Functions Modeling Change

A Preparation for Calculus

Preliminary Edition
Abridged

Connally
Hughes-Hallett
Gleason et al.

for use in the
Department of Mathematics
De Anza College
Cuppertino, California

WILEY
Custom Services

IMPORTANT
PLEASE READ

TO THE STUDENT

This book is a customized textbook, blending chapters from several different books. Here are a few important notes that will help you to best utilize this book.

Table of Contents – The table of contents lists the chapters according to the actual organization of this book.

Chapter Headers – New chapter headers have been created to follow the new organization of the book. The new chapter headers are the ones printed within the black box. However, for your reference, the original chapter headers have been left intact.

Pagination – The book has been repaginated to make it easier for you to follow the new organization. The new page numbers are the ones printed within the black box. The original page numbers have also been left on each page.

Chapter References – Within most of the chapters, the author makes reference to previously discussed concepts, illustrations, problems, etc. When locating these reference points, please use the original chapter numbers and page references, and not the new organization of the book.

Thank you for reading these important notes and good luck with the course!

FUNCTIONS MODELING CHANGE:
A Preparation for Calculus

Produced by the Consortium based at Harvard and funded by a National Science Foundation Grant.
All proceeds from the sale of this work are used to support the work of the Consortium.

Eric Connally
Wellesley College

Deborah Hughes-Hallett
Harvard University

Andrew M. Gleason
Harvard University

Frank Avenoso
Nassau Community College

Philip Cheifetz
Nassau Community College

Jo Ellen Hillyer
Newton North High School

William Mueller
University of Arizona

Andrew Pasquale
Chelmsford High School

Pat Shure
University of Michigan

Carl Swenson
Seattle University

Karen R. Thrash
University of Southern Mississippi

Katherine Yoshiwara
Los Angeles Pierce College

Coordinated by
Ann J. Ryu

John Wiley & Sons, Inc.
New York Chichester Weinheim Brisbane Singapore Toronto

Dedicated to Maria, Ben, and Jonah

COVER PHOTO: Dennis O'Clair/Tony Stone Images/New York, Inc.

This material is based upon work supported by the National Science Foundation under Grant No. DUE-9352905. All royalties from the sale of this book will go toward the furtherance of the project.

ISBN-0-471-17081-X (Paper); 0-471-31787-X (Cloth)

Printed in the United States of America

10 9 8 7

PRECALCULUS

JOHN R. DURBIN
THE UNIVERSITY OF TEXAS
AT AUSTIN

JOHN WILEY & SONS
New York   Chichester   Brisbane   Toronto   Singapore

Cover Design: Renée Kilbride Edelman

Library of Congress Cataloging in Publication Data:

Durbin, John R.
  Precalculus.

  Includes index.
  1. Mathematics—1961–   I. Title.

QA39.2.D87 1986   512'.1   85-26493
ISBN 0-471-88603-3

Printed in the United States of America

10 9 8 7 6 5 4

MULTIVARIABLE CALCULUS

*Produced by the Consortium based at Harvard and funded by a
National Science Foundation Grant.*

William G. McCallum
University of Arizona

Deborah Hughes-Hallett
Harvard University

Daniel Flath
University of South Alabama

Douglas Quinney
University of Keele

Andrew M. Gleason
Harvard University

Wayne Raskind
University of Southern California

Sheldon P. Gordon
Suffolk County Community College

Jeff Tecosky-Feldman
Haverford College

David Mumford
Harvard University

Joe B. Thrash
University of Southern Mississippi

Brad G. Osgood
Stanford University

Thomas W. Tucker
Colgate University

with the assistance of

Adrian Iovita
*Centre Interuniversitaire en
Calcul Mathématique Algébrique*

John Wiley & Sons, Inc.
New York   Chichester   Weinheim   Brisbane   Singapore   Toronto

Dedicated to Amy, Nell, Abby, and Sally.

Cover Photo by Greg Pease

This material is based upon work supported by the National Science Foundation under Grant No. DUE-9352905.

This book was set in Times Roman by the Consortium based at Harvard using LaTeX, Mathematica, and the package AsTeX, which was written by Alex Kasman for this project.

ISBN: 0-471-31151-0

Printed in the United States of America

10 9 8 7 6 5 4 3

Contents

Math 49A

Chapter 0

Polynomial Inequalities
Absolute Value Equations
and Inequalities

SECTION 5

POLYNOMIAL INEQUALITIES

A. Order Properties

Order properties relate to inequality. In Section 1 we looked briefly at inequality in terms of a real line directed to the right:

$$a < b \quad \text{iff} \quad a \text{ is to the left of } b.$$

Also, a number was defined to be *positive* if it is to the right of 0 and *negative* if it is to the left of 0. It is advantageous to restate the condition for $a < b$ in the following equivalent form:

$$\boxed{a < b \quad \text{iff} \quad b - a \text{ is positive.}}$$

Example 5.1 (See Figure 5.1.)

(a) $2 < 7$ because $7 - 2 = 5$ is positive.

(b) $-6 < -4.5$ because $-4.5 - (-6) = -4.5 + 6 = 1.5$ is positive.

(c) $-5 < \frac{2}{3}$ because $\frac{2}{3} - (-5) = \frac{2}{3} + 5 = \frac{17}{3}$ is positive.

FIGURE 5.1

    (Appendix B indicates how to define *positive* without appealing to a real line. When *positive* has been defined independently of a real line, then the equivalence "$a < b$ iff $b - a$ is positive" makes the idea of *inequality* also independent of a real line.)

    The notations $a \leq b$, $b > a$, and $b \geq a$, as well as the terminology *less than* and *greater than*, are all defined in terms of $a = b$ and $a < b$ as in Section 1C. The basic properties of inequalities are the order properties that follow. Properties (5.1) and (5.2) are actually axioms; Properties (5.3) through (5.6) can be proved using (5.1), (5.2), and other properties of the real numbers. (See Examples 5.2 and 5.3.) *Pay special attention to Properties (5.5) and (5.6). The former* states that if both sides of an inequality are multiplied by the same *positive* number, then the sense (direction) of the inequality remains *unchanged*; the latter states that if both sides are multiplied by the same *negative* number, then the sense is *reversed*.

Order properties.

If a is any real number, then exactly one of the following is true:

$$a > 0, \quad a = 0, \quad \text{or} \quad -a > 0. \tag{5.1}$$

If $a > 0$ and $b > 0$, then $a + b > 0$ and $ab > 0$. $\qquad$ (5.2)

If $a < b$ and $b < c$, then $a < c$. $\qquad$ (5.3)

If $a < b$, then

$$a + c < b + c \quad \text{and} \quad a - c < b - c \tag{5.4}$$

for every c.

If $a < b$ and $c > 0$, then $ac < bc$. $\qquad$ (5.5)

If $a < b$ and $c < 0$, then $ac > bc$. $\qquad$ (5.6)

The next two examples give proofs of (5.5) and the first part of (5.4) using "$a < b$ iff $b - a$ is positive" as the definition. We use without hesitation the fact that $b > a$ means the same as $a < b$.

Example 5.2 Prove this part of Property (5.4):

$$\text{If } a < b, \text{ then } a + c < b + c.$$

Proof. If $a < b$, then $b - a$ is positive. But $b - a = (b + c) - (a + c)$, so $(b + c) - (a + c)$ is positive and $a + c < b + c$. $\qquad\square$

Example 5.3 Use Property (5.2) to prove Property (5.5).

Assume $a < b$ and $c > 0$. Then $b - a > 0$, and thus $(b - a)c > 0$ by (5.2), since (5.2) states that the product of two positive numbers is positive. Thus $bc - ac > 0$ so $ac < bc$. $\qquad\square$

Chapter 0/ 3

B. Sets and Intervals

This subsection introduces some terminology that will be useful in discussing inequalities that contain variables. We begin with the **set-builder notation**

$$\{x: \ \cdots \},$$

which means

the set of all x such that $\cdots$.

For example,

$$\{x: \ x < 5\}$$

represents

the set of all x such that $x < 5$.

(From the context, x is assumed to represent real numbers in this case. For more examples with set-builder notation, see Appendix C.)

Now assume that a and b are real numbers with $a < b$. The notation $a < x < b$ means that both $a < x$ and $x < b$; that is, x is between a and b. The notations $[a, b]$, $[a, b)$, $(a, b]$, and (a, b) are used to denote the four special sets of real numbers defined in Table 5.1. Each set is called an **interval** with **endpoints** a and b. The keys are that [is used if a is to be *included* in the set, and (is used if a is to be *excluded*. Similarly for] and). [Sometimes a closed circle (●) is used to denote an endpoint that is to be *included*, and an open circle (○) is used to denote an endpoint that is to be *excluded*.]

TABLE 5.1

Interval	Definition	Figure
$[a, b]$	$\{x: \ a \leq x \leq b\}$	
$[a, b)$	$\{x: \ a \leq x < b\}$	
$(a, b]$	$\{x: \ a < x \leq b\}$	
(a, b)	$\{x: \ a < x < b\}$	

Table 5.2 shows the five types of **unbounded intervals**—that is, intervals without an endpoint on one or both ends. The symbols $-\infty$ and ∞ *do not* denote real numbers: "$(-\infty$" simply denotes the absence of an endpoint on the left, and "$\infty)$" denotes the absence of an endpoint on the right.

TABLE 5.2

Interval	Definition	Figure
$[a, \infty)$	$\{x: \ x \geq a\}$	
$(-\infty, b]$	$\{x: \ x \leq b\}$	
(a, ∞)	$\{x: \ x > a\}$	
$(-\infty, b)$	$\{x: \ x < b\}$	
$(-\infty, \infty)$	$\{x: \ x$ is a real number$\}$	

Sometimes it is convenient to use set notation when working with intervals. For this we need the following ideas. (For more examples of these ideas see Appendix C.) Let A and B represent sets (collections of numbers, for example).

$x \in A$ denotes that x is an element of (or is a member of, or belongs to) the set A.

$\{a, b, \ldots\}$ denotes the set whose members are $a, b, \ldots$.

$\varnothing$ denotes the **empty set**, that is, the set that contains no elements.

$A \cup B$ denotes $\{x: \ x \in A \text{ or } x \in B\}$.

$A \cap B$ denotes $\{x: \ x \in A \text{ and } x \in B\}$.

The set $A \cup B$ is called the **union** of A and B ("$x \in A$ or $x \in B$" includes the possibility that x belongs to *both* A and B). The set $A \cap B$ is called the **intersection** of A and B. (See Figure 5.2.)

$A \cup B$
is shaded

$A \cap B$
is shaded

FIGURE 5.2

Example 5.4 Figure 5.3 shows the intervals that appear on the left in these equations.

(a) $[-1, 3] \cup [1, 4) = [-1, 4)$

(b) $[-1, 3] \cap [1, 4) = [1, 3]$

(c) $(-\infty, 1] \cap [1, 4) = \{1\}$

(d) $(-\infty, 1] \cap (-1, \infty) = (-1, 1]$

(e) $(-3, -2) \cap [1, 4) = \varnothing$

(f) The set $(-3, -2) \cup [1, 4)$ is not an interval.

FIGURE 5.3

C. Linear Inequalities

The basic terminology about equations with one variable also applies to inequalities with one variable. A real number is a **solution** of such an inequality (or **satisfies** the inequality) if it leads to a true inequality of numbers when it replaces the variable. Thus 4 is a solution of

$$3x < 15$$

because

$$3 \cdot 4 = 12 \quad \text{and} \quad 12 < 15.$$

The set of all solutions of an inequality is called its **solution set.** To **solve** an inequality is to find its solution set. Two inequalities with the same variable are **equivalent** if they have the same solution set.

As with an equation, the most basic plan for solving an inequality is to replace it by simpler and simpler equivalent inequalities until the solutions (if there are any) become obvious. The most frequently used tools for this are Properties (5.4)–(5.6). For the present we concentrate on **linear inequalities—** that is, inequalities that can be written in the form

$$ax + b < 0 \quad \text{or} \quad ax + b \leq 0, \quad \text{with } a \neq 0.$$

Linear inequalities are solved just like linear equations, except that the sense of the inequality sign must be reversed whenever the sides are interchanged or both sides are multiplied (or divided) by a negative number.

Example 5.5

$$9x - 6 < 7x + 4$$

$9x < 7x + 10$	Add 6 to both sides.
$2x < 10$	Subtract $7x$ from both sides.
$x < 5$	Divide both sides by 2.

The original inequality has been transformed into the equivalent inequality $x < 5$. Thus the solution set of the original inequality is $\{x: \; x < 5\}$, or in interval notation, $(-\infty, 5)$.

Notice that Example 5.5 has an infinite number of solutions. That is typical of linear inequalities—in contrast with linear equations, which have only one solution each.

The rules for solving inequalities with $\leq$ or $\geq$ are the same as those for $<$ and $>$. Here is an example.

Example 5.6

$$\frac{3u - 2}{5} + 3 \geq \frac{4u - 1}{3}$$

$3(3u - 2) + 15 \cdot 3 \geq 5(4u - 1)$	Multiply by 15.
$9u - 6 + 45 \geq 20u - 5$	Distributive property.
$9u \geq 20u - 44$	Subtract 39.
$-11u \geq -44$	Subtract $20u$.
$u \leq 4$	Divide by -11 and change $\geq$ to $\leq$.

Thus the solution set is $(-\infty, 4]$.

Example 5.7 Find the domain of $\sqrt{5 - 2x}$ and write the answer using interval notation. (The *domain* of an expression is defined in Section 3A.)

Solution   The square root of a negative number is not a real number. Thus we require

$$5 - 2x \geq 0$$
$$-2x \geq -5$$
$$x \leq 2.5$$

Therefore, in interval notation the solution set is $(-\infty, 2.5]$.

D. Other Polynomial Inequalities

To solve an inequality with nonlinear polynomials, we first rewrite the inequality with only 0 on one side. We next try to factor the other side, and then use the fact that a product of nonzero real numbers is positive iff either all of the factors are positive or an even number of them are negative.

Chapter 0/   7

Example 5.8   Solve $x(x - 1) > 6$.

Solution

$$x^2 - x > 6 \qquad \text{Distributive law.}$$

$$x^2 - x - 6 > 0 \qquad \text{Add } -6 \text{ to both sides.}$$

$$(x - 3)(x + 2) > 0 \qquad \text{Factor.}$$

It suffices to solve the latter inequality, since it is equivalent to the original inequality. The factors $x - 3$ and $x + 2$ are 0 at $x = 3$ and $x = -2$, respectively. When these numbers are plotted on a number line, three intervals are formed: $(-\infty, -2)$, $(-2, 3)$, and $(3, \infty)$ (Figure 5.4). The factors $x - 3$ and $x + 2$ will not change sign within these intervals. Figure 5.4 shows the sign of each factor within each interval. To determine the sign of a factor within one of the intervals, it suffices to test with any number in that interval. For example, if $x = 4$ then $x - 3 > 0$, so $x - 3 > 0$ throughout the interval $(3, \infty)$. Since $(x - 3)(x + 2) > 0$ iff both factors are positive or both are negative, the signs of $(x - 3)(x + 2)$ are as shown in Figure 5.4. Thus the solution set is

$$(-\infty, -2) \cup (3, \infty).$$

FIGURE 5.4

Once the intervals in Figure 5.4 were determined, we could have completed the solution by considering the signs of $x^2 - x - 6$ directly, rather than the signs of the individual factors. In general, choose whichever method seems easier.

Example 5.9   Solve $2x^3 - 15x \le -7x^2$.

Solution

$$2x^3 + 7x^2 - 15x \le 0$$

$$x(2x^2 + 7x - 15) \le 0$$

$$x(2x - 3)(x + 5) \le 0$$

The factors on the left are zero at $x = 0$, $x = \frac{3}{2}$, and $x = -5$, respectively. Four intervals are determined. The signs of the factors and the product within these intervals are shown in Figure 5.5. In this case we want the intervals where the product is negative. Since the values where the product is 0 also provide solutions, we include -5, 0, and $\frac{3}{2}$. Thus the solution set is

$$(-\infty, -5] \cup [0, \tfrac{3}{2}].$$

FIGURE 5.5

E. Application

Example 5.10   Let C denote temperature in degrees Celsius and F temperature in degrees Fahrenheit. The normal January daily temperature range in Honolulu is 65°F to 79°F. Find the range in degrees Celsius.

Solution   The formula for C in terms of F is

$$F = \tfrac{9}{5}C + 32. \tag{5.7}$$

Therefore, $65 \le F \le 79$ implies

$$65 \le \tfrac{9}{5}C + 32 \le 79$$

$$65 - 32 \le \tfrac{9}{5}C \le 79 - 32$$

$$\tfrac{5}{9}(33) \le C \le \tfrac{5}{9}(47)$$

$$18.\overline{3} \le C \le 26.\overline{1}$$

Thus the range is approximately 18°C to 26°C.

Exercises for Section 5

Replace each □ with the appropriate sign, either < or >. .

1. $-1.4\ \square -1.5$

2. $\tfrac{6}{25}\ \square\ \tfrac{7}{25}$

3. $0\ \square\ -4$

4. $\tfrac{1}{5}\ \square\ \tfrac{1}{6}$

5. $-0.2\ \square\ -0.19$

6. $1/0.2\ \square\ 1/0.1$

7. $3 - x^3\ \square\ 1 - x^3$

8. $-7\pi\ \square\ -5\pi$

9. $-5\sqrt{2}\ \square\ -5\sqrt{3}$

10. $1.2 \times 10^6\ \square\ 1.2 \times 10^7$

11. $1.2 \times 10^{-13}\ \square\ 1.2 \times 10^{-14}$

12. $-1.2 \times 10^7\ \square\ -1.2 \times 10^8$

Solve each inequality and express the solution set with set-builder notation.

13. $6x + 2 > 3x - 4$

14. $5y - 4 < 7y + 2$

15. $1 + 5z < 2 - z$

16. $2(4 - t) \le 5(1 + 2t)$

17. $\tfrac{1}{3}(u + 1) > \tfrac{1}{4}(u - 1)$

18. $\tfrac{1}{2}(3 - 2x) \ge \tfrac{1}{10}(x + 4)$

19. $0.05[v - 3(1 - v)] \le 0.4v$

Chapter 0/   9

20. $1.46 \geq 0.2[1 + 2.1(r - 3)]$

21. $-y \geq 1.4[2(2 - y) + 0.5]$

Graph each interval on a real line. (See Figure 5.3.) Then simplify the set (if possible) as in Example 5.4.

22. $(-2, 1] \cup [-1, 2)$

23. $[0, 3] \cap [2, 4]$

24. $[0, 3] \cup [2, 4]$

25. $(1, 5] \cap [-4, 1)$

26. $[1.5, 2.5] \cap [2.5, \infty)$

27. $(-\infty, -1) \cup (2, \infty)$

28. $[0, \infty) \cup (-\infty, 0]$

29. $(-\infty, 0) \cap (0, \infty)$

30. $(-\infty, -1] \cup [1, \infty)$

Solve and express the solution set with interval notation.

31. $x^2 - 4x < 5$

32. $10 > x^2 - 3x$

33. $x^2 < 2x + 8$

34. $2(x^2 + x + 2) \geq -7x$

35. $4x^2 + 2x \leq x^2 + x + 2$

36. $(2x + 1)^2 \leq x^2 - x + 3$

37. $y^2 > 1.5y + 1$

38. $y^2 - 2.2y \geq 1.21$

39. $y(y + 0.1) > 0.02$

40. $x^3 \leq x$

41. $(x - 2)x \leq (x - 2)x^2$

42. $x^4 \geq 16$

Find the domain of each expression in Exercises 43–48. Write the answer using interval notation.

43. $\sqrt{5x + 15}$

44. $\sqrt{x - 2} + \dfrac{1}{x - 5}$

45. $\sqrt{-x} - \dfrac{1}{x}$

46. $\sqrt{3x + 4} + \dfrac{1}{\sqrt{2 - x}}$

47. $\dfrac{3}{\sqrt{x}} - \dfrac{4}{\sqrt{3x - 6}}$

48. $\dfrac{1}{\sqrt{x + 5}} + 2\sqrt{-2x - 10}$

49. Prove that if $a > b > 0$, then $1/b > 1/a$. [Suggestion: Use Property (5.5) with $c = 1/(ab)$.]

50. Find all values of k for which
$$kx^2 - 3x + 2 = 0$$
has two real solutions for x.

51. Find all values of p for which
$$-x^2 + 5x + p = 0$$
has no real solution for x.

52. Find all values of k for which $x^2 + kx + 1 = 0$ has two real solutions for x.

53. Find all values of p for which $x^2 + px + p = 0$ has no real solution for x.

54. Prove that if $q \neq 0$, then $x^2 + qx + q^2 = 0$ has no real solution for x.

55. The normal January temperature range in Minneapolis-St. Paul is 3°F to 21°F. Find the range in degrees Celsius.

56. What range of temperatures in degrees Fahrenheit corresponds to a range of 10°C to 20°C?

57. Suppose the pressure P (in pounds) and volume V (in cubic inches) of a confined gas are related by the equation $P = 100/V$. What range for the volume corresponds to a range of 20 pounds per square inch to 40 pounds per square inch for pressure? (Suggestion: Use Exercise 49.)

58. What can we conclude about the radius of a circle if we know that the circumference exceeds the perimeter of a square whose edges are each 10 centimeters?

59. For which sets of three consecutive positive integers will four times the sum of the first two integers exceed seven times the third of the integers?

60. What can we conclude about the radius of a circle if we know that the area exceeds that of a square whose edges are each 5 centimeters?

61. Prove that $\sqrt{ab} \le \dfrac{a+b}{2}$ for all positive

real numbers a and b. [Suggestion: Begin with $(\sqrt{a} - \sqrt{b})^2 \ge 0$.]

62. Prove that $\dfrac{a^2 + b^2}{2} \ge \left(\dfrac{a+b}{2}\right)^2$ for all real numbers a and b. [Suggestion: Show that the inequality is equivalent to $(a-b)^2 \ge 0$.]

63. Prove that if $a < b$ and $(x - a)^2 < (x - b)^2$, then $x < (a + b)/2$.

SECTION 6

ABSOLUTE VALUE EQUATIONS AND INEQUALITIES

A. More about Absolute Value

Recall that

$$|a| = \begin{cases} a & \text{if} \quad a \ge 0 \\ -a & \text{if} \quad a < 0 \end{cases}$$

(Section 1D). Also, $|a|$ is the distance between the points with coordinates 0 and a on a real line. Following is a collection of other properties of absolute value. Throughout, a and b denote real numbers, with $b \ne 0$ in (6.5).

$$|a| \ge 0 \tag{6.1}$$

$$|a| = 0 \quad \text{iff} \quad a = 0 \tag{6.2}$$

$$|a| = |-a| \tag{6.3}$$

$$|ab| = |a||b| \tag{6.4}$$

$$\left|\frac{a}{b}\right| = \frac{|a|}{|b|} \tag{6.5}$$

$$|a| = |b| \quad \text{iff} \quad a = -b \quad \text{or} \quad a = b \tag{6.6}$$

Properties (6.1)–(6.3) were stated in Section 1D. Property (6.4) can be proved using Properties (1.6), (1.11), and (1.12):

$$|ab| = \sqrt{(ab)^2} = \sqrt{a^2b^2} = \sqrt{a^2}\sqrt{b^2} = |a||b|.$$

Property (6.5) can be proved from (6.4):

$$\left|\frac{a}{b}\right||b| = \left|\frac{a}{b} \cdot b\right| = |a| \quad \text{so} \quad \left|\frac{a}{b}\right| = \frac{|a|}{|b|} \quad (b \neq 0).$$

B. Absolute Value Equations

If y and c denote real numbers with $c > 0$, then $|y| = c$ iff y is c units to the left of 0 ($y = -c$) or y is c units to the right of 0 ($y = c$). See Figure 6.1.

FIGURE 6.1

> For real numbers y and c such that $c > 0$:
>
> $$|y| = c \quad \text{iff} \quad y = -c \quad \text{or} \quad y = c.$$

(6.7)

Here is an example using (6.7) to solve an equation with an absolute value.

Example 6.1   Solve $|3x| = 12$.

Solution   By (6.7), with $y = 3x$ and $c = 12$, we get a solution iff $3x = -12$ or $3x = 12$. Thus the solution set is $\{-4, 4\}$.

The next example uses (6.6) and the fact that the distance between the points with coordinates a and b on a real line is $|a - b|$ (Section 1D).

Example 6.2   Find all points x on a real line such that x is twice as far from -3 as from 10.

Solution   The distance between x and -3 is $|x - (-3)|$. The distance between x and 10 is $|x - 10|$. Thus we need

$$|x - (-3)| = 2|x - 10|.$$

This can be solved as follows.

$$|x + 3| = |2(x - 10)| \quad \text{Property (6.4)}$$
$$|x + 3| = |2x - 20|$$
$$x + 3 = -(2x - 20) \quad \text{or} \quad x + 3 = 2x - 20 \quad \text{Property (6.6)}$$
$$x = 17/3 \quad \text{or} \quad x = 23$$

The two solutions (17/3 and 23) are shown along with the two given points (−3 and 10) in Figure 6.2.

FIGURE 6.2

C. Absolute Value Inequalities

To solve an inequality that contains absolute values, we can sometimes first convert to one or more inequalities that do not contain absolute values. To do this we use the facts that, for $c > 0$,

$$|y| < c \quad \text{iff} \quad y \text{ is } within \ c \text{ units of 0 (Figure 6.3)},$$

FIGURE 6.3

and

$$|y| > c \quad \text{iff} \quad y \text{ is } more \ than \ c \text{ units from 0 (Figure 6.4)}.$$

FIGURE 6.4

For real numbers y and c such that $c > 0$:

$$|y| < c \quad \text{iff} \quad -c < y < c \tag{6.8}$$
$$|y| > c \quad \text{iff} \quad y < -c \text{ or } y > c \tag{6.9}$$

Example 6.3 Solve $|x| < 3$.

Solution By (6.8), with $y = x$ and $c = 3$, the solution set is $\{x: \ -3 < x < 3\}$. In interval notation, the solution set is $(-3, 3)$.

Example 6.4   Solve $|3x - 2| < 4$.

Solution   Using (6.8) with $y = 3x - 2$ and $c = 4$, we see that the given inequality is equivalent to

$$-4 < 3x - 2 < 4.$$

Now proceed as in Section 5. Add 2 to each part (this is equivalent to adding 2 to both sides of $-4 < 3x - 2$ and to both sides of $3x - 2 < 4$):

$$(-4) + 2 < (3x - 2) + 2 < (4) + 2$$
$$-2 < 3x < 6.$$

Now divide by 3:

$$-\tfrac{2}{3} < x < 2.$$

In interval notation, the solution set is $(-\tfrac{2}{3}, 2)$.

Example 6.5   Solve $|2x| \geq 7$.

Solution   Use (6.9) with $y = 2x$ and $c = 7$, and the corresponding statement with $=$ in place of $>$. We see that the given inequality is equivalent to

$$2x \leq -7 \quad \text{or} \quad 2x \geq 7$$
$$x \leq -\tfrac{7}{2} \quad \text{or} \quad x \geq \tfrac{7}{2}.$$

Thus the solution set is $(-\infty, -3.5] \cup [3.5, \infty)$.

Example 6.6   Solve $5 \leq |4 - x|$.

Solution   This is equivalent to $|4 - x| \geq 5$. Apply (6.9) with $y = 4 - x$ and $c = 5$, and the corresponding statement with $=$ in place of $>$. This leads to

$$4 - x \leq -5 \quad \text{or} \quad 4 - x \geq 5$$
$$-x \leq -9 \quad \text{or} \quad -x \geq 1$$
$$x \geq 9 \quad \text{or} \quad x \leq -1.$$

Thus the solution set is $(-\infty, -1] \cup [9, \infty)$.

Exercises for Section 6

Solve each equation.

1. $|6x| = 4$
2. $|-2x| = 9$
3. $|x + 7| = 0$
4. $|x - 8| = -2$
5. $|x^2 - 5| = 0$
6. $|12 - 5x| = 1$
7. $2|0.3 - x| = |0.5x|$
8. $|\frac{1}{2}x - \frac{1}{3}| = \frac{1}{3}|-x|$
9. $1.5|x + 4| = -|2x|$
10. $x^2 - 5|x - 1| = 0$
11. $|2 - x^2| - |x^2 + x| = 0$
12. $|x^2 - 3| = |x + 2|$
13. $x + 3\,|7 - 2|x|| = 0$
14. $||x| - 2| + 3| = 0$
15. $|2 + |x|| + ||x| - 2| = 0$

Solve each inequality and express the solution set with interval notation.

16. $|x| \leq 4$
17. $|2x| > 14$
18. $|-x| \leq 5$
19. $|6x| > |-3|$
20. $|-6| \geq |-0.1x|$
21. $|-1| < |\frac{1}{2}x|$
22. $|2x - 1| < 7$
23. $|3x + 1| \geq 5$
24. $|\frac{1}{2}x - 1| \leq \frac{3}{2}$
25. $|0.2 - 0.1x| \geq 0.3$
26. $|1 - 5x| < 1$
27. $|3 - 2x| > 1$
28. $4 < |x| < 9$
29. $5 \geq |2x| \geq 1$
30. $2 < |3x - 1| < 5$

Find the domain of each expression in Exercises 31–33.

31. $\sqrt{2 - x}/(|x| - 3)$
32. $\sqrt{x - 1} + \sqrt{5 - |x|}$
33. $\sqrt{|x| - 7}/(\sqrt{|x + 7|})$
34. Write an inequality to represent the fact that x is 8 units from 3 on a real line. Which x satisfy the inequality?
35. Find all points x on a real line such that x is 3 times as far from the origin as from 7.
36. Find all points x on a real line such that x is twice as far from 3 as $2x$ is from 7.

In Exercises 37–39: (a) Write an absolute value inequality to represent each statement. (b) Solve the inequality from part (a) and express the answer with interval notation.

37. The point representing x on a real line is within 2 units of the point representing 5.
38. The point representing x on a real line is at least 6 units from the point representing 3.
39. The point representing x on a real line is more than twice as far from the point representing -1 as from the point representing 2.
40. If $y = 1/x$ and $|x - 3| < 2$, what can you conclude about y? (Suggestion: If $a > b > 0$, then $1/b > 1/a$.)
41. Prove that $-|a| \leq a \leq |a|$ for every real number a. (Suggestion: If $a \geq 0$, then $-a \leq a \leq a$ and $|a| = a$, so $-|a| \leq a \leq |a|$. What about the case $a < 0$?)
42. Prove that $|a + b| \leq |a| + |b|$ for all real numbers a and b. This is known as the **triangle inequality**. [Suggestion: An equivalent form is $-|a| - |b| \leq a + b \leq |a| + |b|$. (Why?) Also, by Exercise 41, $-|a| \leq a \leq |a|$ and $-|b| \leq b \leq |b|$.]

Chapter 1

Functions: An Introduction

1.1 WHAT IS A FUNCTION?

The word *function*, used casually, expresses the notion of dependence. For example, a person might say that election results are a function of the economy, meaning that the winner of an election is determined by how the economy is doing. Another person may claim that car sales are a function of the weather, meaning that the number of cars sold on a given day is affected by the weather.

In mathematics, the meaning of the word *function* is more precise, but the basic idea is the same. A function is a relationship between two quantities. If the value of one quantity uniquely determines the value of the second quantity, we say the second quantity is a function of the first.

Example 1 In the early 1980s, the recording industry introduced the compact disc (CD) as an alternative to vinyl long playing records (LPs). Table 1.1 gives the number of units (in millions) of CDs sold for the years 1982 through 1987.[1] The year uniquely determines the number of CDs sold. Thus, we say the number of CDs sold is a function of the year.

TABLE 1.1 *Millions of CDs sold, by year*

year	sales (millions)
1982	0
1983	0.8
1984	5.8
1985	23
1986	53
1987	102

The quantities described by a function are called *variables*, and are often represented by letters like x and y. In the next example, the variables are named A and n.

Example 2 The number of gallons of paint needed to paint a house depends on the size of the house. A gallon of paint will typically cover 250 square feet. Thus, the number of gallons of paint, n, is a function of the area to be painted, A. For example, if $A = 5000$ ft^2, then $n = 5000/250 = 20$ gallons of paint.

In summary, we say:

> One variable, Q, is a **function** of another variable, t, if each value of t has a unique value of Q associated with it.

---

[1] Data from Recording Industry of America, Inc., 1993.

Representing Functions: Words, Tables, Graphs, and Formulas

There are several ways to represent functions. Depending on the situation, the relationship between two quantities can be described using words, data in a table, points on a graph, or an algebraic formula. In many situations there is more than one way to show the relationship described by a function.

Example 3 It is a surprising biological fact that most crickets chirp at a rate that increases as the temperature increases. For the snowy tree cricket (*Oecanthus fultoni*), the relationship between temperature and chirp rate is so reliable that this type of cricket is called the thermometer cricket. One can estimate the temperature (in degrees Fahrenheit) by counting the number of times a snowy tree cricket chirps in 15 seconds and adding 40. For instance, if we count 20 chirps in 15 seconds, then a good estimate of the temperature would be $20 + 40 = 60°F$.

The rule used to find the estimated temperature T (in °F) based on the measured chirp rate R (in chirps per minute) is an example of a function. Describe this function in four different ways: using words, a table, a graph, and a formula.

Solution
- **Words**: To estimate the temperature, we count the number of chirps in fifteen seconds and then add forty. Alternatively, if we count R chirps per minute, we can divide R by four and add forty. This is because there should be one-fourth as many chirps in fifteen seconds as there are in sixty seconds. For instance, if we count 80 chirps in one minute, that works out to $\frac{1}{4} \cdot 80 = 20$ chirps every 15 seconds, giving an estimated temperature of $20 + 40 = 60°F$.
- **Table**: Table 1.2 gives the estimated temperature T as a function of R, the number of chirps we count per minute. Notice the pattern in Table 1.2: each time the chirp rate R goes up by 20 chirps per minute, temperature T goes up by 5°F.
- **Graph**: The data from Table 1.2 have been plotted in Figure 1.1. For instance, from Table 1.2 we see that a chirp rate of $R = 80$ indicates a temperature of $T = 60$. This pair of values has been plotted as a single point in Figure 1.1 and labeled P. Point P is 80 units along the horizontal axis (or R-axis) and 60 units along the vertical axis (or T-axis). Data represented in this way are said to be plotted on the *Cartesian plane*. The precise position of a point like P on the Cartesian plane is shown by giving the coordinates of the point. The coordinates of P are written $P = (80, 60)$.

TABLE 1.2

R, chirp rate (chirps/minute)	T, predicted temperature (°F)
20	45
40	50
60	55
80	60
100	65
120	70
140	75
160	80

Figure 1.1

- **Formula**: A *formula* is a rule, given algebraically, that tells us how to determine the value of one quantity when given the value of another quantity (or quantities). Here, we would like to use our rule to find a formula for T in terms of R. We know that dividing the chirp rate by four and adding forty gives the estimated temperature:

$$\underbrace{\text{Estimated temperature}}_{T} = \frac{1}{4} \cdot \underbrace{\text{Chirp rate}}_{R} + 40.$$

Rewriting this using the variables T and R gives us the formula:

$$T = \frac{1}{4}R + 40.$$

Let's check our formula. At a chirp rate of $R = 80$, we have

$$T = \frac{1}{4}R + 40$$
$$= \frac{1}{4} \cdot 80 + 40$$
$$= 60$$

which agrees with point $P = (80, 60)$ from Figure 1.1.

All of the descriptions given in Example 3 provide the same information, but each description has a different emphasis. A relationship between variables is often described in words, as at the beginning of Example 3. A table like Table 1.2 is useful because it shows the predicted temperature for various chirp rates. The graph in Figure 1.1 is more suggestive than the table, although it may be harder to read the function's exact values. For example, you might have noticed that every point in Figure 1.1 falls on a straight line that slopes up from left to right. In general, a graph can reveal a pattern that might otherwise go unnoticed. Finally, the formula has the advantage of being both compact and precise. However, this compactness can also be a disadvantage since it is often harder to gain as much immediate insight from the brief notation of a formula as from a table or a graph.

Functions Don't Have to be Defined by Formulas

People sometimes think that a function is the same thing as a formula. However, functions aren't always defined by formulas. Consider the following examples.

Example 4   The last digit, d, of a phone number is a function of n, its position in the phone book. For example, Table 1.3 gives d for the first 10 listings in the 1995 Boston telephone directory. Table 1.3 shows that the last digit of the first listing is 8, the last digit of the second listing is 7, and so on. In principle we could use a phone book to figure out other values of d. For instance, if $n = 300$, we could count down to the 300th listing in order to determine d. However, there is no particular pattern to the values of d. Using the data in the table, we cannot find a formula that will tell us d for every listing in the phone book. Nonetheless, the last digit is uniquely determined by the position of the listing in the phone book, so d is a function of n.

TABLE 1.3   *The number d is the last digit of the nth listing in the 1995 Boston phone book*

n	1	2	3	4	5	6	7	8	9	10
d	8	7	4	3	3	5	9	3	2	0

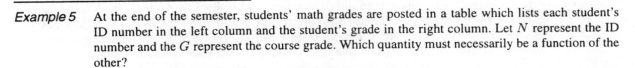

Example 5   At the end of the semester, students' math grades are posted in a table which lists each student's ID number in the left column and the student's grade in the right column. Let N represent the ID number and the G represent the course grade. Which quantity must necessarily be a function of the other?

Solution N is not necessarily a function of G, since each value of G does not need to have a unique value of N associated to it. For example, suppose we choose the value of G to be a B. There may be more than one student who received a B, so there may be more than one ID number corresponding to B.

       G must necessarily be a function of N, because each value of N must have a unique value of G associated with it. That is, each ID number (each student) must receive exactly one grade.

When is a Relationship not a Function?

It is possible for two quantities to be related and yet for neither quantity to be a function of the other.

Example 6   In a certain national park there is a population of foxes that preys on a population of rabbits. Table 1.4 gives these two populations, F and R, over a 12-month period, where $t = 0$ means January 1, $t = 1$ means February 1, and so on.

TABLE 1.4   *Number of foxes and rabbits in a national park, by month*

t, month	0	1	2	3	4	5	6	7	8	9	10	11
	Jan	Feb	Mar	Apr	May	Jun	Jul	Aug	Sep	Oct	Nov	Dec
R, rabbits	1000	750	567	500	567	750	1000	1250	1433	1500	1433	1250
F, foxes	150	143	125	100	75	57	50	57	75	100	125	143

(a)   Is F a function of t? Is R a function of t?
(b)   Is F a function of R?
(c)   Is R a function of F?

Solution   (a)   Both F and R are functions of t. For each value of t, there is a unique value of F and a unique value of R. For example, if $t = 5$, then we see from Table 1.4 that $R = 750$ and $F = 57$. This means that on June 1 there are 750 rabbits and 57 foxes in the park.

(b)   No, F is not a function of R. For example, suppose $R = 750$, meaning there are 750 rabbits. We see that this happens both at $t = 1$ (February 1) and at $t = 5$ (June 1). In the first instance, there are 143 foxes; in the second instance, there are 57 foxes. Since each value of R does not correspond to a unique value of F, we see that F is not a function of R.

(c) R is not a function of F. At time $t = 5$, we have R is 750 when F is 57, while at time $t = 7$, we have R is 1250 when F is again 57. Thus, the value of F does not uniquely determine the value of R.

How to Tell if a Graph Represents a Function: the Vertical Line Test

In Example 6, we saw that the number of foxes is not a function of the number of rabbits, because some values of R are associated with more than one value of F. In general, for y to be a function of x, each value of x must be associated with exactly one value of y.

Let's think about what this requirement means graphically. In order for a graph to represent a function, each x-value must correspond to exactly one y-value. This means that the graph must not intersect any vertical line at more than one point. Otherwise the curve would contain two points with different y-values but the same x-value. This condition can be summarized as follows.

The **vertical line test**:
- If any vertical line intersects a graph in more than one point, then the graph does not represent a function.

Example 7 Which of the graphs in Figures 1.2 and 1.3 could represent a function?

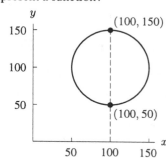

Figure 1.2: Since no vertical line intersects this curve at more than one point, the graph represents y as a function of x

Figure 1.3: Since at least one vertical line intersects this curve at more than one point, the graph does not represent y as a function of x

Solution The curve in Figure 1.2 represents y as a function of x because no vertical line intersects this curve in more than one point.

The curve in Figure 1.3 does *not* represent the graph of a function. The vertical line shown in the figure intersects the curve at $(100, 50)$ and $(100, 150)$. If x equals 100, y could equal 50, or 150. Thus, the value of x does not uniquely determine the value of y.

In Example 7 there are many vertical lines that intersect the circle in Figure 1.3 in more than one point. However, we only need to find one such line in order for a curve to fail the vertical line test. On the other hand, if a graph represents a function, then every vertical line must intersect the graph in at most one point.

Problems for Section 1.1

 Table 1.5 shows the daily low temperature for a one-week period in New York during July.

TABLE 1.5

Date in July	17	18	19	20	21	22	23
Low temperature (°F)	73	77	69	73	75	75	70

(a) What was the low temperature on July 19th? *69°F*
(b) When was the low temperature 73°F? *July 17 & 20th*
(c) Is the daily low temperature a function of the date? Explain. *Yes*
(d) Is the date a function of the daily low temperature? Explain. *No*

2. Table 1.6 shows the number of calories used per minute as a function of body weight for three sports (walking, bicycling, and swimming).

    (a) Determine the number of calories that a 200-lb person uses in one half-hour of walking.

    (b) Who would use more calories, a 120-lb person swimming for one hour or a 220-lb person bicycling for one half-hour?

    (c) Does the number of calories used by a person walking increase or decrease as the person's weight increases?

TABLE 1.6 *Calories used per minute according to body weight in pounds*
Source: 1993 World Almanac

Activity	100 lb	120 lb	150 lb	170 lb	200 lb	220 lb
Walking (3 mph)	2.7	3.2	4.0	4.6	5.4	5.9
Bicycling (10 mph)	5.4	6.5	8.1	9.2	10.8	11.9
Swimming (2 mph)	5.8	6.9	8.7	9.8	11.6	12.7

3. Use the data from Table 1.4 on page 5 to answer the following questions.

    (a) Plot R on the vertical axis and t on the horizontal axis. From this graph show that R is a function of t.

    (b) Plot F on the vertical axis and t on the horizontal axis. From this graph show that F is a function of t.

    (c) Plot F on the vertical axis and R on the horizontal axis. From this graph show that F is not a function of R.

    (d) Plot R on the vertical axis and F on the horizontal axis. From this graph show that R is not a function of F.

4. Tables 1.7–1.9 represent the relationship between the button number, N, which you push, and the snack, S, delivered by three different vending machines. [2]

TABLE 1.7
Vending Machine #1

N	S
1	m&ms
2	pretzels
3	dried fruit
4	Hersheys
5	fat free cookies
6	Snickers

TABLE 1.8
Vending Machine #2

N	S
1	m&ms or dried fruit
2	pretzels or Hersheys
3	Snickers or fat free cookies

TABLE 1.9
Vending Machine #3

N	S
1	m&ms
2	m&ms
3	pretzels
4	dried fruit
5	Hersheys
6	Hersheys
7	fat free cookies
8	Snickers
9	Snickers

    (a) One of these vending machines is not a good one to use, because S is not a function of N. Which one? Explain why this makes it a bad machine to use.   #2

    (b) For which vending machine(s) is S a function of N? Explain why this makes them user-friendly.

    (c) For which of the vending machines is N not a function of S? What does this mean to the user of the vending machine?

---

[2]For each N, vending machine #2 dispenses one or the other product at random.

5. According to Charles Osgood, CBS news commentator, it takes about one minute to read 15 double-spaced typewritten lines on the air.[2]

   (a) Construct a table showing the time Charles Osgood is reading on the air in seconds as a function of the number of double-spaced lines read for $0, 1, 2, \ldots, 10$ lines. From your table, how long does it take Charles Osgood to read 9 lines?

   (b) Plot this data on a graph with the number of seconds on the vertical axis and the number of lines on the horizontal axis.

   (c) From your graph, estimate how long it takes Charles Osgood to read 9 lines. From your graph, estimate how many lines Charles Osgood can read in 30 seconds.

   (d) Construct a formula which relates the time T to n, the number of lines read.

6. A chemical company must spend $2 million to buy machinery before it can start producing chemicals. Then it must spend $0.5 million on raw materials per million liters of chemical produced.

   (a) Suppose the number of liters produced ranges from 0 to 5 million. Make a table showing the relationship between number of liters produced, l, and the cost, C.

   (b) Find a formula that expresses the total cost C, in millions of dollars, as a function of l, the number of liters of chemical produced.

7. (a) Which of the graphs in Figure 1.4 represent y as a function of x?

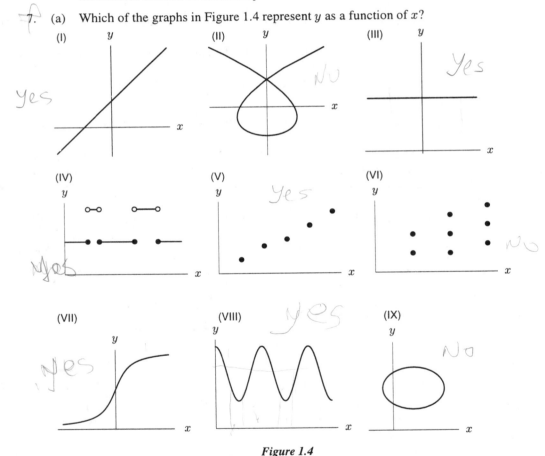

Figure 1.4

---

[2] "Rules of Thumb" by T. Parker, Houghton Mifflin, Boston, 1983.

(b)   Which of the graphs in Figure 1.4 might represent the following situations? Give reasons.
   (i)   SAT Math score versus SAT Verbal score for a number of students.
   (ii)   Total number of daylight hours as a function of the day of the year, shown over a period of several years.
(c)   Among graphs (I)–(IX), find two which could give the cost of train fare as a function of the time of day. Explain the relationship between cost and time for both choices.

8. Consider the following stories about five different bike rides. Match each story to one of the graphs in Figure 1.5. (A graph may be used more than once.)

(a)   This person starts out 5 miles from home and rides 5 miles per hour away from home.
(b)   This person starts out 5 miles from home and rides 10 miles per hour away from home.
(c)   This person starts out 10 miles from home and arrives home one hour later.
(d)   This person starts out 10 miles from home and is halfway home after one hour.
(e)   This person starts out 5 miles from home and is 10 miles from home after one hour.

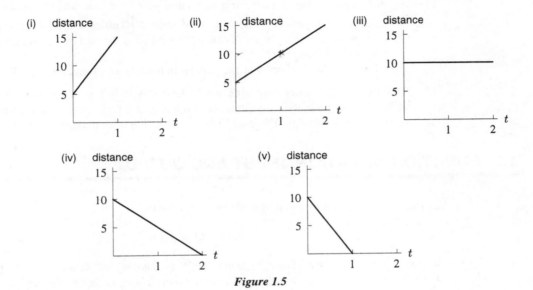

Figure 1.5

9. (a)   Label the axes for a sketch of a problem which begins, "Over the past century we have seen changes in the population, P (in millions), of the city. . ."
   (b)   Label the axes for a problem which says, "Sketch a graph of the cost of manufacturing q items. . ."
   (c)   Label the axes for a problem which says, "Graph the pressure, p, of a gas as a function of its volume, v, where p is in pounds per square inch and v is in cubic inches."
   (d)   Label the axes for a problem which asks you to "Graph D in terms of y. . ."

10. Suppose you are looking at the graph of a function.
   (a)   What is the maximum number of times that the graph can intersect the y-axis? Explain.
   (b)   Can the graph intersect the x-axis an infinite number of times?

11. A bug starts out ten feet from a light, flies closer to the light, then farther away, then closer than before, then farther away. Finally the bug hits the bulb and flies off. Sketch a possible graph of the distance of the bug from the light as a function of time.

12. A light is turned off for several hours. It is then turned on. After a few hours it is turned off again. Sketch a possible graph of the light bulb's temperature as a function of time.

13. Suppose the sales tax on an item is 6%. Express the total cost, C, in terms of the price of the item, P.

14. A cylindrical can is closed at both ends and its height is twice its radius. Express its surface area, S, as a function of its radius, r.

15. Suppose that $y = 3$ no matter what x is.
    (a) Is y a function of x? Explain.
    (b) Is x a function of y? Explain.

16. Suppose that $x = 5$ no matter what y is.
    (a) Is y a function of x? Explain.
    (b) Is x a function of y? Explain.

17. Suppose a person leaves home and walks due west for a time, and then walks due north.
    (a) Suppose the person is known to have walked 10 miles in total. If w is the distance west she walked, and D is her distance from home at the end of her walk, is D a function of w? Why or why not?
    (b) Let x be the distance that she walked in total. Is D a function of x? Why or why not?

18. The distance between Cambridge and Wellesley is 10 miles. A person walks part of the way at 5 miles per hour, then jogs the rest of the way at 8 mph. Find a formula that expresses the total amount of time for the trip, $T(d)$, as a function of d, the distance walked.

1.2 FUNCTION NOTATION: INPUT AND OUTPUT

To indicate that Q is a function of t, we use the notation

$$Q = f(t).$$

We read "$f(t)$" as "f of t." The expression "$f(t)$" does *not* mean "f times t." Instead, $f(t)$ is another symbol for the variable Q. Here, t is called the function's *input*, and Q the function's *output*.

Since we think of the value of Q as being dependent on the value of t, we also call Q the *dependent variable* and t the *independent variable*. The letter f is used to represent the dependence of Q on t. We could have used any letter, not just f, to represent the dependence of Q on t.

Example 1   Let $n = f(A)$ be the amount of paint (in gallons) needed to cover an area of A ft^2. Explain in words what the following statement tells you about painting houses: $f(10{,}000) = 40$.

Solution   Since $n = f(A)$, the input of this function is an area, and the output is an amount of paint. The statement $f(10{,}000) = 40$ tells us that an area of 10,000 ft^2 requires 40 gallons of paint.

In this example, $n = f(A)$ gives the amount of paint, n, as a function of the area, A, to be covered. In that case, the amount of paint we need depends on the area of the house. So n is the dependent variable and A is the independent variable.

Example 2   In Example 6 on page 5, the number of foxes, F, is determined by the month, t. F is the dependent variable and t is the independent variable.

The roles of dependence and independence are not necessarily fixed, as the next example illustrates.

Example 3   If $n = f(A)$ gives the number of gallons of paint required to cover a house of area A ft^2, we think of the amount of paint as being determined by the area to be painted. Suppose 1 gallon of paint covers 250 square feet. Then we can also think of the area as being determined by the amount of paint. For instance, knowing that we have $n = 25$ gallons of paint tells us that we can cover an area of $25 \cdot 250 = 6250$ ft^2. In this case, the area we can cover depends on the amount of paint that we have. Notice that we are defining a *new* function, $A = g(n)$, which tells us the value of A when given the value of n instead of the other way around. For this function, A is the dependent variable and n is the independent variable.

The expression "Q depends on t" does *not* imply a cause-and-effect relationship, as the next example illustrates.

Example 4   In Example 3 on page 3, we saw a formula for estimating air temperature based on the chirp rate of the snowy tree cricket. The formula was

$$T = \frac{1}{4}R + 40.$$

In this formula, T depends on R. In everyday language, however, saying that T depends on R seems to imply that by making the cricket chirp faster we could somehow cause the temperature to go up. Clearly, the cricket's chirping doesn't cause the temperature to be what it is. When we say that the temperature "depends" on the chirp rate, we mean only that knowing the chirp rate is sufficient to determine the temperature.

Finding Output Values: Evaluating a Function

In the housepainting example, the notation $n = f(A)$ indicates that n is a function of A. The expression $f(A)$ by itself is another name for n. It represents the output of the function – specifically, the amount of paint required to cover an area of A ft^2. For example $f(20,000)$ represents the number of gallons of paint required to cover a house of 20,000 ft^2. In other words, $f(20,000)$ represents the output when the area is 20,000 ft^2.

Often, we would like to figure out the value of a function's output when the value of the input is known. This is called *evaluating* the function.

Example 5   Using the fact that 1 gallon of paint will cover 250 ft^2, evaluate the expression $f(20,000)$.

Solution   To evaluate $f(20,000)$, we need to calculate the number of gallons required to cover 20,000 ft^2. Now, 20,000 square feet of area requires

$$\frac{20,000 \text{ ft}^2}{250 \text{ ft}^2/\text{gallon}} = 80 \text{ gallons of paint}, \quad \text{so} \quad f(20,000) = 80.$$

Example 6 Let $F = g(t)$ be the number of foxes in a national park as a function of t, the number of months since January 1. Evaluate $g(9)$ using Table 1.4 on page 5. What does this expression indicate about the fox population?

Solution The input, t, is the number of months since January 1, and the output, F, is the number of foxes. Thus, the expression $g(9)$ represents the number of foxes in the park on October 1. Referring to Table 1.4, we see that when $t = 9$ there are 100 foxes. Thus, $g(9) = 100$.

Evaluating a Function Using a Formula

Recall from geometry that if we know the radius of a circle, we can find its area. If we let $A = q(r)$ represent the area of a circle as a function of its radius, then a formula for $q(r)$ is

$$A = q(r) = \pi r^2.$$

We can use this formula to evaluate $q(r)$ for different values of r.

Example 7 Use the formula $q(r) = \pi r^2$, where r is in cm, to evaluate $q(10)$ and $q(20)$. Explain what your results tell you about circles.

Solution In the expression $q(10)$, the value of r is 10, so

$$q(10) = \pi \cdot 10^2 = 100\pi \approx 314.$$

Similarly, substituting $r = 20$, we have

$$q(20) = \pi \cdot 20^2 = 400\pi \approx 1256.$$

The statements $q(10) \approx 314$ and $q(20) \approx 1256$ tell us that a circle of radius 10 cm has an area of approximately 314 cm^2 and a circle of radius 20 cm has an area of approximately 1256 cm^2.

Example 8 Find a formula for $f(A)$, the amount of paint (in gallons) required to cover a house of area A ft^2.

Solution We use the fact that the

$$\text{Amount of paint required} = \frac{\text{Area to be painted}}{250}.$$

Since $f(A)$ is the amount of paint required and A is the area to be painted, we have

$$f(A) = \frac{A}{250}.$$

This is a formula for $f(A)$ in terms of the variable, A.

You should verify that using the formula in Example 8 to evaluate $f(20,000)$ gives the same answer we found in Example 5.

Finding Input Values

When we know the input value of a function, we can evaluate the function to find the output value. Often the situation is reversed: We know the output value of a function, and want to find the corresponding input value (or values).

Example 9 Let $F = g(t)$ be the number of foxes in month t in the national park described in Example 6 on page 5. Solve the equation $g(t) = 75$. What does your solution tell you about the fox population?

Solution   The output of g stands for a number of foxes. We want to know in what month there are 75 foxes. Table 1.4 tells us that this occurs when $t = 4$ and $t = 8$. This means there are 75 foxes in May and in September.

If the function is given by an algebraic formula, we can find input values by solving an algebraic equation.

Example 10   Recall the cricket function from Example 4, $T = \frac{1}{4}R + 40$. How fast would you expect the snowy tree cricket to chirp if the temperature is 76°F?

Solution   We would like to find R when $T = 76$. Substituting 76 for T into the formula, we need to solve the equation

$$76 = \frac{1}{4}R + 40$$

$$36 = \frac{1}{4}R \quad \text{subtract 40 from both sides}$$

$$144 = R. \quad \text{multiply both sides by 4}$$

We expect the cricket to chirp at a rate of 144 chirps per minute.

Function Notation with Graphs and Tables

So far we have used function notation with functions defined by a formula. The following two examples use function notation with a graph and a table respectively.

Example 11   A man drives from his house to a grocery store and returns home 30 minutes later. Figure 1.6 gives a graph of his velocity $v(t)$ (in mph) as a function of the time t (in minutes) since he left home. A negative velocity indicates that he is traveling from the store back to his house.

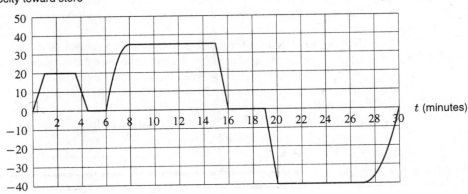

Figure 1.6: Velocity of a man on a trip to the store

Evaluate and interpret (a) – (d). Solve for t and interpret (e) – (h):

(a) $v(5)$ (b) $v(24)$ (c) $v(8) - v(6)$ (d) $v(-3)$

(e) $v(t) = 15$ (f) $v(t) = -20$ (g) $v(t) = v(7)$ (h) $v(t+2) = -10$

Solution   (a)   To evaluate $v(5)$, look on the graph where $t = 5$ minutes. We see from the graph that the velocity is 0 mph. Thus, $v(5) = 0$. Perhaps he had to stop at a light.

(b)   When $t = 24$ minutes we see from the graph that $v(24) = -40$ mph. On his way back from the store, he is traveling at 40 mph.

(c)   From the graph we see that $v(8) = 35$ mph and $v(6) = 0$ mph. Thus, $v(8) - v(6) = 35 - 0 = 35$. This shows that the man's speed increased by 35 mph between $t = 6$ minutes and $t = 8$ minutes.

(d)   The quantity $v(-3)$ is not defined since the trip lasts for $0 \leq t \leq 30$ minutes.

(e)   To solve for t when $v(t) = 15$, look on the graph where the velocity is 15 mph. We see that occurs at $t \approx 0.75$ minute, 3.75 minutes, 6.5 minutes, or 15.5 minutes. Thus, $v(t) = 15$ when $t \approx 0.75, 3.75, 6.5, 15.5$. At each of these four times the man's velocity was 15 mph.

(f)   We must solve for t: $v(t) = -20$. Looking on the graph where the velocity is -20 mph we see that this occurs for $t \approx 19.5$ and $t \approx 29$ minutes.

(g)   First we evaluate $v(7) \approx 27$. To solve $v(t) = 27$, we look for the values of t making the velocity 27 mph. One such t is of course $t = 7$; the other t is $t \approx 15$ mins.

(h)   Look on the graph where the velocity is -10 mph. This occurs at about 19.2 and 29.7 minutes. Therefore, $t + 2 = 19.25$ or $t + 2 = 29.75$, so $t = 17.25$ or 27.75. The times 17.25 minutes and 27.75 minutes are each two minutes prior to a time at which the man is traveling homeward at 10 mph.

Example 12   Table 1.10 shows $N(s)$, the number of sections of Economics 101, as a function of s, the number of students in the course.

TABLE 1.10

Number of students, s	50	75	100	125	150	175	200
Number of sections, $N(s)$	4	4	5	5	6	6	7

Assume that if s is a value in between those listed in the table, then N will be the higher number of sections. Evaluate and interpret (a) – (c) and solve for s and interpret (d) and (e):

(a) $N(150)$ (b) $N(80)$ (c) $N(3.5)$
(d) $N(s) = 4$ (e) $N(s) = N(125)$

Solution   (a)   When $s = 150$ students, the number of sections is 6. So $N(150) = 6$.

(b)   Since 80 is between 75 and 100 students, we choose the higher value for N. So $N(80) = 5$ sections.

(c) $N(3.5)$ is not defined for this function, since 3.5 is not a possible number of students.

(d)   Looking on the table where $N = 4$ sections, we see the numbers 75 and 50 listed for s. We also know that for any integer between those in the table, the section number will be the highest possible one. Therefore, for $50 \leq s \leq 75$, we will have $N(s) = 4$ sections. We do not know what will happen if $s < 50$.

(e)   First evaluate $N(125) = 5$. So we must solve for s: $N(s) = 5$ sections. The enrollment numbers that would result in 5 sections are $76 \leq s \leq 125$.

Problems for Section 1.2

1.   Using Table 1.11, sketch a graph of $n = f(A)$, the number of gallons of paint needed to cover a house of area A. Identify the independent and dependent variables.

TABLE 1.11

A	0	250	500	750	1000	1250	1500
n	0	1	2	3	4	5	6

2. The graph in Figure 1.7 defines $f(x)$. Use it to estimate:

(a) $f(0)$ (b) $f(1)$ (c) $f(b)$ (d) $f(c)$ (e) $f(d)$

Figure 1.7

Figure 1.8

3. Figure 1.8 shows the graph of the function $h(x)$.

(a) Fill in the following table:

x	-2	-1	0	1	2	3
$h(x)$	0	9	8	3	0	4

(b) Evaluate $h(3) - h(-2)$. 4   3 -(0) = +3

(c) Evaluate $h(2) - h(0)$. -8   0 - 8 = 8

(d) Evaluate $2h(0)$. 16   16

(e) Evaluate $h(1) + 3$. 6

$y = f(x) \rightarrow f(x)$:output
output   input

4. Let $f(x) = \sqrt{x^2 + 16} - 5$.

(a) Find $f(0)$.

(b) For what values of x is $f(x)$ zero?

(c) Find $f(3)$.

(d) What is the vertical intercept of the graph of $f(x)$?

(e) Where does the graph cross the x-axis?

5. Use the letters a, b, c, d, e, h in Figure 1.9 to answer the following questions.

Figure 1.9
(b,a)   (d,e)

f(b) = a   f(h) = e

d. c = f(z)   z = 0
    c = y , z = f(x)
    0 = f(x)
    x = h

(a) What are the coordinates of the points P and Q?

(b) Evaluate $f(b)$. output   when $x = b$ $y = a$

(c) Solve $f(x) = e$ for x.   d

(d) Suppose $c = f(z)$ and $z = f(x)$. What is x? h →

(e) Suppose $f(b) = -f(d)$. What additional information does this imply? e
     opposite
     a   - e

6. (a) Let
$$f(x) = 2x(x - 3) - x(x - 5) \quad \text{and} \quad g(x) = x^2 - x.$$
Complete the following table. What do you notice? Draw a graph of these two functions. Are the two functions the same?

x	-2	-1	0	1	2
$f(x)$					
$g(x)$					

  (b) Let
$$h(x) = x^5 - 5x^3 + 6x + 1 \quad \text{and} \quad j(x) = 2x + 1.$$
Complete the following table. What do you notice? Draw a graph of these two functions. Are the two functions the same?

x	-2	-1	0	1	2
$h(x)$					
$j(x)$					

7. If a ball is thrown up from the ground with an initial velocity of 64 ft/sec, its height as a function of time, t, is given by
$$h(t) = -16t^2 + 64t.$$
  (a) Evaluate $h(1)$ and $h(3)$. What does this tell us about the height of the ball?
  (b) Sketch a graph of this function. Using a graphing calculator or computer, determine when the ball hits the ground and the maximum height of the ball.

8. Suppose $v(t) = t^2 - 2t$ gives the velocity, in ft/sec, of an object at time t, in seconds.
  (a) What is the initial velocity, $v(0)$?
  (b) When does the object have a velocity of zero?
  (c) What is the meaning of the quantity $v(3)$? What are its units?

9. Let $s(t) = 11t^2 + t + 100$ be the position, in miles, of a car driving on a straight road at time t, in hours. The car's velocity at any time t is given by $v(t) = 22t + 1$.
  (a) Use function notation to express the car's position after 2 hours. Where is the car then?
  (b) Use function notation to express the question, "When is the car going 65 mph?"
  (c) Where is the car when it is going 67 mph?

10. An epidemic of influenza spreads through a city. Figure 1.10 shows the graph of $I = f(w)$, where I is the number of individuals (in thousands) infected w weeks after the epidemic begins.

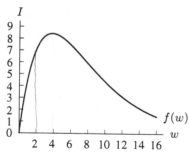

Figure 1.10

(a) Evaluate $f(2)$ and explain its meaning in terms of the epidemic.

(b) Approximately how many people were infected at the height of the epidemic? When did that occur? Write your answer in the form $f(a) = b$.

(c) Solve $f(w) = 4.5$ and explain what the solutions mean in terms of the epidemic.

(d) The graph was obtained using the formula $f(w) = 6w(1.3)^{-w}$. Use the graph to estimate the solution of the inequality $6w(1.3)^{-w} \geq 6$. Explain what the solution means in terms of the epidemic.

11. New York state income tax is based on what is called taxable income. For a person with a taxable income between $65,000 and $100,000, the tax owed is $4635 plus 7.875% of the taxable income over $65,000.

$4871.25

(a) Compute the tax owed by a lawyer whose taxable income is $68,000.

(b) Consider a lawyer whose taxable income is 80% of her total income, x, where x is between $85,000 and $120,000. Write a formula for $T(x)$, the taxable income. $T(x) = 0.8x$

(c) Write a formula for $L(x)$, the amount of tax owed by the lawyer in part (b). $L(x) = 0.063x - 483.75$

(d) Use $L(x)$ to evaluate the tax liability for $x = 85,000$ and compare your results to part (a). $4871.25

12. Consider the functions f and g whose values are given in Table 1.12.

(a) Evaluate $f(1)$ and $g(3)$.

(b) Describe in full sentences the patterns you see in the values for each function.

(c) Assuming that the patterns you observed in part (b) hold true for all values of x, calculate $f(5)$, $f(-2)$, $g(5)$, and $g(-2)$.

(d) Find formulas for $f(x)$ and $g(x)$.

TABLE 1.12

x	-1	0	1	2	3	4
$f(x)$	-4	-1	2	5	8	11
$g(x)$	4	1	0	1	4	9

13. In bowling, ten pins are arranged in a triangular fashion as shown below. If a fifth row were added, the total number of pins would be fifteen. Let $s(n)$ be the sum of the pins in rows 1 to n inclusive. For example, $s(3) = 1 + 2 + 3 = 6$.

row 4

row 3

row 2

row 1

Figure 1.11

(a) Complete Table 1.13.

TABLE 1.13

n	1	2	3	4	5
$s(n)$					

(b)   Using Table 1.13, verify that the following equation holds true for $1 \le n \le 5$:

$$s(n) = \frac{n(n+1)}{2}.$$

(c)   Assuming the formula for $s(n)$ holds for all n, calculate how many pins would be used if there were 100 rows.

14.   The Fibonacci sequence is a sequence of numbers that begins $1, 1, 2, 3, 5 \ldots$.

(a)   Notice that each term in the sequence is the sum of the two preceding terms. For example,

$$2 = 1 + 1, \quad 3 = 2 + 1, \quad 5 = 2 + 3, \ldots .$$

Based on this observation, complete the following table of values for $f(n)$, the nth term in the Fibonacci sequence.

TABLE 1.14

n	1	2	3	4	5	6	7	8	9	10	11	12
$f(n)$	1	1	2	3	5							

(b)   The table of values in part (a) can be completed even though we don't have a formula for $f(n)$. Does the fact that we don't have a formula mean that $f(n)$ is not a function?

(c)   Are you able to evaluate the following expressions in a way that is consistent with the observations from parts (a) and (b)? If so, do so; if not, explain why not.

$$f(0), \quad f(-1), \quad f(-2), \quad f(0.5).$$

1.3 DOMAIN AND RANGE

In Example 4 on page 4, we defined d to be the last digit of the nth listing in the Boston telephone directory. Although d is a function of n, the value of d is not defined for every possible value of n. For instance, it makes no sense to consider the value of d for $n = -3$, or $n = 8.21$, or, for that matter, $n = 10$ billion (since the Boston directory has far fewer than 10 billion listings). Thus, although d is a function of n, this function is defined only for certain values of n.

Notice also that d, the output value of this function, will always be a whole number between 0 and 9. This is because d stands for the last digit of a telephone number. Thus, although the value of d is defined for hundreds of thousands of listings, the values of d will always be a whole number between 0 and 9.

A function is often defined only for certain values of the independent variable. Also, the dependent variable often takes on only certain values. This leads to the following definitions:

> If $Q = f(t)$, then
> - the **domain** of f is the set of values for the independent variable, t.
> - the **range** of f is the set of values for the dependent variable, Q.

Thus, the domain of a function is the set of input values, and the range is the set of output values.

Example 1   The domain of the telephone directory function is $n = 1, 2, 3, \ldots, N$, where N is the total number of listings in the directory. The range of this function is $d = 0, 1, 2, \ldots, 9$, because the last digit of any listing must be one of these numbers.

If the domain of a function is not specified, we will usually take it to be all possible real numbers that make sense for the function. For example, we usually think of the domain of the function $f(x) = x^2$ as all real numbers, because we can substitute any real number into the formula $f(x) = x^2$. Sometimes, however, we may restrict the domain to suit a particular application. If the function $f(x) = x^2$ is used to represent the area of a square of side x, we consider only nonnegative values of x and restrict the domain to nonnegative numbers.

If a function is being used to model a real-world situation, the domain and range of the function are often determined by the constraints of the situation being modeled, as in the next example.

Example 2   The domain of the house-painting function $n = f(A)$, from Example 8 on page 12, is $A > 0$ because all houses have some positive area. There is a practical upper limit to A because houses cannot be infinitely large, but in principle, A can be as large or as small as we like as long as it is positive. Therefore we take the domain of f to be $A > 0$.

The range of this function is $n > 0$, because every house will require some positive amount of paint. In addition, if we assume we can only buy paint by the gallon, the value of n must be a positive integer: $n = 1, 2, 3, \ldots$.

Example 3   Algebraically speaking, the formula

$$T = \frac{1}{4}R + 40$$

can be used for all possible values of R. If we know nothing more about this function than its algebraic formula, we can use the set of all real numbers for its domain. And, as you can see in Figure 1.12, the formula for $T = \frac{1}{4}R + 40$ returns any value of T we like when we choose an appropriate R-value. Thus, the range of the function is also the set of all real numbers.

However, if we want to use this formula to represent the temperature T as a function of a cricket's chirp rate R, as we did in Example 3 on page 3, there are certain values of R we cannot use. For one thing, it doesn't make sense to talk about a negative chirp rate. Also, crickets can only chirp so fast, and there is some maximum chirp rate R_{max} that no cricket can physically exceed. This means that if we want to use this formula to express T as a function of R, we must restrict R to the interval $0 \leq R < R_{max}$, as shown in Figure 1.12.

The range of the cricket function will also be restricted. Since the chirprate must be non-negative, the smallest value of T occurs when $R = 0$. This happens at $T = 40$, as you can check for yourself. On the other hand, if the temperature gets too hot, the cricket won't be able to keep chirping faster, and if the temperature gets *too* hot, the cricket won't chirp at all – it will simply cook. Supposing a cricket can't keep chirping faster if its gets hotter than T_{max}, then the values of T must be restricted to the interval $40 \leq T \leq T_{max}$.

(a)

(b)
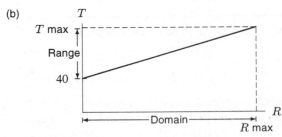

Figure 1.12

Using a Graph to Find the Domain and Range of a Function

One way to get a good idea of the domain and range of a function is to examine a graph of the function. It is customary to plot values of the independent variable (domain values) on the horizontal axis, and values of the dependent variable (range values) on the vertical axis. Consider the next example.

Example 4   Experiments suggest that the height of sunflowers[3] can be modeled by using the *logistic function*.

$$h(t) = \frac{260}{1 + 24(0.9)^t} \quad \text{for } t \geq 0 \text{ days,} \qquad \begin{array}{l}\text{where } h(t) \text{ gives the height of the sunflower}\\ \text{at the end of day } t.\end{array}$$

(a)   Using a graphing calculator or computer, sketch a graph of the height over 80 days.
(b)   What is the domain of this function? What is the range? What does this tell you about the height of these sunflowers?

Solution   (a)

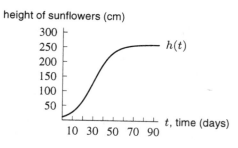

Figure 1.13

(b)   The domain: We could say that the domain is $t \geq 0$. However, note that there will be some upper bound on the domain, since the sunflower will die at some point. If we let T be the day on which the sunflower dies, we could say that the domain is $0 \leq t \leq T$. (However, $t \geq 0$ is also a reasonable answer for the domain.)

The range: We see on the graph that the smallest value of h occurs at $t = 0$. Evaluating, we obtain $h(0) = 10.4$ cm. Larger values of t result in larger values of $h(t)$. Tracing from left to right along the graph, you notice that as t-values get very large, $h(t)$-values approach 260 but never quite reach 260. Thus, the range of this function is $10.4 \leq h(t) < 260$. This information tells us that sunflowers typically grow to a height of about 260 cm.

Using a Formula to Find the Domain and Range of a Function

When a function is defined by a formula, its domain and range can often be determined algebraically. Consider the next example.

Example 5   Let $g(x)$ be defined by the formula

$$g(x) = \frac{1}{x}.$$

State the domain and range of $g(x)$.

Solution   The domain: For a function such as $g(x) = 1/x$, the domain is all real numbers except those which make the function undefined. The expression $1/x$ is defined for any real number x except 0 (division by 0 is undefined). Therefore,

Domain: all real x, $x \neq 0$.

---

[3] Adapted from "Growth of Sunflower Seeds" by H.S. Reed and R.H. Holland, Proc. Nat. Acad. Sci., 5, 1919.

The range: The range is all real numbers that the formula can return as output values. It is not possible for $g(x)$ to equal zero, since 1 divided by a real number is never zero. You can check that all real numbers except 0 are possible output values, so that is the range of $g(x)$.

Range: all real values, $g(x) \neq 0$.

You can confirm the domain and range by looking at Figure 1.14.

Figure 1.14

Example 6   Algebraically find the domain of $y = \dfrac{1}{\sqrt{x-4}}$.

Solution   The domain: The domain is all real numbers except those for which the function is undefined. The square root of a negative number is undefined, and so is division by zero. Therefore we need

$$x - 4 > 0.$$

Solving for x gives

$$x > 4.$$

Thus, the domain is all real numbers greater than 4.

Domain: $x > 4$.

We can often use algebraic methods to find the range of a function, too.

Example 7   Algebraically find the range of $y = 2 + \dfrac{1}{x}$.

Solution   The range is all real numbers which the function can return as output values.

We can determine explicitly which output values are possible by solving for the independent variable. To see why this is true, consider a specific example. Suppose we want to check if $y = -\frac{1}{2}$ is a possible y-value. This means we want to know whether there is an x-value which would result in $y = -\frac{1}{2}$. To see if there is such an x-value, we substitute $y = -\frac{1}{2}$ and solve for x:

$$-\frac{1}{2} = 2 + \frac{1}{x},$$

$$\frac{-5}{2} = \frac{1}{x},$$

or

$$x = \frac{-2}{5}.$$

This means that when we substitute $x = -\frac{2}{5}$, the result will be $y = -\frac{1}{2}$. Thus, $y = -\frac{1}{2}$ is in the range.

In general, we start with $y = 2 + \frac{1}{x}$ and solve for x to see which y-values are possible outputs:

$$y = 2 + \frac{1}{x}.$$

Subtracting 2 from both sides

$$y - 2 = \frac{1}{x}$$

and taking the reciprocal of both sides gives

$$x = \frac{1}{y - 2}.$$

From this formula we can see that if $y = 2$, x is undefined. That is, there is no x-value which makes $y = 2$. All other values of y are possible. Therefore the range of this function is all real numbers except 2. See Figure 1.15.

Range: all y values, $y \neq 2$.

Figure 1.15

Problems for Section 1.3

1. A movie theater seats 200 people. For any particular show, the amount of money the theater makes is a function of the number of people, n, in attendance. If a ticket costs \$4.00, find the domain and range of this function. Sketch its graph.

    D: $0 \leq n \leq 200$
    R: $0 \leq n \leq 800$

2. A car gets the best mileage at intermediate speeds. Sketch a possible graph of the gas mileage as a function of speed. Determine a reasonable domain and range for the function and justify your reasoning.

Use a calculator or computer to sketch a graph of each of the functions in Problems 3–14. Then state the domain and range of the function.

3. $y = \sqrt{x}$ D: $x \geq 0$ R: $y \geq 0$ 4. $y = \sqrt{x - 3}$ 5. $y = \sqrt{8 - x}$ D: $x \leq 8$ R: $y \geq 0$

6. $y = \dfrac{1}{x^2}$ D: all reals except $x = 0$ R: $y \geq 0$ 7. $y = \dfrac{1}{(x - 2)^2}$ D: all reals, $x \neq 2$ $y > 0$ 8. $y = \dfrac{-1}{(x + 1)^2}$

9. $y = x^2 + 1$ D: all reals   R: $y \geq 1$ 10. $y = x^2 - 4$ 11. $y = 9 - x^2$ D: all reals   R: $y \leq 9$

12. $y = x^3$ 13. $y = x^3 + 2$ D: all reals   R: all reals y 14. $y = (x - 4)^3$

In Problems 15–18, use a graph to help you find the range of each function on the given domain.

15. $y = \dfrac{1}{x^2}$, $-1 \leq x \leq 1$ D: all reals $x \neq 0$ R: $y \geq 1$ 16. $y = \dfrac{1}{x}$, $-2 \leq x \leq 2$

17. $y = x^2 - 4$, $-2 \leq x \leq 3$ R: $-4 \leq y \leq 5$ 18. $y = \sqrt{9 - x^2}$, $-3 \leq x \leq 1$

19. In month $t = 0$, a small group of rabbits escapes from a ship onto an island where there are no rabbits. The island rabbit population, $p(t)$, in month t is given by

    fifty rabbit

    $$p(t) = \frac{1000}{1 + 19(0.9)^t}, \quad t \geq 0.$$

    50   131   911

    10 moths later there was about 131 rabbits on island

    (a) Evaluate $p(0)$, $p(10)$, $p(50)$, and explain their meaning in terms of rabbits.
    (b) Sketch a graph of $p(t)$, $0 \leq t \leq 100$, and describe the graph in words. Does it suggest the growth in population you would expect among rabbits on an island?
    (c) Estimate the range of $p(t)$. What does this tell you about the rabbit population?
    (d) Explain how you can find the range of $p(t)$ from its formula.

    y

20. Bronze is an alloy or mixture of the metals copper and tin. The properties of bronze depend on the percentage of copper in the mix. A chemist decides to study the properties of a given alloy of bronze as the proportion of copper is varied. She starts with 9 kg of bronze that contain 3 kg of copper and 6 kg of tin and either adds or removes copper. Let $f(x)$ be the percentage of copper in the mix if x kg of copper are added ($x > 0$) or removed ($x < 0$).

    (a) State the domain and range of f. What does your answer mean in the context of bronze?
    (b) Find a formula in terms of x for $f(x)$.
    (c) If the formula you found in part (b) was not intended to represent the percentage of copper in an alloy of bronze, but instead simply defined an abstract mathematical function, what would be the domain and range of this function?

1.4 WORKING WITH FUNCTION NOTATION

Evaluating functions given by a formula can involve algebraic simplification, as the following example shows. Similarly, solving for the input, or independent variable, involves solving an equation algebraically.

Evaluating a Function

A formula like $f(x) = \frac{x^2+1}{5+x}$ is a rule that tells us what the function f does with its input value. In the formula, the letter x is a place-holder for the input value. Thus, to evaluate $f(x)$, we replace each occurrence of x in the formula with the value of the input.

Example 1   Let $g(x) = \dfrac{x^2 + 1}{5 + x}$. Evaluate the following expressions. Some of your answers will contain a.

   (a) $g(3)$ (b) $g(-1)$ (c) $g(a)$
   (d) $g(a - 2)$ (e) $g(a) - 2$ (f) $g(a) - g(2)$

Solution   (a) To evaluate $g(3)$, replace every x in the formula with 3:

$$g(3) = \frac{3^2 + 1}{5 + 3} = \frac{10}{8} = 1.25.$$

   (b) To evaluate $g(-1)$, replace every x in the formula with (-1):

$$g(-1) = \frac{(-1)^2 + 1}{5 + (-1)} = \frac{2}{4} = 0.5.$$

   (c) To evaluate $g(a)$, replace every x in the formula with a:

$$g(a) = \frac{a^2 + 1}{5 + a}.$$

(d) To evaluate $g(a-2)$, replace every x in the formula with $(a-2)$:

$$g(a-2) = \frac{(a-2)^2 + 1}{5 + (a-2)}$$
$$= \frac{a^2 - 4a + 4 + 1}{5 + a - 2}$$
$$= \frac{a^2 - 4a + 5}{3 + a}.$$

(e) To evaluate $g(a) - 2$, first evaluate $g(a)$ (as we did in part (c)), and then subtract 2:

$$g(a) - 2 = \frac{a^2 + 1}{5 + a} - 2$$
$$= \frac{a^2 + 1}{5 + a} - \frac{2}{1} \cdot \frac{5 + a}{5 + a}$$
$$= \frac{a^2 + 1}{5 + a} - \frac{10 + 2a}{5 + a}$$
$$= \frac{a^2 + 1 - 10 - 2a}{5 + a}$$
$$= \frac{a^2 - 2a - 9}{5 + a}.$$

(f) To evaluate $g(a) - g(2)$, subtract $g(2)$ from $g(a)$.

$$g(2) = \frac{2^2 + 1}{5 + 2} = \frac{5}{7}.$$

From part (c), $g(a) = \dfrac{a^2 + 1}{5 + a}$. Thus

$$g(a) - g(2) = \frac{a^2 + 1}{5 + a} - \frac{5}{7}$$
$$= \frac{7(a^2 + 1) - 5(5 + a)}{7(5 + a)}$$
$$= \frac{7a^2 - 5a - 18}{7(5 + a)}.$$

Example 2   Let $h(x)$ be a function defined by the equation $h(x) = x^2 + bx + c$, where b and c are constants. Evaluate the following expressions. (Your answers will involve b and c.)

(a) $h(2)$ (b) $h(b)$ (c) $h(2b)$ (d) $h(2x)$

Solution   Notice that, in our formula, x stands for the input. It will be helpful to rewrite our formula without using the letter x:

$$\text{Output} = h(\text{Input}) = (\text{Input})^2 + b \cdot (\text{Input}) + c.$$

(a) For $h(2)$, we have Input $= 2$, so

$$h(2) = (2)^2 + b \cdot (2) + c,$$

which simplifies to $h(2) = 2b + c + 4$.

(b) In this case, Input $= b$. Thus, we have

$$h(b) = (b)^2 + b \cdot (b) + c.$$

Simplifying gives $h(b) = 2b^2 + c$.

(c) For the input $2b$, we have

$$h(2b) = (2b)^2 + b \cdot (2b) + c$$
$$= 4b^2 + 2b^2 + c$$
$$= 6b^2 + c.$$

(d) To find $h(2x)$, we have

$$h(2x) = (2x)^2 + b \cdot (2x) + c$$
$$= 4x^2 + 2bx + c.$$

Finding Input Values

Example 3 In Example 6 on Page 21 we found the domain of the function $y = \frac{1}{\sqrt{x-4}}$.
(a) Find an x-value that results in $y = 2$.
(b) Is there an x-value that results in $y = -2$?

Solution (a) To find an x-value that results in $y = 2$, we must solve the equation:

$$2 = \frac{1}{\sqrt{x-4}} \qquad \text{Square both sides}$$
$$4 = \frac{1}{x-4} \qquad \text{Multiply by } x-4$$
$$4(x-4) = 1$$
$$4x - 16 = 1$$
$$x = \frac{17}{4} = 4.25.$$

The x-value is 4.25. (Note that in the second step in the solution, multiplying by $x-4$ was valid because $x \neq 4$, so $x - 4 \neq 0$.)
(b) There is no x-value that results in $y = -2$. Note that $\sqrt{x-4}$ is non-negative when it is defined, so its reciprocal, $y = \frac{1}{\sqrt{x-4}}$ is also non-negative. Thus, y cannot have a negative value for any x input.

If we are using a function to model a physical quantity and we solve an equation involving the function, we must choose the solutions that make sense in the context of the model. Consider the next example.

Example 4 Let $A = q(r)$ be the area of a circle of radius r, where r is in cm. Solve the equation $q(r) = 100$. What does your solution mean in the context of circles?

Solution The output of $q(r)$ is an area. In solving the equation $q(r) = 100$ for r, we are finding the radius of a circle whose area is 100 cm^2. Since the formula for the area of a circle is $q(r) = \pi r^2$, we have

$$q(r) = 100$$
$$\text{so} \quad \pi r^2 = 100$$
$$r^2 = \frac{100}{\pi}$$
$$r = \pm\sqrt{\frac{100}{\pi}}$$
$$\approx \pm 5.64.$$

We found two solutions for r, one positive and one negative. However, a circle cannot have a negative radius. Thus, the only solution that is useful for our model is $r = \sqrt{\frac{100}{\pi}} \approx 5.64$.

Inside and Outside Changes

When we write

$$Q = f(t),$$

we often speak of t, the input, as being "inside" the function and Q, the output, being on the "outside" of the function. A change inside the function's parentheses can be called an "inside change," and a change outside the function's parentheses can be called an "outside change."

Example 5 If $n = f(A)$ gives the number of gallons of paint needed to cover a house of area A ft², explain the meaning of the expressions $f(A + 10)$ and $f(A) + 10$ in the context of painting.

Solution These two expressions are similar in that they both involve adding 10. However, for $f(A + 10)$, the 10 is added on the inside. So we are adding 10 to the area, A. Thus,

$$n = f(\underbrace{A + 10}_{\text{area}}) = \begin{array}{c}\text{Amount of paint needed} \\ \text{to cover an area of } (A + 10) \text{ ft}^2\end{array} = \begin{array}{c}\text{Amount of paint needed} \\ \text{to cover an area 10 ft}^2 \\ \text{larger than } A\end{array}$$

The expression $f(A) + 10$ represents an outside change. We are adding 10 to $f(A)$, which represents an amount of paint, not an area. We have

$$n = \underbrace{f(A)}_{\substack{\text{Amount} \\ \text{of paint}}} + 10 = \begin{array}{c}\text{amount of paint needed} \\ \text{to cover a region of area } A\end{array} + 10 \text{ gals} = \begin{array}{c}\text{10 gallons more paint} \\ \text{than the amount needed} \\ \text{to cover an area } A\end{array}$$

In the first case, we added 10 square feet on the inside of the function, which means that now the house is 10 ft² larger. In the second case, we added 10 gallons to the outside, which means that we have 10 more gallons of paint than we need.

Example 6 Let $s(t)$ be the *average* weight (in pounds) of a baby boy at age t months, $0 \le t \le 12$. Suppose that V is the weight of a *particular* baby boy named Jonah. During Jonah's first year of life, his weight, V, is related to the average weight function $s(t)$ by the equation

$$V = s(t) + 2.$$

Find Jonah's weight at ages $t = 3$ and $t = 6$. What can you say about Jonah's weight in general?

Solution At $t = 3$, Jonah's weight is

$$V = s(3) + 2.$$

Since $s(3)$ is the average weight of a 3-month old boy, we see that at 3 months, Jonah weighs 2 pounds more than average. Similarly, at $t = 6$ we have

$$V = s(6) + 2,$$

which means that, at 6 months, Jonah weighs 2 pounds more than average. In general, Jonah weighs 2 pounds more than average.

Example 7 Suppose W is the weight of another particular baby boy named Ben. Ben's weight, W, is related to $s(t)$ by the equation

$$W = s(t + 4).$$

What can you say about Ben's weight at age $t = 3$ months? At $t = 6$ months? Assuming that babies increase in weight over the first year of life, decide if Ben is of average weight for his age, above average, or below average.

Solution Since Ben's weight is given by $W = s(t+4)$, at age $t = 3$ his weight is given by

$$W = s(3+4) = s(7).$$

We defined $s(7)$ to be the average weight of a 7-month old boy. At age 3 months, Ben's weight is the same as the average weight of 7-month old boys. Since, on average, a baby's weight increases as the baby grows, this means that Ben is heavier than the average for a 3-month old. Similarly, at age $t = 6$, Ben's weight is given by

$$W = s(6+4) = s(10).$$

Thus, at 6 months Ben's weight is the same as the average weight of 10 month old boys. In both cases, we see that Ben is above average in weight.

Notice that in Example 7, the equation

$$W = s(t+4)$$

involves an inside change, or a change in months. This equation tells us that Ben weighs as much as boys who are 4 months older than he is. However in Example 6, the equation

$$V = s(t) + 2$$

involves an outside change, or a change in weight. This equation tells us that Jonah is 2 pounds heavier than the average weight of boys his age. Although both equations tell us that the boys are heavier than average for their age, they do so in different ways.

Problems for Section 1.4

1. The following table shows values for functions $f(x)$ and $g(x)$:

x	0	1	2	3	4	5	6	7	8	9
$f(x)$	−10	−7	4	29	74	145	248	389	574	809
$g(x)$	−6	−7	6	33	74	129	198	281	378	489

(a) Evaluate
   (i) $f(x)$ for $x = 6$. 248   (ii) $f(5) - 3$. 142 378   (iii) $f(5 - 3)$. 4
   (iv) $g(x) + 6$ for $x = 2$. 12 (v) $g(x + 6)$ for $x = 2$.   (vi) $3g(x)$ for $x = 0$. −18
   (vii) $f(3x)$ for $x = 2$. 248 (viii) $f(x) - f(2)$ for $x = 8$. 570 (ix) $g(x+1) - g(x)$ for $x = 1$. 13

(b) Solve $x = 2$
   (i) $g(x) = 6$. $x = 8$ (ii) $f(x) = 574$. $x = 7$ (iii) $g(x) = 281$.

(c) The values in the table were obtained using the formulas $f(x) = x^3 + x^2 + x - 10$ and $g(x) = 7x^2 - 8x - 6$. Use the table to find two solutions to the equation $x^3 + x^2 + x - 10 = 7x^2 - 8x - 6$.

2. Let $f(x) = \left(\dfrac{x}{2}\right)^3 + 2$. The graph of $y = f(x)$ is in Figure 1.16.

    (a) Calculate $f(-6)$.
    (b) Solve $f(x) = -6$.
    (c) Find points that correspond to parts (a) and (b) on the graph of the function.
    (d) Calculate $f(4) - f(2)$. Draw a vertical line segment on the y-axis that illustrates this calculation.
    (e) If $a = -2$, compute $f(a+4)$ and $f(a) + 4$.
    (f) In part (e) above, what x-value corresponds to $f(a+4)$? To $f(a) + 4$?

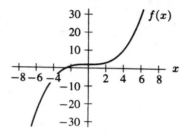

Figure 1.16   *Figure 1.17*

3. Let $g(x) = \dfrac{1}{x+1}$. The graph of $y = g(x)$ is in Figure 1.17.

    (a) Calculate $g(-2)$.
    (b) Solve $g(x) = -2$.
    (c) Find points that correspond to parts (a) and (b) on the graph of the function.
    (d) Calculate $g(0) - g(2)$. Draw a vertical line segment on the y-axis that illustrates this calculation.
    (e) If $a = -3$, compute $g(a-1)$ and $g(a) - 1$.
    (f) In part (e) above, what x-value corresponds to $g(a-1)$? To $g(a) - 1$?

4. Let $h(x) = \sqrt{x+4}$.

    (a) Find a point on the graph of $h(x)$ whose x-coordinate is 5.
    (b) Find a point on the graph whose y-coordinate is 5.
    (c) Sketch the graph and locate the points in parts (a) and (b).
    (d) Let $p = 2$. Calculate $h(p+1) - h(p)$.

5. Let $k(x) = 6 - x^2$.

    (a) Find a point on the graph of $k(x)$ whose x-coordinate is -2.
    (b) Find two points on the graph whose y-coordinates are -2.
    (c) Sketch the graph and locate the points in parts (a) and (b).
    (d) Let $p = 2$. Calculate $k(p) - k(p-1)$.

6. Let f be defined by

    $$f(x) = \frac{1}{x^2 - 5x + 6}.$$

    (a) Use algebra to find the domain of f.
    (b) Estimate the range of f using a graphing calculator or computer.

7. State the domain and range of each of the following functions.

    (a) $f(x) = \sqrt{x-4}$ (b) $r(x) = \sqrt{4 - \sqrt{x-4}}$
    (c) $g(x) = \dfrac{4}{4+x^2}$ (d) $h(x) = x^2 + 8x$

8. The number of gallons of paint, n, needed to cover a house is a function of the surface area, measured in ft^2, of the house. That is, $n = f(A)$. Match each story below to one expression.

   (a) I figured out how many gallons I needed and then bought two extra gallons just in case. iii
   (b) I bought enough paint to cover my house twice. i
   (c) I bought enough paint to cover my house and my welcome sign, which measures 2 square feet. ii

   (i) $2f(A)$ (ii) $f(A + 2)$ (iii) $f(A) + 2$

9. Suppose every day I take the same taxi over the same route from home to the train station. The trip is x miles, so the cost for the trip is $C = f(x)$. Match each story in (a)–(d) to a function in (i)–(iv) which represents the amount paid to the taxi driver.

   (a) I received a raise yesterday, so today I gave my driver a five dollar tip. ii
   (b) I had a new driver today and he got lost. He drove five extra miles and charged me for it. iv
   (c) I haven't paid my driver all week. Today is Friday and I'll pay what I owe for the week. i
   (d) The meter in the taxi went crazy and showed five times the number of miles I actually traveled. iii

   (i) $C = 5f(x)$ (ii) $C = f(x) + 5$ (iii) $C = f(5x)$ (iv) $C = f(x + 5)$

10. Let $R = P(t)$ be the number of rabbits living in the national park in month t. (See Example 6 on page 5.)

    (a) What does the expression $P(t + 1)$ represent?
    (b) What does the expression $2P(t)$ represent?

11. The perimeter of a square is the distance around its sides. If s is the length of one side of a square, then $P = 4s$. Let $P = h(s)$.

    (a) Evaluate $h(3)$.
    (b) Evaluate $h(s + 1)$. What does this expression represent?

12. Suppose $P(t)$ is the US population in millions today. Match each of the statements with one of the following formulas.

    I. The population 10 years before today. b

    II. Today's population plus 10 million immigrants. d

    III. Ten percent of the population we have today. c

    IV. The population after 100,000 people have emigrated. h

    (a) $P(t) - 10$ (b) $P(t - 10)$
    (c) $0.1P(t)$ (d) $P(t) + 10$
    (e) $P(t + 10)$ (f) $P(t)/0.1$
    (g) $P(t) + 0.1$ (h) $P(t) - 0.1$

13. Let $A = f(r)$ be the area of a circle as a function of radius.

    (a) Write a formula for $f(r)$. $= \pi r^2$
    (b) Which expression represents the area of a circle whose radius is increased by 10%? Explain.
        (i) $0.10f(r)$ (ii) $f(r) + 0.10)$ (iii) $f(0.10r)$
        (iv) $f(1.1r)$ (v) $f(r) + 0.10$
    (c) By what percent does the area increase if the radius is increased by 10%?

1.5 SEVERAL TYPES OF FUNCTIONS

Direct and Inverse Proportions

Many functions involve the concepts of *direct* or *inverse proportionality*:

> • A quantity y is **directly proportional to** x if
>
> $$y = kx, \quad k \text{ a constant.}$$
>
> In other words, y is directly proportional to x if y is equal to a constant *times* x.
> • A quantity y is **inversely proportional to** x if
>
> $$y = \frac{k}{x}, \quad k \text{ a constant.}$$
>
> In other words, y is inversely proportional to x if y is equal to a constant *divided* by x.
> • The constant k is called the **constant of proportionality**.

If we say "y is proportional to x," we mean that "y is directly proportional to x."

Example 1   The formula giving the circumference, C, of a circle as a function of the circle's diameter, d, is

$$C = \pi \cdot d.$$

Thus, circumference is directly proportional to diameter, and the constant of proportionality is $\pi \approx 3.14$. Figure 1.18 is a graph of the function $C = \pi \cdot d$. Notice that the graph is a straight line. We will study lines in Chapter 2.

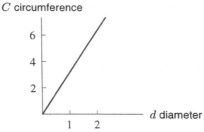

Figure 1.18: A graph of the function $C = \pi \cdot d$.

Figure 1.19: A graph of $T = \frac{50}{R}$

Example 2   If T is the time required to drive a fixed distance, D, at a constant rate, R, then T is inversely proportional to R because

$$T = \frac{D}{R}.$$

Here, the constant of proportionality is D, the distance driven. Suppose $D = 50$ km. Figure 1.19 is a graph of the function $T = 50/R$, which shows the time it takes to drive 50 km as a function of the rate. The graph of this function is called a *hyperbola*.

It is also possible for y to be directly or inversely proportional to a power of x. For example, if $y = kx^2$, where k is a constant, then y is directly proportional to x^2.

Example 3   The period of a pendulum, p, is the amount of time required for the pendulum to make one complete swing. For small swings, the period, p, is approximately proportional to the square root of l, the pendulum's length. So

$$p = k\sqrt{l} \quad \text{where } k \text{ is a constant.}$$

Notice that p is not directly proportional to l itself but to $\sqrt{l}$.

Example 4   An object's weight, w, is inversely proportional to the square of its distance, r, from the earth's center. This gives

$$w = \frac{k}{r^2}.$$

Here w is not inversely proportional to r, but to r^2.

We will now see that these four functions are all in the same family of functions.

Power Functions

We define a power function as follows:

> We say that $Q(x)$ is a **power function** of x if $Q(x)$ is proportional to a constant power of x. If k is the constant of proportionality, and if p is the power, then
>
> $$Q(x) = k \cdot x^p.$$

Note that functions defined by direct or inverse proportionality are examples of power functions. Thus, the function $C = \pi \cdot d$ from Example 1 is a power function with $p = 1$. Because $1/R = R^{-1}$, we can write the function in Example 2 as $T = 50 \cdot R^{-1}$. Thus T is a power function with $p = -1$. Likewise, $p = k\sqrt{l} = kl^{1/2}$ and $w = \frac{k}{r^2} = kr^{-2}$ are examples of power functions.

Graphs of Power Functions

Figure 1.20 shows the graphs of some power functions with positive integer powers and constant of proportionality $k = 1$.

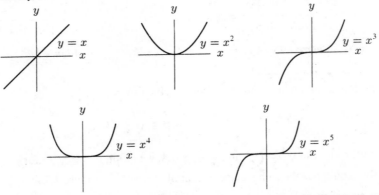

Figure 1.20: Graphs of power functions $Q(x) = x^p$ for $p = 1, 2, 3, 4, 5$

Notice the characteristic shapes of these graphs: the graphs of power functions with odd integer powers are in quadrants I and III, and the graphs of power functions with even integer powers are in quadrants I and II.

Figures 1.21 and 1.22 show the graphs of some power functions with negative integer powers.

Figure 1.21: Graph of
$Q(x) = x^{-1} = 1/x$

Figure 1.22: Graph of
$Q(x) = x^{-2} = 1/x^2$

Notice that the graphs of both functions approach the x- and y-axes. For these functions, the x-axis is called the *horizontal asymptote* and the y-axis is called the *vertical asymptote*.

Figures 1.23 and 1.24 show the graphs of power functions with fractional powers $p = \frac{1}{2}, \frac{1}{3}$.

Figure 1.23: $Q(x) = x^{1/2} = \sqrt{x}$

Figure 1.24: $Q(x) = x^{1/3} = \sqrt[3]{x}$

Many important functions in geometry and physics involve a constant power of the independent variable.

Example 5   Since $A = \pi r^2$, we know that the area of a circle of radius r is proportional to the square of the radius. Figure 1.25 is a graph of the function $A = \pi r^2$ with $r \geq 0$. Notice that the graph looks like the graph of $y = x^2$ in Figure 1.20 (with $x \geq 0$).

Figure 1.25: $A = \pi r^2$

Figure 1.26: $p = 0.8 l^{1/2}$

Example 6   The period, p, of a pendulum of length l is given by

$$p = \sqrt{\frac{2}{\pi}}\sqrt{l}.$$

Since we can write $\sqrt{l} = l^{1/2}$ and $\sqrt{\frac{2}{\pi}} \approx 0.8$, we graph $p = 0.8 l^{1/2}$ for $l \geq 0$ in Figure 1.26. Notice that this graph has the same shape as that of $y = x^{1/2}$ in Figure 1.23.

Example 7   Which of the following functions are power functions? For each power function, state the value of the constants k and p in the formula $Q = kx^p$.

(a) $f(x) = 13\sqrt[3]{x}$ (b) $g(x) = 2(x+5)^3$ (c) $u(x) = \sqrt{\frac{25}{x^3}}$ (d) $v(x) = 6 \cdot (3)^x$

Solution   The functions f and u are power functions; the functions g and v are not.

(a)   The function $f(x) = 13\sqrt[3]{x}$ is a power function because we can write its formula as

$$f(x) = 13x^{1/3}.$$

Here, $k = 13$ and $p = 1/3$.

(b)   Although the value of $g(x) = 2(x+5)^3$ is proportional to the cube of $x+5$, it is *not* proportional to a power of x. We cannot write $g(x)$ in the form $g(x) = kx^p$; thus, g is not a power function.

(c)   We can rewrite the formula for $u(x) = \sqrt{25/x^3}$ as

$$u(x) = \frac{\sqrt{25}}{\sqrt{x^3}}$$
$$= \frac{5}{(x^3)^{1/2}}$$
$$= \frac{5}{x^{3/2}}$$
$$= 5x^{-3/2}.$$

Thus, u is a power function. Here, $k = 5$ and $p = -3/2$.

(d)   Although the value of $v(x) = 6 \cdot 3^x$ is proportional to a power of 3, the power is not a constant – it is the variable x. Thus, $v(x)$ is not a power function. Notice that the similar-looking function $y = 6 \cdot x^3$ *is* a power function. However, $6 \cdot x^3$ and $6 \cdot 3^x$ are quite different.

The Absolute Value Function

Geometrically, the absolute value of a number is the number's distance from 0, measured along the number line. The notation for the absolute value function is

$$f(x) = |x| .$$

For example, $|4| = 4$. This is because the number four is 4 units away from 0 on the number line. Similarly, $|-3| = 3$. This is because -3 is 3 units away from 0 along the number line. (See Figure 1.27.)

Figure 1.27: Diagram showing $|4| = 4$ and $|-3| = 3$.

Notice that for $x \geq 0$, we have $|x| = x$. For $x < 0$, we have $|x| = -x$. Remember that $-x$ is a positive number if x is a negative number. For example, if $x = -3$, then

$$|-3| = -(-3) = 3.$$

We can give a definition of $f(x) = |x|$ in two pieces:

Absolute Value Function

$$f(x) = |x| = \begin{cases} x & \text{for} \quad x \geq 0 \\ -x & \text{for} \quad x < 0 \end{cases} .$$

Figure 1.28 is a graph of $f(x) = |x|$. Table 1.15 gives several values of $f(x)$.

TABLE 1.15
Absolute value function values

x	$|x|$
-3	3
-2	2
-1	1
0	0
1	1
2	2
3	3

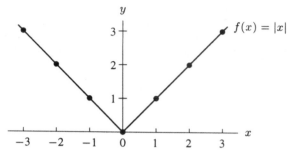

Figure 1.28: Absolute value function graph

The absolute value function is an example of a *piecewise defined function*. Another example is given below.

Piecewise Defined Functions

When we define a function using a formula, we sometimes use different formulas for different intervals of the domain. In that case, the function is said to be *piecewise defined*.

Example 8   Graph the function

$$f(x) = \begin{cases} x + 1, & x \le 2 \\ 1, & x > 2 \end{cases}$$

Solution   For $x \le 2$, we graph the line $y = x + 1$. We use a solid dot at the point $(2, 3)$ to show that it is included in the graph. For $x > 2$, we graph the horizontal line $y = 1$. We use an open circle at the point $(2, 1)$ to show that it is *not* included in the graph. (Note that $f(2) = 3$, and $f(2)$ cannot have more than one distinct value.) The graph is shown in Figure 1.29.

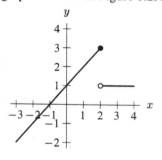

Figure 1.29

Example 9   The Ironman Triathlon is a race that consists of three parts: a 2.4 mile swim followed by a 112 mile bike race and then a 26.2 mile marathon. Suppose a participant swims steadily at 2 mph, cycles steadily at 20 mph, and then runs steadily at 9 mph.[4] Assuming that no time is lost during the transition from one stage to the next, find a formula which shows the distance d, covered in miles, as function of the elapsed time t in hours, from the beginning of the race. Graph the function.

[4]Data supplied by Susan Reid, Athletics Department, University of Arizona

Solution First, we calculate how long it took for the participant to cover each of the three parts of the race. The first leg took $2.4/2 = 1.2$ hours, the second leg took $112/20 = 5.6$ hours, and the final leg took $26.2/9 \approx 2.91$ hours. Thus, the participant finished the race in $1.2 + 5.6 + 2.91 = 9.71$ hours. For each leg of the race, we use the formula Distance = Rate · Time.

If $t \le 1.2$, that is, during the first leg, the speed is 2 mph, so

$$d = 2t \qquad \text{for} \qquad 0 \le t \le 1.2.$$

If $1.2 < t \le 1.2 + 5.6 = 6.8$, that is, during the second leg, the speed is 20 mph. The length of time spent in the second leg is $(t - 1.2)$ hours. Thus, by time t,

$$\text{Distance covered in the second leg} = 20(t - 1.2).$$

When the participant is in the second leg, $1.2 < t \le 6.8$, the total distance covered is the sum of the distance covered in the first leg (2.4 miles) plus the part of the second leg that has been covered by time t.

$$d = 2.4 + 20(t - 1.2)$$
$$= 20t - 21.6 \qquad \text{for } 1.2 < t \le 6.8.$$

Finally, in the third leg, $6.8 < t \le 9.71$, the speed is 9 mph. Since 6.8 hours were spent on the first two parts of the race, the length of time spent on the third leg is $(t - 6.8)$ hours. Thus, by time t,

$$\text{Distance covered in third leg} = 9(t - 6.8).$$

When the participant is in the third leg, the total distance covered is the sum of the distance covered in the first leg (2.4 miles) plus the distance already covered in the second leg (112 miles) plus the part of the third leg that has been covered by time t.

$$d = 2.4 + 112 + 9(t - 6.8)$$
$$= 9t + 53.2 \qquad \text{for } 6.8 < t \le 9.71.$$

We see that the formula for d is different on different intervals of t. We summarize as follows:

$$d = \begin{cases} 2t & \text{for} \quad 0 \le t \le 1.2 \\ 20t - 21.6 & \text{for} \quad 1.2 < t \le 6.8 \\ 9t + 53.2 & \text{for} \quad 6.8 < t \le 9.71. \end{cases}$$

Figure 1.30 gives a graph of the distance covered, d, as a function of time, t. Notice that the graph has three pieces.

Figure 1.30: Ironman Triathlon: d as a function of t

Problems for Section 1.5

1. The volume, V, of a sphere is given as a function of its radius, r, by

$$V = \frac{4}{3}\pi r^3.$$

   (a) Write V as proportional to a power of r. What is the constant of proportionality?
   (b) Write V as power function of r. What is the power?
   (c) Sketch a graph of V against r for $r \geq 0$.

2. The weight of an object a distance r from the earth's center is given by

$$w = \frac{k}{r^2}.$$

   (a) Write w as proportional to a power of r. What is the power of r?
   (b) Suppose $k = 1$. Sketch a graph of w against r.

3. The cost of denim fabric is directly proportional to the amount that you buy. Let $C(x)$ be the cost, in dollars, of x yards of denim fabric.

   (a) Write a formula for the cost, $C(x)$, in terms of x. Your answer will contain a constant, k.
   (b) A particular type of denim costs \$28.50 for 3 yards. Find the value of k and rewrite the formula for $C(x)$ using it.
   (c) How much will it cost to buy 5.5 yards of denim?

4. In Example 2 we saw that the time, T, needed to travel a fixed distance, D, is inversely proportional to the (constant) rate, R.

   (a) Find D if it takes 20 hours to travel this distance at a constant rate of 60 miles per hour.
   (b) Graph T as a function of R for $0 < R < 600$.
   (c) If $T = f(R)$, calculate $f(300)$ and label the corresponding point on your graph. What does $f(300)$ mean in the context of the problem?

Which of the functions in Problems 5–12 represent direct proportionality and which represent indirect proportionality? Write each function in the form $y = kx^p$ and identify the values of k and p.

5. $y = 0.34\left(\dfrac{x}{2}\right)$ 6. $y = x$ 7. $s = \dfrac{-t}{2}$

8. $y = -x$ 9. $C = 2\pi r$ 10. $f(x) = \dfrac{1}{x}$

11. $h(x) = \dfrac{2}{3x}$ 12. $y = mx$

Which of the functions in Problems 13–24 represent power functions? That is, can the function be written in the form $Q = kx^p$ for some Q and x? If so, identify the constant, k, and the power, p.

13. $y = (2x)^5$ 14. $y = \dfrac{3\sqrt{x}}{4}$ 15. $y = \dfrac{3}{x^5}$

16. $y = \dfrac{3}{x^{2/3}}$ 17. $l = \dfrac{-5}{t^{-4}}$ 18. $s = \dfrac{p^{1/2}}{p^3}$

19. $y = \dfrac{\frac{1}{3}}{2x^7}$ 20. $y = \dfrac{6}{\frac{-2}{x^5}}$ 21. $p(x) = 5(3)^x$

22. $f(q) = 2q^3 - 5$ 23. $g(m) = (5m + 1)^4$ 24. $r(y) = \dfrac{1}{2^y}$

25. The circulation time of a mammal—that is, the average time it takes for all the blood in the body to circulate once and return to the heart—is governed by the equation

$$t = 17.4m^{1/4},$$

where m is the body mass of the mammal in kilograms, and t is the circulation time in seconds.[5]

(a) Complete Table 1.16 which shows typical body masses in kilograms for various mammals.[6]

TABLE 1.16   *The mass of various animals*

Animal	Body mass (kg)	Circulation time (sec)
Blue whale	91000	
African elephant	5450	
White rhinoceros	3000	
Hippopotamus	2520	
Black rhinoceros	1170	
Horse	700	
Lion	180	
Human	70	

(b) If the circulation time of one mammal is twice that of another, what can be said about their body masses?

26. Ship designers usually construct scale models before building a real ship. The formula that relates the speed u to the hull length l of a ship is

$$u = k\sqrt{l},$$

where k is a positive constant. This constant k varies depending on the ship's design, but scale models of a real ship have the same k as the real ship after which they are modeled.[7]

(a) How fast should a scale model with hull length 4 meters travel to simulate a real ship with hull length 225 meters traveling 9 meters/sec?

(b) A new ship is to be built whose speed is to be 10% greater than the speed of an existing ship with the same design. What is the relationship between the hull lengths of the new ship and the existing ship?

---

[5]"Scaling–Why is animal size so important?'" by K. Schmidt-Nielsen, Cambridge University Press, England, 1984.

[6]"Dynamics of Dinosaurs and Other Extinct Giants" by R. McNiell Alexander, Columbia University Press, New York, 1989.

[7]"Dynamics of Dinosaurs and Other Extinct Giants" by R. McNiell Alexander, Columbia University Press, New York, 1989.

27. An astronaut's weight, w, is inversely proportional to the square of his distance, r, from the earth's center. Suppose that he weighs 180 pounds at the earth's surface, and that the radius of the earth is approximately 3960 miles.
    (a) Find the constant of proportionality, k.
    (b) Graph w as a function of r for $3960 < r < 6960$.
    (c) If $w = f(r)$, find $f(5000)$ and label the corresponding point on the graph. What does $f(5000)$ mean in the context of the problem?

28. The radius, r, of a sphere is proportional to the cube root of its volume, V.
    (a) A spherical tank has radius 10 centimeters and volume 4188.79 cubic centimeters. Find the constant of proportionality and write r as a function of V, that is, $r = f(V)$.
    (b) Graph $r = f(V)$ for $0 < V < 10,000$.
    (c) Suppose you would like to double the volume of the sphere in part (a). What should the new radius be? Write your answer using function notation, and label the corresponding point on the graph.

29. Express the area, A, of a circle as a function of its diameter, d.

30. Express the volume, V, of a sphere as a function of its diameter, d.

31. Many people believe that $\sqrt{x^2} = x$. We are going to investigate this claim graphically and numerically.
    (a) Use a graphing calculator or computer to graph the two functions x and $\sqrt{x^2}$ in the window $-5 \le x \le 5$, $-5 \le y \le 5$. Based on what you see, do you believe that $\sqrt{x^2} = x$? What function does the graph of $\sqrt{x^2}$ remind you of?
    (b) Complete Table 1.17. Based on this table, do you believe that $\sqrt{x^2} = x$? What function does the table for $\sqrt{x^2}$ remind you of? Is this the same function you found in part (a)?

    TABLE 1.17

x	-5	-4	-3	-2	-1	0	1	2	3	4	5
$\sqrt{x^2}$											

    (c) Prove that $\sqrt{x^2}$ is the same as the function you found in parts (a) and (b).
    (d) Use a graphing calculator or computer to graph the function $\sqrt{x^2} - |x|$ in the window $-5 \le x \le 5$, $-5 \le y \le 5$. Explain what you see.

32. This problem deals with the function $u(x) = |x|/x$.
    (a) Use a graphing calculator or computer to graph $u(x)$ in the window $-5 \le x \le 5$, $-5 \le y \le 5$. Explain what you see.
    (b) Complete Table 1.18. Does this table agree with what you found in part (a)?

    TABLE 1.18

x	-5	-4	-3	-2	-1	0	1	2	3	4	5
$|x|/x$											

    (c) Identify the domain and range of $u(x)$.
    (d) Comment on the claim that $u(x)$ can be written as

    $$u(x) \begin{cases} -1 & \text{if } x < 0, \\ 0 & \text{if } x = 0, \\ 1 & \text{if } x > 0. \end{cases}$$

Graph the piecewise-defined functions in Problems 33–36.

33. $f(x) = \begin{cases} -1, & -1 \le x < 0 \\ 0, & 0 \le x < 1 \\ 1, & 1 \le x < 2 \end{cases}$

34. $f(x) = \begin{cases} x + 4, & x \le -2 \\ 2, & -2 < x < 2 \\ 4 - x, & x \ge 2 \end{cases}$

35. $f(x) = \begin{cases} x^2, & x \le 0 \\ \sqrt{x}, & 0 < x < 4 \\ x/2, & x \ge 4 \end{cases}$

36. $f(x) = \begin{cases} x + 1, & -2 \le x < 0 \\ x - 1, & 0 \le x < 2 \\ x - 3, & 2 \le x < 4 \end{cases}$

37. In a particular city the charge for a taxi ride is \$1.50 for the first 1/8 of a mile, and \$0.25 for each additional 1/8 of a mile (rounded up to the nearest 1/8 mile).

   (a) Make a table showing the cost of a trip as a function of its length. Your table should start at zero and go up to one mile in 1/8-mile intervals.
   (b) What is the cost for a 5/8-mile ride?
   (c) How far can you go for \$3.00?
   (d) Sketch a graph that depicts the cost function for the table in part (a).

38. A contractor purchases gravel one cubic yard at a time.

   (a) A gravel driveway L yards long and 6 yards wide is to be poured to a depth of 1 foot. Find a formula for $n(L)$, the number of cubic yards of gravel the contractor buys, assuming that he buys 10 more cubic yards of gravel than are needed (to be sure he'll have enough).
   (b) Assuming no driveway can be less than 5 yards long, state the domain and range of $n(L)$. Sketch a graph of $n(L)$ showing the domain and range.
   (c) If the function $n(L)$ did not represent an amount of gravel, but was a mathematical relationship defined by the formula in part (a), what would be its domain and range?

39. A floor-refinishing company charges \$1.83 per square foot to strip and refinish a tile floor for up to 1000 square feet. There is an additional charge of \$350 for toxic waste disposal for any job which includes more than 150 square feet of tile.

   (a) Express the cost, y, of refinishing a floor as a function of the number of square feet, x, to be refinished.
   (b) Graph the function. Give the domain and range.

40. A private museum charges \$40 for a group of 10 or fewer people. A group consisting of more than 10 people must, in addition to the \$40, pay \$2 per person for the number of people above 10. For example, a group of 12 pays \$44 and a group of 15 pays \$50. The maximum group size is 50.

   (a) Draw a graph that represents this situation.
   (b) What are the domain and range of the cost function?

1.6 RATES OF CHANGE

The Average Rate of Change of a Function

Two cyclists take a cross-country trip. Figure 1.31 is a graph of their distance traveled as a function of time. (We let $t = 0$ at the start of the trip.)

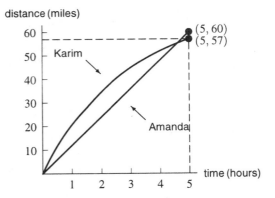

Figure 1.31: The distance traveled as a function of time

We can compare the speeds at which these two cyclists traveled by comparing their average speeds over the trip. Over any time interval, average speed is defined as:

$$\text{Average speed} = \frac{\text{Distance traveled}}{\text{Time elapsed}}.$$

Thus, during the time interval $0 \le t \le 5$ we have

$$\text{Amanda's average speed} = \frac{\text{Distance traveled}}{\text{Time elapsed}} = \frac{60 \text{ miles}}{5 \text{ hours}} = 12 \text{ mph}.$$

Over the same interval $0 \le t \le 5$,

$$\text{Karim's average speed} = \frac{\text{Distance traveled}}{\text{Time elapsed}} = \frac{57 \text{ miles}}{5 \text{ hours}} = 11.4 \text{ mph}.$$

Thus, Amanda's average speed was faster than Karim's.

The average speed is a special case of an average rate of change of a function. In general, if $Q = f(t)$ we write ΔQ for a change in Q and Δt for a change in t. Then we define:

The **average rate of change** of Q with respect to t over a given interval is

$$\text{Average rate of change} = \frac{\text{Change in the value of } Q}{\text{Change in the value of } t} = \frac{\Delta Q}{\Delta t}.$$

The average rate of change of the function $Q = f(t)$ is the ratio of the change in Q to the change in t. This ratio tells us how much Q changes for each unit change in t. For example, Figures 1.32 and 1.33 show that during the third hour of the trip, $2 \le t \le 3$,

$$\text{Karim's average speed} = \frac{10 \text{ miles}}{1 \text{ hour}} = 10 \text{ mph},$$

while

$$\text{Amanda's average speed} = \frac{12 \text{ miles}}{1 \text{ hour}} = 12 \text{ mph}.$$

Note that while Karim's average speed over the entire 5-hour trip was 11.4 mph, during the third hour his average speed was 10 mph. The average rate of change of a function may well be different on different intervals.

Figure 1.32: Karim   *Figure 1.33:* Amanda

Function Notation for the Average Rate of Change

Suppose we want to find the average rate of change of a function $Q = f(t)$ on the interval $a \le t \le b$.

$$\frac{\text{Average rate of change}}{\text{from } t = a \text{ to } t = b} = \frac{\text{Change in value of } Q}{\text{Change in value of } t} = \frac{\Delta Q}{\Delta t}.$$

On the interval from $t = a$ to $t = b$, the change in the value of t is given by

$$\Delta t = b - a.$$

Now, at $t = a$, the value of Q is $f(a)$, and at $t = b$, the value of Q is $f(b)$. Therefore, the change in the value of Q is given by

$$\Delta Q = f(b) - f(a).$$

This is illustrated in Figure 1.34. Notice that the average rate of change is given by the slope of the line segment joining the two points on the graph.

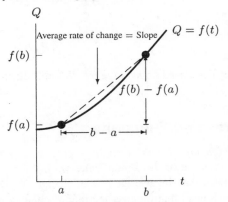

Figure 1.34: The graph of a function
$Q = f(t)$

Using function notation, we can express the average rate of change as follows:

$$\frac{\text{Average rate of change}}{\text{of a function } Q = f(t)} = \frac{\text{Change in the value of } Q}{\text{Change in the value of } t} = \frac{\Delta Q}{\Delta t} = \frac{f(b) - f(a)}{b - a}.$$
on the interval $a \le t \le b$

Example 1   Table 1.19 gives the annual sales (in millions) of compact discs (CDs) and vinyl long playing records (LPs) between 1982 to 1987. What were the average rates of change of the annual sales of CDs and of LPs between 1982 and 1987?

TABLE 1.19   *Annual Sales of CDs and LPs (in millions)*

year	1982	1983	1984	1985	1986	1987
	$t = 0$	$t = 1$	$t = 2$	$t = 3$	$t = 4$	$t = 5$
CD sales	0	0.8	5.8	23	53	102
LP Sales	244	210	205	167	125	105

Solution   Let $s = C(t)$ be the sales (in millions) of CDs during year t, where $t = 0$ represents the year 1982. We see from Table 1.19 that

$$\begin{array}{c} \text{Average rate of change of } s \\ \text{from } t = 0 \text{ to } t = 5 \end{array} = \frac{\Delta s}{\Delta t} = \frac{C(5) - C(0)}{5 - 0}$$

$$= \frac{102 - 0}{5}$$

$$= 20.4 \text{ million discs/year.}$$

Thus, CD sales increased on average by 20.4 million discs/year between 1982 and 1987.

Let $q = L(t)$ be the sales (in millions) of LPs during year t. We see from Table 1.19 that

$$\begin{array}{c} \text{Average rate of change of } q \\ \text{from } t = 0 \text{ to } t = 5 \end{array} = \frac{\Delta q}{\Delta t} = \frac{L(5) - L(0)}{5 - 0}$$

$$= \frac{105 - 244}{5}$$

$$= -27.8 \text{ million records/year.}$$

Thus, LP sales decreased on average by 27.8 million records/year between 1982 and 1987.

Increasing and Decreasing Functions

The terms *increasing* or *decreasing* have precise definitions when referring to functions. Consider the previous example of the annual sales (in millions) of both CD's and LP's between 1982 and 1987. We showed that the average rate of change of CD sales is positive on the interval $0 \le t \le 5$. Similarly, we showed that the average rate of change of LP sales is negative on the same interval. The annual sales of CDs is an example of an *increasing function*, and the annual sales of LPs is an example of a *decreasing function*. In general we say the following:

If $Q = f(t)$,
- f is an **increasing function** if the average rate of change of f with respect to t is positive on every interval.
- f is a **decreasing function** if the average rate of change of f with respect to t is negative on every interval.

Saying that $Q = f(t)$ is an increasing function means that any increase in the value of t results in an increase in the value of Q. Similarly, $Q = f(t)$ is a decreasing function if any increase in the value of t results in a decrease in the value of Q.

Example 2 Let $A = q(r)$ give the area, A, of a circle as a function of its radius, r. An increase in the radius, r, results in an increase in the area, A. Therefore, $A = q(r)$ in an increasing function. Remember that this means that the average rate of change $\Delta A / \Delta r$ is always positive.

Notice that the graph of $q(r)$ in Figure 1.35 climbs as we move from left to right.

Figure 1.35: The graph of $A = q(r)$, the area of a circle of radius r, rises when read from left to right

Example 3 Carbon-14 is a radioactive element that exists naturally in the atmosphere. Over time, carbon-14 turns slowly into other elements in a process known as radioactive decay. The tissues of living organisms absorb carbon-14 from the atmosphere. When an organism dies, carbon-14 is no longer absorbed and the amount present at death begins to decay.

If we let $L = g(t)$ be the quantity of carbon-14 (in micrograms, μg) present in a tree t years after its death, then g is a decreasing function of t. The average rate of change of the level of carbon-14 with respect to time is always negative, since the amount of carbon-14 is decaying over time. Suppose a tree's tissues contain 200 μg (micrograms) of carbon-14 at the time of the tree's death. Table 1.20 gives the amount of carbon-14 in the tree at year t (where $t = 0$ is the year of the tree's death).

TABLE 1.20 *Quantity of carbon-14*

t, years	0	1000	2000	3000	4000	5000
L, quantity of carbon-14 (μg)	200	177	157	139	123	109

The graph of $L = g(t)$ is shown in Figure 1.36. The function is a decreasing function, and its graph falls as we move from left to right.

Figure 1.36: The graph of $L = g(t)$, the amount of carbon-14 remaining in year t, falls when read from left to right

In general, we can identify an increasing or decreasing function from its graph as follows:

- The graph of an increasing function rises when read from left to right.
- The graph of a decreasing function falls when read from left to right.

Many functions have intervals on which they are increasing and others on which they are decreasing. These intervals can be identified from the graph. Whenever the function is increasing, the average rate of change on any subinterval is positive and the graph climbs; whenever the function is decreasing, the average rate of change on any subinterval is negative and the graph falls.

Concavity and Rates of Change

In the example at the beginning of this section, we considered the distance traveled by two bikers as functions of time.

Figure 1.37: Karim's distance from the biking club as a function of time

Figure 1.38: Amanda's distance from the biking club as a function of time

We found that Amanda's average speed was 12 mph during the five hour trip. The fact that her graph is a straight line means that her speed was constant throughout the trip. If the graph of a function is not a straight line, then the rate of change of the function is not constant. If a graph shows upward curvature, it is described as *concave up*, and if it shows downward curvature, it is described as *concave down*.

Example 4   What is the concavity of the graph of Karim's distance traveled as a function of time? Was Karim's speed (that is, the rate of change of distance with respect to time) increasing, constant, or decreasing?

Solution   Figure 1.37 shows downward curvature so the graph is concave down. Table 1.21 shows Karim's speed was decreasing throughout the entire five hour trip. Figure 1.39 shows how the decreasing speed can be visualized on the graph.

TABLE 1.21   Karim's distance as a function of time, with the average speed for each hour

t, time (hours)	d, distance (miles)	average speed, $\Delta d / \Delta t$ (mph)
0	0	
		20 mph
1	20	
		15 mph
2	35	
		10 mph
3	45	
		7 mph
4	52	
		5 mph
5	57	

Figure 1.39: Karim's distance as a function of time

Example 5   Table 1.22 gives values of $L = g(t)$, the quantity of carbon-14 (in μg) remaining in a tree t years after its death. These data have been plotted in Figure 1.40 and a dashed curve has been drawn in to help us see the trend in the data. We see from the graph that L is a decreasing function, so its rate of change is always negative. What can we say about the concavity of the graph, and what does this mean about the rate of change of the function?

TABLE 1.22 $L = g(t)$

t, time (years)	L, amount (grams)	rate of change $\Delta g / \Delta t$ (gm/yr)
0	200	
		−0.0182 gm/yr
5,000	109	
		−0.0098 gm/yr
10,000	60	
		−0.0054 gm/yr
15,000	33	

Figure 1.40: Graph of $L = g(t)$, the quantity of carbon-14 in a tree t years after its death

Solution   The graph shows upward curvature, so its shape is concave up. Table 1.21 shows that the rate of change of the function is increasing. Figure 1.40 shows how the increasing rate of change can be visualized on the graph.

Summary

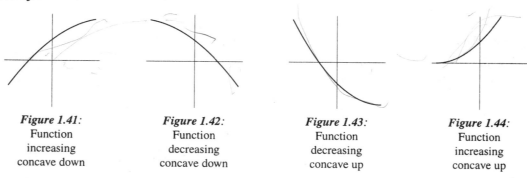

Figure 1.41:
Function
increasing
concave down

Figure 1.42:
Function
decreasing
concave down

Figure 1.43:
Function
decreasing
concave up

Figure 1.44:
Function
increasing
concave up

As we can see in Figures 1.41-1.44, concavity does not depend upon whether the function is increasing or decreasing. If the function's rate of change is constant, its graph is a line and has no concavity. Otherwise, we have the following relationships between concavity and rate of change:

- If f is a function whose average rate of change increases (gets less and less negative or more and more positive as you move from left to right), then the graph of f is **concave up**. That is, the graph bends upward.

- If f is a function whose average rate of change decreases (gets less and less positive or more and more negative as you move from left to right), then the graph of f is **concave down**. That is, the graph bends downward.

Problems for Section 1.6

1. Table 1.19 on page 42 gives the annual sales (in millions) of compact discs and vinyl long playing records. What was the average rate of change of annual sales between
   (a) 1982 and 1983?   (b) 1986 and 1987?
   (c) Interpret these results in terms of sales.

2. Because scientists know how much carbon-14 a living organism should have in its tissues, they can measure the amount of carbon-14 present in the tissue of a fossil and then calculate how long it took for the original amount to decay to the current level, thus determining the time of the organism's death. Suppose a tree fossil is found to contain 130 μg of carbon-14, and scientists determine from the size of the tree that it would have contained 200 μg of carbon-14 at the time of its death. Using Table 1.20 on page 43, approximately how long ago did the tree die?

3. The surface of the sun has dark areas known as *sunspots*. Sunspots are cooler than the rest of the sun's surface, although they are still quite hot. It has been discovered that the number of visible sunspots fluctuates with time, as shown in Figure 1.45. Based on the figure, is the number of sunspots, s, observed during year t a function of t? If so, is s a strictly increasing or strictly decreasing function of t?

Figure 1.45: The number of sunspots as a function of time

4. Using the graph from Figure 1.45, state approximate time intervals on which s is an increasing function of t.

5. The graph of the function $y = f(x)$ is in Figure 1.46.

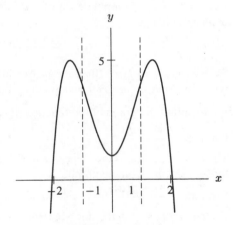

Figure 1.46: $y = f(x)$

On which intervals is $f(x)$ increasing? decreasing? concave up? concave down?

6. Use Table 1.22 to compute the average rate of change of $L = g(t)$, the quantity of carbon-14 remaining in a tree t-years after its death. Do this for the intervals $0 \leq t \leq 5000$, and $5000 \leq t \leq 10,000$ and $10,000 \leq t \leq 15,000$. Are these rates of change increasing?

7. The most freakish change in temperature ever recorded was from $-4°$F to $45°$F between 7:30 am and 7:32 am on January 22, 1943 at Spearfish, South Dakota.[8] What was the average rate of change of the temperature for this time period?

----

[8]"The Guinness Book of Records", 1995.

8. Table 1.23 gives two populations (in thousands) over a 17–year period.

    TABLE 1.23

year	1980	1982	1985	1990	1997[9]
P_1 (thousands)	42	46	52	62	76
P_2 (thousands)	82	80	77	72	65

    (a) Find the average rate of change of each population on the following intervals:
         (i)   1980 to 1990   (ii)   1980 to 1997   (iii)   1985 to 1997
    (b) What do you notice about the average growth rate for each population? Explain what the growth rate tells you about each population.

9. Table 1.24 shows two populations for five different years. Find the average rate of change of each population over the following intervals.
    (a)   1980 to 1990   (b)   1985 to 1997   (c)   1980 to 1997

    TABLE 1.24

year	1980	1982	1985	1990	1997
P_1 (hundreds)	53	63	73	83	93
P_2 (hundreds)	85	80	75	70	65

10. Let $f(x) = 16 - x^2$. Compute each of the following expressions, and interpret each as an average rate of change.
    (a) $\dfrac{f(2) - f(0)}{2 - 0}$ (b) $\dfrac{f(4) - f(2)}{4 - 2}$ (c) $\dfrac{f(4) - f(0)}{4 - 0}$

    (d) Sketch a graph of $f(x)$. Illustrate each ratio in parts (a)–(c) by sketching the line segment with the given slope. Over which interval is the average rate of decrease the greatest?

11. Figure 1.47 shows the graph of the function $g(x)$.
    (a) Estimate $\dfrac{g(4) - g(0)}{4 - 0}$.
    (b) The ratio in part (a) is the slope of a line segment joining two points on the graph. Sketch this line segment on the graph.
    (c) Estimate $\dfrac{g(b) - g(a)}{b - a}$ for $a = -9$ and $b = -1$.
    (d) On the graph, sketch the line segment whose slope is given by the ratio in part (c).

    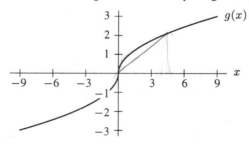

    Figure 1.47

---

[9] 1997 figures are projected estimates

12. Table 1.25 is a data set corresponding to the times achieved every 10 meters by Carl Lewis in the 100 meter final of the World Championship in Rome in 1987.[10]

TABLE 1.25   *Carl Lewis' times at 10 meter intervals*

Time (sec)	0.00	1.94	2.96	3.91	4.78	5.64	6.50	7.36	8.22	9.07	9.93
Distance (meters)	0	10	20	30	40	50	60	70	80	90	100

(a) For each successive time interval, calculate the average rate of change of distance. What is a common name for the average rate of change of distance?

(b) Where did Carl Lewis attain his maximum speed during this race? Some runners are running their fastest as they cross the finish line. Does that seem to be true in this case?

13. Table 1.26 gives the amount of garbage produced in the US (in millions of tons per year) as reported by the EPA.[11]

TABLE 1.26

t (year)	1960	1965	1970	1975	1980	1985	1990
G (millions of tons of garbage)	90	105	120	130	150	165	180

(a) What is the value of Δt for consecutive entries in this table? 5

(b) Calculate the value of ΔG for each pair of consecutive entries in this table. 15,15,10,20,15,15

(c) Are all the values of ΔG you found in part (b) the same? What does this tell you? No G is not a linear fn. of t the rate of change is not constant

14. Figure 1.48 shows distance traveled as a function of time.

(a) Find ΔD and Δt between:

(i) $t = 2$ and $t = 5$ (ii) $t = 0.5$ and $t = 2.5$ (iii) $t = 1.5$ and $t = 3$

(b) Compute the rate of change, $\Delta D/\Delta t$, and interpret its meaning.

D (miles)

t (hours)

Figure 1.48

15. Table 1.19 on page 42 shows that CD sales are a function of LP sales. Is it an increasing or decreasing function? decreasing

16. If $f(x)$ is increasing and concave down and $f(0) = 1$ and $f(10) = 7$, What can be said about $f(5)$?

---

[10]"Mathematical Models of Running" by W. G. Pritchard, SIAM Review, 35, 1993, pages 359 - 379

[11]adapted from Characterization of Solid Waste in the United States, 1992, EPA

17. Match each story with the table and graph which best represent it.

(a) When you study a foreign language, the number of new verbs you learn increases rapidly at first, but slows almost to a halt as you approach your saturation level. E   (II)

(b) You board an airplane in Philadelphia heading west. Your distance from the Atlantic Ocean, in kilometers per minute, increases at a constant rate. G I

(c) The interest on your savings plan is compounded annually. At first your balance grows slowly, but its rate of growth continues to increase. F II

(E)

x	0	5	10	15	20	25
y	20	275	360	390	395	399

(F)

x	0	5	10	15	20	25
y	20	36	66	120	220	400

(G)

x	0	5	10	15	20	25
y	20	95	170	245	320	395

(I)   (II)   (III)

Follow these steps for each of the functions in Problems 18–23 to investigate its rate of change and concavity.

(a) Complete the table of values for the functions. (If the function is undefined for a given x value, say so.)

x	-5	-4	-3	-2	-1	$-\frac{3}{4}$	$-\frac{1}{2}$	$-\frac{1}{4}$
y								

x	0	$\frac{1}{4}$	$\frac{1}{2}$	$\frac{3}{4}$	1	2	3	4	5
y									

(b) Sketch a graph of the function for $-5 \leq x \leq 5$. Based on your table in part (a), choose a suitable range of y-values.

(c) Give the domain and range of the function.

(d) For what values of x is the function increasing? Decreasing?

(e) For what values of x is the function concave up? Concave down?

18. $y = x^2$ 19. $y = x^3$ 20. $y = \dfrac{1}{x}$

21. $y = \dfrac{1}{x^2}$ 22. $y = \sqrt{x}$ 23. $y = \sqrt[3]{x}$

The graphs of $y = \dfrac{1}{x}$ and $y = \dfrac{1}{x^2}$ approach the x- and y-axes. The x-axis (the horizontal line $y = 0$) is called a *horizontal asymptote* for the graph, and the y-axis (the vertical line $x = 0$) is called a *vertical asymptote*. In Problems 24–27, you will see that other horizontal and vertical lines can be asymptotes for a graph.

24. Let $f(x) = \dfrac{1}{x - 3}$.

    (a) Complete Table 1.27 for x-values close to 3. What happens to the values of $f(x)$ as x approaches 3 from the left? From the right?

TABLE 1.27

x	2	2.5	2.75	2.9	2.99	3	3.01	3.1	3.25	3.5	4
$f(x)$											

    (b) Complete Tables 1.28 and 1.29. What happens to the values of $f(x)$ as x takes very large positive values? As x takes very large negative values?

TABLE 1.28

x	5	10	100	1000
$f(x)$				

TABLE 1.29

x	-5	-10	-100	-1000
$f(x)$				

    (c) Sketch a graph of $y = f(x)$. Give the equations of the horizontal and vertical asymptotes.

25. Let $g(x) = \dfrac{1}{(x + 2)^2}$.

    (a) Complete Table 1.30 for x-values close to -2. What happens to the values of $g(x)$ as x approaches -2 from the left? From the right?

TABLE 1.30

x	-3	-2.5	-2.25	-2.1	-2.01	-2	-1.99	-1.9	-1.75	1.5	-1
$g(x)$											

    (b) Complete Tables 1.31 and 1.32. What happens to the values of $g(x)$ as x takes very large positive values? As x takes very large negative values?

TABLE 1.31

x	5	10	100	1000
$g(x)$				

TABLE 1.32

x	-5	-10	-100	-1000
$g(x)$				

    (c) Sketch a graph of $y = g(x)$. Give the equations of the horizontal and vertical asymptotes.

26.   Let $F(x) = \dfrac{x^2 - 1}{x^2}$.

   (a)   Complete Table 1.33 for x-values close to 0. What happens to the values of $F(x)$ as x approaches 0 from the left? From the right?

TABLE 1.33

x	-1	-0.5	-0.25	-0.1	-0.01	0	0.01	0.1	0.25	0.5	1
$F(x)$											

   (b)   Complete Tables 1.34 and 1.35. What happens to the values of $F(x)$ as x takes very large positive values? As x takes very large negative values?

TABLE 1.34

x	5	10	100	1000
$F(x)$				

TABLE 1.35

x	-5	-10	-100	-1000
$F(x)$				

   (c)   Sketch a graph of $y = F(x)$. Give the equation of the horizontal and vertical asymptotes.

27.   Let $G(x) = \dfrac{2x}{x + 4}$.

   (a)   Complete Table 1.36 for x-values close to -4. What happens to the values of $G(x)$ as x approaches -4 from the left? From the right?

TABLE 1.36

x	-5	-4.5	-4.25	-4.1	-4.01	-4	-3.99	-3.9	-3.75	-3.5	-3
$G(x)$											

   (b)   Complete Tables 1.37 and 1.38. What happens to the values of $G(x)$ as x takes very large positive values? As x takes very large negative values?

TABLE 1.37

x	5	10	100	1000
$G(x)$				

TABLE 1.38

x	-5	-10	-100	-1000
$G(x)$				

   (c)   Sketch a graph of $y = G(x)$. Give the equations of the horizontal and vertical asymptotes.

28.   When a sky-diver free-falls vertically from a plane, his speed increases from 0 ft/sec and approaches a final speed of between 176 ft/sec (120 mph) and 352 ft/sec (240 mph), depending on the individual's body and its position.

   (a)   Sketch a possible graph of the speed of a sky-diver as a function of the time of the fall.
   (b)   Sketch a graph which shows the distance the sky-diver has fallen as a function of the time of the fall. Make sure the concavity of your graph is consistent with the graph you drew in part (a).
   (c)   When a sky-diver opens his parachute his speed drops to a new terminal speed of about 22 ft/sec (15 mph) within 5 seconds no matter how fast he was traveling before opening the parachute. (Landing at 22 ft/sec is like jumping down from a 10 foot wall.) Draw a graph of the speed of a sky-diver as a function of the time of the fall, for a sky diver who free falls, reaching a speed of 180 ft/sec, and then opens his parachute, eventually landing at 22 ft/sec. Based on practical knowledge, when do you expect that the sky-diver experiences the greatest discomfort? Identify this place on your graph.

(d)   Table 1.39 contains data obtained from the United States Parachute Association that show the sky diver's distance fallen (in feet) as a function of the time (in seconds). Graph the data and sketch a curve connecting the data points. How well does your graph from part (b) match the general shape of this graph?

From Table 1.39 calculate the average rate of change—for example, the first average rate of change would be $(16 - 0)/(1 - 0) = 16$ and would be placed at time 0.5 sec, the average of 0 and 1. Is this graph similar to the one you drew in part (a)?

TABLE 1.39   *Sky-diver's distance fallen (Free-fall, spread-eagle position)*

(sec)	0	1	2	3	4	5	6	7	8	9	10	11	12
Distance (feet)	0	16	62	138	242	366	504	652	808	971	1138	1309	1483

29.   The rate at which water is entering a reservoir is given for time $t > 0$ by the graph in Figure 1.49. A negative rate means that water is leaving the reservoir. For each of the following statements, give every interval on which it holds true:

Figure 1.49

(a)   The volume of water is increasing.
(b)   The volume of water is constant.
(c)   The volume of water is increasing fastest.
(d)   The volume of water is decreasing.

REVIEW PROBLEMS FOR CHAPTER ONE

1.   The nautilus, a multi–chambered mollusk, the canal of the inner ear, and petals of certain flowers have the spiral shape shown in Figure 1.50.

Figure 1.50

(a)   Is y a function of x?   No
(b)   Is x a function of y?   NO
(c)   Is there any interval on the x-axis for which y is a function of x?   yes

2. Figure 1.51 represents the depth of the water at Montauk Point, New York for a given day in November. Using the graph determine the following:

    (a)   How many high tides took place on this day?
    (b)   How many low tides took place on this day?
    (c)   How much time elapsed in between high tides?

depth of water (feet)

```
                  time (hours)
   4  8  12 16 20 24
```

Figure 1.51

3. Figure 1.52 shows the average monthly temperature in Albany, New York, over a twelve-month period. (January is month 1.)

    (a)   Make a table showing average temperature as a function of the month of the year.
    (b)   What is the warmest month in Albany?
    (c)   Over what interval of months is the temperature increasing? Decreasing?

average temperature (°F)

Figure 1.52

4. According to Jill Phillips, a home economist, the ideal size refrigerator for a family is 8 cubic feet for two people, plus 1 cubic foot for each additional member of the family for families with 3 through 10 members.[12]

    (a)   Construct a table showing the size of the ideal refrigerator as a function of the number of family members. From your table, what size refrigerator should a family of 5 own?
    (b)   Plot a graph with refrigerator size on the vertical axis and the number of family members on the horizontal axis.
    (c)   From your graph, estimate the ideal sized refrigerator for a family of 6.
    (d)   Construct a formula which relates the size S to n, the number of family members.

---

[12]"Rules of Thumb" by T. Parker, Houghton Mifflin, Boston, 1983.

5. In 1947, Jesse Owens, the US gold medal track star of the 1930s and 1940s, ran a 100 yard race against a horse. The race, "staged" in Havana, Cuba, is filled with controversy; some say Owens received a head start, others claim the horse was drugged. Owens himself revealed some years later that the starting gun was placed next to the horse's ear causing the animal to rear and remain at the gate for a few seconds. Figure 1.53 depicts speeds measured against time for the race.

   (a) How fast were Owens and the horse going at the end of the race?
   (b) When were the participants both traveling at the same speed?

Figure 1.53

6. (a) Is the area, A, of a square a function of the length of one of its sides, s?
   (b) Is the area, A, of a rectangle a function of the length of one of its sides, s?

7. Consider the graph in Figure 1.54. An open circle represents a point which is not included.

   (a) Is y a function of x? Explain.
   (b) Is x a function of y? Explain.
   (c) The domain of $y = f(x)$ is $0 \le x < 4$. What is the range of $y = f(x)$?

Figure 1.54

8. Is the graph of $y = |x|$ concave up?

9. A person's blood sugar level at a particular time of the day is partially determined by the time of the most recent meal. After a meal, blood sugar level increases rapidly, then slowly comes back down to a normal level. Sketch a graph showing a person's blood sugar level as a function of time over the course of a day. Label the axes to indicate normal blood sugar level and the time of each meal.

10. Match each of the following descriptions with an appropriate graph and table of values.

   (a) The weight of your jumbo box of Fruity Flakes decreases by an equal amount every week.

   (b) The machinery depreciated rapidly at first, but its value declined more slowly as time went on.

   (c) In free fall, your distance from the ground decreases at an increasing rate.

   (d) For a while it looked like the decline in profits was slowing down, but then they began declining ever more rapidly.

(A)

x	0	1	2	3	4	5
y	400	384	336	256	144	0

(B)

x	0	1	2	3	4	5
y	400	320	240	160	80	0

(C)

x	0	1	2	3	4	5
y	400	184	98	63	49	43

(D)

x	0	1	2	3	4	5
y	412	265	226	224	185	38

(I)   (II)

(III)   (IV)

11. From December 1906 until July 1907, Bombay experienced a plague spread by rats. Table 1.40 shows the total number of deaths at the end of each month.[13]

   TABLE 1.40   *The total number of deaths at the end of each month during the Bombay plague*

Month	0	1	2	3	4	5	6	7
Deaths	4	68	300	1290	3851	7140	8690	8971

[13]Data extracted from "A contribution to the mathematical theory of epidemics" by W. O. Kermack and A. G. Mckendrick, Proc. Roy. Soc., 115A, 1927, pages 700-721

O-7

(a) When was the number of deaths increasing? Decreasing?
(b) For each successive month, construct a table showing the average rate of change in the number of deaths.
(c) From the table you constructed in part (b) when will the graph of the number of deaths be concave up? Concave down?
(d) When was the average rate of change of deaths the greatest? How is this related to part (c)? What does this mean in human terms as far as the spread of this epidemic is concerned?
(e) Enter Table 1.40 on a graph and dash in a curve to help you see the trend in the data. From this graph identify where the curve is increasing, decreasing, concave up, concave down. Compare your answers to those you found in parts (a) and (c). On the graph identify your answer to part (d), namely, the place when the average rate of change of deaths was greatest.
(f) Ultimately 9100 people died due to this plague. Estimate at what time half this number was dead.

12. A price increases 5% due to inflation and is then reduced 10% for sale. Express the final price as a function of the original price, P.

13. The surface area of a cylindrical aluminum can is a measure of how much aluminum the can requires. If the can has radius r and height h, its surface area A and its volume V are given by the equations:
$$A = 2\pi r^2 + 2\pi rh \quad \text{and} \quad V = \pi r^2 h.$$

(a) The volume, V, of a 12 oz cola can is 355 cm^3. A cola can is approximately cylindrical. Express its surface area A as a function of its radius r, where r is measured in centimeters. [Hint: First solve for h in terms of r.]
(b) Sketch a graph of $A = s(r)$, the surface area of a cola can whose volume is 355 cm^3, for $0 \le r \le 10$. Label your axes.
(c) What is the domain of $s(r)$? Based on the sketch you made in (b), what, approximately, is the range of $s(r)$?
(d) The cola manufacturers wish to use the least amount of aluminum (in cm^2) necessary to make a 12 oz cola can. Use your answer in (c) to determine the minimum amount of aluminum needed. State the values of r and h that would minimize the amount of aluminum used.
(e) The radius of a real 12 oz cola can is about 3.25 cm. Show that real cola cans use more aluminum than necessary to hold 12 oz of cola. Why do you think cola cans are not made to these specifications?

14. Consider an 8-foot tall cylindrical water tank with a base of diameter 6 feet.
(a) How much water can the tank hold?
(b) How much water is in the tank if the water is 5 feet deep?
(c) Write a formula for the volume of water as a function of its depth in the tank.

15. The purchase of batches of goods is a common practice in business. Goods are purchased periodically throughout the year in lots and put into storage. The stored goods are used as needed until the supply is exhausted or reaches a predetermined minimum, called the safety stock. Then a new order is placed.
(a) Sketch a graph of time versus quantity in inventory without a safety stock.
(b) On the same graph, draw the curve with a safety stock. Mark the interval between orders and the points when the shipment is received.

16.   An incumbent politician running for reelection declared that the number of violent crimes is no longer rising and is presently under control. Does the graph shown in Figure 1.55 support this claim? Why or why not?

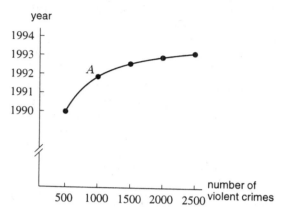

Figure 1.55

17.   If $g(x) = x\sqrt{x} + 100x$, find
(a) $g(100) = 11000$
(b) $g(4/25) = 16.064$
(c) $g(1.21 \cdot 10^4)$

18.   Let $h(x) = x^2 + bx + c$. Evaluate and simplify:
(a) $h(1)$
(b) $h(b + 1)$

19.   For n a positive integer, the product $1 \times 2 \times 3 \times \cdots \times (n-1) \times n$ is called n *factorial*, and is written $n!$.

(a)   Let $p(n) = n!$ for n a positive integer. Evaluate $p(n)$ for $n = 1, 2, 3, \ldots, 10$. Compile your results in a table.
(b)   Most calculators can evaluate $n!$. What is the largest value of n for which your calculator will compute $n!$?

20.   Let $r(x)$ be the average number of pounds of trash recycled in a given week by those households producing a total of x pounds of trash in a week. For example, $r(10)$ is the average amount of trash recycled per household among all households producing 10 pounds of trash per week.

(a)   Give lower and upper bounds for $r(q)$, where q is some quantity of trash.
(b)   A study indicates that, as a rule, when $A > B$, $r(A) > r(B)$. The authors of the study conclude that households producing more trash are also more conscientious about recycling. Do you think the study supports this conclusion? If not, what additional evidence would be needed?

21.   Find the domain and range for each of the following functions:
(a) $m(x) = 9 - x$
(b) $n(x) = 9 - x^4$
(c) $q(x) = \sqrt{x^2 - 9}$

22.   The cruising speed V of birds at sea-level (in meters/sec) is determined [14] by the mass M of the bird (in grams), and the surface area S of the wings exposed to the air (in square meters). It is given by

$$V = 0.164\sqrt{\frac{M}{S}}.$$

---

[14]"The Simple Science of Flight" by H. Tennekes, MIT Press, Cambridge, 1996.

(a) The mass of a partridge is half the mass of a hawk. Their wing surface areas are typically 0.043 and 0.166 square meters, respectively. Which bird has the faster cruising speed? The cruising speed of the partridge is 15.6 meters/sec. What are the masses of the partridge and the hawk?

(b) The wing surface area of a Canadian goose is typically 12 times that of an American robin, whereas the mass of the goose is 70 times that of the robin. Which bird has the faster cruising speed? The mass and cruising speed of the American robin are typically 80 grams and 9.5 meters/sec, respectively. What are the wing surface areas of the Canadian goose and the American robin?

(c) Using a graphing calculator or computer to plot V against different masses M, for birds with the same surface area of 0.01 square meters—swallows, martins, swifts, and so on. How would you describe the graph in words? What happens to the cruising speed as the mass increases?

(d) Use a graphing calculator or computer to plot V against different wing surface areas S, for birds with the same mass 784 grams—falcons, hawks, and so on. How would you describe the graph in words? What happens to the cruising speed as the wing surface area increases?

(e) When a bird dives it draws in its wings. What happens to its cruising speed? Is this realistic?

23. In Example 3 we saw that the period, p, of a pendulum is proportional to the square root of its length, l.

(a) The pendulum in a grandfather clock is 3 feet long and has a period of 1.924 seconds. Find the constant of proportionality, and write p as a function of l, $p = f(l)$.

(b) Graph $p = f(l)$ for $0 < l < 250$.

(c) The period of Foucault's pendulum, built in 1851 in the Pantheon in Paris, was 15.59 seconds. Find the length of the pendulum, and write your answer using function notation. Locate the corresponding point on your graph.

24. A certain subway train serves 19 stations, numbered 1 through 19. Although passengers can board the train at any of its 19 stops, most of its passengers board at the first station. The train has a capacity of 700 people. Define $p(n)$ to be the number of passengers on a given day who board the train at the first station and exit at station number n or lower.

(a) State the domain and range of $p(n)$.

(b) Interpret the expression $p(1)$. Describe a scenario where $p(1) > 0$.

(c) Is $p(n)$ increasing, decreasing, neither, or can't we tell? Explain.

25. While white-water rafting, the guide in a kayak accompanies the raft. At points where the river is narrow, the kayak moves ahead of the raft, then waits for the raft to catch up. Where the river is wide, the kayak stays alongside the raft. The raft moves faster in regions where the river is narrow than in regions where the river is wide. Suppose that a kayak and a raft travel down the Reventazón River in Costa Rica. The river is narrow for the first half-mile, then wide for the next three quarters of a mile, then narrow for another two miles, and lastly wide for a mile.

(a) Sketch the graph of the raft's distance from its starting point as a function of time. Label the narrow and wide regions of the river on your graph.

(b) On the same graph as in part (a), sketch the position of the kayak as a function of time.

26. Academics have suggested that loss of worker productivity can result from sleep deprivation. An article in the Sunday, September 26, 1993, *New York Times* quotes David Poltrack, the senior vice president for planning and research at CBS, as saying that seven million Americans are staying up an hour later than usual to watch talk show host David Letterman. The article goes on to quote Timothy Monk, a professor at the University of Pittsburgh School of Medicine, as saying ". . . my hunch is that the effect [on productivity due to sleep deprivation among this group] would be in the area of a 10 percent decrement." The article next quotes Robert Solow, a Nobel prize-winning professor of economics at MIT, who suggests the following procedure to estimate the impact that this loss in productivity will have on the US economy – an impact he dubbed "the Letterman loss." First, Solow says, we find the percentage of the work force who watch the program. Next, we determine this group's contribution to the gross domestic product (G.D.P.). Then we reduce the group's contribution by 10% to account for the loss in productivity due to sleep deprivation. The amount of this reduction is "the Letterman loss."

    (a) The article estimated that the G.D.P. is $6.325 trillion, and that 7 million Americans watch the show. Assume that the nation's work force is 118 million people and that 75% of David Letterman's audience belongs to this group. What percentage of the work force is in Dave's audience?

    (b) What percent of the G.D.P. does David Letterman's audience contribute? How much money do they contribute?

    (c) How big is "the Letterman Loss"?

27. Table 1.41 shows the population of Ireland [15] at various times between 1780 and 1910, where 0 corresponds to 1780.

TABLE 1.41 *The population of Ireland from 1780 to 1910, where 0 corresponds to 1780*

Year	0	20	40	60	70	90	110	130
Population (millions)	4.0	5.2	6.7	8.3	6.9	5.4	4.7	4.4

0 – 60 years   60 – 130 years

    (a) When was the population increasing? Decreasing?

    (b) For each successive time interval, construct a table showing the average rate of change of the population.

    (c) From the table you constructed in part (b), when is the graph of the population concave up? Concave down?

    (d) When was the average rate of change of the population the greatest? The least? How is this related to part (c)? What does this mean in human terms?

    (e) Graph the data in Table 1.41 and join the points by a curve to help you see the trend in the data. From this graph identify where the curve is increasing, decreasing, concave up and concave down. Compare your answers to those you got in parts (a) and (c). Identify the region you found in part (d).

    (f) Something catastrophic happened in Ireland between 1780 and 1910. When? Do you know what happened in Ireland at that time to cause this catastrophe?

---

[15] Adapted from "Mathematical Models in the Social, Management and Life Sciences" by D. N. Burghes and A. D. Wood, Ellis Horwood, 1980, page 104.

28. The relationship [16] between the swimming speed U (in cm/sec) of a salmon to the length l of the salmon (in cm) is given by the equation

$$U = 19.5\sqrt{l}.$$

(a) If one salmon is 4 times the length of another salmon, how are their swimming speeds related?

(b) Use a graphing calculator or computer to graph the function $U = 19.5\sqrt{l}$. Describe what you see using words such as increasing, decreasing, concave up, concave down.

(c) What property that you described in part (b) allows you to answer the question "Do larger salmon swim faster than smaller ones?"

(d) What property that you described in part (b) allows you to answer the following question? Imagine you have four salmon—two small and two large. The smaller salmon differ in length by 1 cm, as do the two larger. Is the difference in speed between the two smaller fish, greater than, equal to, or smaller than the difference in speed between the two larger fish?

29. At a supermarket checkout, a scanner records the prices of the foods you buy. In order to protect consumers, the state of Michigan passed a "scanning law" that says something similar to the following:

> If there is a discrepancy between the price marked on the item and the price recorded by the scanner, the consumer is entitled to receive 10 times the difference between those prices; this amount given must be at least $1 and at most $5. Also, the consumer will be given the difference between the prices, in addition to the amount calculated above.

For example: If the difference is 5¢, you should receive $1 (since 10 times the difference is only 50¢ and you are to receive at least $1), plus the difference of 5¢. Thus, the total you should receive is $1.00 + $0.05 = $1.05,

If the difference is 25¢, you should receive 10 times the difference in addition to the difference, giving $(10)(0.25) + 0.25 = \$2.75$,

If the difference is 95¢, you should receive $5 (because $10(.95) = \$9.50$ is more than $5, the maximum penalty), plus 95¢, giving $5 + 0.95 = \$5.95$.

(a) What is the lowest possible refund?

(b) Suppose x is the difference between the price scanned and the price marked on the item, and y is the amount refunded to the customer. Write a formula for y in terms of x. (Hints: Look at the sample calculations. Your answer may be a function defined in pieces.)

(c) What would the difference between the price scanned and the price marked have to be in order to obtain a $9.00 refund?

(d) Sketch a graph of y as a function of x.

30. Many printing presses are designed with large plates that print a fixed number of pages as a unit. Each unit is called a *signature*. Suppose a particular press prints signatures of 16 pages each. Suppose $C(p)$ is the cost of printing a book of p pages, assuming each signature printed costs $0.14.

(a) What would be the cost of printing a book of 128 pages? 129 pages? p pages?

(b) What are the domain and range of C?

(c) Sketch a graph of $C(p)$ for $0 \le p \le 128$.

---

[16] From K. Schmidt-Nielsen, *Scaling—Why is animal size so important?* (London: Cambridge University Press, 1984).

Chapter 2

Linear Functions

2.1   WHAT MAKES A FUNCTION LINEAR?

A Constant Rate of Change

In Chapter 1, we considered the average rate of change of a function on an interval. We saw that any function whose average rate of change is constant has a graph which is a straight line on that interval. For example, suppose we are driving on Interstate 5 from Los Angeles to San Francisco. If we drive at a constant speed of 60 mph, that is, at a constant rate of travel (the rate of change of the distance driven with respect to time), then the graph of distance as a function of time is a straight line. If a function's average rate of change stays the same on every interval, we can refer to it as *the* rate of change of the function.

A function whose rate of change is constant is called a *linear function*, and any quantity which grows or changes at a constant rate can be modeled by a linear function. The set of all such functions is called the *family of linear functions*.

Population Growth

Mathematical models of population growth are used by city planners to project the growth of towns and cities and by federal policymakers to project the growth of states and countries. Biologists and ecologists model the growth (or decline) of animal populations in the wild and physicians model the spread of a viral infection in the bloodstream. A linear growth model assumes that the population grows (or decreases) at a constant rate. Consider the following example:

Example 1   Suppose a town of 30,000 people grows by 2000 people every year. If P gives the town's population, then P is a linear function of the time, t, measured in years, because the population is growing at the constant rate of 2000 people per year.

   (a) Make a table that gives the town's population every five years over a 20-year period. Sketch a graph of the population over time.
   (b) Find a formula for P in terms of t.

Solution   (a) Let's calculate the population every five years for the first 20 years. The initial population in year $t = 0$ is $P = 30{,}000$ people. Since the town grows by 2000 people every year, after five years it will have grown by

$$5 \text{ years} \times \frac{2000 \text{ people}}{\text{year}} = 10{,}000 \text{ people}.$$

Thus, in year $t = 5$ the population is given by

$$P = \text{initial population} + \text{new people} = 30{,}000 + 10{,}000 = 40{,}000.$$

Similarly, after ten years the population is given by

$$P = 30{,}000 + \underbrace{10 \text{ years} \times 2000 \text{ people/year}}_{20{,}000 \text{ new people}} = 50{,}000.$$

In year $t = 15$ the population is given by

$$P = 30{,}000 + \underbrace{15 \text{ years} \times 2000 \text{ people/year}}_{30{,}000 \text{ new people}} = 60{,}000,$$

and in year $t = 20$,

$$P = 30{,}000 + \underbrace{20 \text{ years} \times 2000 \text{ people/year}}_{40{,}000 \text{ new people}} = 70{,}000.$$

These results are shown in Table 2.1 and Figure 2.1, where a dashed line shows the trend in the data.

TABLE 2.1 *The size of the population over a 20-year period*

t, years	P, population
0	30,000
5	40,000
10	50,000
15	60,000
20	70,000

Figure 2.1: The town's population over 20 years

(b)   From part (a), we see that the size of the population is given by

$$P = \text{initial population} + \text{new people}$$
$$= 30{,}000 + \text{years} \times 2000 \text{ people/year},$$

so a formula for P in terms of t is

$$P = 30{,}000 + t \cdot 2000, \quad \text{or} \quad P = 30{,}000 + 2000t.$$

Since the population increases at a constant rate, the graph of the population data in Figure 2.1 is a straight line. If we calculate the population for other years, the new points will also fall along the *same* straight line. This is not a coincidence. In fact, the family of linear functions gets its name from this property. In general:

- A **linear function** describes a quantity that changes at a constant rate.
- The graph of any linear function is a straight line.

Financial Applications of Linear Functions

Economists and accountants often use linear models, such as *straight-line depreciation*.

Example 2   Suppose that a small business spends $20,000 on new computer equipment. For tax purposes, the value of this equipment is considered to go down, or *depreciate*, over time. This makes sense: Computer equipment may be state-of-the-art today, but after several years it will be outdated and run-down. Suppose that this business chooses to depreciate its computer equipment over a five-year period. This means that after five years the equipment is valued (for tax purposes) at $0. Straight-line depreciation means that the rate of change of value with respect to time is assumed to be constant.

Chapter 2/   3

If V is the value and t the number of years, we see that the

$$\begin{array}{l}\text{Average rate of}\\\text{change of value}\\\text{from } t=0 \text{ to } t=5\end{array} = \frac{\text{change in value}}{\text{change in time}} = \frac{\Delta V}{\Delta t} = \frac{-\$20{,}000}{5 \text{ years}} = -\$4000 \text{ per year.}$$

In other words, since the equipment's value depreciates by \$20,000 in five years, it drops at the constant rate of \$4000 per year. (Notice that ΔV is negative because the value of the equipment decreases.) Table 2.2 gives the value of the equipment each year. The data have been plotted in Figure 2.2. Since $V = f(t)$ is a linear function, its graph is a straight line.

TABLE 2.2 *The value of computer equipment depreciates over a 5-year period*

t, year	V, value (\$)
0	20,000
1	16,000
2	12,000
3	8,000
4	4,000
5	0

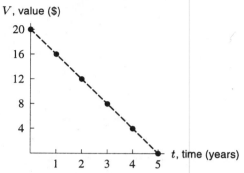

Figure 2.2: The value of computer equipment depreciates over a 5-year period

The total cost of producing a product is another application of linear functions in economics.

Example 3 A woodworker goes into business selling fine wooden rocking horses. His start-up costs, including tools, plans, and advertising, total \$5000. Labor and materials for each horse cost \$350.
(a) Calculate the woodworker's total cost to make 1, 2, 5, 10, and 20 rocking horses. Sketch a graph of C, the woodworker's total cost, versus n, the number of rocking horses that he carves.
(b) Find a formula for C in terms of n.
(c) What is the rate of change of this function? What does the rate of change tell you about the woodworker's expenses?

Solution (a) To carve one horse would cost the woodworker \$5000 in start-up costs plus \$350 for labor and material, a total of \$5350. Thus, if $n = 1$, we have

$$C = \underbrace{5000}_{\text{start-up costs}} + \underbrace{350}_{\text{extra cost for 1 horse}} = 5350.$$

Similarly, for 2 horses

$$C = \underbrace{5000}_{\text{start-up costs}} + \underbrace{2 \cdot 350}_{\text{extra cost for 2 horses}} = 5700,$$

and for 5 horses

$$C = \underbrace{5000}_{\text{start-up costs}} + \underbrace{5 \cdot 350}_{\text{extra cost for 5 horses}} = 6750.$$

Similar calculations show that for 10 horses the cost is \$8500, and for 20 horses $C = 12{,}000$. These results have been recorded in Table 2.3 and plotted in Figure 2.3.

TABLE 2.3 *The total cost of carving n rocking horses*

n, number of horses	C, total cost (\$)
0	5000
1	5350
2	5700
5	6750
10	8500
20	12,000

Figure 2.3: The total cost of carving n wooden rocking horses

Notice that it costs the woodworker \$5000 to carve 0 horses since he buys all the necessary tools, plans, and advertising even if he never carves a single horse.

(b) From part (a), the woodworker's total cost is given by

$$C = \underbrace{5000}_{\text{start-up costs}} + \underbrace{n \cdot 350}_{\text{extra cost for } n \text{ horses}},$$

so a formula for C in terms of n is

$$C(n) = 5000 + 350n.$$

(c) According to the definition given in Section 1.6, the average rate of change of this function is

$$\text{Rate of change} = \frac{\Delta C}{\Delta n} = \frac{\text{change in cost}}{\text{change in number of horses carved}}.$$

We know that each additional horse costs an extra \$350. We can write

$$\Delta C = 350 \qquad \text{if} \qquad \Delta n = 1.$$

Thus, the rate of change is given by

$$\frac{\Delta C}{\Delta n} = \frac{\$350}{1 \text{ horse}} = \$350 \text{ per horse}.$$

This tells us that the total cost increases at a constant rate of \$350 per horse.

A General Formula for the Family of Linear Functions

In Example 1, we considered a town whose population is growing at a constant rate. We found that a formula for this function is

$$\underset{\text{population}}{\text{Current}} = \underbrace{\underset{\text{population}}{\text{Initial}}}_{\text{30,000 people}} + \underbrace{\underset{\text{rate}}{\text{Growth}}}_{\substack{\text{2000 people} \\ \text{per year}}} \times \underbrace{\underset{\text{years}}{\text{Number of}}}_{t}$$

$$P = 30,000 + 2000t.$$

In Example 3, the woodworker's total cost, C, as a function of the number of horses that he carves, n, is given by

$$\underset{\text{cost}}{\text{Total}} = \underbrace{\underset{\text{cost}}{\text{Start-up}}}_{\$5000} + \underbrace{\underset{\text{horse}}{\text{Cost per}}}_{\$350 \text{ per horse}} \times \underbrace{\underset{\text{horses}}{\text{Number of}}}_{n}$$

$$C = 5000 + 350n.$$

The formulas for both of these linear functions follow the same overall pattern:

$$\underset{\text{quantity}}{\text{Dependent}} = \underset{\text{value}}{\text{Initial}} + \underset{\text{change}}{\text{Rate of}} \times \underset{\text{quantity}}{\text{Independent}}.$$

This word equation is a *general formula* for the family of linear functions. It turns out that *every* linear function has a formula that fits this word equation. We can use algebraic symbols to make this general equation more compact. To do this, suppose that y is a linear function of x and that the rate of change, or slope, of this function is called m. Also suppose that b is the initial value of y (that is, b is the value of y when $x = 0$, or the y-intercept). Then the word equation can be written as

$$\underset{\substack{\text{Dependent}\\\text{quantity}}}{y} = \underset{\substack{\text{Initial}\\\text{value}}}{b} + \underset{\substack{\text{Rate of}\\\text{change}}}{m} \cdot \underset{\substack{\text{Independent}\\\text{quantity}}}{x}.$$

Different linear functions have different values for m and b. In summary:

If $y = f(x)$ is a linear function, then a formula for y in terms of x can be written as

$$y = b + m \cdot x$$

where b and m are constants known as the **parameters** of the general equation.

- m is called the **slope**, and gives the rate of change of y with respect to x. Thus,

$$m = \frac{\Delta y}{\Delta x}.$$

If (x_0, y_0) and (x_1, y_1) are any two distinct points on the graph of f, then

$$m = \frac{\Delta y}{\Delta x} = \frac{y_1 - y_0}{x_1 - x_0}.$$

- b is called the y**-intercept** and gives the value of y for $x = 0$. In mathematical models, b typically represents an initial or starting value of the dependent quantity.

Example 4   In Example 1, the population is given by $P = 30{,}000 + 2000t$. The slope, $m = 2000$, tells us that the town grows by 2000 people per year. The vertical intercept, $b = 30{,}000$, tells us that in year $t = 0$ the town had 30,000 people. In Example 3, the rocking-horse function is $C = 5000 + 350n$. The slope, $m = 350$, indicates that the total cost increases at a rate of \$350 per horse. The value $b = 5000$ indicates that the carpenter's start-up costs are \$5000.

Example 5   If V is the value of computer equipment t years after the equipment is purchased, find a formula for V in terms of t. Assume that the value of the new equipment is \$20,000 and that the value drops to \$0 after five years have elapsed. (See Example 2.)

Solution   In Example 2, we established that $V = f(t)$ is a linear function, that is, its rate of change is constant. Therefore, we have $V = b + mt$. Since b is the initial value, $b = \$20{,}000$. We calculated the constant rate of change of this function:

$$\frac{\Delta V}{\Delta t} = \frac{-\$20{,}000}{5 \text{ years}} = -4000 \text{ dollars per year.}$$

Since m is the rate of change, $m = -4000$. Thus,

$$V(t) = 20{,}000 - 4000t.$$

The general formula for a linear function is

$$y = b + mx.$$

This is called the *slope-intercept formula*, since it gives the slope, m, and the y-intercept, b, for the line.

Another common form is called the *standard form* of a line. For constants $A, B,$ and C, the standard form is

$$Ax + By = C.$$

If (x_0, y_0) is a point on the line and its slope is m, then the *point-slope form* is

$$\frac{y - y_0}{x - x_0} = m$$

or

$$y - y_0 = m(x - x_0).$$

You can verify that these formulas do indeed represent linear functions.

Tables for Linear Functions

We know how to recognize the graph of a linear function: it is a straight line. Now we can recognize a linear function given by a formula: it can be written as $y = b + mx$. How can we tell if a table of data represents a linear function?

The slope of a linear function given by $y = b + mx$ is $m = \Delta y / \Delta x$. Because the ratio of Δy to Δx is constant, this means that Δy is proportional to Δx, with a constant of proportionality m. In other words, changes in the value of y are proportional to changes in the value of x. Consequently, if the value of x goes up by equal steps in a table for a linear function, then the value of y should go up (or down) by equal steps as well.

Example 6   Table 2.4 gives values of two functions, p and q. Which (if either) of these functions could be linear?

TABLE 2.4   *Values of two functions p and q*

x	50	55	60	65	70
$p(x)$	0.10	0.11	0.12	0.13	0.14
$q(x)$	0.01	0.03	0.06	0.14	0.15

Solution   The value of x goes up by equal steps of Δx ($= 5$): from 50 to 55 to 60, and so on. The value of $p(x)$ also goes up by equal steps $\Delta p(x)$ ($= 0.01$): from 0.10 to 0.11 to 0.12 and so on. Thus p could be a linear function.

TABLE 2.5

x	$p(x)$	$\Delta p/\Delta x$
50	0.10	
		.002
55	0.11	
		.002
60	0.12	
		.002
65	0.13	
		.002
70	0.14	

TABLE 2.6

x	$q(x)$	$\Delta q/\Delta x$
50	0.01	
		.004
55	0.03	
		.006
60	0.06	
		.016
65	0.14	
		.002
70	0.15	

In contrast, the value of $q(x)$ does *not* go up by equal steps. The value climbs from 0.01 to 0.03 to 0.06, and so on. This means that Δq is not constant, even though Δx is. Thus, q is not a linear function.

A table of values could represent a linear function if the rate of change is constant, that is, if the

$$\frac{\text{Change in the dependent variable}}{\text{Change in the independent variable}} = \text{constant.}$$

It is possible to have a data set for a linear function in which neither the x-values nor the y-values go up by equal steps, as long as the ratio is constant. Consider the following example.

Example 7   The former republic of Yugoslavia began exporting cars called Yugos in 1985. Table 2.7 gives the quantity of Yugos sold, Q, and the sale price, p, for each year from 1985 to 1988.
(a)   Based on the data in Table 2.7, show that Q is a linear function of p.
(b)   What does the rate of change of this function tell you about Yugos?

TABLE 2.7   *Price of Yugos and number sold, by year*

Year	Price in \$, p	Number sold, Q
1985	3990	49,000
1986	4110	43,000
1987	4200	38,500
1988	4330	32,000

Solution   (a)   Begin by plotting some points to see the shape of the graph. From Figure 2.4 we see that the data points appear to fall along a straight line, suggesting a linear function.

Figure 2.4: Since the data from Table 2.7 falls on a straight line, the table could represent a linear function

To provide further evidence that Q is a linear function we can show that the rate of change of Q with respect to p is constant. We calculate the rate of change for each year from 1985 to 1988. Between 1985 and 1986, the price of a Yugo rose from \$3990 to \$4110, while the number sold fell from 49,000 to 43,000. Thus,

$$\Delta p = 4110 - 3990 = 120,$$

and

$$\Delta Q = 43,000 - 49,000 = -6000.$$

Notice that ΔQ is negative because the number of Yugos sold decreased. Thus, between 1985 and 1986,

$$\text{Rate of change} = \frac{\Delta Q}{\Delta p} = \frac{-6000}{120} = -50.$$

Next, we will calculate the rate of change for the years 1986 to 1987 and 1987 to 1988 to see if it remains constant. We have

$$\begin{array}{l}\text{Rate of change} \\ \text{from 1986 to 1987}\end{array} = \frac{\Delta Q}{\Delta p} = \frac{38{,}500 - 43{,}000}{4200 - 4110} = \frac{-4500}{90} = -50,$$

and

$$\begin{array}{l}\text{Rate of change} \\ \text{from 1987 to 1988}\end{array} = \frac{\Delta Q}{\Delta p} = \frac{32{,}000 - 38{,}500}{4330 - 4200} = \frac{-6500}{130} = -50.$$

For each year from 1985 to 1988, the rate of change is -50. Since the rate of change is a constant, we conclude that Q is a linear function of p. (It is still possible that, given additional data, $\Delta Q/\Delta p$ may not remain constant. However, based on the data in the table, it appears that the function is linear.)

(b) ΔQ is the change in the number of cars sold while Δp is the change in price. Thus, the rate of change is -50 cars per dollar, which indicates that the number of Yugos sold decreases by 50 each time the price goes up by \$1. Car buyers are less interested in Yugos at higher prices than at lower prices.

Warning: Not All Graphs That Look Like Lines Represent Linear Functions

The graph of any linear function is a line. However, a function's graph can look like a line without actually being one. Consider the following example.

Example 8   The function $P = 67.38(1.026)^t$ is a good model of the population of Mexico in the early 1980s. Here P is the population (in millions) and t is the number of years since 1980. Table 2.8 gives values of P over a six-year period. These points have been plotted in Figure 2.5.

TABLE 2.8   *Population of Mexico (in millions) t years after 1980*

t	P
0	67.38
1	69.13
2	70.93
3	72.77
4	74.67
5	76.61
6	78.60

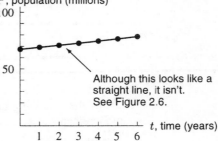

Although this looks like a straight line, it isn't. See Figure 2.6.

Figure 2.5: The graph of $P(t)$ for $0 \le t \le 6$

The graph of P *appears* to be a straight line, but is it? The formula for P does not fit the general form $P = b + mt$. But, the *defining* property for linear functions is that their rate of change is constant. The general formula and the fact that the graph must be a line are both results of this property. We can check Table 2.8 to see if P's rate of change is constant. Note that $P(0) = 67.38$

and $P(1) = 69.13$. Thus, between 1980 and 1981,

$$\begin{array}{c}\text{Rate}\\\text{of change}\end{array} = \frac{\Delta P}{\Delta t} = \frac{69.13 - 67.38}{1 - 0} = 1.75.$$

Between 1981 and 1982, we have

$$\begin{array}{c}\text{Rate}\\\text{of change}\end{array} = \frac{\Delta P}{\Delta t} = \frac{70.93 - 69.13}{2 - 1} = 1.80,$$

and from $t = 5$ (1985) to $t = 6$ (1986), we have

$$\begin{array}{c}\text{Rate}\\\text{of change}\end{array} = \frac{\Delta P}{\Delta t} = \frac{78.60 - 76.61}{6 - 5} = 1.99.$$

Thus, P's rate of change is not constant. In fact, P appears to be increasing at a faster and faster rate. In fact, the graph of P is concave up.

Table 2.9 gives values of P over a longer (60-year) period. These points have been plotted in Figure 2.6. As you can see on this larger scale, these points do not fall on a straight line. In fact, the graph of P is concave up. The portion of P's graph shown by Figure 2.5 is indicated by a shaded box in Figure 2.6. The graph of P curves upward so gradually at first that over the short interval shown in Figure 2.6, it barely curves at all. The graphs of many non-linear functions, when viewed on a relatively small scale, appear to be linear.

TABLE 2.9   *Population of Mexico predicted by the formula* $P = f(t) = 67.38(1.026)^t$ *(in millions)*

t	P
0	67.38
10	87.10
20	112.58
30	145.53
40	188.12
50	243.16
60	314.32

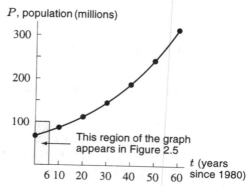

Figure 2.6: The graph of $P = f(t)$ for $0 \leq t \leq 60$ is not a straight line

Problems for Section 2.1

1. Which of the following tables could represent a linear function? Check by determining if equal increments in x cause equal increments in the function values. $2.10, 2.11, 2.12$

TABLE 2.10	
x	$f(x)$
0	10
5	20
10	30
15	40

TABLE 2.11	
x	$g(x)$
0	50
100	100
300	150
600	200

TABLE 2.12	
x	$h(x)$
0	20
10	40
20	50
30	55

TABLE 2.13	
x	$j(x)$
-3	5
-1	1
0	-1
3	-7

2. At a university, campus food services decides to sell gourmet coffee from a cart in front of the library. Table 2.14 is a projection of the cost to the university of selling various amounts of coffee.

    TABLE 2.14 *Total cost to serve x cups of coffee in a day*

x (cups)	0	5	10	50	100	200
C (dollars)	50.00	51.25	52.50	62.50	75.00	100.00

    (a) Using the table, show that the relationship is linear.
    (b) Plot the data found in the table.
    (c) Find the slope of the line. Explain what this means in the context of the given situation.
    (d) Why should it cost $50 to serve zero cups of coffee?

3. Suppose $P(t)$, the population (in millions) of a country in year t, is defined by the formula

    $$P(t) = 22 + 0.3t.$$

    (a) Construct a table of values for $t = 0, 10, 20, \dots ,50$.
    (b) Plot the points you found in part (a).
    (c) What is the country's initial population?
    (d) What is the country's annual growth rate (in millions of people/year)?

4. Table 2.15 gives the area and perimeter of a square as a function of the length of its side.

    TABLE 2.15

length of side	0	1	2	3	4	5	6
area of square	0	1	4	9	16	25	36
perimeter of square	0	4	8	12	16	20	24

    (a) From the table, determine if there is a linear relationship between either side length and area or side length and perimeter.
    (b) From the data make two graphs, one showing side length and area, the other side length and perimeter. Connect the points.
    (c) If you find a linear relationship give its corresponding rate of change and interpret its significance.

5. Make two tables, one comparing the radius of a circle to its area, the other comparing the radius of a circle to its circumference. Repeat parts (a), (b), and (c) from Problem 4, this time comparing radius with circumference, and radius with area.

6. Let $r = f(v)$ be the fine imposed on a motorist for speeding, where v is his speed and 55 mph is the speed limit. Table 2.16 gives the fine for several different speeds.

    (a) Decide whether $f(v)$ is linear.
    (b) What does the rate of change represent in practical terms?
    (c) Plot the data points.

    TABLE 2.16 *The fine imposed for driving v mph, v > 55*

v (mph)	60	65	70	75	80	85
r (dollars)	75	100	125	150	175	200

7. Let $f(x) = 0.003 - (1.246x + 0.37)$
    (a) Calculate the following average rates of change:
         (i) $\dfrac{f(2) - f(1)}{2 - 1}$ (ii) $\dfrac{f(1) - f(2)}{1 - 2}$ (iii) $\dfrac{f(3) - f(4)}{3 - 4}$
    (b) Rewrite $f(x)$ in the form $f(x) = b + mx$.

8. A new Toyota RAV4 costs $21,000. The car's value depreciates linearly to $10,500 in three years time. Write a formula which expresses its value, V, in terms of its age, t, in years.

9. The population of a certain town was 18,310 in 1978, and began to grow by 58 people per year. Find a formula for P, the town's population, in terms of t, the number of years since 1978.

10. Sri Lanka is a tropical island in the Indian Ocean which experienced approximately linear population growth from 1970 to 1990. On the other hand, Afghanistan, a country in Asia, was torn by warfare in the 1980s and did not experience linear or near-linear growth.
    (a) In Table 2.17 which of these two countries is Country A and which is Country B?

    TABLE 2.17

Year	1970	1975	1980	1985	1990
Population of Country A (millions)	13.5	15.5	16	14	16
Population of Country B (millions)	12.2	13.5	14.7	15.8	17

    (b) What is the approximate rate of change of the linear function? What does the rate of change represent in practical terms?
    (c) Estimate the population of Sri Lanka in 1988.

11. Owners of a long-inactive small quarry in northeastern Australia have decided to resume production. They have old equipment and they figure that it will cost them $1000 per month to maintain and insure it. They estimate that monthly salaries will be $3000. Furthermore they know that it costs $80 to mine a ton of rocks. Write a formula that expresses the total cost each month, c, as a function of r, the number of tons of rock mined per month.

12. Tuition cost T (in dollars) for part-time students at Stonewall College is given by $T = 300 + 200C$, where C represents the number of credits taken.

    (a) Find the tuition cost for eight credits.
    (b) How many credits were taken if the tuition was $1700?
    (c) Make a table showing costs for taking from one to twelve credits. For each value of C, give both the tuition cost, T, and the cost per credit, $\frac{T}{C}$. Round to the nearest dollar.
    (d) Which of these values of C has the smallest cost per credit?
    (e) What might the $300 represent in the formula for T?

13. To convert temperature from Celsius, C, to Fahrenheit, F, we use the formula

    $$F = \frac{9}{5}C + 32.$$

    Outside the United States, temperature readings are usually given in degrees Celsius. A rough approximation of the equivalent Fahrenheit temperature is obtained by doubling the Celsius reading and adding 30°.

    (a) Write a formula to express this approximation, where F represents Fahrenheit temperature and C represents Celsius temperature.

(b)   How far off would the approximation be if the Celsius temperature was $-5°$, $0°$, $15°$, $30°$?

(c)   For what temperature (in Celsius) will the approximation agree with the actual formula?

14.   Let $r(t)$ be the rate that water enters a reservoir:

$$r(t) = 800 - 40t,$$

where $r(t)$ is in units of gallons/second and t is time in seconds.

(a)   Evaluate the expressions $r(0), r(15), r(25)$, and explain their physical significance.

(b)   Graph $y = r(t)$ for $0 \leq t \leq 30$, labeling the intercepts. What is the real-life significance of the slope and the intercepts?

(c)   For $0 \leq t \leq 30$, when does the reservoir have the most water? When does it have the least water?

(d)   What are the domain and range of $r(t)$?

15.   Hooke's Law states that the force in pounds, $F(x)$, necessary to keep a spring stretched x units beyond its natural length is directly proportional to x, so $F(x) = kx$. The positive constant k is called the spring constant. Stiffer springs have larger values of k.

(a)   Would you expect $F(x)$ to be an increasing function or a decreasing function of x? Explain.

(b)   A force of 2.36 pounds is required to hold a certain spring stretched 1.9 inches beyond its natural length. Find the value of k for this spring and rewrite the formula for $F(x)$ using this value of k.

(c)   How much force would be needed to stretch this spring 3 inches beyond its natural length?

16.   A company has found that there is a linear relationship between the amount of money that it spends on advertising and the number of units it sells. If it spends no money on advertising, it will nonetheless sell 300 units. Moreover, for each additional $5000 spent, an additional 20 units will be sold.

(a)   If x is the amount of money that the company spends on advertising, find a formula for y, the number of units sold as a function of x.

(b)   How many units will the firm sell if it spends $25,000 on advertising? $50,000?

(c)   How much advertising money must be spent to sell 700 units?

(d)   What is the slope of the equation you found in part (a)? Give an interpretation of the slope that relates units sold and advertising costs.

17.   The graph of $y = x^2/100 + 5$ in the standard viewing window of a graphing calculator is shown in Figure 2.7. Discuss whether this is a linear function.

Figure 2.7

18.   Graph the equation

$$y = -x \left(\frac{x - 1000}{900} \right)$$

in the standard window of your calculator. Is this graph a line? Explain.

19.   Graph $y = 2x + 400$ on the standard window. Describe what happens, and how you can fix it by using a better window.

20.   Graph $y = 200x + 4$ on the standard window. Describe what happens and how you can fix it by using a better window.

21.   Suppose we model the cost of a cab ride by the function $C = 1.50 + 2d$, where d is the number of miles traveled and C is measured in dollars. Choose an appropriate window and graph the cost of a ride for a cab that travels no farther than a 10 mile radius from the center of the city.

22.   Sometimes a relationship is defined by two independent variables. The wind chill index is one such function. The wind chill, denoted W, is a measure of how cold it *feels*; it takes into account both the temperature, T, and the wind velocity, V. The function can be called $W(T, V)$ to show that W depends on both T and V. One model for wind chill is the piecewise function shown below.

$$W(T, V) = \begin{cases} T & \text{for } 0 \leq V \leq 4 \\ 0.0817(5.81 + 3.71\sqrt{V} - 0.25V)(T - 91.4) + 91.4 & \text{for } 4 < V \leq 45 \\ 1.60T - 55 & \text{for } V > 45. \end{cases}$$

The table below shows wind chill for various combinations of temperature and wind velocity.

TABLE 2.18   *Wind chill as a function of temperature and wind velocity (Adapted from UMAP)*

							V						
		0	4	10	15	20	25	30	35	40	45	50	55
	50	50	50	40.5	35.8	32.5	30.1	28.4	27.0	26.2	25.6	25	25
	45	45	45	34.4	29.1	25.4	22.7	20.8	19.3	18.3	17.7	17	17
	40	40	40	28.2	22.4	18.3	15.3	13.2	11.6	10.5	9.7	9	9
	35	35	35	22.1	15.7	11.2	8.0	5.6	3.8	2.6	1.8	1	1
	30	30	30	15.9	9.0	4.1	0.6	−2.1	−4.0	−5.3	−6.1	−7	−7
	25	25	25	9.8	2.3	−3.0	−6.8	−6.7	−11.7	−13.2	−14.1	−15	−15
	20	20	20	3.7	−4.4	−10.1	−14.2	−17.3	−19.5	−21.0	−22.0	−23	−23
T	15	15	15	−2.5	−11.1	−17.2	−21.6	−24.9	−27.2	−28.9	−30.0	−31	−31
	10	10	10	−8.6	−17.9	−24.3	−29.0	−32.5	−35.0	−36.8	−37.9	−39	−39
	5	5	5	−14.8	−24.6	−31.4	−36.4	−40.1	−42.8	−44.7	−45.9	−47	−47
	0	0	0	−20.9	−31.3	−38.5	−43.8	−47.7	−50.5	−52.5	−53.8	−55	−55
	−5	−5	−5	−27.1	−40.0	−45.7	−51.2	−55.3	−58.3	−60.4	−61.8	−63	−63
	−10	−10	−10	−33.2	−44.7	−52.8	−58.6	−62.9	−66.1	−68.3	−69.7	−71	−71
	−15	−15	−15	−39.4	−51.4	−59.9	−66.0	−70.6	−73.8	−76.1	−77.7	−79	−79
	−20	−20	−20	−45.5	−58.1	−67.0	−73.4	−78.3	−81.6	−84.0	−85.6	−87	−87

(a)   Two of the three rules of the piecewise function are linear. Which are they?

(b)   Beyond which velocity will the wind have no further effect on the perceived temperature?

(c)   How hard must the wind blow so that a temperature of 40°F feels like 9°F?

2.2 FINDING FORMULAS FOR LINEAR FUNCTIONS

A linear function is completely determined by its slope, m, and its y-intercept, b. Therefore, finding a formula for a particular linear function amounts to finding the values of m and b.

Finding a Formula for a Linear Function from a Table of Data

If a table of data represents a linear function, we can use the table values to calculate m, the slope. Having found m, we can then determine the value of b.

Example 1   A grapefruit is thrown into the air. Table 2.19 gives the grapefruit's velocity, v (in feet per second) as a function of t, the number of seconds elapsed. A positive velocity indicates the grapefruit is rising and a negative velocity indicates the grapefruit is falling. Show that v is a linear function of t and find a formula for v in terms of t.

TABLE 2.19   *The velocity (in ft/sec) of a grapefruit t seconds after being thrown into the air.*

t, time (sec)	1	2	3	4
v, velocity (ft/sec)	48	16	-16	-48

Solution   Figure 2.8 gives a plot of the data points in Table 2.19. The points *seem* to fall on a line. To confirm that the velocity is linear, we show that v's rate of change is constant. For the first second, that is from time $t = 1$ to $t = 2$, we have

$$\text{Rate of change} = \frac{\Delta v}{\Delta t} = \frac{16 - 48}{2 - 1} = -32.$$

For the next second, from $t = 2$ to $t = 3$, we have

$$\text{Rate of change} = \frac{\Delta v}{\Delta t} = \frac{-16 - 16}{3 - 2} = -32.$$

As you can check for yourself, the rate of change for the third second is also -32.

Figure 2.8: The velocity of a grapefruit that has been thrown into the air

To find a formula for v in terms of t, we begin with the general formula $v = f(t) = b + mt$. Since m is the rate of change, we have $m = -32$. The initial velocity (at $t = 0$) is represented by b. We are not given $f(0)$ in the table, but we can use any data point to determine b. For example, the table tells us that $v(1) = 48$. We can substitute $t = 1$, $f(1) = 48$, and $m = -32$ into the formula $f(t) = b + mt$ and solve for b:

$$48 = b + (-32) \cdot (1)$$

so

$$b = 80.$$

Thus, a formula for the velocity is $f(t) = 80 - 32t$.

What does the rate of change in the last example tell us about the grapefruit? Let's think about the units of m, the slope. We have

$$m = \frac{\Delta v}{\Delta t} = \frac{\text{change in velocity}}{\text{change in time}}$$
$$= \frac{-32 \text{ ft/sec}}{\text{sec}}$$
$$= -32 \text{ ft/sec}^2.$$

Thus, the value of m is -32 ft/sec per second. This tells us that the grapefruit's velocity is decreasing by 32 ft/sec for every second that goes by. We say the grapefruit is *accelerating* at -32 ft/sec per second.[1] (Negative acceleration is also called deceleration.)

Finding a Formula for a Linear Function from a Graph

We can calculate the slope, m, of a linear function by using the coordinates of two points on its graph. Having found m we can then determine the value of b, the y-intercept.

Example 2 Figure 2.9 shows the oxygen consumption as a function of heart rate of two people running on treadmills.

(a) Assuming linearity, find formulas for these two functions.

(b) Interpret the slope of each graph in terms of oxygen consumption.

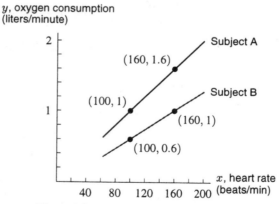

Figure 2.9: Measuring the slopes of these lines from their graphs

---

[1] Note: The notation ft/sec^2 is shorthand for ft/sec per second; it is not meant to imply the existence of a "square second" in the same way that there are areas measured in square feet or square meters.

Solution   (a)   We will find the formula for subject A first. Let x be the heart rate and y the corresponding oxygen consumption. Since we're assuming this is a linear function, we have $y = b + mx$. From Figure 2.9 we can find the coordinates of two points on person A's line, such as $(100, 1)$ and $(160, 1.6)$. The first point indicates that when person A's heart rate is 100 beats/minute, she consumes oxygen at a rate of 1 liter/minute. We have

$$m = \frac{\Delta y}{\Delta x} = \frac{1.6 - 1}{160 - 100} = 0.01.$$

Thus $y = b + 0.01x$. To determine b, we use the fact that $y = 1$ when $x = 100$:

$$1 = b + 0.01(100)$$
$$1 = b + 1$$
$$b = 0.$$

Alternatively, we could have found b using the fact that $x = 160$ if $y = 1.6$. Either way leads us to the same formula for person A, $y = 0.01x$.

For person B, we again begin with the general equation $y = b + mx$. In Figure 2.9, we see that two points on the line are $(100, 0.6)$ and $(160, 1)$, so we have

$$m = \frac{\Delta y}{\Delta x} = \frac{1 - 0.6}{160 - 100} = \frac{0.4}{60} = \frac{1}{150}.$$

To determine b, we use the fact that $y = 1$ when $x = 160$:

$$1 = b + \left(\frac{1}{150}\right)(160)$$
$$1 = b + \frac{16}{15}$$
$$b = -\frac{1}{15}.$$

Thus, for person B, $y = -\frac{1}{15} + \frac{1}{150}x$.

(b)   The slope for person A is $m = 0.01$, or

$$m = \frac{\text{change in oxygen consumption}}{\text{change in heart rate}} = \frac{\text{change in liters/min}}{\text{change in beats/min}} = 0.01 \frac{\text{liters}}{\text{heart beat}}.$$

Every additional heart beat (per minute) for person A translates to an additional 0.01 liters (per minute) of oxygen consumed.

The slope for person B is $m = 1/150$. Thus, for every additional beat per minute that her pulse rises, she will consume an additional 1/150 of a liter of oxygen. We could also express the slope as $m \approx 0.0067$ which tells us that person B consumes an additional 0.0067 liters (per minute) of oxygen each time her pulse goes up by 1 beat per minute. Notice that the slope for person B is smaller than for person A. Thus person B consumes less additional oxygen than person A does for the same increase in pulse.

You may be wondering what the y-intercepts of the functions in Example 2 tell us about oxygen consumption. Often the y-intercept of a function is a starting value. Here however, the y-intercept would be the oxygen consumption of a person whose pulse is zero (i.e. $x = 0$). Since a person running on a treadmill must have a pulse, it makes no sense to interpret the y-intercept this way. In other words, a formula for oxygen consumption is only useful for realistic values of the pulse.

Finding a Formula for a Linear Function from a Verbal Description

Sometimes the verbal description of a linear function is less straightforward than those we saw in Section 2.1. Consider the following example.

Example 3 Suppose we have $24 to spend on soda and chips for a party. If a six-pack of soda costs $3 and a bag of chips costs $2, then y, the number of six-packs we can afford, is a function of x, the number of bags of chips we decide to buy.
(a) Find an equation relating x and y.
(b) Graph the equation from part (a) and interpret the intercepts and the slope in the context of the party.

Solution (a) If we spend all $24 on soda and chips, then we have the following equation:

$$\text{Amount spent on chips} + \text{Amount spent on soda} = \$24.$$

If we buy x bags of chips at $2 per bag, then the amount spent on chips is given by $2x$. Similarly, if we buy y six-packs of soda at $3 per six-pack, then the amount spent on soda is $3y$. Thus,

$$2x + 3y = 24.$$

This equation is in the standard form. We can also put it in slope-intercept form by solving for y:

$$3y = 24 - 2x$$
$$y = 8 - \frac{2}{3}x.$$

Thus, we see that this is a linear equation with slope $m = -\frac{2}{3}$ and y-intercept $b = 8$.

(b) The graph of this function is a discrete set of points, since the number of bags of chips and the number of six-packs of soda must be integers. We can start by finding the x- and y-intercepts. If $x = 0$, then $2 \cdot 0 + 3y = 24$. So $3y = 24$, giving

$$y = 8.$$

If $y = 0$, then $2x + (3 \cdot 0) = 24$. So $2x = 24$, giving

$$x = 12.$$

Thus the points $(0, 8)$ and $(12, 0)$ are on the graph.

The point $(0, 8)$ indicates that we can buy 8 six-packs of soda if we buy no chips. Likewise, the point $(12, 0)$ indicates that we can buy 12 bags of chips if we buy no soda. The other points on the line describe affordable options between these two extremes. For example, the point $(6, 4)$ is on the line, because

$$2 \cdot 6 + 3 \cdot 4 = 24.$$

This means that if we buy 6 bags of chips, we can afford 4 six-packs of soda. The graph is shown in Figure 2.10. The points shown represent affordable options, and the line $2x + 3y = 24$ is sketched in as a dotted line to indicate that all affordable options lie on or below this line. Note that not all of the points on the line are affordable options. For example, suppose we

Figure 2.10: Number of six-packs, y, as a function of number of bags of chips, x

purchase one six-pack of soda for \$3.00. That leaves \$21.00 to spend on chips, meaning we would have to buy 10.5 bags of chips, which is not possible. Therefore, the point $(10.5, 1)$ is not included as a solution to our problem, although it is a point on the line $2x + 3y = 24$.

To interpret the slope in the context of the party, notice that

$$m = \frac{\Delta y}{\Delta x} = \frac{\Delta(\text{number of six-packs})}{\Delta(\text{number of bags of chips})},$$

which means that the units of m are six-packs per bags of chips. Since $m = -2/3$, we conclude that for each additional 3 bags of chips purchased, we must purchase 2 fewer six-packs of soda. This is reasonable since 2 six-packs cost \$6, as do 3 bags of chips. Thus, $m = -2/3$ is the rate at which the amount of soda we can buy decreases as we buy more chips.

Problems for Section 2.2

1. Graphing a linear equation is often easier if the equation is in the form $y = b + mx$. (This is often referred to as *slope-intercept form*.) If possible rewrite the following equations in slope-intercept form.

   (a) $3x + 5y = 20$
   (b) $0.1y + x = 18$
   (c) $y - 0.7 = 5(x - 0.2)$
   (d) $5(x + y) = 4$
   (e) $5x - 3y + 2 = 0$
   (f) $\frac{x+y}{7} = 3$
   (g) $3x + 2y + 40 = x - y$
   (h) $x = 4$

2. Find formulas for the following linear functions.

   (a) This function has slope 3 and y-intercept 8.
   (b) This function passes through the points $(-1, 5)$ and $(2, -1)$.
   (c) This function has slope -4 and x-intercept 7.
   (d) This function has x-intercept 3 and y-intercept -5.
   (e) This function has slope $2/3$ and passes through the point $(5, 7)$.

3. If $y = f(x)$ is a linear function and if $f(-2) = 7$ and $f(3) = -3$, find a formula for f.

4. Describe a linear (or nearly linear) relationship that you have encountered in your life. Determine the rate of change of the relationship and interpret its meaning.

5. Given that a linear function generated the data in Table 2.20, find a formula for the function.

TABLE 2.20

t	1.2	1.3	1.4	1.5
$f(t)$	0.736	0.614	0.492	0.37

6. Table 2.21 gives values of g, a linear function. Find a formula for g.

TABLE 2.21   *Values of g, a linear function*

x	200	230	300	320	400
$g(x)$	70	68.5	65	64	60

7. A bullet is shot straight up into the air from ground level. The velocity of the bullet, in meters per second, after t seconds can be approximated by the formula

$$v = f(t) = 1000 - 9.8t.$$

(a) Evaluate the following: $f(0)$, $f(1)$, $f(2)$, $f(3)$, $f(4)$. Compile your results in a table.
(b) Describe in words what is happening to the speed of the bullet. Discuss whether this makes sense or not.
(c) Evaluate and interpret the slope and both intercepts of $f(t)$.
(d) The gravitational field near the surface of Jupiter is stronger than that near the surface of the Earth, which, in turn, is stronger than the field near the surface of the moon. How would the formula of $f(t)$ be different for a bullet shot from Jupiter's surface? From the moon?

8. An empty champagne bottle is tossed from a hot-air balloon, and its velocity is measured every second. (See Table 2.22.)

TABLE 2.22

t (sec)	v (ft/s)
0	40
1	8
2	−24
3	−56
4	−88
5	−120

(a) Describe the motion of the bottle in words. What do negative values of v represent?
(b) Find a formula for v in terms of t.
(c) Explain the physical significance of the slope of your formula.
(d) Explain the physical significance of the t-axis and v-axis intercepts.

9. John wants to buy a dozen rolls. The local bakery sells sesame and poppy seed rolls for the same price.

(a) Make a table of all the possible combinations of rolls if he buys a dozen, where s is the number of sesame seed rolls and p is the number of poppy seed rolls.
(b) Find a formula for p as a function of s.
(c) Graph this function.

Chapter 2/ 20

10. According to one economic model, a person's demand for gasoline is a linear function of price. Suppose that one month, the price of gasoline is $p = \$1.10$ per gallon, and that the quantity demanded is $q = 65$ gallons. The following month, the price rises to $1.50 per gallon, while the quantity demanded falls to only 45 gallons. *(handwritten: (p,q) (1,10,65) (1,5* $\frac{\Delta q}{\Delta p} = \frac{20}{.4} = -50$ gal/dollar*)*

   (a) Find a formula for q in terms of p, assuming a linear relationship.

   (b) Explain the economic significance of the slope of your formula. *(handwritten: b.for each dollar, the gas is)*

   (c) Explain the economic significance of the q-axis and p-axis intercepts. *(handwritten: decrease 50 gal.)*

(handwritten left margin:
b. $q = mp + b$
$q = -50p + b$
$65 = -50(1.1) + b$
$b = 120$
$\boxed{q = -50p + 120}$ *)*

11. In a meal plan at a college you pay a monthly membership fee, and then you receive all meals at a predetermined fixed price per meal.

   (a) If 30 meals cost $152.50 and 60 meals cost $250, find the membership fee and the fixed price for a meal.

   (b) Write a formula for the cost of a meal plan, C, in terms of the number of meals, m.

   (c) Find the cost for 50 meals.

   (d) Now find m in terms of C.

   (e) Use part (d) to determine the maximum number of meals you can buy on a budget of $300.

12. Suppose you can type four pages in 50 minutes and nine pages in an hour and forty minutes.

   (a) Find a linear function for the number of pages produced, p, as a function of time, t. If time is measured in minutes, what values of t make sense in this example?

   (b) How many pages can be typed in two hours?

   (c) Interpret the slope of the function in practical terms.

   (d) Solve the function in (a) for time as a function of pages.

   (e) How long will it take to type a 15 page paper?

   (f) Write a short paragraph explaining why it would be useful to know both the formulas obtained in (a) and in (d).

13. Find the equation of the line l, shown in Figure 2.11, if its slope is $m = 4$.

(handwritten near figure 2.11: $y = 4x - 4$)

(handwritten between figures: $y = 4x + m$, $y = 4(2) \times m$, $4 = 8 + m$, $4 = m$)

Figure 2.11

Figure 2.12

14. Find the equation of the line l in Figure 2.12. Assume that the shapes under the line are squares.

15. Over the past year a theater manager graphed weekly profits as a function of the number of patrons. She found that the relationship was linear. One week the profit was $11,328$ when 1324 patrons attended. Another week 1529 patrons produced a profit of $13,275.50$

   (a) Find the equation of the line that expresses weekly profit, y, as a function of the number of patrons, x.

(handwritten left: $(1324, 11,298)$ $(1529, 13,275.50)$

(handwritten: $m = \frac{\Delta y}{\Delta y} = 9.5$ dollars/patron)

b. For each addition patron, profit increases by $9.5

c. $y = 9.5x - 1250 \rightarrow$ if nobody come, you lost 1250.)

(b) Interpret the slope and the y-intercept of the line.

(c) What is the break-even point (the number of patrons for which there is zero profit)?

(d) Find a formula for the number of patrons as a function of profit.

(e) If the weekly profit was $17,759.50, how many patrons attended the theater?

16. Find the equation of line l in Figure 2.13.

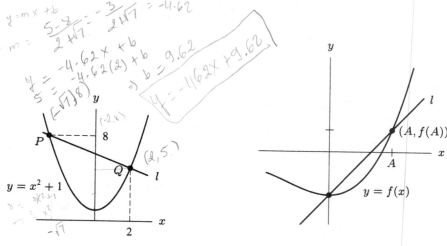

Figure 2.13

Figure 2.14

17. Find an equation for the line l in Figure 2.14 in terms of the constant A and function values of $f(x)$.

18. A business consultant works 10 hours a day, 6 days a week. She divides her time between meetings with clients and meetings with co-workers. A client meeting requires 3 hours while a co-worker meeting requires only 2 hours. Let x be the number of co-worker meetings the consultant holds during a given week. If y is the number of client meetings for which she has time remaining, then y is a function of x. Assume this relationship is linear and that meetings can be split up and continued on different days.

(a) Sketch a graph that describes this relationship. [Hint: consider the maximum number of client and co-worker meetings that can be held.]

(b) Find a formula for this function.

(c) Explain what the slope and the x- and y-intercepts represent in the context of the consultant's meeting schedule.

(d) Suppose that, due to a procedural change, co-worker meetings now take 90 minutes instead of two hours. Sketch the graph for this solution. Describe those features of this graph that have changed from the one sketched in part (a) and those that have remained the same.

19. You have c dollars to spend on x apples and y bananas. In Figure 2.15, line l gives y as a function of x, assuming you spend all of the c dollars.

(a) If apples cost p dollars a piece and bananas cost q a piece, label the x- and y-intercepts of l. [Note: Your labels involve the constants p, q or c.]

(b) What is the slope of l?

Figure 2.15: Note: Axes not necessarily to scale

Figure 2.16

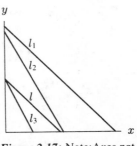

Figure 2.17: Note:Axes not necessarily drawn to same scale

20. Assume that apples from Problem 19 cost more than bananas–in other words assume that $p > q$. If we label the graph as shown in Figure 2.16, which of the two lines, l_1 or l_2, could represent $y = f(x)$ where y is the number of bananas purchased and x is the number of apples purchased?

21. Figure 2.17 gives line l from Problem 19, and three other lines l_1, l_2, l_3. Match the following stories (if possible) to lines l_1, l_2, l_3.

   (a) Your total budget, c, has increased, but the prices of apples and bananas have not changed.
   (b) Your total budget and the cost of bananas do not change, but the cost of apples increases.
   (c) Your budget increases, as does the price of apples, but the price of bananas stays fixed.
   (d) Your budget increases, but the price of apples goes down, and the price of bananas stays fixed.

2.3 THE GEOMETRIC PROPERTIES OF LINEAR FUNCTIONS

Interpreting the Parameters of a Linear Function

We have seen that the general formula for a linear function is $y = b + mx$, where b is the y-intercept and m is the slope. The parameters b and m are useful in describing linear models. As we see in the following example, the parameters can be used to compare two or more linear functions.

Example 1   Suppose the populations of four different towns, P_A, P_B, P_C and P_D, are given by the following equations, where t is the year:

$$P_A = 20{,}000 + 1600t$$
$$P_B = 50{,}000 - 300t$$
$$P_C = 650t + 45{,}000$$
$$P_D = 15{,}000(1.07)^t$$

   (a) Which populations are represented by linear functions?
   (b) Describe in words what each of the linear models tells you about that town's population. Which town starts out with the most people? Which town is growing fastest?

Solution   (a)   The populations of towns A, B, and C are represented by linear functions. Each of these formulas can be written in the general form for linear functions, $y = b + mt$. For example, the equation for town A is $P_A = 20{,}000 + 1600t$. This is a linear equation with $m = 1600$ and $b = 20{,}000$. Town B also has linear population growth with $m = -300$ and $b = 50{,}000$. To see this, notice that we can rewrite the formula for P_B as

$$P_B = \underbrace{50{,}000}_{b} + \underbrace{(-300)}_{m} \cdot t.$$

Town C's growth is also linear with $m = 650$ and $b = 45{,}000$. We can rewrite the formula for P_C as

$$P_C = \underbrace{45{,}000}_{b} + \underbrace{650}_{m} \cdot t.$$

Town D's population does not grow linearly since its formula, $P_D = 15{,}000(1.07)^t$, cannot be expressed in the form $P_D = b + mt$.

(b)   For town A, $m = 1600$ and $b = 20{,}000$. This means that in year $t = 0$, town A has 20,000 people. It grows by 1600 people per year.

For town C, $m = 650$ and $b = 45{,}000$. This means that town C begins with 45,000 people and grows by 650 people per year.

For town B, $m = -300$ and $b = 50{,}000$. This means that town B starts with 50,000 people. But what does it mean for its slope to be negative? Recall from Chapter 1 that a function with a negative rate of change is a decreasing function. Thus, the population of town B must be decreasing at the rate of 300 people per year.

In conclusion, town B starts out with the most people, (50,000), but town A, with a growth rate of 1600 people per year, grows the fastest of the three towns that have linear population growth.

The Effect of the Parameters on the Graph of a Linear Function

We have seen that the graph of a linear function is a line. What do the values of m and b in the general formula $y = b + mx$ tell us about the appearance of this line?

Since b is the initial value of y (that is, the value of y at $x = 0$) it tells us where the line crosses the y-axis. This is why b is called the y-intercept of the function.

We know that m, the slope, represents the rate of change of the function. From Chapter 1 we know that the greater the rate of change of a function on an interval, the steeper the function's graph will be on that interval. Extreme positive rates of change correspond to steeply rising graphs while extreme negative rates of change correspond to steeply falling graphs. If $m = 0$, the line neither rises nor falls; it is horizontal. (See page 87 for a discussion of this case.)

In summary:

Let $y = f(x)$ be a linear function whose formula is $y = b + mx$. Then:

- The graph of f is a line.

- The y-intercept, b, tells us where the line crosses the y-axis.

- If the slope, m, is positive, the line climbs from left to right. If the slope, m, is negative, the line falls from left to right.

- The larger the absolute value of m, the steeper the graph of f.

Varying the values of b and m gives us different members of the family of linear functions.

Example 2   Figure 2.18 gives graphs of the populations of three of the towns described in Example 1:

$$P_A = 20{,}000 + 1600t, \qquad P_B = 50{,}000 - 300t, \quad \text{and} \quad P_C = 45{,}000 + 650t.$$

The graphs of these functions are lines. Figure 2.19 gives a graph of the population of the fourth town clearly illustrating that it is not a linear function.

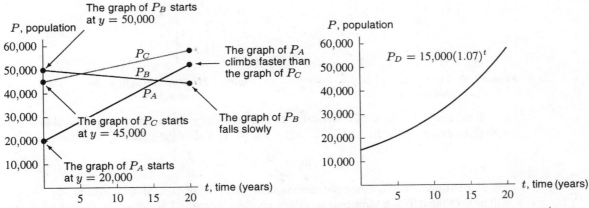

Figure 2.18: The graphs of the three linear population functions, P_A, P_B, and P_C

Figure 2.19: The graph of $P_D = 15{,}000(1.07)^t$ is not a line

Figure 2.18 shows that the graph of P_A starts at $y = 20{,}000$, the graph of P_B starts at $y = 50{,}000$, and the graph of P_C starts at $y = 45{,}000$. These starting values correspond to the y-intercepts of the respective formulas of these functions and they tell us the size of each population in year $t = 0$.

Notice also that the graphs of P_A and P_C are both climbing and that P_A climbs faster than P_C. This corresponds to the fact that the slopes of these two functions are positive and the slope of P_A, $m = 1600$, is larger than the slope of P_C, $m = 650$.

Finally, notice that the graph of P_B falls when read from left to right, indicating that population decreases over time. This corresponds to the fact that the slope of P_C, $m = -300$, is negative.

The Equations of Horizontal and Vertical Lines

An increasing linear function has positive slope and a decreasing linear function has negative slope. What about a line with slope $m = 0$?

If the rate of change of a quantity is zero, then the quantity never changes — that is, the quantity remains constant. Thus, if the slope of a line is zero, the value of y must be constant. We can see this algebraically. If the slope $m = 0$ we have

$$\frac{\Delta y}{\Delta x} = 0.$$

Multiplying both sides by Δx gives $\Delta y = 0$. This tells us that the value of y never changes for a line with slope zero, no matter how large the change in x. Such a line, having a constant y-value, is horizontal.

Example 3   The equation $y = 4$ describes a linear function that has slope $m = 0$. To see this, notice that this equation can be rewritten as $y = 4 + 0 \cdot x$. Thus, y will equal 4 no matter what the value of x is. This line is graphed in Figure 2.20.

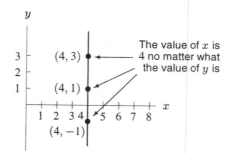

Figure 2.20: The horizontal line $y = 4$ has slope 0

Figure 2.21: The vertical line $x = 4$ has an undefined slope

What about the slope of a vertical line? Figure 2.21 gives the graph of a vertical line together with three points on the line, $(4, -1)$, $(4, 1)$, and $(4, 3)$. Calculating the slope, we have

$$m = \frac{\Delta y}{\Delta x} = \frac{3 - 1}{4 - 4} = \frac{2}{0}.$$

The slope is undefined because the denominator, Δx, is 0. In general, the slope of any vertical line will be undefined for the same reason: all the x-values on such a line are equal. Thus, Δx is 0, making the denominator of the slope expression always 0.

A vertical line does not represent the graph of a function, since it fails the vertical line test. It cannot be described by the general formula for linear functions, $y = b + mx$. What, then, is the equation of a vertical line? Note that every point on a vertical line has the same x-value. For example, every point on the line in Figure 2.21 has x equal to 4. Thus the equation of this line is simply

$$x = 4.$$

In summary,

> For any constant k:
> * The graph of the equation $y = k$ is a horizontal line and its slope is zero.
> * The graph of the equation $x = k$ is a vertical line and its slope is undefined.

The Slopes of Parallel and Perpendicular Lines

Figure 2.22 shows two parallel lines. We can see that what makes these lines parallel is that they have equal slopes.

Figure 2.22: Parallel lines have equal slopes

Figure 2.23: Perpendicular lines: l_1 has a positive slope and l_2 has a negative slope

What about perpendicular lines? Two perpendicular lines are graphed in Figure 2.23. We can see that if one line has a positive slope, then any line perpendicular to it must have a negative slope. Perpendicular lines have slopes with opposite signs.

It can be shown that if l_1 and l_2 are two perpendicular lines with slopes, m_1 and m_2, then their slopes are related by the following equation:

$$m_1 = -\frac{1}{m_2}.$$

We say that m_1 is the *negative reciprocal* of m_2.[2]

In summary:

Let l_1 and l_2 be two lines having slopes m_1 and m_2, respectively. Then:
- These lines are parallel if and only if $m_1 = m_2$.

- These lines are perpendicular if and only if $m_1 = -\dfrac{1}{m_2}$.

Another way to remember the relationship between the slopes of perpendicular lines is to rewrite the equation $m_1 = -\dfrac{1}{m_2}$ as

$$m_1 m_2 = -1.$$

This means that two lines are perpendicular if the product of their slopes is -1.

In addition, any two horizontal lines are parallel, any two vertical lines are parallel, and a horizontal line is perpendicular to a vertical line, as the graphs below show.

Figure 2.24: Any two horizontal lines are parallel

Figure 2.25: Any two vertical lines are parallel

Figure 2.26: A horizontal line and a vertical line are perpendicular

The Intersection of Two Lines

Sometimes we need to find the point at which two lines intersect. The (x, y)-coordinates of such a point must satisfy the equations for both lines. Thus, in order to find the point of intersection algebraically, we must solve the equations simultaneously.[3]

Example 4   Find the point of intersection of the lines $y = 3 - \frac{2}{3}x$ and $y = -4 + \frac{3}{2}x$.

Solution   Since the y-values of the two lines are equal at the point of intersection, we have

$$-4 + \frac{3}{2}x = 3 - \frac{2}{3}x.$$

Notice that we have converted a pair of equations into a single equation by eliminating one of the

---

[2]For an explanation of this relationship between slopes of perpendicular lines, see the notes at the end of this section.
[3]If you have questions about the algebra in this section, please refer to the Appendix.

Figure 2.27

two variables. This equation can be simplified by multiplying both sides by 6:

$$6\left(-4+\frac{3}{2}x\right) = 6\left(3-\frac{2}{3}x\right)$$
$$-24 + 9x = 18 - 4x$$
$$13x = 42$$
$$x = \frac{42}{13}.$$

We can evaluate either of the original equations at $x = \frac{42}{13}$ to find y. For example, $y = -4 + \frac{3}{2}x$ gives

$$y = -4 + \frac{3}{2}\left(\frac{42}{13}\right) = \frac{11}{13}.$$

Therefore, the point of intersection is $\left(\frac{42}{13}, \frac{11}{13}\right)$. You can check for yourself that this point also satisfies the other equation. The lines and their point of intersection are shown in Figure 2.27.

If linear functions are modeling real-world quantities, their points of intersection often have special significance. Consider the next example.

Example 5 The cost in dollars of renting a car for one day from three different rental agencies and driving it d miles is given by the following equations:

$$C_1 = 50 + 0.10d$$
$$C_2 = 30 + 0.20d$$
$$C_3 = 0.50d.$$

  (a) Describe in words the rental arrangements made by these three agencies.
  (b) Which agency is cheapest?

Solution (a) Agency 1 charges $50 plus $0.10 per mile driven. Agency 2 charges $30 plus $0.20 per mile. Agency 3 charges $0.50 per mile driven.
  (b) The answer depends on how far we want to drive. If we aren't driving far, agency 3 may be cheapest because it only charges for miles driven and has no other fees. If we want to drive a long way, agency 1 may be cheapest (even though it charges $50 up front) because it has the lowest per-mile rate. Next we will determine the exact number of miles for which each agency is the cheapest.

Chapter 2/ 28

All three functions have been graphed in Figure 2.28 and the points of intersection have been found. (The calculations follow.) From the graph, we see that for d up to 100 miles, the value of C_3 is less than C_1 and C_2 because its graph is below the other two. For d between 100 and 200 miles, the value of C_2 is less than C_1 and C_3. For d more than 200 miles, the value of C_1 is less than C_2 and C_3.

If we graph these three functions using graphing technology, we can estimate the coordinates at the points of intersection by tracing on the graphs. To find the exact coordinates of the intersection points, we must solve simultaneous equations. Let's start with the intersection of lines C_1 and C_3. We can set the costs equal, $C_1 = C_3$, and solve to find the distance, d, that makes costs equal:

$$50 + 0.10d = 0.50d$$
$$50 = 0.40d$$
$$d = 125.$$

This tells us that if we drive 125 miles, agency 1 will cost the same as agency 3. What about agencies 1 and 2? Solving the equation $C_1 = C_2$ gives

$$50 + 0.10d = 30 + 0.20d$$
$$20 = 0.10d$$
$$d = 200.$$

Thus, the cost for driving 200 miles is the same for companies 1 and 2. Finally, solving $C_2 = C_3$ gives

$$30 + 0.20d = 0.50d$$
$$0.30d = 30$$
$$d = 100,$$

which means the cost of driving 100 miles is the same for companies 2 and 3.

Thus, agency 3 is cheapest for someone who plans to drive less than 100 miles. Agency 1 is cheapest for someone who plans to drive more than 200 miles. Agency 2 is the cheapest for someone who plans to drive between 100 and 200 miles.

Notice that the point of intersection between lines C_1 and C_3, $(125, 62.5)$, does not influence our decision as to which agency is the cheapest. Although agency 1 is cheaper than agency 3 for d greater than 125 miles, for those distances, agency 2 is cheaper still.

Figure 2.28: The cost of driving a car d miles when renting from three different companies

Notes on the Slopes of Perpendicular Lines

Let l_1 and l_2 be two perpendicular lines with slope m_1 and m_2. We will prove here that

$$m_1 m_2 = -1.$$

Figure 2.29 shows a graph of two perpendicular lines. A horizontal line has been dashed in through point P, the point where these two lines intersect. This horizontal line meets the y-axis at point R and forms two similar triangles, one labeled $\triangle PQR$ and one labeled $\triangle SPR$.

To justify that $\triangle PQR$ and $\triangle SPR$ are similar, we will show that two pairs of corresponding angles have equal measures. We see that $m < QRP = m < SRP$ since they are both right angles. Since $\triangle QPS$ is a right triangle, $< S$ is complementary to $< Q$, and since $\triangle QRP$ is a right triangle, $< QPR$ is complementary to $< Q$. Therefore $m < S = m < QPR$. We have shown that two pairs of angles in $\triangle PQR$ and $\triangle SPR$ have equal measure; the triangles are similar.

Now, corresponding sides of similar triangles are proportional. Therefore, the ratio of side RQ to side RP equals the ratio of side RP to side RS. (See Figure 2.30.) In other words,

$$\frac{\|RQ\|}{\|RP\|} = \frac{\|RP\|}{\|RS\|},$$

where $\|RQ\|$ means the length of side RQ. We can rewrite this equation as

$$\frac{\|RS\|}{\|RP\|} \cdot \frac{\|RQ\|}{\|RP\|} = 1.$$

Next, we'll calculate m_1, using points S and P and m_2 using points Q and P. In Figure 2.29, we see that

$$\Delta x = \|RP\|, \quad \Delta y_1 = \|RS\|, \quad \text{and} \quad \Delta y_2 = -\|RQ\|, \quad \text{because } \Delta y_2 \text{ is negative.}$$

Thus,

$$m_1 = \frac{\Delta y_1}{\Delta x} = \frac{\|RS\|}{\|RP\|} \quad \text{and} \quad m_2 = \frac{\Delta y_2}{\Delta x} = -\frac{\|RQ\|}{\|RP\|}.$$

Therefore

$$m_1 m_2 = -\frac{\|RS\|}{\|RP\|} \cdot \frac{\|RQ\|}{\|RP\|}.$$

But by considering the triangles in Figure 2.30, we showed that

$$\frac{\|RS\|}{\|RP\|} \cdot \frac{\|RQ\|}{\|RP\|} = 1.$$

Thus, $m_1 m_2 = -1$ which is the result we wanted.

Figure 2.29

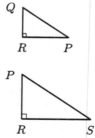

Figure 2.30

Problems for Section 2.3

1. Figure 2.31 gives the graphs of five different linear functions, labeled A, B, C, D, and E. Match each of these graphs to one of the functions f, g, h, u and v, whose equations are given below:

$$f(x) = 20 + 2x \quad A$$
$$g(x) = 20 + 4x \quad B$$
$$h(x) = 2x - 30 \quad C$$
$$u(x) = 60 - x \quad D$$
$$v(x) = 60 - 2x \quad E$$

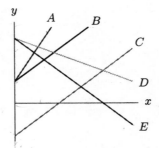

Figure 2.31

2. Using a calculator or computer and the viewing window $-10 \le x \le 10$ by $-10 \le y \le 10$, graph the lines $y = x$, $y = 10x$, $y = 100x$, and $y = 1000x$.

   (a) Explain what happens to the graphs of the lines as the slopes become large.
   (b) Write an equation of a line that passes through the origin and is horizontal.

3. On a calculator or computer, graph $y = x + 1$, $y = x + 10$, and $y = x + 100$ in the window $-10 \le x \le 10$ by $-10 \le y \le 10$.

   (a) Explain what happens to the graph of a line, $y = b + mx$, as b becomes large.
   (b) Write a linear equation whose graph cannot be seen within the standard viewing window because all its y-values are less than the y-values shown.

4. The graphical interpretation of the slope is that it shows steepness. Using a calculator or a computer, graph the function $y = 2x - 3$ in the following windows:

   (a) $-10 \le x \le 10$ by $-10 \le y \le 10$
   (b) $-10 \le x \le 10$ by $-100 \le y \le 100$
   (c) $-10 \le x \le 10$ by $-1000 \le y \le 1000$
   (d) Write a sentence about steepness being related to the window in which it is viewed.

5. Match the following functions to the graphs in Figure 2.32.

   (a) $f(x) = 3x + 1$ ii   (b) $g(x) = -2x + 1$ iii   (c) $h(x) = 1$ i

(i)   (ii)   (iii)

Figure 2.32: Three graphs

6. Match the following functions to the lines in Figure 2.33: $f(x) = 5 + 2x$, $g(x) = -5 + 2x$, $h(x) = 5 + 3x$, $j(x) = 5 - 2x$, and $k(x) = 5 - 3x$.

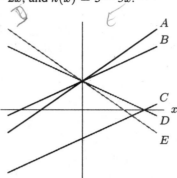

Figure 2.33: Three lines

7. Match the graphs in Figure 2.34 with the equations below.
   (a) $y = x - 5$ V   (b) $-3x + 4 = y$ IV   (c) $5 = y$ I   (d) $y = -4x - 5$ VI
   (e) $y = x + 6$ II   (f) $y = x/2$ III   (g) $5 = x$ VII

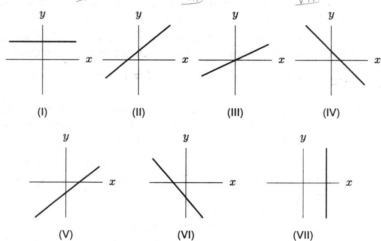

(I)   (II)   (III)   (IV)

(V)   (VI)   (VII)

Figure 2.34

8. Estimate the slope of the line shown in Figure 2.35 and use the slope to find an equation for that line.

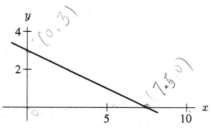

Figure 2.35

9. (a) Sketch, by hand, the graph of $y = 3$.
   (b) Sketch, by hand, the graph of $x = 3$.
   (c) Can you write the equation in part (a) in slope intercept form?
   (d) Can you write the equation in part (b) in slope intercept form?

10. Let line l be given by $y = 3 - \frac{2}{3}x$ and point P have the coordinates $(6, 5)$.
    (a) Find the equation of the line containing P and parallel to l.
    (b) Find the equation of the line containing P and perpendicular to l.
    (c) Graph the equations in (a) and (b).

11. Two straight lines are given by $y = b_1 + m_1 x$ and $y = b_2 + m_2 x$, where b_1, b_2, m_1, and m_2 are constants.
    (a) What conditions are imposed on b_1, b_2, m_1, and m_2 if the two straight lines have no points in common?
    (b) What conditions are imposed on b_1, b_2, m_1, and m_2 if the two straight lines have all points in common?
    (c) What conditions are imposed on b_1, b_2, m_1, and m_2 if the two straight lines have exactly one point in common?
    (d) What conditions are imposed on b_1, b_2, m_1, and m_2 if the two straight lines have exactly two points in common?

12. Find the equation of the line, l_2 in Figure 2.36.

Figure 2.36   **Figure 2.37**

13. Line, l, in Figure 2.37 is parallel to the line represented by $y = 2x + 1$. Find the coordinates of the point P.

14. Find the coordinates of point P in Figure 2.38.

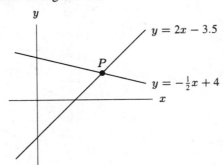

Figure 2.38: Axes not necessarily drawn to the same scale

15. The cost of a Frigbox refrigerator is $950, but it depreciates $50 each year. The cost of an ArcticAir refrigerator is $1200, but it depreciates $100 per year.

   (a)   When will the two refrigerators have equal value?
   (b)   What happens in 20 years time? What does this mean?

16. The total costs, in dollars, of producing three goods are defined below. The number of goods produced is represented by n. For each good, state the fixed and unit costs.

   (a) $C_1 = 8000 + 200n$ (b) $C_2 = 5000 + 200n$
   (c) $C_3 = 10{,}000 + 100n$ (d) $C_4 = 50n$

17. Graph the functions defined in Problem 16 on a single coordinate system.

18. Solve the system of equations given by $3x - y = 17$ and $-2x - 3y = -4$ algebraically.

19. You need to rent a car and compare the charges of three different companies. Company A charges 20 cents per mile plus a fixed rate of $20 per day. Company B charges 10 cents per mile plus a fixed rate of $35 per day. Company C charges a flat rate of $70 per day with no mileage charge.

   (a)   Find formulas for the cost of driving cars rented from companies A, B, and C, in terms of x, the distance driven in miles in one day.
   (b)   Graph the costs for each company for $0 \leq x \leq 500$. Put all three graphs on the same set of axes.
   (c)   What do the slope and the vertical intercept tell you in this situation?
   (d)   Use the graph in part (b) to find under what circumstances would company A be the cheapest? Company B? Company C? Do your results make sense?

20. You are comparing long-distance telephone calling plans. You can only choose one long-distance telephone company, and you have the following options.

   • Company A charges $0.37 per minute.
   • Company B charges $13.95 per month plus $0.22 per minute.
   • Company C charges a fixed rate of $50 per month.

   Let Y_A, Y_B, Y_C represent the monthly charges using Company A, B, and C, respectively. Let x denote the number of minutes spent on long distance calling during a month.

   (a)   Find equations for Y_A, Y_B, Y_C as functions of x.
   (b)   Figure 2.39 gives the graphs of the functions found in part (a). Which function corresponds to which graph?

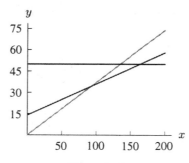

Figure 2.39

   (c)   Find the values of x for which Company B is the cheapest.

21. The solid waste generated each year in the cities of the United States is increasing. The solid waste generated, in millions of tons, was 82.3 in 1960 and 139.1 in 1980.[4] The trend appears linear during this time.

(a) Construct a mathematical model of the amount of municipal solid waste generated in the US by finding the equation of the line through these two points.

(b) Use this model to predict the amount of municipal solid waste generated in the US, in millions of tons, in the year 2000.

2.4 FITTING LINEAR FUNCTIONS TO DATA

When real data are collected in the laboratory or the field, they are often subject to experimental error. Even if there is an underlying linear relationship between two quantities, real data may not fit this relationship perfectly. Suppose we observe empirically that a certain quantity, Q, depends linearly on another quantity, t, and we find a linear function that models this dependence. If we plug a specific t-value into the function, it will predict a unique Q-value. However, in practice, the value of Q may be influenced by other factors besides the choice of t, and therefore the actual Q-value may differ from the Q-value predicted by the model.

However, even if a data set does not perfectly conform to a linear function, we may still be able to use linear functions to help us analyze the data.

Laboratory Data: The Viscosity of Motor Oil

The *viscosity* of a liquid, or its resistance to flow, depends on the liquid's temperature. Pancake syrup is a familiar example: straight from the refrigerator, it pours very slowly. When warmed on the stove it becomes quite runny, indicating that its viscosity has decreased.

Viscosity plays an important role inside the engine of a car. The viscosity of motor oil is a measure of its effectiveness as a lubricant. Thus, the effect of high engine temperature is a significant factor in motor-oil performance. Table 2.23 gives the viscosity of a certain grade of motor oil as measured in the lab at different temperatures. These data have been plotted in Figure 2.40. A plot of data points such as Figure 2.40 is called a *scatter plot*.

TABLE 2.23 *The measured viscosity, v, of motor oil as a function of the temperature, T*

T, temperature (°F)	v, viscosity (lbs·sec/in²)
160	28
170	26
180	24
190	21
200	16
210	13
220	11
230	9

Figure 2.40: The viscosity data from Table 2.23

[4]*Statistical Abstracts of the US*, 1988, p. 193, Table 333.

From the figure we see that, the viscosity of motor oil decreases as its temperature rises. If we want to study the relationship between engine temperature and motor-oil performance it would be useful to have a formula. In order to decide what kind of function would be the best model for our data, it is helpful to look at the scatter plot to see if the data fall roughly in the shape of a familiar family of functions.

Looking at Figure 2.40 again, the graph suggests a nearly linear relationship between v, viscosity, and T, temperature. The relationship is *nearly* linear but not completely so because not all the data points fall on one straight line. Thus we need to decide which line best fits these data points.

The process of fitting a line to a set of data is called *linear regression* and the line which fits best is called the *regression line*. There are several ways to go about fitting a line to data. One way is to draw in a line "by eye" that looks like a reasonable fit. In this case we can pick two appropriate points on the line and find its formula using those points. Alternatively, many computer programs and calculators will give you the regression line if you enter the data points.

Figure 2.41 shows the data from Table 2.23 together with the regression line. Its formula,

$$v = 75.6 - 0.293T,$$

was provided by a calculator (and the parameters were rounded for convenience).

Figure 2.41: A graph of the viscosity data from Table 2.23, together with a regression line (provided by a calculator)

It is easy to see why the line in Figure 2.41 can be considered a good fit. It captures the downward trend in the plotted points and these points all lie close to the line. However, none of the data points fall exactly on this regression line. The regression line summarizes behavior over a stated interval but does not necessarily represent any particular point on that interval.

The Assumptions Involved In Finding a Regression Line

When we determine a regression line for the data in Table 2.23, we are assuming that the value of v is in some way related to the value of T. However, we realize that other factors might influence the value of v. For example, there may be some experimental error in our viscosity measurements. In other words, if we measure viscosity twice at the same temperature, we may observe slightly different values for the viscosity. Alternatively, something besides engine temperature could be affecting the oil's viscosity (the oil pressure, for example). In either case, our viscosity readings may vary somewhat erratically with respect to temperature because we are neglecting to consider some other factors. Thus, even if we assume that our temperature readings are exact, our viscosity readings may include some degree of uncertainty.

Interpolation and Extrapolation

Now that we have a formula for viscosity, we can use it to make predictions. Suppose we want to know the viscosity of motor oil at $T = 196°$. Using our formula, we have

$$v = 75.6 - 0.293(196) \approx 18.2.$$

To see that this is a reasonable estimate, we can compare it to the entries in Table 2.23. At $190°$, the measured viscosity was 21 and at $200°$ it was 16. Our predicted viscosity of 18.2 is between 16 and 21, which makes sense because it corresponds to a temperature between $190°$ and $200°$. Figure 2.42 shows our predicted point in relation to the data points from Table 2.23. Of course, if we measured the viscosity at $T = 196°$ in the lab, we might obtain something different from 18.2. The regression equation allows us to make predictions, but does not necessarily provide exact results.

Figure 2.42: We can use a regression line to predict the viscosity at 196°

Figure 2.43: The data from Table 2.23 together with the predicted viscosity at $T = 240°$ and $T = 300°$

Since the temperature $T = 196°$ is *between* two temperatures for which v is known ($190°$ and $200°$), our estimate is said to be an *interpolation*. If instead we estimate the value of v for a temperature *outside* the known values for T in Table 2.23, our estimate would be called an *extrapolation*.

Example 1   Predict the viscosity of motor oil at 240°F and at 300°F.

Solution   At $T = 240°$F, we predict that the viscosity of motor oil is

$$v = 75.6 - 0.293(240) = 5.3.$$

This seems reasonable. As you can see from Figure 2.43, the predicted point – shown as an open circle on the graph – is consistent with the observed trend in the data points from Table 2.23.

On the other hand, at $T = 300°$F our regression-line formula gives

$$v = 75.6 - 0.293(300) = -12.3.$$

This is entirely unreasonable because it makes no sense to talk about a negative viscosity. To understand what went wrong, notice that in Figure 2.43, the open circle indicating the point $(300, -12.3)$ is quite far from the plotted data points. The predictive value of our regression line is compromised because we are using it to extend an observed trend too far beyond the bounds of our laboratory measurements. Based on the data in Table 2.23, we have no real way of knowing what happens to the viscosity of motor oil at temperatures much higher than 230°F or much lower than 160°F. If we want to extend the scope of our model we need to spend more time in the laboratory.

In general:

The process of using a regression line to find the value of the dependent quantity corresponding to a given value of the independent quantity is called:

- **interpolation** if the value of the independent quantity is *within* the interval of known values or

- **extrapolation** if the value of the independent quantity is *outside* the interval of known values.

Interpolation tends to be more reliable than extrapolation because we are making a prediction on an interval we already know something about instead of making a prediction beyond the limits of our knowledge.

How Regression Works

Often, the easiest way to fit a line to a set of data is to plot the data points and then fit the line "by eye." However, it is sometimes more convenient and more accurate to have a calculator or computer provide the line of best fit. How does a calculator or computer determine which line is best?

Figure 2.44 illustrates one good way for a calculator or computer to do this. Note that we are assuming that the value of y is in some way related to the value of x although we admit that other factors could influence y as well. Thus, we assume that we can pick the value of x exactly but that the value of y may be only partially determined by this x-value.

One way to fit a line to the data is to find the line that minimizes the sum of the squares of the vertical distances between the data points and the line. Such a line is shown in Figure 2.44, and it is called a *least-squares line*. There are straightforward techniques for calculating the slope m and the y-intercept b of the least-squares line for a given set of data. Your calculator or computer uses these techniques when it determines the formula for the regression line. The least-squares line is sometimes referred to as the *line of best fit*.

Figure 2.44: A given set of data and the corresponding least-squares regression line

Correlation

Another useful piece of information you can get from a computer or calculator is called the *correlation coefficient*, r. This number tells you something about how well a particular regression line fits your data. The correlation coefficient is a number between -1 and $+1$. If $r = 1$, the data lie exactly on a line of positive (or zero) slope. If $r = -1$, the data lie exactly on a line of negative slope. If r is close to 0, the data may be completely scattered, or perhaps there is a non-linear relationship between the variables. (See Figure 2.45.)

Figure 2.45: Various data sets and correlation coefficients

Example 2   Using a calculator or computer, we learn that the correlation coefficient for the viscosity data in Table 2.23 on page 97 is $r \approx -0.99$. The fact that r is negative tells us that the regression line has negative slope. The fact that r is so close to -1 tells us that the regression line is an excellent fit to this data set.

The Difference between Relation, Correlation, and Causation

It's important to understand that a high correlation (either positive or negative) between two quantities does *not* imply causation. For example, a study of children's reading level and shoe size would show a high correlation between them. However, it is certainly not true that having large feet causes a child to read better (or vice versa). Larger feet and improved reading ability are both a consequence of growing older.

Notice also that a correlation of 0 does not imply that there is no relationship between x and y. For example, Figure 2.45(d) exhibits a strong relationship between x and y-values, while Figure 2.45(c) exhibits no apparent relationship. Both data sets have a correlation coefficient of $r \approx 0$. Thus a correlation of $r = 0$ usually implies there is no *linear* relationship between x and y, but this doesn't mean there is no relationship at all.

Problems for Section 2.4

1. Table 2.24 shows Calories used per minute when walking at 3 mph.

    TABLE 2.24   *Calories burned from walking 3 mph*

Body Weight (lb)	100	120	150	170	200	220
Calories	2.7	3.2	4.0	4.6	5.4	5.9

    (a) Make a scatter plot of this data.
    (b) Draw a regression line.
    (c) Estimate the correlation coefficient.

2. Using the correlation coefficient values given below, match the r that best describes each scatter plot in Figure 2.46.

$$r = -0.98, \quad r = -0.5, \quad r = -0.25, \quad r = 0, \quad r = 0.7, \quad r = 1$$

(a)

(b)

(c)

(d)

(e)

(f)
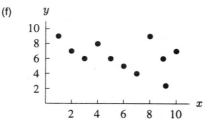

Figure 2.46

3. The rate of oxygen consumption for Colorado beetles increases with temperature. See Table 2.25.

TABLE 2.25

° C	10	15	20	25	30
oxygen rate	90	125	200	300	375

(a) Make a scatter plot of this data.
(b) Draw in an estimated regression line.
(c) Use a calculator or computer to find the equation of the least square best fit line or find the equation of your line in part (b); round slope and intercept parameters to whole integer values.
(d) Interpret the slope and each intercept of the estimated regression equation.
(e) Is there a correlation between temperature and oxygen rate?

4. An ecologist has tracked and studied 145 deer that were born in 1987. The number of these deer still living each year in the study is shown in Table 2.26.

   TABLE 2.26

year	1987	1988	1989	1990	1991	1992	1993	1994	1995
s	145	144	134	103	70	45	32	22	4

   Set 1987 to be $t = 0$.

   (a) Make a scatter plot of this data.
   (b) On the scatter plot, draw by hand a good fitting line and estimate its equation, rounded to whole integer values.
   (c) Use a calculator or computer to find the equation of the least square best fit line, rounded to whole integer values.
   (d) Interpret the slope and each intercept of the line graph.
   (e) Is there a correlation between time and the number of deer born in 1987 that are still alive?

5. Consider Table 2.27, which shows IQ and hours of watching TV per week for ten students.

   TABLE 2.27 *Ten students' IQ and hours of TV viewing per week*

IQ	110	105	120	140	100	125	130	105	115	110
Hours	10	12	8	2	12	10	5	6	13	3

   (a) Make a scatter plot of the data.
   (b) Estimate the correlation coefficient.
   (c) Use a calculator or computer to find the least squares regression line and the correlation coefficient. Your values should be correct to four decimal places.

6. The data on hand strength in Table 2.28 was collected from a freshman college class by using a grip meter.

   TABLE 2.28 *Hand strength for 20 students*

Preferred hand (kg)	28	27	45	20	40	47	28	54	52	21
Nonpreferred hand (kg)	24	26	43	22	40	45	26	46	46	22
Preferred hand (kg)	53	52	49	45	39	26	25	32	30	32
Nonpreferred hand (kg)	47	47	41	44	33	20	27	30	29	29

   (a) Make a scatter plot of these data treating the strength of the preferred hand as the independent quantity and the strength of the nonpreferred hand as the dependent quantity.
   (b) Draw a line on your scatter plot that is a good fit for these data and use it to find an approximate regression line equation.
   (c) Using a graphing calculator or computer find the least squares line equation.
   (d) What would the predicted grip strength in the nonpreferred hand be for a student with a preferred hand strength of 37?
   (e) Discuss interpolation and extrapolation using specific examples in relation to this regression line.
   (f) Discuss why r, the correlation coefficient, is both positive and close to 1.
   (g) Why do the points tend to "cluster" into two groups on your scatter plot?

7. In baseball, Henry Aaron holds the record for the greatest number of home-runs hit in the major leagues. Table 2.29 shows his cumulative yearly record from the start of his career, 1954, until 1973.[5]

TABLE 2.29 *Aaron's cumulative home-run record from 1954 to 1973*

Year	1	2	3	4	5	6	7	8	9	10	11	12	13	14	15	16	17	18	19	20
Home-runs	13	40	66	110	140	179	219	253	298	342	366	398	442	481	510	554	592	639	673	713

(a) Plot Aaron's cumulative number of home runs H on the vertical axis, and the time t in years along the horizontal axis, where $t = 1$ corresponds to 1954.

(b) By eye draw a straight line that best fits these data and write down the equation of that line.

(c) Using calculator or computer to find the equation of the regression line for these data. What is the correlation coefficient, r, to 4 decimal places? To 3 decimal places? What does this tell you?

(d) What does the slope of the regression line mean in terms of Henry Aaron's home-run record?

(e) From the results you found in earlier parts of this problem how many home-runs do you estimate Henry Aaron hit in each of the years 1974, 1975, 1976, and 1977. How confident are you with your estimates? If you were told that Henry Aaron retired at the end of the 1976 season, would this affect your confidence?

8. Table 2.30 shows the men's and women's freestyle swimming world records for distances from 50 meters to 1500 meters.[6]

TABLE 2.30   *Men's and women's freestyle swimming world records*

Distance (meters)	50	100	200	400	800	1500
Men (seconds)	21.81	48.21	106.69	223.80	466.00	881.66
Women (seconds)	24.51	54.01	116.78	243.85	496.22	952.10

(a) What values would you add to Table 2.30 that would represent the time taken by both men and women to swim 0 meters?

(b) Plot the men's time against distance, with time t in seconds on the vertical axis and distance d in meters on the horizontal axis. It is claimed that a straight line models this behavior well. What is the equation for that line? What does its slope represent? On the same graph plot the women's time against distance and find the equation of the straight line that models this behavior well. Is this line steeper or flatter than the men's line? What does that mean in realistic terms? What are the values of the y-intercepts? Do these values have a practical interpretation?

(c) On another graph plot the women's times against the men's times, with women's times, w, on the vertical axis and men's times, m, on the horizontal axis. It should look linear. How could you have predicted this linearity from the equations you found in part (b)? What is the slope of this line and how can it be interpreted? A newspaper reporter claims that the men's records are about 93% of the women's. Do the facts support this statement? What is the value of the y-intercept? Does this value have a practical interpretation?

---

[5] Adapted from "Graphing Henry Aaron's home-run output" by H. Ringel, The Physics Teacher, January 1974, page 43.
[6] Accurate as of August 1995. Data from "The World Almanac and Book of Facts: 1996" edited by R. Famighetti, Funk and Wagnalls, New Jersey, 1995.

REVIEW PROBLEMS FOR CHAPTER TWO

1.
   TABLE 2.31
   Calories Used Per Minute According to Body Weight in Pounds (rounded)
   Source: 1993 World Almanac

Activity	100 lb	120 lb	150 lb	170 lb	200 lb	220 lb
Walking(3 mph)	2.7	3.2	4.0	4.6	5.4	5.9
Bicycling(10 mph)	5.4	6.5	8.1	9.2	10.8	11.9
Swimming(2 mph)	5.8	6.9	8.7	9.8	11.6	12.7

   (a) Use Table 2.31 to determine the number of calories that a person weighing 200 lb uses in a half–hour of walking.

   (b) Table 2.31 illustrates a relationship between the number of calories used per minute walking and a person's weight in pounds. Describe in words what is true about this relationship. Identify the dependent and independent variables. Specify whether it is an increasing or decreasing function.

   (c) (i) Graph the linear function for walking, as described in part (b) and find its equation.

   (ii) Interpret the meaning of the y–intercept of the graph of the function.

   (iii) Specify a meaningful domain and range for your function.

   (iv) Use your function to determine how many calories per minute a person who weighs 135 lb would use per minute of walking (3 mph).

2. Suppose you start 60 miles east of Pittsburgh and drive east at a constant speed of 50 miles per hour. (Assume that the road is straight and will permit you to do this.) Find a formula for d, your distance from Pittsburgh as a function of t, the number of hours of travel.

3. Suppose a small café makes all of its money on the sale of coffee. It sells coffee for $0.95 per cup. On average, it costs the café $0.25 to make a cup of coffee (for grounds, hot water, filters, etc.). The café also faces a fixed daily cost of $200 (for rent, wages, utilities, etc.).

   (a) Let R, P, and C be the café's daily revenue, profit, and costs, respectively, for selling x cups of coffee on a given day. Find equations for R, P, and C as a function of x. [Hint: The cost C includes the fixed daily cost as well as the cost for all x cups of coffee sold. R is the total amount of money that the café brings in. P is the café's profit after costs have been accounted for.]

   (b) Plot P against x. When is the graph of P below the x-axis? Above the x-axis? Interpret your results.

   (c) Interpret the slope and both intercepts of your graph in practical terms.

Table 2.32 describes the cost, $C(n)$, of producing a certain good as a linear function of n, the number of units produced. Use the table to answer Problems 4–6.

TABLE 2.32

n (units)	100	125	150	175
$C(n)$ (dollars)	11000	11125	11250	11375

4. Evaluate the expressions below. Give economic interpretations for each.

   (a) $C(175)$ (b) $C(175) - C(150)$ (c) $\dfrac{C(175) - C(150)}{175 - 150}$

5. Estimate $C(0)$. What is the economic significance of this value?

6. The *fixed cost* of production is the cost incurred before any goods are produced. The *unit cost* is the cost of producing an additional unit. Use the fact that

$$\begin{pmatrix} \text{total} \\ \text{cost} \end{pmatrix} = \begin{pmatrix} \text{fixed} \\ \text{cost} \end{pmatrix} + \begin{pmatrix} \text{unit} \\ \text{cost} \end{pmatrix} \cdot \begin{pmatrix} \text{number} \\ \text{of units} \end{pmatrix}$$

   to find a formula for $C(n)$ in terms of n.

7. A linear function, $f(t)$, generated the data below. Find a formula for $f(t)$.

   TABLE 2.33

t	1.2	1.3	1.4	1.5
$f(t)$	0.736	0.614	0.492	0.37

   $f(t) = -1.2t + 2.2$

8. Find the equation of the line parallel to $3x + 5y = 6$ and passing through $(0, 6)$.

9. A rock is thrown into the air. Suppose $v = f(t) = 80 - 32t$ gives the rock's velocity in feet per second after t seconds.

   (a) Construct a table of values of v for $t = 0, 0.5, 1, 1.5, 2, 2.5, 3, 3.5, 4$.
   (b) Describe the motion of the rock. How can you interpret negative values of v?
   (c) At what time t is the rock highest above the ground?
   (d) Interpret the slope and both intercepts of the graph of $v = f(t)$.
   (e) How would the slope of v be different on the moon, whose gravitational pull is less than the earth's? How would the slope be different on Jupiter, which has a greater gravitational pull than the earth?

10. Wire is sold by gauge size, where the diameter of the wire is a decreasing linear function of gauge. Gauge 2 wire has a diameter of 0.2656″ and gauge 8 wire has a diameter of 0.1719″. Find the diameter for wires of gauge 12 1/2 and gauge 0. What values of the gauge do not make sense in this model?

11. Suppose that there are x male job-applicants at a certain company, and y female applicants. Suppose that 15% of the men are accepted, and that 18% of the women are accepted.

    (a) Write an expression in terms of x and y representing the total number of applicants to the company. $x+y$
    (b) Write an expression in terms of x and y representing the total number of applicants accepted. $y = .15x + .18y$
    (c) Write an expression in terms of x and y representing the percentage of all applicants accepted. $(15x + 18y)(x+y)$

12. One of the problems that challenged early Greek mathematicians was whether it was possible to construct a square whose area was the same as that of a given circle.

    (a) If the radius of a given circle is r, what expression, in terms of r, describes the side, s, of the square with area equal to that of the circle?
    (b) The side, s, of such a square is a function of the radius of the circle. What kind of function is it? How do you know?
    (c) For what values of r is the side, s, equal to zero? Explain why your answer makes sense.

13. A *dose-response function* can be used to describe the increase in risk associated with the increase in exposure to various hazards. For example, the risk of contracting lung cancer depends upon, among other things, the number of cigarettes a person smokes per day. This risk can be described by a linear dose-response function. For example, it is known that smoking 10 cigarettes per day increases a person's probability of contracting lung cancer by a factor of 25, while smoking 20 cigarettes a day increases the probability by a factor of 50.

   (a) Find a formula for $i(x)$, the increase in the probability of contracting lung cancer for a person who smokes x cigarettes per day as compared to a non-smoker.

   (b) Evaluate $i(0)$.

   (c) Interpret the slope of i.

14. Match the graphs in Figure 2.47 with the equations below.

   (a) $y = -2.72x$ (c) $y = 27.9 - 0.1x$ (e) $y = -5.7 - 200x$

   (b) $y = 0.01 + 0.001x$ (d) $y = 0.1x - 27.9$ (f) $y = x/3.14$

(I)   (II)   (III)   (IV)   (V)   (VI)

Figure 2.47

15. Find the equation of the line passing through the point $(2, 1)$, and which is perpendicular to the line $y = 5x - 3$.

16. Find the equations of the lines parallel to and perpendicular to the line $y + 4x = 7$ through the point $(1, 5)$.

17. Sketch a family of five functions $y = -2 - ax$ for different values of $a < 0$.

18. Assume the equation

$$Ax + By = C \quad (A, B, C \text{ are constants}, B \neq 0, \ A \neq 0)$$

is true for all x.

   (a) Show that $y = f(x)$ is linear. State the slope and the x- and y-intercepts of $f(x)$.

   (b) Graph $y = f(x)$, labeling the x- and y-intercepts in terms of A, B, and C, assuming

   (i) $A > 0, B > 0, C > 0$;   (ii) $A > 0, B > 0, C < 0$;

   (iii) $A > 0, B < 0, C > 0$.

19. In economics, the *demand* for a product reflects the amount of that product that consumers are willing to buy at a given price. The quantity demanded of a product will usually go down if the price of that product goes up. Suppose that a certain company believes there is a linear relationship between the consumer demand for its product and the price charged. Furthermore, it knows that when the price of its product was \$3 per unit, the weekly quantity demanded was 500 units, and that when the unit price was raised to \$4, the weekly quantity demanded dropped to 300 units. Let D represent the weekly quantity demanded for the product at a unit price of p, dollars.

(a) Calculate D when $p = 5$. Interpret your result.
(b) Find a formula for D in terms of p.
(c) Suppose that the company raises the price of the good, and that the new weekly quantity demanded is only 50 units. What is the new price?
(d) Give an interpretation of the slope of the equation you found above in practical terms.
(e) Find D when $p = 0$. Find p when $D = 0$. Interpret both of these results.

20. In economics, the *supply* of a product reflects the quantity of that product suppliers are willing to provide at a given price. In theory, the quantity supplied of a product will go up if the price of that product goes up. Suppose that there is a linear relationship between the quantity supplied, S, of the product described in Problem 19 and the unit price, p. Suppose furthermore that the weekly quantity supplied is 100 when the price is $2, and that the quantity supplied rises by 50 units when the price rises by $0.50.

(a) Find a formula for S in terms of p.
(b) Interpret the slope of your formula in practical terms.
(c) Is there a price below which suppliers will not provide this product?
(d) The *market clearing price* is the price at which supply equals demand. According to theory, the free-market price of a product will be its market clearing price. Find the market clearing price for the product under consideration.

21. When economists graph demand or supply equations, they place quantity on the horizontal axis and unit price on the vertical axis.

(a) On the same set of axes, graph the demand and supply equations you found in Problems 19 and 20, being sure to place price on the vertical axis.
(b) Indicate how you could estimate the market clearing price from your graph.

22. Bill has an initial investment of $12,467.00. Suppose that the investment grows according to the following table.

TABLE 2.34

Month	1	2	3	4	5	6	7	8
Interest	$95.48	$96.21	$96.95	$97.70	$98.47	$99.23	$99.99	$100.74

(a) Let $M(t)$ be the amount of money the investment is worth after t months. Complete a similar table showing t and $M(t)$.
(b) Plot the data points you got from part (a).
(c) Find an equation for a regression line for the data points.
(d) Use the equation of the line to predict $M(9)$ and $M(100)$.
(e) Are these reasonable extrapolations?

23. A student exercised for 30 minutes and then measured her ten-second pulse count at one minute intervals as she rested. The data are shown in Table 2.35.

TABLE 2.35 *Ten-second pulse count, t minutes after exercise*

t, time	0	1	2	3	4	5
pulse	22	18	15	12	10	10

   (a) Make a scatter plot of this data.

   (b) Because the pulse values are the same after 4 and 5 minutes, these data are clearly not linear. Is there a domain on which a regression line is a good model for these data? If so, what is it?

   (c) Discuss the correlation between minutes after exercising and pulse rate.

24. Repeat Problem 23 after collecting your own data in a table like Table 2.35.

25. Record the height and shoe size of at least five females or five males in your class and make a data table.

   (a) Make a scatter plot of these data, with height on the y-axis and shoe size on the x-axis.

   (b) Draw a line on your scatter plot that is a good fit for this data and use it to find an approximate regression line equation.

   (c) Use a graphing calculator or computer to find the equation of the least-squares line.

   (d) Discuss interpolation and extrapolation using specific examples in relation to this regression line. Try to check the interpolation with a student in the class whose shoe size is close to the one you have chosen.

   (e) Discuss r, the correlation coefficient, for this regression line.

Chapter 3

Exponential and Logarithmic Functions

3.1 INTRODUCTION TO THE FAMILY OF EXPONENTIAL FUNCTIONS

Growing at a Constant Percent Rate

Linear functions represent quantities that change at a constant rate. In this section we introduce functions that represent quantities that change at a constant *percent* rate. These functions are members of the family of *exponential functions*.

The Balance in a Savings Account

Example 1   Suppose you deposit $1000 into an account that earns 6% annual interest compounded annually (i.e. interest is paid once at the end of the year). Provided you make no additional deposits or withdrawals, your balance grows at a constant 6% annual rate; thus, the balance is an exponential function of time.

Let's calculate the balance for the first several years. If t represents the number of years since the deposit was made, then for $t = 0$ the balance is $1000. At the end of the first year, when $t = 1$, the balance increases by 6% so

$$\text{Balance when } t = 1 = \text{old balance } + 6\% \text{ of old balance}$$
$$= 1000 + 0.06(1000) = 1000 + 60$$
$$= 1060.$$

After the second year, the balance again increases by 6%, so

$$\text{Balance when } t = 2 = \text{old balance } + 6\% \text{ of old balance}$$
$$= 1060 + 0.06(1060) = 1060 + 63.60$$
$$= 1123.60.$$

Notice that the account earned more interest in the second year than in the first since the account earned interest on the original $1000 deposit *and* on the $60 interest earned in the first year. In effect, the account is earning interest on its interest.

The balance calculations for the first four years have been rounded and recorded in Table 3.1. At the end of the third and fourth years the balance again increases by 6%, but the balance grows by a larger amount each time; it grows by $60 the first year, by $63.60 in the second, then by $67.42, and finally by $71.46 at the end of year 4. The balance grows by the same *percentage* every year, but the dollar amount earned in interest increases each time.

TABLE 3.1   *The interest and balance of an account earning 6% annual interest. (Note that interest is credited at the end of the year.)*

year	interest earned ($)	balance ($)
0		1000.00
1	60.00	1060.00
2	63.60	1123.60
3	67.42	1191.02
4	71.46	1262.48

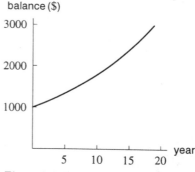

Figure 3.1: The account balance over a 20-year period

Figure 3.1 gives a graph of the account balance over a 20-year period assuming that no other deposits or withdrawals were made and that the annual interest rate remained at 6% compounded annually. The graph of this function is not a line; the graph is concave up, indicating that the balance increased by a larger amount each year. In other words, it increased at an increasing rate.

Population Growth

Exponential functions can also provide reasonable models for growing populations. Consider the following example.

Example 2   During the early 1980s, the population of Mexico increased at a constant annual percent rate of 2.6%. Since the population increased at a constant annual percent rate, it can be modeled by an exponential function.

Let's calculate the population of Mexico for the first few years after 1980. In 1980, the population was 67.38 million. Since the population grew by 2.6% each year, we see that

$$\text{Population in 1981} = \text{Population in 1980} + 2.6\% \text{ of population in 1980}$$
$$= 67.38 + 0.026(67.38)$$
$$\approx 67.38 + 1.75$$
$$\approx 69.13.$$

Similarly,

$$\text{Population in 1982} = \text{Population in 1981} + 2.6\% \text{ of population in 1981}$$
$$= 69.13 + 0.026(69.13)$$
$$\approx 69.13 + 1.80$$
$$\approx 70.93.$$

The calculations for years 1980 through 1984 have been rounded and recorded in Table 3.2. As you can see, the population of Mexico increased by slightly more each year than it did the year before. This is because each year the increase is 2.6% of a larger number.

Figure 3.2 gives a graph of the population of Mexico over a 30-year period, assuming a constant 2.6% annual growth rate. Notice that this graph has the same concave-up appearance as the graph of the account balance shown in Figure 3.1.

TABLE 3.2   *Calculated values for the population model of Mexico*

t, year	*P*, population (millions)	ΔP increase
1980	67.38	—
1981	69.13	1.75
1982	70.93	1.80
1983	72.77	1.84
1984	74.67	1.90

Figure 3.2: The population of Mexico over a 30-year period, assuming 2.6% annual growth

Growth Factors and Percent Growth Rates

The bank account in Example 1 earns 6% annual interest compounded annually. Thus, we say that the annual percent growth rate of the account is 6%. But there is another way to think about the growth of this account. We know that each year,

New balance = Old balance + 6% of old balance.

We can rewrite this word equation as follows:

New balance = 100% of old balance + 6% of old balance.

or

New balance = 106% of old balance.

For example, the account begins with $1000. Thus, when $t = 1$,

$$\text{New balance} = 106\% \text{ of } \$1000$$
$$= 1.06(1000) \quad \text{(because 106\% = 1.06)}$$
$$= 1060.$$

We see that multiplying the old balance by 1.06 gives the same result as adding 6% interest to the old balance. In fact, each value of M in Table 3.1 can be obtained by multiplying the previous value by 1.06:

$$1060(1.06) = 1123.60$$
$$1123.60(1.06) = 1191.02$$

and so on.

We call the multiplying factor of 1.06 the account's *annual growth factor*. As you can see,

Annual growth factor = 1 + Annual interest rate,

where the percent interest is expressed in decimal form.

Example 3   What is the annual growth factor of the population of Mexico (in the early 1980s)? What does this tell you about the population?

Solution   During the early 1980s the population of Mexico grew at the constant annual percent rate of 2.6%. Thus,

$$\text{Annual growth factor} = 1 + \text{Annual growth rate}$$
$$= 1 + 0.026$$
$$= 1.026.$$

This tells us that each year the population increased by a factor of 1.026. You can check that each value of P in Table 3.2 can be obtained by multiplying the previous value by 1.026.

In general:

Q is an increasing exponential function of t if
- Q increases by the same percent on all intervals of t that are the same length, or equivalently,
- Q increases by the same growth factor on all intervals of t that are the same length.

If r is the percent growth rate then the growth factor, B, is given by

$$B = 1 + r.$$

Example 4   On August 2, 1988, a US District Court judge imposed a fine on the city of Yonkers, New York, for defying a federal court order involving housing desegregation.[1] The fine was set at $100 for the first day and was to double daily until the city chose to obey the court order. In other words, the fine increased each day by a factor of 2. Thus, the fine grew exponentially with growth factor $B = 2$.

To find the percent growth rate we set $B = 1 + r = 2$, from which we find $r = 1$, or 100%. Thus the daily percent growth rate is 100%. This makes sense because when a quantity increases by 100% it doubles in size.

Decreasing Exponential Functions

Exponential functions can also model decreasing quantities. A quantity which decreases at a constant percent rate is said to be decreasing exponentially.

Example 5   Over time the isotope carbon-14 decays radioactively into other more stable isotopes. The decay rate of carbon-14 is 11.4% every 1000 years. For example, if we begin with a 200 microgram (μg) sample of carbon-14 then

$$\begin{aligned}\text{Amount remaining after 1000 years} &= \text{Initial amount} - 11.4\% \text{ of initial amount}\\ &= 200 - 0.114(200)\\ &= 177.2.\end{aligned}$$

Similarly,

$$\begin{aligned}\text{Amount remaining after 2000 years} &= \text{Amount remaining after 1000 years} - 11.4\% \text{ of } \left(\text{Amount remaining after 1000 years}\right)\\ &= 177.2 - 0.114(177.2)\\ &\approx 157,\end{aligned}$$

and

$$\begin{aligned}\text{Amount remaining after 3000 years} &= \text{Amount remaining after 2000 years} - 11.4\% \text{ of } \left(\text{Amount remaining after 2000 years}\right)\\ &= 157 - 0.114(157)\\ &\approx 139.1.\end{aligned}$$

These calculations have been recorded in Table 3.3. Notice that during each 1000-year period, the amount of carbon-14 that decays decreases. This is because we are taking 11.4% of a smaller quantity each time.

TABLE 3.3   *The amount of carbon-14 remaining over time*

years elapsed	amount remaining (μg)	amount decayed (μg)
0	200.0	—
1000	177.2	22.8
2000	157.0	20.2
3000	139.1	17.9

Figure 3.3: Amount of carbon-14 over 10,000 years

[1]*The Boston Globe*, August 27, 1988.

Figure 3.3 gives a graph of the amount of carbon-14 left from a 200μg sample over 10,000 years. The graph goes down when read from left to right, which tells us that the amount of carbon-14 decreases over time. The graph is concave up, which means that it decreases by a smaller amount over each time interval.

The Growth Factor of a Decreasing Exponential Function

We have seen that exponential functions can be used to model quantities that change at a constant percent rate. In Example 5 the rate of change of carbon-14 is -11.4% every 1000 years. The negative growth rate tells us that the carbon-14 level decreases over time. The growth factor for carbon-14 is

$$B = 1 - 0.114$$
$$= 0.886.$$

The fact that B is less than 1 indicates that the amount of carbon-14 is decreasing, since multiplying a quantity by a factor between 0 and 1 decreases the quantity.

Although it may sound strange to refer to the growth factor of a decreasing quantity, that is the term people tend to use. In general:

Let $Q = f(t)$ be an exponential function. Let r be the percent growth rate and $B = 1 + r$ the growth factor.
- If $r > 0$, then $B > 1$ and f is increasing.
- If $r < 0$, then $0 < B < 1$ and f is decreasing.

Notice that if the percent growth rate is 0% the growth factor would be $B = 1$. Then the exponential function would be $Q = A \cdot (1)^t = A$ (since $1^t = 1$ for any t). This function is constant, and its graph is the horizontal line $y = A$. Therefore, the family of exponential functions is defined for $B > 0$, $B \neq 1$.

A General Formula for the Family of Exponential Functions

In Example 1 we considered a bank account that begins with $1000 and earns 6% annual interest compounded annually. Let's find a formula that gives M, the balance, in terms of t, the year, where t represents the number of years since the account was opened. Since the annual growth factor is $B = 1.06$, we know that for each year,

New balance = Old balance $\cdot$ 1.06.

Thus, after one year, or when $t = 1$,

$$M = \underbrace{1000}_{\text{old balance}} \cdot 1.06.$$

Similarly, when $t = 2$,

$$M = \underbrace{1000(1.06)}_{\text{old balance}} \cdot 1.06$$
$$= 1000(1.06)^2.$$

Here there are *two* factors of 1.06 because the balance has increased by 6% twice. When $t = 3$,

$$M = \underbrace{1000(1.06)^2}_{\text{old balance}} \cdot 1.06$$

$$= 1000(1.06)^3.$$

Here there are *three* factors of 1.06 because the balance has increased by 6% three times. Generalizing, we see that after t years have elapsed,

$$M = 1000 \underbrace{(1.06)(1.06)\ldots(1.06)}_{t \text{ factors of } 1.06}$$

$$= 1000(1.06)^t.$$

After t years the balance has increased by a factor of 1.06 a total of t times. Thus,

$$M(t) = 1000(1.06)^t.$$

These results are summarized in Table 3.4. Notice that in this formula we assume that t is an integer, $t \geq 0$, since the account pays interest only once a year.

TABLE 3.4 *The balance of an account in year t*

t, year	M, balance($\$$)
0	1000
1	1000(1.06)
2	1000(1.06)(1.06)
3	1000(1.06)(1.06)(1.06)
t	$1000(1.06)^t$

This account-balance formula can be written as

$$M = \text{initial balance} \times (\text{annual growth factor})^t.$$

In general, if Q is an exponential function of t, then a formula for Q is given by

$$Q = \text{initial value} \times (\text{growth factor})^t.$$

Thus, we have:

> A general formula for the exponential function $Q = f(t)$ is
>
> $$f(t) = AB^t, \quad B \neq 1,$$
>
> where the parameter A is the initial value of Q (at $t = 0$) and the parameter B is the growth factor.
> - If $B > 1$, then f is an increasing function. We say that f describes exponential growth.
> - If $0 < B < 1$, then f is a decreasing function. We say that f describes exponential decay.

The formula indicates where the name *exponential function* comes from: the independent variable, t, appears in the exponent.

Example 6   Using the formula $M = 1000(1.06)^t$, calculate the balance when $t = 4$, when $t = 12$, and when $t = 100$.

Solution   When $t = 4$, we have
$$M = 1000(1.06)^4 \approx 1262.48.$$
Notice that this agrees with Table 3.1 on page 112. When $t = 12$, we have
$$M = 1000(1.06)^{12} \approx 2012.20.$$
So after 12 years, the balance has more than doubled from the initial deposit of $1000. When $t = 100$ we have
$$M = 1000(1.06)^{100} \approx 339{,}302.08.$$
Thus if we are willing to wait 100 years, our balance will be over a third of a million dollars.

Example 7   Find a formula for P, the population of Mexico (in millions), in year t where $t = 0$ means 1980. (See Example 2 on page 113.)

Solution   In 1980, the population of Mexico was 67.38 million, and it was growing at a constant 2.6% annual rate. Thus, the growth factor is $B = 1 + 0.026 = 1.026$, and $A = 67.38$.
Thus,
$$P(t) = 67.38(1.026)^t.$$
Because the growth factor may change eventually, this formula may not give accurate results for very large values of t.

Example 8   What does the formula $P = 67.38(1.026)^t$ predict when $t = 0$? When $t = -5$? What do these values tell you about the population of Mexico?

Solution   If $t = 0$, then

$$P = 67.38(1.026)^0$$
$$= 67.38. \quad \text{(because } 1.026^0 = 1\text{)}$$

This makes sense because $t = 0$ stands for 1980, and in 1980 the population was 67.38 million. What about when $t = -5$? We have
$$P = 67.38(1.026)^{-5}$$
$$= 67.38 \left(\frac{1}{1.026^5} \right) \quad \text{(Using a property of exponents)}$$
$$\approx 59.26.$$

This also makes sense, provided we are willing to interpret the year $t = -5$ as 5 years *before* 1980 – that is, as the year 1975. If the population of Mexico had been growing at a 2.6% annual rate from 1975 to 1980 as well as in the early 1980s, then our formula says that in 1975 the Mexican population was 59.26 million, quite a bit less than the 1980 level.

Example 9   Suppose that the annual inflation rate in a certain state is 3.5%.
(a)   If a movie ticket costs $7.50, find a formula for p, the price of the ticket t years from today, assuming that movie tickets keep up with inflation and that the inflation rate stays at 3.5%.
(b)   According to your formula, how much will movie tickets cost in 20 years?

Chapter 3/   8

Solution (a) We assume that the price of a movie ticket increases at the rate of 3.5% per year. This means that the price is rising exponentially, so a formula for p is of the form $p = AB^t$. In this formula, A is the initial price and B is the growth factor. Thus, $A = 7.50$ and $B = 1 + r = 1.035$. We conclude that a formula for p is

$$p = 7.50(1.035)^t.$$

  (b) In 20 years ($t = 20$) we have $p = 7.50(1.035)^{20} \approx 14.92$. Thus, in 20 years, movie tickets will cost almost $15.

Solving Exponential Equations Graphically

We will often be interested in solving equations involving exponential functions. However, as the next two examples illustrate, this cannot always be done algebraically.

Example 10 In 1988, the entire annual budget of the city of Yonkers was $337 million. The fine imposed on the city is given by $F = f(t) = 100 \cdot 2^t$ where t is the number of days after August 2. If the city chose to disobey the court order, at what point would the fine have wiped out its entire annual budget? (See Example 4 on page 115.)

Solution We need to find the day on which the fine reaches $337 million. That is, we would like to solve the equation

$$100 \cdot 2^t = 337{,}000{,}000.$$

Dividing by 100 gives

$$2^t = 3{,}370{,}000.$$

At this point, we see that we cannot bring t down from the exponent (at least not using basic arithmetic). We will have to try another approach to solve this equation.

Using a computer or graphing calculator we can graph $f(t) = 100 \cdot 2^t$ to find the point at which the fine reaches 337 million. Figure 3.4 gives such a graph. From the figure we see that after about 15 days the fine grows quite rapidly.

At day $t = 21$, or August 23, the fine is (rounded to the nearest dollar):

$$F = 100 \cdot 2^{21} = 209{,}715{,}200,$$

or just over $200 million. On day $t = 22$, or August 24, the fine is

$$F = 100 \cdot 2^{22} = 419{,}430{,}400,$$

or almost $420 million – quite a bit more than the city's entire annual budget! Thus, the city's entire budget will be wiped out after only 22 days.

Figure 3.4: The fine imposed on Yonkers exceeds $337 million after 22 days

Example 11   In Example 5 we saw that carbon-14 decays radioactively at a rate of 11.4% every 1000 years. A 200 microgram sample of carbon-14 will decay according to the formula

$$Q(t) = 200(0.886)^t$$

where t is given in thousands of years. Estimate when there will be only 25 micrograms of carbon-14 left.

Solution   We must solve the equation

$$200(0.886)^t = 25.$$

This equation cannot be solved algebraically with basic arithmetic operations. However, we can estimate the solution graphically. Figure 3.5 shows a graph of $Q(t)$ and the line $Q = 25$. The amount of carbon-14 decays to 25 micrograms at $t \approx 17.2$, or, since t is measured in thousands of years, about 17,200 years later.

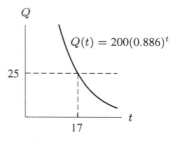

Figure 3.5: The graph of $Q(t)$ and line $Q = 25$

We will return to the question of solving exponential equations in Section 3.4 when we discuss logarithmic functions.

Problems for Section 3.1

1. Let $f(x) = 2^x$.

    (a) Prepare a table of values for f for $x = -3, -2, -1, 0, 1, 2, 3$.
    (b) Draw a graph of $f(x)$. (You can plot points from part (a), or you can use your calculator.) Describe the graph in words.

2. Suppose you owe $2000 on a credit card. The card charges 1.5% *monthly* interest on your balance, and requires a minimum monthly payment of 2.5%. All transactions (payments and interest charges) are recorded at the end of the month. Suppose you make only the minimum required payment every month, and that you incur no additional debt.

    (a) Complete Table 3.5 below for a twelve-month period. (The first two rows have been filled in.)

    TABLE 3.5

Month	Balance	Interest	Minimum payment
0	$2000.00	$30.00	$50.00
1	$1980.00	$29.70	$49.50
2	$1960.20		
⋮			

(b) What will your unpaid balance be after one year has passed? How much of your debt will you have paid off? How much money in interest charges will you have paid your creditors?

3. The HOME section of many Sunday newspapers includes a mortgage table similar to Table 3.6. Mortgage tables allow readers to compute the monthly payment of a mortgage given the amount of the loan. The table gives the required monthly payment per $1000 borrowed for loans at various interest rates and time periods. Use the table to determine the monthly payment on a

   (a) $60,000 mortgage at 8% for fifteen years.
   (b) $60,000 mortgage at 8% for thirty years.
   (c) $60,000 mortgage at 10% for fifteen years.
   (d) Over the life of the loan how much money would be saved on a 15-year mortgage of $60,000 if the rate were 8% instead of 10%?
   (e) Over the life of the loan how much money would be saved on an 8% mortgage of $60,000 if the term of the loan was fifteen years rather than thirty years?

TABLE 3.6 *Monthly payment per $1000 borrowed for mortgages at different interest rates and loan periods*

Mortgage Rate	15–year loan	20–year loan	25–year loan	30–year loan
8.00	9.56	8.37	7.72	7.34
8.50	9.85	8.68	8.06	7.69
9.00	10.15	9.00	8.40	8.05
9.50	10.45	9.33	8.74	8.41
10.00	10.75	9.66	9.09	8.78
10.50	11.06	9.99	9.45	9.15
11.00	11.37	10.33	9.81	9.53
11.50	11.69	10.67	10.17	9.91

4. Let the value V of a $100,000 investment that earns 3% annual interest be denoted by $V = f(t)$ where t is measured in years. How much is the investment worth in 3 years?

5. In 1988, the population of a country was 70 million and growing at a rate of 1.9% per year. Express the population of this country as a function of t, the number of years after 1988.
$$70(1.019)^t$$

6. Suppose the city of Yonkers is offered two alternative fines by the judge. (Refer to Example 4 on page 115.)

   Penalty A: $1 million on August 2 and the fine increases by $10 million each day thereafter.

   Penalty B: 1¢ on August 2 and the fine doubles each day thereafter.

   (a) If the city of Yonkers plans to defy the court order until the end of the month (August 31), compare the fines incurred under Penalty A and Penalty B.
   (b) If t represents the number of days after August 2, express the fine incurred as a function of t under

   (i) Penalty A   (ii) Penalty B

   (c) Assuming your formulas in part (b) hold true for $t \geq 0$, is there a value of t such that the fines incurred under both penalties are equal? If so, estimate that value.

7. Let $P = f(t)$ be the population of a community in year t, where a formula for $f(t)$ is

$$f(t) = 1000(1.04)^t.$$

(a) Evaluate $f(0)$ and $f(10)$. What do these expressions represent in terms of the population?
(b) Using a graphing calculator a computer find appropriate viewing windows on which to graph the population for the first 10 years and for the first 50 years. Give the dimensions of the viewing windows you used, and sketch the resulting graphs.

8. A pill is taken and the amount (in milligrams) of the drug in the body at time t (in hours) is given by: $A(t) = 25(0.85)^t$.

(a) What is the initial dose given?
(b) What percent of the drug leaves the body each hour?
(c) What is the amount of drug left after 10 hours?
(d) After how many hours will there be less than 1 milligram left in the body?

9. In 1980 the population of the United States was about 222.5 million. Assume the population increases at a constant rate of 1.3% per year. In what year is the population projected to reach 350 million?

10. Suppose the population of a small town increases by a growth factor of 1.134 during a period of two years.

(a) By what percent does the town increase in size during a period of two years?
(b) If the town grows by the same percent each year, what is its annual percent growth rate?

11. Every year, teams from 64 colleges qualify to compete in the NCAA basketball playoffs. For each round, every team is paired with an opponent. A team is eliminated from the tournament once it loses any round. So, at the end of a round, only one half the number of teams move on to the next round. Define $N(r)$ to be the number of teams remaining in competition after r rounds of the tournament have been played.

(a) Find a formula for $N(r)$, and sketch the graph of $y = N(r)$.
(b) How many rounds will it take to determine the winner of the tournament?

12. Suppose y, the number of cases of a disease, is reduced by 10% each year.

(a) If there are initially 10,000 cases, express y as a function of t, the number of years elapsed.
(b) How many cases will there be 5 years from now?
(c) How long will it take to reduce the cases to 1000 per year?

13. Polluted water is passed through a series of filters. Each filter removes 85% of the remaining impurities. Initially, the untreated water contains impurities at a level of 420 parts per million (ppm). Find a formula for L, the remaining level of impurities, after the water has been passed through a series of n filters.

14. A one-page letter is folded into thirds to go into an envelope. If it were possible to repeat this kind of tri-fold 20 times, how many miles thick would the letter be? (A stack of 150 pieces of stationery is one inch thick.)

15. Suppose a one-celled animal is in a petri dish and reproduces (by division) once every minute, as do its offspring. In one hour the dish is full.

(a) At what time was the jar half full?
(b) One quarter full?

16. Use a graphing calculator or computer to plot the three functions $f(x) = 10(1.0001)^x$, $g(x) = 10(1.0000)^x$, and $h(x) = 10(0.9999)^x$ in the window $0 \leq x \leq 20, 0 \leq y \leq 20$. If you were presented only with this picture and told that you were looking at the graphs of three functions, what would you conclude? Would this be accurate? What actually happens to $f(x)$, $g(x)$, and $h(x)$ as $x \to \infty$?

17. The Earth's atmospheric pressure, P, in terms of height above sea level is often modeled by an exponential decay function. Suppose the pressure at sea level is 1013 millibars (about 14.7 pounds per square inch) and that the pressure decreases by 14% for every kilometer above sea level. $P = 1013(.86)^k$

    (a) What is the atmospheric pressure at 50 km? $.538$
    (b) Estimate the altitude h at which the pressure equals 900 millibars. $.7811$

18. The radioactive isotope gallium-67 decays by 1.48% every hour. $67(.9852)^t$

    (a) If there are initially 100 milligrams of gallium-67, find a formula for the amount remaining after t hours. $100(.9852)^t$ 70 mil. 8.2 mi
    (b) How many milligrams will be left after 24 hours? After 1 week?
    (c) When will 50 mg of gallium-67 remain?

19. Suppose you want to use your calculator to graph $y = 1.04^{5x}$. You correctly enter $y = 1.04\text{^}(5x)$ and see the graph in Figure 3.6.

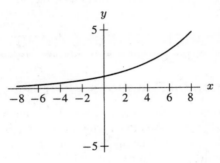

Figure 3.6

A friend graphed the function by entering $y = 1.04\text{^}5x$ and said, "the graph is a straight line, so I must have the wrong window." Explain why changing the window will not correct the error of your friend.

20. Set a window of $-4 \leq x \leq 4, -1 \leq y \leq 6$ and graph the following functions using several different values of a for each. (Be sure to try some fractional values for a.)

    (a) $y = a(2)^x$, $0 < a < 5$.   (b) $y = 2(a)^x$, $0 < a < 5$.

21. Write a paragraph that compares the function $f(x) = a^x$, where $a > 1$ and $g(x) = b^x$ when $0 < b < 1$. Include graphs in your answer.

22. There have been frequent debates concerning the inequity of health care for children in the US. Figure 3.7 shows infant mortality rate, or number of deaths in the first year of life for every 1000 live births, for African-American and Caucasian children.

Deaths per thousands

Figure 3.7: Infant mortality rate for African-American and Caucasian children. Source: New York Times 7/10/95, B9.

(a) Use average rate of change to determine whether the infant mortality rate declined faster for Caucasian or African-American infants from 1950 to 1992.

(b) Compare the ratio of African-American to Caucasian infant mortality in 1950 to that in 1992. Would your answer to part (a) change?

(c) Construct two tables for the data in Figure 3.7, one for Caucasian infants and one for African-American infants (use 5-year intervals).

(d) Using the tables constructed in (c), determine if Caucasian or African-American infant mortality rate declined exponentially.

(e) List some factors that might have the effect of narrowing the gap in mortality rates.

3.2 MORE ON EXPONENTIAL FUNCTIONS

The Graphs of Exponential Functions

In the last section, we showed that a general formula for an exponential function $Q = f(t)$ is given by $f(t) = AB^t$ where A is the starting value and B is the growth factor. Knowing this formula and the significance of the parameters A and B can help us analyze various exponential functions. Consider the following example.

Example 1   The following formulas give the populations (in 1000s) of four different cities, A, B, C, and D. Describe in words how these populations are changing over time.

$$P_A = 200 + 1.3t$$
$$P_B = 270(1.021)^t$$
$$P_C = 150(1.045)^t$$
$$P_D = 600(0.978)^t$$

Solution   The formula for city A, $P_A = 200 + 1.3t$, tells us that this population is growing linearly. In year $t = 0$, the city has 200,000 people and each year, the population grows by 1.3 thousand people – that is, by 1,300 people.

The formulas for cities B, C, and D indicate that those populations are growing (or decreasing) exponentially. Since $P_B = 270(1.021)^t$, city B starts with 270,000 people and grows at a constant

Figure 3.8: The graphs of three different populations

2.1% annual rate. Since $P_C = 150(1.045)^t$, city C starts with 150,000 people and grows at a constant 4.5% annual rate.

Finally, since $P_D = 600(0.978)^t$, city D starts with 600,000 people, but its population *decreases* at a constant 2.2% annual rate. We find the annual percent rate by taking growth factor $= 0.978 = 1 + r$, which gives $r = -0.022 = -2.2\%$

So city D starts out with more people than the other three but is shrinking. Figure 3.8 gives the graphs of the three exponential populations from Example 1.

Notice that the y-intercepts of the graphs correspond to the initial populations (when $t = 0$) of the towns. Although the graph of P_C starts below the graph of P_B, it eventually catches up and rises above the graph of P_B. This is because the population of city C, which is increasing by 4.5% each year, is growing faster than city B, which is increasing by only 2.1% each year.

All three graphs are concave up, telling us that the rate of change is increasing. This means that populations B and C are increasing faster and faster while the population of city D is decreasing slower and slower (that is, its rate of change is getting less and less negative).

The Effect of the Parameter B

In general, for the exponential function $Q = AB^t$, the parameters A and B tell us what the graph of the function will look like. Figure 3.9 shows how the graph of $Q = AB^t$ will appear for $B > 1$ and for $0 < B < 1$. (In both cases the value of A is positive.) If $B > 1$, the graph climbs when read from left to right; if $0 < B < 1$, the graph falls when read from left to right.

Figure 3.10 shows how the value of B affects the steepness of the graph of $Q = AB^t$. Each graph in the figure has a different value of B but the same value of A (and thus the same y-intercept). Notice that for $0 < B < 1$, the smaller the value of B, the more rapidly the graph falls. Similarly, for $B > 1$, the greater the value of B, the more rapidly the graph rises.

The Effect of the Parameter A

We have seen that in the equation $Q = AB^t$, the value of A can be thought of as an initial (or starting) value. Thus the value of A tells us where the graph crosses the Q-axis. Figure 3.11 shows how the value of A affects the graph of $Q = AB^t$. Each graph in the figure has the same value of B but different values of A (and thus different y-intercepts).

In general:

If $Q = AB^t$ is an exponential function, and if $A > 0$, then
- The graph of $Q = AB^t$ is concave up.
- If $B > 1$, the graph rises when read from left to right; the larger the value of B, the more rapidly the graph rises.
- If $0 < B < 1$, the graph falls when read from left to right; the smaller the value of B, the more rapidly the graph falls.
- The graph crosses the Q-axis at A, the initial value.

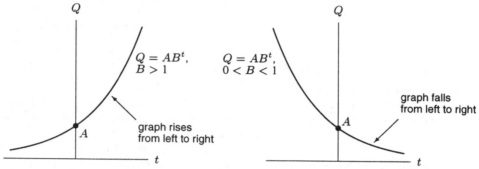

Figure 3.9: For $A > 0$, if $B > 1$, the graph of $Q = AB^t$ rises when read from left to right; if $0 < B < 1$, the graph falls when read from left to right

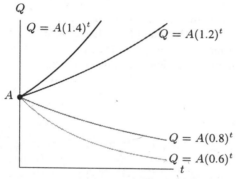

Figure 3.10: The graphs of $Q = AB^t$ for $B = 0.6, 0.8, 1.2$ and 1.4

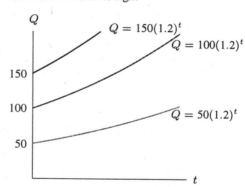

Figure 3.11: The graphs of $Q = A(1.2)^t$ for $A = 50, 100$ and 150

The Horizontal Asymptote of an Exponential Function

A *horizontal asymptote* is a horizontal line the graph of a function approaches for extreme values of x, either positive or negative (or sometimes both). Both of the graphs in Figure 3.9 have horizontal asymptotes at $Q = 0$, the t-axis. For the graph on the right ($0 < B < 1$), the value of Q gets closer and closer to 0 as t gets larger and larger. We say that *Q approaches zero as t approaches infinity* and we write

$$Q \to 0 \quad \text{as} \quad t \to \infty,$$

to describe this behavior. When we say that $Q \to 0$ as $t \to \infty$, we mean specifically that we can make Q as close to 0 as we like by choosing a large enough value for t. For the graph on the left ($B > 1$), the value of Q approaches zero as t grows more and more negative. We say that Q

approaches zero as t approaches negative infinity and we write

$$Q \to 0 \quad \text{as} \quad t \to -\infty.$$

This means that we can make Q as close to 0 as we like by choosing an extreme enough negative value for t. In general:

> Any exponential function $Q = AB^t$ has a horizontal asymptote at $Q = 0$,
> - if $B > 1$ then $Q \to 0$ as $t \to -\infty$.
> - if $0 < B < 1$ then $Q \to 0$ as $t \to +\infty$.

Example 2 A *capacitor* is an electrical circuit element that stores electric charge. The quantity of charge stored in the capacitor decreases exponentially with time. Stereo amplifiers provide a familiar example: when an amplifier is turned off, the display lights fade slowly because it takes time for the capacitors to discharge completely. (This is why it can be unsafe to open a stereo or a computer even after it is turned off.)

Suppose that in a given circuit, the quantity of stored charge (in micro-Coulombs) is given by

$$Q = 200(0.9)^t, \quad t \geq 0,$$

where t is the number of seconds after the circuit is switched off.

(a) Describe in words how the stored charge changes over time.

(b) What level of charge remains after 10 seconds? 20 seconds? 30 seconds? 1 minute? 2 minutes? 3 minutes?

(c) Sketch a graph of the charge level over the first minute. What does the horizontal asymptote of the graph tell you about the charge level?

Solution (a) The charge is initially 200 micro-coulombs. Since $B = 1 + r$, then $1 + r = 0.9$. So we have

$$r = -0.10$$

which means that the charge level decreases by 10% each second.

(b) Table 3.7 gives the value of Q at $t = 0, 10, 20, 30, 60, 120,$ and 180. Notice that as t increases, Q gets closer and closer to, but doesn't quite reach, zero. The charge stored by the capacitor is getting smaller and smaller, but never completely vanishes.

(c) Figure 3.12 gives a graph of Q over a 60-second interval. The graph horizontal asymptote at $Q = 0$ corresponds to the fact that the value of Q grows quite small as t increases. The graph gets very close to, but does not reach, the asymptote.

TABLE 3.7 *The charge stored by a capacitor over time*

t (seconds)	Q, charge level (micro-coulombs)
0	200
10	69.7
20	24.3
30	8.48
60	0.359
120	0.000646
180	0.00000116

Figure 3.12: The charge stored by a capacitor over 1 minute

Using Ratios to Tell if Data Comes From an Exponential Function

Table 3.8 gives two functions, f and g. Notice that the value of x goes up by equal steps of $\Delta x = 5$. The function f is linear because the value of $f(x)$ increases by the same amount, 15, each time x goes up by 5. In other words, the *difference* between consecutive values of f is a constant.

On the other hand, the difference between consecutive values of g is *not* constant:

$$1200 - 1000 = 200$$
$$1440 - 1200 = 240$$
$$1728 - 1440 = 288,$$

and so on. Because x increases by the same amount each time, we see that g is not linear. However, the *ratio* of consecutive values of g is constant:

$$\frac{1200}{1000} = 1.2, \quad \frac{1440}{1200} = 1.2, \quad \frac{1728}{1440} = 1.2,$$

and so on. This means that each time x increases by 5, $g(x)$ increases by a factor of 1.2. In other words, g is exponential.

In general:

> Suppose a table of data gives y as a function of x and that the value of Δx is constant. Then,
> - if the *difference* of consecutive y-values is constant, the table could represent a linear function.
> - if the *ratio* of consecutive y-values is constant, the table could represent an exponential function.

TABLE 3.8   *Two functions, one linear and one exponential*

x	20	25	30	35	40	45
$f(x)$	30	45	60	75	90	105
$g(x)$	1000	1200	1440	1728	2073.6	2488.32

Finding a Formula for an Exponential Function

Let's find a formula for g, the exponential function in Table 3.8. Since g is exponential, its formula can be written as $g(x) = AB^x$, where we must determine the values of A and B. From the table, we see that $g(20) = 1000$ and that $g(25) = 1200$. The ratio of $g(25)$ to $g(20)$ is

$$\frac{g(25)}{g(20)} = \frac{1200}{1000} = 1.2.$$

Now, from our formula we also see that $g(25) = AB^{25}$ and that $g(20) = AB^{20}$. Thus we can also write the ratio as

$$\frac{g(25)}{g(20)} = \frac{AB^{25}}{AB^{20}} = B^5.$$

Notice that the value of A cancels out when taking this ratio. We can equate these two expressions for $\frac{g(25)}{g(20)}$ to obtain an equation relating the ratio value to the growth constant:

$$B^5 = 1.2.$$

We solve for B by raising each side to the $1/5$th power:

$$(B^5)^{\frac{1}{5}} = B = 1.2^{\frac{1}{5}}$$

$$\approx 1.0371.$$

Having found the value of B, we can now solve for A. Since $g(20) = AB^{20} = 1000$, we have

$$A(1.0371)^{20} = 1000$$

$$A = \frac{1000}{1.0371^{20}} \approx 482.6.$$

Thus, a formula for g is $g(x) = 482.6(1.0371)^x$. (Note: We could have used $g(25)$ or any other data point from the table to find A.) This method of finding a formula for an exponential function is called the *ratio method*.

Modeling Linear and Exponential Growth Using Two Points

As is the case with linear functions, given two points on the graph of an exponential function, we can find the function's formula. Consider the following example.

Example 3   At time $t = 0$ a species of turtle is accidentally released into a wetland. When $t = 4$ a biologist estimates there are 300 turtles in the wetland. Three years later she estimates there are 450 turtles. Let P represent the size of the turtle population in year t.
  (a) Find a formula for $P = f(t)$ assuming linear growth. Interpret the slope and P-intercept of your formula in terms of the turtle population.
  (b) Now find a formula for $P = g(t)$ assuming exponential growth. Interpret the parameters of your formula in terms of the turtle population.
  (c) Five years later, in year $t = 12$, the biologist estimates that there are 900 turtles in the wetland. What does this indicate about the two population models?

Solution   (a) Assuming linear growth, we have $P = f(t) = b + mt$, with $P = 300$ when $t = 4$ and $P = 450$ when $t = 7$. This gives

$$m = \frac{\Delta P}{\Delta t} = \frac{450 - 300}{7 - 4} = \frac{150}{3} = 50.$$

Solving for b, we have

$$300 = b + 50 \cdot 4$$

$$b = 100,$$

which gives $P = f(t) = 100 + 50t$. This formula tells us that 100 turtles were originally released into the wetland and that the number of turtles increases at the constant rate of 50 turtles per year.
  (b) Assuming exponential growth we have $P = g(t) = AB^t$. We will find the values of A and B by using the ratio method. Since $P = 300$ when $t = 4$, we have

$$g(4) = AB^4 = 300.$$

Similarly, since $P = 450$ when $t = 7$, we have

$$g(7) = AB^7 = 450.$$

Taking ratios we have

$$\frac{g(7)}{g(4)} = \frac{AB^7}{AB^4} = B^3.$$

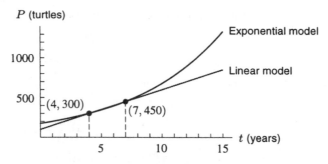

Figure 3.13: Graphs of the linear and exponential models of the turtle population

We also know that

$$\frac{g(7)}{g(4)} = \frac{450}{300} = 1.5.$$

Putting these two statements together gives us

$$B^3 = 1.5$$

so

$$B = (1.5)^{1/3} \approx 1.145.$$

Having determined the value of B, we can now solve for A. Using the fact that $g(4) = AB^4 = 300$, we have

$$AB^4 = 300$$
$$A(1.145)^4 = 300$$
$$A = \frac{300}{1.145^4}$$
$$A \approx 175, \quad \text{(rounding to the nearest whole turtle)}$$

which gives $P = g(t) = 175(1.145)^t$. This formula indicates that, assuming exponential growth, 175 turtles were originally released into the wetland and their numbers increased at the constant rate of about 14.5% per year.

(c)   The biologist counts approximately 900 turtles in year $t = 12$. Using the linear formula from part (a) we would expect to find,

$$100 + 50 \cdot 12 = 700 \text{ turtles.}$$

Using the exponential formula from part (b), however, we would expect to find

$$175(1.145)^{12} \approx 889 \text{ turtles.}$$

This provides the biologist with evidence that exponential growth gives a better model of the turtle population than does linear growth. The two different models are graphed in Figure 3.13.

Similarities and Differences between Linear and Exponential Functions

In some ways the general formulas for linear and exponential functions are quite similar. If y is a linear function of x, $y = b + mx$. This can be written (assuming x is an integer) as

$$y = b + \underbrace{m + m + m + \ldots + m}_{x \text{ times}}.$$

Similarly, we see that if y is an exponential function of x, so that $y = A \cdot B^x$, we can write (again assuming x is an integer)

$$y = A \cdot \underbrace{B \cdot B \cdot B \cdot \ldots \cdot B}_{x \text{ times}}.$$

Thus, linear functions involve repeated sums whereas exponential functions involve repeated products. In either case, the independent variable x determines the number of repetitions.

There are other similarities between the formulas for linear and exponential functions. For example, we can interpret the slope m of a linear function as a rate of change of some physical quantity and the y-intercept as a starting value. The constants B and A in the exponential formula $y = A \cdot B^x$ have similar interpretations.

Exponential Growth Will Always Outpace Linear Growth in the Long Run

Figure 3.13 shows the graphs of the linear and exponential models for the turtle population from Example 3. The graphs highlight a major difference between linear and exponential growth: although the two graphs remain fairly close for the first ten or so years, the exponential model predicts explosive growth as more time passes.

In fact, it can be shown that an exponentially increasing quantity will, in the long run, *always* outpace a linearly increasing quantity. This fact led the 19th-century clergyman and economist, Thomas Malthus, to make some rather gloomy predictions, the essence of which is illustrated by the next example.

Example 4 Suppose that the population of a country is initially 2 million people and is increasing at the rate of 4% per year. Suppose also that the country's annual food supply is initially adequate for 4 million people and is increasing at a constant rate adequate for an additional 0.5 million people per year.
  (a) Based on these assumptions, in approximately what year will this country first experience shortages of food?
  (b) If the country could somehow double its initial food supply, would shortages still occur? If so, when? (Assume the other conditions do not change).
  (c) If the country could somehow double the rate at which its food supply increases, in addition to doubling its initial food supply, would shortages still occur? If so, when? (Again, assume the other conditions do not change.)

Solution Let $P = f(t)$ represent the country's population (in millions), and $N = g(t)$ the number of people it can feed (in millions). The population increases at a constant percent rate, so it can be modeled by an exponential function. Its formula is

$$P = f(t) = 2(1.04)^t$$

because the initial population is $A = 2$ million people and the annual growth factor is $B = 1 + 0.04 = 1.04$. In contrast, the food supply increases by a constant amount each year and is therefore modeled by a linear function. Its formula is

$$N = g(t) = 4 + 0.5t$$

because the initial food supply is adequate for $b = 4$ million people and the growth rate is $m = 0.5$ million per year.
  (a) Figure 3.14(a) gives the graphs of P and N over a 105-year span. The country enjoys great prosperity for many years because its food supply is far in excess of its needs. However, after about 78 years the population has begun to grow so rapidly that it catches up to the food supply and then outstrips it. After that time, the country will suffer from shortages.
  (b) If the country could initially feed eight million people rather than four, the formula for N would be

$$N = g(t) = 8 + 0.5t.$$

However, as you can see from Figure 3.14(b), this measure only buys the country three or four extra years. After 81 years, the population is growing so rapidly that the head start given to the food supply makes little difference.

(c)   If the country doubles the rate at which its food supply increases, from 0.5 million per year to 1.0 million per year, the formula for N will be

$$N = g(t) = 8 + 1.0t.$$

Unfortunately the country will still run out of food eventually. Judging from Figure 3.14(c), this will happen in about 102 years.

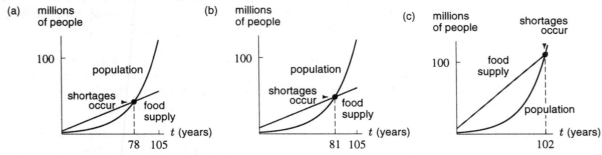

Figure 3.14: These graphs illustrate the fact that an exponentially growing population will eventually outstrip a linearly growing food supply

Since Malthus believed that populations tend to increase exponentially while food production tends to increase only linearly, the last example should explain his gloomy predictions. After all, as Malthus knew, any exponentially increasing population will eventually outstrip a linearly growing food supply. This situation, he predicted, would inevitably lead to famine and war.

Exponential Functions with Negative Values

So far, the exponential functions we have studied have all had positive output values. But if $Q = AB^t$ and A is negative, the value of Q is negative, not positive.

Example 5   Figure 3.15 gives graphs of two exponential functions,

$$Q = -1000(1.25)^t \quad \text{and} \quad Q = -1000(0.80)^t.$$

Both graphs are concave down and have horizontal asymptotes at $Q = 0$. Notice that the function $Q = -1000(1.25)^t$ is decreasing, whereas the function $Q = -1000(0.8)^t$ is increasing.

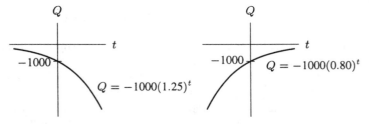

Figure 3.15: Two exponential functions with negative values

In general:

Let $y = f(x) = AB^x$ be an exponential function. Then the graph of f will have a horizontal asymptote at $y = 0$.

- If $A > 0$, then the graph of f will lie above the x-axis. For $B > 1$, f is increasing, and for $0 < B < 1$, f is decreasing.

- If $A < 0$, then the graph of f will lie below the x-axis. For $B > 1$, f is decreasing, and for $0 < B < 1$, f is increasing.

Notes on the General Formula: Why $B > 0$ for Exponential Functions

Let's look at a specific example to see why the base B of an exponential function is restricted to positive values. To keep the function simple, let $A = 1$ so that $f(x) = 1 \cdot (-2)^x$. Here, the base is -2. At first, f seems like a reasonable function. For example,

$$f(1) = (-2)^1 = -2,$$
$$f(2) = (-2)^2 = +4,$$
$$f(3) = (-2)^3 = -8,$$

and so on. Granted, the value of f changes signs depending on whether x is even or odd, but that isn't the reason negative bases aren't allowed. We exclude negative bases because of the following even more unusual behavior:

$$f(x) = (-2)^x$$
$$f(1/2) = (-2)^{1/2} = \sqrt{-2} \quad \text{(undefined)}$$
$$f(1/3) = (-2)^{1/3} = \sqrt[3]{-2} \approx -1.260$$
$$f(1/4) = (-2)^{1/4} = \sqrt[4]{-2} \quad \text{(undefined)}$$
$$f(1/5) = (-2)^{1/5} = \sqrt[5]{-2} \approx -1.149$$

and so on. For some values of x, f is defined, but for many others it isn't. In fact, on *any* interval of x there are infinitely many values of x for which $f(x)$ is undefined! We avoid this awkward situation by requiring $B > 0$. In fact, many calculators and computer software packages are programmed so they will not evaluate some powers of negative numbers, even if the answer actually exists.

Problems for Section 3.2

1. The graphs of $y = (1.1)^x$, $y = (1.2)^x$, and $y = (1.25)^x$ are given in Figure 3.16. Explain how you can match these formulas and the graphs without using a calculator.

Figure 3.16

$B > 1$, the larger the value of B, the more rapidly the graph rises.

2. The graphs of $y = (0.7)^x$, $y = (0.8)^x$, and $y = (0.85)^x$, are given in Figure 3.17. Explain how you can match these formulas and the graphs without using a calculator.

B < 1, the smaller the value of B, the more rapidly the graph falls.

Figure 3.17

3. Match each of the following formulas to the graph in Figure 3.18 that best characterizes it. (Note: The axes are unscaled so a graph is general and may correspond to more than one formula.)

(a) $y = 0.8^t$ (b) $y = 5(3)^t$ (c) $y = -6(1.03)^t$

(d) $y = 15(3)^{-t}$ (e) $y = -4(0.98)^t$ (f) $y = 82(0.8)^{-t}$

(i)   (ii)   (iii)   (iv)

Figure 3.18

4. Let f be a piecewise-defined function given by

$$f(x) = \begin{cases} 2^x, & x < 0 \\ 0, & x = 0 \\ 1 - \frac{1}{2}x, & x > 0 \end{cases}$$

(a) Graph f for $-3 \leq x \leq 4$.

(b) The domain of $f(x)$ is all real numbers. What is its range?

(c) What are the intercepts of f?

(d) Describe what happens to f as $x \to +\infty$ and $x \to -\infty$.

(e) Over what intervals is f increasing? Decreasing?

5. (a) Determine from the tables below which of the given functions could be linear and which of them could be exponential.

TABLE 3.9

x	$f(x)$
0	12.5
1	13.75
2	15.125
3	16.638
4	18.301

TABLE 3.10

x	$g(x)$
0	0
1	2
2	4
3	6
4	8

TABLE 3.11

x	$h(x)$
0	14
1	12.6
2	11.34
3	10.206
4	9.185

TABLE 3.12

x	$i(x)$
0	18
1	14
2	10
3	6
4	2

(b) Find formulas for functions f and g and sketch their graphs.

6. Determine which of the following functions is linear and which is exponential. Write formulas for the linear and exponential functions.

TABLE 3.13

x	$f(x)$	$g(x)$	$h(x)$
-2	0.43982	1.02711	0.95338
-1	1.31947	1.13609	1.88152
0	2.19912	1.25663	2.82743
1	3.07877	1.38996	3.77375
2	3.95842	1.53743	4.72713

7. Table 3.14 shows the concentration of theophylline, a common asthma drug, in the blood stream as a function of time after injection of a 300 mg initial dose given to a subject weighing 50 kg.[2] It is claimed that this data set is consistent with an exponential decay model $C = ab^t$ where C is the concentration and t is the time. Estimate the values of a and b. How good is this model?

TABLE 3.14 *Concentration of theophylline in the blood*

Time (hours)	0	1	3	5	7	9
Concentration (mg/l)	12.0	10.0	7.0	5.0	3.5	2.5

8. Determine whether the function defined in Table 3.15 could be exponential.

TABLE 3.15 *Table of values*

x	1	2	4	5	8	9
$f(x)$	4096	1024	64	16	0.25	0.0625

9. Let $p(x) = 2 + x$ and $q(x) = 2^x$. Estimate the values of x such that $p(x) < q(x)$. $x < -1.7$ and $x > 2$

10. This problem deals with the two functions x^2 and 2^x.
   (a) Complete Table 3.16 by computing the values of x^2 and 2^x for 0, 1, 2, ... ,5.

TABLE 3.16 *Complete this table*

x	0	1	2	3	4	5
x^2						
2^x						

   (b) Use Table 3.16 to identify the values of x for which
      (i) $x^2 < 2^x$,

---

[2] Based on "Applying Mathematics" by D.N. Burghes, I. Huntley, and J. McDonald, Ellis Horwood 1982.

(ii) $x^2 = 2^x$,

(iii) $x^2 > 2^x$.

(c)   Use a graphing calculator or computer to plot x^2 and 2^x in the window $0 \le x \le 5$, $0 \le y \le 35$. From this plot, identify the values of x for which

(i) $x^2 < 2^x$,

(ii) $x^2 = 2^x$,

(iii) $x^2 > 2^x$.

(d)   Do the answers you gave in parts (b) and (c) agree?

(e)   As $x \to \infty$, which function grows faster, x^2 or 2^x?

11.   The functions $f(x) = (\frac{1}{2})^x$ and $g(x) = 1/x$ are similar in that they both tend toward zero as x becomes large. Using your calculator, determine which function, f or g, approaches zero faster.

12.   Suppose $f(-3) = \frac{5}{8}$ and $f(2) = 20$. Find a formula for f assuming it is

(a)   linear   (b)   exponential

13.   Find formulas for the exponential functions h, f, and g given that:

(a) $h(0) = 3$ and $h(1) = 15$.
(b) $f(3) = -3/8$ and $f(-2) = -12$.
(c) $g(1/2) = 4$ and $g(1/4) = 2\sqrt{2}$.

For Problems 14–18, find possible formulas for the graphs of the exponential functions.

14.

Figure 3.19

15.

Figure 3.20

16.

Figure 3.21

17.

Figure 3.22

18.

Figure 3.23

19.   Figure 3.24 gives the balance, P, of a bank account in year t.

Figure 3.24

(a)   Find a possible formula for $P = f(t)$ assuming the balance grows exponentially.
(b)   What was the initial balance?
(c)   What annual interest rate does the account seem to pay?

20.   Five different stories are given below. Following the stories are five formulas. Match each formula to the story it models and state what the variables represent. You should assume that the constants P_0, r, B, A are all positive.

(a)   The percent of a lake's surface covered by algae, initially at 35%, was halved each year since the passage of anti-pollution laws.
(b)   The amount of charge on a capacitor in an electric circuit decreases by 30% every second.
(c)   Polluted water is passed through a series of filters. Each filter removes all but 30% of the remaining impurities from the water.
(d)   In 1920, the population of a town was 3000 people. Over the course of the next 50 years, the town grew at a rate of 10% per decade.
(e)   In 1920, the population of a town was 3000 people. Over the course of the next 50 years, the town grew at a rate of 250 people per year.

(i) $f(x) = P_0 + rx$ (ii) $g(x) = P_0(1 + r)^x$
(iii) $h(x) = B(0.7)^x$ (iv) $j(x) = B(0.3)^x$
(v) $k(x) = A(2)^{-x}$

21.   Three scientists, working independently of each other, arrive at the following formulas to model the spread of a certain species of mussel in a system of fresh water lakes:

$$f_1(x) = 3(1.2)^x$$
$$f_2(x) = 3(1.21)^x$$
$$f_3(x) = 3.01(1.2)^x$$

where $f_n(x)$, $n = 1, 2, 3$, is the number of individual mussels (in 1000s) predicted by model number n to be living in the lake system after x months have elapsed.

(a)   Graph these three functions for $0 \le x \le 60, 0 \le y \le 40{,}000$.
(b)   The graphs of these three models don't seem all that different from each other. But do they make significantly different predictions about the future mussel population? To answer this, graph the *difference* function, $f_2(x) - f_1(x)$, of the population sizes predicted by models 1 and 2, as well as the difference function, $f_3(x) - f_1(x)$, of the predictions made by models 1 and 3. (Use the same window you used for part (a).)
(c)   Based on the graphs you made in part (b), discuss the assertion that all three models are in good agreement as far as long-range predictions of mussel population are concerned. What conclusions can you draw about exponential functions in general?

22. A colony of bacteria is growing exponentially. At the end of 3 hours there are 1000 bacteria. At the end of 5 hours there are 4000.

    (a) Write a formula for the population of bacteria at time t, in hours.
    (b) By what percent does the number of bacteria increase each hour?

23. At 12 noon, a bacteria colony was growing exponentially. The population was 12,000 at 3 pm and 15,000 at 5 pm. What was the population at 12 noon?

24. A 1993 Lexus costs $39,375 and the car depreciates during its first 7 years a total of 46%.

    (a) Suppose the depreciation is exponential. Find a formula for the value of the car at time t.
    (b) Suppose instead that the depreciation is linear. Find a formula for the value of the car at time t.
    (c) If this were your car and you were trading it in after 4 years, which depreciation model would you prefer (exponential or linear)?

25. The *New York Times* reported that wildlife biologists have found a direct link between the increase in the human population in Florida and the decline of the local black bear population. From 1953 to 1993, the human population increased, on average, at a rate of 8% per year, while the black bear population decreased at a rate of 6% per year. In 1953 the black bear population was 11,000.

    (a) The 1993 human population of Florida was 13 million. What was the human population in 1953?
    (b) Find the black bear population for 1993.
    (c) If this trend continues, when will the black bear population number less than 100?

26. According to a letter written to the editorial page of the April 10, 1993 *New York Times*, ". . . the probability of [a driver's] involvement in a single-car accident increases exponentially with increasing levels of blood alcohol." The letter goes on to state that when a driver's blood-alcohol content (BAC) is 0.15, the risk of such an accident is about 25 times greater than for a nondrinker.

    (a) Let p_0 be a nondrinker's probability of being involved in a single-car accident. Define $f(x)$ to be the probability of an accident for a driver whose blood alcohol level is x. Find a formula for $f(x)$. (Note that this only makes sense for some values of x.)
    (b) In many states, the legal definition of intoxication is having a BAC of 0.1 or higher. According to your formula for $f(x)$, how many times more likely is a driver at the legal limit to be in a single-car accident than a nondrinker?
    (c) Suppose that new legislation was proposed that would change the definition of legal intoxication. The new definition would hold that a person was legally intoxicated when their likelihood of involvement in a single-car accident is three times that of a non-drinker. To what BAC would the new definition of legal intoxication correspond?

27. The field of probability was born in France as an attempt to answer questions about gambling. One puzzling question concerned betting on rolling a six on a die given three attempts. Common sense suggested that given three attempts and the probability of rolling a six being one-sixth on each attempt, it would be an even bet to get at least one six. In practice this was not the case. The mathematician Blaise Pascal reasoned that the chance of *not* getting a six on the first roll was five-sixths, and that the probability of continuing with no six decreased by a factor of 5/6 on each subsequent roll.

    (a) Find a formula for the probability of *not* getting a 6 after n throws of the die.
    (b) How many rolls are needed for there to be at least a 50% chance of rolling a 6?
    (c) At least a 90% chance?

3.3 LOGARITHMS

The Solar System and Beyond

Table 3.17 gives the distance from the Sun (in millions of kilometers) to a number of different astronomical objects. Notice that the planet Mercury is 58,000,000 km from the Sun, that Earth is 149,000,000 km from the Sun, and that Pluto is 5,900,000,000 km, or almost 6 *billion* kilometers from the Sun. The table also gives the distance to Alpha Centauri, the star closest to the Sun; to the Andromeda Galaxy, the spiral galaxy closest to our own (the Milky Way); and to the most distant quasars, mysterious, luminous objects at the edge of the known universe.

TABLE 3.17 *The distance from the Sun to various astronomical objects*

object	distance (millions of kilometers)
Mercury	58
Venus	108
Earth	149
Mars	228
Jupiter	778
Saturn	1426
Uranus	2869
Neptune	4495
Pluto	5900
Alpha Centauri	4.1×10^7
Andromeda Galaxy	2.4×10^{13}
quasars	10^{17}

Linear Scales

We can represent the information in Table 3.17 graphically in order to get a better feel for the distances involved. Figure 3.25 shows the distance from the Sun to the first 5 planets on a *linear scale*, which means that the evenly spaced units shown in the figure represent equal distances. In this case, each unit represents 100 million kilometers.

Figure 3.25: The distance from the Sun of the first five planets (in millions of kilometers)

The drawback of Figure 3.25 is that the scale is too small to show all of the astronomical distances described by the table. For example, to show the distance to Pluto on this scale would require over 6 times as much space on the page. Even worse, assuming that each 100 million km unit on the scale measures half an inch on the printed page, we would need 3 miles of paper to show the distance to Alpha Centauri!

You might conclude that we could fix this problem by choosing a larger scale. In Figure 3.26 each unit on the scale is 1 billion kilometers. Notice that all five planets shown by Figure 3.25 are crowded into the first unit of Figure 3.26; even so, the distance to Pluto barely fits. The distances to the other objects certainly don't fit. For instance, to show the Andromeda Galaxy, Figure 3.26 would have to be almost 200,000 miles long. Choosing an even larger scale will not improve the figures.

Figure 3.26: The distance to all nine planets (in billions of kilometers)

Logarithmic Scales

The point is that the data in Table 3.17 cannot be represented graphically on a linear scale. If the scale is too small, the more distant objects will not fit; if the scale is too large, the less distant objects will be indistinguishable. The problem is not that the numbers are too big or too small; the problem is that the numbers vary in size over too great a range.

If we can't represent this information graphically on a linear scale, is there another option? We will consider a different type of scale on which equal distances are not evenly spaced. All the objects from Table 3.17 are represented in Figure 3.27. The nine planets get a bit cramped, but it's still possible to tell them apart. Each tick mark on the scale in Figure 3.27 represents a larger distance than the one before it. Moving from left to right, each successive tick mark indicates a distance ten times larger than the previous one. This kind of scale is called *logarithmic*.

Figure 3.27: The distance from the Sun (in millions of kilometers)

How Do We Plot Data on a Logarithmic Scale?

A logarithmic scale is marked off with increasing powers of 10: 10^1, 10^2, 10^3, and so on. In this case, the units are millions of kilometers, so 10^1 means 10 million kilometers, 10^2 means 100 million kilometers, and so on. In order to plot the distance to Mercury, 58 million kilometers, we note that

$$10 < 58 < 100.$$

Thus, Mercury's distance is between 10^1 and 10^2, as shown in Figure 3.28.

Example 1   Locate the distances from the Sun to Saturn and to the Andromeda Galaxy on the logarithmic scale in Figure 3.28.

Solution   To plot Saturn's distance of 1,426 million kilometers, we note that

$$1,000 < 1,426 < 10,000,$$

so Saturn's distance comes between 10^3 and 10^4.

The Andromeda Galaxy's distance is 2.4×10^{13} million kilometers from the Sun. Therefore, since

$$10^{13} < 2.4 \times 10^{13} < 10^{14}$$

its distance comes between 10^{13} and 10^{14}.

Figure 3.28: The distances of Saturn and the Andromeda Galaxy from the Sun

Using Exponents To Indicate Distance

While we know that the distance to Mercury, 58 million kilometers, falls between 10 million and 100 million kilometers, you may be wondering how this distance is represented on the scale. To solve this problem, think in terms of exponents. Even though the distances in Figure 3.28 are not evenly spaced, the exponents are.

We would like to know what power of 10 gives 58. Table 3.18 gives exponents ranging from $n = 1.5$ to $n = 2.0$, and the corresponding values of 10^n, which we can find with a calculator. From Table 3.18, we see that $10^{1.75} = 56.23$, and $10^{1.80} = 63.10$. Thus,

$$10^{1.75} < 58 < 10^{1.80}.$$

This means that we should indicate Mercury's distance somewhere between $10^{1.75}$ and $10^{1.80}$ as shown in Figure 3.29. (which shows an enlargement of part of Figure 3.28.)

TABLE 3.18   *Exponents ranging from $n = 1.5$ to $n = 2$, and values of 10^n*

n, exponent	1.50	1.55	1.60	1.65	1.70	1.75	1.80	1.85	1.90	1.95	2.00
10^n	31.62	35.48	39.81	44.67	50.12	56.23	63.10	70.79	79.43	89.13	100

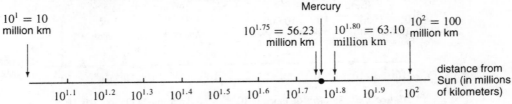

Figure 3.29: Mercury's distance, 58 million kilometers falls between $10^{1.75} = 56.23$ and $10^{1.80} = 63.10$ million kilometers

Logarithms

On logarithmic scales like the ones shown in Figures 3.27 through 3.29, we represent a distance by using an exponent of 10. The distance to Mercury, 58 million kilometers, is represented by an exponent between 1.75 and 1.80, because 58 is between $10^{1.75} = 56.73$ and $10^{1.80} = 63.10$. But which exponent of 10 will give us *exactly* 58?

To answer this question, we introduce a new function, called the *common logarithmic function*, or simply the *common log function*, which is written $\log x$. We define the log function as follows.

If x is a positive number,

$$\log x \text{ is the exponent of 10 that gives } x.$$

For example, $\log 10 = 1$, because 1 is the exponent of 10 that gives 10, and $\log 100 = 2$, because 2 is the exponent of 10 that gives 100.

For the distance to Mercury, we must find $\log 58$, the exponent of 10 that gives 58. Using a calculator, we can approximate this exponent. We find

$$\log 58 \approx 1.763427994.$$

This means that $10^{1.763427994} \approx 58$. Notice that this exponent is between 1.75 and 1.80 as predicted.

Example 2 Where should Saturn's distance be indicated on the logarithmic scale? What about the Andromeda Galaxy's distance? The quasars' distance?

Solution For Saturn's distance we would like to find the exponent of 10 that gives 1,426. This exponent is given by $\log 1426$, and using a calculator, we have

$$\log 1426 \approx 3.154119526.$$

Thus $10^{3.154} \approx 1426$, so we use 3.154 to indicate Saturn's distance.

Similarly, the distance to the Andromeda Galaxy is 2.4×10^{13} million kilometers so the exponent of 10 that represents this distance should lie between 13 and 14. We have

$$\log(2.4 \times 10^{13}) \approx 13.38,$$

so we use 13.38 to represent the galaxy's distance. Finally, the distance to the quasars is 10^{17} million kilometers. Notice that

$$\log 10^{17} = 17.$$

The value of $\log 10^{17}$ is exactly 17 because 17 is the exponent of 10 that gives 10^{17}.

The distances are shown in Figure 3.30.

Figure 3.30: Saturn's distance is $10^{3.154}$, the Andromeda Galaxy's is $10^{13.38}$, and the quasars' is 10^{17}

Logs of Small Numbers

The history of the world, like the distance to the stars and planets, involves numbers of vastly different sizes. Table 3.19 gives the ages of certain events (in millions of years)[3]. Let's plot the ages of these events on a logarithmic scale. For example, the demise of the dinosaurs occurred 67 million years ago. Using a calculator, we have

$$\log 67 \approx 1.83.$$

This tells us that $10^{1.83} \approx 67$ so we use $10^{1.83}$ on the log scale to indicate approximately how long ago the dinosaurs became extinct. Table 3.19 gives the logarithms of the other ages have been used to plot the events in Figure 3.31. Notice that the emergence of *homo erectus* occurred 1 million years ago, and that

$$\log 1 = 0.$$

This is because 0 is the exponent of 10 that gives 1.

The events described by Table 3.19 all happened at least 1 million years ago. Suppose we would like to include some relatively recent events, such as the construction of the pyramids or the signing of the Declaration of Independence, which occurred less than 1 million years ago. How can we indicate these events on our log scale?

The pyramids were built about 5000 years ago, or

$$\frac{5000}{1,000,000} = 0.005 \text{ million years ago.}$$

TABLE 3.19   *Ages of various events in Earth's history and logarithms of the ages*

Event	Age of event (millions of years ago)	log (age)
Homo erectus emerges	1	0
Ape man fossils	5	0.70
Rise of cats, dogs, pigs	37	1.57
Demise of dinosaurs	67	1.83
Rise of dinosaurs	245	2.39
Vertebrates appear	570	2.76
First plants	2500	3.40
Earth forms	4450	3.65

Figure 3.31: Logarithmic scale showing the ages of various events (in millions of years ago)

---

[3]CRC Handbook, 14-8, 75th edition

Notice that 0.005 is between 0.001 and 0.01, that is,

$$10^{-3} < 0.005 < 10^{-2}.$$

Thus, the exponent of 10 that yields 0.005 is negative and lies between -3 and -2. Using a calculator, we see that

$$\log 0.005 \approx -2.30,$$

which is indeed between -2 and -3. The construction of the pyramids is located between 10^{-3} and 10^{-2} in Figure 3.32.

Example 3   Where should the signing of the Declaration of Independence be indicated on the log scale?

Solution   The Declaration of Independence was signed in 1776, more than 220 years ago. We can write this number as

$$\frac{220}{1,000,000} = 0.00022 \text{ million years ago.}$$

This number is between $10^{-4} = 0.0001$ and $10^{-3} = 0.001$. Using a calculator, we have

$$\log 0.00022 \approx -3.66,$$

which, as expected, lies between -3 and -4. Figure 3.32 shows all these historical events plotted on a logarithmic scale.

Figure 3.32: Logarithmic scale showing the ages of various events. Note that events that are less than 1 million years old are indicated by negative exponents

We Can't Plot Negative Numbers on a Log Scale

Notice that 10 raised to a positive exponent gives a number greater than 1, while 10 raised to a negative exponent gives a number between 0 and 1. For example,

$$10^2 = 100 \quad \text{and} \quad 10^{-3} = 0.001.$$

We also saw that raising 10 to the power of 0 gives exactly 1. Can we represent 0 or a negative number as an exponent of 10? The answer is no, at least not using real-valued exponents. Therefore, the log function is defined only for positive values of x.

Summary of the Log Function

In summary:

> The **common logarithmic function** is written $\log x$ and is defined for $x > 0$ as follows:
>
> $$\log x \text{ is the exponent of 10 that gives } x.$$
>
> Note that:
> - $\log 1 = 0$
> - $\log x$ is positive if $x > 1$
> - $\log x$ is negative if $0 < x < 1$

Problems for Section 3.3

1. Use a calculator to fill in the following three tables (round to 4 decimal digits).

   TABLE 3.20

n	1	2	3	4	5	6	7	8	9
$\log n$									

   TABLE 3.21

n	10	20	30	40	50	60	70	80	90
$\log n$									

   TABLE 3.22

n	100	200	300	400	500	600	700	800	900
$\log n$									

2. Plot the integer points 2 through 9 and the multiples of 10 from 20 to 90 on the log scaled axis shown in Figure 3.33.

Figure 3.33

3. (a) Draw a line segment about 5 inches long. On it, choose an appropriate scale and mark points that represent the integral powers of two from zero to six. What is true about the location of the points as the exponents get larger?

   (b) Draw a second line segment. Repeat the process in (a) but this time use a logarithmic scale so that the units are now powers of ten. What do you notice about the location of these points?

(4.) Table 3.23 shows the typical body masses in kilograms for various animals.[4]

TABLE 3.23 *The mass of various animals in kilograms*

Animal	Body Mass	log of Body Mass
Blue Whale *A*	91000	4.96
African Elephant *B*	5450	3.74
White Rhinoceros *C*	3000	3.48
Hippopotamus *D*	2520	3.40
Black Rhinoceros *E*	1170	3.07
Horse *F*	700	2.85
Lion *G*	180	2.26
Human *H*	70	1.85
Albatross *I*	11	1.04
Hawk *J*	1	0
Robin *K*	0.08	-1.10
Hummingbird *L*	0.003	-2.52

(a) Complete Table 3.23 to two decimal places using a calculator.

(b) Plot the body masses for each animal in Table 3.23 on a linear scale using A to identify the Blue Whale, B to identify the African Elephant, and so on down to L to identify the Hummingbird.

(c) Plot the body masses for each animal in Table 3.23 on a logarithmic scale using the same identification scheme outlined in part (b).

(d) Which figure in parts (b) and (c) is most helpful?

5. The usual distances for track (running) events are 100 meters, 200 meters, 400 meters, 800 meters, 1500 meters, 3000 meters, 5000 meters, and 10,000 meters.

(a) Plot the length of each track event on a linear scale.

(b) Plot the length of each track event on a logarithmic scale.

(c) Which figure in parts (a) and (b) is the most helpful?

(d) On each figure identify the point corresponding to 50 meters.

6. Figure 3.34 shows a graph of two data points from an ecological study of the relationship between the diameter, d, and height, h, of trees. This relationship is known to be of the form $h = kd^n$. (In practice, hundreds of data points might have been included instead of only two.) Notice that even though h is not a linear function of d, the graph is a straight line. This is because both axes have log scales. When both axes are log scaled, we say that the graph has been drawn on a *log-log scale*. Log-log scaling causes the graph of a power function to appear as a straight line.

---

[4]"Dynamics of Dinosaurs and Other Extinct Giants" by R. McNiell Alexander, Columbia University Press, New York, 1989, and "The Simple Science of Flight" by H. Tennekes, MIT Press, Cambridge, 1996.

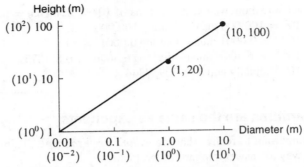

Figure 3.34: Log-log scaling of graph showing the relationship between tree height and trunk diameter

(a)   It is traditional to show zero on axes scaled in the usual way. It is not possible to show zero on a log scaled axis. Why?

(b)   Find a formula for $h = f(d)$, the height as a function of diameter. [Hint: Use a power function.]

3.4 USING LOGARITHMS TO SOLVE EXPONENTIAL EQUATIONS

What is a Logarithm?

We have seen convincing evidence that any positive number, large or small, can be uniquely represented as 10 raised to an exponent. In the last section, we defined the common logarithmic function as follows:

> For $x > 0$, $\log x$ is the exponent of 10 that gives x.

In other words,

> If $y = \log x$ then $10^y = x$.

The next two examples show how to use logarithms to change the form of an equation.

Example 1   Rewrite the following equations without using logs.

(a) $\log 100 = 2$

(b) $\log 0.01 = -2$

(c) $\log 30 = 1.477$

Solution   For each equation, we use the fact that if $y = \log x$ then $10^y = x$.

(a) $2 = \log 100$ means that $10^2 = 100$.

(b) $-2 = \log 0.01$ means that $10^{-2} = 0.01$.

(c) $1.477 = \log 30$ means that $10^{1.477} = 30$. (Actually, this is only an approximation. Using a calculator, we see that $10^{1.477} = 29.9916\ldots$ and that $\log 30 = 1.47712125\ldots$.)

Example 2   Rewrite the following equations without using exponents.

(a) $10^5 = 100,000$

(b) $10^{-4} = 0.0001$

(c) $10^{0.8} = 6.3096$.

Solution　For each equation, we use the fact that if $10^y = x$, then $y = \log x$.
- (a)　$10^5 = 100{,}000$ means that $\log 100{,}000 = 5$.
- (b)　$10^{-4} = 0.0001$ means that $\log 0.0001 = -4$.
- (c)　$10^{0.8} = 6.3096$ means that $\log 6.3096 = 0.8$. (This, too, is only an approximation because $10^{0.8}$ actually equals $6.30957344\ldots$.)

Logarithms are the same as exponents

It is important to realize that *logarithms are exponents*. Thinking in terms of exponents is often a good way to answer a logarithm problem.

Example 3　Evaluate the following, if possible.
- (a)　$\log 1{,}000{,}000$
- (b)　$\log 0.001$
- (c)　$\log \frac{1}{\sqrt{10}}$
- (d)　$\log(-100)$

Solution
- (a)　Since $1{,}000{,}000 = 10^6$, the exponent of 10 that gives $1{,}000{,}000$ is 6. Thus $\log 1{,}000{,}000 = 6$.
- (b)　Since $0.001 = 10^{-3}$, the exponent of 10 that gives 0.001 is -3. Thus, $\log 0.001 = -3$.
- (c)　Since

$$\frac{1}{\sqrt{10}} = 10^{-1/2},$$

$-\frac{1}{2}$ is the exponent of 10 that gives $1/\sqrt{10}$. Thus $\log(1/\sqrt{10}) = -\frac{1}{2}$.
- (d)　Since 10 to any power is positive, -100 cannot be written as a power of 10. Thus, $\log(-100)$ is undefined.

The function $y = \log x$ "undoes" the function $y = 10^x$

Example 3 illustrates a particularly important point. The fact that $1{,}000{,}000 = 10^6$ means that

$$\log 1{,}000{,}000 = \log 10^6 = 6.$$

Similarly,

$$\log 0.001 = \log 10^{-3} = -3 \quad \text{and} \quad \log \frac{1}{\sqrt{10}} = \log 10^{-1/2} = -1/2.$$

In each case, $\log 10^N = N$. This is true in general. The operation of taking a logarithm "undoes" the effect of applying the exponential function $f(x) = 10^x$. For example, the number $1{,}000{,}000$ is the result using 6 as the input to $f(x) = 10^x$. The log function, then, takes the number $1{,}000{,}000$ and "undoes" this process, giving back 6. Symbolically,

$$\log \underbrace{1{,}000{,}000}_{\substack{\text{the result} \\ \text{of raising} \\ \text{10 to 6}}} = \underbrace{\log(10^6)}_{\substack{\log \text{ "undoes"} \\ \text{this operation}}} = \underbrace{6}_{\substack{\text{we get} \\ \text{our 6 back}}}.$$

Similarly, applying the exponential function 10^x "undoes" the effect of taking a logarithm. For example, start with $N = 1000$ and take its log: $\log N = \log 1000 = 3$. Now apply the function 10^x to $\log N$:

$$10^{\log N} = 10^3 = 1000.$$

We get N back again. Thus, $10^{\log N} = N$.

In summary,

The log function has the following properties:

$$\log(10^N) = N \quad \text{for all } N \qquad \text{and} \qquad 10^{\log N} = N \quad \text{provided that } N > 0.$$

Solving Exponential Equations Using Logarithms

The log function is often useful when answering questions about exponential models. Because logarithms "undo" the effects of the exponential function 10^x, we can use them to solve equations that include powers of 10. Using logarithms, we can solve many exponential equations algebraically.

Example 4   Solve the equation $480(10)^{0.06x} = 1320$ algebraically.

Solution   First, isolate the power of 10 on one side of the equation:

$$480(10)^{0.06x} = 1320$$
$$10^{0.06x} = 2.75.$$

To get the variable out of the exponent, we take the log of both sides of the equation:

$$\log 10^{0.06x} = \log 2.75.$$

Now we use the property that $\log(10^N) = N$ to simplify the left side of the equation. This gives

$$0.06x = \log 2.75,$$

so

$$x = \frac{\log 2.75}{0.06} \approx 7.3$$

where we have used a calculator to evaluate the answer.

An Important Property of the Log Function

There is an important property of the log function that enables us to solve exponential equations with any base, not just base 10. Suppose that a and b are numbers and that a is positive. Because $a > 0$, we can find a number $k = \log a$, so that $10^k = a$. Then we can rewrite the expression a^b as

$$a^b = (10^k)^b.$$

Notice that we have rewritten the expression a^b so that the base is a power of 10. Using a familiar property of exponents, we can write $(10^k)^b$ as 10^{kb}. Therefore, if we take the log of the number a^b, we write

$$\log a^b = \log 10^{kb}$$
$$= kb \qquad (\log 10^p = p)$$
$$= (\log a)b \qquad (k = \log a)$$
$$= b \cdot \log a.$$

We have therefore found the following important property of the log function:

For $a > 0$,

$$\log a^b = b \cdot \log a.$$

In particular, note that

$$\log \frac{1}{a} = \log a^{-1} = -\log a.$$

Let's see how this property can be used to solve equations.

Example 5   In Section 3.1 we used a graph to solve the equation $200(0.886)^t = 25$, finding that a 200 microgram sample of carbon-14 will decay to 25 micrograms in approximately $17,200$ years. Using logarithms, we can now solve $200(0.886)^t = 25$ algebraically.

Solution   First, isolate the power on one side of the equation

$$200(0.886)^t = 25$$
$$(0.886)^t = 0.125.$$

Take the log of both sides, and use the fact that $\log(0.886)^t = t \log 0.886$. Then

$$\log(0.886)^t = \log 0.125$$
$$t \log 0.886 = \log 0.125$$

so

$$t = \frac{\log 0.125}{\log 0.886} \approx 17.18.$$

This answer, $17,180$ years, compares well with the value we found using a graph.

Example 6   Solve the equation $3 \cdot 2^x + 8 = 25$ for x.

Solution   First, we isolate the power on one side of the equation:

$$3 \cdot 2^x = 17$$
$$2^x = \frac{17}{3}.$$

Now, we use the fact that $\log(2^x) = x \cdot \log 2$. Taking the log of both sides of the equation gives

$$\log(2^x) = \log \frac{17}{3}$$
$$x \cdot \log 2 = \log \frac{17}{3}$$
$$x = \frac{\log \frac{17}{3}}{\log 2} \qquad \text{(dividing by log 2)}$$
$$x \approx 2.5025 \qquad \text{(using a calculator).}$$

We must be very careful when using a calculator to evaluate expressions like $\log \frac{17}{3}$. On many calculators if you enter log 17/3, the result will be 0.410, which is incorrect. This is because the calculator assumes that you mean $(\log 17)/3$, which is not the same as $\log(17/3)$. Notice further that

$$\frac{\log 17}{\log 3} \approx \frac{1.230}{0.477} \approx 2.579,$$

which is not the same as either $(\log 17)/3$ or $\log(17/3)$. Thus, the following expressions are all different.

$$\log \frac{17}{3} \approx 0.753, \qquad \frac{\log 17}{3} \approx 0.410, \qquad \text{and} \qquad \frac{\log 17}{\log 3} \approx 2.579.$$

Sometimes, instead of using logs to solve an equation, we need to solve an equation that involves logs.

Example 7   Solve $\log(2x + 1) + 3 = 0$.

Solution   To solve for x, we isolate the log expression and use the inverse function, in this case, the exponential to base 10.

$$\log(2x + 1) = -3$$
$$10^{\log(2x+1)} = 10^{-3}$$
$$2x + 1 = 10^{-3} \qquad \text{(since } 10^{\log(2x+1)} = 2x + 1\text{)}$$
$$2x = 10^{-3} - 1 \qquad \text{(solving for } x\text{)}$$
$$x = \frac{10^{-3} - 1}{2}$$
$$x = -0.4995.$$

Other Properties of the Log Function

We have seen one useful property of the log function, namely that

$$\log a^b = b \cdot \log a \quad \text{for } a > 0.$$

There are two other useful properties involving logs of products and quotients. First, recall that if a and b are both positive, then $10^{\log a} = a$ and $10^{\log b} = b$ because 10^x "undoes" $\log x$. Thus, the product $a \cdot b$ can be written

$$a \cdot b = \underbrace{10^{\log a}}_{a} \cdot \underbrace{10^{\log b}}_{b}.$$

When we multiply two powers with the same base we can add the exponents, so

$$a \cdot b = 10^{\log a + \log b}.$$

This last equation tells us that the exponent of 10 that gives $a \cdot b$ is $\log a + \log b$. But, by definition $\log ab$ is the exponent of 10 that gives ab, so

$$\log(a \cdot b) = \log a + \log b \quad \text{for } a, b > 0.$$

By writing $\frac{a}{b}$ as $a(\frac{1}{b})$, we can also show that

$$\log\left(\frac{a}{b}\right) = \log\left(a\left(\frac{1}{b}\right)\right) = \log a - \log b, \quad \text{for } a, b > 0.$$

These three properties and several others we have established are summarized below:

Properties of the common logarithm:

- By definition, $y = \log x$ has the same meaning as $10^y = x$.
- The function $y = \log x$ "undoes" the function $y = 10^x$; this means that

$$\log 10^x = x \qquad \text{for all } x,$$
$$10^{\log x} = x \qquad \text{for } x > 0.$$

- Two important values of the log function are

$$\log 1 = 0 \quad \text{and} \quad \log 10 = 1.$$

- For a and b both positive,

$$\log(ab) = \log a + \log b$$
$$\log\left(\frac{a}{b}\right) = \log a - \log b.$$

- For a positive,

$$\log a^b = b \cdot \log a.$$

Example 8   At time $t = 0$, the population of city A begins with 50,000 people and grows at a constant 3.5% annual rate. The population of city B begins with a larger population of 250,000 people but grows at the slower rate of 1.6% per year. Assuming that these growth rates hold constant, will the population of city A ever catch up to the population of city B? If so, when?

Solution   If P_A and P_B are the respective populations of these two cities, then

$$P_A = 50{,}000(1.035)^t \qquad \text{and} \qquad P_B = 250{,}000(1.016)^t.$$

Thus, we would like to solve the equation $50{,}000(1.035)^t = 250{,}000(1.016)^t$. Using the properties of logs, we have

$$\log 50{,}000(1.035)^t = \log 250{,}000(1.016)^t$$
$$\log 50{,}000 + \log(1.035)^t = \log 250{,}000 + \log(1.016)^t$$
$$\log 50{,}000 + t\log(1.035) = \log 250{,}000 + t\log(1.016)$$
$$t(\log 1.035 - \log 1.016) = \log 250{,}000 - \log 50{,}000$$
$$t = \frac{\log 250{,}000 - \log 50{,}000}{\log 1.035 - \log 1.016}$$
$$\approx 86.9.$$

Thus, the cities' populations will be equal in just under 87 years. To verify this, notice that when $t = 86.9$,

$$P_A = 50{,}000(1.035)^{86.9} \approx 993{,}771$$

and

$$P_B = 250{,}000(1.016)^{86.9} \approx 993{,}123.$$

The answers aren't exactly equal because we rounded off when evaluating t. Rounding can introduce significant errors, especially when logs and exponentials are involved. If we used the 8 decimal place value shown by our calculator, $t = 86.86480867$, the values of P_A and P_B would agree.

Misconceptions Involving Logs

It is important to know how to use the properties of logarithms. It is equally important to recognize statements that are *not* true.

In general,

The following expressions are different:

- $\log(a + b)$ is not the same as $\log a + \log b$
- $\log(a - b)$ is not the same as $\log a - \log b$
- $\log(ab)$ is not the same as $(\log a)(\log b)$
- $\log\left(\frac{a}{b}\right)$ is not the same as $\frac{\log a}{\log b}$
- $\log\left(\frac{1}{a}\right)$ is not the same as $\frac{1}{\log a}$.

Notice that there are no formulas to simplify either $\log(a + b)$ or $\log(a - b)$. Another common mistake is to assume that the expression $\log 5x^2$ is the same as $2 \cdot \log 5x$. It is not, because the exponent, 2, belongs only to the x and not to the 5. However, it is correct to write

$$\log 5x^2 = \log 5 + \log x^2 = \log 5 + 2 \log x.$$

Problems for Section 3.4

1. Evaluate the following expressions. (Try not to use a calculator.)
   (a) $\log 1$ $= 0$
   (b) $\log 0.1$ $= -1$
   (c) $\log(10^0)$ $= 0$
   (d) $\log \sqrt{10}$ $= 1/2$
   (e) $\log(10^5)$ $= 5$
   (f) $\log(10^2)$ $= 2$
   (g) $\log \frac{1}{\sqrt{10}}$ $= -\frac{1}{2}$
   (h) $10^{\log 100}$ $= 100$
   (i) $10^{\log 1}$ $= 1$
   (j) $10^{\log(0.01)}$ $= 0.01$

2. Evaluate the following pairs of expressions. (Try not to use a calculator.)
   (a) $\log(10 \cdot 100)$ and $\log 10 + \log 100$
   (b) $\log(100 \cdot 1000)$ and $\log 100 + \log 1000$
   (c) $\log\left(\frac{10}{100}\right)$ and $\log 10 - \log 100$
   (d) $\log\left(\frac{100}{1000}\right)$ and $\log 100 - \log 1000$
   (e) $\log(10^2)$ and $2 \log 10$
   (f) $\log(10^3)$ and $3 \log 10$

3. (a) Write general formulas based on what you observed in Problem 2.
   (b) Apply your formulas to rewrite $\log\left(\frac{AB}{C}\right)^p$ at least two different ways.

4. Write the following quantities in terms of $\log(15)$ and/or $\log(5)$.
   (a) $\log(3)$
   (b) $\log(25)$ $= \log(5 \times 5)$ $= 2 \log 5$
   (c) $\log(75)$ $3 \log 5$

5. True or false?
   (a) $\log AB = \log A + \log B$ T
   (b) $\log A \log B = \log A + \log B$ F
   (c) $\frac{\log A}{\log B} = \log A - B$ F
   (d) $p \cdot \log A = \log A^p$ T
   (e) $\log \sqrt{x} = \frac{1}{2} \log x$ T
   (f) $\sqrt{\log x} = \log(x^{1/2})$ F

6. Let $p = \log m$ and $q = \log n$. Write the following expressions in terms of p and/or q without using logs.

   (a) $\log m$ (b) n^3 (c) $\log(mn^3)$ (d) $\log\sqrt{m}$

7. Suppose that $x = \log A$ and that $y = \log B$. Write the following expressions in terms of x and y.

   (a) $\log(AB)$ (b) $\log(A^3 \cdot \sqrt{B})$ (c) $\log(A - B)$
   (d) $\frac{\log A}{\log B}$ (e) $\log\frac{A}{B}$ (f) AB

8. Solve for x: $\log(1 - x) - \log(1 + x) = 2$.

9. Express the following in terms of x without using logs.

   (a) $\log 100^x$ (b) $1000^{\log x}$ (c) $\log 0.001^x$

10. Let $x = 10^U$ and $y = 10^V$. Write the following expressions in terms of U and/or V without using logs.

    (a) $\log xy$ (b) $\log\frac{x}{y}$ (c) $\log x^3$ (d) $\log\frac{1}{y}$

11. A calculator will confirm that $5 \approx 10^{0.7}$. Show how to use this fact to approximate the value of $\log 25$.

12. Given that $10^{1.3} \approx 20$, approximate the value of $\log 200$.

13. Simplify the following expressions. Try not to use a calculator.

    (a) $\log \log 10$ (b) $\sqrt{\log 100} - \log\sqrt{100}$ (c) $\log(\sqrt{10}\sqrt[3]{10}\sqrt[5]{10})$
    (d) $1000^{\log 3}$ (e) $0.01^{\log 2}$ (f) $\frac{1}{\log\frac{1}{\log\sqrt[10]{10}}}$

14. Assume that f and g are exponential functions, and that h is a linear function. All three functions are defined by the graphs in Figure 3.35.

Figure 3.35

    (a) Find formulas for f, g, and h.
    (b) Find the *exact* value(s) of x such that $f(x) = g(x)$.
    (c) Estimate the value(s) of x such that $f(x) = h(x)$.

15. Solve the following equations for t:

    (a) $1.04^t = 3$ (b) $3(1.081)^t = 14$ (c) $84(0.74)^t = 38$
    (d) $5(1.014)^{3t} = 12$ (e) $5(1.15)^t = 8(1.07)^t$ (f) $12(1.221)^t = t + 3$

16. A rubber ball is dropped onto a hard surface from a height of 6 feet, and it bounces up and down. At each bounce it rises to 90% of the height from which it fell.

    (a) If n is the number of bounces, find a formula for $h(n)$, the height reached by the ball on bounce n.
    (b) How high will the ball bounce on the 12th bounce?
    (c) How many bounces before the ball rises no higher than an inch?

    $3(100)^{3t}$

17. A colony of bacteria grows exponentially. The colony begins with 3 bacteria, but 3 hours after the beginning of the experiment, it has grown to 100 bacteria.

    $3 \text{ hour} = 100$

    3

    (a) Give an equation for the number of bacteria as a function of time.
    (b) Exactly how long does it take for the colony to triple in size?

18. The populations (in thousands) of two different cities are given by

    $$P_1 = 51(1.031)^t \quad \text{and} \quad P_2 = 63(1.052)^t,$$

    where t is the number of years since 1980.

    (a) When does the population of P_1 equal that of P_2?
    (b) Explain why it makes sense that your solution to part (a) is negative.

19. Solve the following equations exactly.

    (a) $5(1.031)^x = 8$ $1.031^x = 1.6 \Rightarrow x = \dfrac{\log 1.6}{\log 1.031} = 15.4$
    (b) $4(1.171)^x = 7(1.088)^x$ 7.6
    (c) $3\log(2x + 6) = 6$ 47

20. Solve the following equations for x.

    (a) $1.7(2.1)^{3x} = 2(4.5)^x$ (b) $3^{4\log x} = 5$
    (c) $\log x + \log(x - 1) = \log 2$

21. In 1990, the population of the country Erehwon was 50 million people and has since been increasing by 2.9% every year. The population of the country Ecalpon, on other hand, was 45 million people and increasing by 3.2% every year.

    (a) For each country, write a formula expressing the population as a function of time t, where t is the number of years since 1990.
    (b) Find the value(s) of t, if any, when the two countries will have the same population.
    (c) Give an expression which represents the exact value of t when the population of Ecalpon is double that of Erehwon.

22. Three students try to solve the equation

    $$11 \cdot 3^x = 5 \cdot 7^x.$$

    The first student finds that $x = \dfrac{\log \frac{11}{5}}{\log \frac{7}{3}}$. The second finds that $x = \dfrac{\log \frac{5}{11}}{\log \frac{3}{7}}$. The third finds that

    $x = \dfrac{\log 11 - \log 5}{\log 7 - \log 3}$. Which student (or students) is correct?

23. A student is asked to solve the equation

    $$3 \cdot 10^{-t} = \frac{3}{2}.$$

    (a) The student finds that $t = -\log \frac{1}{2} \approx 0.30103$. Show that this answer is correct.

(b) The solution provided by the student, including several marginal comments, is given below. Are the steps followed by the student correct? Discuss.

$$3 \cdot 10^{-t} = \frac{3}{2}$$

$$\log(3 \cdot 10^{-t}) = \log\left(\frac{3}{2}\right)$$

$$-t \log(3 \cdot 10) = \log\left(\frac{3}{2}\right) \qquad \text{(because } \log A^B = B \log A\text{)}$$

$$-t \log(3 \cdot 10) = \frac{\log 3}{\log 2}$$

$$-t(\log 3)(\log 10) = \frac{\log 3}{\log 2}$$

$$-t \log 3 = \frac{\log 3}{\log 2} \qquad \text{(because } \log 10 = 1\text{)}$$

$$-t = \frac{1}{\log 2} \qquad \text{(dividing by } \log 3\text{)}$$

$$t = -\frac{1}{\log 2}$$

$$t = -\log \frac{1}{2}$$

3.5 APPLICATIONS OF THE LOG FUNCTION

The Graph of the Log Function

In Section 3.3 we saw that the log function is defined only for positive numbers. In other words, the domain of $\log x$ consists of all positive real numbers. By considering its graph, we can determine the range of $\log x$. The log graph crosses the x-axis at $x = 1$, because $\log 1 = \log(10^0) = 0$. It climbs to $y = 1$ at $x = 10$, because $\log 10 = \log(10^1) = 1$. In order for the log graph to climb to $y = 2$, the value of x must reach 100, or 10^2. And in order for it to climb to $y = 3$, the value of x must be 10^3, or 1000. To reach the modest height of $y = 20$ requires x to equal 10^{20}, or 100 billion billion! The log function increases so slowly that it often serves as a benchmark for other slow-growing functions. Nonetheless, the graph of $y = \log x$ will eventually climb to any value we choose, so that range of $\log x$ is all real numbers. The graph of $y = \log x$ has a vertical asymptote at $x = 0$. To see why, notice that as x decreases to 0, the value of $\log x$ gets large and negative. For example,

$$\log 0.1 = \log 10^{-1} = -1,$$
$$\log 0.01 = \log 10^{-2} = -2,$$

and so on. Thus, large negative values of y correspond to exceedingly small positive values of x.

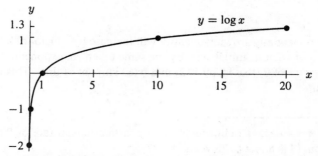

Figure 3.36: The log function grows very rapidly for $0 < x < 1$
and very slowly for $x > 1$. It has a vertical asymptote at $x = 0$

Doubling Time

Recall that exponential functions model growth at a constant percent rate. Eventually, *any* exponentially growing quantity will double, or increase by 100%. Since its percent growth rate is constant, the time it takes for it to grow by 100% is also constant. This period of time is called the *doubling time*.

Example 1   (a)   Find the amount of time needed for the turtle population described by the equation $P = 175(1.145)^t$ to double its initial size.

(b)   How long does it take this population to quadruple its initial size? To increase by a factor of 8?

Solution   (a)   The initial size is 175 turtles; doubling this gives 350 turtles. Thus, we need to solve the following equation for t:

$$175(1.145)^t = 350$$
$$1.145^t = 2$$
$$\log 1.145^t = \log 2$$
$$t \cdot \log 1.145 = \log 2$$
$$t = \frac{\log 2}{\log 1.145} \approx 5.12 \text{ years.}$$

We can check this by noting that

$$175(1.145)^{5.12} \approx 350,$$

which is double the initial population. In fact, at any time it will take the turtle population about 5.12 years to double in size.

(b)   We see that this population doubles, or increases by 100%, in 5.12 years. Since the population function is exponential, its percent growth rate is constant, which means that it increases by 100% *every* 5.12 years. Thus it will double its initial size in the first 5.12 years, quadruple its initial size in the next 5.12 years, and increase it by a factor of 8 in the next 5.12 years after that. We can verify these results by noting that

$$175(1.145)^{10.24} \approx 700,$$

or 4 times the initial size, and that

$$175(1.145)^{15.36} \approx 1400,$$

or 8 times the initial size.

Chapter 3/ 47

Half-Life

An exponentially growing quantity will increase by a factor of 2 (double) in a fixed amount of time, no matter what its initial size. By the same token, an exponentially decaying quantity will *decrease* by a factor of 2 (that is, by $1/2$) in a fixed amount of time. This time period is called the quantity's *half-life*.

Example 2   Carbon-14 decays radioactively at a constant annual rate of 0.0121%. Show that the half-life of carbon-14 is about 5728 years.

Solution   Suppose that Q_0 is the initial quantity of carbon-14 present. The growth rate is -0.000121 because carbon-14 is decaying. So the growth factor is $B = 1 - 0.000121 = 0.999879$. Thus, after t years the amount left will be

$$Q = Q_0(0.999879)^t.$$

We want to find how long it takes for the quantity to drop to half its initial level. Thus, we need to solve for t in the equation

$$Q_0(0.999879)^t = \frac{1}{2}Q_0.$$

Dividing each side by Q_0, we have

$$0.999879^t = \frac{1}{2}$$
$$\log 0.999879^t = \log \frac{1}{2}$$
$$t \cdot \log 0.999879 = \log 0.5$$
$$t = \frac{\log 0.5}{\log 0.999879} \approx 5728.14.$$

Thus, no matter how much carbon-14 an item initially contains, after about 5728 years only half of it will remain.

Log Scales and Orders of Magnitude

We often compare sizes or quantities by computing their ratios. If A is twice as tall as B, then

$$\frac{\text{height of } A}{\text{height of } B} = 2.$$

If one object is 10 times heavier than another, we say it is an *order of magnitude* heavier. If one quantity is two factors of 10 greater than another, we say it is two orders of magnitude greater, and so on. For example, the value of a dollar is two orders of magnitude greater than the value of a penny, because the exponent of their ratio is 2 in base 10:

$$\frac{\$1}{\$0.01} = 100 = 10^2.$$

Comparing quantities by order of magnitude is really the same as using a logarithmic scale as we did in Section 3.3: in both applications we use exponents to measure magnitudes.

Example 3   The sound intensity of a refrigerator motor is 10^{-11} watts/cm^2. A typical school cafeteria has sound intensity of 10^{-8} watts/cm^2. How many orders of magnitude more intense is the sound of the cafeteria?

Solution   To compare the two intensities, we compute their ratio:

$$\frac{\text{Sound intensity of cafeteria}}{\text{Sound intensity of refrigerator}} = \frac{10^{-8}}{10^{-11}} = 10^{-8-(-11)} = 10^3.$$

Thus, the sound intensity of the cafeteria is 1000 times greater than the sound intensity of the refrigerator. The log of this ratio is 3. We say that the sound intensity of the cafeteria is three orders of magnitude greater than the sound intensity of the refrigerator.

Decibels

The intensity of audible sound varies over an enormous range. The range is so enormous that, like the distances to the stars and planets described in Section 3.3, it is useful to treat comparisons of intensity logarithmically. This is the idea behind the *decibel* (abbreviated dB). To measure a sound in decibels, we compare the sound's intensity, I, to the intensity of a standard benchmark sound, I_0. The intensity of this benchmark sound, I_0, is defined to be 10^{-16} watts/cm^2 and is roughly the lowest intensity audible to humans. The comparison between a given sound intensity I and the benchmark sound intensity I_0 is made in the following way:

$$\left(\begin{array}{c} \text{noise level} \\ \text{in decibels} \end{array} \right) = 10 \times \left(\log \frac{I}{I_0} \right).$$

For instance, let's find the decibel rating of the refrigerator in Example 3. First, we find how many orders of magnitude more intense the refrigerator sound is than the benchmark sound:

$$\frac{I}{I_0} = \frac{\text{sound intensity of refrigerator}}{\text{benchmark sound intensity}} = \frac{10^{-11}}{10^{-16}} = 10^5.$$

Thus, the refrigerator's intensity is 5 orders of magnitude more than I_0, the benchmark intensity. We have

$$\begin{array}{c} \text{Decibel rating of} \\ \text{refrigerator noise} \end{array} = 10 \times \underbrace{\text{number of orders of magnitude}}_{5} = 50 \text{ dB}.$$

Note that 5, the number of orders of magnitude, is the log of the ratio I/I_0. We use the log function because it "counts" the number of powers of 10. Thus if N is the decibel rating, then

$$N = 10 \log \frac{I}{I_0}.$$

Example 4   (a)   If a sound doubles in intensity, how many units does its decibel rating go up?
 (b)   Loud music can measure 110 dB whereas normal conversation measures 50 dB. How many times more intense is loud music than normal conversation?

Solution (a) Let I be the sound's intensity before it doubles. Once doubled, the new intensity is $2I$. The decibel rating of the original sound is $10\log(\frac{I}{I_0})$, and the decibel rating of the new sound is $10\log(\frac{2I}{I_0})$. The difference in decibel ratings is given by

$$\text{Difference in decibel ratings} = 10\log(\frac{2I}{I_0}) - 10\log(\frac{I}{I_0})$$

$$= 10\left(\log(\frac{2I}{I_0}) - \log(\frac{I}{I_0})\right) \quad \text{(factor out 10)}$$

$$= 10\cdot\log\left(\frac{2I/I_0}{I/I_0}\right) \quad \text{(using the property } \log a - \log b = \log\frac{a}{b}\text{)}$$

$$= 10\cdot\log 2 \quad \text{(canceling } I/I_0\text{)}$$

$$\approx 3\text{ dB} \quad \text{(because } \log 2 \approx 0.3\text{)}.$$

Thus, if the sound intensity is doubled, the decibel rating goes up by approximately 3 dB.

(b) If I_M is the sound intensity of loud music, then

$$110 = 10\log\left(\frac{I_M}{I_0}\right).$$

Similarly, if I_C is the sound intensity of conversation, then

$$50 = 10\log\left(\frac{I_C}{I_0}\right).$$

Computing the difference of the decibel ratings gives

$$10\log\left(\frac{I_M}{I_0}\right) - 10\log\left(\frac{I_C}{I_0}\right) = 60.$$

Dividing by 10 gives

$$\log\left(\frac{I_M}{I_0}\right) - \log\left(\frac{I_C}{I_0}\right) = 6$$

$$\log\left(\frac{I_M/I_0}{I_C/I_0}\right) = 6 \quad \text{(using the property } \log b - \log a = \log\frac{b}{a}\text{)}$$

$$\log\frac{I_M}{I_C} = 6 \quad \text{(canceling } I_0\text{)}$$

$$\frac{I_M}{I_C} = 10^6. \quad \text{(}\log x = 6\text{ means that } x = 10^6\text{)}$$

So $I_M = 10^6 I_C$, which means that loud music is 10^6 times, or one million times, as intense as normal conversation.

Chemical Acidity

In chemistry, the acidity of a liquid is expressed using a rating called pH. The acidity depends on the hydrogen ion concentration in the liquid (in moles per liter); this concentration is written $[H^+]$. The greater the hydrogen ion concentration, the more acidic the solution. The pH rating is defined as:

$$pH = -\log[H^+].$$

Example 5 The hydrogen ion concentration of seawater is $[H^+] = 1.1 \times 10^{-8}$. Estimate the pH of seawater and then check your answer with a calculator.

Solution 1.1×10^{-8} is slightly greater than 1×10^{-8}, and so $\log(1.1 \times 10^{-8})$ should be slightly greater than $\log 10^{-8}$. Thus, $-\log(1.1 \times 10^{-8})$ should be slightly less than $-\log 10^{-8}$. Since $-\log 10^{-8} = -(-8) = +8$, we expect the pH to be slightly less than $+8$. Checking our answer, we have

$$pH = -\log(1.1 \times 10^{-8})$$
$$\approx -(-7.96) = +7.96$$

Example 6   A vinegar solution has a pH of 3. Determine the hydrogen ion concentration.

Solution   Since $3 = -\log[H^+]$, we have $-3 = \log[H^+]$. This means that $10^{-3} = [H^+]$. So the hydrogen ion concentration is 10^{-3} moles per liter.

Problems for Section 3.5

1. Each of the functions defined by a graph in Figure 3.37 corresponds to exactly one function described by the tables below. Find the match and justify your answers.

(a)   (b)   (c)

Figure 3.37

TABLE 3.24	
x	$r(x)$
2	1
4	1.3010
10	1.6990

TABLE 3.25	
x	$s(x)$
0.5	−0.06021
5	0.379
10	0.6990

TABLE 3.26	
x	$t(x)$
0.1	−3
2	0.9031
100	6

2. Graph the equations $y_1 = \log(x)$, $y_2 = \log(10x)$, and $y_3 = \log(100x)$. How do the graphs compare? Why is this happening?

3. Immediately following the gold medal performance of the US women's gymnastic team in the 1996 Olympic Games, an NBC commentator, John Tesh, said of one of the team members: "Her confidence and performance have grown logarithmically." He clearly thought this was an enormous compliment. Is it a compliment? Is it realistic?

4. A manager at Saks Fifth Avenue wants to estimate the number of customers to expect on the last shopping day before Christmas. She collects data from three previous years, and determines that the crowds follow the same general pattern. When the store opens at 10 AM, 500 people enter, and the total number in the store doubles every 40 minutes. When the number of people in the store reaches 10,000, security guards need to be stationed at the entrances to control the crowds. At what time should the guards be commissioned?

5. Scientists observing owl and hawk populations collect the following data. Their initial count for the owl population is 245 owls, and the population seems to grow by 3% per year. They initially observe 63 hawks, and this population doubles every 10 years.

   (a) Find a formula for the size of the population of owls in terms of time t.

   (b) Find a formula for the size of the population of hawks in terms of time t.

   (c) Use a graph to find how long it will take for these populations to be equal in number.

6. The Richter Scale is a measure of the ground motion that occurs during an earthquake. The intensity R of an earthquake as measured on the Richter Scale is given by

$$R = \log\left(\frac{a}{T}\right) + B$$

   where a is the amplitude (in microns) of vertical ground motion, T is the period (in seconds) of the seismic wave, and B is a constant. Let $B = 4.250$ and suppose $T = 2.5$ seconds. Find a if

   (a) $R = 6.1$ (b) $R = 7.1$

   (c) How do the values of R in (a) and (b) compare? How do the corresponding values of a compare?

7. To compare the acidity of different solutions, chemists use the pH. The pH (which is a single number not the product of a p and an H) is defined in terms of the concentration of hydrogen ions in the solution:

$$pH = -\log x$$

   (a) Find the concentrations of hydrogen ions in solutions with

   (i) pH= 2 (ii) pH= 4 (iii) pH= 7

   (b) A high concentration of hydrogen ions corresponds to an acidic solution. From your answer to part (a), decide if solutions with high pHs are more or less acidic.

3.6 MODELS OF INVESTMENT AND THE NUMBER e

Exponential Models of Investment

What is the difference between a bank account that pays 12% interest once per year and one that pays 1% interest every month? Imagine we deposit $1000 into the first account. Then, after 1 year, we will have (assuming no other deposits or withdrawals)

$$\$1000(1.12) = \$1120.$$

But if we deposit $1000 into the second account, then after 1 year, or 12 months, we will have

$$\$1000 \underbrace{(1.01)(1.01)\ldots(1.01)}_{12 \text{ months of 1\% monthly interest}} = 1000(1.01)^{12} = \$1126.83.$$

Thus, we will earn $6.83 more in the second account than in the first. To see why this happens, notice that the 1% interest we earn in January will itself start earning interest at a rate of 1% per month. Similarly, the 1% interest we earn in February will start earning interest, and so will the interest earned in March, April, May, and so on. This is where the extra $6.83 comes from – it is interest earned on interest. This effect is known as *compounding*. We say that the first earns 12% interest *compounded annually* and the second account earns 12% interest *compounded monthly*.

Nominal versus Effective Rates

As we have seen, it is preferable to earn 12% annual interest compounded monthly instead of annually. By leaving our interest payments in the bank, we can actually earn more money, when the interest is compounded frequently. Thus we draw a distinction between the *nominal rate* and the *effective yield* of an investment. The nominal rate is the rate we will earn each year if we don't leave our interest in the bank. The effective yield is the rate we will earn by leaving our interest and therefore allowing it to earn interest as well. Due to the compounding effect, the effective yield is usually larger than the nominal rate.

Example 1   What are the nominal and effective rates of an account paying 12% interest, compounded annually? compounded monthly?

Solution   Since an account paying 12% annual interest, compounded annually, grows by exactly 12% in one year, we see that its nominal rate is the same as its effective rate: both are 12%.

The account paying 12% interest, compounded monthly, also has a nominal rate of 12%. On the other hand, since it pays 1% interest every month, after 12 months, its balance will increase by a factor of

$$\underbrace{(1.01)(1.01)\ldots(1.01)}_{\text{12 months of 1\% monthly growth}} = 1.01^{12} \approx 1.1268250.$$

This means that it will grow by about 12.68% in one year; this is its effective yield.

Example 2   What is the effective annual yield of an account that pays interest at the nominal rate of 6% per year, compounded daily? compounded hourly?

Solution   Since there are 365 days in a year, daily compounding pays interest at the rate of

$$\frac{6\%}{365} = 0.0164384\% \text{ per day.}$$

Thus, the daily growth factor is

$$1 + \frac{0.06}{365} = 1.000164384.$$

If at the beginning of the year the account balance is P, after 365 days the balance will be

$$P \cdot \underbrace{\left(1 + \frac{0.06}{365}\right)^{365}}_{\substack{\text{365 days of} \\ \text{0.0164384\% daily interest}}} = P(1.0618313).$$

Thus, this account earns interest at the effective annual rate of 6.18313%.

Notice that daily compounding results in a higher rate than yearly compounding (6.183% versus 6%). If interest is compounded hourly, since there are 24×365 hours in a year, the balance at year's end would be

$$P\left(1 + \frac{0.06}{24 \times 365}\right)^{(24 \times 365)} = P(1.0618363).$$

The effective yield is now roughly 6.18363% instead of 6.18313% – that is, just slightly better than the yield of the account that compounds interest daily.

7 ×365

Introducing the Number e

In Example 2 we calculated the effective yield for two accounts with a 6% nominal interest rate, but compounded at different time intervals. We saw that the account for which the interest was compounded more frequently earned a better (higher) effective yield.

We could extend this process further so that interest is compounded every minute or every second or even hundreds of times per second. Notice, however, that compounding daily yields a markedly higher rate than compounding annually, but compounding hourly is only slightly better than compounding daily. The improvement is even less substantial if the interest is compounded more frequently, like every second. Thus, it appears that there is a limit to how much more an account will earn if interest is compounded more and more frequently.

The effective yields for several compounding periods are shown in Table 3.27. The last entry in the table is the value to which the effective yields converge as the compounding periods grow shorter and shorter. The exact value of this number involves a new constant called e. Like π, e is an irrational number that occurs in a surprising number of applications in mathematics. You will learn more about e in calculus. For now, you can use your calculator to find an approximation for the value of e,

$$e = 2.718281828\cdots,$$

and to confirm that

$$e^{0.06} \approx 1.0618365,$$

which is the final value for the effective yields in Table 3.27. If an account with a 6% nominal interest rate delivers this effective yield, we say that the interest has been compounded "continuously."

TABLE 3.27 *Compounding frequency and effective yield*

compounding frequency	effective yield
Annual	1.0600000
Monthly	1.0616778
Daily	1.0618313
Hourly	1.0618363
⋮	⋮
Continuously	$e^{0.06} \approx 1.0618365$

Continuous Growth Rates

We have seen that a general formula for the family of exponential functions is given by

$$Q = AB^t, \quad B > 0.$$

Here, B is the growth factor, and it is related to the percent growth rate, r, by the equation

$$B = 1 + r.$$

For example, if \$1000 is deposited at 6% annual interest, compounded annually, then the value of the deposit after t years is given by

$$V = 1000(1.06)^t.$$

Here, $A = 1000$, $B = 1.06$, and $r = 0.06$ or 6%.

There is another way to write the general formula for the family of exponential functions. If

$$Q = Ae^{kt},$$

$e^{(.3)5}$

then the parameter A has the usual interpretation as the initial value (at $t = 0$) of Q. The parameter, k, is called the *continuous percent growth rate*. For example, suppose \$1000 is deposited at 6% annual interest, compounded continuously. Then the value of the deposit is given by

$$V = 1000e^{0.06t}.$$

Here, $A = 1000$ and $k = 0.06$, or 6%, and we say that the balance grows at the continuous annual percent rate of 6%.

What is the Relationship Between the Parameters k and B?

Using the exponent law that says $a^{(bc)} = (a^b)^c$ we can rewrite the equation $V = 1000e^{0.06t}$ as:

$$V = 1000(e^{0.06})^t.$$

Now, using a calculator, $e^{0.06} \approx 1.06184$, so

$$V = 1000(1.06184)^t.$$

This tells us that V, the value of the deposit, increases by 6.184% each year. Notice that V goes up by more than 6% each year because of the effects of compounding. In this case, we say that the account earns interest at the continuous annual percent rate of 6%, but the effective annual yield is 6.184%.

In general, if $Q = Ae^{kt}$, then we can rewrite the formula for Q as

$$Q = A(e^k)^t \quad \text{(using an exponent law)}$$
$$= AB^t \quad \text{(where } B = e^k\text{).}$$

This shows that any exponential base can be written in terms of a growth factor B. To rewrite the function $Q = Ae^{kt}$, with a growth factor B instead of a continuous percent growth rate k, all we have to do is let $B = e^k$. However, the number e turns out to be very handy in calculus. As a result, there are actually many occasions when we might prefer to use e^k rather than B. In summary:

If Q is an exponential function growing at a continuous percent growth rate, we can write the formula for Q as a function of t as:
- $Q = Ae^{kt}$, where A is the starting value and k is the continuous percent growth rate.

or as,
- $Q = AB^t$, where A is the starting value and B is the growth factor. If r is the effective annual percent growth rate, then $B = 1 + r$.

In the two formulas, B and k are related by the equation $B = e^k$.

Example 3 Find the effective annual percent growth rate and the continuous percent growth rate if $P = 54.7\,e^{0.19t}$.

Solution The continuous growth rate is $k = 0.19 = 19\%$ per year. To calculate the effective annual percent growth rate, we use the fact that $B = e^k$,

$$B = e^{0.19} = 1.209.$$

This means that

$$P = 54.7(1.209)^t,$$

and so the effective annual growth rate is 20.9% per year.

It's important to realize that, in the last example, the formulas $P = 54.7e^{0.19t}$ and $P = 54.7(1.209)^t$ both represent the *same* exponential function – they just describe it in different ways. (Actually, this isn't quite true, because we rounded off when we found $B = 1.209$. However, we can find B to as many digits as we want, and to this extent the two formulas are the same.) In the next example we will see what a negative continuous percent rate means.

Example 4   Consider the functions

$$P = 5e^{-0.2t}, \qquad Q = 5e^{0.2t}, \qquad \text{and} \quad R = 5e^{0.3t}.$$

Find the continuous and annual percent growth rates of the population functions and draw a graph showing all three functions.

Solution   The function $P = 5e^{-0.2t}$ has a continuous percent growth rate of -20% per year. Since the annual growth factor is

$$e^{-0.2} \approx 0.819$$

we can write

$$P = 5(0.819)^t.$$

Thus, P is decreasing, and the annual percent growth rate is $(0.819 - 1) = -0.181$ or -18.1%. The negative sign in the exponent of e tells us that P is decreasing instead of increasing.

If $Q = 5e^{0.2t}$, since $e^{0.2} \approx 1.22$, the continuous growth rate of Q is 20% per year and the annual growth rate is 22% per year.

For $R = 5e^{0.3t}$, the continuous growth rate is 30% per year and the annual growth rate is 35% (since $e^{0.3} \approx 1.35$).

Because the 5 appears in all three formulas, all three populations start at 5. All three graphs are shown in Figure 3.38.

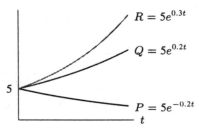

Figure 3.38: Comparing three exponential functions

Notice that in Example 4 the continuous and annual growth rates are nearly equal. This is generally true if these rates are small (say, less than 10%). For higher percents, there is a greater discrepancy between the two rates.

We can summarize as follows:

If Q is an exponential function whose continuous percent growth rate is k, then

$$Q = Ae^{kt}$$

where A is the initial value of Q (at $t = 0$). For positive values of A:

- If $k > 0$, then Q is increasing. The larger the value of k, the faster the function increases.

- If $k < 0$, then Q is decreasing. The more negative the value of k, the faster the function decreases.

Example 5   Which is better: An account that pays 8% annual interest compounded quarterly or an account that pays 7.5% annual interest compounded continuously?

Solution   The account that pays 8% interest compounded quarterly pays 2% interest 4 times a year. Thus, in one year the balance will be

$$B_0(1.02)^4 \approx B_0(1.0824),$$

which means the effective annual yield is 8.24%.

The account that pays 7.5% interest compounded continuously will have a year-end balance of

$$B_0 e^{0.075} \approx B_0(1.0779).$$

Thus, the effective annual yield is only 7.79%. Here, we see that compounding more frequently (or even continuously) isn't necessarily as advantageous as having a higher nominal rate.

Problems for Section 3.6

1. $1000 is deposited into an account paying interest at a nominal rate of 8% per year. Find the balance 3 years later if the interest is compounded

    (a) monthly   (b) weekly
    (c) daily   (d) continuously

2. Suppose an account pays interest at a nominal rate of 8% per year. Find the effective annual yield if interest is compounded

    (a) monthly   (b) weekly
    (c) daily   (d) continuously

3. A bank pays 6% annual interest, compounded daily. About how many days will it take for a deposit of $1000 to reach $1500?

4. How many years must you invest $850 at an annual rate of 3.9%, compounded quarterly, in order to have $5,000 in the account?

5. One student deposits $500 into a savings account earning 4.5% annual interest compounded annually. Another deposits $800 into an account earning 3% annual interest compounded annually. When are the balances equal?

6. An investment grows by 3% per year for 10 years. By what total percent does it increase?

7. An investment grows by 30% over a 5-year period. What is its annual percent growth rate?

8. An investment decreases by 60% over a 12-year period. At what annual percent rate does it decrease?

9. The balance of a bank account that compounds its interest payments monthly is given by

    $$M = M_0(1.07763)^t,$$

    where t is the number of years.

    (a) What is the effective annual yield paid by this account?
    (b) What is the nominal annual rate?

10. Find the annual growth rates of the following quantities.

    (a) This quantity doubles in size every 7 years.
    (b) This quantity triples in size every 11 years.
    (c) This quantity grows by 3% per month.
    (d) This quantity grows by 18% every 5 months.

11. If you need $25,000 six years from now, what is the minimum amount of money you need to deposit into a bank account that pays 5% annual interest, compounded:

    (a) annually   (b) monthly   (c) daily

    (d) Your answers get smaller as the number of times of compounding increases. Why is this so?

12. Prices climb at a constant 3% annual rate.

    (a) By what percent will prices have climbed after 5 years?
    (b) How long will it take for prices to climb 25%?

13. An investment decreases by 5% per year for 4 years. By what total percent does it decrease?

14. $850 is invested for 10 years and the interest is compounded quarterly. There is $1000 in the account at the end of 10 years. What is the nominal annual rate?

15. Let $P(t) = 32(1.047)^t$ give the population of a town (in thousands) in year t. What is the town's annual growth rate? Monthly growth rate? Growth rate per decade?

16. Let $Q(t) = 8(0.87)^t$ give the level of a pollutant (in tons) remaining in a lake after t months. What is the monthly rate of decrease of the pollutant? The annual rate? The daily rate?

17. A population grows from its initial level of 22,000 at a continuous annual growth rate of 7.1%.

    (a) Find a formula for $P(t)$, the population in year t.
    (b) By what percent does the population increase each year?

18. A population begins in year $t = 0$ with 25,000 people and grows at a continuous annual rate of 7.5%.

    (a) Find a formula for $P(t)$, the population in year t.
    (b) By what percent does the population increase each year? Explain why this is more than 7.5%.

19. Suppose 2 mg of a certain drug is injected into a person's bloodstream. As the drug is metabolized, the quantity diminishes at the continuous rate of 4% per hour.

    (a) Find a formula for $Q(t)$, the quantity of the drug remaining in the body after t hours.
    (b) By what percent does the drug level decrease during any given hour?
    (c) Suppose the person must receive an additional 2 mg of the drug whenever its level has diminished to 0.25 mg. When must the person receive the second injection?
    (d) When must the person receive the third injection?

20. A population begins to grow exponentially. Let $P(t)$ be the population (in thousands) in year t, and suppose that $P(0) = 30$ and $P(10) = 45$.

    (a) If $P(t) = AB^t$, find A and B. What does B tell you about the population?
    (b) If $P(t) = P_0 e^{kt}$, find the approximate value of k. What does k tell you about the population?

21. Rank the following three investments in order from best to worst:

TABLE 3.28

Investment A	Investment B	Investment C
Placing $875 in an account giving 13.5% per year compounded daily for 2 years.	Placing $1000 in an account giving 6.7% per year compounded continuously for 2 years.	Placing $1050 in an account giving 4.5% per year compounded monthly for 2 years.

22. Consider the following bank deposit options:

TABLE 3.29

Bank A	Bank B	Bank C
7% compounded daily	7.1% compounded monthly	7.05% compounded continuously

Rank the three investments from best to worst. What observations can you make?

23. It can be shown that $e = 1 + \frac{1}{1} + \frac{1}{1\cdot2} + \frac{1}{1\cdot2\cdot3} + \frac{1}{1\cdot2\cdot3\cdot4} + \cdots$, where the approximation improves as more terms are included.

(a) Use your calculator to find the sum of the five terms shown.

(b) Find the sum of the first seven terms.

(c) Compare your sums with the calculator's displayed value for e (which you can find by entering $e\hat{\ }1$) and state the number of correct digits in the five and seven term sum.

(d) How many terms of the sum are needed in order to give a nine decimal digit approximation equal to the calculator's displayed value for e?

24. (a) Using a computer or a graphing calculator, sketch a graph of $f(x) = 2^x$.

(b) Find the slope of the line tangent to f at $x = 0$ to an accuracy of two decimals. [Hint: Zoom in on the graph until it is indistinguishable from a line and estimate the slope using two points on the graph.]

(c) Find the slope of the line tangent to $g(x) = 3^x$ at $x = 0$ to an accuracy of two decimals.

(d) Find a base b (to two decimals) such that the line tangent to the function $h(x) = b^x$ at $x = 0$ has slope 1.

25. In the 1980s a northeastern bank experienced an unusual robbery. Each month an armored car delivered cash deposits from local branches to the main office, a trip requiring only 1 hour. One day, however, the delivery was six hours late. This delay turned out to be a scheme devised by an employee to defraud the bank. The armored car drivers had loaned the money, a total of approximately \$200,000,000, to arms merchants who then used it as collateral against the purchase of illegal weapons. The interest charged for this loan was 20% per year compounded continuously. How much was the fee for the six-hour period?

3.7 THE NATURAL LOGARITHM FUNCTION

The number $e = 2.71828\ldots$ is a useful base for exponential functions. With this in mind, we will now define a new logarithm function called log base e. The numbers 10 and e are the most frequently used log bases. Most scientific calculators can calculate logs to both of these bases. The log base e is used so frequently that it has its own notation: $\ln x$, read as the *natural log* of x. In other words, $\ln x = \log_e x$. We make the following definition:

> For $x > 0$, if $x = e^y$ then
> $$\ln x = y,$$
> and y is called the **natural logarithm** of x.

Recall that $\log x$ is the exponent of 10 that yields x. Similarly, $\ln x$ is the exponent of e that yields x. Just as the functions 10^x and $\log x$ "undo" each other, so do the functions e^x and $\ln x$. This gives us the following result:

The natural logarithm function satisfies the following conditions:

$$\ln e^x = x \quad \text{for all } x \quad \text{and} \quad e^{\ln x} = x \quad \text{for } x > 0$$

Example 1   Graph the natural log function, $f(x) = \ln x$, and compare this graph to the graph of the exponential function $g(x) = e^x$.

Solution   Values of $\ln x$ and e^x are shown in Table 3.30. (Those with decimals have been rounded.) The first value, $\ln 0$, is undefined since no power of e gives 0. Next, if $x = 1$, then $\ln x = 0$. As x increases past $x = 1$, the natural log function increases. The graphs of f and g are shown in Figure 3.39. Note that $\ln x$ grows very slowly whereas the exponential function grows rapidly.

TABLE 3.30   *Values of $\ln x$ and e^x, rounded*

x	$\ln x$	x	e^x
0	undefined	0	1
1	0	1	e
2	0.7	2	7.4
e	1	e	15.2
3	1.1	3	20.1
4	1.4	4	54.6
⋮		⋮	

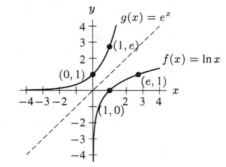

Figure 3.39: The graph of $y = e^x$ and $y = \ln x$. These graphs are symmetric across the line $y = x$

As with the common log function, the natural log function is not defined for $x \leq 0$ and has a vertical asymptote at $x = 0$. The range of $g(x) = e^x$ is $y > 0$. The natural log function crosses the x-axis at $x = 1$, and the exponential function crosses the y-axis at $y = 1$.

Properties of the Natural Log Function

The function $\ln x$ has the same properties as the common log function:

Properties of the natural logarithm
By definition,
$$e^{\ln x} = x \quad \text{for } x > 0$$
$$\ln e^x = x \quad \text{for all } x.$$

In particular,
$$\ln 1 = 0 \quad \text{and} \quad \ln e = 1.$$

For a and b both positive,
$$\ln(ab) = \ln a + \ln b$$
$$\ln\left(\frac{a}{b}\right) = \ln a - \ln b$$

For a positive,
$$\ln a^b = b \cdot \ln a$$

Using Natural Logarithms to Solve Equations

Like common logarithms, natural logarithms can often be used to solve equations where the variable is in the exponent. Consider the following examples.

Example 2   A population increases from its initial level of 7.3 million at the continuous rate of 2.2% per year. When will the population reach 10 million?

Solution   If P gives the population (in millions) in year t, then

$$P = 7.3e^{0.022t}.$$

Solving the equation $P = 10$ for t, we have

$$7.3e^{0.022t} = 10$$

$$e^{0.022t} = \frac{10}{7.3}$$

$$\ln e^{0.022t} = \ln\left(\frac{10}{7.3}\right) \quad \text{(taking ln of both sides)}$$

$$0.022t = \ln\left(\frac{10}{7.3}\right) \quad \text{(because } \ln e^x = x\text{)}$$

$$t = \frac{\ln(10/7.3)}{0.022} \approx 14.3.$$

Thus, it will take about 14.3 years for the population to reach 10 million.

We could have solved the equation in Example 2 by using log base 10 instead of log base e. This would give

$$\log e^{0.022t} = \log\frac{10}{7.3}$$

$$0.022t \log e = \log\frac{10}{7.3}$$

$$t = \frac{\log(10/7.3)}{0.022 \log e}.$$

This process is slightly more complicated than before because it involves $\log e$, the log base 10 of e. However, note that

$$t = \frac{\log(10/7.3)}{0.022 \log e} \approx 14.3,$$

is the same answer that we got before. As a general rule, though, $\ln x$ will result in neater calculations when e^x is involved for the same reason that $\log x$ results in neater calculations when 10^x is involved.

Example 3   Consider a population that begins at 5.2 million and grows at the constant annual rate of 3.1%. Will this population catch up to the population in Example 2? If so, when?

Solution   The new population is given by the formula $P_2 = 5.2(1.031)^t$. The population in Example 2 is given by $P_1 = 7.3e^{0.022t}$. Thus, we must solve the equation

$$5.2(1.031)^t = 7.3e^{0.022t}.$$

Taking the natural log of both sides gives

$$\ln(5.2(1.031)^t) = \ln(7.3e^{0.022t}).$$

Using the properties of the natural log, we get

$$\ln 5.2 + \ln 1.031^t = \ln 7.3 + \ln e^{0.022t} \quad \text{(using } \ln ab = \ln a + \ln b)$$
$$\ln 5.2 + t \ln 1.031 = \ln 7.3 + 0.022t \quad \text{(using } \ln a^b = b \cdot \ln a)$$
$$t \ln 1.031 - 0.022t = \ln 7.3 - \ln 5.2 \quad \text{(grouping like terms)}$$
$$t(\ln 1.031 - 0.022) = \ln 7.3 - \ln 5.2 \quad \text{(factoring } t)$$
$$t = \frac{\ln 7.3 - \ln 5.2}{\ln 1.031 - 0.022} \approx 39.8.$$

Thus, the populations are equal after about 39.8 years. You can use a computer or graphing calculator to verify that the two functions intersect at $t \approx 39.8$.

Logs can often help us solve equations involving a variable in the exponent, but this is not always the case.

Example 4 The population of a country (in millions) is given by $P = 2(1.02)^t$, while the food supply (in millions of people that can be fed) is given by $N = 4 + 0.5t$. Determine the year in which the country will first experience food shortages.

Solution The country will start to experience shortages when the population equals the number of people that can be fed—that is, when $P = N$. We attempt to solve the equation $P = N$ by using logs:

$$2(1.02)^t = 4 + 0.5t$$
$$1.02^t = 2 + 0.25t \quad \text{(dividing by 2)}$$
$$\ln 1.02^t = \ln(2 + 0.25t)$$
$$t \ln 1.02 = \ln(2 + 0.25t).$$

However, this equation cannot be solved algebraically. We can approximate the solution numerically (by taking successive "guesses") or graphically. The graphs of P and N are shown in Figure 3.40. We see that the two functions are equal when $t \approx 199.4$. Thus, it will be almost 200 years before shortages occur.

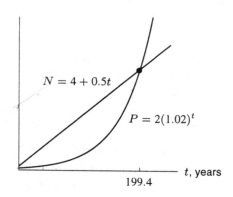

Figure 3.40

Using Logs to Change Bases

We can use logs to change the base of an exponential function. In particular, we can use logs to write a function in the form $Q = AB^t$ as a function in the form $Q = Ae^{kt}$.

Example 5   A population increases from 5.2 million at the constant rate of 3.1% per year. Find the continuous growth rate of the population.

Solution   We have $P = AB^t$ where $A = 5.2$ and $B = 1.031$. If we let $k = \ln B$, then

$$e^k = e^{\ln 1.031} = 1.031.$$

Thus, we can write

$$P = 5.2(1.031)^t$$
$$= 5.2e^{(\ln 1.031)t}$$
$$\approx 5.2e^{0.03053t}.$$

Thus, the continuous growth rate is $k = \ln 1.031 \approx 0.03053$, or 3.053% per year.

In general, suppose $Q = AB^t$, and that we want to change bases from B to e. If we let $k = \ln B$, we can rewrite our formula for Q as $Q = Ae^{kt}$. To see that this works, notice that

$$Q = Ae^{kt}$$
$$= A(e^k)^t \quad \text{(using a property of exponents)}$$
$$= A(e^{\ln B})^t \quad \text{(because } k = \ln B\text{)}$$
$$= AB^t \quad \text{(because } e^{\ln x} = x \text{ for } x > 0\text{).}$$

Thus, even though the formulas $Q = Ae^{kt}$ and $Q = AB^t$ look different, they are the same function.

In summary:

- If $Q = Ae^{kt}$, we can rewrite the formula for Q as $Q = AB^t$ by letting $B = e^k$.
- If $Q = AB^t$, we can rewrite the formula for Q as $Q = Ae^{kt}$ by letting $k = \ln B$.

Recall that the constant B is called the **growth factor** and if $B = 1 + r$, then r is called the **percent growth rate**. The constant k is called the **continuous percent growth rate**. If k is small, say, $k \leq 10\%$, then $k \approx r$. The constant A is the **initial value** of Q at $t = 0$.

Calculating Half-Lives and Doubling Times

Recall that the half-life of a radioactive substance is the time required for one-half of the substance to decay.

Example 6   A substance decays at the continuous rate of 2.3% per minute. What is the half-life of the substance?

Solution   If Q represents the quantity of the substance at time t, then $Q = Q_0 e^{-0.023t}$. Since Q_0 is the initial amount, $\frac{1}{2}Q_0$ is the amount remaining once half of the substance has decayed. Solving $Q = \frac{1}{2}Q_0$ for t gives

$$Q_0 e^{-0.023t} = \frac{1}{2}Q_0$$

$$e^{-0.023t} = \frac{1}{2}$$

$$-0.023t = \ln\frac{1}{2}$$

$$t = \frac{\ln(1/2)}{-0.023} \approx 30.14,$$

and so the half-life is $t = 30.14$ minutes or a little more than half an hour.

Alternatively, given the half-life of a substance, we can determine its decay rate.

Example 7   A substance has a half-life of 11 minutes. What is its continuous decay rate?

Solution   Let $Q = Q_0 e^{-kt}$, where k is the continuous decay rate. We know that after 11 minutes, $Q = \frac{1}{2}Q_0$. Thus, solving for k, we get

$$Q_0 e^{-k \cdot 11} = \frac{1}{2}Q_0$$

$$e^{-11k} = \frac{1}{2}$$

$$-11k = \ln\frac{1}{2}$$

$$k = \frac{\ln(1/2)}{-11} \approx 0.063,$$

so the continuous decay rate is $k = 0.063$, or 6.3% per minute.

The *doubling time* of an exponentially growing quantity is the time required for it to double in size.

Example 8   A population doubles in size every 20 years. What is its continuous growth rate?

Solution   We have $P = P_0 e^{kt}$. After 20 years, $P = 2P_0$, and so

$$P_0 e^{k \cdot 20} = 2P_0$$

$$e^{20k} = 2$$

$$20k = \ln 2$$

$$k = \frac{\ln 2}{20} \approx 0.0347.$$

Thus, the population grows at the continuous annual rate of 3.47%.

The Rule of 70

The Rule of 70 is a rule of thumb that gives an easy way to estimate the doubling time of an exponentially growing quantity. If $r\%$ is the constant annual growth rate of a quantity, then the rule of 70 tells us that

$$\text{doubling time} \approx \frac{70}{r}.$$

Example 9   Verify the Rule of 70 by finding how long it takes a $1000 investment to double provided that it grows at the following constant annual rates: 1%, 2%, 5%, 7%, 10%.

Solution   At an annual growth rate of 1%, the rule of 70 tells us this investment will double in $\frac{70}{r} = 70$ years. At a 2% rate, the doubling time should be about $\frac{70}{2} = 35$ years. The doubling times for the other rates are, according to the Rule of 70,

$$\frac{70}{5} = 14 \text{ years}, \qquad \frac{70}{7} = 10 \text{ years}, \qquad \text{and} \qquad \frac{70}{10} = 7 \text{ years}.$$

To verify these predictions, we can use logs to calculate the actual doubling times. If V is the dollar value of the investment in year t, then at a 1% rate, $V = 1000(1.01)^t$. To find the doubling time, we set $V = 2000$ and solve for t:

$$1000(1.01)^t = 2000$$
$$1.01^t = 2$$
$$\log(1.01)^t = \log 2$$
$$t \log 1.01 = \log 2$$
$$t = \frac{\log 2}{\log 1.01} \approx 69.7.$$

We see that this agrees well with our prediction of 70 years. Doubling times for the other rates have been calculated and recorded in Table 3.31 together with the doubling times predicted by the Rule of 70.

TABLE 3.31   *Rule of 70 predicted doubling times*

rate (%)	1	2	5	7	10
predicted doubling time (in years)	70	35	14	10	7
actual doubling time (in years)	69.7	35	14.2	10.2	7.3

Example 10   Explain why the Rule of 70 works.

Solution   Let $Q = Ae^{kt}$ be an increasing exponential function, so that k is positive. Then to find the doubling time, we need to find how long it takes Q to double from its initial value of A to $2A$:

$$Ae^{kt} = 2A$$
$$e^{kt} = 2 \qquad \text{(dividing by } A)$$
$$\ln e^{kt} = \ln 2$$
$$kt = \ln 2 \qquad \text{(because } \ln e^x = x \text{ for all } x)$$
$$t = \frac{\ln 2}{k}.$$

Now, using a calculator, $\ln 2 = 0.693 \approx 0.70$. This is where the 70 comes from.

Thus, for example, if the continuous growth rate is $k = 0.07 = 7\%$, the doubling time would be

$$\frac{\ln 2}{0.07} = \frac{0.693}{0.07} \approx \frac{0.70}{0.07} = \frac{70}{7} = 10.$$

Stating a function's half-life or doubling time gives us another way to state the function's growth rate. In summary:

- The time required for an exponentially growing quantity to double is a constant known as the **doubling time**.
- The time required for a positive, exponentially decaying quantity to fall to half its size is a constant known as the **half-life**.
- **The Rule of 70** states that if the annual percent growth (or decay) rate of a quantity is $r\%$, then the doubling time (or half-life) is approximately

$$\frac{70}{r},$$

provided that r is not much larger than 10%.

Notice that for small growth rates, the annual growth rate is approximately equal to the continuous annual growth rate. For example, if the continuous growth rate is $k = 0.07$ per year, the annual growth factor is $e^{0.07} = 1.073$, and so the annual growth rate is 7.3%. This is why the Rule of 70 works even for the annual growth rate, provided that the growth rate is small. The Rule of 70 does not give good estimates for growth rates much higher than 10%. For example, at an annual rate of 35%, the Rule of 70 predicts that the doubling time is $\frac{70}{35} = 2$ years. But in 2 years at 35% growth rate, the $1000 investment from the last example would be worth only

$$1000(1.35)^2 = \$1822.50,$$

not $2000.

Problems for Section 3.7

1. The number of bacteria present in a culture after t hours is given by the formula $N = 1000e^{0.69t}$.
   (a) How many bacteria will there be after 1/2 hour?
   (b) How long will it be before there are 1,000,000 bacteria?
   (c) What is the doubling time?

2. A population grows from 11000 to 13000 members in three years. Assuming exponential growth, find
   (a) the annual growth rate;   (b) the continuous annual growth rate.
   (c) Why are your answers different?

3. A population doubles in size every 15 years. Assuming exponential growth, find
   (a) the annual growth rate;   (b) the continuous growth rate.

4. A population increases exponentially. Let $P(t)$ be the population (in millions) in year t, and suppose $P(8) = 20$ and $P(15) = 28$.
   (a) Find a formula for $P(t)$. (b) If $P(t) = Ae^{kt}$, find k.

5. You place $800 in an account that earns 4% annual interest, compounded annually. How long will it be until you have $2000?

6. If $f(x) = 3(1.072)^x$ is rewritten as $f(x) = 3e^{kx}$, find k exactly.

7. Suppose that P is the population (in thousands) of a certain town in year t, where $t = 0$ represents 1980, and that P is given by the formula $P(t) = P_0 e^{kt}$. Suppose also that in 1985 the town's population was 18 thousand and in 1989 the town's population was 21 thousand.

    (a) Find the values of P_0 and k. Explain the significance of these quantities in terms of the town's population.

    (b) By what percent does the town's population increase during a given year?

8. Suppose 1000 dollars earns 6% annual interest, compounded monthly.

    (a) Write a formula for the account balance, $V(t)$, as a function of t, the number of years elapsed.

    (b) What continuous annual interest rate would result in the same annual yield?

9. Suppose Washington State's population is being projected by the function $N(t) = 5.3e^{0.03t}$ where N is in millions and t is the number of years since the base year.

    (a) What is the population's continuous growth rate?   3%

    (b) What is the population of Washington in year $t = 0$?   5.3 million

    (c) How many years will it be before the population triples?   36.6

    (d) In what year does this model predict a population of only one person? Is this prediction reasonable or unreasonable?

10. Solve the following equations for t. Use a graph to answer if the equation cannot be solved analytically.

    (a) $e^{0.044t} = 6$ (b) $121e^{-0.112t} = 88$ (c) $58e^{4t+1} = 30$

    (d) $17e^{0.02t} = 18e^{0.03t}$ (e) $44e^{0.15t} = 50(1.2)^t$ (f) $87e^{0.066t} = 3t + 7$

11. Solve for t. (Use a graph to answer if the equation cannot be solved analytically.)

    (a) $16.3(1.072)^t = 18.5$ (b) $13e^{0.081t} = 25e^{0.032t}$ (c) $5(1.044)^t = t + 10$

12. (a) Find the time required for an investment to triple in value if it earns 4% annual interest, compounded continuously.

    (b) Now find the time required assuming that the interest is compounded annually.

13. A population increases from 30,000 to 34,000 over a 5-year period at a constant annual percent growth rate.

    (a) By what percent did the population increase in total?

    (b) At what constant percent rate of growth must the population have increased each year?   2.53

    (c) At what *continuous* annual growth rate did this population grow?   2.50

14. Let $f(t)$ and $g(t)$ be the respective dollar balances of two different bank accounts, where t is the elapsed number of years. The formulas for f and g are given below:

$$f(t) = 1100(1.05)^t \quad \text{and} \quad g(t) = 1500e^{0.05t}.$$

    (a) Describe in words the bank account modeled by f.

    (b) Now describe the account modeled by g.

    (c) Suppose the account modeled by f keeps the same growth but needs to be converted to continuous compounding. What must its continuous interest rate be?

15. The voltage V across a charged capacitor is given by $V(t) = 5e^{-0.3t}$ where t is in seconds.
    (a) What is the voltage after 3 seconds?
    (b) When will the voltage be 1?
    (c) By what percent does the voltage decrease each second?

16. Oil leaks from a tank. At hour $t = 0$ there are 250 gallons of oil in the tank. Each hour after that, 4% of the oil leaks out.

    (a) What percent of the original 250 gallons has leaked out after 10 hours? Why is it less than $10 \times 4\% = 40\%$?
    (b) If $Q(t) = Q_0 e^{kt}$ is the quantity of oil remaining after t hours, find the value of k. What does k tell you about the leaking oil?

17. I just poured myself a nice cup of coffee at 8:00 AM. The temperature of my coffee is H (in degrees Fahrenheit) and is a function of the time, t, in minutes since I poured it. I have determined the equation to be:

$$H = 75e^{-0.06t} + 65.$$

    (a) Sketch a graph of $H(t)$.
    (b) Explain what the H-intercept of your graph tells you about my coffee.
    (c) What will be the temperature of my coffee at 8:10 AM? 9 AM?
    (d) What will happen to the temperature of my cup of coffee after a long period of time? To what feature of the graph does this fact correspond?
    (e) If my coffee is too hot, I will burn my tongue. If it is cold, it will not taste good. However, I know that if the temperature of my coffee is between 100°F and 125°F, then I will be able to appreciate its flavor to its fullest. If I want to enjoy my coffee, when should I start drinking it, and how much time do I have to finish my coffee before it is too cold?

18. The probability of a transistor failing within t months is given by $P(t) = 1 - e^{-0.016t}$.

    (a) What is the probability of failure within the first 6 months? Within the second six months?
    (b) Within how many months will the probability of failure be 99.99%?

19. In a country where inflation is a concern, prices have risen by 40% over a 5-year period.

    (a) By what percent do the prices rise each year?
    (b) How long does it take prices to rise by 5%?
    (c) Economists often use continuous growth rates in the form $P = P_0 e^{rt}$. Find an r to model the inflation.

20. You deposit $4000 into an account that earns 6% annual interest, compounded annually. A friend deposits $3500 into an account that earns 5.95% annual interest, compounded continuously. Will your friend's balance ever equal yours? If so, when?

21. Solve for x exactly.
    (a) $e^{x+4} = 10$ (b) $e^{x+5} = 7 \cdot 2^x$ (c) $\log(2x + 5) \cdot \log(9x^2) = 0$

22. In the early 1960s, radioactive strontium-90 was released during atmospheric testing of nuclear weapons and got into the bones of people alive at the time. If the half-life of strontium-90 is 29 years, what fraction of the strontium-90 absorbed in 1960 remained in people's bones in 1993?

23. Radioactive carbon-14 decays according to the equation $Q(t) = Q_0 e^{-0.000121t}$ where t is time in years and Q_0 is the amount of carbon-14 present at time $t = 0$. Estimate the age of a skull if 23% of the original amount of carbon-14 is still present.

24. What is the half-life of a radioactive substance that decays at a continuous rate of 11% per minute?

25. The following is excerpted from an article that appeared in the January 8, 1990 *Boston Globe*.

> Men lose roughly 2 percent of their bone mass per year in the same type of loss that can severely affect women after menopause, a study indicates.
>
> "There is a problem with osteoporosis in men that hasn't been appreciated. It's a problem that needs to be recognized and addressed," said Dr. Eric Orwoll, who led the study by the Oregon Health Sciences University.
>
> The bone loss was detected at all ages and the 2 percent rate did not appear to vary, Orwoll said.

   (a) Assume that the average man starts losing bone mass at age 30. Let M_0 be the average man's bone mass at this age. Express the amount of remaining bone mass as a function of the man's age a.

   (b) At what age will the average man have lost half his bone mass?

26. If 17% of a radioactive substance decays in 5 hours, what is the half-life of the substance?

27. In 1991, the body of a man was found in melting snow in the Alps of Northern Italy. An examination of the tissue sample revealed that 46% of the C^{14} present in his body at the time of his death had already decayed. The half-life of C^{14} is approximately 5,728 years. How long ago did this man die?

28. Find the domain of the following functions.

   (a) $f(x) = \ln(\ln x)$ (b) $g(x) = \ln\left(\ln(\ln x)\right)$ (c) $h(x) = \ln(x^2)$

29. The spread of rumor among 100 people can be described by the equation $\ln(x) - \ln(100-x) = 0.48t - \ln(99)$, where x is the number of people who have heard the rumor after t days.

   (a) Solve this equation for t.   (b) Solve this equation for x.

3.8 FITTING CURVES TO DATA

In Section 2.4 we used linear regression to find the equation for a line of "best fit" for a set of data. What if the data do not lie close to a straight line, but instead approximate the graph of some other function? In this section we will see how logarithms can help us find an equation of best fit for some non-linear curves .

The Sales of Compact Discs

Earlier in the text, we looked at data relating the fall in LP record sales and the advent of compact discs. Table 3.32 gives the number of units (in millions) of CDs and LPs sold for the years 1982 through 1992.[5]

[5] Data from Recording Industry Association of America, Inc., 1993

TABLE 3.32   *CD and LP sales (millions of units sold)*

t, years since 1982	c, CDs (millions)	l, LPs (millions)
0	0	244
1	0.8	210
2	5.8	205
3	23	167
4	53	125
5	102	107
6	150	72
7	207	35
8	287	12
9	333	4.8
10	408	2.3

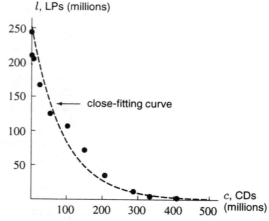

Figure 3.41: The number of LPs sold, l, as a function of number of CDs sold, c

From the table, we see that while CD sales rose dramatically during the 1980s, LP sales declined just as dramatically. Figure 3.41 gives a graph of l, the number of LPs sold in a given year, as a function of c, the number of CDs sold that year. Figure 3.41 also shows a close-fitting curve that summarizes the apparent trend in the data.

Using a Log Scale to Linearize Data

In Section 3.3, we saw that a log scale allows us to compare values that vary over a wide range. Let's see what happens when we use a log scale to plot the data in Figure 3.42.

Figure 3.42 shows the same data as shown in Figure 3.41, except that the vertical axis is now a logarithmic scale, instead of a linear scale. This scale is slightly different from the ones in Section 3.3, because each unit is a power of e, not a power of 10. However, the basic principle is the same. Notice that plotting the data in this way tends to *linearize* the graph – that is, make it look more like a line and less like a curve.

Figure 3.42: The sales of LPs (in millions) have been plotted on a logarithmic scale. The sales of CDs are plotted on a linear scale

Fitting An Exponential Function To Data

Figure 3.43 gives the same graph as Figure 3.42, and a dashed line has been drawn in to emphasize the trend in the data. The difference between Figure 3.43 and Figure 3.42 is the way the vertical axis has been labeled. The axis in Figure 3.43 is marked off in units of $y = \ln l$ rather than in millions of LPs, l, and the points plotted in Figure 3.43 have y-coordinates given by $\ln l$, instead of l. For instance, the point in Figure 3.42 with coordinates $(c, l) = (102, 107)$ is identified in Figure 3.43 by the coordinates $(c, y) = (102, 4.67)$, because $\ln 107 \approx 4.67$. The coordinates of the other points in Figure 3.43 are shown in Table 3.33.

We say that the data values in Table 3.33 have been *transformed*. We can use a calculator or computer program to find a regression line for the transformed data in Table 3.33.

$$y = 5.53 - 0.011c.$$

Notice that this equation gives y in terms of c. We don't really care about the relationship between y and c. Instead we would like to transform the equation back to our original variables, l and c. To do this, we substitute $\ln l$ for y to obtain

$$\ln l = 5.53 - 0.011c.$$

Now we solve for l by raising e to both sides:

$$e^{\ln l} = e^{5.53 - 0.011c}$$
$$= (e^{5.53})(e^{-0.011c}) \qquad \text{(using an exponent rule)}$$

Since $e^{\ln l} = l$ and $e^{5.53} \approx 252$, we have

$$l = 252e^{-0.011c}.$$

This is the equation of the original dashed curve shown in Figure 3.41. Note that the curve is a "close fit" model for the data in the table. This method of transforming a data set using logarithms allows us to use the techniques of linear regression to find formulas for exponential functions. To fit

TABLE 3.33 *Values of $y = \ln l$ as a function of c.*

c	$y = \ln l$
0	5.50
0.8	5.35
5.8	5.32
23	5.12
53	4.83
102	4.67
150	4.28
207	3.56
287	2.48
333	1.57
408	0.83

Figure 3.43: The y-axis of this graph gives the natural log of LP sales

an exponential formula, $N = Ae^{kt}$, to a set of data of the form (t, N), we use three steps. First, we transform the data by making the substitution $y = \ln N$. This leads to the equation

$$y = \ln N = \ln\left(Ae^{kt}\right)$$
$$= \ln A + \ln e^{kt}$$
$$= \ln A + kt.$$

Setting $b = \ln A$ gives the familiar linear equation with k as the slope and b as the y-intercept.

$$y = b + kt.$$

Secondly we can now use linear regression on the variables t and y. (Remember that $y = \ln N$.) Finally, as step three, we transform the regression equation back into our original variables by substituting $\ln N$ for y and solving for N. As we will see, transforming data will also help us find formulas for power functions.

The Spread of AIDS

The data in Table 3.34 give the total number of deaths in the US from AIDS since the start of 1981. Figure 3.44 suggests that a linear function may not give the best possible fit for these data.

Fitting an Exponential

We will first try to fit the data in Table 3.34 using an exponential function

$$N = Ae^{kt},$$

where N is the total number of deaths t years after 1980. We begin by "linearizing" the data, using logs.

Table 3.35 shows the transformed data, where $y = \ln N$. For example, from Table 3.34, we see that in year $t = 1$, $N = 268$ so $y = \ln 268 \approx 5.60$. Thus, the first data point is $(1, 5.60)$. Similarly, the second data point is $(2, \ln 1209) \approx (2, 7.10)$, the third is $(3, \ln 3826) \approx (3, 8.25)$, and so on. These data have been plotted in Figure 3.45. We see that the transformed data lie close to a straight line.

We can now use regression to estimate a line to fit the data points $(t, \ln N)$. The formula provided by a calculator (and rounded) is

$$y = 5.384 + 0.82t.$$

TABLE 3.34 *Domestic deaths from AIDS, 1981–87*

t, year since 1980	N, Total number of deaths to date
1	268
2	1209
3	3826
4	8712
5	17386
6	29277
7	41128

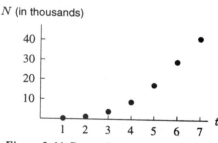

Figure 3.44: Domestic deaths from AIDS, 1981–87

TABLE 3.35
Transformed data from Table 3.34

t	$y = \ln N$
1	5.59
2	7.10
3	8.25
4	9.07
5	9.76
6	10.29
7	10.62

Figure 3.45: Domestic deaths from AIDS, 1981–87 ($\ln N$ against t)

The values obtained by a computer or a calculator may very slightly from the ones given. Finally, to find the formula for N in terms of t, we substitute $\ln N$ for y:

$$\ln N = 5.384 + 0.82t$$
$$N = e^{5.384 + 0.82t}$$
$$= \left(e^{5.384}\right)\left(e^{0.82t}\right),$$

and since $e^{5.384} \approx 218$

$$N \approx 218 e^{0.82t}.$$

Refer to Figure 3.47 on page 185 to see how the graph of this formula fits the data points.

Fitting a Power Function

Some epidemiologists have suggested that a power function might be a better model for the growth of AIDS than an exponential function. Suppose we want to try to fit a power function of the form

$$N = At^p$$

to the AIDS data. We can linearize the power function by making the substitution $y = \ln N$ to obtain

$$y = \ln N = \ln\left(At^p\right)$$
$$= \ln A + \ln t^p$$
$$= \ln A + p \ln t.$$

As before, we make the substitution $b = \ln A$, so the equation becomes

$$y = b + p \ln t.$$

Notice that this substitution does not result in y being a linear function of t. However, if we make a second substitution, $x = \ln t$, we have

$$y = b + px.$$

So y *is* a linear function of x.

We can now use linear regression to find a formula for y in terms of x. From there we can determine a formula for N in terms of t. Let's carry out this procedure for the AIDS data. We first transform the data in Table 3.34, using the two substitutions $x = \ln t$ and $y = \ln N$. For example, the first data point from Table 3.34 is $(t, N) = (1, 268)$. Transforming this data point gives $x = \ln 1 = 0$ and $y = \ln 268 \approx 5.59$. Thus, the first data point in Table 3.36 is $(0, 5.59)$. Similarly, the second data point is $(\ln 2, \ln 1209) \approx (0.69, 7.10)$, the third data point is $(\ln 3, \ln 3826) \approx (1.10, 8.25)$, and so on.

The data from Table 3.36 have been plotted in Figure 3.46. We see that the points show a more linear pattern than the points in Figure 3.45. Using regression to fit a line to these data gives the equation

$$y = 5.435 + 2.65x.$$

Now transform the equation back to the original variables, t and N. Since our original substitutions were $y = \ln N$ and $x = \ln t$, this equation becomes

$$\ln N = 5.435 + 2.65 \ln t.$$

We know how to solve for N by raising e to the power of both sides

$$e^{\ln N} = e^{5.435 + 2.65 \ln t}$$
$$N = (e^{5.435})(e^{2.65 \ln t}).$$

Since $e^{5.435} \approx 229$ and $e^{2.65 \ln t} = \left(e^{\ln t}\right)^{2.65} = t^{2.65}$, we have

$$N \approx 229 t^{2.65},$$

which is the formula of a power function. To see how the graph of this formula fits the data, refer to Figure 3.47.

Which Function Best Fits the Data?

Both the exponential function

$$N = 218 e^{0.82t}$$

and the power function

$$N = 229 t^{2.65}$$

fit the AIDS data reasonably well. By visual inspection alone, the power function arguably provides the better fit. If we fit a linear function to the original data we get

$$N = -12924 + 6867t.$$

TABLE 3.36

x	y
0	5.59
0.69	7.10
1.10	8.25
1.39	9.07
1.61	9.76
1.79	10.29
1.95	10.62

Figure 3.46: Domestic deaths from AIDS, 1981–87 ($\ln N$ against $\ln t$)

Even this linear function gives a passable fit for $t \geq 2$, that is, for 1982 to 1986. (See Figure 3.47.)

Figure 3.47: The AIDS data shown together with an exponential model, a power-function model, and a linear model

Despite the fact that all three functions fit the data reasonably well up to 1987, it's important to realize that they give wildly different predictions for the future. If we use each model to predict the total number of AIDS deaths by the year 2000 (when $t = 20$), the exponential model gives

$$N = 218e^{(0.82)(20)} \approx 2.9 \times 10^9, \quad \text{or about 10 times the current US population;}$$

the power model gives

$$N = 229(20)^{2.65} \approx 650{,}000, \quad \text{or about 0.25\% of the current population;}$$

and the linear model gives

$$N = -12924 + 6867 \cdot 20 \approx 125{,}000, \quad \text{or about 0.05\% of the current population.}$$

Which function is the best predictor? This is an extremely hard question and one which cannot be answered by mathematics alone. An understanding of the processes leading to the data, in this case the nature of the disease and the behavior of the US population, is necessary in order to tackle such a question.

Problems for Section 3.8

1. (a) Complete the following table for $y = 3^x$.

TABLE 3.37

x	0	1	2	3	4	5
$y = 3^x$						

   (b) Construct a table of values for $y = \log(3^x)$.

TABLE 3.38

x	0	1	2	3	4	5
$y = \log(3^x)$						

   What kind of function is this?

   (c) Complete tables for $f(x) = 2 \cdot 5^x$ and $g(x) = \log(2 \cdot 5^x)$. What kinds of functions are these?

   (d) What seems to be true about a function which is the logarithm of an exponential function? Is this true in general?

2. Repeat part (b) and (c) of Problem 1 using the natural log function. Is your answers to part (a) still the same?

3. (a) Plot the following data.

TABLE 3.39

x	0.2	1.3	2.1	2.8	3.4	4.5
y	5.7	12.3	21.4	34.8	52.8	113.1

(b) What kind of function might the data from part (a) represent?
(c) Now plot $\log y$ versus x instead of y versus x. What do you notice?

4. An analog radio dial can be measured in millimeters from left to right. Although the scale of the dial can be different from radio to radio, Table 3.40 gives typical measurements. (Note that x is in millimeters.)

TABLE 3.40

x, millimeters	5	15	25	35	45	55
FM (MHz)	88	92	96	100	104	108
AM (kHz/10)	53	65	80	100	130	160

(a) Which radio band data appear linear? Graph and connect the data points for each band.
(b) Which radio band data appear exponential?
(c) Find a possible formula for the FM station number in terms of x.
(d) Find a possible formula for the AM station number in terms of x.

5. To study how recognition memory decreases with time, the following experiment was conducted. The subject read a list of 20 words slowly aloud, and later, at different time intervals, was shown a list of 40 words containing the 20 words that he or she had read. The percentage P of words recognized was recorded as a function of t, the time elapsed in minutes. Table 3.41 shows the averages for 5 different subjects.[6] This is modeled by $P = a \ln t + b$.

(a) Estimate a and b.
(b) Graph the data points and regression line on a coordinate system of P against $\ln t$.
(c) When does this model predict that the subjects will recognize no words? All words?
(d) Graph the data points and curve $P = a \ln t + b$ on a coordinate system with P against t, with $0 \le t \le 10,500$.

TABLE 3.41   *The percentage P of words recognized as a function of the time elapsed in minutes*

t	5	15	30	60	120	240	480	720	1440	2880	5760	10,080
P	73.0	61.7	58.3	55.7	50.3	46.7	40.3	38.3	29.0	24.0	18.7	10.3

[6]Adapted from "Quantitative Methods in Psychology" by D. Lewis, McGraw-Hill, New York, 1960.

6. A light, flashing regularly, consists of cycles, each cycle having a dark phase and a light phase. The frequency of this light is measured in cycles per second. As the frequency is increased, the eye initially perceives a series of flashes of light, then a coarse flicker, a fine flicker, and ultimately a steady light. The frequency at which the flickering disappears is called the *fusion frequency*.[7] Table 3.42 shows the results of an experiment[8] in which the fusion frequency F was measured as a function of the light intensity I. It is modeled by $F = a \ln I + b$.

TABLE 3.42 *The fusion frequency F as a function of the light intensity I*

I	0.8	1.9	4.4	10.0	21.4	48.4	92.5	218.7	437.3	980.0
F	8.0	12.1	15.2	18.5	21.7	25.3	28.3	31.9	35.2	38.2

(a) Estimate a and b.
(b) Plot F against $\ln t$, showing the data points and equation.
(c) Plot F against I, showing the data points, and give the regression graph of the equation.
(d) The units of I are described as arbitrary, that is, not given. If the units of I were changed, which of the constants a and b would be affected, and in what way?

7. Let x be the number of years since 1985 and y be the cost of US imports from China (in millions of dollars).

TABLE 3.43 *US total imports from China*

Year, x	1985	1986	1987	1988	1989	1990	1991
x (years since 1985)	0	1	2	3	4	5	6
Cost of imports, y (millions of dollars)	3862	4771	6293	8511	11,990	15,237	18,976

(a) Find a formula for a linear function $y = b + mx$ that approximates the data from Table 3.43.
(b) Find $\ln y$ for each y value, and use x and $\ln y$ values to find a formula for a linear function $\ln y = b + mx$ that approximates the data.
(c) Use the equation in part (b) to find an exponential function of the form $y = Ae^{kx}$ that fits the data.

8. Repeat Problem 7 with Table 3.44, this time approximating the percent share as a function of years since 1950.

TABLE 3.44 *Newspapers' share of all spending by national advertisers*

Year	1950	1960	1970	1980	1990	1992
x	0	10	20	30	40	42
Percent share, y	16.0	10.8	8.0	6.7	5.8	5.0

[7]"Experimental Psychology" by R. S. Woodworth, Holt and Company, New York, 1948.
[8]"Quantitative Methods in Psychology" by D. Lewis, McGraw-Hill, New York, 1960.

For the tables in Problem 9–11,

(a)   Use linear regression to find a linear function $y = b + mx$ that fits the data. Record the correlation coefficient.

(b)   Use linear regression on the values x and $\ln y$ to find a function $\ln y = b + mx$. Record the correlation coefficient. Translate the equation into an exponential function $y = Ae^{kx}$.

(c)   Use linear regression on the values $\ln x$ and $\ln y$ to find a function $\ln y = b + m \ln x$. Record the correlation coefficient. Translate the equation into a power function $y = ax^p$.

(d)   Compare the correlation coefficients to assess the best fit of the three functions.

9.

x	y
30	70
85	120
122	145
157	175
255	250
312	300

10.

x	y
8	23
17	150
23	496
26	860
32	2720
37	8051

11.

x	y
3.2	35
4.7	100
5.1	100
5.5	150
6.8	200
7.6	300

12.   A subject was given some objects and asked to judge their weights, where a 98 gram object was assigned the value of 100. Table 3.45 shows the result of such an experiment, where w is the physical weight of the object in grams, and J is the judged weight of the object.[9] This is an example of a "judgment of magnitude" experiment, which is modeled by the power law $J = aw^b$, where a and b are constants.

(a)   Estimate a and b.

(b)   What does the w-intercept suggest about the value implicitly assigned to an object with no weight?

(c)   Someone observes that the doubling of physical weight results in the judged weight being multiplied by 2.6. Is that an accurate observation?

TABLE 3.45   *The judged weight as a function of the physical weight*

Physical weight, w	19	33	46	63	74	98	136	212
Judged weight, J	10	25	35	60	90	100	150	280

13.   (a)   Find a linear function that fits the data in Table 3.46. How good is the fit?

(b)   The data in the table was generated using the power function $y = 5x^3$. Explain why (in this case) a linear function gives such a good fit to a power function. Does the fit remain good for other values of x?

TABLE 3.46

x	2.00	2.01	2.02	2.03	2.04	2.05
y	40.000	40.603	41.212	41.827	42.448	43.076

14.   On a piece of paper draw a straight line through the origin with slope 2 in the first quadrant.

(a)   If the horizontal axis is labeled x and the vertical axis is labeled y, what is the equation of the function represented by your straight line?

(b)   If the horizontal axis is labeled $\ln x$ and the vertical axis is labeled $\ln y$, what is the equation of the function represented by your straight line?

(c)   If the horizontal axis is labeled x and the vertical axis is labeled $\ln y$, what is the equation of the function represented by your straight line?

---

[9]"Elementary Theoretical Psychology" by J. G. Greeno, Addison-Wesley, Massachusetts, 1968.

15. In this problem, we will determine whether or not the compact disc data from Table 3.32 can be well modeled using a power function of the form $l = kc^p$, where l and c give the number of LPs and CDs (in millions) respectively, and where k and p are constant.

   (a) Based on the plot of the data given in Figure 3.41, what do you expect to be true about the sign of the power p?

   (b) Let $y = \ln l$ and $x = \ln c$. Find a linear formula for y in terms of x by making substitutions in the equation $l = kc^p$.

   (c) Transform the data in Table 3.32 to create a table comparing $x = \ln c$ and $y = \ln l$. What data point must necessarily be omitted?

   (d) Plot your transformed data from part (c). Based on your plot, is there a power function that gives a good fit to the data from Table 3.32? If so, find its formula; if not, explain why not.

REVIEW PROBLEMS FOR CHAPTER THREE

1. Decide whether the following functions (See Tables 3.47, 3.48, and 3.49) are approximately linear, exponential, or neither. For those that are nearly linear or exponential, find a possible formula.

Linear   exponential   neither

(a) **TABLE 3.47**   (b) **TABLE 3.48**   (c) **TABLE 3.49**

t	$Q(t)$
3	7.51
10	8.7
14	9.39

t	$R(t)$
5	2.32
9	2.61
15	3.12

t	$S(t)$
5	4.35
12	6.72
16	10.02

Figure 3.48

$20,000 \ (1.0414)^t$

2. In 1980, the population of a town was 20,000, and it grew by 4.14% that year. By 1990, the town's population had reached 30,000.

   (a) Can this town be best described by a linear or an exponential model, or neither? Explain.

   (b) If possible, find a formula for $P(t)$, this town's population t years after 1980. $P(t) = 20,000(1.04\ldots$

3. The populations of several different countries are graphed in Figure 3.48. Based on the graphs, answer the following questions.

   (a) Which population has the fastest constant annual growth rate? The slowest?

   (b) Which two countries seem to be growing at the same constant annual rate? C, E

   (c) Which population is initially ($t = 0$) the largest? The smallest?

   (d) Which population is growing faster and faster? D

   (e) Which population seems to be leveling off? F

   (f) Suppose the population (in millions) of country A is given by the formula $P = 11.5 + 1.2t$. Which of the following formulas could possibly describe the population of country D? (Assume all formulas are in millions.)

   (i) $P = 25 + 0.7t$ (ii) $P = 10 + 0.6t$ (iii) $P = 19.8 + 1.44t$

4. In 1980, the population of a town was 18,500 and it grew by 250 people by the end of the year. By 1990, its population had reached 22,500.

   (a) Can this town be best described by a linear or an exponential model, or neither? Explain.
   (b) If possible, find a formula for $P(t)$, this town's population t years after 1980.

5. The annual inflation rate r for a five-year period is given in Table 3.50.

   TABLE 3.50

t	1980	1981	1982	1983	1984
r	5.1%	6.2%	3.1%	4.7%	3.3%

   (a) By what total percent did prices rise between the start of 1980 and the end of 1984? $2\text{12}.5$
   (b) What is the average annual inflation rate for this time period? 4.5%
   (c) At the beginning of 1980, a shower curtain costs \$20. Make a prediction for the good's cost at the beginning of 1990, using the inflation factor.

6. Claverly Hall is invaded by 100 termites, and the population triples every two days.

   (a) If the population reaches 800,000, the building will be in danger of severe structural damage. How many days before this happens?
   (b) Suppose the building also becomes infested with 2,000 cockroaches. This cockroach population doubles every five days. If the population exceeds 32,000, the dorm will be condemned. If the exterminator can only address one problem at a time, which is more pressing?

7. If $f(x) = 12 + 20x$ and $g(x) = \dfrac{1}{2} \cdot 3^x$, for what values of x is $g(x) < f(x)$?

For Problems 8–10, find a formula for each exponential function graphed:

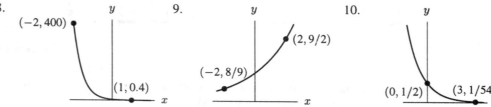

8. $(-2, 400)$ $(1, 0.4)$

9. $(2, 9/2)$ $(-2, 8/9)$

10. $(0, 1/2)$ $(3, 1/54)$

11. Suppose that f is an exponential function and that $f(2) = \frac{1}{27}$ and $f(-1) = 27$. Find a formula for $f(x)$.

12. Suppose f is an exponential function and that $f(-8) = 200$ and $f(30) = 580$. Find a possible formula for f.

13. One of the functions below is linear and the other is exponential. Find formulas for these functions.

    TABLE 3.51

x	0.21	0.37	0.41	0.62	0.68
$f(x)$	0.03193	0.04681	0.05053	0.07006	0.07564
$g(x)$	3.324896	3.423316	3.448373	3.582963	3.622373

14. Determine which of the functions given in Table 3.52 is linear and which is exponential. Write a formula for the linear and the exponential function.

TABLE 3.52

x	$f(x)$	$g(x)$	$h(x)$
-2	4	48	20/3
-1	1	12	16/3
0	0	3	4
1	1	3/4	8/3

15. In the Fibonacci sequence $1, 1, 2, 3, 5, 8 \ldots$, each term in the sequence is the sum of the two preceding terms. For example, the seventh term in this sequence is the sum of the sixth and fifth terms, $8 + 5 = 13$. Let $f(n)$ be the nth term in the Fibonacci sequence, for $n \geq 1$.

    (a) Complete Table 3.53 for the first twelve terms of Fibonacci's sequence:

    TABLE 3.53

n	1	2	3	4	5	6	7	8	9	10	11	12
$f(n)$	1	1	2	3	5							

    (b) Show that $f(n)$ is not an exponential function.
    (c) Show, by taking ratios, that for adequately large values of n, $f(n)$ seems to grow at roughly a constant percent rate.
    (d) Find an exponential function that approximates $f(n)$ for large values of n (say, $n > 5$).

16. Suppose a colony of bacteria is known to grow exponentially with time. At the end of 3 hours there are 10,000 bacteria. At the end of 5 hours there are 40,000. How many bacteria were present initially?

17. Suppose the constants u and v are defined by the equations $u = \log 2$, and $v = \log 5$.

    (a) Find possible formulas for the following expressions in terms of u and/or v. Your answers should not involve logs.
        (i) $\log(0.4)$ (ii) $\log 0.25$ (iii) $\log 40$ (iv) $\log \sqrt{10}$
    (b) Justify the following statement: $\log(7) \approx \frac{1}{2}(u + 2v)$.

18. Before the advent of computers, logarithms were calculated by hand. Various tricks were used to evaluate different logs. One such trick exploits the fact that $2^{10} \approx 1000$. (It actually equals 1024.) Using this fact and the log properties, show that
    (a) $\log(2) \approx 0.3$ (b) $\log(7) \approx 0.85$

19. Let $P = 15(1.04)^t$ give the population (in thousands) of a certain town, where t is in years.
    (a) Describe the population growth in words.
    (b) If the formula for P is written $P = 15(b)^{12t}$, find b exactly. What is the meaning of b in the context of the population?
    (c) If the formula for P is written $P = 15(2)^{t/c}$, find the value of c correct to 2 decimals. What is the meaning of c in this context?

20. The price P of a good is rising due to inflation. If $P(t) = 5(2)^{t/7}$, where t is the time in years.
    (a) What is the price doubling time?
    (b) What is the annual inflation rate (i.e., the annual percent increase in price)?

21.   A high-risk investment reports the following annual yields:

TABLE 3.54

t	1990	1991	1992	1993	1994
growth	27%	36%	19%	44%	57%

What is the average annual yield of this investment over the five-year period shown?

22.   Suppose $300 was deposited into one of five different bank accounts. Each of the equations below gives the balance of an account in dollars, as a function of the number of years elapsed, t. Following the equations are verbal descriptions of five different situations. For each situation, state which equation or equations could possibly describe it.

(a) $B = 300(1.2)^t$ (b) $B = 300(1.12)^t$ (c) $B = 300(1.06)^{2t}$
(d) $B = 300(1.06)^{t/2}$ (e) $B = 300(1.03)^{4t}$

(i)   This investment earned 12% annually, compounded annually.
(ii)   This investment earned, on average, more than 1% each month.
(iii)   This investment earned 12% annually, compounded semi-annually.
(iv)   This investment earned, on average, less than 3% each quarter.
(v)   This investment earned, on average, more than 6% every 6 months.

23.   If you look at the graph of $y = b^x$ for $b = 10$, $b = e$ and $b = 2$, you will see that none of these graphs cross the line $y = x$.

(a)   For $x > 0$, which graph comes closest to crossing the line $y = x$?
(b)   Experiment with lower values of b until you find the largest value that makes the two graphs $y = b^x$ and $y = x$ intersect. (Your answer will be approximate.)
(c)   Do you recognize the value of x at the intersection point of the graphs from part (b)? Can you use this fact to find the exact value of b?
(d)   Use the value of x from part (c) to guess the exact value of b. Check your guess against your answer to part (b). [Hint: if b is exact, then $y = b^x$ intersects $y = x$, so $b^x = x$.]

24.   Rewrite the following formulas as indicated.

(a)   If $f(x) = 5(1.121)^x$, find A and k such that $f(x) = Ae^{kx}$.
(b)   If $g(x) = 17e^{0.094x}$, find A and B such that $f(x) = AB^x$.
(c)   If $h(x) = 22(2)^{x/15}$, find A and B such that $h(x) = AB^x$, and A and k such that $h(x) = Ae^{kx}$.

25.   Solve the following equations. Give approximate solutions if exact ones can't be found.

(a) $e^{x+3} = 8$ (b) $4(1.12^x) = 5$ (c) $e^{-0.13x} = 4$
(d) $\log(x - 5) = 2$ (e) $2\ln(3x) + 5 = 8$ (f) $\ln x - \ln(x - 1) = 1/2$
(g) $e^x = 3x + 5$ (h) $3^x = x^3$ (i) $\ln x = -x^2$

26.   Solve for x exactly.

(a) $\dfrac{3^x}{5^{(x-1)}} = 2^{(x-1)}$ (b) $-3 + e^{x+1} = 2 + e^{x-2}$

(c) $\ln(2x - 2) - \ln(x - 1) = \ln x$ (d) $\dfrac{\ln(8x) - 2\ln(2x)}{\ln x} = 1$

(e) $\ln\left(\dfrac{e^{4x} + 3}{e}\right) = 1$ (f) $9^x - 7 \cdot 3^x = -6$

27. New-product sales often follow one of the following two patterns. Sales can start off slowly, then pick up as more people learn about the product, and finally level off as the market becomes saturated. Or, if the product has been highly anticipated, sales can start off rapidly and then level off. The *logistic function* $S = \dfrac{1}{k + ae^{-bt}}$ is often used to model sales following the first pattern; the *Gompertz function* $S = k \cdot a^{(b^t)}$ is often used to model sales following the second pattern.

    In these models, S is number of sales (in millions), t is time elapsed (in weeks), and a, b, and k are positive constants.

    (a) Graph the logistic function for $k = 0.2$, $a = 3$ and $b = 0.25$. Estimate from the graph when 1 million sales will be reached and the total sales expected.
    (b) Graph the Gompertz function for $k = 5$, $a = 0.1$ and $b = 0.8$. Estimate from the graph when 1 million sales will be reached and the total sales expected.

28. A certain bank pays interest at the nominal rate of 4.2% per year. The *annual percentage rate* (APR) is the actual percentage of principal paid in the course of one year.

    (a) Suppose interest is compounded annually. What is the APR?
    (b) Suppose interest is compounded monthly. What is the APR?
    (c) Suppose interest is compounded continuously. What is the APR?

29. (a) Let $B = 5000(1.06)^t$ give the balance of a bank account after t years. If the formula for B is written $B = 5000e^{kt}$, estimate the value of k correct to four decimal places. What is the meaning of k in financial terms?
    (b) The balance of a bank account after t years is given by the formula $B = 7500e^{0.072t}$. If the formula for B is written $B = 5000b^t$, find b exactly, and state the value of b correct to four decimal places. What is the meaning of b in financial terms?

30. Forty percent of a radioactive substance decays in five years. By what percent does the substance decay each year?

31. Each of the following functions describes a population P (in millions) in year t. Describe the populations in words. Give both the percent annual growth rates and the continuous annual growth rates.

    (a) $P(t) = 51(1.03)^t$ (b) $P(t) = 15e^{0.03t}$ (c) $P(t) = 7.5(0.94)^t$
    (d) $P(t) = 16e^{-0.051t}$ (e) $P(t) = 25(2)^{t/18}$ (f) $P(t) = 10(\tfrac{1}{2})^{t/25}$

32.

TABLE 3.55

x	0.21	0.55	1.31	3.22	5.15	12.48
y	-11	-2	6.5	16	20.5	29

    (a) Plot the data given by Table 3.55. What kind of function seems as though it might fit this data well?
    (b) Using the substitution $z = \ln x$, transform the data in Table 3.55, and compile your results into a new table. Plot the transformed data as $\ln x$ versus y.
    (c) What kind of function gives a good fit to the plot you made in part (b)? Find a formula for y in terms of z that fits the data well.
    (d) Using the formula from part (c), find a formula for y in terms of x that gives a good fit to the data in Table 3.55.
    (e) What does your formula from part (d) tell you about x as a function of y (as opposed to y as a function of x)?

33. If y and x are given by the graphs in Figure 3.49, find an equation giving y in terms of x.

(a)

(b)

(c)

(d)

(e)

(f)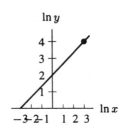

Figure 3.49

34. Table 3.56 shows the minimum wage from 1950 to 1991. In this problem you will fit the data with an exponential function of the form $f(t) = ae^{b(t-1950)}$.

TABLE 3.56 *Minimum wage*[10]

Year	1950	1956	1961	1963	1967	1968	1974	1975
New Wage	0.75	1.00	1.15	1.25	1.40	1.60	2.00	2.10

Year	1976	1978	1979	1980	1981	1990	1991	
New Wage	2.30	2.65	2.90	3.10	3.35	3.80	4.25	

(a) Using $t = 1950$ find the coefficient a. Notice the convenience of the shift $t - 1950$ from a standard equation $f(t) = ae^{bt}$.
(b) By trial and error find an acceptable b.
(c) By the year 2000, what is your prediction for the minimum wage?
(d) Hand draw a graph of the data as a step function. Why is this realistic?

35. Let $P(x) = P_0 a^x$ and $Q(x) = Q_0 b^x$ describe two different populations, where P_0, Q_0, a and b are positive constants not equal to 1.

(a) Solve the equation $P_0 a^x = Q_0 b^x$ for x.
(b) If $P_0 = Q_0$, and $a \neq b$, what does x equal? What does this tells you? Justify your answer graphically.
(c) If $P_0 \neq Q_0$, and $a = b$, what does x equal? What does this tell you? Justify your answer graphically.

[10]Source: The American Almanac, Table 658, 1992-1993

Chapter 4

Transformations of Functions

4.1 VERTICAL AND HORIZONTAL SHIFTS OF A FUNCTION'S GRAPH

In this chapter we will study certain kinds of transformations of functions, and we will consider the relationship between changes made to the graph of a function and changes made to its formula. For example, suppose we transform the graph of a function, $f(x)$, into a new function, $g(x)$, by shifting the graph of $f(x)$ vertically. How do we transform the formula for $f(x)$ to obtain the formula for $g(x)$? We will consider vertical and horizontal shifts, reflections, and stretches of the graphs of functions and the corresponding effect on their formulas.

An Example of a Horizontal Shift: The Heating Schedule For an Office Building

We start with an example of a horizontal shift in the context of the heating schedule for an office building.

Example 1   A graph showing temperature as a function of time in a certain office building is given by Figure 4.1. To save money, the building is kept warm only during business hours. Figure 4.1 shows $H = f(t)$, the building's temperature (in °F), t hours after midnight.

Figure 4.1: The heating schedule at an office building

Figure 4.2: The graph of the new heating schedule, $H = p(t)$, can be found by shifting the original schedule's graph 2 units to the left

Figure 4.1 shows that at midnight (time $t = 0$), the building's temperature is 50°F. This temperature is maintained until 4 am. Then the building begins to warm up steadily so that by 8 am the temperature reaches 70°F. The 70°F temperature is maintained until 4 pm, when the building gradually begins to cool. By 8 pm, the temperature is again 50°F.

Suppose that the building superintendent decides to change the heating schedule by starting it two hours earlier. Specifically, she wants to begin warming the building at 2 am instead of 4 am, to reach 70°F at 6 am instead of 8 am, to begin cooling off at 2 pm instead of 4 pm, and to reach 50°F at 6 pm instead of 8 pm. How would these changes affect the graph in Figure 4.1?

Figure 4.2 gives a graph of $H = p(t)$, the new heating schedule. Notice that this new graph can be obtained by shifting the graph of the original heating schedule, $H = f(t)$, two units to the left.

An Example of a Vertical Shift: The Heating Schedule Revisited

We have seen an example of a graph shifted horizontally. The next example involves shifting a graph vertically.

Example 2   Suppose the graph of f, the heating schedule function of Example 1, is shifted upward by 5 units. Sketch a graph of the resulting function. Describe in words how this shift would affect the building's heating schedule.

Solution   Figure 4.3 gives a graph of $H = q(t)$, the vertically shifted heating schedule. The heating schedule described by this graph is the same as the original schedule except that the building is always 5°F warmer than it was before. For example, its overnight temperature is 55°F instead of 50°F and its daytime temperature is 75°F instead of 70°F. The 5°F increase in temperature corresponds to the 5-unit vertical shift in the graph. In particular, notice that the *upward* shift resulted in a *warmer* temperature, whereas, in the previous example, the *leftward* shift resulted in an *earlier* schedule.

Figure 4.3: The result of shifting $H = f(t)$ upward by 5 units is $H = q(t)$

Finding a Formula to Represent a Vertical or Horizontal Shift

How does a horizontal or vertical shift of a function's graph affect its formula?

Example 3   In Example 2 we shifted the graph of the original heating schedule, $H = f(t)$, upward by 5 units; the result was the warmer heating schedule $H = q(t)$. How are the formulas for $f(t)$ and $q(t)$ related?

Solution   The temperature under the new schedule, $q(t)$, is always 5°F warmer than the temperature under the old schedule, $f(t)$. Thus, we can write the word equation

New temperature at time t = (Old temperature at time t) + 5.

We can rewrite this word equation algebraically:

$$\underbrace{q(t)}_{\substack{\text{new temperature} \\ \text{at time } t}} = \underbrace{f(t)}_{\substack{\text{old temperature} \\ \text{at time } t}} + 5.$$

The relationship between the formulas for q and f is given by the equation $q(t) = f(t) + 5$.

Although we determined in Example 3 that the relationship between f and q is $q(t) = f(t) + 5$, we do not have an explicit formula for f or for q. However, we do not need the specific formulas to glean information from the equation $q(t) = f(t) + 5$.

Suppose we need to know the office temperature at 6 am under the new heating schedule given by $q(t)$. We already know from the graph of $f(t)$ that the temperature under the old schedule at time $t = 6$ is $f(6) = 60$. Since we have an equation relating $q(t)$ and $f(t)$, we can plug in $t = 6$ to find $q(6)$, the temperature under the new schedule at 6 am:

$$q(6) = f(6) + 5.$$

Substituting $f(6) = 60$ gives

$$q(6) = 60 + 5 = 65.$$

Thus, at 6 am the temperature under the new schedule is 65°.

Example 4   Recall Example 1 in which the heating schedule was changed to 2 hours earlier, causing the graph to shift horizontally 2 units to the left. Find a formula for p, this new schedule, in terms of f, the original schedule.

Solution   If we hold the temperature constant and compare the time values, the old schedule will always reach a certain temperature 2 hours after the new schedule. For example, at 4 am the temperature under the new schedule reaches 60°. The temperature under the old schedule reaches 60° at 6 am, 2 hours later. The temperature reaches 65° at 5 am under the new schedule, but not until 7 am, 2 hours later, under the old schedule. In general, we see that

$$\text{Temperature under new schedule at time } t = \text{Temperature under old schedule at time } (t+2), \text{ two hours later.}$$

Expressing this word equation algebraically, we write

$$p(t) = f(t + 2).$$

This is a formula for p in terms of f.

Let's check our formula from Example 4 by using it to calculate $p(14)$, the temperature under the new schedule at 2 pm. We have

$$p(14) = f(14 + 2) \quad \text{(because } p(t) = f(t + 2)\text{)}$$
$$= f(16).$$

From Figure 4.1 we see that $f(16) = 70$. Since $p(14) = f(16)$, this means $p(14) = 70$. This agrees with the graph of $H = p(t)$ in Figure 4.2. The building reaches 70°F initially at 6 am with the new schedule and remains at 70°F until 2 pm, whereas the building reaches 70°F initially at 8 am with the old schedule and remains there until 4 pm.

Summary of Function Translations

In the last example, we studied both vertical and horizontal shifts, or *translations*, of the heating schedule function, f. We saw that

$$q(t) = f(t) + 5$$

is a vertically shifted version of f, representing a warmer schedule, whereas

$$p(t) = f(t + 2)$$

is a horizontally shifted version of f, representing an earlier schedule. Notice that by adding 5 to the temperature, or output value, $f(t)$, we shift its graph *up* five units. By adding 2 to the time, or input value, t, we shift its graph to the *left* two units. It makes sense that a change to the output of a function will result in a vertical change in the graph while a change to the input results in a horizontal change. This is because the output of a function is measured along the vertical axis, whereas the input of a function is measured along the horizontal axis. We can generalize these observations to any function g:

If $y = g(x)$ is a function and $|k|$ is a constant, then the graph of
- $y = g(x + k)$ is the graph of $y = g(x)$ shifted horizontally $|k|$ units. If k is positive, the shift is k units to the left; if k is negative, the shift is $|k|$ units to the right.
- $y = g(x) + k$ is the graph of $y = g(x)$ shifted vertically $|k|$ units. If k is positive, the shift is k units up; if k is negative, the shift is $|k|$ units down.

Note that a horizontal or vertical shift of the graph of a function does not change the shape of the graph, but simply translates it to another position in the plane. For the heating schedule function, the shape of the graph gives us information about the rate at which the building heats up or cools down, and this rate remains unchanged under vertical and horizontal shifts.

Inside and Outside Changes

Since $y = g(x + k)$ involves a change to the input value, x, we will call it an *inside change* to g. Similarly, since $y = g(x) + k$ involves a change to the output value, $g(x)$, we will call it an *outside change*. As we study other transformations we will see that, as with horizontal and vertical shifts, an inside change in a function results in a horizontal change in its graph, whereas an outside change in a function results in a vertical change in its graph.

Combining Horizontal and Vertical Shifts

We have seen what happens when we shift a function's graph either horizontally or vertically. What would happen if we shifted it both horizontally *and* vertically?

Example 5   Let $H = f(t)$ be the heating schedule function from Example 2. Let r be a transformation of f defined by the equation

$$r(t) = f(t - 2) - 5.$$

(a) Sketch the graph of $H = r(t)$.
(b) Describe in words the heating schedule determined by r.

Solution (a) To figure out what the graph of r looks like, we can break this transformation into two separate steps. First, we sketch a graph of $H = f(t - 2)$. This is an inside change to the function f and it results in the graph of f being shifted 2 units to the right. Next, we sketch a graph of $H = f(t - 2) - 5$. This graph can be found by shifting our sketch of $H = f(t - 2)$ down 5 units. The resulting graph is shown in Figure 4.4. Notice that the graph of r is shifted 2 units to the right and 5 units down from the graph of f.

Chapter 4/   5

Figure 4.4: The graph of $r(t) = f(t - 2) - 5$

(b)   The function r determines a schedule that is both 2 hours later and 5 degrees cooler than the schedule determined by f.

It is often possible to use our knowledge of function transformations to understand an unfamiliar function by relating it to a function we already know.

Example 6   Let f be defined by $f(x) = x^2$. A graph of $y = f(x)$ is given in Figure 4.5. Let g be the transformation defined by shifting f to the right 2 units and down 1 unit. The graph of g is shown in Figure 4.6. Find a formula for g in terms of f. Then, find a formula for g in terms of x.

Figure 4.5: The graph of $f(x) = x^2$

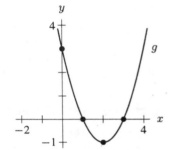

Figure 4.6: The graph of g, a transformation of f

Solution   Since the graph of g is the graph of f shifted to the right 2 units and down 1 unit, a formula for g is $g(x) = f(x - 2) - 1$. Now that we have a formula for g in terms of f, we need to find a formula for g in terms of x. Since $f(x) = x^2$, we have $f(x - 2) = (x - 2)^2$. Therefore,

$$g(x) = (x - 2)^2 - 1.$$

It is a good idea to check our result by graphing $g(x) = (x - 2)^2 - 1$ on a computer or graphing calculator and comparing it with Figure 4.6, or by checking some points on the graph. For example, Figure 4.6 shows that $g(2) = -1$. According to our formula,

$$g(2) = (2 - 2)^2 - 1 = -1,$$

which agrees with Figure 4.6.

Problems for Section 4.1

1. The function $H(t)$, graphed in Figure 4.1, gives the heating schedule of an office building during the winter months. $H(t)$ is the building's temperature in degrees Fahrenheit t hours after midnight.

    (a) Graph the function $H(t) - 2$. If the company decides to schedule its heating according to this function, what has it decided to do?

    (b) Graph the function $H(t - 2)$. If the company decides to schedule its heating according to this function, what has it decided to do?

    (c) When you get to work at 8 am, will the building be warmer under the $H(t)$ schedule, the $H(t) - 2$ schedule, or the $H(t - 2)$ schedule? What will the temperature be under that schedule?

    (d) Which schedule will save the company on heating costs, assuming that the hourly cost of heating depends only on the thermostat setting?

2. Complete Tables 4.1, 4.2, and 4.3 using the fact that $f(p) = p^2 + 2p - 3$, $g(p) = f(p + 2)$, and $h(p) = f(p - 2)$. Compare the graphs of the three functions using graphing technology. Explain your results.

TABLE 4.1

p	-3	-2	-1	0	1	2	3
$f(p)$							

TABLE 4.2

p	-3	-2	-1	0	1	2	3
$g(p)$							

TABLE 4.3

p	-3	-2	-1	0	1	2	3
$h(p)$							

3. The values for the function $f(x)$ are given in Table 4.4.

TABLE 4.4

x	-2	-1	0	1	2
$f(x)$	-3	0	2	1	-1

Complete Tables 4.5 to 4.8 where:

(a) $g(x) = f(x - 1)$

(b) $h(x) = f(x + 1)$

(c) $k(x) = f(x) + 3$

(d) $m(x) = f(x - 1) + 3$

TABLE 4.5

x	-1	0	1	2	3
$g(x)$	-3	0	2	1	-1

TABLE 4.6

x	-3	-2	-1	0	1
$h(x)$	-3	0	3	1	0

TABLE 4.7

x	-2	-1	0	1	2
$k(x)$	0	3	5	4	2

TABLE 4.8

x	-1	0	1	2	3
$m(x)$	0	3	5	4	2

Explain how the graph of each function compares to the graph of $y = f(x)$.

4. If $m(n) = \frac{1}{2}n^2$, sketch a graph of m. Then write the formula and sketch the graph of the following transformations.

(a) $y = m(n) + 1$ (b) $y = m(n + 1)$

(c) $y = m(n) - 3.7$ (d) $y = m(n - 3.7)$

(e) $y = m(n) + \sqrt{13}$ (f) $y = m(n + 2\sqrt{2})$

(g) $y = m(n + 3) + 7$ (h) $y = m(n - 17) - 159$

5. If $k(w) = 3^w$, write a formula and sketch a graph for the following transformations:

(a) $y = k(w) - 3$ (b) $y = k(w - 3)$

(c) $y = k(w) + 1.8$ (d) $y = k(w + \sqrt{5})$

(e) $y = k(w + 2.1) - 1.3$ (f) $y = k(w - 1.5) - 0.9$

6. Let $f(x) = \left(\frac{1}{3}\right)^x$, $g(x) = \left(\frac{1}{3}\right)^{x+4}$, and $h(x) = \left(\frac{1}{3}\right)^{x-2}$. How do the graphs of $g(x)$ and $h(x)$ compare to $f(x)$?

7. Match each graph with the corresponding formula.

(i) $y = |x|$ (ii) $y = |x| - 1.2$ (iii) $y = |x - 1.2|$

(iv) $y = |x| + 2.5$ (v) $y = |x + 3.4|$ (vi) $y = |x - 3| + 2.7$

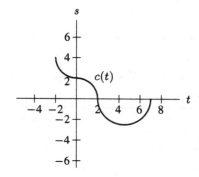

(a)   (b)   (c)

(d)   (e)   (f)

Figure 4.7

8. The graph in Figure 4.8 defines the function $s = c(t)$. Sketch graphs of the following transformations:

(a) $s = c(t) + 3$ (b) $s = c(t + 3)$

(c) $s = c(t) - 1.5$ (d) $s = c(t - 1.5)$

(e) $s = c(t - 2) + 2$ (f) $s = c(t + 0.5) - 3$

Figure 4.8

9. Sketch graphs of the following functions by treating them as transformations of $y = |x|$.

   (a) $g(x) = |x| + 1$ (b) $h(x) = |x + 1|$ (c) $j(x) = |x - 2| + 3$

10. The graph of $y = m(r)$ is given in Figure 4.9. The graph of each function in parts (a) – (d) resulted from translations of $y = m(r)$. Give a formula for each of these functions in terms of m.

Figure 4.9

(a)

(b)

(c)

(d)

Figure 4.10

11. Let $f(x) = 4^x$, $g(x) = 4^x + 2$, and $h(x) = 4^x - 3$. What is the relationship between the graph of $g(x)$ and the graphs of $h(x)$ and $f(x)$?

12. Suppose that the function $f(x)$ is given by the data in Table 4.9. Each of the functions in parts (a) – (c) can be obtained via translations of $f(x)$. Find formulas for these functions in terms of f. For example, if you were given the data in Table 4.10, you could say that $k(x) = f(x) + 1$.

TABLE 4.9

x	0	1	2	3	4	5	6	7
$f(x)$	0	0.5	2	4.5	8	12.5	18	24.5

TABLE 4.10

x	0	1	2	3	4	5	6	7
$k(x)$	1	1.5	3	5.5	9	13.5	19	25.5

(a)

$h(x) = f(x) - 2$

TABLE 4.11

x	0	1	2	3	4	5	6	7
$h(x)$	-2	-1.5	0	2.5	6	10.5	16	22.5

(b)

$g(x) = f(x+1)$

TABLE 4.12

x	0	1	2	3	4	5	6	7
$g(x)$	0.5	2	4.5	8	12.5	18	24.5	32

(c)

$i(x) = f(x+1) - 2$

TABLE 4.13

x	0	1	2	3	4	5	6	7
$i(x)$	-1.5	0	2.5	6	10.5	16	22.5	30

13. The function $g(t)$ is defined by Table 4.14.

TABLE 4.14

t	-2	-1.5	-1	-0.5	0	0.5	1	1.5	2
$g(t)$	-0.48	0	0.48	0.84	1.0	0.91	0.60	0.14	-0.35

Each of the functions in parts (a) – (e) can be obtained via translations of $g(x)$. Find formulas for these functions in terms of g.

(a)

t	-2	-1.5	-1	-0.5	0	0.5	1	1.5	2
$a(t)$	0.02	0.5	0.98	1.34	1.50	1.41	1.10	0.64	0.15

(b)

t	-2	-1.5	-1	-0.5	0	0.5	1	1.5	2
$b(t)$	0.84	1.0	0.91	0.60	0.14	-0.35	-0.76	-0.98	-0.96

(c)

t	-2	-1.5	-1	-0.5	0	0.5	1	1.5	2
$c(t)$	0.54	0.7	0.61	0.30	-0.16	-0.65	-1.06	-1.28	-1.26

(d)

t	-2	-1.5	-1	-0.5	0	.5	1	1.5	2
$d(t)$	1.32	-0.48	0	.48	.84	1	.91	.6	.14

(e)

t	-2	-1.5	-1	-0.5	0	0.5	1	1.5	2
$e(t)$	2.52	.72	1.2	1.68	2.04	2.20	2.11	1.80	1.34

14. If you start with the function $f(x) = 2^x$, describe the family of functions that you can obtain from $f(x)$ by

   (a) shifting horizontally,
   (b) shifting vertically,
   (c) shifting horizontally and vertically.

15. Suppose $S(d)$ gives the height of high tide in Seattle on a specific day, d, of the year. Use a shift of the function $S(d)$ to describe each of the following functions:

   (a) $T(d)$, the height of high tide in Tacoma on day d, given that high tide in Tacoma is always one foot higher than high tide in Seattle. $T(d) = S(d) + 1$
   (b) $P(d)$, the height of high tide in Portland on day d, given that high tide in Portland is the same height as high tide in Seattle on the previous day. $P(d) = S(d-1)$

16. Suppose $H(t)$ is a function which gives the temperature of a cup of coffee in degrees Fahrenheit, t minutes after it is brought to class. We are told that $H(t) = 68 + 93(0.91)^t$ for $t \geq 0$.

   (a) Find formulas for $H(t+15)$ and $H(t) + 15$.
   (b) Sketch graphs of $H(t)$, $H(t+15)$, and $H(t) + 15$ using a calculator or computer.
   (c) Describe in practical terms what situation might be modeled by the function $H(t+15)$. What about $H(t) + 15$?
   (d) Which function, $H(t+15)$ or $H(t) + 15$, approaches the same final temperature as the function $H(t)$? What is that temperature?

17. Suppose $T(d)$ gives the average temperature in your hometown on the dth day of last year (where $d = 1$ is January 1st, and so on).

   (a) Sketch a possible graph of $T(d)$ for $1 \leq d \leq 365$.
   (b) Give a possible value for each of the following: $T(6); T(100); T(215); T(371)$.
   (c) What is the relationship between $T(d)$ and $T(d + 365)$? Explain.
   (d) If you were to graph $w(d) = T(d + 365)$ on the same axes as $T(d)$, how would the two graphs compare?
   (e) Do you think the function $T(d) + 365$ has any practical significance? Explain.

18. A carpenter remodeling your kitchen quotes you a price based on the cost of labor and materials. Materials are subject to a sales tax of 8.2%. Labor is not taxed.

   (a) One option is based on a fixed labor cost of $800 and the variable cost of materials. The total cost $C(x)$ is given by $C(x) = 800 + x + 0.082x$ where x is the cost of materials in dollars. Later she says the job will actually cost $C(x) - 50$. Find a formula for $C(x) - 50$ and describe in practical terms what might have changed.
   (b) Another option has you pay a fixed amount of $1000 for the materials and the sales tax on them plus an hourly labor rate. This time, total cost $D(x)$ is given by $D(x) = 1000 + 15x$ where x is the number of hours to complete the job. Find $D(x) + 250$ and explain what this might mean in terms of the job.
   (c) Using the option from part (b), find a formula for $D(x - 8)$ and explain what this might suggest about the job.

19. At a local jazz club, the cost of an evening is based on a cover charge of $5 plus a beverage charge of $3 per drink.

   (a) If x is the number of drinks consumed and $t(x)$ is the total cost, write a formula for $t(x)$. $t(x) = 5 + 3x$
   (b) If the price of the cover charge is raised by $1, express the new total cost function $n(x)$ as a transformation of $t(x)$. $n(x) = t(x) + 1$

$P(x) = t(x-2)+5 \quad x \geq 2$

$P(x) = 10 \quad 0 \leq x < 2$

(c)   The management decides to increase the cover charge to $10, leave the price of a drink at $3, but include the first two drinks for free. Write a function for $x \geq 2$ that gives the new total cost $p(x)$. For $x \geq 2$, express $p(x)$ as a transformation of $t(x)$.

20.   You have a budget of $60 with which to buy soda and nuts for a party. Let s represent the number of six-packs of soda you buy, at $4 per six-pack, and n represent the number of cans of nuts, at $3 per can. Suppose you spend your entire $60 budget.

   (a)   Find a formula for n in terms of s.
   (b)   Sketch a graph of n versus s. Interpret the slope and both intercepts of your graph.
   (c)   Suppose your budget is increased to $72, find a new formula for n in terms of s and sketch its graph. What are the slope and intercepts of the new graph? Interpret the changes in common sense terms.
   (d)   Suppose you decided to buy a brand of soda costing $5 per six-pack instead of $4. If the cost of nuts stays the same and your budget is $60, how would the graph you made in part (b) change? What are the slope and intercepts of the new graph? Interpret the slope and intercepts in common sense terms.

21.   A hot brick is removed from a kiln and set on the floor to cool. According to a law devised by Isaac Newton, the difference, $D(t)$, between the brick's temperature and room temperature will decay exponentially over time. Suppose that the brick's temperature is initially 350°F, and that room temperature is 70°F. Suppose also that the temperature difference, $D(t)$, decays exponentially at the constant rate of 3% per minute. The function $H(t)$, the brick's temperature t minutes after being removed from the kiln, is a transformation of $D(t)$. Find a formula for $H(t)$. Compare the graphs of $D(t)$ and $H(t)$, paying attention to the asymptotes.

22.   If your total taxable income for one year is d dollars, let $I(d)$ be the federal income tax that you owe. For 1993, the value of $I(d)$ was given (approximately) by:

$$I(d) = \begin{cases} 0.15d & \text{if } 0 \leq d \leq 20{,}000 \\ 3000 + 0.28(d - 20{,}000) & \text{if } 20{,}000 < d \leq 49{,}000 \\ 11{,}120 + 0.31(d - 49{,}000) & \text{if } d > 49{,}000. \end{cases}$$

   (a)   Sketch a graph of $I(d)$.
   (b)   Suppose the Internal Revenue Service (IRS) suddenly declared that your new tax obligation was $I(d) + 200$. Sketch a graph of this new function. Explain how this changes your tax obligation.
   (c)   Suppose the IRS suddenly declared that your new tax obligation was $I(d+1000)$. Sketch a graph of this new function. Explain how this changes your tax obligation.
   (d)   If your taxable income were $15,000, would you prefer the $I(d) + 200$ system or the $I(d + 1000)$ system? Explain your reasoning.
   (e)   Would your answer to part (d) be different if your taxable income were $30,000?
   (f)   At what income level do the $I(d) + 200$ system and the $I(d + 1000)$ system produce the same tax obligation?

4.2 REFLECTIONS OF A FUNCTION'S GRAPH ACROSS AN AXIS

In Section 4.1 we saw that a horizontal shift of the graph of a function is represented in its formula by making an inside change, that is, by adding or subtracting a constant inside the function's parentheses. Similarly, a vertical shift of the graph corresponds to an outside change in the formula.

In this section we will consider the effect on the formula of reflecting a function's graph over the x or y-axis. A reflection over the x-axis is a vertical reflection, and a reflection over the y-axis is a horizontal reflection.

Finding a Formula to Represent a Reflection

Figure 4.11 shows the graph of a function $y = f(x)$ and Table 4.15 gives a table of values corresponding to some points on the graph. Note that we do not have an explicit formula for f; we do not need it here.

TABLE 4.15
Values of the function
$y = f(x)$

x	y
-3	1
-2	2
-1	4
0	8
1	16
2	32
3	64

Figure 4.11: A graph of the function $y = f(x)$

Figure 4.12 shows three graphs. The first is a graph of a function $y = g(x)$, resulting from a vertical reflection of the graph of f across the x-axis. The second is a graph of a function $y = h(x)$, resulting from a horizontal reflection of the graph of f across the y-axis. The third is a graph of a function $y = k(x)$, resulting from both a horizontal reflection of the graph of f across the y-axis and then a vertical reflection of the resulting graph across the x-axis.

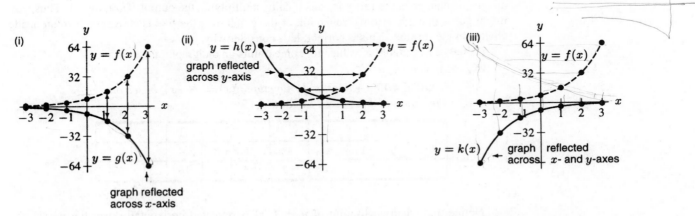

Figure 4.12: The graph of f after being reflected across (i) the x-axis, (ii) the y-axis, and (iii) the x- and y-axes

Example 1   (a)   Find a formula for $y = g(x)$ in terms of f.
       (b)   Find a formula for $y = h(x)$ in terms of f.
       (c)   Find a formula for $y = k(x)$ in terms of f.

Solution   (a)   The graph of the function $y = g(x)$ was obtained by reflecting the graph of f vertically across the x-axis. For example, consider the point $(3, 64)$ on the graph of f. This point reflects over the x-axis to become the point $(3, -64)$ on the graph of g. The point $(2, 32)$ on the graph of f becomes $(2, -32)$ on the graph of g. Table 4.16 is a table of values for some points on the graph of $y = g(x)$.

TABLE 4.16   *Values of the function $g(x) = -f(x)$, based on the values of $f(x)$ given by Table 4.15.*

x	-3	-2	-1	0	1	2	3
$g(x) = -f(x)$	-1	-2	-4	-8	-16	-32	-64
$f(x)$	1	2	4	8	16	32	64

Notice that when each point of $y = f(x)$ is reflected vertically over the x-axis, the x-value, or input value, stays fixed, while the y-value, or output value, changes sign. That is, for a given x-value,

the y-value of g is the opposite sign of the y-value of f.

Algebraically, this word equation can be written as

$$g(x) = -f(x).$$

For example, since $f(3) = 64$ and $g(3) = -64$, we have $g(3) = -f(3)$. And, since $f(2) = 32$ and $g(2) = -32$, we have $g(2) = -f(2)$.

The vertical reflection of the graph of f is accomplished by multiplying the output, $f(x)$, by -1. Multiplying the output value, or y-value, by -1 makes positive y-values negative and negative y-values positive, thus reflecting the entire graph over the x-axis.

    (b)   The graph of the function $y = h(x)$ was obtained by reflecting the graph of $y = f(x)$ horizontally across the y-axis. We saw in part (a) that a vertical reflection of the graph corresponds to an outside change in the formula, specifically, multiplying the output, $f(x)$, by -1. Thus, you might guess that a horizontal reflection of the graph over the y-axis corresponds to an inside change in the formula. This is correct; let's consider why.

Table 4.17 is a table of values for some points on the graph of $y = h(x)$.

TABLE 4.17   *Values of the function $h(x) = f(-x)$, based on the values of $f(x)$ given by Table 4.15.*

x	-3	-2	-1	0	1	2	3
$h(x) = f(-x)$	64	32	16	8	4	2	1
$f(x)$	1	2	4	8	16	32	64

Notice that when each point of $y = f(x)$ is reflected horizontally over the y-axis, the y-value, or output value, stays fixed, while the x-value, or input value, changes sign. For example, since $f(-3) = 1$ and $h(3) = 1$, we have $h(3) = f(-3)$. And, since $f(-1) = 4$ and $h(1) = 4$, we have $h(1) = f(-1)$. In general,

$$h(x) = f(-x).$$

Multiplying inside the function's parentheses, or the x-value, by -1 makes positive x-values negative and negative x-values positive, thus reflecting the entire graph over the y-axis.

(c)   The graph of the function $y = k(x)$ resulted from both a horizontal reflection of the graph of f across the y-axis and then a vertical reflection of the resulting function across the x-axis. Now we know that a horizontal reflection corresponds to multiplying the inputs by -1, and a vertical reflection corresponds to multiplying the outputs by -1. Thus,

vertical reflection over the x-axis
$$k(x) = -f(-x).$$
horizontal reflection over the y-axis

Let's check some points to see if this appears to work. For example, let $x = 1$. Then using our formula, $k(x) = -f(-x)$, gives:

$$k(1) = -f(-1) = -4 \quad \text{since } f(-1) = 4.$$

Our formula is consistent with the graph, since $(1, -4)$ is a point on the graph of $k(x)$. Let's check one more point, letting $x = -3$. Then

$$k(-3) = -f(-(-3)) = -f(3) = -64 \quad \text{since } f(3) = 64.$$

Again, $(-3, -64)$ is a point on the graph of k, so our formula is consistent with the graph. You can check for yourself that the rest of the points on the graph of k agree with our formula, $k(x) = -f(-x)$.

In general, if f is any function,
- the graph of $y = -f(x)$ is a reflection of the graph of $y = f(x)$ across the x-axis;
- the graph of $y = f(-x)$ is a reflection of the graph of $y = f(x)$ across the y-axis.

Symmetry of Graphs

Symmetry About the y-Axis

In Figure 4.13 we can see that the graph of $p(x) = x^2$ is *symmetric* about the y-axis. In other words, the part of the graph to the left of the y-axis is the mirror image of the part to the right of the y-axis. If we reflect the graph of $p(x)$ across the y-axis, we will simply obtain the graph of $p(x)$ again.

Figure 4.13: Reflecting the graph of $p(x) = x^2$ across the y-axis does not change its appearance

Symmetry about the y-axis is called even symmetry, because all power functions with even powers have this property. There are also many other functions that have even symmetry.

Since $y = p(-x)$ is a reflection of the graph of p across the y-axis we have,

$$p(x) = p(-x).$$

We can check this equation for a specific x-value. For example, let $x = 2$. Then $p(2) = 2^2 = 4$, and $p(-2) = (-2)^2 = 4$. Since $4 = 4$, we have $p(2) = p(-2)$. This means that, since the point $(2, 4)$ is on the graph of $p(x)$, its reflection over the y-axis, $(-2, 4)$, must also be on the graph of $p(x)$.

Example 2   For the function $p(x) = x^2$, verify algebraically that $p(x) = p(-x)$ for any x.

Solution   We substitute $-x$ into the formula for $p(x)$ giving

$$p(-x) = (-x)^2$$
$$= (-x) \cdot (-x)$$
$$= x^2$$
$$= p(x).$$

Thus, $p(x) = p(-x)$.

In general,

> If f is a function and if
> $$f(-x) = f(x)$$
> for all values of x in the domain of f, then f is called an **even function** and the graph of f is symmetric across the y-axis.

Symmetry About the Origin

Figures 4.14 and 4.15 show the graph of $q(x) = x^3$. If we reflect the graph of q first across the y-axis and then across the x-axis (or vice-versa), we obtain the graph of q again.

This kind of symmetry is called symmetry about the origin, and functions which are symmetric about the origin are called **odd functions**.

In the solution to part (c) of Example 1, we concluded that $y = -f(-x)$ is a reflection of the graph of $y = f(x)$ across both the y-axis and the x-axis. In our example, $q(x) = x^3$ is symmetric about the origin. Therefore, q is the same function as this double reflection. That is,

$$q(x) = -q(-x).$$

We can check this equation for a specific x-value. For example, let $x = 2$. Then $q(2) = 2^3 = 8$, and $-q(-2) = -(-2)^3 = -(-8) = 8$, so $q(2) = -q(-2)$. Since the point $(2, 8)$ is on the graph of q, this means that its reflection across the origin, $(-2, -8)$, must also be on the graph of q.

Figure 4.14: Reflecting the graph of $q(x) = x^3$ across the y-axis and then across the x-axis does not change its appearance.

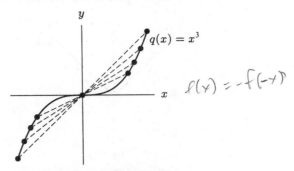

Figure 4.15: If every point on this graph is reflected across the origin, the resulting graph appears unchanged.

Example 3   For the function $q(x) = x^3$, verify algebraically that $q(x) = -q(-x)$ for all x.

Solution   We evaluate $-q(-x)$ giving

$$
\begin{aligned}
-q(-x) &= -1 \cdot q(-x) \\
&= -1 \cdot (-x)^3 \\
&= -1 \cdot (-x) \cdot (-x) \cdot (-x) \\
&= -1 \cdot (-x^3) \\
&= x^3 \\
&= q(x).
\end{aligned}
$$

Thus, $q(x) = -q(-x)$.

In general,

If f is a function and if

$$f(x) = -f(-x)$$

for all values of x in the domain of f, then f is called an **odd function** and the graph of f is symmetric across the origin.

Example 4   Formulas for three functions are given. Determine whether each function is symmetric across the y-axis, the origin, or neither.
   (a) $a(x) = |x|$ (b) $b(x) = \frac{1}{x}$ (c) $c(x) = -x^3 - 3x^2 + 2$

Solution   One way to identify the symmetry is to graph the functions, as we have done in Figures 4.16, 4.17, and 4.18.

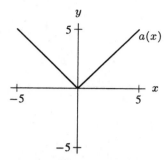

Figure 4.16: The graph of $a(x) = |x|$ appears to be symmetric about the y-axis

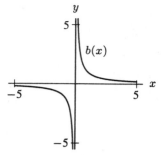

Figure 4.17: The graph of $b(x) = \frac{1}{x}$ appears to be symmetric about the origin

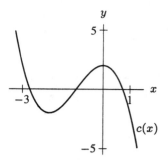

Figure 4.18: The graph of $c(x) = -x^3 - 3x^2 + 2$ is symmetric neither about the y-axis nor the origin

From the graphs it appears that a is symmetric about the y-axis (even symmetry), b is symmetric about the origin (odd symmetry), and c has neither type of symmetry. However, how can we be sure that $a(x)$ and $b(x)$ are symmetric and not just close in appearance? We should check algebraically.

If a has even symmetry, then the equation $a(x) = a(-x)$ must hold. Let's check the formula:

$$a(-x) = |-x| \quad \text{(plugging } -x \text{ in for } x\text{)}$$
$$= |x|$$
$$= a(x).$$

Thus, a does have even symmetry as we predicted.

If b is symmetric about the origin, then the equation $b(x) = -b(-x)$ must hold. We see that

$$-b(-x) = -\left(\frac{1}{-x}\right)$$
$$= \frac{1}{x}$$
$$= b(x).$$

Thus, b is symmetric about the origin as we predicted.

We can see from the graph that c does not exhibit odd or even symmetry. Using its formula, we can give a counterexample to verify that c does not have odd or even symmetry. A counterexample is a specific example that shows a claim is false. First, evaluate $c(x)$ for a particular x-value, say $x = 1$:

$$c(x) = c(1) = -1^3 - 3 \cdot 1^2 + 2 = -2.$$

Now if $x = 1$, then $-x = -1$, so

$$c(-x) = c(-1) = -(-1)^3 - 3 \cdot (-1)^2 + 2 = 0.$$

Thus $c(x) \neq c(-x)$, so the function is not symmetric about the y-axis. Also, $c(x) \neq -c(-x)$, so the function is not symmetric about the origin.

Chapter 4/ 18

Combining Shifts and Reflections

We can combine the horizontal and vertical shift transformations from Section 4.1 with the horizontal and vertical reflections of this section.

Example 5   A frozen yam is placed in a hot oven. According to Newton's Law of Cooling, the difference between the yam's temperature and the oven's temperature can be modeled by an exponential decay function. If the yam's temperature is initially 0°F, and if the oven's temperature is a constant 300°F, find a formula for $Y(t)$, the yam's temperature at time t, provided that the temperature difference decreases by 3% per minute.

Solution   Let d be the difference between the oven's temperature and the yam's temperature. The temperature difference decays exponentially over time at a rate of 3% per minute. This means that d is an exponential function given by $d(t) = AB^t$. Since the difference in temperatures is initially 300°F − 0°F = 300°F, we know that $A = 300$. Since the temperature difference goes down by 3% per minute, this means that $B = 1 - 0.03 = 0.97$. Thus, a formula for d is

$$d(t) = 300(0.97)^t.$$

Figure 4.19 shows a graph of the temperature difference function, $Y = d(t)$.

The yam's temperature is given by the oven temperature minus the temperature difference, so

$$Y(t) = 300 - d(t),$$

so using $d(t)$ from above,

$$Y(t) = 300 - 300(0.97)^t.$$

If we write

$$Y(t) = \underbrace{-d(t)}_{\text{flip}} + \underbrace{300}_{\text{shift}},$$

we see that the graph of Y can be obtained by first reflecting the graph of d across the t-axis and then shifting it vertically up 300 units. Notice that the horizontal asymptote of d, which is on the t-axis, is also shifted upward, resulting in the asymptote at $T = 300$ for Y.

Figures 4.19 and 4.20 give the graphs of d and Y. As you can see in Figure 4.20, the yam heats up rapidly at first and then its temperature levels off toward 300°F, the oven temperature. This is indicated by the horizontal asymptote $T = 300$ on the graph of Y.

Figure 4.19: The graph of $d(t) = 300(0.97)^t$, the temperature difference between the yam and the oven

Figure 4.20: The graph of $Y(t) = -300(0.97)^t + 300$ is a transformation of $d(t) = 300(0.97)^t$

Note: The temperature difference function, d, is a decreasing function, so its average rate of change is negative. However, Y, the yam's temperature function, is an increasing function, so its average rate of change is positive. Reflecting of the graph of d over the t-axis to obtain the graph of Y altered the average rate of change.

Problems for Section 4.2

1. Complete Tables 4.18, 4.19, and 4.20 using the fact that $y = f(p) = p^2 + 2p - 3$, $y = g(p) = f(-p)$, and $y = h(p) = -f(p)$. Using graphing technology, compare the graphs of the three functions. Explain your results.

TABLE 4.18

p	−3	−2	−1	0	1	2	3
$f(p)$							

TABLE 4.19

p	−3	−2	−1	0	1	2	3
$g(p)$							

TABLE 4.20

p	−3	−2	−1	0	1	2	3
$h(p)$							

2. If $m(n) = n^2 - 4n + 5$, sketch a graph of m. Then give a formula and graph for each of the following transformations of m.

   (a) $y = m(-n)$ (b) $y = -m(n)$ (c) $y = -m(-n)$
   (d) $y = -m(n + 2)$ (e) $y = m(-n) - 4$ (f) $y = -m(-n) + 3$
   (g) $y = 1 - m(n)$

3. If $k(w) = 3^w$, sketch a graph of k. Then give a formula and graph for each of the following transformations of k.

   (a) $y = k(-w)$ (b) $y = -k(w)$ (c) $y = -k(-w)$
   (d) $y = -k(w - 2)$ (e) $y = k(-w) + 4$ (f) $y = -k(-w) - 1$
   (g) $y = -3 - k(w)$

4. Figure 4.21 shows the graph of a function $y = f(x)$.

Figure 4.21: $y = f(x)$

Match each graph with the corresponding formula.

(i) $y = f(-x)$ (ii) $y = -f(x)$ (iii) $y = f(-x) + 3$

(iv) $y = -f(x - 1)$ (v) $y = -f(-x)$ (vi) $y = -2 - f(x)$

(a)

(b)

(c)

(d)

(e)

(f)

Figure 4.22

5. Below is the graph of $y = f(x) = 3 \cdot 2^x$ (Figure 4.23). Sketch a graph of:

(a) $y = f(-x)$ (b) $y = -f(x)$ (c) $y = 4 - f(-x)$

Figure 4.23

Figure 4.24

6. Given the graph of $y = f(x)$ in Figure 4.24, graph the following transformations on separate axes.

(a) $y = f(x) - 2$ (b) $y = f(x - 2)$ (c) $y = -f(x)$ (d) $y = f(-x)$

7. Sketch the graphs of $y = f(x) = 4^x$ and $y = f(-x)$ on the same set of axes. How are these graphs related? Give an explicit formula for $y = f(-x)$.

8. Sketch the graphs of $y = g(x) = \left(\frac{1}{3}\right)^x$ and $y = -g(x)$ on the same set of axes. How are these graphs related? Give an explicit formula for $y = -g(x)$.

9. (a) If $f(x) = \sqrt{4 - x^2}$, find a formula for $f(-x)$.
   (b) Graph $y = f(x)$, $y = f(-x)$ and $y = -f(x)$ on the same axes.
   (c) Is the function $f(x) = \sqrt{4 - x^2}$ even, odd, or neither?

10. (a) If $g(x) = \sqrt[3]{x}$, find a formula for $g(-x)$.
    (b) Graph $y = g(x)$, $y = g(-x)$, and $y = -g(x)$ on the same axes.
    (c) Is $g(x) = \sqrt[3]{x}$ even, odd, or neither?

11. Let $g(x) = 3(2)^x$. Write a paragraph that compares the graph of $y = g(x)$ to the graphs of $y = -g(x)$, $y = g(-x)$, and $y = -g(-x)$.

12. Let f be defined by the graph in Figure 4.25. Find formulas (in terms of f) for the following transformations of f and sketch a graph of each. Show that these transformations lead to different outcomes.

(a) First shift the graph of f upward by 3 units, then reflect it across the x-axis.

(b) First reflect the graph of f across the x-axis. Then, shift it upward by 3 units.

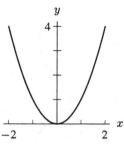

Figure 4.25: The graph of
$y = f(x)$

13. Let $f(x) = x^3$.

(a) Sketch the graph of the function obtained from f by first reflecting about the x-axis, then translating up two units. Write a formula for the resulting function.

(b) Sketch the graph of the function obtained from f by first translating up two units, then reflecting about x-axis. Write a formula for the resulting function.

(c) Are the functions you found in parts (a) and (b) the same?

14. Let $g(x) = 2^x$.

(a) Sketch the graph of the function obtained from g by first reflecting about the y-axis, then translating down three units. Write a formula for the resulting function.

(b) Sketch the graph of the function obtained from g by first translating down three units, then reflecting about y-axis. Write a formula for the resulting function.

(c) Are the functions you found in parts (a) and (b) the same?

15. The functions graphed in Figure 4.26 are transformations of some basic functions that were introduced in Chapter 1. Give a possible formula for each one.

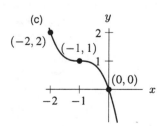

Figure 4.26

16. The function $d(t)$ in Figure 4.27 gives the winter temperature in degrees Fahrenheit, at Newton H.S., t hours after midnight.

Figure 4.27

(a) Describe the heating schedule for this building during the winter months.
(b) Sketch a graph of $c(t) = 142 - d(t)$.
(c) Explain why c might describe the cooling schedule for summer months.

17. On the graph in Figure 4.28, the value c is labeled on the x-axis. Locate the following quantities on the y-axis:

   (a) $f(c)$ (b) $f(-c)$ (c) $-f(c)$

Figure 4.28

18. Consider the formula for the force exerted by an electric charge Q on a moving charge q,

$$F = qQr^{-2},$$

where r is the distance between the charges q and Q.
Suppose that the fixed positive charge $Q = +1$ is located at $x = 0$ on a number line.

   (a) A charge $q = +1$ moves along the positive half of the number line, so its position is given by x, where $x > 0$. Write a formula for the force F as a function of x, $F = R(x)$. Sketch a graph of $R(x)$.
   (b) A charge $q = +1$ moves along the negative half of the number line, so its position is given by x, where $x < 0$. Write a formula for the force F as a function of x, $F = L(x)$. Sketch a graph of $L(x)$.
   (c) Compare the graphs of $R(x)$ and $L(x)$. Can you express $L(x)$ as a transformation of $R(x)$?

19. Consider the following table of values for a function $y = f(x)$:

   TABLE 4.21

x	-3	-2	-1	0	1	2	3
y	-5		$+4$			$+8$	

   (a) Fill in as many y-values as you can if you know that f is an even function.
   (b) Fill in as many y-values as you can if you know that f is an odd function.

20. Are the following functions even, odd, or neither?

(a) $m(x) = \dfrac{1}{x^2}$

(b) $n(x) = x^3 + x$

(c) $p(x) = x^2 + 2x$

(d) $q(x) = 2^{x+1}$

21. For each table decide whether the function is symmetric about the y-axis, across the origin, or neither.

(a)

TABLE 4.22

x	-4	-3	-2	-1	0	1	2	3	4
$f(x)$	13	6	1	-2	-3	-2	1	6	13

(b)

TABLE 4.23

x	-4	-3	-2	-1	0	1	2	3	4
$g(x)$	-19.2	-8.1	-2.4	-0.3	0	0.3	2.4	8.1	19.2

(c)

TABLE 4.24

x	-4	-3	-2	-1	0	1	2	3	4
$f(x) + g(x)$	-6.2	-2.1	-1.4	-2.3	-3	-1.7	3.4	14.1	32.2

(d)

TABLE 4.25

x	-4	-3	-2	-1	0	1	2	3	4
$f(x+1)$	6	1	-2	-3	-2	1	6	13	22

22. A function is called symmetric across the line $y = x$ if interchanging x and y gives the same graph. The simplest example is the function $y = x$. Sketch the graph of another straight line that is symmetric across the line $y = x$. What is its equation?

23. Figure 4.29 shows the graph of a function f in the second quadrant. Sketch the graphs of $y = f(x)$ if you are given the following information.

Figure 4.29: The graph of $f(x)$ in the second quadrant

(a) f is symmetric across the y-axis.

(b) f is symmetric across the origin.

(c) f is symmetric across the line $y = x$.

24. Comment on the following justification that the function $f(x) = x^3 - x^2 + 1$ is an odd function: For a function to be odd we need $f(x) = -f(-x)$. With $x = 1$ we find $f(1) = 1^3 - 1^2 + 1 = 1$. With $x = -1$ we find $f(-1) = (-1)^3 - (-1)^2 + 1 = -1$. So $f(1) = -f(-1)$ and the function is odd.

25. Comment on the following justification that the function $f(x) = x^3 - x^2 + 1$ is an even function:

    Because $f(0) = 1 \neq -f(0)$, we know that $f(x)$ is not odd. If a function is not odd, it must be even.

26. Is it possible to for an odd function which is defined on the domain of all real numbers to be strictly concave up?

27. If f is an odd function and defined at $x = 0$, what is the value of $f(0)$? Explain how you can use this result to show that the following functions are not odd. *odd func. has to go through origin*
    (a) $c(x) = x + 1$ *Not odd* $c(x) = x + 1$ $c(0) = 1$ $(0, 0)$
    (b) $d(x) = 2^x$ *not odd*

    If f is odd and if f is defined at 0, then f(0) = 0

28. In the first quadrant a given even function is increasing and concave down. What can you say about the function's behavior in the second quadrant?

29. Show that the power function $f(x) = x^{1/3}$ is an odd function. Give a counterexample to the statement that all power functions are odd.

30. Using graphing technology, graph the functions $s(x) = 2^x + (\frac{1}{2})^x$, $c(x) = 2^x - (\frac{1}{2})^x$, and $n(x) = 2^x - (\frac{1}{2})^{x-1}$. State whether you think these functions are even, odd or neither. Show that your statements are true using algebra. That is, prove or disprove statements such as $s(x) = s(-x)$.

31. Consider $f(x) = b + mx$.
    (a) Can $f(x)$ be even? How?   (b) Can $f(x)$ be odd? How?
    (c) Can $f(x)$ be both odd and even?

32. There are functions which are *neither* even nor odd. Is there a function that is *both* even and odd?

33. Some functions are symmetric across the y-axis. Is it possible for a function to be symmetric across the x-axis?

4.3 VERTICAL STRETCHES OF A FUNCTION'S GRAPH

The Effect of a Vertical Stretch or Compression on a Function's Formula

We have studied vertical and horizontal translations and reflections of the graphs of functions and the resulting effects on their formulas. In this section we will consider vertical stretches and compressions of graphs. As was the case with vertical translations, we will see that vertical stretches and compressions are represented by outside changes to the formulas.

Example 1   A stereo amplifier can take a weak signal from a cassette-tape deck, compact disc player, or radio tuner, and transform it into a much stronger signal suitable for powering a set of stereo speakers.

Figure 4.30 shows a graph of a typical radio signal (measured in volts) as a function of time, t, both before and after amplification. In this illustration, the amplifier has boosted the strength of the original signal by a factor of 3. (The amount of amplification, or *gain*, of most stereos is considerably greater than this.)

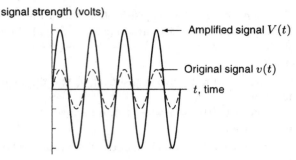

signal strength (volts)

Figure 4.30: A stereo amplifier can transform a weak signal into a stronger signal

Notice that in Figure 4.30, the wave crests of the amplified signal are 3 times as high as those of the original signal; similarly, the amplified wave troughs are 3 times deeper than the original wave troughs.

If we let v be the original signal function, and V be the amplified signal function, then since

$$\underbrace{\text{Amplified signal strength at time } t}_{V(t)} = 3 \cdot \underbrace{\text{Original signal strength at time } t,}_{v(t)}$$

we have

$$V(t) = 3 \cdot v(t).$$

This formula tells us that values of the amplified signal function can be found by multiplying values of the original signal function by 3. Notice that we did not need to have a formula for v in order to obtain this result.

Notice from Figure 4.30 that the graph of V, the amplified signal function, is a vertically "stretched" version of the graph of v, the original signal function. In general,

---

If f is any function and if k is a positive constant, then the graph of $y = k \cdot f(x)$ is
- a vertically stretched version of the graph of $y = f(x)$, for $k > 1$,
- a vertically compressed version of the graph of $y = f(x)$, for $0 < k < 1$.

We refer to k as the **stretch factor** of f.

As we expected, a vertical stretch of the graph of $v(t)$ corresponds to an outside change to the formula. Specifically, the output value in this example, $v(t)$, is multiplied by 3. This means that all v-values are multiplied by 3, causing the graph to stretch vertically, away from the t-axis. The t-intercepts remain fixed under a vertical stretch, because the v-value of these points is 0, which is unchanged when multiplied by 3.

Example 2 A yam is placed in a 300°F oven. Table 4.26 gives values of $T = r(t)$, the yam's temperature t minutes after being placed in the oven. These data have been plotted in Figure 4.31, and a curve has been drawn in to emphasize the trend.

TABLE 4.26   *The temperature of a yam*

t, time (minutes)	$r(t)$, temperature (°F)
0	0
10	150
20	225
30	263
40	281
50	291
60	295

Figure 4.31: The temperature of a yam at time t

(a) Describe the function r in words. What do the data indicate about changes in the yam's temperature?

(b) Prepare a table of values for $p(t) = \frac{1}{2}r(t)$. Sketch a graph of this new function. Under what conditions might p describe the yam's temperature?

(c) Prepare a table of values for $q(t) = 1.5r(t)$. Sketch a graph of this new function. Under what conditions might q describe the yam's temperature?

Solution   (a) The function r is increasing and concave down. The yam starts out at 0°F and at first warms up very quickly, reaching 150°F after only 10 minutes. Although it continues heating up, it does so more and more slowly, climbing by 75°F in the next 10 minutes and by only 38°F in the 10 minutes after that. The temperature levels off around 300°F, the oven's temperature. The horizontal asymptote in Figure 4.31 indicates that the yam's temperature will approach, but not reach, this temperature.

(b) We can use the table of values for $r(t)$ to prepare a table of values for $p(t)$. For example, from Table 4.26, we see that $r(0) = 0$. Since $p(t) = \frac{1}{2}r(t)$, this means that

$$p(0) = \frac{1}{2}r(0)$$
$$= \frac{1}{2} \cdot 0$$
$$= 0.$$

Similarly, from Table 4.26 we see that $r(10) = 150$ (so $p(10) = 75$) and that $r(20) = 225$ (so $p(20) = 112.5$). Table 4.27 gives values of $p(t)$ for $t = 0, 10, \ldots, 60$. The values for $p(t)$ in Table 4.27 are exactly half the corresponding values for $r(t)$ in Table 4.26.

TABLE 4.27   *Values of* $p(t) = \frac{1}{2}r(t)$

t, time (minutes)	0	10	20	30	40	50	60
$p(t)$, temperature (°F)	0	75	112.5	131.5	140.5	145.5	147.5

The data in Table 4.27 have been plotted in Figure 4.32 along with a curve containing the data points. Notice that because the stretch factor $k = 1/2$ is less than 1, the graph of p is a vertically compressed version of the graph of r. While the horizontal asymptote of r was

$T = 300$, the horizontal asymptote of p is $T = 1/2 \cdot 300 = 150$. Now, the yam's temperature is approaching 150°F, suggesting that the yam has been placed in a 150°F oven, instead of a 300°F oven.

Figure 4.32: A graph of $p(t) = \frac{1}{2}r(t)$

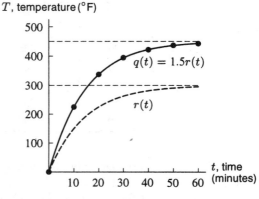

Figure 4.33: A graph of $q(t) = 1.5r(t)$

(c)   We can calculate values of $q(t)$ in much the same way that we calculated values of $p(t)$. For example, from Table 4.26, we know that $r(0) = 0, r(10) = 150$, and $r(20) = 225$. Thus,

$$q(0) = 1.5r(0)$$
$$= 1.5 \cdot 0$$
$$= 0.$$

Similarly, $q(10) = 1.5(150) = 225$ and $q(20) = 1.5(225) = 337.5$. Table 4.28 gives values of $q(t)$ for $t = 0, 10, \dots, 60$. The values for $q(t)$ are 1.5 times as large as the values for $r(t)$ given by Table 4.26.

TABLE 4.28   *Values of $q(t) = 1.5r(t)$*

t, time (minutes)	0	10	20	30	40	50	60
$q(t)$, temperature (°F)	0	225	337.5	394.5	421.5	436.5	442.5

The data in Table 4.28 have been plotted in Figure 4.33 and a curve has been drawn in. The graph of q is a vertically stretched version of the graph of r, because the stretch factor of $k = 1.5$ is larger than 1. While the horizontal asymptote of r was $T = 300$, the horizontal asymptote of q is $T = 1.5 \cdot 300 = 450$. This suggests that the yam has been placed in a 450°F oven instead of a 300°F oven.

Stretch Factors and Rates of Change

Consider again the graph of the radio signal and its amplification in Figure 4.30. Notice that the amplified signal, V, is increasing on the same intervals as the original signal, v. Similarly, both functions decrease on the same intervals. Stretching or compressing a function vertically does not change the intervals on which the function increases or decreases.

However, the average rate of change of a function, visible in the steepness of the graph, is altered by a vertical stretch or compression.

Example 3   In Example 2 on page 220, the function $T = r(t)$ describes the temperature (in °F) of a yam placed in a 300°F oven. We saw that the function $p(t) = \frac{1}{2}r(t)$ describes the temperature of the yam if it is placed in a 150°F oven, and that $q(t) = 1.5r(t)$ describes the temperature of the yam if it is placed in a 450°F oven.

(a)   Calculate the average rate of change of r on 10-minute intervals. What does this tell you about the yam's temperature?

(b)   Now calculate the average rate of change of p and q on 10-minute intervals. What does this tell you about the yam's temperature?

Solution   (a)   On the first interval, from $t = 0$ to $t = 10$, we have

$$\begin{aligned} \text{Average rate of change of } r = \frac{\Delta T}{\Delta t} &= \frac{r(10) - r(0)}{10 - 0} \\ &= \frac{150 - 0}{10} \quad \text{(referring to Table 4.26)} \\ &= 15. \end{aligned}$$

Thus, during the first 10 minute interval, the average rate of increase in the yam's temperature was 15°F per minute.

On the second time interval, from time $t = 10$ to $t = 20$, the average rate of increase in temperature was

$$\frac{\Delta T}{\Delta t} = \frac{225 - 150}{10} = 7.5°\text{F/min},$$

and on the third interval, from $t = 20$ to $t = 30$, it was

$$\frac{\Delta T}{\Delta t} = \frac{263 - 225}{10} = 3.8°\text{F/min}.$$

Table 4.29 gives values of the average rate of change of r on each 10 minute interval.

TABLE 4.29   *The average rate of change of r (in °F per minute)*

time interval	0 − 10	10 − 20	20 − 30	30 − 40	40 − 50	50 − 60
average rate of change of r	15	7.5	3.8	1.8	1.0	0.4

(b)   We can use the data in Tables 4.27 and 4.28 to calculate the average rate of change of $p(t) = \frac{1}{2}r(t)$ and $q(t) = 1.5r(t)$. This has been done in Table 4.30.

TABLE 4.30   *The average rate of change of p and q*

time interval	0 − 10	10 − 20	20 − 30	30 − 40	40 − 50	50 − 60
average rate of change of p	7.5	3.75	1.9	0.9	0.5	0.2
average rate of change of q	22.5	11.25	5.7	2.7	1.5	0.6

If you compare the average rates of change on each 10 minute interval, you can see that p's average rate of change is 1/2 times r's, and q's average rate of change is 1.5 times r's. Thus, p depicts a yam whose temperature increases more slowly than r does, and q depicts a yam whose temperature increases more quickly than r does.

From the last example, we see that multiplying a function by a positive stretch factor k has the effect of multiplying the function's average rate of change on a given interval by the same factor. We can verify this statement algebraically. Suppose that f is a function and that $g(x) = k \cdot f(x)$ for $k > 0$. The average rate of change of $y = g(x)$ on the interval from a to b is given by

$$\frac{\Delta y}{\Delta x} = \frac{g(b) - g(a)}{b - a}.$$

But $g(b) = k \cdot f(b)$ and $g(a) = k \cdot f(a)$. Thus, the average rate of change of $y = g(x)$ can be written as

$$\frac{\Delta y}{\Delta x} = \frac{k \cdot f(b) - k \cdot f(a)}{b - a}$$

$$= k \cdot \frac{f(b) - f(a)}{b - a} \quad \text{(factoring out } k\text{)}$$

$$= k \cdot \left(\begin{array}{c} \text{average rate of change} \\ \text{of } f \text{ from } a \text{ to } b \end{array} \right).$$

In general,

If f is a function and k a stretch factor, then the average rate of change of g, where $g(x) = k \cdot f(x)$ on any interval is given by

$$\begin{array}{c} \text{Average rate of} \\ \text{change of } g \end{array} = k \cdot \begin{array}{c} \text{average rate of} \\ \text{change of } f \end{array}.$$

Negative Stretch Factors

We have seen what happens when we multiply a function by a positive stretch factor, k. But what happens if we multiply a function by a negative stretch factor?

Figure 4.34 gives a graph of a function $y = f(x)$, together with a graph of $y = -2 \cdot f(x)$. The stretch factor of f is $k = -2$. Notice that we can write

$$y = -2f(x)$$
$$= 2 \cdot (-f(x)).$$

This tells us that we can think of $y = -2f(x)$ as a combination of two separate transformations of $y = f(x)$: First, it has been reflected across the x-axis, and second, it has been stretched by a factor of 2 away from the x-axis.

Figure 4.34: The graph of $y = -2f(x)$ is a vertically stretched version of the graph of $y = f(x)$ that has been flipped across the x-axis

In general:

> If $g(x) = k \cdot f(x)$, and if $k < 0$, then the graph of $y = g(x)$ is given by the graph of $y = f(x)$ stretched vertically by a factor of $|k|$ and reflected vertically across the x-axis.

Combining Transformations

In general, any transformations of functions can be combined.

Example 4   Let $y = f(x)$ be the function graphed in Figure 4.35. Sketch a graph of the function $g(x) = (-1/2)f(x+3) - 1$.

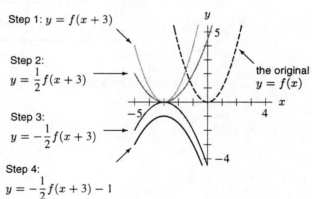

Figure 4.35: The graph of
$y = f(x)$

Solution   The function g combines several of the transformations we have studied in this chapter. When there are several transformations in the formula at once, it is necessary to consider them in the correct order. Always work from inside the parentheses outward.

Step 1: horizontal
shift left 3 units

Step 2: vertical
compression

$$g(x) = -\tfrac{1}{2}f(x+3) - 1$$

Step 3: vertical reflection
over the x-axis

Step 4: vertical
shift down 1 unit

Figure 4.36

Step 1: $y = f(x+3)$

Step 2:
$y = \dfrac{1}{2}f(x+3)$

Step 3:
$y = -\dfrac{1}{2}f(x+3)$

Step 4:
$y = -\dfrac{1}{2}f(x+3) - 1$

Figure 4.37: The graph of $y = f(x)$ transformed in four steps
into $g(x) = -(1/2)f(x+3) - 1$

Figure 4.36 shows the graphs corresponding to each step. Note that we did not need a formula for f in order to be able to graph g.

Problems for Section 4.3

1. Let $f(x)$ be defined by Table 4.31:

   TABLE 4.31

x	-3	-2	-1	0	1	2	3
$f(x)$	2	3	7	-1	-3	4	8

   Prepare tables for the following transformations of f using an appropriate domain.

   (a) $\frac{1}{2}f(x)$ (b) $-2f(x+1)$ (c) $f(x)+5$

   (d) $f(x-2)$ (e) $f(-x)$ (f) $-f(x)$

2. Table 4.32 gives a partial set of values for a function f. Fill in all the blanks for which you have sufficient information.

   TABLE 4.32

x	-3	-2	-1	0	1	2	3
$f(x)$	-4	-1	2	3	0	-3	-6
$f(-x)$							
$-f(x)$							
$f(x)-2$							
$f(x-2)$							
$f(x)+2$							
$f(x+2)$							
$2f(x)$							
$-f(x)/3$							

3. Let $y = f(x)$ be given by the graph in Figure 4.38.

Figure 4.38

   Choose the letter corresponding to the graph that represents the given function:

   (i) $y = 2f(x)$ (ii) $y = \frac{1}{3}f(x)$ (iii) $y = -f(x) + 1$

   (iv) $y = f(x+2) + 1$ (v) $y = f(-x)$

(a)   (b)   (c)

(d)   (e)   (f)

(g)   (h)   (i)

Figure 4.39

4. Figure 4.40 shows a graph of the power function $y = x^{3/2}$. Match the following functions with the graphs in Figure 4.41.

(a) $y = x^{3/2} - 1$ (b) $y = (x - 1)^{3/2}$

(c) $y = 1 - x^{3/2}$ (d) $y = \frac{3}{2}x^{3/2}$

Figure 4.40

Figure 4.41

5. Graph the indicated functions using the graph of f in Figure 4.42.

(a) $y = -f(x) + 2$ (b) $y = 2f(x)$

(c) $y = f(x - 3)$ (d) $y = -\frac{1}{2}f(x + 1) - 3$

Figure 4.42

6. Sketch graphs of the following transformations. Label at least three points on each graph.

    (a) $y = f(x + 3)$ if $f(x) = |x|$ (b) $y = f(x) + 3$ if $f(x) = |x|$

    (c) $y = -g(x)$ if $g(x) = x^2$ (d) $y = g(-x)$ if $g(x) = x^2$

    (e) $y = 3h(x)$ if $h(x) = 2^x$

7. Graph the transformations (a) – (f) of the function f given in Figure 4.43. Be sure to relabel points A and B as well as the horizontal asymptote, if it does not occur at the x-axis.

Figure 4.43

    (a) $y = 2f(x)$ (b) $y = f(-x)$ (c) $y = -f(x)$

    (d) $y = f(x + 3)$ (e) $y = f(x) + 3$ (f) $y = \dfrac{1}{2}f(x)$

8. Find formulas, in terms of f, for the transformations (a) – (c) of the graph of $y = f(x)$ shown in Figure 4.43.

(a)

(b)

(c)

Figure 4.44

9. Let $f(x) = 2^x$. Find formulas in terms of f and then in terms of x for the transformations of f in (a) – (d). *Example:* The graph in Figure 4.45 appears to be f flipped across the y-axis. Because the horizontal asymptote is at $y = -3$ instead of $y = 0$, it also appears that f is shifted downward by 3 units. Therefore, the formula should be

$$y = f(-x) - 3 = 2^{-x} - 3.$$

Figure 4.45

(a)

(b)

(c)

(d)

Figure 4.46

$y = f(-x) = 2^{-x}$

$y = f(x) + 1.5$
$y = 2^x + 1.5$

10. For each of the following formulas, if possible find a graph or graphs in Figure 4.47, which might represent the function.

(a) $y = 3 \cdot 2^x$

(b) $y = 5^{-x}$

(c) $y = -5^x$

(d) $y = 2 - 2^{-x}$

(e) $y = 1 - \left(\frac{1}{2}\right)^x$

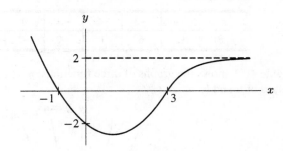

Figure 4.47

11. The graph of $y = f(x)$ is given in Figure 4.48.

Figure 4.48

Graph each of the following functions on separate sets of axes, together with the graph of the original function. Label any intercepts or special points.

(a) $y = 3f(x)$

(b) $y = f(x - 1)$

(c) $y = f(x) - 1$

(d) $y = -2f(x)$

(e) $y + 1 = \frac{1}{2}f(x + 2)$

(f) $-y = f(-x)$

12. The graph of $y = f(t)$ given in Figure 4.49. Find formulas in terms of f for transformations (a) – (c) found in Figure 4.50. What is the equation of the asymptote in each case?

Figure 4.49

(a)

(b)

(c)

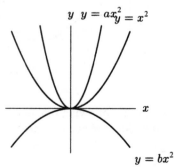

Figure 4.50

13. Using Table 4.33 to define $f(x)$, create a table of values for
    (a) $f(-x)$.   (b) $-f(x)$.   (c) $3f(x)$.
    (d) Which of these tables from part (a), (b), and (c) represents an even function?

    TABLE 4.33

x	-4	-3	-2	-1	0	1	2	3	4
$f(x)$	13	6	1	-2	-3	-2	1	6	13

14. Figure 4.51 shows the graphs of three functions: $y = x^2$, $y = ax^2$, and $y = bx^2$. Estimate the values of a and b.

Figure 4.51

Chapter 4/ 36

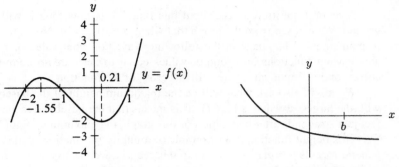

Figure 4.52   Figure 4.53

15. Figure 4.52 gives a graph of $y = f(x)$. Consider the transformations $y = \frac{1}{2}f(x)$ and $y = 2f(x)$. Which points on the graph of $y = f(x)$ stay fixed under these transformations? Compare the intervals on which all three functions are increasing and decreasing.

16. The Heaviside step function, $H(x)$, is defined as follows:

$$H(x) = 1 \text{ for } x \geq 0$$
$$H(x) = 0 \text{ for } x < 0.$$

   Sketch the graph of the Heaviside function, $H(x)$. Use the graph of $H(x)$ to sketch the graphs of the following transformations.

   (a) $y = H(x) - 2$ (b) $y = H(x + 2)$ (c) $y = -3H(-x) + 4$

17. On the graph in Figure 4.53, b is labeled on the x-axis. On the y-axis, locate and label the output values:

   (a) $f(b)$ (b) $-2f(b)$ (c) $-2f(-b)$

18. Start with the function $f(x) = 2^x$, and describe in words the family of functions that you obtain from f by

   (a) stretching vertically,
   (b) stretching vertically and shifting horizontally.

4.4 THE FAMILY OF QUADRATIC FUNCTIONS

Suppose that a baseball is "popped" straight up by a batter. The height of the ball can be modeled by the function $y = f(t) = -16t^2 + 64t + 3$, where t is given in seconds after the ball leaves the bat and y is in feet. The graph of the function is shown in Figure 4.54.

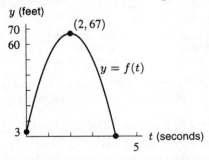

Figure 4.54: The height of a ball t seconds after being "popped up"

A natural question to ask about this function is how long it will be before the ball hits the ground. We can see from the graph that when $y = 0$, $t \approx 4$. Note that we can phrase the question in mathematical language in the following way: For what value of t does $f(t) = 0$? Questions about when functions have output values equal to zero are so common in applications that the corresponding input values are called "zeros" of the function.

We might also ask what will be the maximum height of the baseball. The point on the graph with the largest y-value is $(2, 67)$. This means that the baseball reaches its maximum height of 67 feet just 2 seconds after being hit. For this graph, the maximum point $(2, 67)$ is called the vertex.

This height function is an example of a family of functions called quadratic functions, whose general form is $y = ax^2 + bx + c$. In this section, we discuss how to find the vertex of a quadratic function algebraically, and how to find its zeros (if they exist).

The Vertex of a Quadratic Function

We have seen one member of the quadratic family before: the function $y = x^2$, whose graph is a parabola with vertex at the origin. All other functions in the quadratic family are transformations of this simple function. Let's first see how to graph a quadratic function of the form $y = a(x - h)^2 + k$, and to locate its vertex.

Example 1   Let $f(x) = x^2$ and $g(x) = -2(x + 1)^2 + 3$.

    (a)   Express the function g in terms of f.

    (b)   Sketch a graph of f. Explain how to transform the graph of f into the graph of g, and sketch a graph of g.

    (c)   Multiply out and simplify the formula for g.

    (d)   Explain how the formula for g can be used to obtain the vertex of the graph of g.

Solution   (a)   Since $f(x + 1) = (x + 1)^2$, we have

$$g(x) = -2f(x + 1) + 3.$$

    (b)   The graph of $f(x) = x^2$ is shown in Figure 4.55. The graph of g can be obtained from the graph of f in four steps, as shown in Figure 4.55.

| The graph of $f(x) = x^2$ | Step 1: shift left 1 unit $y = f(x + 1)$ | Step 2: stretch vertically $y = 2f(x + 1)$ | Step 3: reflect vertically $y = -2f(x + 1)$ | Step 4: shift up 3 units $g(x) = -2f(x + 1) + 3$ |

Figure 4.55: The graph of $f(x) = x^2$, on the left, is transformed in four steps into the graph of $g(x) = -2(x + 1)^2 + 3$, on the right

    (c) $g(x) = -2(x^2 + 2x + 1) + 3 = -2x^2 - 4x + 1$

    (d)   The vertex of the graph of f is $(0, 0)$. Notice that in Step 1 the vertex shifts one unit to the left, and in Step 4 the vertex shifts 3 units up. Thus, the vertex of the graph of g is at $(-1, 3)$.

In general, the graph of $g(x) = a(x - h)^2 + k$ is obtained from the graph of $f(x) = x^2$ by shifting horizontally $|h|$ units, stretching vertically by a factor of a (and reflecting vertically over the x-axis if $a < 0$), and shifting vertically $|k|$ units. In the process, the vertex is shifted from $(0, 0)$ to the point (h, k). The graph of the function is symmetrical about a vertical line through the vertex, called the axis of symmetry. Thus, we see that the vertex form is useful for graphing quadratic functions.

Formulas for Quadratic Functions

Notice that the function g in Example 1 can be written in two ways:

$$g(x) = -2(x + 1)^2 + 3$$

and

$$g(x) = -2x^2 - 4x + 1.$$

The first version, called the *vertex form*, is helpful for graphing; the second version is called *standard form*. In general, we have the following:

The **standard form** for the family of quadratic functions is

$$y = ax^2 + bx + c, \quad \text{where } a, \ b, \ c \text{ are constants, } a \neq 0.$$

The **vertex form** is

$$y = a(x - h)^2 + k, \quad \text{where } a, \ h, \ k \text{ are constants, } a \neq 0.$$

The graph of a quadratic function is called a **parabola** and

- has vertex (h, k),
- has an axis of symmetry, $x = h$,
- opens upward if $a > 0$ or downward if $a < 0$,
- is a vertical compression of the graph of $y = x^2$ if $|a| < 1$, or a vertical stretch if $|a| > 1$.

Thus, any quadratic function can be expressed in both standard form and vertex form. To convert from vertex form to standard form, we expand the squared term and simplify by collecting like terms. To convert from standard form to vertex form, we use the method of *completing the square*.

Example 2   Put the following quadratic functions into vertex form by the method of completing the square and graph them.

(a) $s(x) = x^2 - 6x + 8$ 　　　　　　　　　(b) $t(x) = -4x^2 - 12x - 8$

Solution   (a)   To complete the square,[1] we find the square of half of the coefficient of the x-term, $(6/2)^2 = 9$. Add and subtract this number after the x-term:

$$s(x) = \underbrace{x^2 - 6x + 9}_{\text{perfect square}} - 9 + 8,$$

so

$$s(x) = (x - 3)^2 - 1.$$

---

[1] A fuller explanation of this method is included in the Appendix.

The vertex of s is $(3, -1)$ and the axis of symmetry is the vertical line $x = 3$. There is no vertical stretch since $a = 1$, and the parabola opens upward. Figure 4.56 shows a graph of s.

Figure 4.56: $s(x) = x^2 - 6x + 8$ Figure 4.57: $t(x) = -4x^2 - 12x - 8$

(b)   To complete the square, we first factor out -4, the coefficient of x^2, giving

$$t(x) = -4(x^2 + 3x + 2).$$

Now add and subtract the square of half the coefficient of the x-term, $(3/2)^2 = 9/4$ inside the parenthesis. This gives

$$t(x) = -4(\underbrace{x^2 + 3x + \frac{9}{4}}_{\text{perfect square}} - \frac{9}{4} + 2)$$

$$t(x) = -4\left(\left(x + \frac{3}{2}\right)^2 - \frac{1}{4}\right)$$

$$t(x) = -4\left(x + \frac{3}{2}\right)^2 + 1.$$

The vertex of t is $(-3/2, 1)$, the axis of symmetry is $x = -3/2$, the vertical stretch factor is 4, and the parabola opens downward. The graph is shown in Figure 4.57.

Finding a Formula for a Parabola

If we are given the vertex of a quadratic function, we can use the vertex form to find its formula.

Example 3   Find the formula for the quadratic function graphed in Figure 4.58.

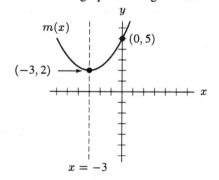

Figure 4.58

Solution   Since the vertex is given, we will use the vertex form $m(x) = a(x - h)^2 + k$ to find a, h, and k. The vertex of m is $(-3, 2)$, so $h = -3$ and $k = 2$. Thus,

$$m(x) = a(x - (-3))^2 + 2,$$

or

$$m(x) = a(x + 3)^2 + 2.$$

To find a, we can use the y-intercept $(0, 5)$. Substitute $x = 0$ and $m(0) = 5$ into the formula and solve for a:

$$5 = a(0 + 3)^2 + 2$$
$$3 = 9a$$
$$a = \frac{1}{3}.$$

Thus, the formula is

$$m(x) = \frac{1}{3}(x + 3)^2 + 2.$$

If we want the formula in standard form, we can multiply it out:

$$m(x) = \frac{1}{3}x^2 + 2x + 5.$$

If we are given the intercepts of a parabola, it is easier to use the standard form to find its formula.

Example 4   Find a formula for the parabola in Figure 4.59.

y

6

1 3 x

Figure 4.59

Solution   In standard form the parabola has equation

$$y = ax^2 + bx + c.$$

Since the y-intercept is 6, we know the point $x = 0, y = 6$ satisfies the equation. Substituting gives

$$6 = a(0)^2 + b(0) + c$$
$$c = 6$$

so $y = ax^2 + bx + 6$.

The parabola goes through the points $x = 1, y = 0$ and $x = 3, y = 0$ so we have

$$0 = a(1)^2 + b(1) + 6$$
$$0 = a(3)^2 + b(3) + 6$$

or

$$a + b = -6$$
$$9a + 3b = -6.$$

To solve these simultaneous equations, first divide both sides of the second equation by 3 to get

$$a + b = -6$$
$$3a + b = -2.$$

Then subtract the first equation from the second to get

$$2a = 4$$

and we divide by 2 to give

$$a = 2.$$

Now solve for b, using $a + b = -6$

$$2 + b = -6$$
$$b = -8.$$

Thus we have found a, b, and c, so the equation of the parabola is

$$y = 2x^2 - 8x + 6.$$

Finding the Zeros of a Quadratic Function

Recall that the zeros of a function f are values of x for which $f(x) = 0$. It is easy to find the zeros of a quadratic function if the formula can be factored.

Example 5   Find the zeros of $f(x) = x^2 - x - 6$.

Solution   To find the zeros, set $f(x) = 0$:

$$x^2 - x - 6 = 0$$
$$(x - 3)(x + 2) = 0.$$

Solving this equation gives us the zeros: $x = 3$ or $x = -2$.

Recall that any quadratic function can be expressed in standard form or vertex form. Some quadratic functions can also be expressed in *factored form*, $q(x) = a(x - r)(x - s)$, where a, r, and s are constants, $a \neq 0$. Note that r and s are zeros of the function. The factored form of the function f in Example 5 is $f(x) = (x - 3)(x + 2)$.

Example 6   Find the equation of the parabola in Example 4 using factored form.

Solution   Since the parabola has x-intercepts at $x = 1$ and $x = 3$, the formula is of the form

$$y = k(x - 1)(x - 3)$$
$$y = k(x^2 - 4x + 3)$$

Substituting $x = 0, y = 6$ gives

$$6 = k(3)$$
$$k = 2.$$

Thus, the equation is

$$y = 2(x - 1)(x - 3).$$

Multiplying out gives the same result as before.

Many quadratic functions, however, cannot be easily factored.

Example 7   Find the zeros of $g(x) = x^2 - (8/3)x - 1$.

Solution   To find the zeros of g, set $g(x) = 0$:

$$x^2 - \frac{8}{3}x - 1 = 0.$$

Since the formula for g cannot be factored easily, we complete the square. We take $(8/3)/2 = 4/3$, and $(4/3)^2 = 16/9$. Add and subtract $16/9$ to make a perfect square:

$$\underbrace{x^2 - \frac{8}{3}x + \frac{16}{9}}_{\text{perfect square}} \underbrace{- \frac{16}{9} - 1}_{-\frac{16}{9} - 1 = -\frac{25}{9}} = 0$$

$$\left(x - \frac{4}{3}\right)^2 - \frac{25}{9} = 0$$

$$\left(x - \frac{4}{3}\right)^2 = \frac{25}{9}$$

$$x - \frac{4}{3} = \pm\sqrt{\frac{25}{9}} = \pm\frac{5}{3} \qquad \text{(taking the square root)}$$

$$x = \frac{4}{3} \pm \frac{5}{3} \qquad \text{(adding 4/3 to both sides).}$$

So the zeros are $x = 3$ and $x = -1/3$.

Instead of completing the square every time we we would like to find the zeros of a quadratic function, we can use the quadratic formula, which is derived by completing the square for the general quadratic function, $y = ax^2 + bx + c$. A derivation of the formula is given in the Appendix.

The solutions to the equation $ax^2 + bx + c = 0$ are given by the **quadratic formula**:

$$x = \frac{-b \pm \sqrt{b^2 - 4ac}}{2a}.$$

You should use the quadratic formula to find the zeros of the function in Example 7. Of course, you should get the same answers as we did by completing the square.

The zeros of a function occur at the x-intercepts of its graph. Not every quadratic function has x-intercepts, as we see in the next example.

Example 8   Figure 4.60 shows a graph of $h(x) = -(1/2)x^2 - 2$. What happens if we try to use the quadratic formula to find its zeros?

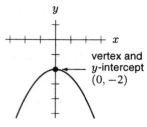

Figure 4.60

vertex and
y-intercept
$(0, -2)$

Solution   To find the zeros we solve the equation

$$-\frac{1}{2}x^2 - 2 = 0.$$

Substitute $a = -1/2, b = 0, c = -2$ into the quadratic formula:

$$x = \frac{-0 \pm \sqrt{0^2 - 4(-\frac{1}{2})(-2)}}{2(-\frac{1}{2})} = \frac{\pm\sqrt{-4}}{-1}.$$

Since $\sqrt{-4}$ is not a real number, there are no real solutions. That is, h has no real zeros, as we can see in the graph in Figure 4.60.

An Application of Quadratic Functions

When quadratic functions occur in applications, it is often useful to find the maximum or minimum value of the function.

Example 9   As part of a campaign to increase its endowment, Harvard decides to fence off a particularly popular section of the University's property on the Charles River and charge admission to the park. It is decided that funds will be allotted to provide 80 meters of fence. The area enclosed will be a rectangle, but only three sides will be enclosed by fence — the other side will be bound by the river. What is the maximum area that can be enclosed in this way?

Solution   Two sides are perpendicular to the bank of the river, and have equal lengths. Call the length of either of these sides h. The other side is parallel to the bank of the river. Call its length b. See Figure 4.61. Since the fence is 80 meters long,

$$2h + b = 80$$
$$b = 80 - 2h.$$

The river

h h

b

Figure 4.61

Since the area of the park, A, is the product of two adjacent sides, it is a quadratic function:

$$A = bh = (80 - 2h)h$$
$$= -2h^2 + 80h.$$

The zeros of this function are $h = 0$ and $h = 40$, so the axis of symmetry is $h = 20$. (Recall that the vertex of a parabola occurs on its axis of symmetry.) Since the coefficient of h^2 is negative, we know that the parabola is concave down, and therefore we have a maximum at the vertex. Thus, when $h = 20$

$$A = (80 - 2(20))(20) = (80 - 40)(20) = (40)(20) = 800,$$

so the maximum area that can be enclosed is 800 m^2.

Problems for Section 4.4

1. Using graphing technology, sketch the following quadratic functions and identify the values of the parameters a, b, and c. Label the zeros, axis of symmetry, vertex, and y-intercept of both graphs.
   (a) $f(x) = -2x^2 + 4x + 16$ (b) $g(x) = x^2 + 3$

2. Let $f(x) = x^2$ and let $g(x) = (x - 3)^2 + 2$.
   (a) Give the formula for g in terms of f, and describe the relationship between f and g in words.
   (b) Is g a quadratic function? If so, find its parameters.
   (c) Sketch a graph of g, labeling all important features.

3. (a) Sketch a graph of the quadratic function $h(x) = -2x^2 - 8x - 8$.
   (b) Compare this graph to the graph of $f(x) = x^2$. How are these two graphs related? Be specific.

4. Let f represent a quadratic function whose graph is a concave up parabola with a vertex at $(1, -1)$, and a zero at the origin. $f(x) = (x-1)^2 - 1$ $(x+h)^2 + k$
   (a) Sketch a graph of $y = f(x)$.   (b) Determine a formula for $f(x)$. $a(x+h)$
   (c) Determine the range of f. ≥ -1 (d) Find any other zeros. $a(x-2)^2 + 0$
   : 2

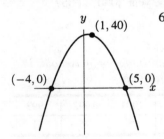

For Problems 5–7, give a possible formula for the function graphed.

5.

Figure 4.62

6.

Figure 4.63

7.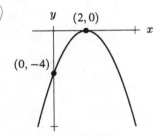

Figure 4.64

8. Find formulas for the quadratic functions shown in Figure 4.65.

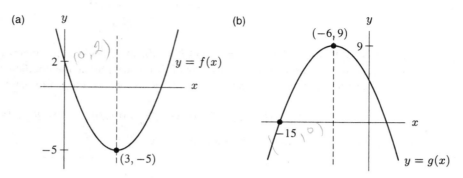

Figure 4.65

9. Let $f(x) = x^2$ and $g(x) = x^2 + 2x - 8$.
   (a) Sketch graphs f and g in the window $-10 \le x \le 10, -10 \le y \le 10$. How are the two graphs similar? How are they different?
   (b) Graph f and g in the window $-10 \le x \le 10, -10 \le y \le 100$. Why do the two graphs appear more similar on this window than on the window from part (a)?
   (c) Graph f and g in the window $-20 \le x \le 20, -10 \le y \le 400$, the window $-50 \le x \le 50, -10 \le y \le 2500$, and the window $-500 \le x \le 500, -2500 \le y \le 250,000$. Describe the change in appearance of f and g on these three successive windows.

10. Find a formula for the quadratic function f which has zeros at $x = 1$ and $x = 2$ and whose vertex is $(3/2, -1)$.

11. If we know a quadratic function f has a zero at $x = -1$ and vertex at $(1, 4)$, do we have enough information to find a formula for this function? If your answer is yes, find it; if not, give your reasons.

12. The percentage of households in the US engaged in gardening activities each year from 1990 to 1993 is shown in Table 4.34.[2]
   (a) Show that this data set can be modeled by the quadratic equation $q(x) = -\frac{1}{2}x^2 - \frac{3}{2}x + 80$ where x measures the years since 1990.
   (b) According to this model, when was the percentage highest? What was that percentage?
   (c) When is the percentage predicted to be 50%?
   (d) What does this model predict for the year 2000? 2005?
   (e) Is this a good model?

TABLE 4.34   *The percentage of households in the US engaged in gardening*

Year	1990	1991	1992	1993
Percentage	80	78	75	71

[2]Data from "The American Almanac: 1995 – 1996", The Reference Press, Texas, 1995.

13. The percentage of schools with interactive videodisc players each year from 1992 to 1995 is shown in Table 4.35.[3] Show that this data set can be modeled by the quadratic equation $p(x) = \frac{1}{2}x^2 + \frac{11}{2}x + 8$ where x measures the years since 1992. What does this model predict for the year 2002? How good is this model for predicting the future.

TABLE 4.35 *The percentage of schools with interactive videodisc players from 1992 to 1995*

Year	1992	1993	1994	1995
Percentage	8	14	21	29

14. Graph $y = x^2 - 10x + 25$ and $y = x^2$. Use a shift transformation to explain the relationship between the two graphs.

15. Gwendolyn, a common parabola, was taking a peaceful nap when her dream turned into a nightmare: she dreamt that a low-flying pterodactyl was swooping towards her. Startled, she flipped over the horizontal axis, darted up (vertically) by three units, and to the left (horizontally) by two units. Finally she woke up and realized that her equation was $y = (x - 1)^2 + 3$. What was her equation before she had the bad dream?

16. Graph and describe the differences between $f(x) = 2^x$, $g(x) = x^2$, and $h(x) = 2x$.

17. A tomato is thrown vertically into the air at time $t = 0$. Its height, $d(t)$ (in feet), above the ground at time t (in seconds) is given by:

$$d(t) = -16t^2 + 48t.$$

(a) Sketch a graph of $d(t)$.
(b) Find t when $d(t) = 0$. What is happening to the tomato the first time $d(t) = 0$? What is happening the second time?
(c) When does the tomato reach its maximum height?
(d) What is its maximum height?

18. Suppose the height (in feet) of a ball thrown into the air is given by

$$h(t) = 80t - 16t^2,$$

where t is the time (in seconds) elapsed since throwing the ball.

(a) Evaluate and interpret $h(2)$.
(b) Solve the equation $h(t) = 80$. (Your solution(s) can be approximate.) Interpret your solution(s) and illustrate your answers in a graph of $h(t)$.

19. During a hurricane, a brick breaks loose from the top of a chimney, 38 feet above the ground. As the brick falls, its distance from the ground after t seconds is given by:

$$d(t) = -16t^2 + 38.$$

(a) Find formulas for $d(t) - 15$ and $d(t - 1.5)$.

---

[3]Data from *The World Almanac and Book of Facts: 1996*, ed. R. Famighetti,(New Jersey: Funk and Wagnalls, 1995).

(b) On the same axes, sketch graphs of $d(t)$, and $d(t) - 15$ and $d(t - 1.5)$.

(c) Suppose $d(t)$ represents the height of a brick which began to fall at noon. What might $d(t) - 15$ represent? $d(t - 1.5)$?

(d) Using algebra, determine when the brick will hit the ground:

(i) If $d(t)$ represents the distance of the brick from the ground,

(ii) If $d(t) - 15$ represents the distance of the brick from the ground.

(e) Use one of your answers in part (d) to determine when the brick will hit the ground if $d(t - 1.5)$ represents its distance above the ground at time t.

For Problems 20–23, factor:

20. $x^2 + 3x - 28$

21. $x^2 - 1.4x - 3.92$

22. $a^2x^2 - b^2$

23. $c^2 + x^2 - 2cx$

24. Sketch the graph of the function $y = 3x^2 - 16x - 12$ by factoring and plotting the zeros.

25. Sketch the graph of the following function by factoring and plotting the zeros:

$$y = -4cx + x^2 + 4c^2 \quad \text{for} \quad c > 0$$

26. Find two quadratic functions with roots $x = 1, x = 2$.

27. Is there a quadratic function with roots $x = 1, x = 2$ and $x = 3$?   No

28. Solve for x by completing the square: $8x^2 - 1 = 2x$.

29. Put the equation in standard form by completing the square and then graph it.

$$y - 12x = 2x^2 + 19$$

30. Complete the square in the quadratic function $r(x) = x^2 - 12x + 28$. Then find the vertex and axis of symmetry.

31. Find the vertex and axis of symmetry of the graph of $v(t) = t^2 + 11t - 4$.

32. Find the vertex and axis of symmetry of the graph of $w(x) = -3x^2 - 30x + 31$.

33. Find the zeros of $y = x^2 + 8x + 5$ by completing the square.

34. Show that the function $y = -x^2 + 7x - 13$ has no real-valued zeros.

35. Solve for x using the quadratic formula, and demonstrate your solution graphically:

(a) $6x - \frac{1}{3} = 3x^2$ (b) $2x^2 + 7.2 = 5.1x$

36. If $f(x) = ax^2 + bx + c \ (a \neq 0)$, then

$$f\left(\frac{-b + \sqrt{b^2 - 4ac}}{2a}\right) = f\left(\frac{-b - \sqrt{b^2 - 4ac}}{2a}\right) = 0.$$

Explain briefly why this is so without carrying out any calculations.

37. Solve for x:

$$\frac{x^2 - 5mx + 4m^2}{x - m} = 0.$$

38.   Consider the data in Table 4.36.

   TABLE 4.36

x	0	1	2	3	50
y	1.0	3.01	5.04	7.09	126.0

   (a)   Using the first three points, find the formula for a quadratic function that fits the data. Use the fifth point as a check.

   (b)   Find the formula for a linear function that passes through the second two points.

   (c)   Find the value of the linear function at $x = 3$, and compare that value to the value of the quadratic at $x = 3$.

   (d)   Compare the values of the linear and quadratic functions at $x = 50$.

   (e)   Approximately what x values would you have to use so that the resulting function values for the quadratic function and the linear function would not differ from each other by more than 0.5? Use a graphing calculator or computer graph of both functions on the same axes to estimate your answers.

39.   If you have a string of length 50 cm, what are the dimensions of the rectangle of maximum area that you can enclose with your string? Show mathematically why your answer is true. What about a string of length k cm?

40.   The graphs of two lines, $f(x)$ and $g(x)$ are shown in figure 4.66. We can inscribe different rectangles underneath each line, and define an area of the rectangle function for each line:

$$R(x) = x \cdot f(x) \qquad S(x) = x \cdot g(x)$$

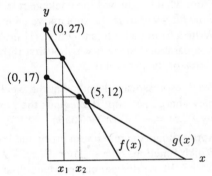

Figure 4.66

   (a)   Give formulas for $f(x)$ and $g(x)$.

   (b)   Solve $f(x) - g(x) = 4$ for x.

   (c)   For what value of x will the area of the rectangle under $f(x)$ be 40?

   (d)   Define a new function $D(x) = R(x) - S(x)$. What information is given by $D(x)$?

   (e)   Find the x-value for which $D(x)$ is a maximum. What information do you now have about the diagram?

41.   If a football player kicks a ball at an angle of 37° above the ground with an initial speed of 20 meters/second, then the height, h, as a function of the horizontal distance traveled, d, is given by:

$$h = 0.75d - 0.01914d^2.$$

   (a)   Sketch a graph of the path the ball follows.

(b) When the ball hits the ground, how far away is it from the spot where the football player kicked it?

(c) What is the maximum height the ball reached during its flight?

(d) What is the horizontal distance the ball has traveled when it reaches its maximum height?[4]

42. A relief package is dropped from an airplane moving at a speed of 500 km/hr. Since the package is initially released with this forward horizontal velocity, it follows a trajectory of projectile motion (instead of dropping straight down). The graph in Figure 4.67 defines the height of the package, h, as a function of the horizontal distance, d, it has traveled since it was dropped.

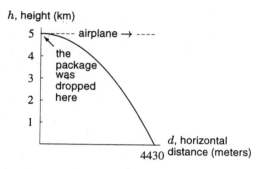

Figure 4.67:

(a) From what height was the package released?

(b) How far away from the spot above which it started does it hit the ground?

(c) Write a formula for this function. (Hint: We know that projectile motion follows the path of a parabola. Since it was not first thrown upwards, the package started falling at the vertex of the parabola).

43. A sidewalk espresso stand finds that the weekly profit for their business is a function of the price they charge per cup. If x equals the price (in dollars) of one cup, the weekly profit is given by $P(x) = -2900x^2 + 7250x - 2900$.

(a) Approximate the maximum profit and the price per cup that produces that profit.

(b) Which function, $P(x-2)$ or $P(x)-2$, gives a function that has the same maximum profit? What price per cup produces that maximum profit?

(c) Which function, $P(x+50)$ or $P(x)+50$, gives a function where the price per cup that produces the maximum profit remains unchanged? What is the maximum profit?

44. The height h, in feet, of a vertical jump performed by a ballet dancer at time t in seconds is determined by the function[5]

$$h(t) = -16t^2 + 16Tt,$$

where T is the total time in seconds that the ballet dancer is in the air.

(a) Why is t restricted to $0 \le t \le T$?

(b) If H is the maximum height of the jump, when does this occur in terms of T?

(c) Show that the time T that the dancer is in the air is related to H, the maximum height of the jump, by

$$H = 4T^2.$$

---

[4] Adapted from Physics, by Halliday and Resnick, p.58
[5] "The Physics of Dance" by K. Laws, Schirmer, 1984.

4.5 HORIZONTAL STRETCHES OF A FUNCTION'S GRAPH

In Section 4.3, we observed that a vertical stretch of a function's graph corresponds to an outside change in its formula, specifically, by a constant multiple or "stretch factor" of its outputs. Since we have seen that horizontal changes to the graphs of functions correspond to inside changes in their formulas, it is reasonable to expect that a horizontal stretch is represented in the formula by a constant multiple of its inputs. We will see that this is in fact the case.

A Lighthouse Beacon

The beacon in a lighthouse turns once per minute, and its beam sweeps across the wall of a beach house. Figure 4.68 gives a graph of $L(t)$, the intensity, or brightness, of the light striking the beach house wall as a function of time on a 4-minute interval.

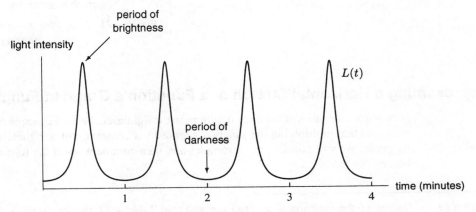

Figure 4.68: A graph of $L(t)$, light intensity as a function of time

Now suppose the lighthouse beacon begins turning twice as fast as before, so that its beam sweeps past the beach house wall twice instead of once each minute. This corresponds to speeding up by a factor of 2, or multiplying the input values (time) by 2. Figure 4.69 gives a graph of $f(t)$, the intensity of light from this faster beacon as a function of time. If we imagine horizontally squeezing or compressing the original graph of $L(t)$ in Figure 4.68, the result is the graph in Figure 4.69.

Figure 4.69: A graph of $f(t)$, the light intensity of the fast beacon as a function of time

Figure 4.70: Comparing the fast beacon to the original beacon

If the lighthouse beacon were to turn at half its original rate, so that its beam sweeps past the beach house wall once every two minutes instead of once every minute, there would only be 2 periods of brightness and 2 periods of darkness in a 4-minute interval. Slowing the beacon's speed results in a horizontal stretch of the original graph, illustrated in Figure 4.72.

Figure 4.71: A graph of $s(t)$, the light intensity of the slow beacon as a function of time

Figure 4.72: Comparing the slow beacon to the original beacon

Representing a Horizontal Stretch of a Function's Graph In Functional Notation

How are the formulas of the three functions in the lighthouse beacon example related? It is reasonable to expect that multiplying the function's input by a constant will horizontally stretch or compress its graph. We will consider two examples and then comment about the formulas for the lighthouse beacon functions.

Example 1   Values of the function $y = f(x)$ are given in Table 4.37 and its graph is shown in Figure 4.73. Prepare a table and a graph of the function $g(x) = f(\frac{1}{2}x)$.

TABLE 4.37

x	$f(x)$
-3	0
-2	2
-1	0
0	-1
1	0
2	-1
3	1

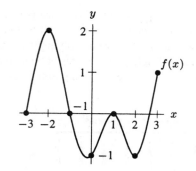

Figure 4.73

Solution   To prepare a table for $g(x) = f(\frac{1}{2}x)$, we will substitute some x-values into the formula. For example, if $x = 4$, then

$$g(4) = f\left(\frac{1}{2} \cdot 4\right) = f(2).$$

From Table 4.37 we see that $f(2) = -1$, we have

$$g(4) = f(2) = -1.$$

Thus, $(4, -1)$ is a point on the graph of g. If $x = 6$, then

$$g(6) = f\left(\frac{1}{2} \cdot 6\right) = f(3),$$

and since Table 4.37 gives $f(3) = 1$, so $g(6) = 1$. If $x = 3$, then

$$g(3) = f\left(\frac{1}{2} \cdot 3\right) = f(1.5).$$

Table 4.37 does not give the value of $f(1.5)$. However, from Figure 4.73 it appears that $f(1.5) \approx -0.5$. Thus, $g(3) \approx -0.5$;

In general:

$$g(\underbrace{x}_{\text{input to } g}) = f(\underbrace{\tfrac{1}{2}x}_{\text{input to } f \text{ is } \frac{1}{2}\text{input to } g}).$$

Table 4.38 gives values of $g(x)$ for $x = -6, -4, \dots, 6$. Notice that the table of values for g can be obtained by keeping the same output values from the table for f and multiplying the corresponding input values by 2.

TABLE 4.38

x	$g(x) = f(\frac{1}{2}x)$
-6	0
-4	2
-2	0
0	-1
2	0
4	-1
6	1

Figure 4.74: The graph of $g(x) = f(\frac{1}{2}x)$ resembles the graph of $y = f(x)$ stretched away from the y-axis

The formula for f in Example 1 was transformed into the formula for g by multiplying f's input by 1/2. The corresponding transformation of f's graph was a horizontal stretch by a factor of 2. Notice that the graph stretches horizontally away from the y-axis. If we let $x = 0$, then

$$g(0) = f\left(\frac{1}{2} \cdot 0\right) = f(0),$$

so $g(0) = -1$; the y-intercept remains fixed under a horizontal stretch.

The next example shows the effect on the graph of an inside multiple of 2.

Example 2   Let $f(x)$ be the function defined in Example 1. Prepare a table and a graph of the function $h(x) = f(2x)$.

Solution   We can use Table 4.37 and the formula $h(x) = f(2x)$ to evaluate $h(x)$ at several values of x. For example, if $x = 1$, then

$$h(1) = f(2 \cdot 1) = f(2).$$

From Table 4.37, we see that $f(2) = -1$ which means that $h(1) = -1$. Similarly, letting $x = 1.5$, we have

$$h(1.5) = f(2 \cdot 1.5) = f(3).$$

Since $f(3) = 1$, this means $h(1.5) = 1$. Observe that $h(0) = f(2 \cdot 0) = f(0)$; the y-intercept remains fixed. The graph is compressed horizontally toward the y-axis. Continuing in this fashion, Table 4.39 gives values of $h(x)$ for $x = -1.5, -1.0, \ldots, 1.5$. These points have been plotted in Figure 4.75 and a curve has been drawn in.

TABLE 4.39

x	$h(x) = f(2x)$
-1.5	0
-1.0	2
-0.5	0
0.0	-1
0.5	0
1.0	-1
1.5	1

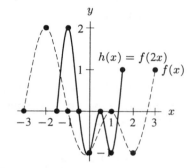

Figure 4.75: The graph of $h(x) = f(2x)$ resembles the graph of $y = f(x)$ compressed horizontally.

In Example 2, multiplying f's input by 2 caused a horizontal stretch of the graph by a factor of 1/2, that is, a horizontal compression.

In general:

Let f be a function and k a constant. The graph of $y = f(kx)$ can be obtained from the graph of f by

- a horizontal compression if $|k| > 1$,
- a horizontal stretch if $|k| < 1$.

If $k < 0$, then the graph of f must also be reflected horizontally across the y-axis to obtain the graph of $y = f(kx)$.

Finally let's consider the lighthouse beacon functions again. Speeding the beacon up resulted in a horizontal compression of the graph, so for the fast beacon we have $f(t) = L(2t)$. Slowing the beacon down resulted in a horizontal stretch of the original graph, so for the slow beacon we have $s(t) = L(\frac{1}{2}t)$.

Problems for Section 4.5

1. Let $f(x)$ be defined by Table 4.40:

   TABLE 4.40

x	−3	−2	−1	0	1	2	3
$f(x)$	2	3	7	−1	−3	4	8

   Prepare a table of values for $f(\frac{1}{2}x)$ using an appropriate domain.

2. Table 4.41 gives a partial set of values for a function f. Fill in all the blanks for which you have sufficient information.

   TABLE 4.41

x	−3	−2	−1	0	1	2	3
$f(x)$	−4	−1	2	3	0	−3	−6
$f(\frac{1}{2}x)$							
$f(2x)$							

3. Let $y = f(x)$ be given by the graph in Figure 4.76.

$$y = f(x)$$

Figure 4.76

Choose the letter corresponding to the graph (if any) that represents the given function:

   (i) $y = f(2x)$ (ii) $y = 2f(2x)$ (iii) $y = f(\frac{1}{2}x)$

(a)   (b)   (c)

(d)   (e)   (f)

(g)   (h)   (i)

Figure 4.77

4.   Sketch a graph of $y = h(3x)$ if $h(x) = 2^x$.

5.   Graph the following transformations of the function f given in Figure 4.78. Be sure to relabel points A and B as well as the horizontal asymptote, if it does not occur at the x-axis.

Figure 4.78

(a) $y = f(2x)$ (b) $y = f\left(-\dfrac{x}{3}\right)$

6.   Find a formula in terms of f for the following transformation of the graph of $y = f(x)$ shown in Figure 4.78.

7.   The graph of $y = f(x)$ is given in Figure 4.80. Graph the following functions on separate sets of axes, together with the graph of the original function. Label any intercepts or special points.

(a) $y = f(3x)$ (b) $y = f(-2x)$ (c) $y = f(\tfrac{1}{2}x)$

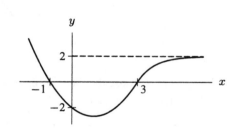

Figure 4.79   **Figure 4.80**

8.   Graph $m(x) = e^x$, $n(x) = e^{2x}$, and $p(x) = 2e^x$ on the same axes and describe how the graphs of $n(x)$ and $p(x)$ compare with that of $m(x)$.

9.   On the graph in Figure 4.81, c is labeled on the x-axis. On the y-axis, locate and label output values: (a) $g(c)$ (b) $2g(c)$ (c) $g(2c)$

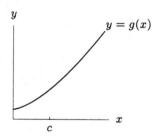

Figure 4.81

10. The age at which 41,000 Australian men, born in the same year, were married is shown in Figure 4.82, and a function has been added that models these data.[6] The vertical axis shows the percentage of the 41,000 men who were married, while the horizontal axis shows the age, measured from 22 years, at which they were married. Thus, the point $(3.5, 50)$ tells us that 50% of these men were married by the age of 25.5. It is claimed that US men who get married at some point in their lives follow a similar pattern to the Australians, but the US graph is horizontally stretched by a factor of 0.7. Sketch the corresponding figure for US men. In general, are Australian men older or younger than their US counterparts when they get married? By what age are 50% of the US men married?

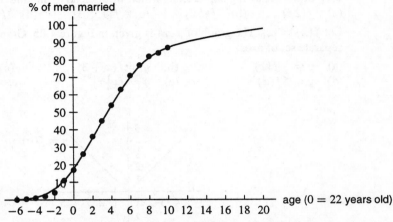

Figure 4.82: The percentage of married male Australians as a function of marrying age

11. Figure 4.83 shows the graphs of two functions, $f(x)$ and $g(x)$. It is claimed that $f(x)$ is a horizontal stretch of $g(x)$. If that is true, find the stretch. If that is not true, explain.

12. Figure 4.84 shows three functions: $y = 2^x$, $y = 2^{ax}$, and $y = 2^{bx}$. Estimate the values of a and b.

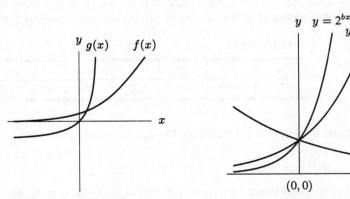

Figure 4.83: The graphs of $f(x)$ and $g(x)$

Figure 4.84: The graphs of $y = 2^x$, $y = 2^{ax}$, and $y = 2^{bx}$

---

[6]"What is a Growth Cycle?" by S.A. Coutis, Growth, **1**, 1937, 155—174.

REVIEW PROBLEMS FOR CHAPTER FOUR

1. Suppose $x = 2$. Determine the value of the input of the function f in each of the following expressions.
    (a) $f(2x)$ (b) $f(\frac{1}{2}x)$ (c) $f(x+3)$ (d) $f(-x)$

2. Now suppose that the input of the function f in Question 1 is 2. Determine the value of x in each of the following expressions which would lead to an input of 2.
    (a) $f(2x)$ (b) $f(\frac{1}{2}x)$ (c) $f(x+3)$ (d) $f(-x)$

3. Let $f(x) = |x|$. The graph of $f(x)$ is given in Figure 4.85. Graph each of the following on a separate set of axes.
    (a) $y = -f(x)$ (b) $y = f(x+3)$ (c) $y = f(x) - 4$
    (d) $y = 5f(x)$ (e) $y = f(\frac{1}{4}x)$

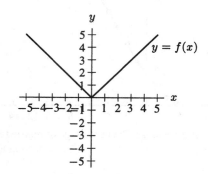

Figure 4.85

4. Let $f(x) = ax^2 + bx + c, a \neq 0$. Simplify: $f\left(\frac{-b+\sqrt{b^2-4ac}}{2a}\right)$.

Problems 5–9 use the following: The total cost C for a carpenter to build n wooden chairs is given below for several values of n. We write $C = f(n)$ to represent the cost C of building n chairs.

TABLE 4.42

n	0	10	20	30	40	50
$f(n)$	5000	6000	6800	7450	8000	8500

5. Evaluate the following expressions. Explain in plain English what they mean.
    (a) $f(10)$ (b) $f(x)$ if $x = 30$
    (c) z if $f(z) = 8000$ (d) $f(0)$

6. Find approximate values for p and q if $f(p) = 6400$ and $q = f(26)$.

7. Let $d_1 = f(30) - f(20)$, $d_2 = f(40) - f(30)$, and $d_3 = f(50) - f(40)$.
    (a) Evaluate d_1, d_2 and d_3.
    (b) What do these numbers tell you about the carpenter's cost of building chairs?

8. Sketch a graph of $f(n)$. Label the quantities you found in Questions 5–7 on your graph.

9. Suppose the carpenter currently builds k chairs per week.

    (a) What do the following expressions represent?

        (i) $f(k + 10)$ (ii) $f(k) + 10$ (iii) $f(2k)$ (iv) $2f(k)$

    (b) If the carpenter sells his chairs at 80% above cost, plus an additional 5% sales tax, write an expression for his gross income (including sales tax) each week.

10. Let $g(x) = 2^x$. The graph of g is given in Figure 4.86. Graph the following pairs of functions on the same set of axes.

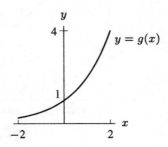

Figure 4.86

    (a) $y = -g(x)$ and $g(x)$ (b) $y = g(-x)$ and $g(x)$ (c) $y = -g(-x)$ and $g(x)$

    (d) $y = g(x) + 3$ and $g(x)$ (e) $y = 5 - g(x)$ and $g(x)$

11. Figure 4.87 gives the graph of $y = h(x)$. Each of the graphs in Figure 4.88 is a transformation of the function $y = h(x)$. Find formulas for these graphs in terms of $h(x)$.

Figure 4.87

Figure 4.88

12. The graph of $h = L(d)$ shown in Figure 4.89 gives the number of hours of daylight in Charlotte, North Carolina on a given day d of the year, where $d = 0$ means January 1. Sketch a graph that gives the number of hours of daylight in Buenos Aires, which is as far south of the equator as Charlotte is north. (Hint: Recall that when it is summer in the Northern Hemisphere, it is winter in the Southern Hemisphere.)

Figure 4.89

13. $T(d)$ is the low temperature in degrees Fahrenheit on the dth day of last year (where $d = 1$ is January 1st, and so on).

    (a) Sketch a possible graph of T for your home town for $1 \le d \le 365$.
    (b) Suppose n is a new function that reports the low temperature on day, d, in terms of degrees above (or below) freezing. (For example, if the low temperature on the 100th day of the year is 42°F, then $n(100) = 42 - 32 = 10$.) Write an expression for $n(d)$ as a shift of T. Graph n. How does the graph of n relate to the graph of T?
    (c) This year, something different has happened. The temperatures for each day are exactly the same as they were last year, except each temperature occurs a week earlier than it did last year. Suppose $p(d)$ gives the low temperature on the dth day of this year. Write an expression for $p(d)$ in terms of $T(d)$. Graph p. How does the graph of p relate to the graph of T?

14. A box in the shape of a cube has an edge of length x centimeters.

    (a) Write a formula in terms of x for the function L that gives the length of tape necessary to run a layer of tape around all the edges.
    (b) Explain what would happen if your roll of tape contained $L(x) - 6$ cm of tape. What about $L(x - 6)$ cm of tape?
    (c) If the tape must be wrapped beyond each corner for a distance of 1 cm, express the length of tape necessary in terms of a shift of the function L.
    (d) Write a formula in terms of x for the function S that gives the surface area of the box.
    (e) Write a formula in terms of x for the function V that gives the volume of the box.

    Suppose the box is very fragile and must be packed inside a larger box so that there is room for packing material to surround it. Assume that there must be 5 cm of clearance between the smaller and larger boxes on every side.

    (f) Express the surface area of the larger box as a shift of the function S.
    (g) Express the volume of the larger box as a shift of V.
    (h) Suppose the larger box must also have its edges taped. Express the length of tape necessary as a shift of the function L.

(i)   Suppose this outside box needs to be double taped to reinforce it for shipping (every edge receives two layers of tape). Express the length of tape that needs to be used in terms of $L(x)$.

(j)   Suppose the edge length of the outside box must be 20% longer than the edge length of the original box. Which expression gives the length of tape necessary to tape the edges, $1.2L(x)$ or $L(1.2x)$? Explain.

15.   On the graph in Figure 4.90, the value of d is labeled on the x-axis. Sketch the graph, then locate the following quantities on the y-axis:

(a) $g(d)$ (b) $g(-d)$ (c) $-g(-d)$

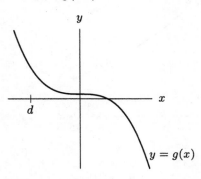

Figure 4.90

16.   On the graph in Figure 4.91, the values c and d are labeled on the x-axis. On the y-axis, locate and label the following quantities:

(a) $h(c)$ (b) $h(d)$
(c) $h(c+d)$ (d) $h(c) + h(d)$

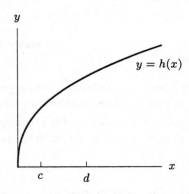

Figure 4.91

17.   A component of some natural-gas meters is a spherical rubber bladder that can expand or contract. The bladder's minimum radius is 2 centimeters, and its maximum radius is 12 centimeters. Suppose that initially the bladder is expanded to its full capacity, but that at time $t = 0$ it begins to contract at the rate of 0.25 centimeters per second, that is, its radius decreases by 0.25 cm each second.

(a)   Find a formula for $r = f(t)$, the radius of the bladder in centimeters as a function of t, the time elapsed in seconds.

(b)   Find a formula for $S = g(t)$, the surface area of the bladder as a function of t.
(c)   What is the domain of the function g?
(d)   Solve the equation $g(t) = 100$ for t, and interpret your solution.
(e)   Will the surface area of the bladder decrease more between $t = 0$ and $t = 10$, or between $t = 10$ and $t = 20$?
(f)   Which of the graphs in Figure 4.92 could be a portion of the graph of $S = g(t)$?

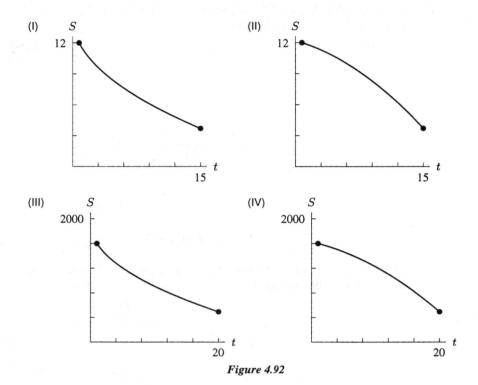

Figure 4.92

18.   Let $w(h)$ represent the quantity of water (in gallons) required each day by an oak tree of height h feet. Answer the following questions in complete sentences.

(a)   What does the expression $w(25)$ represent ?
(b)   What does the following equation tell you about v?

$$w(v) = 50$$

(c)   Find the value of $w(0)$. Explain how you got your answer.
(d)   Suppose oak trees are on average z feet high and that a tree of average height requires p gallons of water. Therefore, $w(z) = p$. Describe what the following expressions represent: $w(2z), 2w(z), w(z + 10), w(z) + 10$.

Chapter 5

Composite, Inverse and Combination Functions

6.1 COMPOSITION OF FUNCTIONS

The Effect of a Drug on Heart Rates

Suppose a patient is given a 250 mg injection of a therapeutic drug that has the side effect of raising her heart rate. Table 6.1 gives the relationship between Q, the amount of drug in her body (in milligrams, or mg), and r, the patient's heart rate (in beats per minute). As you can see from the table, the higher the drug level, the faster the heart rate.

TABLE 6.1   *Heart rate r as a function of drug level Q*

Q, drug level (mg)	0	50	100	150	200	250
r, heart rate (beats per minute)	60	70	80	90	100	110

Over time, the patient's body metabolizes the drug, and the level of drug in her bloodstream falls accordingly. Table 6.2 gives the drug level, Q, as a function of t, the number of hours since the injection was given.

TABLE 6.2   *Drug level Q, as a function of time, t*

t, time (hours)	0	1	2	3	4	5	6	7	8
Q, drug level (mg)	250	200	160	128	102	82	66	52	42

Since the patient's heart rate depends on the drug level, and the drug level depends on time, her heart rate depends, via the drug level, on time. We can combine Tables 6.1 and 6.2 to give the patient's heart rate, r, directly as a function of time, t. For example, according to Table 6.2, at time $t = 0$ the drug level is 250 mg. According to Table 6.1, at this drug level her heart rate is 110 beats per minute. This gives the point $(0, 110)$ in Table 6.3.

We can use similar arguments to estimate the drug level for later times. These results have been compiled in Table 6.3. Note that many of the entries, such as $r = 92$ when $t = 2$, are estimates.

TABLE 6.3   *Heart rate, r, as a function of time, t*

t, time (hours)	0	1	2	3	4	5	6	7	8
r, heart rate (beats per minute)	110	100	92	86	80	76	73	70	68

Suppose that $r = f(Q)$ gives the patient's heart rate as a function of the drug level (Table 6.1) and that $Q = g(t)$ gives the drug level as a function of time (Table 6.2). Let $r = h(t)$ give the heart rate as a function of time (Table 6.3). How can we express h in terms of the functions from which it was derived, f and g? We know that

$$r = f(Q) \quad or \quad \underbrace{\text{heart rate}}_{r} = f(\underbrace{\text{drug level}}_{Q})$$

and

$$Q = g(t) \quad or \quad \underbrace{\text{drug level}}_{Q} = g(\underbrace{\text{time}}_{t}).$$

Therefore,

$$r = f(\underbrace{Q}_{g(t)}),$$

and substituting $Q = g(t)$ gives

$$r = f(g(t))$$

or

$$h(t) = f(g(t)).$$

This equation represents the process that we used to make the table of values 6.3 for $r = h(t)$. For example, if $t = 0$, then

$$r = h(0) = f(g(0)).$$

Table 6.2 shows that $g(0) = 250$, so

$$r = h(0) = f(\underbrace{250}_{g(0)}).$$

We see from Table 6.1 that $f(250) = 110$. Thus,

$$r = h(0) = \underbrace{110}_{f(250)}.$$

This tells us that the patient's heart rate at time $t = 0$ is 110 beats per minutes, which agrees with our previous result and Table 6.3.

Example 1   Estimate the value of $h(4)$.

Solution   We have $h(t) = f(g(t))$ so, if $t = 4$, then

$$h(4) = f(g(4)).$$

We must work from the innermost set of parentheses outward, so we start by evaluating $g(4)$. From Table 6.2, we see that $g(4) = 102$. Thus,

$$h(4) = f(\underbrace{102}_{g(4)}).$$

We do not have a value for $f(102)$ in Table 6.1, but since $f(100) = 80$ and $f(150) = 90$, we estimate that $f(102)$ is close to 80. Thus, we let

$$h(4) \approx \underbrace{80}_{f(102)}.$$

This indicates that four hours after the injection, the patient's heart rate is approximately 80 beats per minute.

Composition of functions

The function $h(t) = f(g(t))$ from the preceding example is said to be a *composition* of the functions f and g. For example, suppose that $p(x) = 2x + 1$ and $q(x) = x^2 - 3$. We can define a function $u(x)$ by writing

$$u(x) = p(q(x)).$$

The function u is a composition of p and q. Let's see how this works with $x = 3$. We have

$$u(3) = p(q(3)).$$

We start with the innermost set of parentheses, so we first evaluate $q(3)$. Using the formula, we find that $q(3) = 3^2 - 3 = 6$. We then substitute 6 for $q(3)$

$$u(3) = p(6) \qquad \text{(because } q(3) = 6\text{).}$$

We now use the formula for p to find $p(6) = 2 \cdot 6 + 1 = 13$, so

$$u(3) = 13.$$

Chapter 5/   3

Alternatively, we can define a function $v(x)$ by writing

$$v(x) = q(p(x)).$$

The function v is also a composition of p and q. If we substitute $x = 3$, will we find $v(3)$ equal to $u(3)$?

$$v(3) = q(p(3))$$
$$= q(7) \quad \text{(because } p(3) = 2 \cdot 3 + 1 = 7)$$
$$= 46 \quad \text{(because } q(7) = 7^2 - 3).$$

Thus, $v(3) \neq u(3)$. The function $v(x) = q(p(x))$ is different from the function $u(x) = p(q(x))$.

Finding Formulas for Composite Functions

We will now revisit the heart rate and drug example using formulas. A formula for $r = f(Q)$, the heart rate as a function of drug level (Table 6.1), is

$$f(Q) = 60 + 0.2Q.$$

A formula for $Q = q(t)$, the drug level as a function of time (Table 6.2), is

$$g(t) = 250(0.8)^t.$$

Given these formulas, let's compose them to find a formula for $r = h(t)$, the heart rate as a function of time. Recall that

$$r = h(t) = f(g(t))$$

where $Q = g(t)$. The formula $f(Q) = 60 + 0.2Q$ can be written in words as

$$f(\text{input}) = 60 + 0.2(\text{input}).$$

In the expression $f(g(t))$, the function $g(t)$ is the input to f. Thus,

$$f(\underbrace{\text{input}}_{g(t)}) = 60 + 0.2(\underbrace{\text{input}}_{g(t)})$$

and so

$$f(g(t)) = 60 + 0.2g(t).$$

To finish, we can substitute in the formula for $g(t)$. This gives

$$h(t) = f(g(t)) = 60 + 0.2 \cdot \underbrace{250(0.8)^t}_{g(t)}$$

so

$$r = h(t) = 60 + 0.2 \cdot 250(0.8)^t$$
$$= 60 + 50(0.8)^t.$$

We can verify our formula by checking it against the entries we estimated in Table 6.3. For example, setting $t = 4$ gives

$$h(4) = 60 + 50(0.8)^4$$
$$= 80.48.$$

In Table 6.3, we made the estimate $h(4) = 80$, so our formula is in good agreement with the table value.

Example 2   Let us return to the two functions $p(x) = 2x + 1$ and $q(x) = x^2 - 3$.
(a)   Find a formula in terms of x for $u(x) = p(q(x))$.
(b)   Find a formula in terms of x for $v(x) = q(p(x))$.

Solution   (a)   In the formula $u(x) = p(q(x))$, $q(x)$ is the input to p.

$$u(x) = p(\ \underbrace{q(x)}_{\text{input for } p}\ )$$

$$= 2q(x) + 1 \qquad \text{because } p(\text{input}) = 2 \cdot \text{input} + 1$$
$$= 2(x^2 - 3) + 1 \qquad \text{substituting } q(x) = x^2 - 3$$
$$= 2x^2 - 5.$$

To check this formula, we can use it to evaluate $u(3)$ which we found before equals 13. We have

$$u(3) = 2 \cdot 3^2 - 5 = 13.$$

(b)   In the formula $v(x) = q(p(x))$, $p(x)$ is the input to q. A variation of the technique used in part (a) is

$$v(x) = q(\ \underbrace{p(x)}_{\text{input for } q}\ )$$

$$= q(2x + 1) \qquad \text{because } p(x) = 2x + 1$$
$$= (2x + 1)^2 - 3 \qquad \text{because } q(\text{input}) = \text{input}^2 - 3$$
$$= 4x^2 + 4x - 2.$$

To check this formula, we can use it to evaluate $v(3)$, which we found before equals 46. We have

$$v(3) = 4 \cdot 3^2 + 4 \cdot 3 - 2 = 46.$$

So far we have considered examples of two functions composed together, but there is no limit on the number of functions that can be composed. Functions can even be composed with themselves.

Example 3   Let $p(x) = 2x + 1$ and $q(x) = x^2 - 3$. Find a formula in terms of x for $w(x) = p(p(q(x)))$.

Solution   We work from inside the parentheses outward. First we find $p(q(x))$, and then input the result to p.

$$w(x) = p(p(q(x)))$$
$$= p(\underbrace{2x^2 - 5}_{\text{input for } p}) \qquad \text{because we found in example 2 that } p(q(x)) = 2x^2 - 5$$
$$= 2(2x^2 - 5) + 1 \qquad \text{because } p(\text{input}) = 2(\text{input}) + 1$$
$$= 4x^2 - 9.$$

Composition of Functions Defined by Graphs

So far we have considered composing functions defined by tables and formulas. In the next example, we will use graphs to evaluate expressions involving function composition.

Example 4   Let u and v be two functions defined by the graphs in Figure 6.1. Find:

(a) $v(u(-1))$,

(b) $u(v(5))$,

(c) $v(u(0)) + u(v(4))$.

Figure 6.1: The functions u and v are defined by their graphs

Solution   (a) To find $v(u(-1))$ we work from the inside the parentheses outward, thus we must start with $u(-1)$. From the graph in Figure 6.1, we see that $u(-1) = 1$. Thus,

$$v(u(-1)) = v(1).$$

From the graph we see that $v(1) = 2$, so

$$v(u(-1)) = 2.$$

(b) Since $v(5) = -2$, we have $u(v(5)) = u(-2) = 0$.

(c) Since $u(0) = 0$, we have $v(u(0)) = v(0) = 3$.

Since $v(4) = -1$, we have $u(v(4)) = u(-1) = 1$.

Thus $v(u(0)) + u(v(4)) = 3 + 1 = 4$.

Decomposition of Functions

In Example 2 we composed p and q to find $u(x) = p(q(x)) = 2x^2 - 5$. If we start with the formula $u(x) = 2x^2 - 5$, we can *decompose* it by finding other functions, such as p and q, which when composed give us u.

Example 5   Let $h(x) = \sqrt{x + 1}$. Decompose h into two functions. That is, if $h(x) = f(g(x))$, find possible formulas for $f(x)$ and $g(x)$.

Solution   In the formula $h(x) = \sqrt{x + 1}$, we think of the expression $x + 1$ as being inside the square root sign. Thus, we could say that the inside function is $x + 1$. Since in the formula $h(x) = f(g(x))$ the inside function is $g(x)$, we have $g(x) = x + 1$. This means that we can write

$$h(x) = \sqrt{\underbrace{x + 1}_{g(x)}} = \sqrt{g(x)}.$$

It follows that our outside function, $f(x)$, is a square root; in other words, $f(x) = \sqrt{x}$. We can check our result:

$$h(x) = f(g(x)) = f(x + 1) = \sqrt{x + 1},$$

as required.

The solution of Example 5 is not unique. For example, we might have chosen $f(x) = \sqrt{x-1}$ and $g(x) = x + 2$. Then

$$h(x) = f(g(x)) = \sqrt{(x+2)-1} = \sqrt{x+1},$$

as required.

Alternatively, we might have chosen $f(x) = \sqrt{x+1}$ and $g(x) = x$. Although this satisfies the condition that $h(x) = f(g(x))$, it is not a very interesting decomposition, because f would be the same as h. This kind of decomposition is referred to as *trivial*. Another example of a trivial decomposition of $h(x)$ is $f(x) = x$ and $g(x) = \sqrt{x+1}$.

Example 6   The vertex formula for the family of quadratic functions is

$$p(x) = a \cdot (x - h)^2 + k.$$

Decompose the formula into three functions. That is, let

$$p(x) = u(v(w(x))),$$

and find formulas for $u, v,$ and w.

Solution   There are many ways to decompose a function. One strategy is to work from inside the parentheses outward. In the formula $p(x) = a(x - h)^2 + k$, we have the expression $x - h$ inside the parentheses. In the formula $p(x) = u(v(w(x)))$, $w(x)$ is the innermost function. Thus, we can start by letting $w(x) = x - h$. In the formula $p(x) = a(x - h)^2 + k$, the first operation done to the $x - h$ is that it is squared. Thus, we let

$$v(\text{input}) = \text{input}^2$$
$$v(x) = x^2.$$

In the formula $p(x) = u(v(w(x)))$, we must evaluate $v(w(x))$ and then substitute the result into u. Using $w(x) = x - h$ and $v(x) = x^2$, we have

$$v(w(x)) = v(x - h) = (x - h)^2.$$

Finally, in order to obtain $p(x) = a(x - h)^2 + k$, we can start with $v(w(x)) = (x - h)^2$, and then we must multiply by a and add k. Thus, we let

$$u(\text{input}) = a \cdot \text{input} + k$$
$$u(x) = ax + k.$$

Let's check to see that $u(v(w(x))) = p(x) = a(x - h)^2 + k$:

$$u(v(w(x))) = u(v(x - h)) \qquad \text{since } w(x) = x - h$$
$$= u(\underbrace{(x - h)^2}_{\text{input for } u}) \qquad \text{since } v(x - h) = (x - h)^2$$
$$= a(x - h)^2 + k \qquad \text{since } u(x - h)^2 = a(x - h)^2 + k.$$

Thus, our decomposition of p is:
$p(x) = u(v(w(x)))$ with $u(x) = ax + k, v(x) = x^2, w(x) = x - h$.

Chapter 5/   7

LyNA-NGAy THO (handwritten)

Functions of Related Quantities

The process of composition can be used to relate two quantities by means of an intermediate quantity.

Example 7 The formula for the volume of a cube of side s is $V = s^3$. The formula for the surface area of a cube is $A = 6s^2$. Express the volume of a cube, V, as a function of its surface area, A.

Solution We can express V as a function of A by exploiting the fact that V is a function of s, which can in turn be expressed as a function of A. To see that s is a function of A, from $A = 6s^2$ we write

$$s^2 = \frac{A}{6} \qquad \text{so} \qquad s = +\sqrt{\frac{A}{6}} \qquad \text{(because the length of a side of a cube is positive).}$$

Therefore, in our formula for $V = s^3$, we can replace s with $\sqrt{\frac{A}{6}}$. This gives

$$V = s^3 = \left(\sqrt{\frac{A}{6}}\right)^3 ,$$

which gives V as a function of A.

Problems for Section 6.1

1. Let p and q be functions defined by Table 6.4 for $x = 0, 1, \ldots, 5$. If $r(x) = p(q(x))$, construct a table of values for r.

TABLE 6.4 *The functions p and q are defined for $x = 0, 1, \ldots, 5$*

x	0	1	2	3	4	5
$p(x)$	1	0	5	2	3	4
$q(x)$	5	2	3	1	4	8

(handwritten, right of table)
$r(x) = P(q(x))$
$r(0) = P(q(0)) = 4$
$r(1) = 5$
$r(2) = 2$
$r(3) = 0$
$r(4) = 3$
$r(5) = $ under.

2. Let p and q be the functions defined in Problem 1. If $s(x) = q(p(x))$, construct a table of values for s.

3. Complete Table 6.5 to show values for functions f, g, and h, given the following conditions:

(i) f is symmetric about the y-axis (even).
(ii) g is symmetric about the origin (odd).
(iii) h is the composition of g on f [that is, $h(x) = g(f(x))$].

TABLE 6.5

x	-3	-2	-1	0	1	2	3
$f(x)$	0	2	2	0	2	2	0
$g(x)$	0	2	2	0	-2	-2	0
$h(x)$	0	-2	-2	0	-2	-2	0

4. Values for $f(x)$ and $g(y)$ are given in Tables 6.6 and 6.7. Complete Table 6.8:

TABLE 6.6

x	$f(x)$
0	0
$\pi/6$	$1/2$
$\pi/4$	$\sqrt{2}/2$
$\pi/3$	$\sqrt{3}/2$
$\pi/2$	1

TABLE 6.7

y	$g(y)$
0	$\pi/2$
$1/4$	π
$\sqrt{2}/4$	0
$1/2$	$\pi/3$
$\sqrt{2}/2$	$\pi/4$
$3/4$	0
$\sqrt{3}/2$	$\pi/6$
1	0

TABLE 6.8

x	$g(f(x))$
0	$\pi/2$
$\pi/6$	$\pi/3$
$\pi/4$	$\pi/4$
$\pi/3$	$\pi/6$
$\pi/2$	0

5. Let $f(x) = x^2 + 1$, $g(x) = \dfrac{1}{x-3}$, and $h(x) = \sqrt{x}$. Find simplified formulas for the following functions.

   (a) $f(g(x))$ (b) $g(f(x))$ (c) $f(h(x)) = x + 1$

   (d) $h(f(x)) = \sqrt{x^2+1}$ (e) $g(g(x))$ (f) $g(f(h(x))) = \dfrac{1}{x-2}$

6. Let $f(x) = 3x - 2$ and $h(x) = 3x^2 - 5x + 2$. Find an equation for $y = f(h(x))$.

Let $m(x) = \dfrac{1}{x-1}$, $k(x) = x^2$, and $n(x) = \dfrac{2x^2}{x+1}$. Find formulas for the functions in Problems 7–15.

7. $k(m(x)) = $ 8. $m(k(x))$ 9. $k(n(x))$ 10. $n(k(x)) = n(x^2) = \dfrac{2x^2}{x^2+1}$

11. $m(n(x))$ 12. $n(m(x))$ 13. $m(m(x))$ 14. $(m(x))^2$

15. $m(x^2) = \dfrac{1}{x^2-1}$

16. Let $y = f(x)$ be defined in the following way:

$$f(x) = \begin{cases} 2 & \text{if } x \le 0 \\ 3x + 1 & \text{if } 0 < x < 2 \\ x^2 - 3 & \text{if } x \ge 2 \end{cases}$$

Find the value of $f(f(1))$. Show all your steps.

17. Let $f(x) = \dfrac{1}{x}$. For n a positive integer, define $f_n(x)$ as the composition of f with itself n times. For example, $f_2(x) = f(f(x))$ and $f_3(x) = f(f(f(x)))$.

   (a) Evaluate $f_7(2)$.   (b) Evaluate $f_{23}(f_{22}(5))$.

18. Express (decompose) each of the following functions as a composition of two new functions.

   (a) $f(x) = \sqrt{3 - 5x}$ (b) $g(x) = \dfrac{1}{1-x}$

19. Decompose each of the following functions into two new functions.

  (a) $f(x) = \sqrt{x+8}$ (b) $g(x) = \frac{1}{x^2}$ (c) $h(x) = x^4 + x^2$

  (d) $j(x) = 1 - \sqrt{x}$ (e) $k(x) = \sqrt{1-x}$ (f) $l(x) = 2 + \frac{1}{x}$

20. Decompose each of the following functions into two new functions.

  (a) $F(x) = (2x+5)^3$ (b) $G(x) = \frac{2}{1+\sqrt{x}}$ (c) $H(x) = 3^{2x-1}$

  (d) $J(x) = 8 - 2|x|$ (e) $K(x) = \sqrt{1-4x^2}$ (f) $L(x) = x^6 - 2x^3 + 1$

21. Decompose each of the following functions into three new functions.

  (a) $m(x) = \sqrt{1-x^2}$ (b) $n(x) = \frac{1}{1-2x}$ (c) $o(x) = 1 - \sqrt{x-1}$

  (d) $p(x) = \sqrt[3]{5 - \sqrt{x}}$ (e) $q(x) = (1 + \frac{1}{x})^2$ (f) $r(x) = \frac{1}{1+\frac{1}{x+1}}$

For Problems 22–25, $k(x) = x^2 + 2$

22. Find a possible $h(x)$ if $h(k(x)) = (x^2 + 2)^3$.

23. Find a possible $j(x)$ if $k(j(t)) = \left(\frac{1}{t}\right)^2 + 2$.

24. Find a possible $g(x)$ if $g(k(v)) = \frac{1}{v^2 + 2}$.

25. Find a possible $m(x)$ if $m(k(\pi)) = \frac{1}{\sqrt{\pi^2 + 2}}$.

26. Complete the following tables given that $h(x) = g(f(x))$.

TABLE 6.9

x	$f(x)$
-2	4
-1	2
0	3
1	5
2	1

TABLE 6.10

x	$g(x)$
1	
2	1
3	2
4	0
5	-1

TABLE 6.11

x	$h(x)$
-2	
-1	1
0	2
1	
2	-2

27. Suppose that $h(x) = f(g(x))$. Complete the following table.

x	$f(x)$	$g(x)$	$h(x)$
0	1	2	5
1	9	0	
2		1	

28. Let $g(x) = x^2 + 3$.

  (a) Find $f(x)$ if $g(f(x)) = (x+1)^2 + 3$.   (b) Find $h(x)$ if $h(g(x)) = \frac{1}{x^2+3} + 5x^2 + 15$.

  (c) Find $j(x)$ if $j(x) = g(g(x))$.

29. Suppose $p(x) = \frac{1}{x} + 1$ and $q(x) = x - 2$.
    (a) Let $r(x) = p(q(x))$. Find a formula for $r(x)$ and simplify it.
    (b) Write possible formulas for $s(x)$ and $t(x)$ such that $p(x) = s(t(x))$ where neither $s(x)$ nor $t(x)$ are trivial.
    (c) Let a be different from 0 and -1. Find a simplified expression for $p(p(a))$.

30. If $s(x) = 5 + \dfrac{1}{x+5} + x$, $k(x) = x + 5$, and $s(x) = v(k(x))$, what is $v(x)$?

31. Suppose $u(v(x)) = \dfrac{1}{x^2 - 1}$ and $v(u(x)) = \dfrac{1}{(x-1)^2}$. Find formulas for $u(x)$ and $v(x)$.

32. Currency traders often move investments from one country to another in order to make a profit. Table 6.12 gives exchange rates for US dollars, Japanese yen, and German marks. For example, from Table 6.12, we see that 1 US dollar can purchase 100 Japanese yen or 1.600 German marks. Similarly, the investment of 1 German mark will purchase 62.5 Japanese yen or 0.625 US dollar.

    Suppose that, given the information in Table 6.12,

    $$f(x) = \text{number of yen one can buy with } x \text{ dollars}$$
    $$g(x) = \text{number of marks one can buy with } x \text{ dollars}$$
    $$h(x) = \text{number of marks one can buy with } x \text{ yen}$$

    (a) Find formulas for f, g, and h.
    (b) Evaluate $h(f(1000))$ and interpret what this means.

    TABLE 6.12 *Exchange rate for US dollars, Japanese yen and German marks*

Amount invested	dollars purchased	yen purchased	marks purchased
1 dollar	1.0000	100	1.6000
1 yen	0.0100	1.0000	0.016
1 mark	0.6250	62.5	1.0000

33. Suppose you have two money machines, both of which increase any money inserted into them. The first machine doubles your money. The second adds five dollars to your deposit. The two machines actually act like functions and the money that comes out could be described by $d(x) = 2x$, in the first case, and $a(x) = x + 5$, in the second, where x is the number of dollars you start with. While the two machines are good deals in themselves, it is even better when they can get hooked up so that the money is processed through one machine and then through the other. The working of the two machines together is a composition. Find formulas for each of the two composition functions and decide if one is a more profitable arrangement than the other.

34. Assume that $f(x) = 3 \cdot 9^x$ and that $g(x) = 3^x$.
    (a) If $f(x) = h\big(g(x)\big)$, find a formula for $h(x)$.
    (b) If $f(x) = g\big(j(x)\big)$, find a formula for $j(x)$.

6.2   INVERSE FUNCTIONS IN GENERAL

In Section 3.3, we defined a new function called $\log x$ which helped us solve exponential equations. In Section 5.6, we defined a new function called the inverse cosine which helped us solve equations involving $\cos x$. In this section, we study such functions, called inverse functions, in a general way.

Using Electrical Resistance to Measure Temperature

Resistance is an electrical property that measures the extent to which a given material resists the flow of electric current. The resistance of certain materials varies significantly with temperature. Table 6.13 gives values of R, the electrical resistance of a certain circuit element (in ohms), for values of T, the temperature (in °C). From the table, we see that as temperature rises, resistance increases. We can also see that for each value of T, there is a unique value of R, so in fact R is a function of T.

TABLE 6.13   *The resistance R of a certain circuit element depends on the temperature T*

T, temperature (°C)	R, resistance (ohms)
−20	50
−10	100
0	150
10	200
20	250
30	300
40	350
50	400

TABLE 6.14   *The temperature, T, can be determined from the resistance R of the circuit element*

R, resistance (ohms)	T, temperature (°C)
50	−20
100	−10
150	0
200	10
250	20
300	30
350	40
400	50

Now, not only can R be determined from T, but T can also be determined from R. For example, suppose the resistance is measured and found to be $R = 300$ ohms. According to Table 6.14 this corresponds to a temperature of $T = 30°C$ and to no other temperature. Thus, T is also a function of R. (This is the principle behind an electrical device called a *thermocouple*, which determines temperature by measuring resistance.)

Table 6.14 gives T as a function of R. Notice that Table 6.14 is the same as Table 6.13 except that the columns are reversed. In Table 6.14, we are thinking of the temperature as depending on the resistance, instead of the other way around.

Inverse Function Notation

To express the fact that the resistance R is a function of the temperature T, we write

$$R = f(T).$$

To express the additional fact that the temperature T is uniquely determined by R, or in other words that T is also a function of R, we write

$$T = f^{-1}(R).$$

This statement is read, "T equals f-inverse of R." The symbol f^{-1} is used to represent the function that gives the output T for a given input R.

Example 1   Evaluate the expressions $f(50)$ and $f^{-1}(50)$. Describe the significance of these expressions in terms of the thermocouple.

Solution   From Table 6.13, we have

$$f(50) = 400.$$

Since f has temperature as an input and gives resistance as an output, this means that at 50°C, the electrical resistance will be 400 ohms.

On the other hand, the function f^{-1} has resistance as an input and gives temperature as an output. From Table 6.14 we see that

$$f^{-1}(50) = -20.$$

This tells us that if the electrical resistance of the thermocouple is measured to be 50 ohms, then the temperature must be $-20°$ C.

Definition of Inverse Function

Note that the statement $f^{-1}(50) = -20$ in Example 1 conveys the same information as $f(-20) = 50$. In fact, the values of f^{-1} are determined in just this way. For example, we know that $f^{-1}(400) = 50$ because $f(50) = 400$. In general, for any specific values of the variables,

$$f^{-1}(b) = a \quad \text{if and only if} \quad f(a) = b$$

The definition of inverse function should look familiar to you, because we have encountered specific example of inverse functions in earlier chapters. Recall, for instance, that

$$y = \log x \quad \text{if and only if} \quad x = 10^y,$$

and

$$y = \cos^{-1} x \quad \text{if and only if} \quad x = \cos y.$$

Thus, the function $y = \log x$ is the inverse function for $x = 10^y$.

Example 2   Find the radian value of the angle labeled x in Figure 6.2.

Solution

Figure 6.2

From the Figure 6.2, we see that

$$\sin x = \frac{0.83}{1},$$

so

$$x = \sin^{-1}(0.83).$$

Using a calculator, we find that $x = \sin^{-1}(0.83) \approx 0.979$.

We summarize our discussion with the following definitions.

Suppose f is a function and $Q = f(t)$. If, in addition, knowing the value of Q is sufficient to determine the value of t, we say that f has an **inverse** or that f is **invertible**, and we write $t = f^{-1}(Q)$. Here, f^{-1} is called the **inverse function** of f. The values of f^{-1} are determined as follows:

$$t = f^{-1}(Q) \quad \text{if and only if} \quad Q = f(t).$$

Example 3   Suppose that g is an invertible function, with $g(10) = -26$ and $g^{-1}(0) = 7$. What else can you say about the values of g and g^{-1}?

Solution   Because $g(10) = -26$, we know that $g^{-1}(-26) = 10$, and because $g^{-1}(0) = 7$, we know that $g(7) = 0$.

Warning: Inverse Function Notation is not an Exponent

Unfortunately, the notation used to indicate the inverse function of f looks just like an exponent. However, the -1 in the expression $f^{-1}(x)$ is *not* an exponent. In other words, $y = f^{-1}(x)$ is *not* meant to be interpreted as $y = \frac{1}{f(x)}$.

For this reason, it is not a good idea to read the expression $f^{-1}(x)$ as "f to the minus one of x," since this implies that inverse functions have something to do with exponents. Instead, the expression $f^{-1}(x)$ should be read as "f-inverse of x."

Example 4   Suppose a population is described by the equation $P = f(t) = 20 + 0.4t$ where P is the number of people (in thousands) and t is the number of years since 1970.
(a)   Evaluate $f(25)$. Explain in words what this tells you about the population.
(b)   Evaluate $f^{-1}(25)$. Explain in words what this tells you about the population.

Solution   (a)   We have
$$f(25) = 20 + 0.4 \cdot 25 = 30.$$
This tells us that in 1995 (year $t = 25$), the population is $P = 30{,}000$ people.
(b)   Since $P = f(t)$, we know that $t = f^{-1}(P)$. In other words, an input for f^{-1} is a P-value, or population, and the output for f^{-1} will be a year. In particular, $f^{-1}(25)$ gives us the year in which the population reaches 25 thousand. To evaluate $f^{-1}(25)$, we are looking for t such that $f(t) = 25$. Thus, we can find t by solving the equation $f(t) = 25$, or
$$20 + 0.4t = 25.$$
We find $0.4t = 5$, or $t = 12.5$. Therefore, $f^{-1}(25) = 12.5$, which means that at the year 12.5, or midway into 1982, the population reaches 25,000 people.

We can also evaluate $f^{-1}(25)$ graphically, using the graph of $P = f(t)$. In this context 25 is an input for f^{-1}, but an output for f. After locating 25 on the P-axis, we use the graph of f "backwards" as shown in Figure 6.3 to locate $f^{-1}(25) = 12.5$ on the t axis.

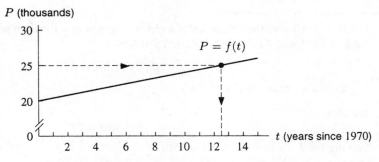

Figure 6.3: The population P (in thousands) since 1970

How to Find a Formula for a Function's Inverse

If $Q = f(t)$ is an invertible function defined by a formula, then it is sometimes possible to find a formula for its inverse function, $t = f^{-1}(Q)$.

In Example 4, the function $P = f(t)$ gives the population (in thousands) of a town in year t. Consequently, the function $t = f^{-1}(P)$ gives the year in which the town's population is P. To evaluate $f^{-1}(P)$, we must find the year in which the population reaches the value P. In Example 4, we found $f^{-1}(P)$ for a specific value of P, namely 25, but we can perform the same calculations for P in general. Thus, we have

$$P = 20 + 0.4t.$$

Solving for t we have $0.4t = P - 20$, so

$$t = \frac{P - 20}{0.4},$$

which can be simplified to give $t = 2.5P - 50$. Thus, a formula for f^{-1} is

$$f^{-1}(P) = 2.5P - 50.$$

The values in Table 6.15 were calculated using the formula for $f(t)$, $P = 20 + 0.4t$, and the values in Table 6.16 were calculated using the formula for $f^{-1}(P)$, $t = 2.5P - 50$. Note that the table for f^{-1} can be obtained from the table for f by interchanging its columns. We see again that the inverse function reverses the roles of inputs and outputs: the function f gives us P in terms of t, while f^{-1} gives t in terms of P.

TABLE 6.15

t	P
0	20
5	22
10	24
15	26
20	28
25	30
30	32

TABLE 6.16

P	t
20	0
22	5
24	10
26	15
28	20
30	25
32	30

Chapter 5/ 15

Example 5 Let $R = f(T)$ give the resistance of a circuit element as a function of temperature, as described by Table 6.13. Thus, f is a linear function given by

$$f(T) = 150 + 5T.$$

Find a formula for $T = f^{-1}(R)$.

Solution We have

$$R = 150 + 5T.$$

Solving for T we have $5T = R - 150$, so

$$T = \frac{1}{5}R - 30.$$

Thus, for the values of R shown in Table 6.14, a formula for f^{-1} is $f^{-1}(R) = \frac{1}{5}R - 30$.

Example 6 Suppose you deposit \$500 into a savings account that pays 4% interest compounded annually. The balance in the account after t years is given by $B = f(t) = 500(1.04)^t$.

(a) Find a formula for $t = f^{-1}(B)$.
(b) What does the inverse function represent in terms of the account?

Solution (a) To find a formula for f^{-1}, we solve the equation

$$B = 500(1.04)^t$$

for t in terms of B. This gives

$$\frac{B}{500} = (1.04)^t$$

$$\log\left(\frac{B}{500}\right) = t \log 1.04 \qquad \text{Taking logs of both sides}$$

$$t = \frac{\log(B/500)}{\log 1.04}.$$

Thus,

$$t = f^{-1}(B) = \log(B/500)/\log 1.04$$

is a formula for the inverse function.

(b) The function $t = f^{-1}(B)$ gives the number of years it takes for the account to grow to a balance of B.

The Graphs of a Function and its Inverse

In Example 4 we saw how to find values of $t = f^{-1}(P)$ using the graph of $P = f(t)$. However, $t = f^{-1}(P) = 2.5P - 50$ is a function in its own right, and we can consider its graph as well. Compare the graphs of $P = f(t)$ and $t = f^{-1}(P)$ shown in Figure 6.4.

It is clear that these are definitely two different functions. Nonetheless, because they are inverses of each other, there is an interesting relationship between their graphs. To see this, it is helpful to graph both functions on the same coordinate system. We will write both functions in terms of some common, "neutral" variables, say x and y:

$$P = f(t) = 20 + 0.4t \quad \rightarrow \quad y = f(x) = 20 + 0.4x$$
$$t = f^{-1}(P) = 2.5P - 50 \quad \rightarrow \quad y = f^{-1}(x) = 2.5x - 50.$$

Figure 6.4: The graphs of $P = f(t)$ and its inverse $t = f^{-1}(P)$

The graphs of f and f^{-1} are shown together in Figure 6.5

Perhaps you can see that the graph of f^{-1} is the mirror-image of the graph of f across the line $y = x$, which appears as a dotted line in Figure 6.5. Why this should occur is not hard to understand when we consider how a function is related to its inverse.

If f is a function with an inverse and if, for example, $f(2) = 5$, then we also know that $f^{-1}(5) = 2$. Consequently, while the point $(2, 5)$ is on the graph of f, the point $(5, 2)$ is on the graph of f^{-1}.

Generalizing, if (a, b) is any point on the graph of f, then (b, a) will be a point on the graph of f^{-1}. In Figure 6.6 note that the points (a, b) and (b, a) appear to be reflected across the line $y = x$. Consequently, the graph of f^{-1} is a reflection of the graph of f across the line $y = x$.

For function values in a table such as Table 6.15 and 6.16, recall the columns we interchanged from f to f^{-1}. This reflection property is easier to see on the graph of a non-linear function.

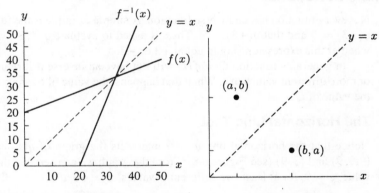

Figure 6.5: The graphs of f and f^{-1} *Figure 6.6*

Example 7   Given the fact that $f(x) = x^3$ is invertible, find f^{-1} and sketch its graph.

Solution   Let's set $y = f(x)$ and find a formula for $x = f^{-1}(y)$ as we did in Example 5. The formula for f is

$$y = x^3.$$

Solving for x we have

$$x = y^{1/3},$$

$(a, b) \rightarrow (b, a)$

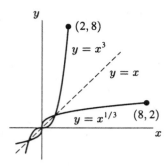

Figure 6.7: The graphs of $y = x^3$ and $y = x^{1/3}$. The graph
and its inverse are symmetrical across the line $y = x$

so $f^{-1}(y) = y^{1/3}$. (It should come as no surprise that the inverse of the cubing function is the cube root function.) Now in order to graph both functions on the same axes, we will write the function f^{-1} using the same variables as the function f, thus:

$$f(x) = x^3 \quad \text{and} \quad f^{-1}(x) = x^{1/3}.$$

Figure 6.7 shows the graphs of f and f^{-1}. Notice that these graphs are symmetric about the line $y = x$. For instance,

$$f(2) = 2^3 = 8 \quad \text{and} \quad f^{-1}(8) = 8^{1/3} = 2,$$

hence the point $(2, 8)$ lies on the graph of f and the point $(8, 2)$ lies on the graph of f^{-1}.

Noninvertible Functions

Not every function has an inverse function. A simple example is the function $q(x) = x^2$. Notice that $q(-3) = 9$ and that $q(+3) = 9$. Thus, if asked to evaluate $q^{-1}(9)$, we would be unable to decide whether this expression should equal $+3$ or -3.

In general, a function $Q = f(t)$ will not have an inverse if it returns the same Q-value for two or more different values of t. When that happens, the value of t cannot be uniquely determined from the value of Q.

The Horizontal Line Test

Notice that the horizontal line $y = 9$ intersects the graph of $q(x) = x^2$ at two different points: $(-3, 9)$ and $(3, 9)$ (see Figure 6.8). From the graph we can see that the function q returns the same value, $y = 9$, for at least two different x-values, $x = +3$ and $x = -3$.

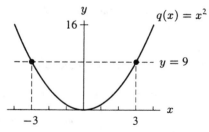

Figure 6.8: The graph of $q(x) = x^2$ fails
the horizontal line test

In general,

If a horizontal line can be found that intersects a function's graph in at least two different points, then the function fails the **horizontal line test**. Such a function does not have an inverse function and is said to be **noninvertible**.

Sometimes it is difficult or impossible to find a formula for a function's inverse, even if the function is invertible. However, this does not mean that the inverse function does not exist.

Example 8   Let $u(x) = x^3 + x + 1$. Estimate $u^{-1}(4)$.

Solution   We could try to find a formula for u^{-1} and use it to estimate $u^{-1}(4)$. To do this, we would use the formula $y = x^3 + x + 1$ and solve for x in terms of y. Unfortunately, solving this equation algebraically is quite difficult. Let's try a graphical approach. To evaluate $u^{-1}(4)$, we must find an x-value such that

$$x^3 + x + 1 = 4.$$

From Figure 6.9, we see that the graph of $y = u(x)$ and the horizontal line $y = 4$ intersect at one and only one point. Using a computer or a calculator, we find that the solution is $x \approx 1.213$.

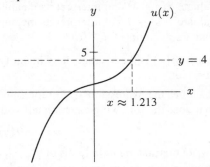

Figure 6.9: Since $u(1.213) \approx 4$, $u^{-1}(4) \approx 1.213$

From the graph of $y = u(x)$ we see that u passes the horizontal line test. Thus we can find $u^{-1}(a)$ for any value of a using the same process as above. In other words, using the graph of $u(x)$, we can find $u^{-1}(5), u^{-1}(6), \ldots, u^{-1}(a)$, for all a. Using this process we can find values of the function $u^{-1}(x)$ even though there is no familiar algebraic formula for this function.

Problems for Section 6.2

1. Suppose Table 6.17 shows the cost of a taxi ride as a function of miles traveled.

    TABLE 6.17

m	0	1	2	3	4	5
$C(m)$	0	2.50	4.00	5.50	7.00	8.50

    (a)   What does $C(3.5)$ mean in practical terms? Estimate $C(3.5)$. $= \$ 6.25$
    (b)   What does $C^{-1}(3.5)$ mean in practical terms? Estimate $C^{-1}(3.5)$. 1.67

2. Let f be defined by the following graph.

Rank the following quantities in order from least to greatest: $0, f(0), f^{-1}(0), 3, f(3), f^{-1}(3)$.

3. The area, in square centimeters, of a circle whose radius is r cm is given by $A = \pi r^2$.

    (a) Write this formula using function notation.
    (b) Evaluate $f(0)$.
    (c) Evaluate and interpret $f(r + 1)$.
    (d) Evaluate and interpret $f(r) + 1$.
    (e) What are the units of $f^{-1}(4)$?

4. The perimeter, in meters, of a square whose side is s meters is given by $P = 4s$.

    (a) Write this formula using function notation, where f is the name of the function.
    (b) Evaluate $f(s + 4)$ and interpret its meaning.
    (c) Evaluate $f(s) + 4$ and interpret its meaning.
    (d) What are the units of $f^{-1}(6)$?

5. Suppose $w = j(x)$ is the average daily quantity of water (in gallons) required by an oak tree of height x feet.

    (a) What does the expression $j(25)$ represent? What about $j^{-1}(25)$?
    (b) What does the following equation tell you about v?

$$j(v) = 50.$$

    Rewrite this statement in terms of j^{-1}.
    (c) Suppose oak trees are on average z feet high and that a tree of average height requires p gallons of water. Represent this fact in terms of j and then in terms of j^{-1}.
    (d) Using the definition of z from part (c), describe what the following expressions represent:
    $j(2z), \quad 2j(z), \quad j(z + 10), \quad j(z) + 10, \quad j^{-1}(2p), \quad j^{-1}(p + 10), \quad j^{-1}(p) + 10.$

6. Let $P = f(t) = 37.8(1.044)^t$ be the population of a town (in thousands) in year t.

    (a) Describe the town's population in words.
    (b) Evaluate $f(50)$. What does this expression tell you about the population?
    (c) Find a formula for $f^{-1}(P)$ in terms of P.
    (d) Evaluate $f^{-1}(50)$. What does this expression tell you about the population?

7. Let $t(x)$ be the time required, in seconds, to completely melt 1 gram of a certain compound, when x is the temperature you apply, in °C.

    (a) Express the following statement in an equation using $t(x)$: it takes 272 seconds to melt 1 gram of the compound at 400°C.
    (b) Explain the following equation using complete sentences: $t(800) = 136$.
    (c) Explain the following equation using complete sentences: $t^{-1}(68) = 1600$.
    (d) Suppose it can be experimentally demonstrated that, above a certain temperature, by doubling the temperature x, the melting time is halved. Express this fact with an equation involving $t(x)$.

8. Let f and g be defined Table 6.18.

Chapter 5/   20

TABLE 6.18

x	-3	-2	-1	0	1	2	3
$f(x)$	9	7	6	-4	-5	-8	-9
$g(x)$	3	15	3	2	-3	-1	3

not invert [handwritten on g(x) row]
3 different answer not 1 to 1 [handwritten below table]

Based on this table, answer the following questions:

(a) Is $f(x)$ invertible? If not, explain why; if so, construct a table of values of $f^{-1}(x)$ for all values of x for which $f^{-1}(x)$ is defined. *yes*

(b) Answer the same question as in part (a), only this time for $g(x)$. *NO*

(c) Make a table of values for $h(x) = f(g(x))$, with $x = -3, -2, -1, 0, 1, 2, 3$.

(d) Explain why you cannot define a function $j(x)$ by the equation $j(x) = g(f(x))$.

9. Suppose that $f(x)$ is an invertible function and that both f and f^{-1} are defined for all values of x. Suppose also that $f(2) = 3$ and $f^{-1}(5) = 4$. Evaluate each of the following expressions, or, if the given information is insufficient, write *unknown*.

(a) $f^{-1}(3) = 2$ (b) $f^{-1}(4) = $ *Unknow*   (c) $f(4) = 5$ (d) $f(f^{-1}(2)) = 2$

10. Suppose that $j(x) = h^{-1}(x)$, and that both j and h are defined for all values of x. If $h(4) = 2$ and $j(5) = -3$, evaluate the following expressions where possible.

(a) $j(h(4))$ (b) $j(4)$ (c) $h(j(4))$
(d) $j(2)$ (e) $h^{-1}(-3)$ (f) $j^{-1}(-3)$
(g) $h(5)$ (h) $h(-3)^{-1}$ (i) $h(2)^{-1}$

11. Using a graphing calculator or computer software, determine whether or not the following functions are invertible.

(a) $y = x^4 - 6x + 12$ *not*   (b) $y = x^3 + 7$ *Yes*
(c) $y = x^6 + 2x^2 - 10$ *not*   (d) $y = x^5$ *yes*
(e) $y = \sqrt{x} + x$ *Yes*   (f) $y = |x|$

12. Let $y = P(t)$ give the population of a town (in thousands) t years after 1980. Suppose that the population was 18,000 in 1985 and 21,000 in 1989.

(a) Assuming P is a linear function, find a formula for $P(t)$.

(b) Evaluate and interpret $P(20)$ and $P(-10)$ using the formula from part (a).

(c) Interpret the slope and the axis-intercepts of P.

(d) Find a formula for $P^{-1}(y)$.

(e) Evaluate and interpret the quantities $P^{-1}(20)$ and $P^{-1}(5)$.

(f) Interpret the slope of P^{-1}.

13. A company believes there is a linear relationship between the consumer demand for its products and the price charged. When the price was \$3 per unit, the demand was 500 units per week. However, when the unit price was raised to \$4, the weekly demand dropped to 300 units. Define $D(p)$ as the quantity per week demanded by consumers at a unit price of \$p.

(a) Estimate and interpret $D(5)$.

(b) Find a formula for $D(p)$ in terms of p, assuming that $D(p)$ is linear.

(c) Calculate and interpret $D^{-1}(5)$.

(d) Give an interpretation of the slope of $D(p)$.

(e) Currently, the company can produce 400 units every week. What should the price of the product be if the company wants to sell all 400 units?

(f) Were the company to resume producing 500 units per week instead of 400 units per week, would it realize an increase in weekly revenues, and if so, by how much?

14.   Table 6.19 gives the number of cows in a herd.

TABLE 6.19

t (years)	$P(t)$ (cows)
0	150
1	165
2	182

(a)   Find an exponential function that approximates the data.
(b)   Find the inverse function of the function in part (a).
(c)   When do you predict that the herd will contain 400 cows?

15.   Suppose $P = f(t)$ is the population (in thousands) in year t, and that $f(7) = 13$ and $f(12) = 20$,

(a)   Find a formula for $f(t)$ assuming f is exponential.
(b)   Find a formula for $f^{-1}(P)$.
(c)   Evaluate $f(25)$ and $f^{-1}(25)$. Explain what these expressions mean.

Find formulas for the inverses of the functions in Problems 16–20:

16. $f(x) = -2x - 7$ 17. $h(x) = 12x^3$ 18. $g(x) = 1/(x - 3)$

19. $k(x) = \dfrac{x + 2}{x - 2}$ 20. $m(x) = \sqrt{\dfrac{x + 1}{x}}, \; x > 0$

21.   Suppose $h(x) = \dfrac{\sqrt{x}}{\sqrt{x} + 1}$. Find a formula for $h^{-1}(x)$.

22.   Let f be a function with an inverse. Explain, in full sentences, the relationship between the graphs of $y = f(x)$ and $y = f^{-1}(x)$.

23.   (a)   Explain how you find the equation of the inverse function from the equation of the original. Illustrate your explanation with an example.
(b)   Explain how you find the graph of the inverse function from the graph of the original, and why you do it this way. Illustrate your explanation with an example.
(c)   Describe what kind of symmetry is found between the graph of a function and the graph of its inverse. Illustrate your explanation with at least one example.

24.   The function $y = \sin(t)$ is not invertible because it fails the horizontal line test.

(a)   Explain in your own words the way that the domain of $\sin(t)$ is restricted in order to define the inverse function, $\sin^{-1} y$.
(b)   Find some other restriction of the domain and explain why it would be a valid one to use.

25.   Solve the following equations exactly. Use an inverse function when appropriate.

(a) $7 \sin(3x) = 2$ (b) $2^{x+5} = 3$ (c) $x^{1.05} = 1.09$

(d) $\ln(x + 3) = 1.8$ (e) $\dfrac{2x + 3}{x + 3} = 8$ (f) $\sqrt{x + \sqrt{x}} = 3$

26.   Find the inverse of each of the following functions. You need not state the domains of the inverses, and you may assume that the given functions are defined on domains on which they are invertible.

(a) $f(x) = \arcsin\left(\dfrac{3x}{2 - x}\right)$ (b) $g(x) = \ln(\sin x) - \ln(\cos x)$

(c) $h(x) = \cos^2 x + 2 \cos x + 1$

6.3 MORE ABOUT INVERSE FUNCTIONS

A Property of Inverse Functions

Recall the thermocouple function from Section 6.2, $R = f(T) = 150 + 5T$, and its inverse function $T = f^{-1}(R) = \frac{1}{5}R - 30$. If we evaluate f for a specific value of T, say $T = 60$, we find

$$f(60) = 10 + 5(60) = 450.$$

If we now apply f^{-1} to $R = 450$, we expect that $f^{-1}(450) = 60$, and in fact this is true:

$$f^{-1}(450) = \frac{1}{5}(450) - 30 = 90 - 30 = 60.$$

We can state our result using composition of functions:

$$f^{-1}(f(T)) = T$$

for any value of T in the domain of f. This statement tells us that f^{-1} "undoes" what f "does" to T. It is also true that

$$f(f^{-1}(R)) = R.$$

Both of these statements can be verified algebraically by composing the formulas for f and f^{-1}. To verify that $f^{-1}(f(T)) = T$ we have

$$f^{-1}(f(T)) = f^{-1}(150 + 5T)$$
$$= \frac{1}{5}(150 + 5T) - 30$$
$$= 30 + T - 30 = T.$$

(You should verify algebraically that $f(f^{-1}(R)) = R$ also).

We see that applying a function and its inverse function in succession to a given value will return that original value as the end result. We can use this property to decide whether two given functions are actually inverses.

Example 1   Show that the functions $f(x) = 2\sqrt[3]{x - 4}$ and $g(x) = x^3/8 + 4$ are inverse functions.

Solution   We need to show that $f(g(x)) = x$ and $g(f(x)) = x$.

$$f(g(x)) = f\left(\frac{x^3}{8} + 4\right) = 2\sqrt[3]{\left(\frac{x^3}{8} + 4\right) - 4}$$
$$= 2\sqrt[3]{\frac{x^3}{8}} = 2\left(\frac{x}{2}\right) = x$$

and

$$g(f(x)) = g(2\sqrt[3]{x - 4}) = \frac{1}{8}(2\sqrt[3]{x - 4})^3 + 4$$
$$= \frac{1}{8}(8(x - 4)) + 4 = (x - 4) + 4 = x.$$

Thus, f and g are inverse functions. In Example 1 we showed that g is the inverse function for f, so in fact $g = f^{-1}$. Thus, we may write

$$f^{-1}(x) = \frac{x^3}{8} + 4.$$

It is also true that $f = g^{-1}$, so we could also write

$$g^{-1}(x) = 2\sqrt[3]{x - 4}.$$

Note that the two functions in Example 1 each "undo" the results of the other:

The function f performs the three operations on an input value x:

subtract 4	$x \to x - 4$
take the cube root	$x - 4 \to \sqrt[3]{x - 4}$
multiply by 2	$\sqrt[3]{x - 4} \to 2\sqrt[3]{x - 4}$

The function g "undoes" these operations in reverse order:

divide by 2	$x \to \frac{x}{2}$
cube the result	$\frac{x}{2} \to \left(\frac{x}{2}\right)^3$
add 4	$\left(\frac{x}{2}\right)^3 \to \left(\frac{x}{2}\right)^3 + 4$

Thus, it makes sense that each of these functions should be the other's inverse. We state this important property of inverse functions as follows:

> If $y = f(x)$ is a function and $y = f^{-1}(x)$ is its inverse, then
> - $f^{-1}(f(x)) = x$ for all values of x for which $f(x)$ is defined, and
> - $f(f^{-1}(x)) = x$ for all values of x for which $f^{-1}(x)$ is defined.

There is a systematic approach we can use to find the inverse of a function that takes advantage of this property. Suppose we would like to find the inverse function for $g(x) = 2x + 5$. Then, starting from the fact that $g(g^{-1}(x)) = x$, we solve for $g^{-1}(x)$ as follows:

$$2 \cdot g^{-1}(x) + 5 = x \qquad \text{because } g(\text{input}) = 2 \cdot \text{input} + 5$$
$$2 \cdot g^{-1}(x) = x - 5$$
$$g^{-1}(x) = \frac{x - 5}{2}.$$

Note that the function g multiplies by 2 then adds 5, while g^{-1} subtracts 5 and then divides by 2.

The notation in this calculation can be simplified by using a single variable, say y, to represent $g^{-1}(x)$. This allows us to avoid repeatedly writing the awkward symbol $g^{-1}(x)$. Our property $g(g^{-1}(x)) = x$ becomes $g(y) = x$, and we now solve for y instead of $g^{-1}(x)$:

$$g(y) = 2y + 5 = x$$
$$2y = x - 5$$
$$y = \frac{x - 5}{2},$$

and, as before:

$$y = g^{-1}(x) = \frac{x - 5}{2}.$$

Example 2   Suppose $h(x) = \dfrac{x}{2x + 1}$. Find a formula for $h^{-1}(x)$.

$$\frac{x}{2(h^{-1}(x)) + 1} = x$$

Solution   Start with our property of inverse functions

$$h(h^{-1}(x)) = x,$$

and substitute y for $h^{-1}(x)$ to get $h(y) = x$. Now, using the formula for h we get

$$h(y) = \frac{y}{2y+1} = x$$

and solving for y yields

$$\frac{y}{2y+1} = x$$

$$y = x(2y+1)$$

$$= 2yx + x \qquad \text{multiplying through by the denominator}$$

$$y - 2yx = x \qquad \text{collecting } y\text{-terms on the left}$$

$$y(1 - 2x) = x \qquad \text{factoring}$$

$$y = \frac{x}{1-2x}.$$

Now replacing y by $h^{-1}(x)$, we have our formula, $h^{-1}(x) = \frac{x}{1-2x}$. The graphs of both functions are shown in Figure 6.10. Note that the two graphs are symmetric about the line $y = x$.

Figure 6.10: The graph of $h(x) = x/(2x+1)$ and the inverse $h^{-1}(x) = x/(1-2x)$

The Domain and Range of a Function's Inverse

We know that the inverse function interchanges the roles of a function's inputs and outputs. This is expressed in the statement $f^{-1}(b) = a$ if and only if $f(a) = b$, and also in the fact that we can obtain a table for f^{-1} by interchanging the columns of a table for f. Consequently, the domain and range for f^{-1} can be determined by interchanging the domain and range of f. In other words,

> The domain of f^{-1} equals the range of f, and the range of f^{-1} equals the domain of f.

For example, consider the function $f(x) = \frac{x}{2x+1}$ and its inverse $f^{-1}(x) = \frac{x}{1-2x}$ in Example 2. f is a rational function that is undefined at $x = -1/2$, so its domain consists of all real numbers except $-1/2$. The range of f can be determined most easily from its graph, shown in Figure 6.10. Because f has a horizontal asymptote at $y = 1/2$, its range is all real numbers except $1/2$.

Now consider the inverse function, $f^{-1}(x) = \frac{x}{1-2x}$. Because $f^{-1}(x)$ in undefined at $x = 1/2$, its domain is all real numbers except $1/2$. Note that this is the same as the range of f. Because the graph of f^{-1} has a horizontal asymptote at $y = -1/2$, we see that its range is all real numbers except $-1/2$, which is the same as the domain of f.

Example 3   Let $P(x) = 2^x$.

    (a)   Show that $P(x)$ is invertible.

    (b)   Sketch a graph and find the domain and range of P^{-1}.

    (c)   Find a formula for $P^{-1}(x)$.

Solution (a) $P(x)$ is an exponential function with base 2. It is always increasing, and therefore passes the horizontal line test (see the graph of P in Figure 6.11). Thus, P has an inverse function.

    (b)   Table 6.20 gives values of $P(x)$ for $x = -3, -2, \cdots, 3$. By interchanging the columns of Table 6.20, we obtain a table for P^{-1}, as shown in Table 6.21. We can use Table 6.21 to sketch a graph of $P^{-1}(x)$. For example, $P(-3) = 2^{-3} = 0.125$, so $P^{-1}(0.125) = -3$. Consequently, while $(-3, 0.125)$ is a point on the graph of P, $(0.125, -3)$ is a point on the graph of P^{-1}. The graphs of both functions are shown in Figure 6.11.

          The domain of P, an exponential function, is all real numbers, and its range is $0 < x < \infty$. Therefore, the domain of P^{-1} is $0 < x < \infty$ and its range is all real numbers.

    (c)   To find a formula for $P^{-1}(x)$, we start with the equation $P(P^{-1}(x)) = x$. Substituting y for $P^{-1}(x)$, we have $P(y) = x$, or

$$2^y = x.$$

To solve for y we can take the log of both sides of the equation to get

$$\log 2^y = \log x$$

$$y \log 2 = \log x$$

$$y = \frac{\log x}{\log 2}.$$

Thus, a formula for P^{-1} is $P^{-1}(x) = \frac{\log x}{\log 2}$.

TABLE 6.20
Values of $P(x) = 2^x$

x	$P(x) = 2^x$
-3	0.125
-2	0.25
-1	0.5
0	1
1	2
2	4
3	8

TABLE 6.21
Values of $P^{-1}(x)$

x	$P^{-1}(x)$
0.125	-3
0.25	-2
0.5	-1
1	0
2	1
4	2
8	3

Figure 6.11: The graphs of $P(x) = 2^x$ and its inverse are symmetrical across the line $y = x$

Restricting the Domain

We have seen that a function that fails the horizontal line test is noninvertible. For this reason, the function $f(x) = x^2$ does not have an inverse function. However, if we consider only part of the graph of f, we may be able to eliminate the duplication of y-values. Suppose we confine our attention to the half of the parabola corresponding to $x \geq 0$, as shown in Figure 6.12.

    This part of the graph does pass the horizontal line test because now there is only one (positive) x-value for each y-value in the range of f.

17 110 266

Gadi

Figure 6.12   *Figure 6.13*

We can now find an inverse for $f(x)$ on its restricted domain, $x \geq 0$. (Technically, changing the domain results in a new function, but we will continue to call it $f(x)$.) The algebraic procedure for finding a formula for f^{-1} is the same as before: Substitute y for f^{-1} into the equation $f(f^{-1}(x)) = x$ to get

$$f(y) = y^2 = x$$

or

$$y = \pm\sqrt{x}.$$

This formula does not define a function, because there are two possible values for y, $\sqrt{x}$ or $-\sqrt{x}$. However, the range of f^{-1} must be the same as the domain of f. We decided that the domain of f would be all non-negative real numbers, so we must choose non-negative values for the range of f^{-1}. Therefore, our formula for the inverse function is $f^{-1}(x) = \sqrt{x}$.

The graphs of f and f^{-1} are shown in Figure 6.13. Note that the domain of f is the same as the range of f^{-1}, and the domain of f^{-1} (all real numbers) is the same as the range of f.

You may recall that in Section 5.6 we restricted the domains of the sine, cosine, and tangent functions in order to define their inverse functions. The inverse trigonometric functions are defined as follows.

$$y = \sin^{-1} x \quad \text{if and only if} \quad x = \sin y \quad \text{and} \quad \frac{-\pi}{2} \leq y \leq \frac{\pi}{2}$$

$$y = \cos^{-1} x \quad \text{if and only if} \quad x = \cos y \quad \text{and} \quad 0 \leq y \leq \pi$$

$$y = \tan^{-1} x \quad \text{if and only if} \quad x = \tan y \quad \text{and} \quad \frac{-\pi}{2} \leq y \leq \frac{\pi}{2}$$

The graphs of each of the inverse trigonometric functions are shown in Figures 6.14- 6.16. Note the symmetry about the line $y = x$ for each trigonometric function and its inverse.

Figure 6.14   *Figure 6.15*   *Figure 6.16*

Problems for Section 6.3

Using the property of inverse functions, show that the pairs of functions in Problems 1–2 are inverses.

1. $h(x) = \sqrt{(2x)}$ and $k(t) = \dfrac{t^2}{2}$, for $x, t \geq 0$

2. $f(x) = \dfrac{x}{4} - \dfrac{3}{2}$ and $g(t) = 4(t + \dfrac{3}{2})$

3. Let $f(x) = x^2$ and $g(x) = \sqrt{x}$.
   (a) Show that $f(g(x))$ will always equal x but that $g(f(x))$ sometimes doesn't equal x.
   (b) Does f have an inverse? Does g have an inverse? Discuss. [Hint: compare the domains of these two functions.]

4. The inverse of $h(x) = \sqrt{\dfrac{1-x}{x}}$, $0 < x \leq 1$ is $h^{-1}(x) = \dfrac{1}{x^2+1}$, $x \geq 0$. Verify this formula by calculating $h^{-1}(h(x))$.

5. Verify that if $f(x) = 1 + 7x^3$, then $f^{-1}(x) = \sqrt[3]{\dfrac{x-1}{7}}$.

6. Verify that if $g(x) = 1 - \dfrac{1}{x-1}$, then $g^{-1}(x) = 1 + \dfrac{1}{1-x}$.

7. (a) What is the formula for the area of a circle in terms of its radius?
   (b) Graph this function for the domain all real numbers.
   (c) What is the domain that actually applies in this situation? On separate axes, graph the function for this domain.
   (d) Find a formula for the inverse of the function in part (c).
   (e) Graph the inverse for the domain you gave in part (c) on the same axes as you graphed in part (c).
   (f) So, if area is a function of the radius, should radius be a function of area? Explain carefully why your answer makes sense.

8. A gymnast at Ringling Brothers, Barnum, & Bailey Circus is fired straight up in the air from a cannon. While she is in the air, a trampoline is moved into the spot where the cannon was. Below is a graph of the gymnast's height, h, as a function of time, t.

height (m)

36

time (s)

6

Figure 6.17

   (a) Approximately what is her maximum height?
   (b) Approximately when does she land on the trampoline?
   (c) Take the function $h(t)$ and restrict its domain so that it has an inverse which is a function. That is, pick a piece of the graph which does have an inverse. Graph this new restricted function.
   (d) Change the story to go with your new graph in part (c).
   (e) Graph the inverse of the function you graphed in part (c). Explain in your story why it makes sense that the inverse is a function.

9. A 100 ml solution contains 99% alcohol and 1% water. Define $y = C(x)$ to be the concentration of alcohol in the solution after x ml of alcohol are removed, so

$$C(x) = \frac{\text{Amount of alcohol}}{\text{Amount of solution}}.$$

(a) What is $C(0)$?
(b) Find a formula in terms of x for $C(x)$.
(c) Find a formula in terms of y for $C^{-1}(y)$.
(d) Explain the physical significance of $C^{-1}(y)$.

10. Suppose that in Question 9 you need an alcohol solution that is 98% alcohol, instead of 99%.

(a) How much alcohol do you think should be removed from the 99% solution described in Problem 9 in order to obtain a 98% solution? (You should make an educated guess.)
(b) Express the exact answer to part (a) using the function C^{-1}.
(c) Determine the exact answer to part (a). Are you surprised by your result?

11. Find the inverses of the following functions.

(a) $f(x) = 10^x$ (b) $g(x) = e^{3x+1}$ (c) $h(x) = \log(1 - 2x)$
(d) $j(x) = \log(x - 1) + 2$

12. Find a formula for the inverse function in each of the following.

(a) $f(x) = 10^x$ (b) $g(x) = e^x$ (c) $k(x) = 3 \cdot e^{2x}$

(d) $n(x) = \log(x - 3)$ (e) $p(x) = 2\ln\dfrac{1}{x}$ (f) $q(x) = \ln(x+3) - \ln(x-5)$

(g) $s(x) = \dfrac{3}{2 + \log x}$

13. Let $p(x) = 3\pi x^3$ and $q(x) = \dfrac{x^2}{2\pi}$. Suppose $A = p(x)$ and $B = q(x)$. Express B as a function of A.

14. Suppose that f, g, and h are all invertible functions, and that

$$f(x) = g(h(x)).$$

Find a formula for $f^{-1}(x)$ in terms of $g^{-1}(x)$ and $h^{-1}(x)$.

15.
TABLE 6.22

Taxable income	Taxes owed
$0–$20,350	15% of income
$20,350–$49,300	$3,052.50 + 28% of income exceeding $20,350
$49,300 and over	$11,158.50 + 31% of income exceeding $49,300

(a) Find a formula $f(x)$ that expresses the amount of taxes owed as a function of taxable income.
(b) What is the domain and range of $f(x)$?
(c) Graph $f(x)$.
(d) Using your graph from part (c), determine how much money a person making $30,000 would owe.
(e) Using your graph from part (c), determine the income of a person who owes $1000 in taxes.
(f) Is $f(x)$ invertible? How do you know?

16. Using the data given in Problem 15, we define the average tax rate as a function of taxable income as follows:

$$\text{Average tax rate} = \frac{\text{Taxes owed}}{\text{Annual taxable income}}.$$

   (a) Find the average tax rate for a person with a taxable income of $25,000.
   (b) The average tax rate can be interpreted as the slope of the line through $(0,0)$ and $(x, f(x))$. Sketch this line for the person with a taxable income of $25,000.
   (c) From the shape of your graph of $f(x)$, do you expect the average tax rate for $50,000 to be larger or smaller than the average tax rate for $25,000?
   (d) Using your graph, if the average tax rate is 20%, what is the annual taxable income and the amount of taxes owed?
   (e) Is the average tax rate function invertible?

17. Find the inverse of each of the following functions.

   (a) $f(x) = \dfrac{3 + 2x}{2 - 5x}$

   (b) $f(x) = \sqrt{\dfrac{4 - 7x}{4 - x}}$

   (c) $f(x) = \dfrac{1}{9 - \sqrt{x - 4}}$

   (d) $f(x) = \dfrac{\sqrt{x} + 3}{11 - \sqrt{x}}$

6.4 COMBINATIONS OF FUNCTIONS

In arithmetic, we learn how to combine numbers using addition, subtraction, multiplication, and division. Functions also can be combined using these operations.

The Quotient of Two Functions Defined by Tables: Per Capita Crime Rate

Table 6.23 gives the number of violent crimes committed in two different cities each year between 1990 and 1995. The table indicates that crime in both cities is on the rise, and that it there is less crime in city B than in city A.

TABLE 6.23 *Number of violent crimes committed each year in two different cities*

year	1990	1991	1992	1993	1994	1995
t, years since 1990	0	1	2	3	4	5
Crimes in city A	793	795	807	818	825	831
Crimes in city B	448	500	525	566	593	652

Table 6.24 gives the population for these two cities from 1990 to 1995. The table indicates that the population of city A is larger than that of city B and that both cities have grown considerably in size over this time period.

TABLE 6.24 *Population of the two cities*

year	1990	1991	1992	1993	1994	1995
t, years since 1990	0.	1	2	3	4	5
city A	61,000	62,100	63,220	64,350	65,510	66,690
city B	28,000	28,588	29,188	29,801	30,427	31,066

Can we attribute the growth in crime in both cities solely to the population growth? Is it reasonable to attribute the fact that city A has more crime than city B to the fact that city A is larger than city B? To answer these questions, we need to consider the per capita crime rate in each city. (The term *per capita* means per person, or literally, "per head.")

Let's define $N_A(t)$ to be the number of crimes in city A during year t (where $t = 0$ means 1990). Similarly, let's define $P_A(t)$ to be the population of city A in year t. Then the per capita crime rate in city A, $r_A(t)$, is given by

$$r_A(t) = \frac{\text{number of crimes in year } t}{\text{number of people in year } t} = \frac{N_A(t)}{P_A(t)}.$$

We have defined a new function, $r_A(t)$, as the quotient of $N_A(t)$ and $P_A(t)$. For example, the per capita crime rate for city A in year $t = 0$ is given by

$$r_A(0) = \frac{N_A(0)}{P_A(0)}$$
$$= \frac{793}{61,000} \quad \text{from Tables 6.23 and 6.24}$$
$$= 1.30\%.$$

Similarly, the per capita crime rate for the year $t = 1$ is

$$r_A(1) = \frac{N_A(1)}{P_A(1)}$$
$$= \frac{795}{62,100} \quad \text{from Tables 6.23 and 6.24}$$
$$= 1.28\%.$$

We see that the per capita crime rate in city A actually went down from 1.30% in 1990 to 1.28% in 1991.

Table 6.25 gives values of $r_A(t)$ for $t = 0, 1, \ldots, 5$. The per capita crime rate in city A actually declines between 1990 and 1995 despite the fact that the total number of crimes rises during this period. Table 6.25 also gives values of $r_B(t)$, the per capita crime rate of city B, defined by the formula

$$r_B(t) = \frac{N_B(t)}{P_B(t)},$$

where $N_B(t)$ is the number of crimes in city B in year t, and $P_B(t)$ is the population of city B in year t. For example, in year $t = 0$, the per capita crime rate in city B is given by

$$r_B(0) = \frac{N_B(0)}{P_B(0)}$$
$$= \frac{448}{28,000} \quad \text{from Table 6.23 and Table 6.24}$$
$$= 1.6\%.$$

TABLE 6.25   *Values of* $r_A(t)$ *and* $r_B(t)$, *the per capita violent crime rates of cities A and B*

year	1990	1991	1992	1993	1994	1995
t, years since 1990	0	1	2	3	4	5
$r_A(t) = \frac{N_A(t)}{P_A(t)}$	1.300%	1.280%	1.276%	1.271%	1.259%	1.246%
$r_B(t) = \frac{N_B(t)}{P_B(t)}$	1.600%	1.749%	1.799%	1.899%	1.949%	2.099%

From Table 6.25, we see that, between 1990 and 1995, city A has a lower per capita crime rate than city B. Moreover, the crime rate of city A is decreasing slowly, whereas the crime rate of city B is increasing. Thus, even though Table 6.23 indicates that there are more crimes committed in city A, Table 6.25 tells us that city B is, in some sense, more dangerous. Table 6.25 also tells us that, even though the number of crimes is rising in both cities, city A is getting safer, while city B is getting more dangerous.

The Difference of Two Functions Defined by Formulas: A Measure of Prosperity

In Chapter 3, we discussed the predictions made by Thomas Malthus. Malthus believed that human populations increase exponentially, whereas the food supply increases linearly. Based on these assumptions, Malthus predicted widespread food shortages.

Let, $P(t)$ give the population (in millions) of a country in year t. Assume that the initial population was 2 million people and that the population grows 4% per year. Then a formula for $P(t)$ is

$$P(t) = 2(1.04)^t.$$

Let $N(t)$ be the number of people (in millions) that the country can supply with food in year t. If the initial annual food supply was adequate for 4 million people, and if this amount increases by enough for an additional 0.5 million people every year, then a formula for $N(t)$ is

$$N(t) = 4 + 0.5t.$$

In Chapter 3 we saw that, based on these assumptions the country will first experience shortages after about 78 years. (See Figure 6.18.) When will this country be most prosperous?

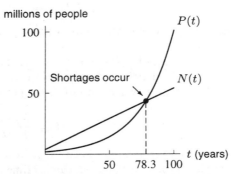

Figure 6.18: The predicted population, $P(t)$, and number of people who can be fed, $N(t)$, over a 100-year period

The answer depends on how we decide to measure "prosperity." Since the only real information we have about the country is its food supply and its population, we might decide to use one of the following measures of prosperity:

- We could measure the prosperity by how much surplus food the country has – that is, the amount of food it has over and above its needs. This surplus food could be warehoused or exported in trade.

- Or, we could measure the prosperity by the per capita food supply—that is, how much food there is per person. This would indicate what share of the nation's wealth the average person might enjoy.

Here we will choose to measure prosperity in terms of food surplus. If $S(t)$ is the surplus food supply in year t, then

$$S(t) = \underbrace{\text{the number of people that can be fed}}_{N(t)} - \underbrace{\text{the number of people living in the country}}_{P(t)}$$

so

$$S(t) = N(t) - P(t).$$

Notice that we defined a new function, the surplus function S, as the difference between the functions N and P. For example, to determine the surplus in year 25, we evaluate

$$S(25) = N(25) - P(25).$$

Since $N(25) = 4 + 0.5(25) = 16.5$ and since $P(25) = 2(1.04)^{25} \approx 5.3$, we have

$$S(25) \approx 16.5 - 5.3 = 11.2.$$

This would indicate that in year 25 the food surplus could feed 11.2 million extra people.

Since we know formulas for N and P, we can use them to find a formula for S. This gives

$$S(t) = \underbrace{N(t)}_{4+0.5t} - \underbrace{P(t)}_{2(1.04)^t},$$

so

$$S(t) = 4 + 0.5t - 2(1.04)^t.$$

Notice that this function is neither linear nor exponential. Instead, it is a combination of the two.

A graph of this function is shown in Figure 6.19. Using a computer or a graphing calculator, we see that the maximum surplus in food will occur sometime during the 48th year. In that year, there will be surplus food sufficient for an additional 14.9 million people.

The Difference of Two Functions Defined by Graphs

Let's determine how the graph of the surplus function S, shown in Figure 6.19, is related to the graphs of N and P, shown in Figure 6.18. For a given value of t, the corresponding values of $N(t)$ and $P(t)$ are represented graphically as vertical distances from the t–axis. Since

$$S(t) = N(t) - P(t),$$

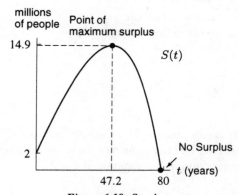

Figure 6.19: Surplus,
$S(t) = 4 + 0.5t - 2(1.04)^t$

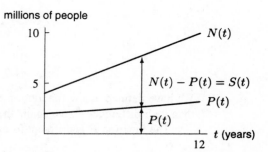

Figure 6.20: The values of $N(t)$, $P(t)$, and $S(t)$ are represented graphically as vertical distances

the value of $S(t)$ is represented graphically as the difference between these distances, or, equivalently, the vertical distance between $N(t)$ and $P(t)$. (See Figure 6.20 for a graph of the first twelve years.) By starting with graphs of N and P, we can measure the vertical distance between the graphs and plot this distance against time. This has been done in Figure 6.21. The resulting graph is the graph of S.

Figure 6.21: For a given value of t, $S(t) = N(t) - P(t)$ is the difference of the vertical distances on the graphs of N and P. This difference is shown graphically in Figure (a) and is plotted against t in Figure (b).

From year $t = 0$ to $t \approx 78.3$, the food supply, N, is greater than the population P. Therefore the surplus, S, is positive on this time interval. At time $t = 78.3$, the food supply equals the population, so $S = 0$, resulting in the x-intercept $(78.3, 0)$ on the graph of S. For times $t > 78.3$, the food supply is less than the population. Therefore the surplus is negative, representing a food shortage.

The Quotient of Functions Defined by Formulas and Graphs:

Now let's think about our second proposed measure of prosperity, the per capita food supply. If we define $R(t)$ to be the per capita food supply, then

$$R(t) = \frac{\text{number of people that can be fed}}{\text{number of people living in the country}},$$

so

$$R(t) = \frac{N(t)}{P(t)}.$$

We have defined a new function, the per capita function R, by taking the ratio of N and P rather than their difference. Once again, the resulting function is neither linear nor exponential.

The function R is different from the function S. For example, if $t = 25$:

$$R(25) = \frac{N(25)}{P(25)} = \frac{16.5}{5.3} \approx 3.1.$$

Figure 6.22: Per Capita $R(t) = \frac{N(t)}{P(t)}$

This indicates that in year 25, everybody in the country could, on average, have three times as much food as he or she needs. Notice that the value of $R(25)$ is not the same as the value of $S(25)$.

To find a formula in terms of t for $R(t)$, we write

$$R(t) = \frac{N(t)}{P(t)} = \frac{4 + 0.5t}{2(1.04)^t}.$$

From the graph of R in Figure 6.22, we see that the maximum per capita food supply occurs during the 18th year. Notice how different this maximum prosperity prediction is from the one made using the surplus function S.

Notice also that both prosperity models show that shortages begin after time $t = 78.3$. This is not a coincidence. The food surplus model shows shortages when $S(t) = N(t) - P(t) < 0$, or $N(t) < P(t)$. The per capita food supply model shows shortages when $R(t) < 1$, meaning that the amount of food available per person is less than the amount necessary to feed 1 person. Since $R(t) = \frac{N(t)}{S(t)} < 1$ is true only when $N(t) < S(t)$, this condition amounts to the same condition we observed in the food surplus model.

Factoring a Function's Formula into the Product of Two Functions

We have just seen the use of division of functions. It is often useful to be able to express a given function as a product of two (or more) other functions.

Example 1 Express the quadratic function $u(x) = 6x^2 - x - 2$ as a product of linear functions and find the zeros of u.

Solution We can do this by factoring $u(x)$ into the product of the linear functions $v(x) = 2x + 1$ and $w(x) = 3x - 2$:

$$u(x) = (2x + 1)(3x - 2) = v(x) \cdot w(x).$$

We can now find the zeros from the factored form:

$$(2x + 1) = 0 \qquad \text{or} \qquad (3x - 2) = 0$$
$$x = -\frac{1}{2} \qquad\qquad\qquad x = \frac{2}{3}.$$

Example 2 Find all zeros of the function

$$p(x) = 2^x \cdot 6x^2 - 2^x x - 2^{x+1}.$$

Solution   We can solve this problem by graphing the function p and finding the points where the graph crosses the x-axis. Unfortunately, our solutions will be approximate, not exact. With a little algebra, we can express p as a product of two functions. Since

$$2^{x+1} = 2^x \cdot 2^1 = 2 \cdot 2^x,$$

we can rewrite the formula for p as

$$p(x) = 2^x \cdot 6x^2 - 2^x x - 2 \cdot 2^x$$
$$= 2^x(6x^2 - x - 2) \qquad \text{(factoring out } 2^x\text{)}.$$

Thus p is the product of the exponential function 2^x and the quadratic function u from Example 1. Since p is a product, it will equal zero if any of its factors equals zero. But 2^x is never equal to 0 so $p(x)$ equals zero if and only if

$$6x^2 - x - 2 = 0.$$

Using the zeros from Example 1, we conclude that the zeros of p are $x = -\frac{1}{2}$ and $x = \frac{2}{3}$.

Problems for Section 6.4

1. Let $f(x)$ and $g(x)$ be defined by Table 6.26. Complete Table 6.27 using the following definitions:

(a) $h(x) = f(x) + g(x)$
(b) $j(x) = 2f(x)$
(c) $k(x) = (g(x))^2$
(d) $m(x) = \dfrac{g(x)}{f(x)}$

TABLE 6.26

x	-1	0	1	2	3	4
$f(x)$	-4	-1	2	5	8	11
$g(x)$	4	1	0	1	4	9

TABLE 6.27

x	$h(x)$	$j(x)$	$k(x)$	$m(x)$
-1	0	-8	16	-1
0	0	-2	1	-1
1	2	4	0	0
2	6	10	1	.2
3	12	16	16	112
4	20	22	81	.82

2. Let $r(x)$, $s(x)$, and $t(x)$ be defined by Table 6.28. Prepare tables for the functions defined below.

(a) $f(x) = r(x) + t(x)$
(b) $g(x) = 4 - 2s(x)$
(c) $h(x) = r(x)t(x)$
(d) $j(x) = \dfrac{r(x) - t(x)}{s(x)}$
(e) $k(x) = r(x)^2$
(f) $l(x) = r(x) + s(x)t(x)$

TABLE 6.28

x	$r(x)$	$s(x)$	$t(x)$
-2	4	-2	8
-1	5	2	5
0	6	-2	7
1	7	2	-3
2	8	-2	2
3	9	2	13

3. Graph the indicated functions using the graph of g in Figure 6.23.

    (a) $y = g(x) - 3$

    (b) $y = g(x) + x$

Figure 6.23

4. Let the functions f and g be defined as in Table 6.29.

    TABLE 6.29

x	$f(x)$	$g(x)$
1	3	2
2	4	1
3	1	4
4	2	3

    Complete the tables for the following functions.

    (a) $n(x) = f(x) + g(x)$

    (b) $p(x) = 2f(x)g(x) - f(x)$

    (c) $q(x) = g(x)/f(x)$

5. Let $f(x) = x + 1$ and $g(x) = x^2$. In parts (a)-(e) write a general formula for the combinations described in terms of $f(x)$ and $g(x)$. Then evaluate the formulas for $x = 3$. Finally, write a formula for each combination in terms of x. Check your formulas for $x = 3$.

    (a) $h(x)$ is the sum of $f(x)$ and $g(x)$.

    (b) $j(x)$ is the difference between $g(x)$ and two times $f(x)$.

    (c) $k(x)$ is the product of $f(x)$ and $g(x)$.

    (d) $m(x)$ is the ratio of $g(x)$ to $f(x)$.

    (e) $n(x)$ is defined by the equation $n(x) = (f(x))^2 - g(x)$.

6. Let $u(x)$, $v(x)$, and $w(x)$ be defined by the following formulas:

    $$u(x) = 2x - 1, \quad v(x) = 1 - x, \quad \text{and} \quad w(x) = \frac{1}{x}.$$

    Find simplified formulas for the following functions.

    (a) $f(x) = u(x) + v(x)$

    (b) $g(x) = v(x)w(x)$

    (c) $h(x) = 2u(x) - 3v(x)$

    (d) $j(x) = \dfrac{u(x)}{w(x)}$

    (e) $k(x) = v(x)^2$

    (f) $l(x) = u(x) - v(x) - w(x)$

7. Table 6.30 gives N, the number of existing warheads, and P, the world's population, both as functions of t, the time elapsed in years since 1980.

TABLE 6.30   *The number of existing warheads, N, and the world's population, P*

t, time in years	$N(t)$, number of warheads	$P(t)$, world population
0	30,000	
5		$4,500,000,000$
10	$21,000$	
15		$5,695,300,000$

(a) Assume that $P(t)$ is an exponential function. Based on Table 6.30, find a formula for $P(t)$.

(b) According to your formula for $P(t)$, by what percent does the population change each year?

(c) Assume that $N(t)$ is a linear function of time. Based on Table 6.30, find a formula for $N(t)$.

(d) Define f by the following formula:

$$f(t) = \frac{N(t)}{P(t)}.$$

Construct a table of values for f for $t = 0, 5, 10, 15$.

(e) Is f an exponential function, a linear function, both, or neither? Justify your answer.

(f) Give the physical significance of $f(t)$; that is, what does the function $f(t)$ represent?

8. Let $f(t)$ be the number of males in Canada in year t.
Let $g(t)$ be the number of females in Canada in year t.
Let $h(t)$ be the average income, in Canadian dollars, of females in Canada in year t.

(a) Find the function $p(t)$ which gives the number of people populating Canada in year t.

(b) Find the total amount of money $m(t)$ earned by Canadian females in year t.

9. If possible, use a computer or graphing calculator for this problem.

(a) Graph the functions $f(x) = (x-4)^2 - 2$ and $g(x) = -(x-2)^2 + 8$ on the same set of axes.

(b) Make a table of values for each function for $x = 0, 1, 2, ..., 6$.

(c) Make a table of values for the function $y = f(x) - g(x)$ for $x = 0, 1, 2, ..., 6$.

(d) On your graph, sketch the vertical line segment of length $f(x) - g(x)$ for each integer value of x from 0 to 6. Check that the segment lengths agree with the table values from part (c).

(e) Plot the values from your table for the function $y = f(x) - g(x)$ on your graph.

(f) Simplify the algebraic formulas for $f(x)$ and $g(x)$ given in part (a). Find a formula for the function $y = f(x) - g(x)$.

(g) Graph the function $y = f(x) - g(x)$ on top of your other graphs. Does the graph pass through the points you plotted in part (e)?

10. The graphs of $f(x)$ and $g(x)$ are given in Figure 6.24. Let $h(x) = g(x) - f(x)$. Sketch a graph of $y = h(x)$. On the graph of $y = h(x)$, label the points whose x-coordinates are $x = a$, $x = b$, and $x = c$. Also label the y-intercept.

11. The graphs of two functions, $f(x)$ and $g(x)$ are shown in Figure 6.25.
    (a) Find possible formulas for the functions.
    (b) Let $h(x) = f(x) \cdot g(x)$. Graph $f(x)$, $g(x)$ and $h(x)$ on the same set of axes.

Figure 6.24

Figure 6.25

12. The function of f in part (a) can you Sketch two linear functions whose product would yield the function of f in part (a). Explain why this is not possible for the function q in part (b).

(a)

(b)

Figure 6.26

13. Suppose that an average of 50,000 people visit Riverside Amusement Park each day in the summer. The park presently charges $15.00 for an admission ticket. The park administrator commissioned consultants who have determined that for each $1.00 increase in the entrance price, the park loses an average of 2500 customers per day. Express the daily revenue from ticket sales as a function of the number of $1.00 price increases. What ticket price will maximize the revenue from ticket sales?

14. Below are the graphs of two functions, $a(x)$ and $b(x)$. Let $c(x) = a(x) \cdot b(x)$. There is not enough information given to determine the formulas for these functions, but still you can do the following: Using what you learned in Problem 11, sketch a graph of $c(x)$ together with $a(x)$ and $b(x)$. (It will be a rough sketch.) Use your calculator to help you by trying out some specific examples.

Figure 6.27

15. Is the following statement true or false? If $f(x) \cdot g(x)$ is an odd function, then both $f(x)$ and $g(x)$ are odd functions. Explain your answer.

16. (a) Is the sum of two even functions even, odd, or neither? Justify your answer.
    (b) Is the sum of two odd functions even, odd, or neither? Justify your answer.
    (c) Is the sum of an even and an odd functions even, odd, or neither? Justify your answer.

17. Suppose $f(x) = kx^2 + B$ and that $g(x) = C^{2x}$. If
$$h(x) = kx^2 C^{2x} + BC^{2x} + C^{2x},$$
and if $f(3) = 7$ and $g(3) = 5$, evaluate $h(3)$.

REVIEW PROBLEMS FOR CHAPTER SIX

1. Define the functions f, g, and h by the following formulas:
$$f(x) = x^2 + x, \qquad g(x) = 2x - 3 \qquad \text{and} \qquad h(x) = \frac{x}{1-x}.$$

   Find formulas, in terms of x, for the following functions.
   (a) $f(2x)$
   (b) $g(x^2)$
   (c) $h(1-x)$
   (d) $(f(x))^2$
   (e) $g^{-1}(x)$
   (f) $(h(x))^{-1}$
   (g) $f(x) \cdot g(x)$
   (h) $h(f(x))$

2. Given f in Figure 6.28 and g in Figure 6.29, graph the indicated functions.
   (a) $f(x) - g(x)$
   (b) $f(g(x))$
   (c) $g(f(x))$
   (d) $g(f(x-2))$

Figure 6.28

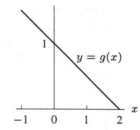

Figure 6.29

3. Table 6.31 gives a range of temperatures in degrees Fahrenheit and the corresponding temperatures in degrees Celsius.

TABLE 6.31   *The temperature Celsius, y, as a function of the temperature Fahrenheit, x*

Temperature in °F, x	−4	5	14	23	32	41	50	59	68	77	86
Temperature in °C, $y = f(x)$	−20	−15	−10	−5	0	5	10	15	20	25	30

Table 6.32 gives a range of temperatures in degrees Celsius and the corresponding temperatures in degrees Fahrenheit.

TABLE 6.32   *The temperature Fahrenheit, y, as a function of the temperature Celsius, x*

Temperature in °C, x	−20	−15	−10	−5	0	5	10	15	20	25	30
Temperature in °F, $y = g(x)$	−4	5	14	23	32	41	50	59	68	77	86

Referring to Tables 6.31 and 6.32, evaluate and interpret the following expressions.

(a) $g(f(23))$ ⁼23 (b) $f(g(5))$ = 5

4. Find inverses for the following functions.

(a) $f(x) = x + 5$ (b) $g(x) = 1 - x$ (c) $h(x) = \sqrt{x}$
(d) $j(x) = \frac{1}{x}$ (e) $k(x) = \frac{x}{x-1}$ (f) $l(x) = \sqrt{1 - 2x^2}$
(g) $m(x) = \frac{1}{x} - x$ (h) $n(x) = (1 + x^2)^2$ (i) $o(x) = \frac{1}{1+\frac{1}{x}}$

5. The graph of $f(x)$ is given in Figure 6.30. Graph $y = f(x) + f(-x)$. Label the y-intercept.

6. The graphs of f and g are given in Figure 6.31.

(a) Evaluate $f(g(a))$.
(b) Evaluate $g(f(c))$. = b
(c) Evaluate $f^{-1}(b) - g^{-1}(b)$.
(d) For what value(s) of x is $f(x) \le g(x)$?

Figure 6.30

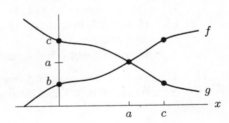

Figure 6.31

7. A research facility on the Isle of Shoals has a limited quantity (800 gal) of fresh water which it must conserve over a two-month period.

(a) If there are 7 members of the research team, and each is allotted 2 gallons of water per day (for cooking and drinking), find a formula for $f(t)$, the amount of fresh water left on the island after t days has elapsed.

(b) Evaluate and interpret the following expressions

(i) $f(0)$ (ii) $f^{-1}(0)$
(iii) t if $f(t) = \frac{1}{2}f(0)$ (iv) $800 - f(t)$

8. A company has found that there is a linear relationship between the number of units of its product it can sell and the amount of money that it spends on advertising. Specifically, the

company knows that if it spends $25,000 on advertising, it will sell 400 units, and that for each $5,000 more or less spent, it will sell 20 units more or less, respectively. Define $N(x)$ to be the number of units sold as a function of the amount spent on advertising, x.

   (a) Calculate and interpret $N(20{,}000)$.

   (b) Find a formula for $N(x)$ in terms of x.

   (c) Give interpretations of the slope and the x- and y-intercepts of $N(x)$ if possible.

   (d) Calculate and interpret $N^{-1}(500)$.

   (e) Suppose that an internal audit reveals that the profit made by the company on the sale of 10 units of its product, before advertising costs have been accounted for, is $2,000. What are the implications regarding the company's advertising campaign? Discuss.

9. Suppose the population of a certain rapidly growing town triples every seven years.

   (a) If in year zero the population is P_0, find a formula for $P(t)$, the population after t years have elapsed.

   (b) By approximately what percent does the town's population increase each year?

   (c) Find a formula for $P^{-1}(x)$. How is this function useful?

   (d) The population's *doubling time* is the amount of time required for it to double. Calculate the doubling time of $P(t)$.

10. A hot brick is removed from a kiln. Initially, the temperature of the brick is 200°C above room temperature. Over time, the brick cools off, so that after 2 hours have elapsed, the brick is only 20°C above room temperature. Let $y = H(t)$ be the brick's temperature above room temperature t hours after removing the brick from the kiln. Assume that $H(t)$ is an exponential function.

   (a) Find a formula for $H(t)$.

   (b) How many degrees does the brick's temperature drop during the first quarter hour? During the next quarter hour?

   (c) Find a formula for and give an interpretation of $H^{-1}(y)$.

   (d) How much time must elapse before the brick's temperature is only 5°C above room temperature?

   (e) Interpret the physical meaning of the horizontal asymptote of $H(t)$.

11. The graph of $y = g(x)$ is given in Figure 6.32. Graph the following related functions on a separate set of axes. Label intercepts and other relevant points.

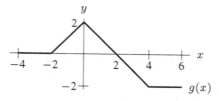

Figure 6.32

   (a) $y = g(2x)$

   (b) $y = g(-2x)$

   (c) $y = 2g(x)$

   (d) $y = -\frac{1}{2}g(x + 1)$

   (e) $y = 3g(x) - 1$

   (f) $y = \dfrac{1}{g(x)}$

   (g) $y = \left(g(x)\right)^2$

   (h) $y = g(g(x))$

   (i) $x = g(y)$

12. Let $f(x)$ be defined by the graph in Figure 6.33:

Figure 6.33

For each function in (a)–(g), indicate the graph in Figure 6.34 to which it corresponds. Note that there may be some functions whose graphs are not shown. Indicate this by writing "none" where appropriate.

(I)   (II)

(III)   (IV)

Figure 6.34

(a) $y = -f(x)$
(b) $y = f(-x)$
(c) $y = f(-x) - 2$
(d) $y = f^{-1}(x)$
(e) $y = -f^{-1}(x)$
(f) $y = f(x + 1)$
(g) $y = -(f(x) - 2)$

13. Figure 6.35 gives the graph of $h(x)$:

Figure 6.35

Sketch the following transformations of $h(x)$. For each graph, label the points corresponding to the points P and Q from the figure. (a) $y = -2h(x)$ (b) $y = h(-x)$
(c) $y = h(-\frac{1}{2}x)$ (d) $y = h^{-1}(x)$

14. Graph the indicated functions using the graphs of f and g shown in Figure 6.36.

   (a) $f(x) + g(x)$ (b) $2g(x)$
   (c) $g(f(x))$ (d) $f(x) - g(x)$
   (e) $g(f(x-2))$ (f) $f(x+1) + g(x+1) + 0.5$

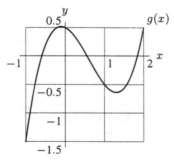

Figure 6.36

Problems 15–18 are based on the following situation:
You want to hire a construction company to build some office space, and decide to hire either Ace Construction or Space Contractors. The two companies seem comparable in terms of quality of work and job-completion time, as well as job-site safety and other concerns.

   Let $f(x)$ be the average total cost in dollars of building x square feet of office space, as estimated by Ace.

15. Describe in words what the following equation tells you: $f(2000) = 200{,}000$

16. Let $g(x) = \frac{f(x)}{x}$. Using the information from Problem 15, evaluate $g(2000)$, and describe in words what $g(2000)$ represents. (Hint: think about the units.)

17. One of Ace's contractors tells you that, due to the economies of scale, "Building twice as much office space always costs less than twice as much." Express the contactor's statement symbolically, in terms of f and x. (Hint: If you are building x square feet, how would you represent the cost? How would you represent twice the cost? How would you represent the cost of building twice as many square feet?)

18. Suppose that $q > p$ and $p > 1$. Assuming that the contractor's statement is correct, rank the following in increasing order, using inequality signs: $f(p)$, $g(p)$, $f(q)$, $g(q)$.

For Problems 19–21, let $h(x)$ be the total number of square feet of office space you can build with x dollars, as estimated by Space Contractors.

19. Describe what the following equation tells you: $h(200{,}000) = 1{,}500$

20. Let $j(x)$ be the average cost per square foot of office space. (The cost is given in dollars.) Give an equation for $j(x)$. (Your equation will have $h(x)$ in it.)

21. You do some research which reveals that $h(f(x)) < x$ for every value of x you checked. Explain the implications of this statement. (Hint: Which construction company seems more economical?)

22. Many college students must work in order to defray tuition costs. However, the number of hours worked usually affects the number of credits taken. In turn, study time in preparation for class is dependent on credits taken. Tables 6.33 and 6.34 show these relationships.

(a) Construct a table showing the relationship between number of hours worked and number of hours of study time.

(b) Make a graph of this relationship. Is it linear?

(c) Can you find a situation in which a student reduces his or her job hours, with the result that the number of credits increases and there is also more time available for leisure activities?

TABLE 6.33

Number of hours worked per week	Number of credits taken
$0 \le h < 4$	18
$4 \le h < 8$	17
$8 \le h < 12$	16
$12 \le h < 16$	15
$16 \le h < 20$	14
$20 \le h < 24$	13
$24 \le h < 28$	12

TABLE 6.34

Number of credits taken	Number of hours of study time per week
12	12
13	14
14	16
15	20
16	25
17	31
18	39

23. Suppose that $f(x) = g(h(x))$. Find possible formulas for $g(x)$ and $h(x)$ assuming that $f(x)$ is defined by the following formulas. (There may be more than one possible answer, but you should assume $g(x) \ne x$ and $h(x) \ne x$.)

(a) $f(x) = 2x + 1$

(b) $f(x) = (x + 3)^2$

(c) $f(x) = \sqrt{1 + \sqrt{x}}$

(d) $f(x) = 9x^2 + 3x$

(e) $f(x) = \dfrac{1}{x^2 + 8x + 16}$

(f) $f(x) = \dfrac{1}{x^2 + 8x + 17}$

24. Suppose that $f(x) = x - 3$ and $g(x) = 2x + 5$.

(a) If $f(h(x)) = \sqrt{x}$, find a formula for $h(x)$.

(b) If $j(g(x)) = \dfrac{2x + 5}{1 + \sqrt{2x + 5}}$, find a formula for $j(x)$.

(c) If $k(g(x)) = \dfrac{2x + 6}{1 + \sqrt{2x + 4}}$, find a formula for $k(x)$.

(d) If $g(l(x)) = 6x - 7$, find a formula for $l(x)$.

25. Find a formula for the inverse function in each of the following. (You may assume these functions are defined on domains on which they are invertible, and you need not state the domain of the inverse.)

(a) $f(x) = 3x - 7$

(b) $g(x) = \dfrac{1}{x} - 2$

(c) $h(x) = \dfrac{2x + 1}{3x - 2}$

(d) $j(x) = \sqrt{1 + \sqrt{x}}$

(e) $k(x) = \dfrac{3 - \sqrt{x}}{\sqrt{x} + 2}$

(f) $l(x) = \dfrac{2 - \dfrac{1}{x}}{3 - \dfrac{2}{x}}$

26. Find the inverses of the following functions.

(a) $f(x) = \dfrac{3 \cdot 2^x + 1}{3 \cdot 2^x + 3}$

(b) $g(x) = \dfrac{\ln x - 5}{2 \ln x + 7}$

(c) $h(x) = \log\left(\dfrac{x + 5}{x - 4}\right)$

27. Let $f(x) = \dfrac{1}{x + 1}$. Find and simplify $f\left(\dfrac{1}{x}\right) + \dfrac{1}{f(x)}$.

28. Let $f(x) = 12 - 4x$, $g(x) = 1/x$, and $h(x) = \sqrt{x - 4}$.
    (a) What must the domain of $u(x)$ be if $u(x) = g(f(x))$?
    (b) What must the domain of $u(x)$ be if, instead, $u(x) = h(f(x))$?

29. Find the inverse of each of the following functions. You do not need to state the domain of the inverse, and you may assume that each of the functions is defined on a domain where it is invertible.
    (a) $f(x) = \cos \sqrt{x}$
    (b) $g(x) = 2^{\sin x}$
    (c) $h(x) = \sin(2x) \cos(2x)$
    (d) $j(x) = \dfrac{\sin x}{2 - \sin x}$

30. Graph $y_1 = \ln(|x - 3|)$ and $y_2 = \ln(|x|)$.

31. For any positive integer x, let $f(x) = 1$ if x is odd and $f(x) = 0$ if x is even. Also, let $g(x) = 1$ if x is even and $g(x) = 0$ if x is odd. Circle those statements which are always true: (Hint: Recall that ab is even unless both a and b are odd.)
    (i) $f(ab) = f(a)f(b)$
    (ii) $g(ab) = g(a)g(b)$
    (iii) $f(g(x)) = f(x)$
    (iv) $g(f(x)) = g(x)$
    (v) $f^{-1}(x)$ does not exist.
    (vi) $f(x) \neq 1 - g(x)$

32. Suppose f and g are invertible functions defined for all values of x. For each of the following statements, write *true* if the statement must be true, being sure to justify your response; otherwise, write *false*, and give a specific example of a function or functions for which the statement does not hold.
    Example: The statement $f(x) + g(x) = g(x) + f(x)$ must be true because the expressions $f(x)$ and $g(x)$ represent numbers, and the order in which you add numbers does not matter.
    Example: The statement $f(a + b) = f(a) + f(b)$ is not necessarily true. For example, if $f(x) = x^2$, then $f(a + b) = (a + b)^2 = a^2 + 2ab + b^2$, whereas $f(a) + f(b) = a^2 + b^2$. Since $a^2 + b^2$ need not equal $a^2 + 2ab + b^2$, $f(a + b)$ need not equal $f(a) + f(b)$.
    (a) $f(a) = g(b)$ implies $f(b) = g(a)$
    (b) $f(g(x)) = g(f(x))$
    (c) $f(ab) = f(a) \cdot f(b)$
    (d) $f(a) = f(b)$ implies $a = b$
    (e) $f(x^2) = (f(x))^2$
    (f) $f(x) \neq f^{-1}(x)$.

33. Recall that a function is said to be *increasing* if the dependent quantity increases whenever the independent quantity increases. A function is said to be *decreasing* if the dependent quantity decreases whenever the independent quantity increases. Let $f(x)$ be an increasing function and $g(x)$ be a decreasing function. Are the following functions increasing, decreasing, or can't we tell? Explain your reasoning in each case.
    (a) $f(f(x))$
    (b) $f(g(x))$
    (c) $g(g(x))$
    (d) $g(f(x))$
    (e) $f(x) + g(x)$
    (f) $f(x) - g(x)$

34. Let $f(x)$ be defined for positive integer values of x as the remainder obtained upon division of x by 3. For example, $f(6) = 0$, because 6 divided by 3 equals 2 with a remainder of 0. Likewise, $f(7) = 1$, because 7 divided by 3 equals 2 with a remainder of 1, and $f(8) = 2$, because 8 divided by 3 equals 2 with a remainder of 2. Answer the following.
    (a) Evaluate $f(17)$, $f(29)$, $f(99)$.
    (b) Find a formula for $f(3x)$.
    (c) Is $f(x)$ invertible?
    (d) Find a formula in terms of $f(x)$ for $f(f(x))$.
    (e) Does $f(x + y)$ necessarily equal $f(x) + f(y)$?

Chapter 6

Polynomial and Rational Functions

7.1 INTRODUCTION TO THE FAMILY OF POWER FUNCTIONS

What is a Power Function?

In Section 1.5, we said that if y is proportional to a constant power of x, then y is called a *power function* of x. Formally:

> If k and p are any constants, then
> $$y = kx^p$$
> is a **power function** of x.

Power functions show up in geometry when discussing areas and volumes. They also show up in physics and chemistry when talking about speed, weight, and energy. We have already encountered several examples of power functions.

Example 1 If A represents the area of a circle of radius r, then

$$A = \pi r^2.$$

From this formula, we see that A is a power function of r. In this case, $p = 2$ and $k = \pi$.

Example 2 If V represents the volume of a sphere of radius r, then

$$V = \frac{4}{3}\pi r^3.$$

V is a power function of r, with $p = 3$ and $k = \frac{4}{3}\pi$.

Example 3 A grandfather clock keeps time by using a pendulum, a long arm with a weight at the bottom that swings back and forth. Such pendulums always take about the same amount of time to complete one swing. This is how the clock keeps time. The *period* of a pendulum is the length of time it takes for the pendulum to complete one full swing. For small swings, the period T is proportional to the square root of l, the length of the pendulum. This gives

$$T = k\sqrt{l} = kl^{\frac{1}{2}}$$

So T is a power function of l. Here, $p = \frac{1}{2}$ and k is a parameter that depends on the clock.

Example 4 The weight of an object is inversely proportional to the square of the object's distance from the earth's center. If w is the object's weight and d is its distance from the center of the earth, then

$$w = \frac{k}{d^2} = kd^{-2}.$$

Since w is proportional to a constant power of d, the quantity w is a power function of d; $p = -2$ and k is a constant.

The Parameter k is a Stretch Factor

For the power function $y = kx^p$, the parameter k is a stretch factor. To begin our study of power functions, we will set $k = 1$, so that the formula becomes $y = x^p$. This will allow us to focus our attention on the effect of the parameter p.

The Graphs of Six Special Power Functions

We will now think about the graphs of six special power functions:

$$y = x^2, \qquad y = x^3, \qquad y = x^{-1}, \qquad y = x^{-2}, \qquad y = x^{\frac{1}{2}}, \quad \text{and} \quad y = x^{\frac{1}{3}}.$$

By studying these six special functions, we can learn quite a bit about the entire family of power functions.

The graphs of $y = x^2$ and $y = x^3$

Figure 7.1 shows the graphs of $y = x^2$ and $y = x^3$ as they appear on the window $-2 \leq x \leq 2$, $-4 \leq y \leq 4$. The graph of $y = x^2$ is a parabola; we discussed it thoroughly in Section 4.4. The function $y = x^3$ is often called a *cubic* function. There are a number of details worth noticing about these graphs.

- Both graphs pass through the origin.
- The graph of $y = x^2$ is symmetric across the y-axis, whereas the graph of $y = x^3$ is symmetric across the origin. Thus, $y = x^2$ is an even function while $y = x^3$ is an odd function.
- As x grows large and positive, both $y = x^2$ and $y = x^3$ tend to positive infinity. But as $x \to -\infty$, $x^2 \to +\infty$ while $x^3 \to -\infty$.
- As x increases, $y = x^3$ increases monotonically for all x, whereas x^2 decreases for $x < 0$ and increases for $x > 0$.
- $y = x^2$ is concave up for all x whereas $y = x^3$ is concave up for $x > 0$ and concave down for $x < 0$.
- The graphs for both functions are very flat for values of x near zero, but for values of x far from zero, both graphs are quite steep.

TABLE 7.1   *The values of x^2 and x^3 grow rapidly for even modest values of x.*

x	0	10	20	30	40	50
$y = x^2$	0	100	400	900	1600	2500
$y = x^3$	0	1000	8000	27,000	64,000	125,000

This last point merits an additional comment. Table 7.1 gives the values of x^2 and x^3 for $x = 0$, 10, 20, 30, 40, and 50. As you can see from the table, both functions grow rapidly as x increases, and $y = x^3$ grows even more rapidly than $y = x^2$.

On the other hand, if you use a calculator or computer to zoom in on the point $(0, 0)$, you will see that at this point both graphs are almost perfectly flat. For $y = x^2$, the point $(0, 0)$ is called the *vertex*. The function $y = x^3$ changes concavity at $(0, 0)$. A point where a function changes concavity is called an *inflection point*.

Figure 7.1: The graphs of $y = x^2$ and $y = x^3$ on the window $-2 \leq x \leq 2$, $-4 \leq y \leq 4$

The graphs of $y = x^{-1}$ and $y = x^{-2}$

Figure 7.2 shows the graphs of $y = x^{-1}$ and $y = x^{-2}$ as they appear on the window $-2 \le x \le 2$, $-4 \le y \le 4$. Since the formula for $y = x^{-1}$ can be written as $y = \frac{1}{x}$, we see that y is the reciprocal of x. Its graph is known as a *hyperbola* or *rectangular hyperbola*. Since the formula for $y = x^{-2}$ can be written as $y = \frac{1}{x^2}$, this function is sometimes called an *inverse-square function*. There are a number of details worth noticing about these graphs.

- Neither graph ever crosses the x-axis or the y-axis. In fact, neither function is defined at $x = 0$, so the graphs are both "broken" at $x = 0$. Such a break is called a *discontinuity*.

- The graph of $y = x^{-1}$ is symmetric across the origin so this is an odd function. On the other hand, the graph of $y = x^{-2}$ is symmetric across the y-axis and is thus even.

- The value of $y = x^{-1}$ is negative for $x < 0$ and positive for $x > 0$. The value of x^{-2} is positive for all $x \ne 0$.

- The graph of $y = x^{-1}$ decreases for all $x \ne 0$. On the other hand, the graph of $y = x^{-2}$ increases for $x < 0$ and decreases for $x > 0$.

- $y = x^{-1}$ is concave down for $x < 0$ and concave up for $x > 0$. On the other hand, $y = x^{-2}$ is concave up for both $x < 0$ and for $x > 0$.

- Both graphs have a horizontal asymptote at $y = 0$ and a vertical asymptote at $x = 0$.

Figure 7.2: The graphs of $y = x^{-1}$ and $y = x^{-2}$ on the window $-2 \le x \le 2, -4 \le y \le 4$

Let's consider this last point more carefully. As x grows large, the values of $\frac{1}{x}$ and $\frac{1}{x^2}$ grow small. Table 7.2 gives values of these functions for $x = 10, 20, \ldots, 50$.

Both $y = \frac{1}{x}$ and $y = \frac{1}{x^2}$ get closer and closer to zero as x increases. In fact, the values of these functions can be brought as close to zero as we like by choosing a sufficiently large x. Graphically, this means that the curves $y = \frac{1}{x}$ and $y = \frac{1}{x^2}$ draw closer and closer to the x-axis for large values of x.

On the other hand, as x gets close to zero, the values of $\frac{1}{x}$ and $\frac{1}{x^2}$ get very large. Table 7.3 gives values of these functions for $x = 0.1, 0.05, 0.01, 0.001, 0.0001$, and 0.

Graphically, this means that the curves $y = \frac{1}{x}$ and $y = \frac{1}{x^2}$ shoot up along the y-axis, climbing higher and higher as positive values of x get closer and closer to zero.

TABLE 7.2 *The values of x^{-1} and x^{-2} approach zero as x grows large*

x	0	10	20	30	40	50
$y = \frac{1}{x}$	—	0.1	0.05	0.033	0.025	0.02
$y = \frac{1}{x^2}$	—	0.01	0.0025	0.0011	0.0006	0.0004

TABLE 7.3 *The values of x^{-1} and x^{-2} grow large as x approaches zero from the positive side. (Notice that x-values are in reverse order.)*

x	0.1	0.05	0.01	0.001	0.0001	0
$y = \frac{1}{x}$	10	20	100	1000	10,000	undefined
$y = \frac{1}{x^2}$	100	400	10,000	1,000,000	100,000,000	undefined

The graphs of $y = x^{\frac{1}{2}}$ and $y = x^{\frac{1}{3}}$

Figure 7.3 shows the graphs of $y = x^{\frac{1}{2}}$ and $y = x^{\frac{1}{3}}$ as they appear on the window $-2 \le x \le 2$, $-2 \le y \le 2$. (Notice that this window is different from the one used for Figures 7.1 and 7.2.)

The formulas for these functions can also be written as $y = \sqrt{x}$ and $y = \sqrt[3]{x}$. Because $\sqrt{x}$ is only defined for $x \ge 0$, the graph of $y = x^{\frac{1}{2}}$ does not extend to the left of the y-axis. However, $\sqrt[3]{x}$ is defined for all x (including negative values). For example, $\sqrt[3]{-8} = -2$, because $(-2)(-2)(-2) = -8$. Thus, the graph of $y = \sqrt[3]{x}$ extends both to the left and the right of the y-axis.

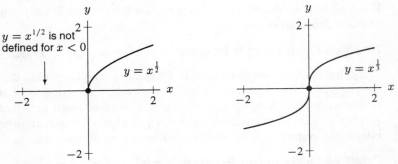

Figure 7.3: The graphs of $y = x^{\frac{1}{2}}$ and $y = x^{\frac{1}{3}}$ on the window
$-2 \le x \le 2$, $-2 \le y \le 2$

Here are some more important details about the graphs of $y = x^{\frac{1}{2}}$ and $y = x^{\frac{1}{3}}$:

- Both graphs contain the origin.
- The graph of $x^{\frac{1}{3}}$ is symmetric across the origin, so this is an odd function.
- As x grows large, both $y = x^{\frac{1}{2}}$ and $y = x^{\frac{1}{3}}$ tend to positive infinity, although they do so very slowly.

Figure 7.4: The graphs of $y = x^2$ (for $x > 0$) and $y = x^{\frac{1}{2}}$ are reflections across the line $y = x$, as are the graphs $y = x^3$ and $y = x^{\frac{1}{3}}$. This is because these functions are inverses.

Chapter 6/   5

- Both functions increase on their domains.
- Both graphs are concave down for $x > 0$. The graph of $y = x^{\frac{1}{3}}$ is concave up for $x < 0$.
- The graphs of both functions are very steep near $x = 0$.

To appreciate this last point better, try zooming in on the graphs near the origin. Both of them are so steep there that they are difficult to distinguish from the y-axis. It's also worth noticing that for $x > 0$, $y = x^2$ and $y = x^{\frac{1}{2}}$ are inverse functions. In other words, if f is defined by the equation $f(x) = x^2$ for $x > 0$, then $f^{-1}(x) = x^{\frac{1}{2}}$ for $x > 0$. Thus, the graph of $y = x^{\frac{1}{2}}$ can be found by flipping the right half of the graph of $y = x^2$ across the line $y = x$. Similarly, $y = x^3$ and $y = x^{\frac{1}{3}}$ are also inverse functions, and their graphs are also reflections of each other across the line $y = x$. (See Figure 7.4.)

Why Did We Pick These Six Functions?

Most power functions have something in common with one of these six functions. For instance, the functions $y = x^4$, $y = x^6$, and $y = x^8$ share many features with the function $y = x^2$. Likewise, the functions $y = x^{-3}$, $y = x^{-5}$, and $y = x^{-7}$ share many features with the function $y = x^{-1}$. Knowing what we do about these six particular functions allows us to say quite a bit about the family of power functions in general.

Positive Even Integer Powers: $y = x^2$, $y = x^4$, $y = x^6$, ...

The graph of any power function with p a positive even integer has the same overall appearance as the graph of x^2. For instance, Figure 7.5 shows the graphs of $y = x^2$ and $y = x^4$. Both graphs are similar in shape, although the graph of $y = x^4$ is much flatter or "blunter" near the origin than the graph of $y = x^2$, and away from the origin $y = x^4$ is much steeper. In general, if p is a positive even integer, the graph of $y = x^p$ will have the same overall appearance as the graph of $y = x^2$.

Positive Odd Integer Powers: $y = x^3$, $y = x^5$, $y = x^7$, ...

Figure 7.6 shows the graphs of $y = x^3$ and $y = x^5$. Although the graph of $y = x^5$ is flatter near the origin and steeper far from the origin than is the graph of $y = x^3$, these graphs do have quite a bit in common. The same can be said for any power function $y = x^p$ for which p is a positive odd integer.

Negative Integer Powers: $y = x^{-1}, x^{-3}, x^{-5}, ...,$ and $y = x^{-2}, x^{-4}, x^{-6}$

Figure 7.7 gives graphs of $y = x^{-1}$ and $y = x^{-3}$, while Figure 7.8 gives graphs of $y = x^{-2}$ and $y = x^{-4}$. If p is a negative odd integer, then the graph of $y = x^p$ will be similar to the graphs

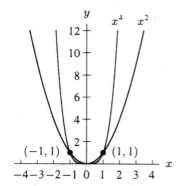

Figure 7.5: Graphs of $y = x^2$ and $y = x^4$

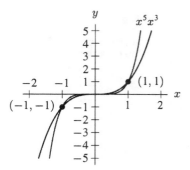

Figure 7.6: Graphs of $y = x^3$, and $y = x^5$

in Figure 7.7, and if p is a negative even integer, then $y = x^p$ will look similar to the graphs in Figure 7.8. There are differences between these graphs, of course. For instance, $y = x^{-3}$ is steeper near the y-axis and flattens towards the x-axis more quickly than $y = x^{-1}$. The same can be said about the graph of $y = x^{-4}$ as compared to $y = x^{-2}$. But overall, these two pairs of graphs serve to indicate the appearance of $y = x^p$ for any negative integer value of p.

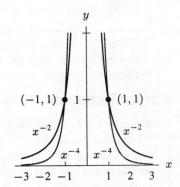

Figure 7.7: Graphs of $y = x^{-1}$ and $y = x^{-3}$

Figure 7.8: Graphs of $y = x^{-2}$ and $y = x^{-4}$

Positive Fractional Powers: $y = x^{\frac{1}{2}}, x^{\frac{1}{3}}, x^{\frac{1}{4}}, ...$

Figure 7.9 shows the graphs of $y = x^{\frac{1}{2}}$ and $y = x^{\frac{1}{4}}$. These graphs have the same overall appearance, although $y = x^{\frac{1}{4}}$ is steeper near the origin and flatter away from the origin than $y = x^{\frac{1}{2}}$. The same can be said about the graphs of $y = x^{\frac{1}{3}}$ and $y = x^{\frac{1}{5}}$ shown in Figure 7.10. In general, if n is a positive integer and if $y = x^{\frac{1}{n}}$, then the graph of this function will look more or less like $y = x^{\frac{1}{2}}$ for n even and more or less like $y = x^{\frac{1}{3}}$ for n odd.

The Symmetry of Power Functions

If $f(x) = kx^p$ and p is an integer, then f will have even symmetry if p is even and odd symmetry if p is odd. This can be shown algebraically and has been left to the exercises. In summary:

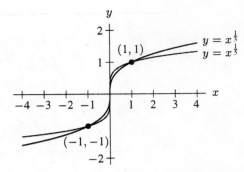

Figure 7.9: The graphs of $y = x^{\frac{1}{2}}$ and $y = x^{\frac{1}{4}}$

Figure 7.10: The graphs of $y = x^{\frac{1}{3}}$ and $y = x^{\frac{1}{5}}$

If $f(x) = kx^p$ and if p is an integer:
- If p is even, f will have even symmetry, that is, symmetry across the y-axis.
- If p is odd, f will have odd symmetry, that is, symmetry across the origin.

If $f(x) = kx^{1/n}$ and if n is an integer:
- If n is odd, f will have odd symmetry.
- If n is even, f will *not* have symmetry, because $f(x)$ is undefined for $x < 0$.

This connection between even and odd powers of x and the symmetry of the graphs of power functions is what led to the terminology "even symmetry" for symmetry across the y-axis and "odd symmetry" for symmetry across the origin.

First Quadrant Behavior of Power Functions

It can be hard to keep track of all the different types of power functions. However, if we focus only on the first quadrant – that is, on the region $x \geq 0, y \geq 0$, – the situation becomes simpler. On this region, the power function $y = x^p$ fits into one of three categories: p greater than 1, p between 0 and 1, and p less than 0. Figure 7.11 shows what these three power functions look like in the first quadrant.

We have left out 2 special cases in Figure 7.11: $p = 1$ and $p = 0$. For $p = 1$, the function $y = x^p$ is the line $y = x$; this line lies midway between the first two graphs in Figure 7.11. For $p = 0$, the function $y = x^p$ is $y = x^0 = 1$, and its graph is a horizontal line. While technically power functions, neither of these functions really fits any of the categories shown by Figure 7.11.

In summary:

In the first quadrant, the power function $y = x^p, p \neq 0, p \neq 1$, belongs to one of the following three categories:
- For $p > 1$, $y = x^p$ is increasing and concave up.
- For $0 < p < 1$, $y = x^p$ is increasing and concave down.
- For $p < 0$, $y = x^p$ is decreasing and concave up.

The following statements are also true:
- For any value of p, the graph of $y = x^p$ contains the point $(1, 1)$.
- For $p > 0$, the graph of $y = x^p$ contains the point $(0, 0)$.
- For $p < 0$, the graph of $y = x^p$ has a vertical asymptote at $x = 0$ and a horizontal asymptote at $y = 0$.

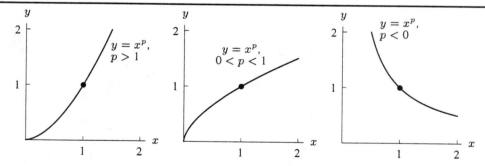

Figure 7.11: Graphs of $y = x^p$ for (respectively) $p > 1, 0 < p < 1$, and $p < 0$

Figure 7.12: The graphs of five power functions for $0 \leq x \leq 10$

The Effect of the Size of p in the First Quadrant

Figure 7.12 gives the graphs of the power functions $y = x^{1/2}$, $y = x^1$, $y = x^2$, $y = x^3$, and $y = x^4$, for $0 \leq x \leq 10$.

All five functions are increasing on this interval, but the higher the power, the more rapid the growth.

In general, in the first quadrant, $y = x^p$ is an increasing function for $p > 0$. The larger the value of p, the more rapid the eventual growth of $y = x^p$. This is also true for $0 < p < 1$.

Example 5 Although we don't normally think of $y = x^{\frac{1}{2}}$ as a rapidly growing function, it grows quite rapidly when compared to functions with smaller powers, such as $y = x^{\frac{1}{4}}$. Figure 7.13 shows the two graphs for $0 \leq x \leq 100$.

Figure 7.13: The graphs of $y = x^{\frac{1}{2}}$ and $y = x^{\frac{1}{4}}$

Figure 7.14: The graphs of the five power functions for $0 \leq x \leq 1.5$

Growth Near the Origin

While the graph of $y = x^4$ eventually climbs much faster than the graphs of $x^{1/2}$, x^1, x^2, and x^3, this situation is reversed near the origin. Figure 7.14 gives the graphs of the functions on the interval $0 \leq x \leq 1.5$. All five functions contain the points $(0,0)$ and $(1,1)$. Notice that, on the interval $0 < x < 1$, the graph of $y = x^{1/2}$ lies *above* the four other graphs, followed in turn by the graphs of x, x^2, x^3, and x^4. The opposite is true for $x > 1$.

To summarize, in the first quadrant $y = x^p$ is an increasing function for $p > 0$. For $x > 1$, higher values of p lead to more rapid growth. For $0 < x < 1$, lower values of p result in more rapid growth.

The Effect of the Size of p for Negative Powers

For $y = x^p$, larger positive values of p indicate more rapid growth in the first quadrant. On the other hand, larger *negative* values of p indicate that the graph of $y = x^p$ will approach its horizontal asymptote more rapidly. Furthermore, larger negative values of p indicate the function $y = x^p$ will climb faster near its vertical asymptote. Figure 7.15 shows the graphs of $y = x^{-1}, y = x^{-2}$, and $y = x^{-3}$ for $0 \leq x \leq 10$. On this scale, we see that $y = x^{-3}$ approaches the x-axis much faster than $y = x^{-2}$ and $y = x^{-1}$.

Figure 7.16 shows these three graphs on a different window, $0 \leq x \leq 0.5, 0 \leq y \leq 20$. On this window we see that near the y-axis, $y = x^{-3}$ climbs much more rapidly than $y = x^{-2}$ and $y = x^{-1}$.

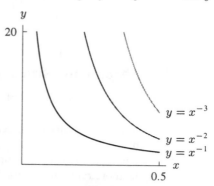

Figure 7.15: The graph of $y = x^{-3}$ approaches the x-axis more rapidly than $y = x^{-2}$ and $y = x^{-1}$

Figure 7.16: The graph of $y = x^{-3}$ climbs faster near the y-axis than do $y = x^{-2}$ and $y = x^{-1}$

In both cases, the asymptotic behavior of $y = x^{-3}$ is more extreme than the other two graphs. The graph of $y = x^{-3}$ "dies off" more rapidly towards $y = 0$ and "blows up" more explosively near $x = 0$. In general, the larger (more negative) the value of p, the more extreme the asymptotic behavior of $y = x^p$.

Problems for Section 7.1

1. Match the functions below with the graphs in Figure 7.17.

   (i) $y = x^5$ (ii) $y = x^2$ (iii) $y = x$ (iv) $y = x^3$

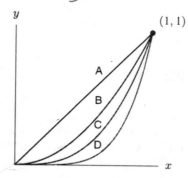

Figure 7.17

2. Describe the behavior of the functions $y = x^{-10}$ and $y = -x^{10}$ as
   (a) $x \to 0$ (b) $x \to \infty$ (c) $x \to -\infty$

3. Compare the graphs of $y = x^2$, $y = x^4$, and $y = x^6$. Describe any similarities or differences you see.

4. Compare the graphs of $y = x^{-2}$, $y = x^{-4}$, and $y = x^{-6}$. Describe any similarities or differences you see.

5. Describe the behavior of the functions $y = x^{-3}$ and $y = x^{1/3}$ as:

   (a) $x \to 0$ from the right   (b) $x \to \infty$

6. (a) Figure 7.18 gives the graphs of two functions f and g. One of these functions can be described by $y = x^n$ and the other by $y = x^{1/n}$, where n is a positive integer. Which is which and why?

Figure 7.18: One of these functions is given by $y = x^n$ and the other is given by $y = x^{1/n}$, n a positive integer.

   (b) What are the coordinates of point A?

7. Assume that $f(x) = 16x^4$ and $g(x) = 4x^2$.

   (a) If $f(x) = g\left(h(x)\right)$ find a possible formula for $h(x)$, assuming $h(x) \le 0$ for all x.

   (b) If $f(x) = j\left(2g(x)\right)$ find a possible formula for $j(x)$, assuming $j(x)$ is a power function.

8. Show that if $f(x) = kx^p$, p an integer, then f will be an even function if p is even, and an odd function if p is odd.

9. A person's weight, w, on a planet of radius d is given by the formula

$$w = kd^{-2}, \quad k > 0,$$

where the constant k depends on the respective masses of the person and the planet; it does not depend on d. (Note that there is a distinction being made here between *mass* and *weight*. For example, an astronaut in orbit may be weightless, but he still has mass.)

   (a) Suppose a man weighs 180 lb on the surface of the earth. How much will he weigh on the surface of a planet as massive as the earth, but whose radius is 3 times as large? One-third as large?

   (b) What fraction of the earth's radius must an equally massive planet have if the surface weight of the man in part (a) is one ton?

10. One of Johannes Kepler's three laws of planetary motion states that the square of the period, P, of a body orbiting the sun is directly proportional to the cube of its average distance, d, from the sun. Symbolically, we have

$$P^2 = kd^3.$$

Solving for P gives

$$P = \sqrt{kd^3} = \sqrt{k}d^{\frac{3}{2}} = k_1 d^{\frac{3}{2}}.$$

For Earth we use a period of 365 days and a distance from the sun of approximately 93,000,000 miles. With this information

$$365 = k_1(93{,}000{,}000)^{\frac{3}{2}},$$

so

$$k_1 = \frac{365}{(93{,}000{,}000)^{\frac{3}{2}}}.$$

This gives

$$P = \frac{365}{(93{,}000{,}000)^{\frac{3}{2}}} \cdot d^{\frac{3}{2}} = 365\frac{d^{\frac{3}{2}}}{(93{,}000{,}000)^{\frac{3}{2}}} = 365\left(\frac{d}{93{,}000{,}000}\right)^{\frac{3}{2}}.$$

Given that the planet Jupiter has an average distance from the sun of 483,000,000 miles, how long in Earth days is a Jupiter year?

11. The radius of a sphere is directly proportional to the cube root of its volume. If a sphere of radius 18.2 cm has a volume of 25,252.4 cm^3, what is the radius of a sphere whose volume is 30,000 cm^3?

12. When an aircraft flies horizontally, the minimum speed required to keep the aircraft aloft (its "stall velocity") is directly proportional to the square root of the quotient of its weight and its wing area. If a breakthrough in materials science allowed the construction of an aircraft with the same weight but twice the wing area, would the "stall velocity" increase or decrease? By what percent?

13. Each of the following functions is a transformation of a power function of the form $y = \frac{1}{x^p}$. For each function:

    - determine p,
    - describe the transformation in words, and
    - graph the function and label any intercepts and asymptotes.

    (a) $f(x) = \dfrac{1}{x - 3} + 4$ (b) $g(x) = -\dfrac{1}{(x - 2)^2} - 3$

    (c) $h(x) = \dfrac{1}{x - 1} + \dfrac{2}{1 - x} + 2$

14. Figure 7.19 gives the graph of $y = f(x)$, which is a transformation of a power function. Find a possible formula for the function.

15. Figure 7.20 gives the graph of $y = g(x)$, which is a transformation of a power function. Find a possible formula for g.

Figure 7.19: The graph of $f(x)$, a transformation of a power function

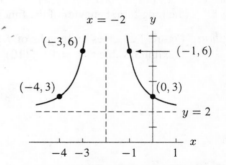

Figure 7.20: The graph of $g(x)$, a transformation of a power function

16. Figure 7.21 gives the graph of $y = f(x)$, a transformation of a power function. Find a formula for f in terms of x.

17. Given the functions $y = kx^{9/16}$, $y = kx^{3/8}$, $y = kx^{5/7}$, $y = kx^{3/11}$. Match the letters in Figure 7.22 with the given functions.

Figure 7.21: The graph of $f(x)$, a transformation of a power function

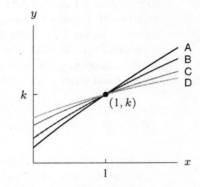

Figure 7.22

18. Our investigation of power functions with rational exponents has been limited to the case of $y = k \cdot x^{p/q}$ with p and q positive integers and $x \geq 0$. Consider the function $y = t(x) = k \cdot x^{p/3}$ where p is *any* integer and x is any real number:

    (a) For what values of p will $t(x)$ have domain restrictions? What will those restrictions be?
    (b) What will be the range of $t(x)$ if p is even?
    (c) What will be the range of $t(x)$ if p is odd?
    (d) What symmetry will the graph of $t(x)$ exhibit if p is even? if p is odd?

7.2 MORE ON POWER FUNCTIONS

The Effect of The Parameter k

From Chapter 4 we know the effect of k on the graph of $y = kx^p$. If $k > 1$, the graph is stretched vertically; if $0 < k < 1$, the graph is compressed vertically. Furthermore, if $k < 0$, the graph is flipped across the x-axis. But how does the value of k affect the long-term growth rate of $y = kx^p$?

Example 1   Let $f(x) = 100x^3$ and $g(x) = x^4$ for $x > 0$. Sketch graphs comparing these two functions. Discuss the long-term behavior of the functions and explain your reasoning.

Solution   Figure 7.23 gives the graphs of f and g on the interval $0 \leq x \leq 10$. On this interval f assumes a maximum value at $x = 10$: $f(10) = 100(10)^3 = 100,000$.

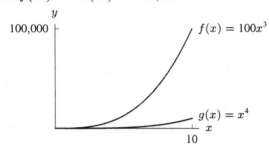

Figure 7.23: On this interval, f climbs faster than g

In Figure 7.23, f seems to be growing faster than g. In fact, g hardly even shows up on this viewing window. This isn't all that surprising, though, since the graph of f is the graph of $y = x^3$ stretched by a factor of 100. Eventually, however, the fact that g has a higher power than f will assert itself. Figures 7.24 and 7.25 demonstrate this by comparing the graphs of f and g on larger intervals. Figure 7.24 shows that $g(x)$ has caught up to $f(x)$ at the point $(100, 1 \times 10^8)$. Figure 7.25 shows that for values of x larger than 100, g remains larger than f. Would it be possible for f to catch back up to g for values of $x > 100$? It is easy to show that this cannot be the case. To see where f and g cross, we must solve the equation $f(x) = g(x)$:

$$x^4 = 100x^3$$
$$x^4 - 100x^3 = 0$$
$$x^3(x - 100) = 0.$$

The solutions to this last equation are $x = 0$ and $x = 100$. Since f and g are never equal for $x > 100$, they cannot meet again. Thus, the function g will remain above f after $x = 100$.

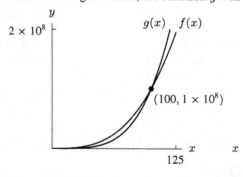

Figure 7.24: On this interval, g catches up to f

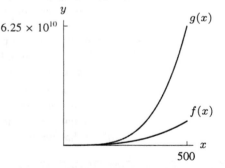

Figure 7.25: On this interval, g is far ahead of f

For $f(x) = kx^p$, the power p has a much more significant effect on the long-range behavior of f than does the constant k, $(k > 0)$. In a race between power functions, the higher power will eventually win — no matter which function starts ahead. We often say that the higher power *dominates* all lower powers of x.

Comparing Exponential Functions and Power Functions

The general formula for the family of power functions,

$$y = kx^p,$$

looks very similar to the general formula for the family of exponential functions,

$$y = AB^x.$$

However, these families are very different. One difference has to do with how fast the functions grow. A power function (for p a positive integer) can increase at phenomenal rates. For example, Table 7.4 shows some values for $y = x^4$ for $0 \le x \le 20$.

TABLE 7.4   *The exponential function $g(x) = 2^x$ eventually grows faster than the power function $f(x) = x^4$*

x	0	5	10	15	20
$f(x) = x^4$	0	625	10,000	50,625	160,000
$g(x) = 2^x$	1	32	1024	32,768	1,048,576

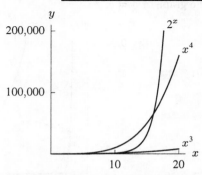

Figure 7.26: The exponential function $y = 2^x$ dominates the power functions $y = x^3$ and $y = x^4$

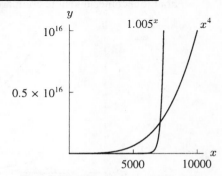

Figure 7.27: The exponential function $y = 1.005^x$ dominates the power function $y = x^4$

Despite the impressive growth in the value of this power function, *any* positive increasing exponential function – no matter how low its percent growth rate – will eventually grow faster than $y = x^4$. In fact, *any* positive increasing exponential function will eventually grow faster than *any* power function – no matter how large its power!

For example, let's compare the growth of $g(x) = 2^x$ to the growth of $f(x) = x^4$. Although g starts off more slowly than f, by the time $x = 20$, $g(20)$ is over 6 times as large as $f(20)$.

Figures 7.26 and 7.27 give two more comparisons of the growth of exponential and power functions. Figure 7.26 compares the graphs of two power functions, $y = x^3$ and $y = x^4$, to the exponential function $y = 2^x$. The exponential function "comes from behind", catching up to x^3 and then to x^4. To get a feel for just how quickly these functions' values are growing, try plotting $y = x^2$ on the viewing window used in Figure 7.26. A fast-growing function in its own right, $y = x^2$ grows so slowly by comparison that it doesn't even show up on this window.

But what about a more slowly growing exponential function? After all, $y = 2^x$ increases at a 100% growth rate. Figure 7.27 compares $y = x^4$ to the exponential function $y = 1.005^x$. Despite the fact that this exponential function creeps along at a 0.5% growth rate, at around $x = 7000$ its values head upward at an explosive rate, leaving the top of the window long before $y = x^4$ gets there. In summary,

> *Any* positive increasing exponential function will eventually grow faster than *any* power function.

Decreasing Exponential Functions

Just as an increasing exponential function will eventually outpace any increasing power function, an exponential decay function will win the race towards the x-axis. In general:

> *Any* positive decreasing exponential function will approach the x-axis faster than any positive decreasing power function.

Figure 7.28 shows the graphs of $y = 0.5^x$, $y = x^{-1}$, and $y = x^{-2}$. Notice that as x increases, the exponential function $y = 0.5^x$ approaches the asymptote at $y = 0$ faster than the power functions $y = x^{-1}$ and $y = x^{-2}$. Figure 7.29 shows what happens for larger values of x. The graph of $y = x^{-1}$ is off the top of the window. The exponential function approaches the x-axis so rapidly that it becomes invisible compared to the graph of $y = x^{-2}$.

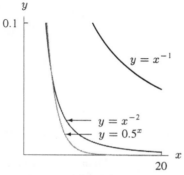

Figure 7.28: The graphs of
$y = x^{-1}$, $y = x^{-2}$, and $y = 0.5^x$

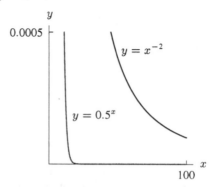

Figure 7.29: The graphs of $y = x^{-2}$ and
$y = 0.5^x$. The graph of $y = x^{-1}$ is off the
top of the window

Comparing Log and Power Functions

Power functions like $y = x^{\frac{1}{2}}$ and $y = x^{\frac{1}{3}}$ grow quite slowly. However, they grow rapidly in comparison to log functions. In fact:

> *Any* positive increasing power function will eventually grow more rapidly than $y = \log x$ and $y = \ln x$.

This statement tells us something about how slowly log functions grow. For example, Figure 7.30 shows the graphs of two power functions which grow very slowly, $y = x^{1/2}$ and $y = x^{1/3}$. However, as slowly as these functions grow, $y = \log x$ eventually grows even more slowly. Similarly, Figure 7.31 shows the functions $y = x^{1/5}$ and $y = \ln x$. The function $y = x^{1/5}$ grows so slowly that even at $x = 2$ million, its value has not reached $y = 20$. Nonetheless, the natural log function eventually grows even more slowly.

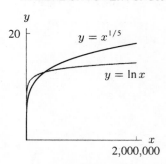

Figure 7.30: Graphs of $y = x^{1/2}$, $y = x^{1/3}$, and $y = \log x$ **Figure 7.31**: Graphs of $y = x^{1/5}$ and $y = \ln x$

Finding the Formula for a Power Function

As is the case for linear and exponential functions, the formula of a power function can be found if we are given two points on the function's graph.

Example 2   Suppose that $g(1) = 6$ and $g(3) = 54$. Find a formula for g, assuming g is:

(a) Linear.   (b) Exponential.   (c) A power function.

Solution   (a) If g is linear, then $g(x) = b + mx$. We use the two points $(1, 6)$ and $(3, 54)$ to solve for m:

$$m = \frac{\Delta y}{\Delta x} = \frac{54 - 6}{3 - 1} = \frac{48}{2} = 24.$$

Solving for b, we have

$$6 = b + 24(1)$$
$$b = -18$$

Thus, if g is linear, its formula is $g(x) = -18 + 24x$.

(b) If g is exponential, then $g(x) = AB^x$. Taking ratios, we have

$$\frac{g(3)}{g(1)} = \frac{AB^3}{AB} = B^2 = \frac{54}{6} = 9.$$

Thus, since B must be positive, we have $B = 3$. Solving for A, we have

$$6 = A(3)^1$$
$$A = 2$$

if g is exponential, its formula is $g(x) = 2 \cdot 3^x$.

(c) If g is a power function, $g(x) = kx^p$. Since $g(1) = 6$,

$$g(1) = k(1)^p = k = 6,$$

so $k = 6$. Solving for p, we have

$$g(3) = 6(3)^p = 54$$

and

$$6(3)^p = 54$$
$$3^p = 9$$
$$3^p = 3^2$$

which gives $p = 2$. Thus, if g is a power function, its formula is $g(x) = 6x^2$.

Chapter 6/ 17

Figure 7.32: The linear function $y = -18 + 24x$, the exponential function $y = 2 \cdot 3^x$, and the power function $y =$ (

The graphs of $y = -18 + 24x$ and $y = 2 \cdot 3^x$, and $y = 6x^2$ are given in Figure 7.32. All three graphs contain the points $(1, 6)$ and $(3, 54)$. However, the graphs have no other points in common. For $x > 3$ the exponential function $y = 2 \cdot 3^x$ will always be larger than the power function $y = 6x^2$, which, in turn, will always be larger than the linear function $y = -18 + 24x$.

Problems for Section 7.2

1. Let $f(x) = 3^x$ and $g(x) = x^3$.

    (a) Complete the following table of values:

    TABLE 7.5

x	-3	-2	-1	0	1	2	3
$f(x)$	.037	.111	.333	1	3	9	27
$g(x)$	-27	-8	-1	0	1	8	27

    (b) Describe the long-range behaviors of f and g as $x \to -\infty$.
    (c) Describe the long-range behaviors of f and g as $x \to +\infty$.

2. The functions $y = x^{-3}$ and $y = 3^{-x}$ both approach zero as $x \longrightarrow \infty$. Which function approaches zero faster? Support your conclusion numerically.

3. The functions $y = x^{-3}$ and $y = e^{-x}$ both approach zero as $x \to \infty$. Which function approaches zero faster? Support your conclusion numerically.

4. Let $f(x) = x^x$. Is f a power function, an exponential function, both, or neither? Discuss.

5. In Figure 7.33, find m, t, and k.

6. Figure 7.34 gives the graphs, for $x \geq 0$, of $f(x) = x^2$, $g(x) = 2x^2$, and $h(x) = x^3$.

    (a) Match these functions to their graphs.
    (b) Does graph (B) intersect graph (A) for $x > 0$? If so, for what value(s) of x? If not, explain how you know.
    (c) Does graph (C) intersect graph (A) for $x > 0$? If so, for what value(s) of x? If not, explain how you know.

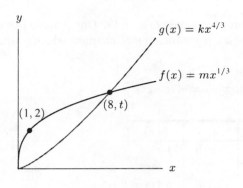

Figure 7.33

Figure 7.34: Three different power functions

7.   Given $t(x) = x^{-2}$ and $r(x) = 40x^{-3}$,
   (a)   Find v such that $t(v) = r(v)$.
   (b)   For $0 < x < v$, which is greater, $t(x)$ or $r(x)$?
   (c)   For $x > v$, which is greater, $t(x)$ or $r(x)$?

Problems 8–10 give tables that represent power functions. Find possible formulas for these functions.

8.   **TABLE 7.6**   *Values of $f(x)$*

x	2	3	4	5
$f(x)$	12	27	48	75

9.   **TABLE 7.7**   *Values of $g(x)$*

x	-6	-2	3	4
$g(x)$	36	4/3	$-9/2$	$-32/3$

10.   **TABLE 7.8**   *Values of $h(x)$*

x	-2	$-1/2$	1/4	4
$h(x)$	$-1/2$	-8	-32	$-1/8$

11.   Find possible formulas for the following power functions.
   (a) $f(1) = \frac{3}{2}$ and $f(2) = \frac{3}{8}$
   (b) $g(-\frac{1}{5}) = 25$ and $g(2) = -\frac{1}{40}$

12.   Suppose that g is a power function and that

$$g(3) = \frac{1}{3} \quad \text{and} \quad g\left(\frac{1}{3}\right) = 27.$$

Find a formula for $g(x)$.

13.   Suppose $f(1) = 18$ and $f(3) = 1458$. Find a formula for f assuming f is
   (a)   a linear function.   (b)   an exponential function.   (c)   a power function.

14.   Repeat Problem 13 for a function f where $f(1) = 16$ and $f(2) = 128$.

15.   Suppose that

$$f(-1) = \frac{3}{4} \quad \text{and} \quad f(2) = 48.$$

   (a)   Assume that f is a linear function. Find a possible formula for $f(x)$.
   (b)   Now assume that f is an exponential function. Find a possible formula for $f(x)$.
   (c)   Finally, assume that f is a power function. Find a possible formula for $f(x)$.

16. Table 7.9 gives approximate values for three functions, f, g, and h. One of these functions is exponential, one is trigonometric, and one is a power function. Determine which is which and find possible formulas for each.

TABLE 7.9 *Approximate values for f, g, and h*

x	$f(x)$	$g(x)$	$h(x)$
-2	4	20.0	1.3333
-1	2	2.5	0.6667
0	4	0.0	0.3333
1	6	-2.5	0.1667
2	4	-20.0	0.0833

17. A hacker unleashed a computer virus onto your network. The number of "infected" computers each day is given in Table 7.10.

TABLE 7.10

Days since infection	Number of infected computers
1	227
2	2580
3	29,311
4	332,944

(a) Graph this information.
(b) What type of function (linear, polynomial, exponential, etc.) seems to fit this data?
(c) Find the formula for a function which fits this data well.
(d) According to your function from part (c), how many computers were initially infected?

18. Recall that the formula of an exponential function can be written as

$$y = AB^x, \qquad B > 0 \quad \text{and} \quad B \neq 1,$$

while the formula of a power function can be written as

$$y = k \cdot x^p, \qquad k \text{ and } p \text{ any constants.}$$

Determine if the formulas of the functions in parts (a) through (h) can be written either in the form of an exponential function or a power function. If not, give an explanation of why the function does not fit either form.

(a) $h(x) = 3(-2)^{3x}$

(b) $j(x) = 3(-3)^{2x}$

(c) $m(x) = 3(3x + 1)^2$

(d) $n(x) = 3 \cdot 2^{(3x+1)}$

(e) $p(x) = (5^x)^2$

(f) $q(x) = 5^{(x^2)}$

(g) $r(x) = 2 \cdot 3^{-2x}$

(h) $s(x) = \dfrac{4}{5x^{-3}}$

19. Figure 7.35 gives the graph of $g(x)$, a mystery function.

    (a) If you learn that the function is a power function and that the point $(-1, 3)$ lies on the graph, do you have enough information to write a formula?

    (b) If you are told that the point $(1, -3)$ also lies on the graph, what new deductions can you make?

    (c) If the point $(2, -96)$ lies on this graph, in addition to the points already mentioned, state two other points which will also lie on it.

Figure 7.35: The graph of $g(x)$, a mystery function

Figure 7.36: The graph of $c(t)$, a power function

20. The graph in Figure 7.36 describes the power function $y = c(t)$. Discuss whether the formula $y = \frac{1}{t}$ is the unique formula that describes c.

21. The period, p, of a planet whose average distance from the sun is d, is given by $p = kd^{3/2}$, where k is a constant. (Note that the average distance from the earth to the sun is 93 million miles.) $2365 = kd^{3/2}$ $d^{3/2} = \frac{365}{k}$

    (a) At what average distance from the sun would the earth have to orbit in order to have a period twice that of 365 earth days? 147.6 million miles

    (b) Is there a planet in our solar system whose yearly cycle is approximately twice the earth's?

22. Refer to Problem 21. If the distance between the sun and the earth were halved, how long (in earth days) would a "year" be?

23. (a) One of the functions in the table below is of the form $y = a \cdot r^{3/4}$ and another is of the from $y = b \cdot r^{5/4}$. Explain how you can tell which is which from the values in the table.

TABLE 7.11

r	2.5	3.2	3.9	4.6
$y = g(r)$	15.9	19.1	22.2	25.1
$y = h(r)$	9.4	12.8	16.4	20.2

    (b) Determine constants a and b for the functions from part (a).

24.

TABLE 7.12		TABLE 7.13	
d	$f(d)$	d	$g(d)$
2	151.6	10	7.924
2.2	160.5	10.2	8.115
2.4	169.1	10.4	8.306
2.6	177.4	10.6	8.498
2.8	185.5	10.8	8.691

One of the functions $f(d)$ and $g(d)$ is of the form $y = a \cdot d^{p/q}$ with $p > q$, while the other is of the form $y = b \cdot d^{p/q}$ with $p < q$. Which is which? How can you tell?

7.3 POLYNOMIAL FUNCTIONS

A *polynomial function* is the sum of one or more power functions, each of which has a non-negative integer power. Because polynomials are defined in terms of power functions, we can use what we learned in Section 7.1 to study them.

Example 1 Suppose you make five separate deposits of $1000 each into a savings account, one deposit per year, beginning today. What annual interest must you earn if you want to close the account with a balance of $6000 five years from today? (Assume the interest rate is constant over these five years.)

Solution Let r be the annual interest rate. Our goal is to determine what value of r gives you $6000 in 5 years. You start in year $t = 0$ by making a $1000 deposit. In one year, you will have $1000 plus the interest earned on that amount. At that point, you add another $1000.

To picture how this works, imagine the account pays 5% annual interest, compounded annually. Then, after one year, your balance will be

$$\begin{pmatrix} \text{Balance after} \\ \text{one year} \end{pmatrix} = [100\% \text{ of (initial deposit)}] + [5\% \text{ of (initial deposit)}] + (\text{second deposit})$$

$$= \left[\underbrace{105\% \text{ of (initial deposit)}}_{\$1000} \right] + \underbrace{(\text{second deposit})}_{\$1000}$$

$$= 1.05(1000) + 1000.$$

Let $x = 1 + r$ be the annual growth factor. For example, if the account paid 5% interest, then x would be given by $x = 1 + 0.05 = 1.05$. We can write the balance after one year in terms of x:

$$\begin{pmatrix} \text{Balance after} \\ \text{one year} \end{pmatrix} = 1000x + 1000.$$

After two years, you will have earned interest on the first-year balance. This gives

$$\begin{pmatrix} \text{Balance after} \\ \text{earning interest} \end{pmatrix} = \underbrace{(1000x + 1000)}_{\text{first-year balance}} x = 1000x^2 + 1000x.$$

The third $1000 deposit brings your balance to

$$\begin{pmatrix} \text{Balance after} \\ \text{two years} \end{pmatrix} = 1000x^2 + 1000x + \underbrace{1000.}_{\text{third deposit}}$$

A year's worth of interest on this amount, plus the fourth $1000 deposit, brings your balance to

$$\begin{pmatrix} \text{Balance after} \\ \text{three years} \end{pmatrix} = \underbrace{(1000x^2 + 1000x + 1000)}_{\text{second-year balance}}x + \underbrace{1000}_{\text{fourth deposit}}$$

$$= 1000x^3 + 1000x^2 + 1000x + 1000.$$

We begin to see a pattern. Each of the $1000 deposits grows to $1000x^n$ by the end of the nth year that the deposit has been held. Thus, at the end of five years you will have

$$1000x^5 + 1000x^4 + 1000x^3 + 1000x^2 + 1000x,$$

minus the $6000 that you withdraw.

If the interest rate r is chosen correctly, then the balance will be zero when we close the account. This gives

$$1000x^5 + 1000x^4 + 1000x^3 + 1000x^2 + 1000x - 6000 = 0.$$

Dividing by 1000, we have the equation

$$x^5 + x^4 + x^3 + x^2 + x - 6 = 0.$$

Since $x = 1 + r$, solving this equation for x will determine how much interest we must earn.

The function

$$Q(x) = x^5 + x^4 + x^3 + x^2 + x - 6$$

Figure 7.37: Finding where $y = Q(x)$ crosses the x-axis, for $x \geq 0$

is an example of a polynomial function. As you can see, Q is a sum of power functions. (Note that the expression -6 can be written as $-6x^0$, so that it, too, describes a power function.) Using a computer or a graphing calculator, we can find where the graph of Q crosses the x-axis. This will tell us how much interest we must earn in order to have the right amount of money in 5 years.

From Figure 7.37, we see that the graph of $y = Q(x)$ crosses the x-axis at $x \approx 1.0614$. Since $x = 1 + r$, this means $r = 0.0614$. So the account must earn 6.14% annual interest for the balance to be $6000 at the end of five years.

You might wonder if Q crosses the x-axis more than once. By graphing Q on a larger scale, you see that it increases for all values of x, and thus crosses the x-axis only once. It makes sense that Q should be an increasing function, at least for $x > 1$: this is because larger values of x indicate higher interest rates. The 5-year balance will be higher if the interest rate goes up, so Q is an increasing function for $x > 1$. Thus, having crossed the axis once, the graph will not "turn around" to cross it at some other point.

A General Formula for the Family of Polynomial Functions

The general formula for the family of polynomial functions can be written as

$$p(x) = a_n x^n + a_{n-1} x^{n-1} + \ldots + a_1 x + a_0,$$

where n is an integer, $n \geq 0$, each of the numbers $a_0, a_1, \ldots, a_n$ is a constant, and $a_n \neq 0$ (unless, perhaps, if $n = 0$). Each member of this sum is called a *term*, and each of the numbers $a_0, a_1, \ldots, a_n$ is called a *coefficient*.

Polynomials are classified by their *degree*, the highest power of any of the terms of the polynomial. In the general formula above, the degree of p is n. For example, the polynomial $Q(x) = x^5 + x^4 + x^3 + x^2 + x - 6$ is a polynomial of degree $n = 5$. So is the polynomial

$$g(x) = 3x^2 - 4x^5 + x - x^3 + 1,$$

because its highest powered term is $-4x^5$. The polynomial g can be written in *standard form* by arranging its terms from left to right so that they go from highest power to lowest power:

$$g(x) = -4x^5 - x^3 + 3x^2 + x + 1.$$

The function g has one other term, $0 \cdot x^4$, which we don't bother writing down. For g, the values of the coefficients are $a_5 = -4, a_4 = 0, a_3 = -1, a_2 = 3, a_1 = 1$, and $a_0 = 1$. In summary:

The general formula for the family of polynomial functions can be written as

$$p(x) = a_n x^n + a_{n-1} x^{n-1} + \ldots + a_1 x + a_0,$$

where n is an integer, $n \geq 0$, called the **degree** of p and where $a_n \neq 0$ (unless, perhaps, $n = 0$).

- Each member of this sum, $a_n x^n$, $a_{n-1} x^{n-1}$, and so on, is called a **term**.
- The constants $a_n, a_{n-1}, \ldots, a_0$ are called **coefficients**.
- The term a_0 is called the **constant term**. The highest-powered term, $a_n x^n$, is called the **leading term**.
- To write a polynomial in **standard form**, we arrange its terms from highest power to lowest power, going from left to right.

Polynomial functions have another important property, which will help us investigate the features of individual members of this family. Since each term of a polynomial is a power function with positive integer exponent, a polynomial function is defined for all values of x. In other words, the domain of a polynomial function is all real values of x. Also, the function has no vertical or horizontal asymptotes. The function is continuous and the graph of a polynomial is smooth and unbroken.

The Long-Run Behavior of Polynomial Functions

We have seen that, as x grows large, $y = x^2$ increases very fast, $y = x^3$ increases even faster, and $y = x^4$ increases faster still. In general, for positive powers, power functions with larger powers will eventually grow much faster than those with smaller powers.

$p(x) = a_n x^n + a_{n-1} x^{n-1} + \dots + a_1 x + a_0$

This tells us something about polynomials. For instance, consider the polynomial $g(x) = 3x^2 - 4x^5 + x - x^3 + 1$. Provided x is large enough, the value of the term $-4x^5$ will be much larger (either positive or negative) than the values of the other terms. In fact, it will be larger than the value of the other terms *combined*. For example, if $x = 100$, we have

$$-4x^5 = -4(100)^5 = -40{,}000{,}000{,}000$$
$$-x^3 = -(100)^3 = -1{,}000{,}000$$
$$3x^2 = 3(100)^2 = 30{,}000.$$

Thus, the value of $-4x^5$ is $-40{,}000{,}000{,}000$ while the value of all the other terms combined is $-x^3 + 3x^2 + x + 1 = -969{,}899$. Therefore, $p(100) = -40{,}000{,}969{,}899$. Clearly, the most important contribution to the value of $p(100)$ is made by the term $-4x^5$. In fact, the contribution of this term is over 40,000 times as large as the contributions of all the other terms combined!

In general, if x is large enough, the most important contribution to the value of a polynomial p will be made by the leading term, or term of highest power. Provided that x is large enough, we say that we can *neglect* or ignore the contributions of the lower-powered terms.

This observation has the following consequence for the graph of p:

When viewed on a large enough scale, the graph of a polynomial will look like the graph of a power function. Specifically the graph of p will look like the graph of $y = a_n x^n$. This behavior is called the **long-run behavior** of the polynomial.

Example 2   Show that the graph of $f(x) = x^3 + x^2$ resembles the power function $y = x^3$ on a large enough scale.

Solution   Figure 7.38 gives the graph of $f(x) = x^3 + x^2$ for $-2 \le x \le 2$, $-1 \le y \le 1$. The graph of $y = x^3$ has been dashed in. On this scale, f does not look like a power function at all. In Figure 7.39, we see that on a larger scale, the graph of f greatly resembles the graph of $y = x^3$. On this larger scale, the "bump" in the graph of f is too small to be seen, and the fact that the graph touches the x-axis more than once is no longer apparent. Finally, Figure 7.40 gives an even larger scale. Here, the graph of f is almost indistinguishable from the graph of $y = x^3$.

Figure 7.38: On this scale, $f(x) = x^3 + x^2$ does not look like a power function

Figure 7.39: On this scale, $f(x) = x^3 + x^2$ resembles the power function $y = x^3$

Figure 7.40: On this scale, $f(x) = x^3 + x^2$ is nearly indistinguishable from $y = x^3$

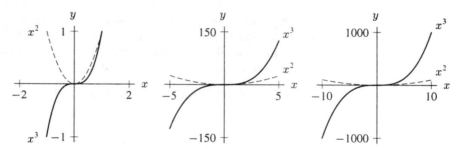

Figure 7.41: As the scale gets larger, the graph of $y = x^2$ becomes much less prominent than the graph of $y = x^3$

To see why the function from the last example behaves the way it does, let's think about its graph more carefully. Since f is the sum of two power functions, x^2 and x^3, we can think about these functions separately. Figure 7.41 gives graphs of $y = x^2$ and $y = x^3$ on the smallest scale that we used, $-2 \le x \le 2$, $-1 \le y \le 1$. On this scale, both functions are equally prominent. Therefore, we would expect each function to make a significant contribution to the appearance of f, their sum.

However, on the next larger scale, $-5 \le x \le 5$, $-150 \le y \le 150$, we see that the graph of $y = x^2$ is much less prominent than the graph of $y = x^3$. On this scale, x^3 attains y-values as large as $5^3 = 125$, whereas x^2 attains y-values no larger than $5^2 = 25$. Therefore, in the sum of these two functions, the largest contributor is $y = x^3$.

Turning to our largest scale, $-10 \le x \le 10$, $-1000 \le y \le 1000$, the values of $y = x^2$ are insignificant compared to the values of $y = x^3$. Thus, when summed, the effect of the x^2 term is almost negligible.

Table 7.14 gives some of the data represented by the graphs in Figure 7.41. The data in the table lead us to the same conclusion as the graphs in the figure: For large enough values of x, the value of x^3 is far more prominent than the value of x^2.

TABLE 7.14 *Values of $f(x) = x^3 + x^2$.*
For large values of x, the x^3 term is more prominent than the x^2 term.

x	x^2	x^3	$f(x) = x^3 + x^2$
-10	100	-1000	-900
-5	25	-125	-100
-2	4	-8	-4
-1	1	-1	0
1	1	1	2
2	4	8	12
5	25	125	150
10	100	1000	1100

Zeros of Polynomials

The *zeros* of a polynomial p are values of x for which $p(x) = 0$. These values are also called the x-intercepts, because they tell us where the graph of p crosses the x-axis. Using algebra to find the zeros of a polynomial can be quite difficult (if not impossible). The graphical approach used in Example 1 is often the only practical way of finding the zeros of a polynomial. Even so, the long-run behavior of the polynomial can give us clues as to how many zeros (if any) there may be.

Example 3   Given the polynomial

$$q(x) = 3x^6 - 2x^5 + 4x^2 - 1,$$

and based on the fact that $q(0) = -1$, is there a reason to expect a solution to the equation $q(x) = 0$? If not, explain why not. If so, how do you know?

Solution   The answer to the first part of the question is yes, the equation $q(x) = 0$ must have at least two solutions. We know this because on a large scale, q must look like the power function $y = 3x^6$. (See Figure 7.42.) The function $y = 3x^6$ takes on large positive values as x grows large (either positive or negative). From the formula for q, we see that $q(0) = -1$. Since the graph of q is smooth and unbroken, it must cross the x-axis at least twice to get from $q(0) = -1$ to the positive values we know it will attain as $x \to \infty$ and $x \to -\infty$.

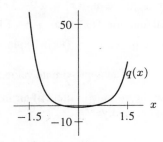

Figure 7.42

In general a sixth degree polynomial can have several real zeros. In fact, it can have as many as six real zeros. We will explore the question of how many zeros a polynomial can have in Section 7.4.

Problems for Section 7.3

1. For each of the following polynomial functions, state the degree of the polynomial, the number of terms in the polynomial, and describe its long-range behavior.
   (a) $y = 2x^3 - 3x + 7$ (b) $y = (x + 4)(2x - 3)(5 - x)$ (c) $y = 1 - 2x^4 + x^3$

2. Let $u(x) = -\frac{1}{5}(x - 3)(x + 1)(x + 5)$ and $v(x) = -\frac{1}{5}x^2(x - 5)$.
   (a)   Draw graphs of u and v on the screen $-10 \le x \le 10$, $-10 \le y \le 10$. How are the graphs similar? How are they different?
   (b)   Now, compare the graphs of u and v on the window $-20 \le x \le 20$, $-1600 \le y \le 1600$, the window $-50 \le x \le 50$, $-25{,}000 \le y \le 25{,}000$, and the window $-500 \le x \le 500$, $-25{,}000{,}000 \le y \le 25{,}000{,}000$. Discuss.

3. Let $f(x) = \left(\dfrac{1}{50{,}000} \right) x^3 + \left(\dfrac{1}{2} \right) x.$
   (a)   For small values of x, which term of f is more important? Explain your answer.
   (b)   Sketch a graph of $y = f(x)$ for $-10 \le x \le 10$, $-10 \le y \le 10$. Is this graph linear? How does the appearance of this graph agree with your answer to part (a)?
   (c)   How large a value of x is required for the cubic term of f to be equal in importance to the linear term?

4. Let $u(x) = \frac{1}{8}x^3$ and $v(x) = \frac{1}{8}x(x - 0.01)^2$. Sketch u and v as they appear on the window $-10 \le x \le 10$, $-10 \le y \le 10$. Do v and u have the exact same graph? If so, explain why their formulas are different; if not, find a viewing window on which their graphs' differences are prominent.

5. Use a computer or graphing calculator to approximate the zeros of the polynomial $f(x) = x^4 - 3x^2 - x + 2$.

6. If $f(x) = x^2$ and $g(x) = (x + 2)(x - 1)(x - 3)$, find all x for which $f(x) < g(x)$.

7. Compare the graphs of $f(x) = x^3 + 5x^2 - x - 5$ and $g(x) = -2x^3 - 10x^2 + 2x + 10$ on an appropriate window. How are the graphs similar? Different? Discuss.

8. Find the equation of the line through the x-intercept of $y = 2x - 4$ and the y-intercept of $y = x^4 - 3x^5 - 1 + x^2$.

9. Find the minimum value of $g(x) = x^4 - 3x^3 - 8$, correct to two decimal places. -16.54

10. The polynomial function $f(x) = x^3 + x + 1$ is invertible—that is, this function has an inverse.

   (a) Sketch a graph of $y = f(x)$. Explain how you can tell from a graph whether f is invertible.

   (b) Find $f(0.5)$ and an approximate value for $f^{-1}(0.5)$.

11. Let V represent the volume in liters of air in the lungs during a 5 second respiratory cycle. A formula for V is given by

$$V = 0.1729t + 0.1522t^2 - 0.0374t^3.$$

   (a) Use your calculator to graph this function, for $0 \le t \le 5$.

   (b) What is the maximum value of V on this interval? What is the practical significance of the maximum value?

   (c) Explain the practical significance of the t- and V-intercepts on the interval $0 \le t \le 5$.

12. Let $C(x)$ be a firm's total cost, in millions of dollars, for producing a given quantity x, in thousands of units, of a certain good.

   (a) Suppose a formula for $C(x)$ is $C(x) = (x - 1)^3 + 1$. Graph $C(x)$.

   (b) Let $R(x)$ be the revenue to the firm (in millions of dollars) for selling a quantity, x, in thousands of units, of the good. Suppose the formula for $R(x)$ is $R(x) = x$. What does this tell you about the price of each unit?

   (c) Profit equals revenue minus cost. For what values of x does the firm make a profit? Break even? Lose money?

13. The town of Smallsville was founded in 1900. Its population y (in hundreds) is given by the equation

$$y = -0.1x^4 + 1.7x^3 - 9x^2 + 14.4x + 5$$

where x is the number of years since the foundation of Smallsville. You can see the graph very well by using the window $0 \le x \le 10$, $-2 \le y \le 13$.

   (a) What was the population of Smallsville when it was founded? 5

   (b) When did Smallsville become a "ghost town" (nobody lived there anymore)? Your answer should give the year and the month. 5 1906 $2,007$

   (c) What was the largest population of Smallsville after 1905? When did Smallsville reach that population? Again, include the month and year. Explain your method.

14. A formula for the volume, V, in milliliters, of 1 kg of water as a function of the temperature T is given by:

$$V = 999.87 - 0.06426T + 0.0085143T^2 - 0.0000679T^3.$$

This formula is only valid for $0 \leq T \leq 30°C$.

(a) Sketch a graph of V.

(b) Describe the shape of the graph. Does V increase or decrease? Does it curve upward or downward? What does the graph tell us about how the volume varies with temperature?

(c) At what temperature will the water have a maximum density? How does that appear on your graph? (*Density* is defined as mass divided by volume: $d = \frac{m}{V}$. Note that in this problem, the mass of the water is 1 kg.)

15. A function that is not a polynomial can often be *approximated* by a polynomial. For example, we can use the fifth-degree polynomial

$$p(x) = 1 + x + \frac{x^2}{2} + \frac{x^3}{6} + \frac{x^4}{24} + \frac{x^5}{120}$$

to approximate the function $f(x) = e^x$ for certain x-values.

(a) Show that $p(1) \approx f(1) = e$. How good is the estimate?

(b) Calculate $p(5)$. How well does $p(5)$ approximate $f(5)$?

(c) Graph $p(x)$ and $f(x)$ together on the same set of axes. Based on your graph, for what range of values of x do you think $p(x)$ gives a good estimate for $f(x)$?

16. Let $f(x) = x - \frac{x^3}{6} + \frac{x^5}{120}$.

(a) Using a graphing calculator, sketch graphs of $y = f(x)$ and $y = \sin x$ for $-2\pi \leq x \leq 2\pi$, $-3 \leq y \leq 3$.

(b) The graph of f resembles the graph of $\sin x$ on a small interval. Based on the graphs you made in part (a), state (approximately) this interval.

(c) Your calculator uses a function similar to f in order to evaluate the sine function. How reasonable an approximation does f give for $\sin(\pi/8)$?

(d) Explain how you could use the function f to approximate the value of $\sin\theta$, $\theta = 18$ radians. (Hint: use the fact that the sine function is periodic.)

17. Let f and g be polynomial functions. Are the compositions

$$f(g(x)) \quad \text{and} \quad g(f(x))$$

also polynomial functions? Explain your answer.

18. Suppose f is a polynomial function of degree n, where n is a positive even integer. For each of the following statements, write *true* if the statement is always true, *false* otherwise. If the statement is false, give an example that illustrates why it is false.

(a) f is even.

(b) f has an inverse.

(c) f cannot be an odd function.

(d) If $f(x) \to +\infty$ as $x \to +\infty$, then $f(x) \to +\infty$ as $x \to -\infty$.

19. A woman opens a bank account with an initial deposit of $1000. At the end of each year thereafter, she deposits an additional $1000.

(a) Suppose the account earns 6% annual interest, compounded annually. Complete the following table.

TABLE 7.15

No. of years elapsed	start-of-year balance	end-of-year deposit	end-of-year interest
0	$1000.00	$1000	$60.00
1	$2060.00	$1000	$123.60
2	$3183.60	$1000	
3		$1000	
4		$1000	
5		$1000	

(b) Does the balance of this account grow linearly, exponentially, or neither? Justify your answer.

20. Suppose the annual percentage rate (APR) paid by the account in Problem 19 is r, where r does not necessarily equal 6%. Define $p_n(r)$ as the balance of the account after n years have elapsed. (For example, $p_2(0.06) = \$3183.60$, because the balance after 2 years is $3183.60 if the APR is 6%, as we know from the table above.)

(a) Find formulas for $p_5(r)$ and $p_{10}(r)$.

(b) What must the APR of the account be if the woman in Problem 19 needs to have $10,000 in 5 years? [Hint: Use a graphing calculator.]

7.4 THE SHORT-RUN BEHAVIOR OF POLYNOMIALS

Polynomials of the Same Degree Can Have Different Short-Run Behaviors

The long-run behavior of a polynomial is determined by its highest-powered, or leading, term. Often, however, we need to look at the behavior of a polynomial near a particular value of x. If x has roughly the same magnitude as the coefficients, then all of the terms of a polynomial can make important contributions to its behavior. For this reason, the *short-run* behavior of a polynomial p – that is, its behavior for relatively small values of x – is often more complicated than its long-run behavior.

Example 1   Compare the graphs of the polynomials f, g, and h given by

$$f(x) = x^4 - 4x^3 + 16x - 16$$
$$g(x) = x^4 - 4x^3 - 4x^2 + 16x$$
$$h(x) = x^4 + x^3 - 8x^2 - 12x.$$

Solution   Each of these functions is a fourth-degree polynomial, and each has x^4 as its highest-powered term. Thus, we expect the long-run behavior of f, g, and h to be the same. Their graphs will resemble the graph of the power function x^4 on a large enough scale. Figure 7.43 gives graphs of these functions on the window $-8 \le x \le 8$, $0 \le y \le 4000$. On this scale, these three functions are difficult to distinguish, and they strongly resemble the function $y = x^4$.

However, on a smaller scale, the functions look very different. Figure 7.44 shows the functions on the scale $-5 \leq x \leq 5$, $-35 \leq y \leq 15$. We see that two of the graphs go through the origin while the third does not. The graphs also differ from one another in the number of bumps or wiggles each one has and in the number of times each one crosses the x-axis.

Figure 7.43: On an adequately large scale, the polynomials f, g, and h resemble the power function $y = x^4$

Figure 7.44: On a smaller scale, the polynomials f, g, and h look quite different from each other

Factored Form

It can be hard to predict the short-run behavior of a polynomial if its formula is written in standard form. However, there is a completely different way to write the formula for some (but not all) polynomials; this is called *factored form*. If we can put a polynomial into factored form, we may be able to say quite a bit about its short-run behavior.

Example 2   Show that the function $u(x) = x(x - 3)(x + 2)$ is a polynomial.

Solution   By multiplying out the expression $x(x - 3)(x + 2)$ and then simplifying the result, we see that

$$u(x) = x^3 - x^2 - 6x,$$

So u is a third-degree polynomial.

Example 3   Show that the function $y = (x^2 - 4)(x^2 - 2x - 3)$ is a polynomial.

Solution   By multiplying out the expression $(x^2 - 4)(x^2 - 2x - 3)$ and then simplifying the result, we see that

$$y = x^4 - 2x^3 - 7x^2 + 8x + 12$$

which is a fourth-degree polynomial.

Notice that in Example 2, the expression $x(x-3)(x+2)$ represents the product of three different first-degree (linear) polynomials, namely, x, $x - 3$, and $x + 2$. We say that the expression has been written as a product of three *linear factors*, because each factor is a linear function. Similarly, in Example 3, the expression $(x^2 - 4)(x^2 - 2x - 3)$ represents the product of two second-degree (quadratic) polynomials, namely, $x^2 - 4$ and $x^2 - 2x - 3$. In general:

Chapter 6/ 31

- The product of any finite number of polynomials is itself a polynomial.
- If the formula for a polynomial p is written as the product of two or more non-constant polynomials, then the formula for p is said to be in **factored form**.

Completely Factored Form

The formula for the function $p(x) = (x^2 - 4)(x^2 - 2x - 3)$ from Example 3 can be factored further. Since $x^2 - 4 = (x + 2)(x - 2)$, and since $x^2 - 2x - 3 = (x + 1)(x - 3)$, we can write the formula for p as

$$p(x) = (x + 2)(x - 2)(x + 1)(x - 3).$$

Since none of the factors in this formula can be factored further, the formula for p is said to be in *completely factored form.*

Factored Form and the Short-Run Behavior of Polynomials

On a large enough scale, the graph of the polynomial $u(x) = x^3 - x^2 - 6x$ from Example 2 will look like the graph of its leading term, $y = x^3$. By placing the formula into factored form, $u(x) = x(x - 3)(x + 2)$, we can also say something about this function's short-run behavior. To do this, we will need the following rule:

If a and b are numbers and if $a \cdot b = 0$, then a must equal 0 or b must equal 0 (or both).

This rule also applies to products of three or more numbers: If such a product equals zero, then at least one of the members of the product must equal zero.

You should note that the number zero is unique in this regard. For example, knowing that $a \cdot b = 12$ doesn't tell us that $a = 12$ or $b = 12$ (or both). For instance, $a = 3$ and $b = 4$ would work, as would $a = 2$ and $b = 6$, or $a = \sqrt{12}$ and $b = \sqrt{12}$, and so on.

Example 4   Describe the graph of $y = u(x) = x^3 - x^2 - 6x$. Where does it cross the x-axis? the y-axis? Where is u positive? negative?

Solution   The following information will be useful for describing the graph of u:

- The zeros, or x-intercepts
- the y-intercept
- the long-run behavior

We will use the factored form of u to find its zeros–that is, those values of x at which $u(x)$ equals zero. This will tell us where the graph of u cross the x-axis. To do this, we can solve the following equation:

$$x(x - 3)(x + 2) = 0.$$

We have a product of 3 numbers that is equal to 0. Thus at least one of these numbers must equal 0. This means that either

$$x = 0, \quad \text{or} \quad x - 3 = 0, \quad \text{or} \quad x + 2 = 0.$$

Therefore,

$$x = 0, \quad \text{or} \quad x = 3, \quad \text{or} \quad x = -2.$$

These are the zeros, or x-intercepts, of u. You can check this by evaluating $u(x)$ for these values of x to see that each is equal to 0. Notice that there are no other zeros because for all other values of x, neither x, $x - 3$, nor $x + 2$ equals zero; thus, their product cannot equal 0.

Now that we know where the graph of u crosses the x-axis, we would like to know where it crosses the y-axis. This is easily determined; since $u(0) = 0^3 - 0^2 - 6 \cdot 0 = 0$, we see that u crosses the y-axis at $y = 0$. Finally, we know that for large enough values of x, the graph of $y = u(x)$ will resemble the graph of $y = x^3$, its leading term. Figure 7.45 indicates the zeros of u and its long-run behavior.

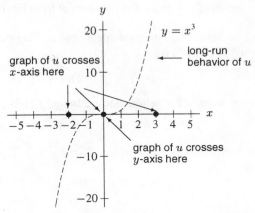

Figure 7.45: The graph of $u(x) = x^3 - x^2 - 6x$ has zeros at $x = -2, 0$, and 3, and its long-run behavior is given by $y = x^3$

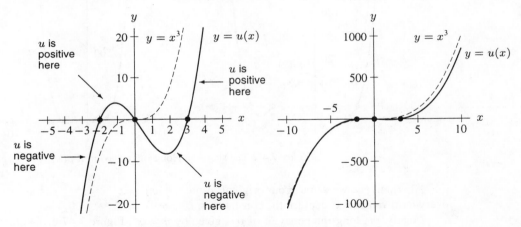

Figure 7.46: The short- and long-run behavior of u

We know (from the long-run behavior of u) that $u(x)$ will be negative for $x < -2$ and positive for $x > 3$. Since u is continuous, the only places the function can change sign are at the zeros $x = 0$, $x = -2$, and $x = 3$. Note that $u(-1) = 4$ and $u(1) = -6$. Thus, the graph of u must lie below the x-axis for $x < -2$ and must cross the x-axis at $x = -2$. It must remain above the x-axis for $-2 < x < 0$ and must cross the x-axis at $x = 0$. It must remain below the x-axis for $0 < x < 3$, and cross the x-axis at $x = 3$. Finally, it remains above the x-axis for $x > 3$. Figure 7.46 shows the short- and long-run behavior of u.

The Bumps in the Graph of a Polynomial

You may be wondering how large the bumps in the graph of a polynomial like u should be. The best way to decide this, given the techniques we have learned so far, is to use a computer or a graphing calculator. Once you know where a polynomial crosses the x-axis, you can choose a good viewing window on which to draw its graph. Note that in general, polynomials may have bumps of different sizes, and the bumps may be lopsided in appearance.

Example 5   Describe the graph of $y = p(x)$, the polynomial from Example 3.

Solution   We will find the zeros of p, its y-intercept, and its long-run behavior. When written in completely factored form, the formula for p is

$$p(x) = (x + 2)(x + 1)(x - 2)(x - 3).$$

(Notice that the order of the factors doesn't matter.) Thus $p(x)$ equals 0 if and only if

$$x + 2 = 0, \quad x + 1 = 0, \quad x - 2 = 0, \quad \text{or} \quad x - 3 = 0.$$

The zeros of p are $x = -2$, $x = -1$, $x = 2$, and $x = 3$. To find the y-intercept of p, we can evaluate $p(0)$. This gives

$$p(0) = (0 + 2)(0 + 1)(0 - 2)(0 - 3) = +12.$$

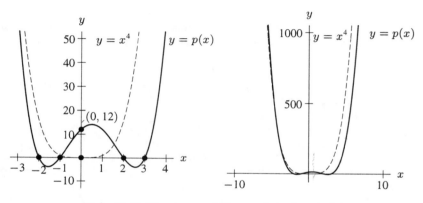

Figure 7.47: The short- and long-run behavior of $p(x)$

Alternatively, we can use our original formula, $p(x) = x^4 - 2x^3 - 7x^2 + 8x + 12$. At $x = 0$ every term vanishes except for the constant term, so $p(0) = 12$.

Finally, the long-run behavior of p is given by $y = x^4$. Figure 7.47 gives graphs of the short- and long-run behavior of $y = p(x)$.

The Relationship Between a Polynomial's Factors and its Short-Run Behavior

We can summarize our observations as follows:

> If p is a polynomial function, and if the formula for p has a **linear factor**, that is, a factor of the form $(x - k)$, then p will have a zero at $x = k$.

We can say more. Although we have not proven this, it is true that

> If p is a polynomial function of degree n with a zero at $x = k$, then the formula for p can be factored as $p(x) = (x - k) \cdot q(x)$, where $q(x)$ is a polynomial of degree $n - 1$.

If p can be written as $p(x) = (x - k) \cdot q(x)$, where q is a polynomial, then it may be that q can also be factored. For instance, as you can check for yourself, the polynomial $y = x^3 - 5x^2 - x + 5$ can be factored as $y = (x - 5)(x^2 - 1)$. Here, q is given by $q(x) = x^2 - 1$. Thus, q can also be factored, because $x^2 - 1 = (x - 1)(x + 1)$. Thus, we can factor $y = x^3 - 5x^2 - x + 5$ completely by writing it as $y = (x - 5)(x - 1)(x + 1)$.

Even though a polynomial with a zero can be factored, this doesn't necessarily mean it can be factored "neatly". Consider the following example.

Example 6   Factor the polynomial $y = x^2 + 2x - 1$.

Solution   Using the quadratic formula, we see that $y = 0$ at $x = \sqrt{2} - 1$ and $x = -\sqrt{2} - 1$. Thus, this polynomial can be factored as

$$y = (x - (\sqrt{2} - 1))(x - (-\sqrt{2} - 1))$$
$$= (x - \sqrt{2} + 1)(x + \sqrt{2} + 1).$$

You can check to see that this works by multiplying out the above expression.

If a polynomial doesn't have a zero, this doesn't mean it can't be factored. For example, the polynomial $y = x^4 + 5x^2 + 6$ has no zeros. To see this, notice that x^4 is never negative; nor is $5x^2$. Thus, y is never less than 6 so it cannot equal 0. However, this polynomial can be factored as $y = (x^2 + 2)(x^2 + 3)$, as you can check for yourself. The important point is that a polynomial with a zero will have a *linear* factor, and a polynomial without a zero will not.

We know that each zero of a polynomial corresponds to a linear factor. This implies that an nth-degree polynomial can have no more than n zeros. For suppose it did have more than n zeros, labeled $x = a$, $x = b$, $x = c$, ... Then its formula could be written as

$$y = (x - a)(x - b)(x - c) \ldots,$$

where there is one factor corresponding to each zero. But there would be more than n factors so if we multiplied out this formula, there would be a term involving a power of x greater than n. This contradicts the assumption that this is an nth-degree polynomial. So we conclude that it cannot have more than n zeros. Thus we are led to the following conclusion:

> An nth-degree polynomial can have up to, but no more than, n different real-valued zeros.

Multiple Zeros

The functions $s(x) = (x - 2)^2$ and $t(x) = (x + 3)^3$ are both polynomials in factored form. Each of these functions is a horizontal shift of a power function. The graph of $y = s(x)$ resembles $y = x^2$ shifted to the right by 2 units. The graph of $y = t(x)$ resembles $y = x^3$ shifted to the left by 3 units.

We refer to the zeros of s and t as *multiple zeros*, because in each case the factor contributing the value of $y = 0$ occurs more than once. For instance, because

$$s(x) = (x-2)^2 = \underbrace{(x-2)(x-2)}_{\text{repeated twice}},$$

we say that $x = 2$ is a *double zero* of s. Likewise, since

$$t(x) = (x+3)^3 = \underbrace{(x+3)(x+3)(x+3)}_{\text{repeated three times}},$$

we say that $x = -3$ is a *triple zero* of t.

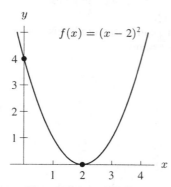

Figure 7.48: The graph of
$f(x) = (x-2)^2$

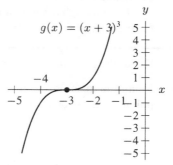

Figure 7.49: The graph of
$g(x) = (x+3)^3$

The graphs of s and t in Figures 7.48 and 7.49 show typical behavior near multiple zeros. In general:

If p is a polynomial with a repeated factor, then p has a **multiple zero**.

- If the factor $(x-k)$ is repeated an even number of times, the graph of $y = p(x)$ does not cross the x-axis at $x = k$, and instead "bounces" off of the x-axis at $x = k$. (See Figure 7.48.)

- If the factor $(x-k)$ is repeated an odd number of times, the graph of $y = p(x)$ crosses the x-axis at $x = k$, but it will have a flattened appearance at this x-intercept. (See Figure 7.49.)

Example 7   Describe in words the zeros of the 4th-degree polynomials f, g, and h, based on their graphs in Figure 7.44, page 421.

Solution   The graph of f has a single zero at $x = -2$. Based on the flattened appearance of the graph at $x = 2$, it has a multiple zero there. Since the graph crosses the x-axis here (instead of bouncing off of it), this zero must be repeated an odd number of times. But since we know f is of degree $n = 4$, this must be a triple zero. Otherwise, we would have too many factors and the degree would be larger than 4.

The graph of g has 4 single zeros. The graph of h has two single zeros and a double zero at $x = -2$. We know that this is not a higher powered zero because h is only of degree $n = 4$.

Finding the Formula for a Polynomial from its Graph

Given the graph of a polynomial, we can often find a formula for a function with the same graphical behavior.

Example 8   Find a possible formula for the polynomial function f shown in Figure 7.50.

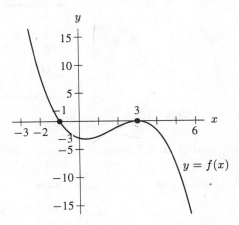

Figure 7.50: The graph of a polynomial function

Solution   Based on its long-run behavior, f must be of odd degree greater than or equal to 3. The polynomial has zeros at $x = -1$ and $x = 3$. We see that $x = 3$ is a multiple zero of even power, because the graph bounces off the x-axis here instead of crossing it. Therefore, we try the formula

$$f(x) = k(x + 1)(x - 3)^2$$

where k represents a stretch factor.

To find k, we use the fact that $f(0) = -3$, so

$$k \cdot (0 + 1)(0 - 3)^2 = -3$$

which gives

$$9k = -3$$
$$k = -\frac{1}{3}.$$

Thus, $f(x) = -\frac{1}{3}(x + 1)(x - 3)^2$ is a possible formula for this polynomial.

The formula for f we found in Example 8 is the polynomial *of least degree* we could have chosen. We could find other formulas with the same overall behavior as the function shown in Figure 7.50. For example, if you graph

$$y = -\frac{1}{27}(x + 1)(x - 3)^4,$$

you can see that this function resembles the one in Figure 7.50.

Problems for Section 7.4

1. Which of the equations in Table 7.16 best describes the polynomial shown in Figure 7.51?

Figure 7.51:

TABLE 7.16   *Equations of five polynomials*

A	$y = (x+2)(x+1)(x-2)(x-3)$
B	$y = x(x+2)(x+1)(x-2)(x-3)$
C	$y = -\frac{1}{2}(x+2)(x+1)(x-2)(x-3)$
D	$y = \frac{1}{2}(x+2)(x+1)(x-2)(x-3)$
E	$y = -(x+2)(x+1)(x-2)(x-3)$

2. Sketch graphs of the following polynomials. Label all the x-intercepts and y-intercepts.
$$f(x) = -5(x^2-4)(25-x^2) \qquad g(x) = 5(x-4)(x^2-25)$$

3. Use the graph of $y = f(x)$ in Figure 7.44 of Section 7.4 to determine the factored form of
$$f(x) = x^4 - 4x^3 + 16x - 16.$$

4. Use the graph of $y = h(x)$ in Figure 7.44 of Section 7.4 to determine the factored form of
$$h(x) = x^4 + x^3 - 8x^2 - 12x.$$

5. Give possible formulas for the following graphs:

Figure 7.52

6. Find possible formulas for the polynomial functions shown in Figure 7.53.

Figure 7.53

7. Figure 7.54 gives the graph of $y = f(x)$, a polynomial. Find a possible formula for f.

8. Figure 7.55 gives the graph of $y = g(x)$, a polynomial. Find a possible formula for g.

Figure 7.54: The graph for $f(x)$, a polynomial

Figure 7.55: The graph of $g(x)$, a polynomial

9. Factor $f(x) = 8x^3 - 4x^2 - 60x$ completely and determine the zeros of f.

10. Find the equation for a polynomial of least possible degree through the points $(-3, 0)$, $(1, 0)$, and $(0, -3)$.

11. Find possible formulas for the following polynomials given:

    (a) f is a third degree polynomial with $f(-3) = 0$, $f(1) = 0$, $f(4) = 0$, and $f(2) = 5$.

    (b) g is a fourth degree polynomial, g has a "double zero" at $x = 3$, $g(5) = 0$, $g(-1) = 0$, and $g(0) = 3$.

12. For each part of this problem, give a possible formula for a polynomial function $f(x)$, with degree ≤ 2, which satisfies the given conditions:

    (a) $f(0) = f(1) = f(2) = 1$

    (b) $f(0) = f(2) = 0$ and $f(3) = 3$

    (c) $f(0) = 0$ and $f(1) = 1$

13. An open-top box is to be constructed from a 6in. x 8in. rectangular sheet of tin by cutting out squares of equal size at each corner, then folding up the resulting flaps. Let x denote the length of the side of each cut-out square.

    (a) Find a formula for the volume of the box as a function of x.

    (b) For what values of x does the formula from part (a) make sense in the context of the problem?

    (c) Sketch a graph of the volume function.

    (d) What, approximately, is the maximum volume of the box?

14. Suppose you wish to pack a cardboard box inside a wooden crate. In order to have room for the packing materials, you need to leave a 0.5-ft space around the front, back, and sides of the box, and a 1-ft space around the top and bottom of the box. If the cardboard box is x feet long, $(x + 2)$ feet wide, and $(x - 1)$ feet deep, find a formula in terms of x for the amount of packing material needed.

15. Which of these functions have inverses that are functions? Discuss.

    (a) $f(x) = (x - 2)^3 + 4$.   (b) $g(x) = x^3 - 4x^2 + 2$.

16. Let $f(x) = x^3 + x + 1$.

    (a) Evaluate $f(-2)$ and $f(2)$.

    (b) Give the approximate value of $f^{-1}(5)$.

17. Find the real zeros of the following polynomials:

(a) $y = x^2 + 5x + 6$

(b) $y = x^4 + 6x^2 + 9$

(c) $y = 4x^2 - 1$

(d) $y = 4x^2 + 1$

(e) $y = 2x^2 - 3x - 3$

(f) $y = 3x^5 + 7x + 1$

18. Find possible formulas for the polynomial functions shown in Figure 7.56.

(a)

(b)

(c)

(d)

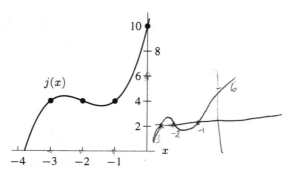

Figure 7.56: Find possible formulas for these polynomial functions.

19. Consider the function $a(x) = x^5 + 2x^3 - 4x$.

(a) Without using a graphing calculator or a computer, what can you say about the graph of a?

(b) Use a calculator or a computer to determine the zeros of this function (correct to three decimal places).

(c) Explain why you think that you have all the possible zeros.

(d) What are the zeros of $b(x) = 2x^5 + 4x^3 - 8x$? Does your answer surprise you?

20. Let $f(x) = x^4 - 17x^2 + 36x - 20$. Sketch a graph of f on the standard viewing screen, $-10 \le x \le 10, -10 \le y \le 10$.

(a) Your graph should appear to have a vertical asymptote at $x = -5$. Does f actually have a vertical asymptote here? Explain.

(b) How many zeros does f have? Can you find a window in which all of the zeros of f are clearly visible? Discuss.

(c) Express the formula of f in factored form.

(d) How many bumps does the graph of f have? Can you find a window in which all of the bumps of f are clearly visible? Discuss.

21. Suppose that f is a polynomial with zeros at $x = -2$, $x = 3$, and $x = 5$.

    (a) If f has a y-intercept of 4, find a possible formula for f.
    (b) Suppose f has the following long-range behavior: as $x \to \pm\infty$, $y \to -\infty$. Find a possible formula for f. [Hint: assume f has a double zero.]
    (c) Now find a formula for f assuming it has the following long-range behavior instead: as $x \to \pm\infty$, $y \to +\infty$.

22. Suppose the following statements about $f(x)$ are true:

    - $f(x)$ is a polynomial function
    - $f(x) = 0$ at exactly four different values of x
    - $f(x) \to -\infty$ as $x \to \pm\infty$

    For each of the following statements, write *true* if the statement must be true, *never true* if the statement is never true, or *neither* if it is sometimes true and sometimes not true.

    (a) $f(x)$ is odd
    (b) $f(x)$ is even
    (c) $f(x)$ is a fourth degree polynomial
    (d) $f(x)$ is a fifth degree polynomial
    (e) $f(-x) \to -\infty$ as $x \to \pm\infty$
    (f) $f(x)$ is invertible

23. (a) Let $f(x) = x^3 - 3x^2 + 3x$. Evaluate $f(0)$, $f(1)$, $f(2)$. What pattern do you notice? Does this pattern hold for other values of x?
    (b) Let $g(x) = x^4 - 6x^3 + 11x^2 - 5x$. Evaluate $g(0)$, $g(1)$, $g(2)$, $g(3)$. What pattern do you notice? Does this pattern hold for other values of x?
    (c) Suppose $h(x)$ is a function that follows the same pattern followed by f and g for $x = 0, 1, 2, 3$, and 4. Find a possible formula for $h(x)$. [Hint: Let $h(x) = p(x) + x$, where $p(x)$ is a polynomial. Decide what $p(0), p(1), p(2), p(3)$, and $p(4)$ must equal given what you want the values of $h(0), h(1), h(2), h(3)$, and $h(4)$ to equal. It isn't necessary to expand the formula you find for $h(x)$.]

24. (a) Let $f(x) = x^3 - 3x^2 + 3x$. Evaluate $f(x)$ for $x = 0$, 1, 2. What pattern do you notice? Does this pattern seem to hold for other values of x?
    (b) Find a non-linear polynomial $g(x)$ such that $g(x) = x$ for $x = 0$, 1, 2, and 3.

7.5 RATIONAL FUNCTIONS

The Average Cost of Producing a Therapeutic Drug

Suppose a pharmaceutical company wants to begin production of a new therapeutic drug. The total cost C, in thousands of dollars, of making q grams of the drug is given by the linear function

$$C(q) = 2500 + 2q.$$

The fact that $C(0) = 2500$ tells us that the company must make an initial \$2,500,000 investment before it starts making the drug. This quantity is known as the *fixed cost* because it does not depend on how much of the drug is made. It represents the cost for research, testing, and the needed equipment. In addition, the slope of C tells us that each gram of the drug costs an extra \$2000 to make. This quantity is known as the *unit cost*.

Now, the fixed cost of \$2.5 million is very large compared to the unit cost of \$2000/gram. This means that it would be impractical for the company to make a small amount of the drug. For instance, if it makes only 10 grams, the total cost is

$$C(10) = 2500 + 2 \cdot 10 = 2520.$$

This means that 10 grams would cost $2,520,000 to make, which works out to an average cost of $252,000 per gram. The company would probably never sell such an expensive drug.

However, as larger and larger quantities of the drug are manufactured, the initial outlay of $2.5 million will seem less significant. The fixed cost will "average out" over a large number of units. For example, if the company makes 10,000 grams of the drug, we have an average cost of

$$\frac{\left(\begin{array}{c}\text{total cost of producing} \\ \text{10,000 grams}\end{array}\right)}{10,000} = \frac{2500 + 2(10,000)}{10,000} = 2.25,$$

or $2250 per gram of drug produced.

To help us think about the average cost of producing q units of the drug, we define the average cost function a as follows:

$$a(q) = \left(\begin{array}{c}\text{average cost of} \\ \text{producing } q \text{ units}\end{array}\right) = \frac{\left(\begin{array}{c}\text{total cost of producing} \\ q \text{ grams}\end{array}\right)}{\left(\begin{array}{c}\text{number of grams} \\ \text{produced}\end{array}\right)} = \frac{C(q)}{q} = \frac{2500 + 2q}{q}.$$

The average cost function $a(q)$ gives the cost per gram the company spends to produce q grams of the drug.

What is a Rational Function?

The function a is an example of a *rational function*. A rational function is a function given by the ratio of two polynomials. Here, the formula of a is the ratio of the linear polynomial $2500 + 2q$ and the linear polynomial q. Figure 7.57 gives a graph of $y = a(q)$ for $q > 0$. In many ways, a is characteristic of rational functions in general. For example, the graph of $y = a(q)$ has two asymptotes: a vertical asymptote at $q = 0$ and a horizontal asymptote at $y = 2$. Often, it is the case that a rational function will have a horizontal asymptote as well as one or more vertical asymptotes.

Figure 7.57: The graph of a, a rational function, has both a horizontal and a vertical asymptote

The horizontal asymptote of a reflects the fact that for large values of q, the value of $a(q)$ draws close to 2. This is reasonable: as more and more of the drug is produced, the initial $2.5 million expenditure grows increasingly less significant, whereas the unit cost of $2000 per gram remains unchanged. Thus, as more and more of the drug is produced, the average cost gets closer and closer to $2000 per gram. Table 7.17 gives the total cost $C(q)$ and the average cost $a(q)$ for producing various quantities of the drug. We see that as q grows large, the value of $a(q)$ approaches 2.

TABLE 7.17   *As the quantity q of drug produced increases, the average cost a(q) draws closer to 2, $2000 per gram*

q	$C(q) = 2500 + 2q$	$a(q) = C(q)/q$
10,000	$2500 + 20,000 = 22,500$	2.250
20,000	$2500 + 40,000 = 42,500$	2.125
30,000	$2500 + 60,000 = 62,500$	2.083
40,000	$2500 + 80,000 = 82,500$	2.063
50,000	$2500 + 100,000 = 102,500$	2.050
100,000	$2500 + 200,000 = 202,500$	2.025
500,000	$2500 + 1,000,000 = 1,002,500$	2.005

On the other hand, the vertical asymptote of Figure 7.57 tells us that the average cost per gram will be very large if only a small amount of the drug is made. Table 7.18 shows values of the average cost function when small amounts of the drug are produced. As q approaches zero, the average cost $a(q)$ becomes extremely large. This is because the $2.5 million initial investment must be averaged out over very few units. For example, as we have seen, to produce only 10 grams costs a staggering $252,000 per gram.

Clearly, some of the values for q shown in Table 7.18 are unreasonably small. For instance, no drug company would consider making only 0.01 grams of a drug. However, the table shows us that, in principle, the average cost will grow enormously large for small values of q.

TABLE 7.18   *As the quantity q of drug produced decreases, the average cost a(q) grows larger*

q	$C(q) = 2500 + 2q$	$a(q) = C(q)/q$
100	2700.00	$2700/100 = 27$
10	2520.00	$2520/10 = 252$
1	2502.00	$2502/1 = 2502$
0.1	2500.20	$2500.2/0.1 = 25,002$
0.01	2500.02	$2500.02/0.01 = 250,002$

In general:

If r is the ratio of the polynomials p and q, that is, if

$$r(x) = \frac{p(x)}{q(x)},$$

where p and q are polynomial functions, then r is called a **rational function**. (We assume that $q(x)$ is not the constant polynomial $q(x) = 0$.)

Note that the formula for a rational function doesn't necessarily need to be written as the ratio of two polynomials. Consider the following example.

Example 1   Show that

$$y = x + 3 - \frac{2}{x-2}$$

is a rational function.

Solution   If we rewrite this formula as

$$y = \frac{x+3}{1} - \frac{2}{x-2},$$

then by finding a common denominator, we have

$$y = \frac{x+3}{1} \cdot \frac{x-2}{x-2} - \frac{2}{x-2}$$
$$= \frac{(x+3)(x-2) - 2}{x-2}$$
$$= \frac{x^2 + x - 8}{x-2}.$$

This is the ratio of the quadratic polynomial $x^2 + x - 8$ and the linear polynomial $x - 2$. Therefore, it is a rational function.

The Long-Run Behavior of Rational Functions

We saw in Section 7.3 that the long-range behavior of a polynomial is decided by its leading term. We can say something similar about rational functions. In general, if r is a rational function given by

$$r(x) = \frac{a_n x^n + a_{n-1} x^{n-1} + \cdots + a_0}{b_m x^m + b_{m-1} x^{m-1} + \cdots + b_0},$$

then the leading term in the numerator is $a_n x^n$ and the leading term in the denominator is $b_m x^m$. For large enough values of x, the value of r will be approximately equal to the ratio of the leading term in the numerator and the leading term in the denominator. Thus, for large x, $r(x)$ will look like the function

$$y = \frac{a_n x^n}{b_m x^m} = \frac{a_n}{b_m} \cdot x^{n-m}.$$

This is a power function, because it can be written as

$$y = kx^p,$$

where $k = \dfrac{a_n}{b_m}$ and where $p = n - m$. This means that:

For large enough values of x (either positive or negative), the graph of the rational function r will look like the graph of a power function. Specifically, if $r(x) = p(x)/q(x)$, then the **long-run behavior** of $y = r(x)$ is given by

$$y = \frac{\text{leading term of } p}{\text{leading term of } q}.$$

Example 2   Describe the positive long-run behavior of the rational function

$$r(x) = \frac{x+3}{x+2}.$$

Solution   If x is a big number, then

$$r(x) = \frac{\text{(big number)} + 3}{\text{(same big number)} + 2} \approx \frac{\text{(big number)}}{\text{(same big number)}} = 1.$$

For example, if $x = 100$, we have

$$r(x) = \frac{103}{102} = 1.0098\ldots \approx 1.$$

If $x = 10,000$, we have

$$r(x) = \frac{10,003}{10,002} = 1.00009998\ldots \approx 1,$$

For large positive x-values, $r(x) \approx 1$. Thus, for large enough values of x, the graph of $y = r(x)$ looks like the horizontal line $y = 1$, and the graph of r has a horizontal asymptote at $y = 1$. (See Figure 7.58.)

Figure 7.58: For large positive values of x, the function r looks like the horizontal line $y = 1$

Example 3   Describe the long-run behavior of the rational function

$$g(x) = \frac{3x + 1}{x^2 + x - 2}.$$

Solution   The leading term in the numerator is $3x$ and the leading term in the denominator is x^2. Thus for large enough values of x,

$$g(x) \approx \frac{3x}{x^2} = \frac{3}{x}.$$

Figure 7.59 shows the graphs of $y = g(x)$ and $y = \frac{3}{x}$ for $0 \le x \le 10, 0 \le y \le 10$. Notice that for large values of x, the two graphs are nearly indistinguishable. Notice also that both graphs have a horizontal asymptote at $y = 0$.

Figure 7.59: For large enough values of x, the function g looks like the rational function $y = 3x^{-1}$

Rational Functions as Transformations of Power Functions

The function a from the beginning of this section can be written as

$$a(q) = \frac{2500 + 2q}{q}$$
$$= 2500q^{-1} + 2.$$

Thus, the graph of a is the graph of the power function $y = 2500q^{-1}$ shifted up two units. Many rational functions can be viewed as translations of power functions. Consider the following example.

Example 4   Show that the rational function

$$r(x) = \frac{x + 3}{x + 2}$$

is a translation of the power function $f(x) = \frac{1}{x}$.

Solution   We can rewrite the numerator of r as follows:

$$r(x) = \frac{x + 3}{x + 2} = \frac{(x + 2) + 1}{x + 2},$$

which gives

$$r(x) = \frac{x + 2}{x + 2} + \frac{1}{x + 2} = 1 + \frac{1}{x + 2}.$$

Thus, the graph of $y = r(x)$ is the graph of $y = \frac{1}{x}$ shifted two units to the left and one unit up. (See Figure 7.60.)

Figure 7.60: The rational function r is a transformation of the power function f

Problems for Section 7.5

1. The total cost C for a producer to manufacture n units of a good is given by

$$C(n) = 5000 + 50n.$$

Define the *average cost*, $A(n)$, for producing n units by the equation

$$A(n) = \frac{C(n)}{n}.$$

(a)   Evaluate and interpret the economic significance of:
    (i) $C(1)$ (ii) $C(100)$ (iii) $C(1000)$ (iv) $C(10000)$
(b)   Evaluate and interpret the economic significance of:
    (i) $A(1)$ (ii) $A(100)$ (iii) $A(1000)$ (iv) $A(10000)$
(c)   Based on part (b), what trend do you notice in the values of $A(n)$ as n gets large? Explain this trend in economic terms.

2. Figure 7.61 gives a graph of $y = C(n)$, defined in Problem 1, together with a line l that passes through the origin.

    (a) What is the slope of line l?
    (b) How does line l relate to $A(n_0)$, the average cost of producing n_0 units (as defined in Problem 1)?

3. Typically, the *average cost* of production (as defined in Problem 1) goes down as the level of production goes up. Is this the case for the goods whose total cost function is graphed in Figure 7.62? Explain your reasoning.

Figure 7.61

Figure 7.62

$$T(y) = 30,000 + 3x$$

4. Suppose it costs a company \$30,000 to begin production of a certain good, plus \$3 for every unit of the good produced. Let x be the number of units produced by the company.

    (a) Find a formula for $T(x)$, the total cost incurred by the company for the production of x units of the good. $P = C(x) = 30,000 + bx$
    (b) The company's average cost per unit, $C(x)$, is defined to be the total cost divided by the number of units, x. Find a formula for $C(x)$ in terms of x.
    (c) Graph $y = C(x)$ for $0 < x \le 50{,}000$ and $0 \le y \le 10$. Label the horizontal asymptote.
    (d) Explain in economic terms why we should expect the graph of C to have the long-range behavior that it does.
    (e) Explain in economic terms why we should expect the graph of C to have the vertical asymptote that it does.
    (f) Find a formula for $C^{-1}(p)$. Give an economic interpretation of $C^{-1}(p)$.
    (g) The company makes a profit if the average cost of its good is less than \$5 per unit. Find the minimum number of units the company should produce in order to make a profit.

    ask for horizontal asymptotes

5. Compare and discuss the long-range behaviors of the following functions:

    $$f(x) = \frac{x^2 + 1}{x^2 + 5}, \qquad g(x) = \frac{x^3 + 1}{x^2 + 5}, \qquad h(x) = \frac{x + 1}{x^2 + 5}.$$

    $\sim \frac{1}{x} \to 0$

    AS $x \to \infty$

    HA $y = 0$

Problems 6–8 each show a graph of a translation of $y = \frac{1}{x}$. In each problem

(a) Find a formula that represents the graph.
(b) Write the formula from part (a) as the ratio of two linear polynomials.

(c)   Find the coordinates of any intercepts of the graph.

Figure 7.63: A translation   Figure 7.64: A translation   Figure 7.65: A translation

Problems 9–11 each show a graph of a translation of $y = \frac{1}{x^2}$. In each problem
(a)   Find a formula that represents the graph.
(b)   Write the formula from part (a) as the ratio of two polynomials.
(c)   Find the coordinates of any intercepts of the graph.

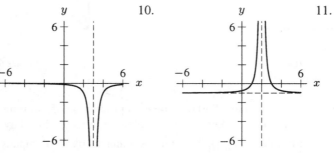

Figure 7.66: A translation   Figure 7.67: A translation   Figure 7.68: A translation

12.   The rational function $r(x)$ shown in Figure 7.69, is a translation of a power function. Find a formula for $r(x)$.

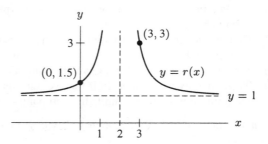

Figure 7.69: $r(x)$ is a translation of a power function

The tables in Problems 13–16 give values for translations of either $y = \frac{1}{x}$ or $y = \frac{1}{x^2}$. In each problem
(a)   Determine if the table values indicate a translation of $y = \frac{1}{x}$ or $y = \frac{1}{x^2}$. Explain your reasoning.
(b)   Find a possible formula for the function given by the table. Express the formula as the ratio of two polynomial functions.

13.

TABLE 7.19

x	y
2.7	12.1
2.9	101
2.95	401
3	undefined
3.05	401
3.1	101
3.3	12.1

14.

TABLE 7.20

x	y
-1000	.499
-100	.490
-10	.400
10	.600
100	.510
1000	.501

15.

TABLE 7.21

x	y
-1000	1.000001
-100	1.00001
-10	1.01
10	1.01
100	1.0001
1000	1.000001

16.

TABLE 7.22

x	y
1.5	-1.5
1.9	-9.5
1.95	-19.5
2	undefined
2.05	20.5
2.1	10.5
2.5	2.5

7.6 THE SHORT-RUN BEHAVIOR OF RATIONAL FUNCTIONS

The Short-Run Behavior of Rational Functions

Recall that the short-run behavior of a polynomial can often be determined from the function's factored form. The same is true of rational functions. If r is a rational function given by

$$r(x) = \frac{p(x)}{q(x)}, \qquad p, q \text{ polynomials,}$$

then knowing the short-run behavior of p and q can tell us something about the short-run behavior of r.

The Zeros of a Rational Function

A fraction will equal zero if and only if its numerator equals zero (and its denominator does not). For the rational function $r(x) = \frac{p(x)}{q(x)}$, this tells us that r will have a zero at $x = a$ if and only if p has a zero at $x = a$, provided q does not also have a zero at $x = a$. In other words, the zeros of r (if any) are the same as the zeros of the numerator p, so long as the zeros of p and q are different.

Example 1   Find the zero(s) of the rational function $r(x) = \dfrac{x + 3}{x + 2}$ from Example 2 in Section 7.5.

Solution   We see that $r(x) = 0$ if

$$\frac{x + 3}{x + 2} = 0.$$

Since this ratio will equal zero only if the numerator is zero (and the denominator is not), we solve

$$x + 3 = 0$$
$$x = -3.$$

The only zero of r is $x = -3$. (Note that $r(-3) = \dfrac{0}{-1} = 0$.)

In summary:

> If r is a rational function given by $r(x) = \dfrac{p(x)}{q(x)}$, where p and q are polynomials, then the **zeros** of r (if any) are the same as the zeros of p, provided that the zeros of p and q are different.

Notice that a rational function may not have any zeros. Consider the following example.

Example 2   Show that the rational function $r(x) = \dfrac{25}{(x + 2)(x - 3)^2}$ has no zeros.

Solution   The numerator of this function is constant and does not equal zero, no matter what the value of x may be. Thus, this function has no zeros, and the graph of r never crosses the x-axis.

The Vertical Asymptotes of a Rational Function

Just as we can find the zeros of a rational function by looking at its numerator, we can find the vertical asymptotes by looking at its denominator. For instance, $y = \frac{1}{x+2}$ is a rational function, and its graph resembles the graph of $y = \frac{1}{x}$ shifted to the left by 2 units. The graph of $y = \frac{1}{x}$ has a vertical asymptote at $x = 0$. When its graph is shifted to the left, so is the vertical asymptote. Figure 7.70 gives a graph of $y = \frac{1}{x+2}$.

In summary:

> If r is a rational function given by $r(x) = \frac{p(x)}{q(x)}$ and $q(a) = 0$, then
> - r is *undefined* at $x = a$, and
> - if $p(a)$ is not also equal to 0, r will have a vertical asymptote at $x = a$.

Figure 7.70: The rational function $y = \frac{1}{x+2}$ has a vertical asymptote at $x = -2$

Essentially, this rule tells us that r will have a vertical asymptote wherever its denominator has a zero, provided its numerator does not also have a zero at the same place. (If the numerator and denominator both have a zero at the same value of x, the situation is more complicated. We will discuss such cases briefly at the end of this section.)

Understanding Vertical Asymptotes in Terms of Power Functions

Suppose $r(x)$ is given by the formula

$$r(x) = \frac{25}{(x+2)(x-3)^2}.$$

The graph of r has vertical asymptotes at $x = -2$ and $x = +3$. What does the graph of r look like near its asymptote at $x = -2$? At $x = -2$, the value of the numerator is 25, and the value of the factor $(x-3)^2$ is $(-2-3)^2$, which also equals 25. For values of x near -2, the value of $(x-3)^2$ stays close to 25; it is nearly constant. However, the value of $1/(x+2)$ becomes quite large, either positively or negatively. It therefore dominates the behavior of the function near $x = -2$. Thus, near the asymptote at $x = -2$, the graph of r looks approximately like the graph of

$$y = \frac{25}{(x+2)(25)}$$
$$= \frac{1}{x+2}.$$

This is the graph of the power function $y = \frac{1}{x}$ shifted to the left by 2 units. Figure 7.71 gives graphs of both functions. Notice that the graphs are similar only near the asymptote at $x = -2$; they look different elsewhere.

Figure 7.71: The rational function $r(x)$ resembles the shifted power function $\dfrac{1}{x+2}$ near its asymptote at $x = -2$

Example 3   Describe the appearance of $r(x) = \dfrac{25}{(x+2)(x-3)^2}$ near its vertical asymptote at $x = 3$.

Solution   At $x = 3$, the function r is undefined. Near $x = 3$, the most important contribution to the value of r is made by the factor $(x - 3)$ because this is the factor responsible for the asymptotic behavior. Near $x = 3$ the value of the numerator equals 25, and value of the factor $x + 2$ is approximately $3 + 2 = 5$. Thus, near $x = 3$, the graph of r will resemble the graph of

$$y = \frac{25}{(5)(x - 3)^2} = \frac{5}{(x - 3)^2}.$$

This is the graph of the power function $y = 5/x^2$ shifted to the right 3 units. Figure 7.72 gives the graphs of both functions.

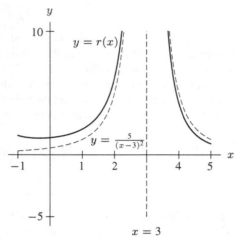

Figure 7.72: The rational function r resembles the shifted power function $\frac{5}{(x-3)^2}$ near its asymptote at $x = 3$.

In general:

> The most significant contribution to the value of a rational function near an asymptote or a zero will be made by the factor whose value is closest to zero.

Drawing the Graph of a Rational Function

We can now summarize what we have learned about the graphs of rational functions.

> If r is a rational function given by $r(x) = \frac{p(x)}{q(x)}$, where p and q are polynomials having different zeros, then:
> - The **long-run behavior** of r resembles the long-run behavior of a power function and this power function is given by the ratio of the leading terms of p and q.
> - The **zeros** of r are the same as the zeros of the numerator, p.
> - The graph of r will have a **vertical asymptote** at each of the zeros of the denominator, q.

Example 4   Draw a graph of $r(x) = \frac{25}{(x+2)(x-3)^2}$, showing all of its important features.

Solution   We have seen that r has no zeros, so its graph does not cross the x-axis. We have also seen that r has a vertical asymptote at $x = -2$ and another one at $x = 3$. Near $x = -2$, its graph resembles the shifted power function $y = \frac{1}{x+2}$, and near $x = 3$ its graph resembles the shifted power function $y = \frac{1}{(x-3)^2}$. We also know that $r(0) = \frac{25}{(0+2)(0-3)^2} = \frac{25}{18}$ so the graph of r crosses the y-axis at this point. Finally, the long-run behavior of r is given by the ratio of the leading term in the numerator to the leading term in the denominator. The numerator is 25 and if we multiply out the denominator, we see that its leading term is x^3. Thus, the long-run behavior of r is given by the graph of $y = \frac{25}{x^3}$. This means that the graph of r has a horizontal asymptote at $y = 0$. Figure 7.73 gives a graph of r, showing all of these features.

Figure 7.73: A graph of the rational function $r(x) = \dfrac{25}{(x+2)(x-3)^2}$

Example 5   Describe the important features of the graph of the rational function $f(x) = \dfrac{18(x+2)^2}{(x-1)(x-4)}$.

Solution   To find the y-intercept, we evaluate

$$f(0) = \frac{18(0+2)^2}{(0-1)(0-4)} = 18.$$

The graph of f crosses the y-axis at the point $(0, 18)$.

   The numerator of this function, $18(x+2)^2$, equals 0 if $x = -2$, thus f has a zero at $x = -2$. Near the zero the most important factor is $18(x+2)^2$. When x is close to -2, the value of $x - 1$ is approximately -3, and the value of $x - 4$ is approximately -6. Thus, near $x = -2$, the graph of $y = f(x)$ resembles the graph of

$$y = \frac{18(x+2)^2}{(-3)(-6)} = (x+2)^2.$$

This is the graph of $y = x^2$ shifted to the left by 2 units. Figure 7.74 shows the graphs of $y = f(x)$ and $y = (x+2)^2$ near $x = -2$. Notice that the graph of f bounces off the x-axis at $x = -2$, just as the graph of a polynomial with a double zero at $x = -2$ would.

   To find the vertical asymptotes, we see that the denominator of f has two zeros, one at $x = 1$ and one at $x = 4$. Near $x = 1$, the graph of f will resemble the shifted power function

$$y = \frac{18(1+2)^2}{(x-1)(1-4)} = \frac{-54}{x-1},$$

and near $x = 4$ the graph of f will resemble the shifted power function

$$y = \frac{18(4 + 2)^2}{(4 - 1)(x - 4)} = \frac{216}{x - 4}.$$

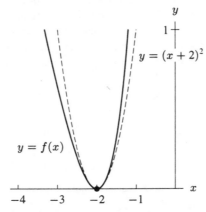

$y = (x + 2)^2$

$y = f(x)$

Figure 7.74: The graph of f resembles the shifted power function $y = (x + 2)^2$ near $x = -2$.

$y = \frac{-54}{x-1}$

$y = \frac{216}{x-4}$

$y = f(x)$

Figure 7.75: The graph of f resembles the shifted power functions, $y = \frac{-54}{x-1}$ and $y = \frac{216}{x-4}$ near $x = 1$ and $x = 4$, respectively.

Figure 7.75 shows the graph of f together with the graphs of these two shifted power functions on the same set of axes.

Finally, the long-run behavior of f is given by the ratio of the leading term in the numerator to the leading term in the denominator. By multiplying out the numerator and denominator, we see that the ratio of the leading terms is given by

$$y = \frac{18x^2}{x^2} = 18.$$

Thus, in the long run, the graph of $y = f(x)$ will resemble the horizontal line $y = 18$. This tells us that the graph of f has a horizontal asymptote at $y = 18$. Figure 7.76 shows the graph of f on two different scales, one emphasizing the short-run behavior of this function and one emphasizing its long-run behavior.

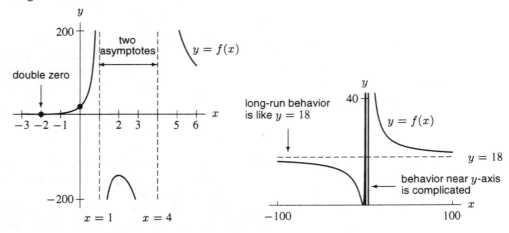

Figure 7.76: These graphs show the short- and long-run behavior of $y = f(x)$.

Can the Graph of a Rational Function Cross its Horizontal Asymptote?

The graph of a rational function can never cross a vertical asymptote because the function is undefined at these x-values. However, the graphs of some rational functions will cross their horizontal asymptotes. For example, we see that the function $f(x)$ from Example 5 will equal 18 if

$$\frac{18(x+2)^2}{(x-1)(x-4)} = 18.$$

Solving this equation gives, after cross multiplying and then dividing by 18,

$$(x+2)^2 = (x-1)(x-4)$$
$$x^2 + 4x + 4 = x^2 - 5x + 4$$
$$9x = 0$$
$$x = 0.$$

Thus, we see that the graph of f crosses its horizontal asymptote at $x = 0$, or the y-axis.

Finding a Formula for a Rational Function from its Graph

Figure 7.77 gives the graph of a rational function, g. From the graph, we see that g has a zero at $x = -1$ and a vertical asymptote at $x = -2$. This means that the numerator of g should have a zero at $x = -1$ and the denominator of g should have a zero at $x = -2$. The zero of g does not seem to be a multiple zero because the graph crosses the x-axis instead of bouncing and does not have a flattened appearance. Thus, we conclude that the numerator of g has one factor of $x + 1$.

As for the denominator, we see that the behavior of g near its vertical asymptote is more like the behavior of $y = \frac{1}{(x+2)^2}$ than like $y = \frac{1}{x+2}$. We conclude that the denominator of g has a factor of $(x+2)^2$. This gives

$$g(x) = k \cdot \frac{x+1}{(x+2)^2},$$

where k is a stretch factor that might or might not equal 1. To figure out the value of k, we use the fact that $g(0) = 0.5$. So

$$0.5 = k \cdot \frac{0+1}{(0+2)^2}$$
$$0.5 = k \cdot \frac{1}{4}$$
$$k = 2.$$

Thus, a possible formula for g is $g(x) = \frac{2(x+1)}{(x+2)^2}$. You can verify this formula by graphing it and comparing the result to Figure 7.77.

Figure 7.77: The graph of $y = g(x)$ a rational function.

When Both the Numerator and Denominator Equal Zero: Holes

The rational function $h(x) = \frac{x^2+x-2}{x-1}$ is undefined at $x = 1$ because the denominator equals zero at $x = 1$. However, the graph of h does not have a vertical asymptote at $x = 1$ because the numerator of h also equals zero at $x = 1$.

$$h(1) = \frac{x^2 + x - 2}{x - 1} = \frac{1^2 + 1 - 2}{1 - 1} = \frac{0}{0},$$

and this ratio is undefined. What does the graph of h look like for $x \neq 1$? If we factor the numerator of h, we have

$$h(x) = \frac{(x - 1)(x + 2)}{x - 1}.$$

By canceling, we can rewrite the formula for h as

$$h(x) = x + 2, \qquad \text{provided } x \neq 1.$$

Thus, the graph of h resembles the line $y = x + 2$ except at $x = 1$, where h is undefined. We see that the line $y = x + 2$ contains the point $(1, 3)$, but that the graph of h does not. Therefore, we say that the graph of h has a *hole* in it at the point $(1, 3)$. See Figure 7.78.

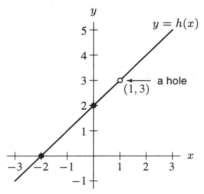

Figure 7.78: The graph of $y = h(x)$ resembles the line $y = x + 2$, except at the point $(1, 3)$, where it has a hole

Problems for Section 7.6

1. Consider the following rational functions. For each, find all zeros and vertical asymptotes and describe its long-range behavior. Then sketch a graph of the function.

   (a) $y = \dfrac{x + 3}{x + 5}$ (b) $y = \dfrac{x + 3}{(x + 5)^2}$ (c) $y = \dfrac{x - 4}{x^2 - 9}$ (d) $y = \dfrac{x^2 - 4}{x - 9}$

2. Let f and g be polynomial functions given by $f(x) = x^2 + 5x + 6$ and $g(x) = x^2 + 1$.

   (a) What are the zeros of f and g?

   (b) Let r be a rational function given by $r(x) = \dfrac{f(x)}{g(x)}$. Sketch a graph of r. Does r have zeros? a vertical asymptote? What is its long-range behavior as $x \to \pm\infty$?

   (c) Let s be a rational function given by $s(x) = \dfrac{g(x)}{f(x)}$. If you graph s on the window $-10 \leq x \leq 10, -10 \leq y \leq 10$, it appears to have a zero near the origin. Does it? Does s have a vertical asymptote? What is its long-range behavior?

3. (a) Give an example of a function for which $f\left(\dfrac{1}{x}\right) \neq \dfrac{1}{f(x)}$

    (b) Show that $f(\frac{1}{x}) = \frac{1}{f(x)}$ must be true for any power function of the form $f(x) = x^{\frac{p}{q}}$.

4. Suppose that n is a constant and that $f(x)$ is a function defined when $x = n$. Complete the following sentences.

    (a) If $f(n)$ is large, then $\dfrac{1}{f(n)}$ is ...

    (b) If $f(n)$ is small, then $\dfrac{1}{f(n)}$ is ...

    (c) If $f(n) = 0$, then $\dfrac{1}{f(n)}$ is ...

    (d) If $f(n)$ is positive, then $\dfrac{1}{f(n)}$ is ...

    (e) If $f(n)$ is negative, then $\dfrac{1}{f(n)}$ is ...

5. (a) Use the results of Problem 4 to graph $y = \frac{1}{f(x)}$ if the graph of $y = f(x)$ is given by Figure 7.79.

    (b) Determine a possible formula for the function shown in Figure 7.79. Use this formula to check your graph you made in part (a).

6. The graph of $y = f(x)$ is given by Figure 7.80. Graph the following functions.
    (a) $y = -f(-x) + 2$ (b) $y = \frac{1}{f(x)}$

Figure 7.79

Figure 7.80

7. Let t be the time in weeks. At time $t = 0$, organic waste is dumped into a pond. Let $f(t)$ represent the level of oxygen in the pond at time t. A formula for $f(t)$ is given by

$$f(t) = \frac{t^2 - t + 1}{t^2 + 1}.$$

Assume $f(0) = 1$ is the normal level of oxygen.

    (a) Sketch a graph of this function.
    (b) Describe the shape of the graph. What is the significance of the minimum in the context of the pond?
    (c) What eventually happens to the oxygen level of the pond?
    (d) Approximately how many weeks must pass in order for the oxygen level to return to 75% of its normal level?

8. Find a formula for $f^{-1}(x)$ given that

$$f(x) = \frac{4 - 3x}{5x - 4}.$$

9. Find possible formulas for the graphs in Figure 7.81.

(a)

(b)

(c)

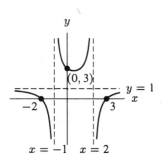

Figure 7.81

10. Find possible formulas for the rational functions in Figure 7.82.

(a)

(b)

(c)

Figure 7.82

In Problems 11–12 find possible equations for the graphs.

11.

Figure 7.83

12.

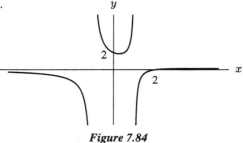

Figure 7.84

13. Define f, g, and h as follows:

$$f(x) = x^2 + 1 \qquad g(x) = x^2 - 4 \qquad h(x) = x + 3$$

Several different functions are described below. Find possible formulas for these functions in terms of $f(x)$, $g(x)$ and $h(x)$. [Example: Suppose j has one zero at $x = -3$, two vertical asymptotes, one at $x = 2$ and one at $x = -2$, and a horizontal asymptote at $y = 0$. Then a possible formula for j would be $j(x) = \frac{h(x)}{g(x)}$.]

(a) k has no zeros, vertical asymptotes at $x = 2$, and $x = -2$, and a horizontal asymptote at $y = 0$.

(b) m has no zeros, vertical asymptotes at $x = 2$, and $x = -2$, and a horizontal asymptote at $y = 1$.

(c) n has no zeros, no vertical asymptotes, and a horizontal asymptote at $y = 0$.

(d) p has two zeros, one at $x = -2$ and one at $x = 2$, no vertical asymptotes, and a horizontal asymptote at $y = 1$.

(e) q has no zeros, one vertical asymptote at $x = -3$, and no horizontal asymptote.

14. Descriptions of the graphs of several rational functions follow. Find a possible formula for each of these functions.

(a)   The graph of $y = f(x)$ has exactly one vertical asymptote, at $x = -1$, and a horizontal asymptote at $y = 1$. The graph of f crosses the y-axis at $y = 3$ and crosses the x-axis exactly once, at $x = -3$.

(b)   The graph of $y = g(x)$ has exactly two vertical asymptotes: one at $x = -2$ and one at $x = 3$. It has a horizontal asymptote of $y = 0$. Furthermore, the graph of g touches the x-axis exactly once, at $x = 5$.

(c)   The graph of $y = h(x)$ has exactly two vertical asymptotes: one at $x = -2$ and one at $x = 3$. It has a horizontal asymptote of $y = 1$. Furthermore, the graph of g crosses the x-axis exactly once, at $x = 5$.

15. Suppose 12 kg of a certain alloy initially contains 3 kg copper and 9 kg tin. Suppose you add x kg of copper to this 12 kg of alloy. Define the concentration of copper in the alloy as a function of x, so that

$$f(x) = \text{Concentration of copper} = \frac{\text{Total amount of copper}}{\text{Total amount of alloy}}.$$

(a)   Find a formula for f in terms of x, the amount of copper added.

(b)   If possible, evaluate the following expressions and explain their significance in the context of the alloy:

   (i) $f(\frac{1}{2})$ (ii) $f(0)$ (iii) $f(-1)$ (iv) $f^{-1}(\frac{1}{2})$ (v) $f^{-1}(0)$

(c)   Graph $y = f(x)$, for $-5 \leq x \leq 5$, $-0.25 \leq y \leq 0.5$. Interpret both axis-intercepts in the context of the alloy.

(d)   Sketch a graph of f for $-3 \leq x \leq 100$, $0 \leq y \leq 1$. Describe the appearance of your graph for large x-values. Does the appearance agree with what you expect to happen when large amounts of copper are added to the alloy?

16. A chemist is studying the properties of an alloy (mixture) of copper and tin. She begins with 2 kg of an alloy that is one-half tin. Keeping the amount of copper constant, she adds small amounts of tin to the alloy. Letting x be the total amount of tin added, define $C(x)$ as the *concentration* of tin in the alloy, where

$$\text{concentration of tin} = \frac{\text{total amount of tin}}{\text{total amount of alloy}}.$$

(a)   Find a formula for $C(x)$.

(b)   Evaluate $C(0.5)$ and $C(-0.5)$. Explain the physical significance of these quantities.

(c)   Sketch a graph of $C(x)$ labeling all interesting features. Describe the physical significance of the features you have labeled.

17. Assume f, g, h, and j are each rational functions of the form

$$y = \frac{(x - A)(x - B)}{(x - C)(x - D)},$$

for different values of A, B, C, and D. The graphs of the four functions are given in Figure 7.85.

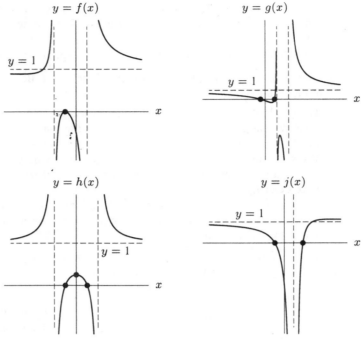

Figure 7.85

Match each of the following statements to one of the graphs in Figure 7.85, or indicate that the statement has no matching function.

(a) $A < C < B < D$ (b) $A < B < C < D$
(c) $A < C < D < B$ (d) $C < A,\ A = B,\ B < D$
(e) $A < C,\ C = D,\ D < B$

18.   Define f, g, and, h as follows:

$$f(x) = x^2 + 9 \qquad g(x) = (x-3)(x-4) \qquad h(x) = x - 5$$

The following polynomial and rational functions are defined in terms of f, g, and, h:

(i) $j(x) = \dfrac{f(x)}{g(x)}$ (ii) $k(x) = \dfrac{g(x)}{f(x)}$ (iii) $m(x) = g(x) \cdot h(x)$

(iv) $n(x) = \dfrac{h(x)}{f(x)}$ (v) $p(x) = \dfrac{g(x)}{h(x)}$ (vi) $q(x) = \frac{1}{g(x)}$

For each of the following descriptions, state which of the functions j, k, m, n, p, q, defined above, that satisfy the description, or indicate that the description has no matching function.

(a)   This function has one zero, no vertical asymptotes, and a horizontal asymptote at $y = 0$.
(b)   This function has three zeros and no asymptotes.
(c)   This function has two zeros, no vertical asymptotes, and a horizontal asymptote at $y = 1$.
(d)   This function has no zeros, two vertical asymptotes, and a horizontal asymptote at $y = 0$.
(e)   This function has no zeros, two vertical asymptotes, and a horizontal asymptote at $y = 1$.
(f)   This function has no zeros, one vertical asymptote, and no horizontal asymptotes.

19. We can use the following procedure to approximate the cube root of a number. If x is a guess for $\sqrt[3]{2}$, for example, then x^3 will equal 2 only if the guess is correct. Note that if $x^3 = 2$ we could also write $x = \frac{2}{x^2}$. If our guess, x, is less than $\sqrt[3]{2}$, then $\frac{2}{x^2}$ will be greater than $\sqrt[3]{2}$. If x is greater than $\sqrt[3]{2}$, then $\frac{2}{x^2}$ will be less than $\sqrt[3]{2}$. However, in either case, if x is an estimate for $\sqrt[3]{2}$, then the *average* of x and $\frac{2}{x^2}$ will provide a better estimate. Define $g(x)$ to be this improved estimate.

   (a) Find a possible formula for $g(x)$, expressed as one reduced fraction.
   (b) Begin with the approximation that $\sqrt[3]{2} \approx 1.26$. Use this as a first guess for $\sqrt[3]{2}$. Explain how to use the function $g(x)$ to improve this approximation and to estimate the value of $\sqrt[3]{2}$, accurate to five decimal places. Construct a table showing any intermediate results, and explain why you believe you have reached the required accuracy for your estimate.

20. Problem 19 outlines a method of approximating $\sqrt[3]{2}$ by guessing. An initial guess, x, is averaged with $2/x^2$ to obtain a better guess, defined as $g(x)$. There exists a better method that returns a more accurate estimate than $g(x)$. This method involves taking a *weighted* average of x and $2/x^2$.

   (a) Let x be a guess for $\sqrt[3]{2}$. Define $h(x)$ by the following equation:

$$h(x) = \frac{1}{3}\left(x + x + \frac{2}{x^2}\right).$$

   Express $h(x)$ as one reduced fraction. Explain why $h(x)$ is referred to as a *weighted* average.
   (b) Explain why $h(x)$ is a better function to use for estimating $\sqrt[3]{2}$ than is $g(x)$. Include specific, numerical examples in your answer.

REVIEW PROBLEMS FOR CHAPTER SEVEN

1. Determine the type of functions that could be described by the following tables of data. They could be linear, exponential, logarithmic, trigonometric, power, or polynomial functions. Find a possible formula for each table.

(a) **TABLE 7.23**

x	-2	-1	0	1	2	3
y	3	-1	3	-1	3	-1

(b) **TABLE 7.26**

x	1/9	1/3	1	3	9
y	-2	-1	0	1	2

(c) **TABLE 7.24**

x	-3	-2	-1	0	1	2	3
y	-40	0	12	8	0	0	20

(d) **TABLE 7.27**

x	-2	-1	0	1	2
y	-24	-3	0	3	24

(e) **TABLE 7.25**

x	-2	-1	0	1	2	3
y	0.02	0.10	0.5	2.50	12.5	62.5

(f) **TABLE 7.28**

x	1	2	3	4	5
y	8	3	-2	-7	-12

2.   Find the function from the list in Table 7.29 that *best* represents each of the following graphs.

(i)

Figure 7.86

(ii)

Figure 7.87

(iii)

Figure 7.88

(iv)

Figure 7.89

TABLE 7.29

A) $y = 0.5\sin(2x)$	**G**) $y = 0.5\sin(0.5x)$	**M**) $y = \frac{1}{x-6}$
B) $y = -\ln x$	**H**) $y = \ln(x+1)$	**N**) $y = \frac{x-2}{x^2-9}$
C) $y = 10(0.6)^x$	**I**) $y = 7(2.5)^x$	**O**) $y = \frac{1}{x^2-4}$
D) $y = 2\sin(2x)$	**J**) $y = 2\sin(0.5x)$	**P**) $y = \frac{x}{x-3}$
E) $y = \ln(-x)$	**K**) $y = \ln(x-1)$	**Q**) $y = \frac{x-1}{x+3}$
F) $y = -15(3.1)^x$	**L**) $y = 2e^{-0.2x}$	**R**) $y = \frac{1}{x^2+4}$

3.   Find possible formulas for the polynomials in Figure 7.90.

(a)

(b)

(c)

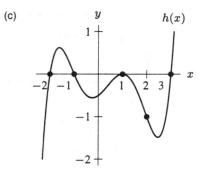

Figure 7.90: Three different polynomials.

4. Find the function from Table 7.30 that best describes each of the following graphs.

(a) (b) (c)

(d) (e) (f)

(g) (h)

Figure 7.91

TABLE 7.30

1) $y = 0.5\sin(2x)$	9) $y = -\ln x$	17) $y = 3e^{-x}$
2) $y = 2\sin(2x)$	10) $y = \ln(-x)$	18) $y = -3e^{x}$
3) $y = 0.5\sin(0.5x)$	11) $y = \ln(x+1)$	19) $y = -3e^{-x}$
4) $y = 2\sin(0.5x)$	12) $y = \ln(x-1)$	20) $y = 3e^{-x^2}$
5) $y = \frac{x-2}{x^2-9}$	13) $y = \frac{x+3}{x^2-4}$	21) $y = \frac{1}{x^2-4}$
6) $y = \frac{x-3}{x^2-1}$	14) $y = \frac{x^2-4}{x^2-1}$	22) $y = \frac{1}{x^2+4}$
7) $y = (x-1)^3 - 1$	15) $y = (x+1)^3 - 1$	23) $y = (x+1)^3 + 1$
8) $y = 2x - 4$	16) $y = -2x - 4$	24) $y = 2(x+2)$

5. Assume that $x = a$ and $x = b$ are zeros of the second degree polynomial function $y = q(x)$.

   (a) Explain what you know and what you don't know about the graph of q (e.g., intercepts, vertex, end behavior).

   (b) Explain why a possible formula for $q(x)$ is given by $q(x) = k(x - a)(x - b)$, with k unknown.

6. Find possible formulas for the polynomial functions in Figure 7.92.

(a) (b)

Figure 7.92: Find possible formulas for these polynomials.

Chapter 6/ 63

7. Figure 7.93 gives the graph of $y = g(x)$, a polynomial. Find a possible formula for g in terms of x.

8. Find an equation for the graph of the polynomial f shown in Figure 7.94. [Note in particular the appearance of the graph of f near the origin.]

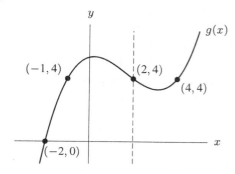

Figure 7.93: The graph of $g(x)$, a polynomial.   **Figure 7.94**

9. (a) Suppose $f(x) = ax^2 + bx + c$. What must be true about the coefficients of f if f is known to be an even function?
    (b) Suppose $g(x) = ax^3 + bx^2 + cx + d$. What must be true about the coefficients of g if g is known to be an odd function?

10. Find the horizontal asymptote, if it exists, of each of the following functions:

    (a) $f(x) = \dfrac{1}{1 + \dfrac{1}{x}}$

    (b) $g(x) = \dfrac{(1 - x)(2 + 3x)}{2x^2 + 1}$

    (c) $h(x) = 3 - \dfrac{1}{x} + \dfrac{x}{x + 1}$

11. The gravitational force exerted by a planet is inversely proportional to the square of the distance to the center of the planet. Thus, the weight, w, of an object at a distance, r, from a planet's center is given by

$$w = \frac{k}{r^2},$$

    where the constant k depends on the masses of the object and the planet.

    Suppose a constant force of one ton (2000 lbs) will kill a 150-pound person. On how small a planet could such a person survive, assuming the planet's mass were the same as the earth's?

12. The following questions involve the behavior of the power function $y = x^{-p}$, for p a positive integer. If a distinction between even and odd values of p is significant, the significance should be indicated.

    (a) What is the domain of $y = x^{-p}$? What is the range?
    (b) What symmetries are exhibited by the graph of $y = x^{-p}$?
    (c) What is the behavior of $y = x^{-p}$ as $x \to 0$?
    (d) What is the behavior of $y = x^{-p}$ for large positive values of x? for large negative values of x?

13. Tradition holds that the ancient Greeks placed great importance on a number known as the *golden ratio*, ϕ (read "phi"). This number can be defined geometrically. Starting with a square, draw a rectangle to one side of the square, so that the resulting rectangle has the same proportions as the rectangle that was added. The golden ratio is defined as the ratio of either rectangle's length to its width. (See Figure 7.95.) Given this information, show that $\phi = \frac{1+\sqrt{5}}{2}$.

Figure 7.95: The large rectangle has the same proportions as the small rectangle

14. The number ϕ, found in Problem 13, has an unusual property:

$$\phi^k + \phi^{k+1} = \phi^{k+2}.$$

(a) Show that the property holds true for $k = 3$ and $k = 10$.
(b) Show that this property follows from the definition of ϕ.

15. Define $f(x)$ as the number that when added to x gives the same result as when multiplied by x. For example, $f(3) = \frac{3}{2}$ because $3 + \frac{3}{2} = 3 \cdot \frac{3}{2} = \frac{9}{2}$.

(a) Evaluate $f(2)$. Explain how you know your answer is correct.
(b) Explain in words why $f(1)$ is undefined.
(c) For $m = 0.25, 0.5, 1, 2, 3$, evaluate $100 + m$ and $100 \times m$, and tabulate your results. Based on your table, guess the approximate value of $f(100)$.
(d) Find a possible formula for $f(x)$.
(e) From its formula, we see that the graph of $f(x)$ has a horizontal asymptote at $y = 1$. Explain why this makes sense in light of the definition of $f(x)$. [Hint: Consider your response to part (c).]
(f) Evaluate $f(f(x))$. What surprising thing happens? Discuss.

16. Suppose an alcohol solution consists of 5 gallons of pure water and x gallons of alcohol, $x > 0$. Let $f(x)$ be the ratio of the volume of alcohol to the total volume of liquid. [Thus, $f(x)$ is the *concentration* of the alcohol in the solution.]

(a) Find a possible formula for $f(x)$.
(b) Evaluate and interpret $f(7)$ in the context of the mixture.
(c) What is the zero of f? Interpret your result in the context of the mixture.
(d) Find an equation for the horizontal asymptote of f, and explain its significance in the context of the mixture..

17. The function $f(x)$ defined in Problem 16 gives the concentration of a solution of x gallons of alcohol and 5 gallons of water.

(a) Find a formula for $f^{-1}(x)$.
(b) Evaluate and interpret $f^{-1}(0.2)$ in the context of the mixture.
(c) What is the zero of f^{-1}? Interpret your result in the context of the mixture.
(d) Find an equation for the horizontal asymptote of f^{-1}, and explain its significance in the context of the mixture.

18. Graph $y = \dfrac{2x^2 - 10x + 12}{x^2 - 16}$ without using a calculator.

19. For each of the following functions, state whether it is even, odd, or neither.

   (a) $f(x) = x^2 + 3$ (b) $g(x) = x^3 + 3$ (c) $h(x) = \frac{5}{x}$

   (d) $j(x) = |x - 4|$ (e) $k(x) = \log x$ (f) $l(x) = \log(x^2)$

   (g) $m(x) = 2^x + 2$ (h) $n(x) = \cos x + 2$

20. Assume f, g, h, and j are each rational functions of the form

$$y = \frac{(x - A)(x - B)}{(x - C)(x - D)},$$

   for different values of A, B, C, and D, where $A \leq B$ and $C \leq D$. The graphs of four rational functions are given in Figures 7.96 and 7.97. For each of these four functions, rank the quantities 0, A, B, C, D in order, from least to greatest.

(a) $y = f(x)$ (b) $y = g(x)$

Figure 7.96: The graphs of two rational functions.

(c) $y = h(x)$ $y = j(x)$

Figure 7.97: The graphs of two rational functions.

21. Find possible formulas for the following polynomials and rational functions.

   (a) This function has zeros at $x = -3$, $x = 2$, $x = 5$, and a double-zero at $x = 6$. It has a y-intercept of 7.

   (b) This function has zeros at $x = -3$ and $x = 2$, and vertical asymptotes at $x = -5$ and $x = 7$. It has a horizontal asymptote of $y = 1$.

   (c) This function has zeros at $x = 2$ and $x = 3$. It has a vertical asymptote at $x = 5$. It has a horizontal asymptote of $y = -3$.

22. Let $f(x) = (x-3)^2$, $g(x) = x^2 - 4$, $h(x) = x+1$, and $j(x) = x^2+1$. Match the following functions to the verbal descriptions below. Some of the descriptions may have no matching function or more than one matching function.

    (i) $p(x) = \dfrac{f(x)}{g(x)}$ (ii) $q(x) = \dfrac{h(x)}{g(x)}$ (iii) $r(x) = f(x)h(x)$

    (iv) $s(x) = \dfrac{g(x)}{j(x)}$ (v) $t(x) = \dfrac{1}{h(x)}$ (vi) $v(x) = \dfrac{j(x)}{f(x)}$

    (a) This function has two zeros, no vertical asymptotes, and a horizontal asymptote.
    (b) This function has two zeros, no vertical asymptote, and no horizontal asymptote.
    (c) This function has one zero, one vertical asymptote, and a horizontal asymptote.
    (d) This function has one zero, two vertical asymptotes, and a horizontal asymptote.
    (e) This function has no zeros, one vertical asymptote, and a horizontal asymptote at $y = 1$.
    (f) This function has no zeros, one vertical asymptote, and a horizontal asymptote at $y = 0$.

23. Find possible formulas for the rational functions defined by their graphs in Figures 7.98 and 7.99.

    (a)   (b)

    Figure 7.98

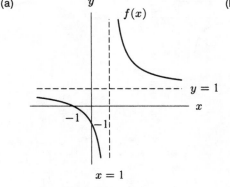

    Figure 7.99

24. Let $f(x) = x^2 - 4$, $g(x) = x^2+4$, and $h(x) = x+5$. Match the given polynomial and rational functions to the descriptions that follow. Note that some of the descriptions may match none of the given functions, and vice versa.

    (a) $y = \frac{f(x)}{g(x)}$ (b) $y = \frac{g(x)}{f(x)}$ (c) $y = \frac{h(x)}{f(x)}$

    (d) $y = f(\frac{1}{x})$ (e) $y = \frac{g(x)}{h(x)}$ (f) $y = \frac{h(x^2)}{h(x)}$

    (g) $y = \frac{1}{g(x)}$ (h) $y = f(x) \cdot g(x)$

    (i)   This function has a horizontal asymptote at $y = 0$ and one zero at $x = -5$.
    (ii)   This function has no horizontal asymptote, no zeros, and a vertical asymptote at $x = -5$.
    (iii)   This function has zeros at $x = -5$, $x = -2$, and $x = 2$.
    (iv)   This function has no zeros, a horizontal asymptote at $y = 0$, and a vertical asymptote at $x = -5$.
    (v)   This function has two zeros, no vertical asymptotes, and a horizontal asymptote at $y = 1$.
    (vi)   This function has no zeros, no vertical asymptotes, and a horizontal asymptote at $y = 1$.
    (vii)   This function has a horizontal asymptote at $y = -4$.
    (viii)   This function has no horizontal asymptotes, two zeros, and a vertical asymptote at $x = -5$.

25. The graphs of six rational functions are shown below followed by six rational function definitions. Match the functions with their graphs by finding the zeros, asymptotes, and end behavior for each function.

(i)

(ii)

(iii)

(iv)

(v)

(vi)

(a) $f(x) = \dfrac{-1}{x^2 - 10x + 25} - 1$

(b) $f(x) = \dfrac{x - 2}{(x + 1)(x - 3)}$

(c) $f(x) = \dfrac{2x + 4}{x - 1}$

(d) $f(x) = \dfrac{1}{x + 1} + \dfrac{1}{x - 3}$

(e) $f(x) = \dfrac{1 - x^2}{x - 2}$

(f) $f(x) = \dfrac{1 - 4x}{2x + 2}$

26. Give examples of rational functions with even symmetry, odd symmetry, and neither. How does the symmetry of $f(x) = \dfrac{p(x)}{q(x)}$ depend on the symmetry of $p(x)$ and $q(x)$?

27. Find inverses for the following functions. (You may assume these functions have been defined on domains where they are invertible.)

(a) $y = \dfrac{2x}{3x + 2}$

(b) $y = \log_3(2x - 7)$

(c) $y = 2^{3x-5}$

(d) $y = \dfrac{e^x + 4}{2 - 3e^x}$

(e) $y = \sqrt{3 + \sqrt{x}}$

(f) $y = 3\sin(2x) + 4$

28. Find formulas for the inverses of the following functions.

(a) $f(x) = 15(x - 2)^3 - 4$

(b) $f(x) = \dfrac{x}{3x + 1},\ x \geq 0$

29. Find the inverse of each of the following functions. You should assume that these functions are defined on domains on which they are invertible.

(a) $f(x) = \dfrac{3x}{x - 1}$

(b) $g(x) = (x - 3)^2 + 4,\quad x \geq 3$

(c) $h(x) = 1 - \dfrac{2}{x - 3}$

(d) $j(x) = \dfrac{2x^3 + 1}{3x^3 - 1}$

(e) $k(x) = (\sqrt{x} + 1)^3$

(f) $x^2 + 4x,\quad x \geq -2$

30. Suppose we want to launch an unpowered spacecraft, initially in free space, so that it hits a planet of radius R. When viewed from a distance, the planet looks like a disk of area πR^2. In the absence of gravity, we would need to aim the spacecraft directly towards this disk. However, because of gravity, the planet will draw the spacecraft towards it, so that even if we are somewhat off the mark, the spacecraft might still hit its target. This means that the area we must aim for is actually larger than the apparent area of the planet. This area is called the planet's *capture cross-section*. The more massive the planet, the larger its capture cross-section, because it exerts a stronger pull on passing objects.

A spacecraft with a large initial velocity has a greater chance of slipping past the planet even if its aim is only slightly off, whereas a spacecraft with a low initial velocity has a good chance of drifting into the planet even if its aim is poor. Thus, the planet's capture cross-section is a function of the initial velocity of the spacecraft, v. If the planet's capture cross-section is denoted by A, and M is the planet's mass then it can be shown that

$$A(v) = \pi R^2 \left(1 + \frac{2MG/R}{v^2} \right),$$

where G is a positive physical constant.

(a) Show from the formula for $A(v)$ that

$$A(v) > \pi R^2$$

for any initial velocity v. Explain why this makes sense.

(b) Consider two planets: The first is twice as massive as the second, while the second has a radius that is twice the radius of the first. Which will have the larger capture cross-section?

(c) The graph of $A(v)$ has both horizontal and vertical asymptotes. Find their equations, and explain their physical significance.

A *table of differences* for a function f is formed by calculating the successive differences between $f(x)$ and $f(x-1)$, where x is an integer. We define $\Delta f(x)$ by the equation

$$\Delta f(x) = f(x) - f(x-1).$$

Thus, a table of differences for $f(x)$ is a table of values for $\Delta f(x)$. For example, the table of differences for the power function $p(x) = x^2$ is given by Table 7.31:

TABLE 7.31

x	-2	-1	0	1	2	3	4
$p(x)$	4	1	0	1	4	9	16
$\Delta p(x)$		-3	-1	1	3	5	7

As you can see, $\Delta p(-1) = -3$, because

$$\Delta p(-1) = p(-1) - p(-1-1) = p(-1) - p(-2) = 1 - 4 = -3.$$

Similarly, $\Delta p(2) = 3$ because

$$\Delta p(2) = p(2) - p(2-1) = p(2) - p(1) = 4 - 1 = 3.$$

Note $\Delta p(-2)$ is not shown because $\Delta p(-3)$ is not in the table.

Problems 31–34 concern the table of differences.

31. (a) What pattern do you notice in the table of differences for $p(x) = x^2$?
     (b) Find a formula for $\Delta p(x)$.

32. (a) Make tables of differences for $f(x) = 2x^2$, $g(x) = 2x^2 + 1$, $h(x) = 3x^2 - 2$, $j(x) = 3x^2 + 4$, $k(x) = 4x^2$. The tables should include values for $x = -2, -1, 0, 1, 2, 3$. Describe any patterns that you see.
     (b) Find a formula for $\Delta p(x)$, given that

$$p(x) = Ax^2 + B.$$

     (c) A table of differences for the function $q(x)$ is given. (See Table 7.32.) Find a formula for $q(x)$.

TABLE 7.32

x	-2	-1	0	1	2	3
$q(x)$	13	-2	-7	-2	13	38
$\Delta q(x)$		-15	-5	5	15	25

33. (a) Make a table of differences for $p(x) = x^3$.
     (b) Find a formula for $\Delta p(x)$ given that $p(x) = x^3$. [Hint: Use the definition of $\Delta p(x)$.]

34. Let $p(x) = x^3$. Define $q(x)$ by the equation

$$q(x) = \Delta p(x).$$

Define $\Delta(\Delta p(x))$ as $\Delta q(x)$. Make a table showing $\Delta q(x)$—that is, make a table of differences for *the table of differences* of $p(x) = x^3$. What pattern do you notice?

35. A group of x people is tested for the presence of a certain virus. Unfortunately, the test is imperfect, and will incorrectly identify some healthy people as being infected and some sick people as being noninfected. There is no way to know when the test is right and when it is wrong. Since the disease is so rare, only 1% of those tested will actually be infected.

     (a) Write expressions in terms of x for the number of people tested that are actually infected and the number who are not.
     (b) Suppose the test correctly identifies 98% of all infected people as being infected. (It incorrectly identifies the remaining 2% as being healthy.) Write an expression in terms of x representing the number of infected people who are correctly identified as being infected. (This group is known as the *true-positive* group.)
     (c) Suppose the test incorrectly identifies 3% of all healthy people as being infected. (It correctly identifies the remaining 97% as being healthy.) Write an expression in terms of x representing the number of noninfected people who are incorrectly identified as being infected. (This group is known as the *false-positive* group.)
     (d) Write an expression in terms of x representing the total number of people the test identifies as being infected, including both true- and false-positives.
     (e) Write an expression in terms of x representing the fraction of those testing positive who are actually infected. Can you evaluate this expression, or do you need to know the value of x?
     (f) Suppose you are among the group of people who test positive for the presence of the virus. Based on your test result, do you think it is likely that you are actually infected?

Problems 36–39 refer to three measures of the accuracy of a test for the presence of a disease: the *sensitivity*, the *specificity*, and the *predictive value*. The sensitivity is the fraction of people having the disease that the test will correctly identify as having the disease. The specificity is the fraction of people not having the disease that the test will correctly identify as not having the disease; the predictive value is the fraction of people testing positive who actually have the disease.

36. Suppose 100,000 people are to be tested for the presence of a rare disease. Since the disease is rare, its prevalence is low, and experts place it at approximately 0.1%. The screening test used is known to have a sensitivity of 95% and a specificity of 90%.

    (a) How many of the 100,000 people tested are likely to be sick? How many of those who are sick will test positive? How many of those who are not sick will test positive?

    (b) By calculating this test's predictive value, show that a person testing positive actually has only about a 1% chance of being sick. Explain how such a highly sensitive and specific test can still have such an incredibly low predictive value.

    (c) Show that the predictive value of the test is independent of the number of people tested. In other words, show that you would get the same predictive value no matter how many people are screened.

37. Suppose a group of people is tested for a rare disease. Since the disease is rare, its prevalence is low, but its precise value is unknown. The screening test itself has a sensitivity of 95% and a specificity of 90%.

    (a) Suppose the number of people tested is P. Letting x represent the prevalence of the disease, write expressions for the numbers of people likely to be infected and likely to not be infected.

    (b) Of those infected, how many will test positive? Of those not infected, how many will test positive?

    (c) Find a simplified formula for $V(x)$, the predictive value of the test as a function of prevalence, x. Recall that the predictive value of a test is defined as the ratio of the number of true positive results to all positive results.

    (d) Make a table showing the test's predictive value for the following values of prevalence: 0.1%, 0.2%, 1%, 2%, 5%, 10%, 20%, 40%, and 80%. Describe the relationship between predictive value and prevalence.

    (e) How prevalent would the disease have to be for a person testing positive to have a 5% chance of actually being infected?

38. The ideal screening test would be both highly sensitive and highly specific. Usually, though, this is not possible, for as a rule there is a tradeoff between the sensitivity and the specificity of a given test. This is because in many cases there are some people who are clearly normal and some who are clearly abnormal, while the rest are somewhere in between. Where one chooses to draw the line between normal and abnormal is arbitrary. Because of this, any test based on such a scale will have an increased sensitivity only at the expense of specificity.

    (a) Naturally, anyone who is clearly normal is assigned a negative test result, because they are known to not be sick. Likewise, anyone who is clearly abnormal is assigned a positive test result, because they are known to be infected. Suppose all those who are neither clearly normal nor clearly abnormal are assigned a positive result. Describe how this decision would affect the sensitivity and the specificity of the test.

    (b) Now suppose that all those who are neither clearly normal nor clearly abnormal are assigned a negative result. Describe how this decision would affect the sensitivity and the specificity of the test.

39. Suppose there are two different screening tests for a disease prevalent in 1% of the population. The first test has a sensitivity of 90% and an undetermined specificity, while the second test has a specificity of 90% and an undetermined sensitivity.

    (a) Find $P_1(x)$, the predictive value of the first test as a function of x, its specificity.
    (b) Find $P_2(x)$, the predictive value of the second test as a function of x, its sensitivity.
    (c) Graph P_1 and P_2 on the same set of axes.
    (d) For what value of x does $P_1(x) = P_2(x)$? Is this what you would expect?
    (e) Suppose you had a test whose sensitivity and specificity were both 90%. If you had to choose, would it be better to try and improve the test's sensitivity or its specificity?

40. Physicists use what are known as *energy diagrams* in the study of planetary motion. An energy diagram is a graph of the *effective potential energy*, U_{eff}, of a sun-planet system, as a function of the planet's distance from the sun, r. By convention, a negative value of U_{eff} signifies an attractive potential, and a positive value of U_{eff} signifies a repulsive potential. Typically, the effective potential of a sun-planet system will have both an attractive term, due to gravity, and a repulsive term, due to the *centrifugal force* any physical body experiences during circular motion. Suppose that the effective potential energy U_{eff} of a hypothetical sun-planet system is given by the formula

    $$U_{eff} = -\frac{3}{r} + \frac{1}{r^2}, \qquad r > 0.$$

    (a) Which of the terms in this expression is attractive? Which is repulsive?
    (b) Sketch an energy diagram for this sun-planet system.
    (c) At what distance is the planet most strongly attracted to the sun?
    (d) Give the equation of the horizontal asymptote of U_{eff}. Explain its physical significance; that is, describe how the planet's attraction to the sun varies as $r \to \infty$.
    (e) Give the equation of the vertical asymptote of U_{eff}, and explain its physical significance.

41. The orbit of a planet around the sun is determined by the effective potential energy of the sun-planet system, U_{eff}, defined in Problem 40, as well as by the system's *total energy*, E, which is a constant. The planet's motion about the sun is confined to those distances r for which $E > U_{eff}$. Suppose the sun-planet system described in Problem 40 has a total energy E given by $E = -1$.

    (a) Sketch a graph of the system's total energy, E, on the same set of axes as its effective potential, U_{eff}. [Hint: because the total energy is a constant, it is represented graphically by a horizontal line.]
    (b) Using the fact that the planet in part (a) is confined to those distances r for which $E > U_{eff}$, determine the planet's *perihelion* – the closest distance to which it can approach the sun.
    (c) Determine the planet's *aphelion* – the farthest distance to which it can move away from the sun.

42. The *total energy* of a sun-planet system is defined in Problem 41.

    (a) Using the fact that E must exceed U_{eff}, determine the minimum possible total energy, E_{min}, of the sun-planet system described in Problem 41.
    (b) Suppose the total energy of this system is E_{min}. Describe the orbit of the planet around the sun.

43. (a) If the total energy E of a sun-planet system, defined in Problem 41, is negative, then the system is referred to as *bound*. The total energy of the system described in Problem 41 is negative. Explain why, based on your answer to Problem 41, it makes sense to refer

to this system as bound.

(b) If the total energy E of a sun-planet system is positive, the system is referred to as *unbound*. Suppose the system described in Problem 40 has a positive total energy of $E = 0.5$. Sketch an energy diagram of this system that shows both E and U_{eff}. Explain why it makes sense to refer to this system as unbound.

44. Recall that a sun-planet system whose total energy is negative is known as a bound system. Figure 7.100 gives the energy diagrams of two different sun-planet systems both having the same effective potential and both having negative total energies. Explain why it makes sense to refer to these systems as bound.

Figure 7.100: Two sun-planet systems with different total energies

45. An *ellipse* resembles a flattened circle. It is known that all bound planetary orbits are elliptical, with circular orbits being special cases.

(a) One of the systems in Figure 7.100, in Problem 44, corresponds to a planet whose orbit about the sun is a circle. What is the total energy of this system? What is the radius of its orbit?

(b) The other system corresponds to a planet whose orbit is elliptical. Draw a sketch of what you think the orbit might look like. Indicate the position of the sun on your sketch. Label the following quantities, if relevant: r_1, r_2, and r_3.

Refer to Problems 40–45 to answer Problems 46–49.

46. Keeping in mind that attractive potentials are negative while repulsive potentials are positive, prepare an energy diagram for a hypothetical sun-planet system whose effective potential is given by

$$U_{eff} = -\frac{1}{r} + \frac{1}{r^2}.$$

Describe the planet's attraction to the sun. At what separation is it strongest? How does the attraction change as the planet moves further from the sun? What happens as the planet draws near the sun?

47. Energy diagrams are sometimes used to study atomic interactions. One standard function used to model diatomic molecules is the *Lennard-Jones 6,12 potential*, given by

$$U(r) = a\left[\left(\frac{b}{r}\right)^{12} - 2\left(\frac{b}{r}\right)^6\right],$$

where a and b are positive constants and r is the distance separating two atoms.

(a) Let $U_1(r), U_2(r)$, and $U_3(r)$ be the Lennard-Jones 6,12 potentials for $a = 1, b = 1$, for $a = 1, b = 2$, and for $a = 2, b = 1$, respectively. Graph these three functions. From your graphs, show that b is the radius at which the potential is a minimum, and that a is the depth of the potential well at its minimum.

(b) Consider two atoms bound by the Lennard-Jones 6,12 potential, where $a = 3$ and $b = 2$. If the total energy E of the system is -1, what is the minimum separation between the two atoms? The maximum?

48. Suppose that a planet (or a spaceship) is somehow brought to a dead stop in space relative to the sun. It will then have no circular motion, and thus experience no repulsive, centrifugal force. Draw a possible energy diagram for this system. Describe the attraction of the planet to the sun as a function of its distance, r. (Assume that there are no other nearby planets contributing to U_{eff}.)

49. Figure 7.101 gives the effective potential of a sun-planet system whose total energy, E, is positive. Recall that the planet will be restricted to regions where $E > U_{eff}$.

    (a) Recall that a planet's perihelion is the distance of its closest approach to the sun. What is the perihelion for the planet in the system represented by Figure 7.101?
    (b) Recall that a sun-planet system whose total energy is positive is referred to as unbound. Explain why it makes sense to refer to the system represented in Figure 7.101 as unbound.

Figure 7.101

Chapter 7

Circles, Parabolas, Elipses, Hyperbolas, and General Quadradics

SECTION **7**

CARTESIAN COORDINATES. CIRCLES

A. Coordinate Systems

The basis for Figures 7.1 and 7.2 is two perpendicular real lines: an **x-axis**, directed to the right, and a **y-axis**, directed upward. The point of intersection of the axes, called the **origin**, corresponds to the zero point on each axis. The origin is denoted by the letter O.

FIGURE 7.1   **FIGURE 7.2**

Each point in the plane of the axes is represented by an ordered pair* of real numbers, called its **coordinates:**

The first coordinate is the directed distance of the point from the y-axis. We say *directed* distance because direction is taken into account—the coordinate is positive if the point is to the right of the y-axis, and negative if the point is to the left.

The second coordinate is the directed distance of the point from the x-axis. This coordinate is positive if the point is above the x-axis, and negative if the point is below.

The first coordinate is called the **x-coordinate** (or the **abscissa**). The second coordinate is called the **y-coordinate** (or the **ordinate**).

By representing points by coordinates in this way we achieve a one-to-one correspondence between the set of points in the plane and the set of ordered pairs of real numbers: each point is assigned to precisely one pair, and each pair

---

* When we say that (a, b) is an **ordered pair,** we mean that it is to be distinguished from (b, a), that is, it is important which symbol appears first (reading from left to right). Thus $(3, 1) \neq (1, 3)$. Coordinate pairs (a, b) and (c, d) are equal iff $a = c$ and $b = d$.

is assigned to precisely one point. This one-to-one correspondence is called a **Cartesian†** (or **rectangular**) **coordinate system** for the plane. A plane with a Cartesian coordinate system is called a **Cartesian plane,** and the coordinates of its points are called **Cartesian coordinates** (or **rectangular coordinates**). When there is no chance of confusion we often refer to a point P with coordinates (x,y) as "the point (x,y)." The notation $P(x,y)$ will also denote the point P with coordinates (x,y).

The axes divide their plane into four **quadrants,** always labeled I, II, III, and IV as shown in Figure 7.1. The same unit of distance is generally used on the two axes unless the circumstances make some other choice more convenient. Also, the letters x and y are the standard labels for the axes, but circumstances will sometimes lead to other choices.

B. Graphs

With each equation involving one or both of the variables x and y we can associate a set of points in the plane, as follows. First, an ordered pair (a,b) of numbers is said to **satisfy** the equation if equality results when x is replaced by a and y is replaced by b.

DEFINITION   The **graph** of an equation involving one or both of the variables x and y is the set of all points in the Cartesian plane whose coordinates satisfy the equation.

Example 7.1 The pair $(1,2)$ satisfies $y = 2x$ because $2 = 2 \cdot 1$. The pairs $(-2, -4)$ and $(3,6)$ also satisfy $y = 2x$. These points have been plotted in Figure 7.3, and the graph of $y = 2x$ is the straight line that passes through them. (We shall see later why the complete graph is a straight line.)

FIGURE 7.3

† In honor of René Descartes (1596–1650), who stressed the value of treating algebraic problems geometrically.

The next two examples concern equations with only one variable, either *x* or *y*.

Example 7.2   Draw the graph (in a Cartesian plane) of the equation *x* = 3.

Solution   A point will be on the graph of *x* = 3 if its *x*-coordinate is 3, regardless of its *y*-coordinate. Therefore, the graph is the line shown in Figure 7.4. Lines such as this, parallel to the *y*-axis, are called **vertical lines.** If *c* is any real number, the graph of *x* = *c* is a vertical line.

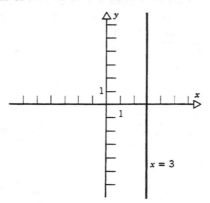

FIGURE 7.4

Example 7.3   Draw the graph of the equation *y* = −2.

Solution   A point will be on the graph of *y* = −2 if its *y*-coordinate is −2, regardless of its *x*-coordinate. Therefore, the graph of *y* = −2 is the line shown in Figure 7.5. Lines such as this, parallel to the *x*-axis, are called **horizontal lines.** If *c* is any real number, the graph of *y* = *c* is a horizontal line.

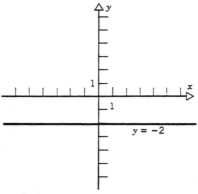

FIGURE 7.5

In the two types of cases just considered, *x* = *c* and *y* = *c*, we can determine what the graph is just by looking at the equation. In the same way, the distance formula that follows will help us determine all of the equations whose graphs are circles. And in the next section we shall determine all of the equations whose graphs are lines.

C. The Distance Formula

Recall that the distance between points with coordinates a and b on a real line is $|a - b|$ (Section 1D). We now derive the corresponding formula for points in a Cartesian plane.

Two points $P_1(x_1, y_1)$ and $P_2(x_2, y_2)$ are on the same vertical line iff $x_1 = x_2$ (first coordinates equal). The distance between such points is

$$|y_1 - y_2|. \tag{7.1}$$

Example 7.4 The points $(7,4)$ and $(7,1)$ are on the same vertical line (Figure 7.6). The distance between them is $|4 - 1| = 3$.

FIGURE 7.6

Two points $P_1(x_1, y_1)$ and $P_2(x_2, y_2)$ are on the same horizontal line iff $y_1 = y_2$ (second coordinates equal). The distance between such points is

$$|x_1 - x_2|. \tag{7.2}$$

Example 7.5 The points $(-2,1)$ and $(7,1)$ are on the same horizontal line (Figure 7.6). The distance between them is $|-2 - 7| = 9$.

> **Distance formula.** The distance d between points $P_1(x_1, y_1)$ and $P_2(x_2, y_2)$ is
>
> $$d = \sqrt{(x_1 - x_2)^2 + (y_1 - y_2)^2}. \tag{7.3}$$

Proof Figure 7.7 shows typical points P_1 and P_2. The vertical and horizontal lines through these points, as shown, intersect at the point with coordinates (x_1, y_2), which has been labeled Q. Triangle P_1QP_2 is a right triangle with

FIGURE 7.7

hypotenuse P_1P_2. The legs P_1Q and QP_2 have lengths $|y_1 - y_2|$ and $|x_1 - x_2|$, respectively. Therefore, using the Pythagorean Theorem and the fact that $|a|^2 = a^2$, we have

$$d^2 = |x_1 - x_2|^2 + |y_1 - y_2|^2$$
$$= (x_1 - x_2)^2 + (y_1 - y_2)^2.$$

Equation (7.3) follows by taking the principal square root. $\square$

Notice that it makes no difference which point is labeled P_1 and which is labeled P_2 in using the distance formula, because $(x_1 - x_2)^2 = (x_2 - x_1)^2$ and $(y_1 - y_2)^2 = (y_2 - y_1)^2$.

Example 7.6   Find the distance between $(7,4)$ and $(-2,1)$ (Figure 7.6).

Solution   By the distance formula,

$$d = \sqrt{[7 - (-2)]^2 + [4 - 1]^2} = \sqrt{9^2 + 3^2} = \sqrt{90}$$
$$= \sqrt{9}\,\sqrt{10} = 3\sqrt{10}.$$

D. Circles

Figure 7.8 shows the graph consisting of all points on the circle with center at $P(h,k)$ and radius r. A point $Q(x,y)$ will be on this circle iff its distance from $P(h,k)$ is r. By the distance formula, this will be true iff

$$\sqrt{(x - h)^2 + (y - k)^2} = r$$

or

$$(x - h)^2 + (y - k)^2 = r^2.$$

FIGURE 7.8

This proves the following result.

If r is a positive real number, then the graph of

$$(x - h)^2 + (y - k)^2 = r^2 \qquad (7.4)$$

is a circle with center at $P(h,k)$ and radius r.

For a circle with center at the origin and radius r, Equation (7.4) becomes $x^2 + y^2 = r^2$.

Example 7.7 Determine an equation of the circle with center at $(3, -2)$ and radius 5.

Solution   By Equation (7.4), the answer is

$$[x - 3]^2 + [y - (-2)]^2 = 5^2$$

or

$$(x - 3)^2 + (y + 2)^2 = 25.$$

Example 7.8 Determine an equation of the circle with center at $(-4, 6)$ and passing through $(-1, 2)$.

Solution   The circle is shown in Figure 7.9. The radius must be the distance between $(-4, 6)$ and $(-1, 2)$, which is

$$\sqrt{[-4 - (-1)]^2 + [6 - 2]^2} = \sqrt{9 + 16} = 5.$$

FIGURE 7.9

Therefore, the answer is

$$(x + 4)^2 + (y - 6)^2 = 25.$$

The equation of the circle in the preceding example can be rewritten as

$$x^2 + 8x + 16 + y^2 - 12y + 36 = 25$$

or

$$x^2 + y^2 + 8x - 12y + 27 = 0.$$

The last equation has the form

$$x^2 + y^2 + ax + by + c = 0, \qquad\qquad (7.5)$$

where a, b, and c are real numbers. To determine the graph of such an equation we first complete the squares on the terms involving x and the terms involving y, as in the following examples. (Completing the square is discussed in Section 4.) The examples will illustrate the following fact.

The graph of an equation that can be written in the form (7.5) is either a circle, a single point, or the empty set.

Example 7.9   Characterize the graph of

$$x^2 + y^2 - 10x + 6y + 30 = 0.$$

Solution   To complete the square on the x terms add 25 to both sides of the equation. To complete the square on y add 9 to both sides.

$$(x^2 - 10x + 25) + (y^2 + 6y + 9) + 30 = 25 + 9$$
$$(x - 5)^2 + (y + 3)^2 = 4$$

Comparison of this equation with Equation (7.4) shows that the graph is the circle with center at $(5, -3)$ and radius 2.

Example 7.10   Characterize the graph of

$$x^2 + y^2 + 10x - 2y + 26 = 0.$$

Solution   If we complete the squares on the x terms and the y terms, the result is

$$(x + 5)^2 + (y - 1)^2 = 0.$$

The only solution of this equation is $(-5, 1)$. Thus the graph consists of a single point.

Example 7.11   Characterize the graph of

$$x^2 - 20x + y^2 + 6y + 113 = 0.$$

Solution   If we complete the squares we obtain

$$(x - 10)^2 + (y + 3)^2 = -4.$$

Since $(x - 10)^2 \geq 0$ for every x and $(y + 3)^2 \geq 0$ for every y, but $-4 < 0$, the equation has no solution. Thus the graph is the empty set (it contains no points).

The method in the last three examples can be used to reduce any equation of the form (7.5) to the form

$$(x - h)^2 + (y - k)^2 = t.$$

The graph will be a circle, a single point, or the empty set, depending on whether the number t on the right is positive, zero, or negative, respectively.

Exercises for Section 7

For each exercise, draw one set of coordinate axes and plot the given points.

1. $(2, 4)$, $(-2, 4)$, $(0, -3)$, $(3.5, 0)$, $(\sqrt{2}, -\pi)$, $(-1, -2)$
2. $(5, 3)$, $(3, -5)$, $(\pi, 0)$, $(0, -\sqrt{2})$, $(-1.5, -2.5)$, $(-4, 2)$
3. $(1, 4)$, $(-1, 0)$, $(\sqrt{2}, -1)$, $(0, \pi)$, $(-4, 3)$, $(1.5, 3.5)$

Give the Cartesian coordinates of each point.

4. 3 units above the x-axis and 2 units to the left of the y-axis.
5. 2.5 units to the right of the y-axis and 4 units below the x-axis.
6. 1.7 units below the x-axis and 3 units to the left of the y-axis.
7. On the y-axis and 4 units below the x-axis.
8. On the x-axis and 2.5 units to the left of the y-axis.
9. On the y-axis and 3.2 units above the x-axis.

In Exercises 10–15, determine which of the given points are on the graph of the given equation.

10. $y = 3x$; $(2, 6)$, $(0.3, 1)$, $(-\frac{1}{2}, -\frac{3}{2})$
11. $y = 2$; $(0, 2)$, $(2, 0)$, $(4, 2)$
12. $x = -3$; $(0, -3)$, $(-3, 0)$, $(-3, 2)$
13. $y = x^2$; $(1, 1)$, $(2, -4)$, $(-2, 4)$
14. $y^3 = x$; $(1, -1)$, $(-\frac{1}{2}, -\frac{1}{8})$, $(-\frac{1}{8}, -\frac{1}{2})$
15. $y^2 + 1 = (x + 1)^2$; $(0, -1)$, $(-1, 0)$, $(-1, -1)$

Draw the graph of each equation.

16. $x = 3$
17. $y = -1$
18. $y = 4$
19. $y = -1.5$
20. $x = 7/5$
21. $x = -2$
22. $x^2 + y^2 = 9$
23. $x^2 + y^2 = 16$
24. $x^2 + y^2 = 4$
25. $(x - 1)^2 + y^2 = 10$

26. $(x + 4)^2 + (y - 3)^2 = 15$

27. $(x + 2)^2 + (y + 1)^2 = 12$

Determine equations of the following lines and circles.

28. The line parallel to and 4 units above the *x*-axis.

29. The line parallel to and 3 units below the *x*-axis.

30. The line parallel to and 2 units to the left of the *y*-axis.

31. The line parallel to and 5 units to the right of the *y*-axis.

32. The line parallel to and 1.5 units to the left of the *y*-axis.

33. The line parallel to and 5 units above the *x*-axis.

34. The circle with center at $(1.5, 0)$ and radius $\sqrt{6}$.

35. The circle with center at $(-2, -3)$ and radius $\sqrt{2}$.

36. The circle with center at $(0, 4.5)$ and radius 10.

37. The circle with center at the origin and passing through $(3, -4)$.

38. The circle with center at $(1, 2)$ and passing through the origin.

39. The circle with center at $(-3, 1)$ and tangent to the *y*-axis.

Find the distance between each pair of points.

40. $(2, 5), (-1, 4)$

41. $(\frac{3}{2}, -2), (\frac{9}{2}, 3)$

42. $(-1, \frac{8}{3}), (7, \frac{2}{3})$

43. $(0, \frac{1}{4}), (\frac{1}{2}, -\frac{3}{5})$

44. $(-\frac{1}{2}, -2), (0.4, 0)$

45. $(2, 0), (-0.5, -1)$

Characterize the graph of each equation.

46. $x^2 + y^2 - 2x + 4y - 4 = 0$

47. $x^2 + y^2 + 12x - 2y - 37 = 0$

48. $x^2 + y^2 - 2x - 8y - 8 = 0$

49. $x^2 + y^2 - 6y = -10$

50. $x^2 + y^2 - 2y = 3$

51. $x^2 - 20x + y^2 = -100$

52. $x^2 + y^2 = 0$

53. $x^2 + y^2 + 9 = 0$

54. $x^2 + y^2 - x + y + 1 = 0$

55. $4x^2 + 4y^2 - 20x + 9 = 0$

56. $9x^2 + 9y^2 - 18x + 12y - 5 = 0$

57. $4x^2 + 4y^2 + 4x - 4y - 22 = 0$

In Exercises 58–66, describe the set of all points in the Cartesian plane whose coordinates satisfy the given condition or conditions. Use a graph where it will help.

58. $x < 0$

59. $xy > 0$

60. $x/y < 0$

61. $x > y$

62. $x^2 + y^2 > 5$

63. $x^2 + y^2 \le 1$

64. Both $|x| = 2$ and $y > 3$

65. Both $|x - 3| < 1$ and $y = 4$

66. Both $|x - 1| \le 1$ and $|y - 1| \le 1$

67. Find all of the points on the *x*-axis that are five units from $(2, 3)$.

68. Find all of the points where the graph of $(x - 2)^2 + (y + 1)^2 = 9$ intersects a coordinate axis.

69. Find all of the points that are 2 units from the *y*-axis and on the graph of $(x + 3)^2 + y^2 = 36$.

70. The point $(x, 1)$ is twice as far from $(-1, 0)$ as from $(1, 0)$. What is *x*? (There are two solutions.)

71. Find an equation that is satisfied by (x, y) iff $P(x, y)$ is on the perpendicular bisector of the segment connecting $P_1(0, 0)$ and $P_2(3, -2)$.

72. Draw the graph of $(x^2 + y^2 - 4)(x^2 + y^2 - 1) \le 0$.

SECTION 59

PARABOLAS

A. Introduction

A **conic section** is a curve formed by the intersection of a plane and a double-napped right circular cone (Figure 59.1). The most important conic sections are *parabolas*, *ellipses*, and *hyperbolas*, which will be studied in turn in this and the next two sections. In each case the conic section will be defined in a way that is equivalent to, but more convenient than, that given in Figure 59.1. Section 62 will show that, with minor exceptions, the conic sections are the same as the graphs of the quadratic equations with variables x and y. Section 63 will give the polar equations of conic sections. Each of these different ways of representing conic sections has its advantages, depending on the application.

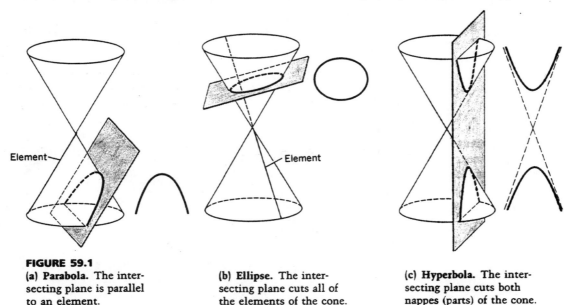

FIGURE 59.1

(a) **Parabola.** The intersecting plane is parallel to an element.

(b) **Ellipse.** The intersecting plane cuts all of the elements of the cone.

(c) **Hyperbola.** The intersecting plane cuts both nappes (parts) of the cone.

B. Definition

DEFINITION   A **parabola** is the set of all points in a plane that are equidistant from a fixed line (the **directrix**) in the plane and a fixed point (the **focus**) in the plane but not on the line.

Chapter 7/ 12

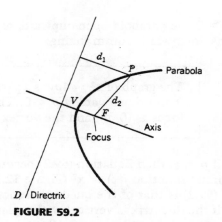

FIGURE 59.2

In Figure 59.2, P is a typical point on the parabola with directrix D and focus F. Thus the distance between P and D, denoted d_1, is equal to the distance between P and F, denoted d_2. The line through F perpendicular to D is called the **axis** of the parabola. The point V where the parabola intersects its axis is called the **vertex** of the parabola. The vertex is the midpoint of the segment cut off on the axis by the focus and the directrix. A parabola is symmetric with respect to its axis.

To derive equations for parabolas in a Cartesian plane, we first consider the special case in which the directrix is horizontal with equation $y = -p$ and the focus is $F(0, p)$, where p is a nonzero constant. Whether $p > 0$ or $p < 0$, the vertex in this case is at the origin and the y-axis is the axis of the parabola. Figure 59.3 shows a case with $p > 0$. A point $P(x, y)$ is on the parabola iff

$$\text{distance between } P \text{ and } Q = \text{distance between } P \text{ and } F \qquad (59.1)$$

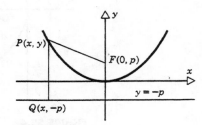

FIGURE 59.3

where $Q(x, -p)$ is the foot of the perpendicular to the directrix from $P(x, y)$. Equation (59.1) is equivalent to

$$\sqrt{(x - x)^2 + (y + p)^2} = \sqrt{(x - 0)^2 + (y - p)^2}$$

$$(y + p)^2 = x^2 + (y - p)^2$$

$$y^2 + 2py + p^2 = x^2 + y^2 - 2py + p^2$$

$$x^2 = 4py. \qquad (59.2)$$

Chapter 7/ 13

If $p > 0$ the parabola opens upward, as in Figure 59.3. If $p < 0$ the parabola opens downward. Summarizing:

> The graph of $x^2 = 4py$ is a parabola opening upward if $p > 0$ and downward if $p < 0$. The directrix is $y = -p$, the focus is $(0, p)$, and the vertex is the origin.

(59.3)

If $p = \frac{1}{4}$, then Equation (59.2) becomes $y = x^2$, whose graph is that of the quadratic function $f(x) = x^2$ (Figure 12.1). More generally, the graph of Equation (59.2) is that of the quadratic function $f(x) = (1/4p)x^2$.

If the directrix is vertical with equation $x = -p$ and the focus is at $(p, 0)$, then a derivation like that for Equation (59.2) shows that the equation of the parabola is

$$y^2 = 4px.$$

(59.4)

Figure 59.4 shows a case with $p > 0$, for which the parabola opens to the right. If $p < 0$ the parabola opens to the left. In either case, the vertex is at the origin and the x-axis is the axis of the parabola.

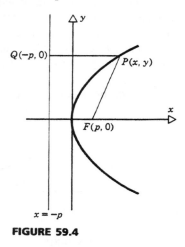

FIGURE 59.4

> The graph of $y^2 = 4px$ is a parabola opening to the right if $p > 0$ and to the left if $p < 0$. The directrix is $x = -p$, the focus is $(p, 0)$, and the vertex is at the origin.

(59.5)

A parabola with vertex at the origin is uniquely determined by its directrix, or by its focus, or by any (nonvertex) point on the parabola together with the direction the parabola opens.

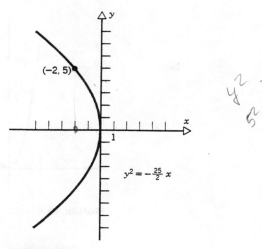

FIGURE 59.5

Example 59.1 Find an equation of the parabola with vertex at the origin and that opens to the left and passes through $(-2, 5)$ (Figure 59.5).

Solution The equation will have the form $y^2 = 4px$, given by Equation (59.4). Since $(-2, 5)$ is on the parabola, we must have

$$5^2 = 4p(-2)$$
$$p = -\tfrac{25}{8}.$$

Thus the equation is

$$y^2 = 4(-\tfrac{25}{8})x$$
$$y^2 = -\tfrac{25}{2}x.$$

Example 59.2 Find the directrix and focus of the parabola whose equation is $y = 2x^2$.

Solution Rewrite $y = 2x^2$ in the form of Equation (59.2).

$$x^2 = \tfrac{1}{2}y$$
$$x^2 = 4 \cdot \tfrac{1}{8}y$$

This shows that $p = \tfrac{1}{8}$, so the parabola opens upward ($p > 0$), the equation of the directrix is $y = -\tfrac{1}{8}$, and the focus is at $(0, \tfrac{1}{8})$. Figure 59.6 shows the graph.

To draw the graph of a parabola, always plot the vertex and several points on one side of the axis, and then take advantage of the symmetry with respect to the axis.

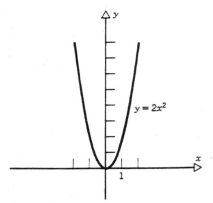

FIGURE 59.6

C. Translations

For a parabola whose directrix is parallel to a coordinate axis but whose vertex is not at the origin, we use the results from Subsection B together with the ideas about translations that were presented in Section 16. The reasoning used to justify Statements (16.2) and (16.3) will also yield the following statements (where the term *Cartesian equation* refers to an equation with variables x and y).

> If x is replaced by $x - h$ in a Cartesian equation, the resulting graph will be the graph of the original equation translated to the right by $|h|$ units if $h > 0$, and translated to the left by $|h|$ units if $h < 0$. If y is replaced by $y - k$ in a Cartesian equation, the resulting graph will be the graph of the original equation translated upward by $|k|$ units if $k > 0$, and translated downward by $|k|$ units if $k < 0$.   (59.6)

Example 59.3 Draw the graph of $y + 3 = 2(x - 1)^2$.

Solution The given equation is $y = 2x^2$ with x replaced by $x - 1$ and y replaced by $y + 3$, or $y - (-3)$. Therefore, by (59.6), the graph of $y + 3 = 2(x - 1)^2$ is the graph of $y = 2x^2$ translated to the right by 1 unit and downward by 3 units. The graph of $y = 2x^2$ is shown in Figure 59.6. The graph of $y + 3 = 2(x - 1)^2$ is shown in Figure 59.7.

By applying Statement (59.6) with Statements (59.3) and (59.5), we obtain the following general results.

$$y + 3 = 2(x - 1)^2$$

$(1, -3)$

FIGURE 59.7

The graph of

$$(x - h)^2 = 4p(y - k)$$

is a parabola with directrix $y = k - p$, focus $(h, k + p)$, vertex (h, k), and axis $x = h$.
The graph of

$$(y - k)^2 = 4p(x - h)$$

is a parabola with directrix $x = h - p$, focus $(h + p, k)$, vertex (h, k), and axis $y = k$.

(59.7)

The equations in (59.7) are called the **standard forms** for the equations of the parabolas they represent. The graph of any equation that can be written in the form

$$y = ax^2 + bx + c, \quad \text{with } a \neq 0,$$

is a parabola with directrix parallel to the x-axis. The graph of any equation that can be written in the form

$$x = ay^2 + by + c, \quad \text{with } a \neq 0,$$

is a parabola with directrix parallel to the y-axis. By completing a square (Section 4), an equation of either of the latter types can be converted to the appropriate standard form. Here is an example.

Example 59.4   Rewrite $x = \frac{1}{6}y^2 - \frac{2}{3}y - \frac{4}{3}$ in standard form and draw the graph of the parabola it represents.

Solution   Multiply both sides by 6 to clear fractions, and isolate the y terms on the right.

$$6x = y^2 - 4y - 8$$

$$6x + 8 = y^2 - 4y$$

Now complete the square on the y terms by adding 4 to both sides. Then put the equation in the second standard form from (59.7).

$$6x + 8 + 4 = y^2 - 4y + 4$$

$$6(x + 2) = (y - 2)^2$$

$$(y - 2)^2 = 4 \cdot \tfrac{3}{2}[x - (-2)]$$

This has the second form in (59.7) with $h = -2$, $k = 2$, and $p = \tfrac{3}{2}$. Thus the graph is a parabola with directrix $x = -2 - \tfrac{3}{2}$, or $x = -\tfrac{7}{2}$, focus $(-2 + \tfrac{3}{2}, 2) = (-\tfrac{1}{2}, 2)$, vertex $(-2, 2)$, and axis $y = 2$. Figure 59.8 shows the graph.

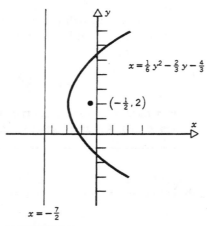

FIGURE 59.8

Example 59.5   Find an equation for the parabola with focus $(1, -2)$ and vertex $(4, -2)$. Also find the directrix and the axis of the parabola.

Solution   The axis is the line through the focus and the vertex, so in this case the axis has equation $y = -2$. The distance between the focus and the vertex is $|p|$, so in this case $|p| = 3$. The focus is to the left of the vertex so the parabola opens to the left and $p = -3$. Using $h = 4$ and $k = -2$, since the vertex is $(4, -2)$, we get the standard form

$$(y + 2)^2 = -12(x - 4).$$

The directrix is $x = 7$. Figure 59.9 shows the result.

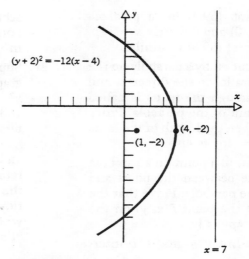

$(y + 2)^2 = -12(x - 4)$

$(4, -2)$

$(1, -2)$

$x = 7$

FIGURE 59.9

Parabolas for which the directrix is not parallel to a coordinate axis will be considered in Section 62. Applications of parabolas are given in Section 12.

Exercises for Section 59

The graph of each equation in Exercises 1–15 is a parabola. In each case, find the directrix, the focus, the vertex, and the axis, and draw the graph.

1. $2x^2 + y = 0$
2. $4x^2 - y = 0$
3. $12x + y^2 = 0$
4. $6x = y^2$
5. $y^2 = -x$
6. $x^2 = 4y$
7. $(x + 2) + (y - 1)^2 = 0$
8. $8x - (y + 4)^2 = 0$
9. $(x - 3)^2 = -10(y - 3)$
10. $x = y^2 + 2y - 2$
11. $2x^2 + y + 3 = 0$
12. $x - 9 = y^2 - 6y$
13. $4y = 4x^2 + 12x + 9$
14. $18x = 9y^2 - 24y + 16$

15. $8x^2 - 8x + 2 = 8y$

In each of Exercises 16–24 find an equation of the parabola satisfying the given conditions.

16. Vertex $(0, 0)$, focus $(-4, 0)$.
17. Vertex $(0, 0)$, directrix $y = 5$.
18. Vertex $(0, 0)$, contains $(-4, -1)$, axis the y-axis.
19. Vertex $(-1, 4)$, directrix $y = 0$.
20. Vertex $(2, 3)$, contains $(0, 0)$, axis $x = 2$.
21. Vertex $(0, -4)$, focus $(0, 0)$.
22. Focus $(-3, 3)$, directrix $x = -5$.
23. Vertex $(5, 1)$, contains $(0, 2)$, symmetric with respect to the line $y = 1$.
24. Focus $(5, 5)$, directrix $y = 10$.
25. A parabolic arch on a bridge has span 30 feet, and 10 feet from each end the rise is 5 feet. (See Exercise 51 in Section 12.) What is the rise at the center?

$y = 4x^2$

$y = -2x^2$

$4 - \frac{1}{8} = \frac{1}{2}$

Chapter 7/ 19

26. Derive Equation (59.4) for a parabola with focus $(p, 0)$ and directrix $x = -p$. The derivation of (59.3) is similar.

27. The segment cut off by a parabola on the line that is parallel to the directrix and that passes through the focus is called the **latus rectum** of the parabola. Prove that if $p > 0$, then the length of the latus rectum of $x^2 = 4py$ is $4p$.

28. The **focal radius** of a point on a parabola is the distance between the point and the focus of the parabola. Prove that the focal radius of the point $P(x, y)$ on the parabola $x^2 = 4py$ is $|y + p|$.

29. Prove that the line $y = mx + b$ inter-

sects the parabola $y^2 = 4px$ in two points if $p^2 > mbp$, in one point if $p^2 = mbp$, and in no point if $p^2 < mbp$.

30. Suppose $p > 0$ and $k > 0$. By (59.6), the graph of $x^2 = 4p(y - k)$ is the graph of $x^2 = 4py$ translated upward by k units, and therefore the two graphs do not intersect. Prove that if $p > 0$, $q > 0$, and $k > 0$, then the graphs of $x^2 = 4q(y - k)$ and $x^2 = 4py$ intersect iff $q > p$. [Interpretation: If two different parabolas have the same axis and open the same direction, then they intersect iff the one whose vertex is "inside" the other is "flatter" (by any amount).]

SECTION **60**

ELLIPSES

A. Definition

DEFINITION   An **ellipse** is the set of all points in a plane such that the sum of the distances from two fixed points (the **foci**) in the plane is a constant. (*Foci* is the plural of **focus**.)

Figure 60.1 shows an example with foci $F'(-c, 0)$ and $F(c, 0)$. The sum $d_1 + d_2$ of the distances to P from F' and F is the same for all points P on the ellipse.

To derive equations for ellipses in a Cartesian plane, we first consider the special case shown in Figure 60.1. Assume $d_1 + d_2 = 2a$ (a constant) for all $P(x, y)$ on the ellipse. Using the distance formula, we have

$$d_1 + d_2 = 2a$$

$$\sqrt{(x + c)^2 + y^2} + \sqrt{(x - c)^2 + y^2} = 2a$$

$$\sqrt{(x + c)^2 + y^2} = 2a - \sqrt{(x - c)^2 + y^2}.$$

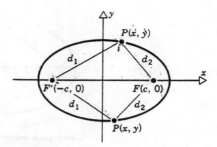

FIGURE 60.1 $d_1 + d_2$ is the same for all points P on the ellipse.

Now square both sides and simplify.

$$x^2 + 2cx + c^2 + y^2 = 4a^2 - 4a\sqrt{(x - c)^2 + y^2} + x^2 - 2cx + c^2 + y^2$$
$$a^2 - cx = a\sqrt{(x - c)^2 + y^2}.$$

Now square again and simplify.

$$a^4 - 2a^2cx + c^2x^2 = a^2(x^2 - 2cx + c^2 + y^2)$$
$$(a^2 - c^2)x^2 + a^2y^2 = a^2(a^2 - c^2)$$

To simplify our result, we introduce the constant b defined by $b > 0$ and

$$b^2 = a^2 - c^2. \qquad (60.1)$$

(Since $d_1 + d_2 = 2a$, we see from Figure 60.1 that $2a > 2c$, or $a > c$, so $a^2 > c^2$.) We now have

$$b^2x^2 + a^2y^2 = a^2b^2$$
$$\frac{x^2}{a^2} + \frac{y^2}{b^2} = 1. \qquad (60.2)$$

The line through the foci intersects the ellipse in two points called the **vertices** of the ellipse. In Figure 60.1, the vertices correspond to the x-intercepts; these are at $(-a, 0)$ and $(a, 0)$, as can be seen by using $y = 0$ in Equation (60.2). The segment connecting the vertices is called the **major axis** of the ellipse. See Figure 60.2. The midpoint of the major axis is called the **center** of the ellipse. In Figure 60.1 the center is the origin. Each segment connecting the center to a vertex is a **semimajor axis**.

Consider the line through the center perpendicular to the major axis. The segment cut off on this line by the ellipse is called the **minor axis** of the ellipse. In Figure 60.1, the minor axis is the segment joining $(0, -b)$ and $(0, b)$. Each segment connecting the center to an endpoint of the minor axis is called a **semiminor axis**.

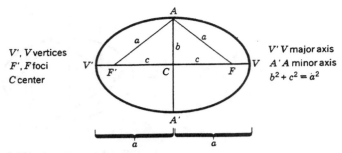

FIGURE 60.2

The length of the minor axis is less than the length of the major axis. For Figure 60.1, this follows from Equation (60.1), which shows $b^2 < a^2$ so that $b < a$ and $2b < 2a$. An ellipse is symmetric with respect to both its major and minor axes. For the ellipse represented by Equation (60.2), this follows because the equations remains unchanged if x is replaced by $-x$ and y is replaced by $-y$.

If the foci of the ellipse are $F'(0, -c)$ and $F(0, c)$ on the y-axis, rather than on the x-axis, then the equation of the ellipse is

$$\frac{x^2}{b^2} + \frac{y^2}{a^2} = 1. \qquad (60.3)$$

As in the derivation of Equation (60.2), the sum of the distances from the foci to any point on the ellipse is $2a$, $b^2 = a^2 - c^2$, and $b < a$. Thus, with the foci on the y-axis, the larger number, a^2, is under y^2 when the equation is written in the form (60.3). The major axis lies along with y-axis in this case. See Figure 60.3.

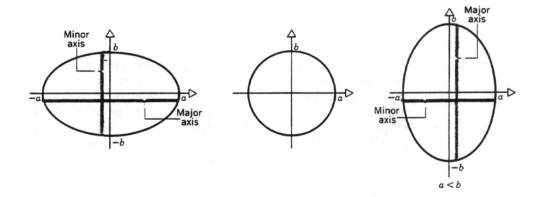

FIGURE 60.3

If $a > b$, then the graph of

$$\frac{x^2}{b^2} + \frac{y^2}{a^2} = 1$$

is an ellipse with center at the origin and foci $(0, -c)$ and $(0, c)$, where $c^2 = a^2 - b^2$. The major axis has endpoints $(0, -a)$ and $(0, a)$, and the minor axis has endpoints $(-b, 0)$ and $(b, 0)$.
If $a > b$, then the graph of

$$\frac{x^2}{b^2} + \frac{y^2}{a^2} = 1$$

is an ellipse with center at the origin and foci $(0, -c)$ and $(0, c)$, where $c^2 = a^2 - b^2$. The major axis has endpoints $(0, -a)$ and $(0, a)$, and the minor axis has endpoints $(-b, 0)$ and $(b, 0)$.

(60.4)

Example 60.1 The graph of $9x^2 + 4y^2 - 36 = 0$ is an ellipse. Find the foci and vertices and draw the graph.

Solution The equation can be rewritten as

$$\frac{x^2}{4} + \frac{y^2}{9} = 1 \qquad \text{or} \qquad \frac{x^2}{2^2} + \frac{y^2}{3^2} = 1.$$

The larger of 2^2 and 3^2 is under y^2, so the foci and vertices are on the y-axis. The vertices are $(0, -3)$ and $(0, 3)$. And from $a = 3$ and $b = 2$ we have $c^2 = 3^2 - 2^2 = 5$, so $c = \sqrt{5}$. Thus the foci are $(0, -\sqrt{5})$ and $(0, \sqrt{5})$. Figure 60.4

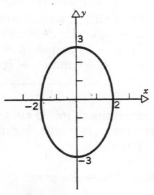

FIGURE 60.4

$c^2 = 3^2 - 4^2 = 9 - 16 = -7$

shows the graph. In addition to the endpoints of the major and minor axes, some other coordinate pairs used to draw the graph are shown in Table 60.1.

TABLE 60.1

x	0	$\pm\frac{1}{2}$	± 1	± 2
y (exact)	± 3	$\pm 3\sqrt{15}/4$	$\pm 3\sqrt{3}/2$	0
y (approximate)	± 3	± 2.90	± 2.60	0

B. Translations

For an ellipse whose axes are parallel to the coordinate axes but whose center is not at the origin, we use the results from (60.4) together with translations. Reasoning as we did for parabolas in Section 59C, we obtain the following results.

If $a > b$, then the graph of

$$\frac{(x - h)^2}{a^2} + \frac{(y - k)^2}{b^2} = 1$$

is an ellipse with center (h, k) and foci $(h - c, k)$ and $(h + c, k)$, where $c^2 = a^2 - b^2$. The major axis has endpoints $(h - a, k)$ and $(h + a, k)$, and the minor axis has endpoints $(h, k - b)$ and $(h, k + b)$. (60.5)
If $a > b$, then the graph of

$$\frac{(x - h)^2}{b^2} + \frac{(y - k)^2}{a^2} = 1$$

is an ellipse with center (h, k) and foci $(h, k - c)$ and $(h, k + c)$, where $c^2 = a^2 - b^2$. The major axis has endpoints $(h, k - a)$ and $(h, k + a)$, and the minor axis endpoints $(h - b, k)$ and $(h + b, k)$.

The equations in (60.5) are called the **standard forms** for the equations of the ellipses they represent. Figure 60.5 shows a typical case of the first possibility in (60.5).

Example 60.2 Draw the graph of $9x^2 + 16y^2 - 18x + 64y - 71 = 0$.

Solution We first rewrite the equation in standard form.

$$\frac{(x-h)^2}{a^2} + \frac{(y-k)^2}{b^2} = 1$$

FIGURE 60.5

Step I. Factor the coefficient of x^2 from the x terms, factor the coefficient of y^2 from the y terms, and write the equation with the constant term on the right of the equality sign.

$$9(x^2 - 2x \quad) + 16(y^2 + 4y \quad) = 71.$$

Step II. Complete the squares on the x and y terms, and add appropriate constants to the right side to compensate.

$$9(x^2 - 2x + 1) + 16(y^2 + 4y + 4) = 71 + 9 + 64$$
$$9(x - 1)^2 + 16(y + 2)^2 \quad = 144.$$

Step III. Divide both sides by the constant on the right, to put the equation in the appropriate form from (60.5).

$$\frac{(x - 1)^2}{16} + \frac{(y + 2)^2}{9} = 1$$
$$\frac{(x - 1)^2}{4^2} + \frac{[y - (-2)]^2}{3^2} = 1. \tag{60.6}$$

Step IV. Draw the graph of (60.6) by following the pattern in Figure 60.5. See Figure 60.6 for the result.

FIGURE 60.6

C. Application

One application of ellipses is given by Kepler's three laws of planetary motion (Figure 60.7):

I. The planets move in elliptical orbits with the sun at one focus.

II. The imaginary line connecting the sun to a planet sweeps out equal areas in equal intervals of time.

III. The ratio of the cube of the semimajor axis to the square of the period is a constant, which is the same for all planets.

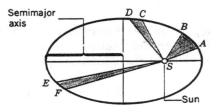

FIGURE 60.7

While the orbits described by the first law are ellipses, they do not differ greatly from circular orbits. To make this more precise, we consider the *eccentricity* of the orbits: Using the notation of (60.4), the **eccentricity** of an ellipse is the number e defined by $e = c/a$. (This number e is not the constant introduced in Section 26, which is the base for the natural logarithms.) From $c^2 = a^2 - b^2$ and $b > 0$, we have $0 \leq c^2 < a^2$ and $0 \leq c < a$, so

$$0 \leq e < 1,$$

with $e = 0$ if $b = a$, and e approaching 1 if b approaches 0. If $e = 0$, then the foci coincide (see Figure 60.2) and the ellipse becomes a circle. If b approaches 0, so that e approaches 1, then F' approaches V' and F approaches V (Figure 60.2), and the ellipse becomes elongated, approaching the segment joining F' and F.

For planetary orbits the eccentricities vary from 0.250 (for Pluto) down to 0.007 (for Venus), with $e = 0.017$ for the Earth. In contrast, some comets travel in elliptical orbits with very large eccentricities.

Kepler's second law implies that if areas such as *ASB*, *CSD*, and *ESF* in Figure 60.7 are all equal, then the planet will move from *A* to *B*, from *C* to *D*, and from *E* to *F* in equal intervals of time. In particular, a planet moves fastest when it is closest to the sun.

Kepler's third law establishes a uniformity among the motions of the different planets. Let R denote the length of the semimajor axis for a planet, measured in millions of miles. Let T denote the *period* of the planet—that is, the time required for one complete orbital revolution about the sun; measure T in Earth years, so that $T = 1$ for the Earth. Then Kepler's third law states that the ratio R^3/T^2 is the same for all planets. If this constant ratio is denoted by K, then

$$R^3/T^2 = K. \tag{60.7}$$

If R and T are known for a single planet, then K can be computed from Equation (60.7). Then, for example, if T can be determined for a second planet, the value of R for the second planet can be computed by solving Equation (60.7) for R:

$$R^3 = KT^2$$
$$R = \sqrt[3]{KT^2}. \tag{60.8}$$

It can be proved that the length of the semimajor axis for an ellipse is also the average distance between a focus and the points on the ellipse. Thus the number R for a planet is also the average distance of the planet from the sun.

Example 60.3 The average distance between the Earth and the sun is approximately 93 million miles. Determine K in Equation (60.7).

Solution With $R = 93$ and $T = 1$, Equation (60.7) becomes

$$K = 93^3/1^2 \approx 8.04 \times 10^5. \qquad \boxed{c} \tag{60.9}$$

Example 60.4 The period of Mars is approximately 1.88 Earth years. What is the average distance between Mars and the sun?

Solution Use Equation (60.8) with $T = 1.88$ and $K = 8.04 \times 10^5$ (from the previous example). Then

$$R = \sqrt[3]{8.04 \times 10^5 \times 1.88^2} \approx 142. \qquad \boxed{c}$$

That is, Mars is approximately 142 million miles from the sun.

Exercises for Section 60

The graph of each equation in Exercises 1–12 is an ellipse. In each case, find the center, the foci, and the endpoints of the major and minor axes, and draw the graph.

1. $16x^2 + 9y^2 - 144 = 0$
2. $9x^2 + 4y^2 - 36 = 0$
3. $25x^2 + 4y^2 - 100 = 0$
4. $(x - 1)^2 + 25y^2 - 25 = 0$
5. $3x^2 + 9(y + 1)^2 - 27 = 0$
6. $3(x - 2)^2 + 4(y - 3)^2 - 12 = 0$
7. $4x^2 + y^2 + 4y = 0$
8. $x^2 + 16y^2 - 32y = 0$
9. $16x^2 + 4y^2 + 160x + 256 = 0$
10. $3x^2 + y^2 - 12x - 6y + 12 = 0$
11. $25x^2 + 16y^2 + 50x + 96y - 231 = 0$
12. $3x^2 + 2y^2 - 24x + 4y + 44 = 0$

In each of Exercises 13–21 find an equation of the ellipse satisfying the given conditions.

13. Endpoints of major axis (2, 0) and (2, 8), endpoints of minor axis (0, 4) and (4, 4).

14. Endpoints of minor axis (0, −1) and (0, 1), semimajor axis of length 5.

15. Center (−3, 2), one vertex (−3, −2), minor axis of length 6.

16. Foci (0, 0) and (6, 0), endpoints of minor axis (3, −2) and (3, 2).

17. Endpoints of major axis (−5, 0) and (5, 0), contains $(3, \frac{16}{5})$.

18. Center (2, 4), one vertex (2, 0), semiminor axis of length 1.

19. Center (0, 0), one vertex (0, −6), contains (1, 1).

20. Foci (−2, 3) and (2, 3), the sum of the distances from the foci to each point on the ellipse equal to 6.

21. Endpoints of minor axis (−5, 0) and (5, 0), contains (1, 5).

22. Find all of the points of intersection of the graphs of $y = x + 1$ and $2x^2 + y^2 - 2 = 0$.

23. Draw the graphs of $3x^2 + 4y^2 - 16 = 0$ and $y = \frac{1}{2}x^2 - 1$ on a single Cartesian coordinate system and find all of the points where the two graphs intersect. (Do the second part of the problem algebraically; do not just estimate the answer from the graph.)

24. Find all of the points of intersection of the graphs of $2x^2 + y^2 - 1 = 0$ and $x^2 + 2y^2 - 1 = 0$.

25. The London Bridge designed by John Rennie and completed in 1831 had five semi-elliptical arches. The central arch had a span of 152 feet 6 inches and a rise at its center of 37 feet 6 inches. Find the rise of this arch 20 feet from either end (Figure 60.8). Ⓒ

FIGURE 60.8

26. The lines $y = x$ and $y = -x$ intersect the ellipse $\frac{x^2}{a^2} + \frac{y^2}{b^2} = 1$ in four points that determine a square. What is the area of the square?

27. Draw the graph of $(4x^2 + 9y^2 - 36)(x^2 + y^2 - 25) \le 0$.

28. Derive Equation (60.3) for an ellipse with foci $F'(0, -c)$ and $F(0, c)$ on the y-axis. The conditions determining a, b, and c are given following (60.3). The derivation of (60.2) is similar.

29. The segment cut off by an ellipse on a line that is perpendicular to the major axis and that passes through a focus is called a **latus rectum** of the ellipse. Prove that the length of a latus rectum of the ellipse determined by Equation (60.2) is $2b^2/a$.

30. Find an equation of the ellipse with center at (0, 0), one focus at (0, −3), and eccentricity $\frac{1}{4}$.

31. The orbit of Pluto, with an eccentricity of 0.250, is the least circular of all the planetary orbits. Find b for an ellipse whose eccentricity is 0.250 and whose equation is $\frac{x^2}{a^2} + \frac{y^2}{b^2} = 1$, with $a = 10$. Now draw the graph of this equation. This graph will have the shape of Pluto's orbit and will give an idea of how close to being circular the planetary orbits are. (The value $a = 10$ was chosen for convenience; it is the relative sizes of a and b that is important here.)

32. The points in the (elliptical) orbit of a satellite of the earth that are farthest

from and nearest to the earth are called the **apogee** and **perigee**, respectively. Let A and P denote the distance from the earth's center to the apogee and perigee, respectively. Prove that the eccentricity of the orbit is $e = (A - P)/(A + P)$.

33. The first artificial satellite was *Sputnik I*, launched October 4, 1957. The greatest and least distances of its orbit from the earth's surface were 584 miles and 143.5 miles, respectively. Use the result in Exercise 32 to compute the eccentricity of its orbit. Use 3960 miles for the radius of the earth.

The next six exercises relate to Subsection C and blanks in Table 60.2. Ⓒ

34. What is the average distance between Mercury and the sun?

35. What is the average distance between Venus and the sun?

TABLE 60.2

Planet	Average distance from sun[a]	Period[b]
Mercury		0.24
Venus		0.62
Earth	93	1.00
Mars	142	1.88
Jupiter		11.86
Saturn	886	
Uranus	1782	
Neptune	2793	
Pluto	3672	248.43

[a] In millions of miles.
[b] As multiples of the Earth's period.

36. What is the average distance between Jupiter and the sun?

37. What is the period for Saturn?

38. What is the period for Uranus?

39. What is the period for Neptune?

SECTION 61

HYPERBOLAS

A. Definition

DEFINITION A **hyperbola** is the set of all points in a plane such that the difference of the distances from two fixed points (called **foci**) in the plane is a constant.

Figure 61.1 shows an example with foci $F'(-c, 0)$ and $F(c, 0)$: $|d_1 - d_2|$ is the same for all points $P(x, y)$ on the hyperbola. The line through the foci intersects the hyperbola in two points called **the vertices** of the hyperbola. The

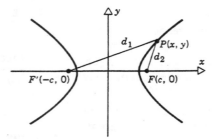

FIGURE 61.1 $|d_1 - d_2|$ is the same for all points P on the hyperbola.

segment connecting the vertices is called the **transverse axis**. The midpoint of the transverse axis is called the **center**.

Suppose $a > 0$ and $c > 0$, and consider the hyperbola shown in Figure 61.1 with $|d_1 - d_2| = 2a$. The method used to derive Equation (60.2) for an ellipse can be used to show that if $b^2 = c^2 - a^2$, then the equation of the hyperbola in Figure 61.1 is

$$\frac{x^2}{a^2} - \frac{y^2}{b^2} = 1. \tag{61.1}$$

The segment connecting $(0, -b)$ and $(0, b)$ is called the **conjugate axis**.

Now suppose $a > 0$ and $c > 0$, and consider the hyperbola in Figure 61.2 with the foci $F'(0, -c)$ and $F(0, c)$ on the y-axis, and, again, $|d_1 - d_2| = 2a$. It can be shown that if $b^2 = c^2 - a^2$, then the equation of this hyperbola is

$$\frac{y^2}{a^2} - \frac{x^2}{b^2} = 1. \tag{61.2}$$

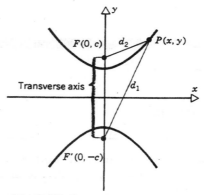

FIGURE 61.2

In this case, the segment connecting $(-b, 0)$ and $(b, 0)$ is the conjugate axis.

Figure 61.3 shows examples representing both of Equations (61.1) and (61.2). The graph of (61.1) has x-intercepts $x = \pm a$, but it has no y-intercept. The x-intercepts are also the vertices. The graph of (61.2) has y-intercepts $y =$

$$\frac{x^2}{a^2} - \frac{y^2}{b^2} = 1$$

$$\frac{y^2}{a^2} - \frac{x^2}{b^2} = 1$$

FIGURE 61.3

$\pm\, a$, but it has no x-intercept. The y-intercepts are the vertices in this case. The two parts of the graph of a hyperbola are called **branches**. The graphs of both (61.1) and (61.2) are symmetric with respect to both the x- and y-axes.

Each dashed line in Figure 61.3 is called an **asymptote** of its hyperbola. This means that the distance to the dashed line from a variable point (x, y) on a branch of the hyperbola approaches zero as the point moves outward along the hyperbola. (The asymptotes are an aid in graphing: they are not part of the hyperbola.) It can be shown that the equations of the asymptotes for Equation (61.1) arise from replacing 1 by 0 on the right side of the equation:

$$\frac{x^2}{a^2} - \frac{y^2}{b^2} = 0$$

$$y^2 = \frac{b^2}{a^2}x^2$$

$$y = \pm\frac{b}{a}x. \tag{61.3}$$

(See Exercise 30.) Similarly, the asymptotes for Equation (61.2) arise from replacing 1 by 0 in that equation; the result in this case is

$$y = \pm\frac{a}{b}x. \tag{61.4}$$

The graph of an equation of the form in either (61.1) or (61.2) can be drawn quickly as follows:

• Draw the asymptotes as dashed lines.
• Plot the intercepts.

- Determine several other points by direct calculation. Also plot the additional points that arise from these by symmetry.
- Complete the graph so that it has the general shape of the appropriate form from Figure 61.3.

Example 60.1 Draw the graph of

$$25x^2 - 4y^2 + 100 = 0. \qquad (61.5)$$

Solution Divide both sides by 100 and then rearrange the terms as shown.

$$\frac{x^2}{4} - \frac{y^2}{25} + 1 = 0$$

$$\frac{y^2}{5^2} - \frac{x^2}{2^2} = 1$$

This is Equation (61.2) with $a = 5$ and $b = 2$. The equations of the asymptotes are

$$\frac{y^2}{5^2} - \frac{x^2}{2^2} = 0 \quad \text{or} \quad y = \pm\frac{5}{2}x.$$

These asymptotes are shown in Figure 61.4, along with the intercepts, $(0, 5)$ and $(0, -5)$. If $x = 1$ in Equation (61.5), then $y^2 = \frac{125}{4}$ so $y = \pm 5\sqrt{5/2} \approx \pm 5.6$. This gives the points $(1, 5.6)$ and $(1, -5.6)$. Symmetry gives the additional points $(-1, 5.6)$ and $(-1, -5.6)$. Other points can be determined in the same way.

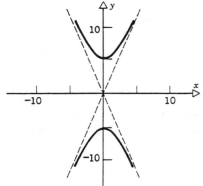

FIGURE 61.4

B. Translations

For a hyperbola whose transverse axis is parallel to a coordinate axis but whose center is not at the origin, the statements in Subsection A together with translations will yield the following results.

If $a > 0$ and $b > 0$, then the graph of

$$\frac{(x - h)^2}{a^2} - \frac{(y - k)^2}{b^2} = 1$$

is a hyperbola with center (h, k) and foci $(h - c, k)$ and $(h + c, k)$, where $c^2 = a^2 + b^2$. The vertices and endpoints of the transverse axis are $(h - a, k)$ and $(h + a, k)$. The conjugate axis has endpoints $(h, k - b)$ and $(h, k + b)$. The asymptotes have equations $y - k = \pm \frac{b}{a}(x - h)$.

If $a > 0$ and $b > 0$, then the graph of

$$\frac{(y - k)^2}{a^2} - \frac{(x - h)^2}{b^2} = 1$$

is a hyperbola with center (h, k) and foci $(h, k - c)$ and $(h, k + c)$, where $c^2 = a^2 + b^2$. The vertices and endpoints of the transverse axis are $(h, k - a)$ and $(h, k + a)$. The conjugate axis has endpoints $(h - b, k)$ and $(h + b, k)$.

The asymptotes have equations $y - k = \pm \frac{a}{b}(x - h)$.

(61.6)

The equations in (61.6) are called the **standard forms** for the equations of the hyperbolas they represent. Figure 61.5 shows a typical case of the first possibility in (61.6).

$$\frac{(x - h)^2}{a^2} + \frac{(y - k)^2}{b^2} = 1$$

FIGURE 61.5

Example 61.2 Draw the graph of $9x^2 - 16y^2 + 36x + 32y + 164 = 0$.

We first rewrite the equation in standard form. The details are similar to those in Example 60.2

$$9(x^2 + 4x \qquad) - 16(y^2 - 2y \qquad) = -164$$

$$9(x^2 + 4x + 4) - 16(y^2 - 2y + 1) = -164 + 36 - 16$$

$$9(x + 2)^2 - 16(y - 1)^2 = -144$$

$$\frac{(y - 1)^2}{9} - \frac{(x + 2)^2}{16} = 1$$

$$\frac{(y - 1)^2}{3^2} - \frac{[x - (-2)]^2}{4^2} = 1$$

Thus we have the second possibility in (61.6). The center is at $(-2, 1)$. The vertices and endpoints of the transverse axis are at $(-2, -2)$ and $(-2, 4)$. The conjugate axis has endpoints $(-6, 1)$ and $(2, 1)$.

To draw the asymptotes, we first draw the rectangle having sides parallel to the coordinate axes and passing through the endpoints of the transverse and conjugate axes (Figure 61.6). The asymptotes are the lines through the pairs of opposite corners of this rectangle.

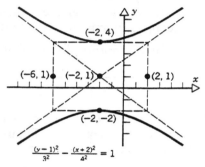

FIGURE 61.6

In addition to the vertices, we can obtain other points by substituting values for x and solving for y. For example, $x = -1$ gives $y = 1 \pm \sqrt{153}/4 \approx 4.09, -2.09$, that is, the points $(-1, 4.09)$ and $(-1, -2.09)$. These two points are located symmetrically with respect to the conjugate axis. And each one gives another point because of the symmetry of the hyperbola with respect to its transverse axis; $(-1, 4.09)$ corresponds to $(-3, 4.09)$, and $(-1, -2.09)$ corresponds to $(-3, -2.09)$. Figure 61.6 shows the graph.

C. Application

The defining property of a hyperbola is fundamental to the *loran* system of navigation. (*Loran* is an acronym for *long range navigation*.) Imagine a pair of stations that can transmit radio signals, such as those labelled master and slave A in Figure 61.7. Suppose pulse signals are transmitted from master and slave

For hyperbolas just worry which one negative or positive

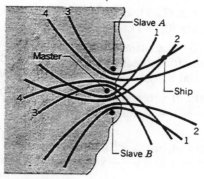

FIGURE 61.7

A at a predetermined time interval. If these signals are received at a ship at different times, then, since the velocity of radio waves is known, this time difference can be converted into a difference in distance of the ship from master and slave A. This locates the ship on a particular one of the hyperbolas with foci at master and slave A. Applying the same idea to master and slave B, the ship can be located on a particular one of the hyperbolas with foci at master and slave B. The intersection of the hyperbolas gives the location of the ship.

Exercises for Section 61

The graph of each equation in Exercises 1–12 is a hyperbola. In each case, find the center, the foci, the endpoints of the transverse and conjugate axes, and draw the graph. Draw the asymptotes as dashed lines.

1. $4x^2 - 9y^2 - 36 = 0$
2. $9x^2 - 16y^2 - 144 = 0$
3. $16x^2 - 4y^2 + 64 = 0$
4. $4(x + 1)^2 - y^2 + 4 = 0$
5. $9(x - 2)^2 - 25(y + 1)^2 + 225 = 0$
6. $x^2 - 25(y + 3)^2 - 25 = 0$
7. $x^2 - 3y^2 - 12y - 21 = 0$
8. $25x^2 - 4y^2 - 200x + 300 = 0$
9. $9x^2 - 16y^2 - 18x - 64y - 199 = 0$
10. $9x^2 - 16y^2 - 54x - 64y + 161 = 0$
11. $9x^2 - 5y^2 - 36x - 60y - 99 = 0$
12. $2x^2 - 3y^2 + 30y - 69 = 0$

In each of Exercises 13–21 find an equation of the hyperbola satisfying the given conditions.

13. Endpoints of transverse axis $(0, -3)$ and $(0, 3)$, endpoints of conjugate axis $(-2, 0)$ and $(2, 0)$.
14. Foci $(-4, 0)$ and $(4, 0)$, vertices $(-2, 0)$ and $(2, 0)$.
15. Foci $(0, -5)$ and $(0, 5)$, endpoints of conjugate axis $(-2, 0)$ and $(2, 0)$.
16. Foci $(0, 1)$ and $(4, 1)$, vertices $(1, 1)$ and $(3, 1)$.
17. Vertices $(-4, 0)$ and $(4, 0)$, contains $(5, \frac{3}{4}\sqrt{5})$.
18. Center $(-2, 1)$, vertex $(-2, 2)$, focus $(-2, 3)$.
19. Vertex $(0, 5)$, asymptotes $y = \pm\frac{5}{3}x$.

$\dfrac{(x-1)^2}{16} = 1$

$(x-1)^2 = 16$

$x - 1 = 4$

$x = 5$

20. Center $(1, -1)$, vertex $(1, 1)$, one end-point of conjugate axis $(0, -1)$.

21. Foci $(-5, 3)$ and $(5, 3)$, the difference of the distances from the foci to each point on the hyperbola equal to 6.

22. Find all of the points of intersection of the graphs of $x - y - 1 = 0$ and $4x^2 - y^2 = 16$.

23. Find all of the points of intersection of the graphs of $y = x^2 - 1$ and $y^2 - x^2 = 1$.

24. Find all of the points of intersection of the graphs of $4x^2 - 9y^2 = 36$ and $x^2 + y^2 = 16$.

25. Two hyperbolas are said to be **conjugate** if the transverse axis of either is the conjugate axis of the other. What is the conjugate of the hyperbola whose equation is $\frac{x^2}{a^2} - \frac{y^2}{b^2} = 1$?

26. A circle with its center at the origin intersects the graph of $\frac{y^2}{a^2} - \frac{x^2}{b^2} = 1$ in exactly two points. What is the area of the circle?

27. A hyperbola is said to be **equilateral** if the length of its transverse and conjugate axes are equal. Find the equations of the asymptotes of an equilateral hyperbola of the form (61.1).

28. An equilateral hyperbola (see Exercise 27) with foci on the x-axis intersects the circle with equation $x^2 + y^2 = 100$ in exactly two points. What is the equation of the hyperbola?

29. Derive Equation (61.1) for a hyperbola with foci $F'(-c, 0)$ and $F(c, 0)$ and with a and b as defined just preceding (61.1).

30. Verify that Equation (61.3) gives asymptotes for the hyperbola defined by Equation (61.1) by carrying out all of the following steps.

(a) Show that Equation (61.1) can be re-written as

$$y^2 = \frac{b^2}{a^2}(x^2 - a^2).$$

(b) Show that the equation in (a) can be rewritten as

$$y^2 = \left(\frac{bx}{a}\right)^2 \left(1 - \frac{a^2}{x^2}\right).$$

(c) Explain why $1 - (a^2/x^2)$ approaches 1 as $|x|$ becomes larger and larger.

(d) Use the preceding steps to explain why a variable point on the graph of Equation (61.1) approaches the graph of $y = \frac{b}{a}x$ or $y = -\frac{b}{a}x$ as $|x|$ becomes larger and larger.

SECTION 62

GENERAL QUADRATICS. ROTATION OF AXES

A. Introduction

In Section 59 we defined a conic section as a curve formed by the intersection of a plane and a double-napped right circular cone. In Sections 59–61 we studied three general types of conic sections: parabolas, ellipses, and hyperbolas. We shall now see that the other possibilities for conic sections are circles and points (special cases of ellipses), lines, and two intersecting lines. Then we shall consider the relationship between conic sections and the graphs of quadratic equations.

In Figure 59.1*b*, the ellipse is a circle if the intersecting plane is perpendicular to the axis of the cone, and the ellipse is a point if the intersecting plane contains the vertex of the cone. The definition of ellipse in Section 60 produces a circle if the foci coincide, and it produces a point if, in addition, the sum of the distances to the foci is allowed to be zero.

Next consider Figure 59.1*a*. If the intersecting plane contains an element of the cone, then the intersection degenerates into a single line. The parabola in Figure 59.2 approaches a straight line as the focus moves away from the directrix, but a straight line is not a parabola (by the definition of parabola in Section 59B).

Now consider Figure 59.1*c*. If the intersecting plane contains the axis of the cone, then the hyperbola degenerates into a pair of intersecting lines. The hyperbola in Figure 61.1 approaches two parallel lines as the distance between the foci increases, but the definition of hyperbola (Section 61A) does not include two parallel lines. Summarizing:

> A conic section (as defined in Section 59) is either a parabola, an ellipse (with a circle and a point as special cases), a hyperbola, a line, or two intersecting lines. (62.1)

B. Quadratic Equations

The **general quadratic equation** with variables x and y has the form

$$Ax^2 + Bxy + Cy^2 + Dx + Ey + F = 0, \tag{62.2}$$

where $A, B, C, D, E,$ and F are real numbers with at least one of $A, B,$ and C not zero. This equation allows for all possible terms of degree two or less in x and y.

The parabolas, ellipses, and hyperbolas in Sections 59–61 all have equations that can be written in the form (62.2). Figure 62.1 shows three other possibilities arising from quadratic equations: intersecting lines, parallel lines, and single lines. In addition, the empty set is the graph of a quadratic equation ($x^2 + 1 = 0$, for example). It turns out that these examples illustrate all of the possibilities arising as graphs of quadratic equations in x and y. If we recall from Statement (62.1) that intersecting lines and single lines are conic sections, we can summarize this as follows.

FIGURE 62.1 (a) **Intersecting lines:** $x^2 - y^2 = 0$ or $y = \pm x$. (b) **Parallel lines:** $y^2 - 4 = 0$ or $y = \pm 2$. (c) **One line:** $y^2 = 0$ or $y = 0$.

> The graph of a quadratic equation in x and y is either a conic section, two parallel lines, or the empty set.   (62.3)

We shall not prove Statement (62.3), but we shall now look at the most significant factor that we have not already considered. Recall that the parabolas, ellipses, and hyperbolas in Sections 59–61 all have directrices and axes parallel to the coordinate axes. The significant difference between these cases and the most general possibilities from Equation (62.2) involve the cross product term Bxy; by allowing an xy term we can write equations for all conic sections appearing as graphs in a Cartesian plane, whatever their orientations. This is done by rotation of axes, which we consider next.

C. Rotation of Axes

Figure 62.2 shows two Cartesian coordinate systems for the plane, an xy-system and an $x'y'$-system. The origins coincide, but the positive x'-axis is inclined at an angle θ to the positive x-axis. Each point P in the plane can be

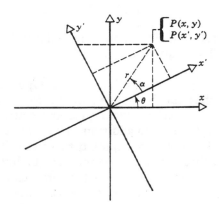

FIGURE 62.2

represented as either $P(x, y)$ or $P(x', y')$, in terms of xy- and $x'y'$-coordinates, respectively. We shall show that the coordinates are related as follows.

$$x = x' \cos\theta - y' \sin\theta \qquad (62.4)$$

$$y = x' \sin\theta + y' \cos\theta \qquad (62.5)$$

$$x' = x \cos\theta + y \sin\theta \qquad (62.6)$$

$$y' = -x \sin\theta + y \cos\theta \qquad (62.7)$$

Proof. Let α denote the angle from the positive x'-axis to OP. Then

$$x' = r \cos\alpha \qquad \text{and} \qquad y' = r \sin\alpha. \qquad (62.8)$$

And the angle from the positive x-axis to OP is $\theta + \alpha$. Therefore, using the addition formulas (32.2) and (32.6) for cosine and sine, we have

$$x = r \cos(\theta + \alpha) = r \cos\theta \cos\alpha - r \sin\theta \sin\alpha \qquad (62.9)$$

$$y = r \sin(\theta + \alpha) = r \sin\theta \cos\alpha + r \cos\theta \sin\alpha. \qquad (62.10)$$

Substituting from (62.8) into (62.9) and (62.10), we obtain

$$x = x' \cos\theta - y' \sin\theta$$

$$y = x' \sin\theta + y' \cos\theta,$$

which establishes (62.4) and (62.5).

Exercise 37 asks you to verify that (62.6) and (62.7) provide solutions for the system (62.4) and (62.5) for x' and y'.

Although Figure 62.2 shows the case where θ and α are both positive and acute, the preceding equations are valid for all values of θ and α. $\qquad\square$

Example 62.1 Transform the equation

$$13x^2 - 10xy + 13y^2 - 72 = 0$$

by rotating the axes through an angle of 45°. Then draw the graph.

Solution If $\theta = 45°$, then $\sin\theta = \cos\theta = 1/\sqrt{2}$. (It is more convenient here to use $1/\sqrt{2}$ than $\sqrt{2}/2$.) From Equations (62.4) and (62.5),

$$x = \frac{1}{\sqrt{2}}(x' - y')$$

$$y = \frac{1}{\sqrt{2}}(x' + y').$$

Substituting for x and y in the given equation, we get

$$13[\tfrac{1}{\sqrt{2}}(x' - y')]^2 - 10[\tfrac{1}{\sqrt{2}}(x' - y')\tfrac{1}{\sqrt{2}}(x' + y')] + 13[\tfrac{1}{\sqrt{2}}(x' + y')]^2 - 72 = 0$$

$$13[\tfrac{1}{2}x'^2 - x'y' + \tfrac{1}{2}y'^2] - 10[\tfrac{1}{2}x'^2 - \tfrac{1}{2}y'^2] + 13[\tfrac{1}{2}x'^2 + x'y' + \tfrac{1}{2}y'^2] - 72 = 0$$

$$8x'^2 + 18y'^2 - 72 = 0$$

$$\frac{x'^2}{9} + \frac{y'^2}{4} = 1.$$

We recognize this as the equation of an ellipse. Figure 62.3 shows the graph.

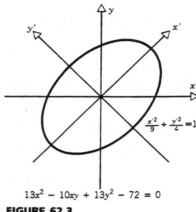

$$13x^2 - 10xy + 13y^2 - 72 = 0$$

FIGURE 62.3

In the preceding example the effect of rotating the axes was to eliminate the cross product (xy) term; the new equation has no cross product ($x'y'$) term. The following result shows that the cross product term can always be eliminated with an appropriate choice for the angle of rotation.

An equation of the form

$$Ax^2 + Bxy + Cy^2 + Dx + Ey + F = 0, \quad B \neq 0, \qquad (62.11)$$

will be transformed into an equation of the form

$$A'x'^2 + C'y'^2 + D'x' + E'y' + F' = 0 \qquad (62.12)$$

if the $x'y'$-system is obtained from the xy-system by rotation through an angle θ such that

$$\cot 2\theta = \frac{A - C}{B}. \qquad (62.13)$$

Proof. To transform Equation (62.11) by rotation through an angle θ, substitute from Equations (62.4) and (62.5).

$$A(x' \cos \theta - y' \sin \theta)^2 + B(x' \cos \theta - y' \sin \theta)(x' \sin \theta + y' \cos \theta)$$
$$+ C(x' \sin \theta + y' \cos \theta)^2 + D(x' \cos \theta - y' \sin \theta)$$
$$+ E(x' \sin \theta + y' \cos \theta) + F = 0$$

Simplification will lead to

$$A'x'^2 + B'x'y' + C'y'^2 + D'x' + E'y' + F' = 0,$$

where

$$A' = A \cos^2 \theta + B \cos \theta \sin \theta + C \sin^2 \theta$$
$$B' = B(\cos^2 \theta - \sin^2 \theta) + 2(C - A) \sin \theta \cos \theta$$
$$C' = A \sin^2 \theta - B \sin \theta \cos \theta + C \cos^2 \theta$$
$$D' = D \cos \theta + E \sin \theta$$
$$E' = -D \sin \theta + E \cos \theta$$
$$F' = F$$

(Exercise 38). To eliminate $B'x'y'$ we need $B' = 0$, that is,

$$B(\cos^2 \theta - \sin^2 \theta) + 2(C - A) \sin \theta \cos \theta = 0.$$

From the double-angle formulas for $\cos 2\theta$ and $\sin 2\theta$ [Equations (33.2) and (33.1)], this is equivalent to

$$B \cos 2\theta + (C - A) \sin 2\theta = 0$$
$$\frac{\cos 2\theta}{\sin 2\theta} = \frac{A - C}{B}$$
$$\cot 2\theta = \frac{A - C}{B}. \qquad \square$$

Example 62.2 Rotate the axes to eliminate the cross product term from

$$36x^2 + 96xy + 64y^2 - 20x + 15y = 0 \qquad (62.14)$$

and then draw the graph.

Solution Using (62.13), we rotate through an angle θ such that

$$\cot 2\theta = \frac{36 - 64}{96} = -\frac{7}{24}.$$

FIGURE 62.4

The other functions of 2θ can be computed from Figure 62.4. To use Equations (62.4) and (62.5), we need $\sin\theta$ and $\cos\theta$, which we can get by using the half-angle formulas (33.6) and (33.7). Here $\pi/2 < 2\theta < \pi$, so $\pi/4 < \theta < \pi/2$ and both $\sin\theta$ and $\cos\theta$ are positive.

$$\sin\theta = \sqrt{\frac{1 - \cos 2\theta}{2}} = \sqrt{\frac{1 - (-7/25)}{2}} = \frac{4}{5}$$

$$\cos\theta = \sqrt{\frac{1 + \cos 2\theta}{2}} = \sqrt{\frac{1 + (-7/25)}{2}} = \frac{3}{5}$$

From (62.4) and (62.5),

$$x = \tfrac{3}{5}x' - \tfrac{4}{5}y'$$
$$y = \tfrac{4}{5}x' + \tfrac{3}{5}y'.$$

If these equations are used to replace x and y in Equation (62.14), the resulting equation simplifies to

$$36(\tfrac{3}{5}x' - \tfrac{4}{5}y')^2 + 96(\tfrac{3}{5}x' - \tfrac{4}{5}y')(\tfrac{4}{5}x' + \tfrac{3}{5}y')$$
$$+ 64(\tfrac{4}{5}x' + \tfrac{3}{5}y')^2 - 20(\tfrac{3}{5}x' - \tfrac{4}{5}y')$$
$$+ 15(\tfrac{4}{5}x' + \tfrac{3}{5}y') = 0$$
$$4x'^2 + y' = 0$$
$$y' = -4x'^2.$$

We recognize this as the equation of a parabola. Figure 62.5 shows the graph. From $\sin\theta = \tfrac{4}{5}$ and $\cos\theta = \tfrac{3}{5}$, the angle θ satisfies $\tan\theta = \tfrac{4}{3}$, so $\theta = \arctan\tfrac{4}{3}$.

For some equations, after the cross product term has been eliminated a translation will be needed. This requires no new ideas; after the rotation,

$$36x^2 + 96xy + 64y^2 - 20x + 15y = 0$$

FIGURE 62.5

simply work with the $x'y'$-coordinate system using the ideas for translations that were introduced in previous sections. Several of the exercises will illustrate this.

D. The Discriminant

Again consider the general quadratic equation,

$$Ax^2 + Bxy + Cy^2 + Dx + Ey + F = 0. \qquad (62.15)$$

The quantity $B^2 - 4AC$ is called the **discriminant** of this equation, and the next result, which we shall not prove, shows that it can be used to classify the graph of the equation.

> If $B^2 - 4AC < 0$, then the graph of (62.15) is either an ellipse, a circle, a point, or the empty set.
>
> If $B^2 - 4AC = 0$, then the graph of (62.15) is either a parabola, a line, two parallel lines, or the empty set. $\qquad$ (62.16)
>
> If $B^2 - 4AC > 0$, then the graph of (62.15) is either a hyperbola or two intersecting lines.

Notice that Statement (62.16) implies Statement (62.3).

Example 62.3 Use the discriminant to classify the graph of

$$16x^2 - 24xy + 9y^2 - 300x - 400y = 0.$$

Solution In this case

$$B^2 - 4AC = (-24)^2 - 4(16)(9) = 0.$$

Therefore, the graph is either a parabola, a line, two parallel lines, or the empty set. (Exercise 22 asks for the graph.)

Exercises for Section 62

1. Suppose an $x'y'$-coordinate system is obtained from an xy-coordinate system by rotation through an angle of 45°.
   (a) Find the $x'y'$-coordinates of the point with xy-coordinates $(2, -3)$.
   (b) Find the xy-coordinates of the point with $x'y'$-coordinates $(5, 0)$.

2. Suppose an $x'y'$-coordinate system is obtained from an xy-coordinate system by rotation through an angle of 120°.
   (a) Find the $x'y'$-coordinates of the point with xy-coordinates $(0, -4)$.
   (b) Find the xy-coordinates of the point with $x'y'$-coordinates $(6, 1)$.

3. Suppose an $x'y'$-coordinate system is obtained from an xy-coordinate system by rotation through an angle of $\pi/4$.
   (a) Find the $x'y'$-coordinates of the point with xy-coordinates $(-4, 2)$.
   (b) Find the xy-coordinates of the point with $x'y'$-coordinates $(-2, 0)$.

The graph of each equation in Exercises 4–18 is either the empty set, one point, one line, or two lines. In each case draw the graph or, if appropriate, indicate that it is the empty set.

4. $x^2 - 9 = 0$
5. $9x^2 - y^2 = 0$
6. $y^2 = 0$
7. $4x^2 - 9y^2 = 0$
8. $2x^2 + 3y^2 + 4 = 0$

9. $x^2 - 4 = 0$
10. $-y^2 = 0$
11. $10x^2 = 0$
12. $x^2 + y^2 + 2 = 0$
13. $3x^2 + 5y^2 = 0$
14. $-x^2 - y^2 = 0$
15. $5x^2 + 3y^2 = 0$
16. $4x^2 + 3y^2 + 2 = 0$
17. $y^2 - 16 = 0$
18. $x^2 - 4y^2 = 0$

In Exercises 19–30, rotate the axes to eliminate the cross product term, and then draw the graph. In some cases a translation will be needed, also.

19. $4x^2 - 10xy + 4y^2 + 9 = 0$
20. $x^2 + 2\sqrt{3}xy - y^2 - 50 = 0$
21. $5x^2 + 2\sqrt{3}xy + 7y^2 - 8 = 0$
22. $16x^2 - 24xy + 9y^2 - 300x - 400y = 0$
23. $13x^2 + 6\sqrt{3}xy + 7y^2 - 16 = 0$
24. $7x^2 + 48xy - 7y^2 - 100 = 0$
25. $34x^2 + 24xy + 41y^2 - 100 = 0$
26. $6x^2 - 4\sqrt{3}xy + 2y^2 - x - \sqrt{3}y = 0$
27. $5x^2 - 6xy + 5y^2 - 8 = 0$
28. $xy + y - 1 = 0$
29. $48x^2 + 72xy + 27y^2 - 225x - 200y + 275 = 0$
30. $16x^2 - 24xy + 9y^2 + 160x - 120y + 225 = 0$

Use the discriminant to classify the graph of each equation in Exercises 31–36.

31. $x^2 + 3xy + 5y^2 - 22 = 0$

32. $34x^2 - 24xy + 41y^2 - 25 = 0$

33. $xy + x - 2y + 3 = 0$

34. $16x^2 - 24xy + 9y^2 - 120x - 160y = 0$

35. $5x^2 + 6xy + 5y^2 - 9 = 0$

36. $x^2 - 4xy + 4y^2 = 4$

37. Verify that x' and y' as given by (62.6) and (62.7) satisfy (62.4) and (62.5).

38. Verify the statement regarding the coefficients A', B', C', D', E', and F' in the proof of the statement containing (62.11)–(62.13).

39. Prove that the equation $x^2 + y^2 = r^2$ is transformed into the equation $x'^2 + y'^2 = r^2$ (same r) by any rotation of axes. Is this a surprise? (What are the graphs of the two equations?)

40. Prove that if an equation of the form (62.2) is transformed by rotation using (62.4) and (62.5), then $B'^2 - 4A'C' = B^2 - 4AC$.

41. Prove that if an equation of the form (62.2) is transformed by rotation using (62.4) and (62.5), then $A' + C' = A + C$.

42. (This exercise depends on ideas from Sections 51 and 52.)

(a) Prove that the pair of Equations (62.4) and (62.5) is equivalent to the matrix equation $X = AX'$, where

$$X = \begin{bmatrix} x \\ y \end{bmatrix}, \qquad A = \begin{bmatrix} \cos\theta & -\sin\theta \\ \sin\theta & \cos\theta \end{bmatrix},$$

$$\text{and} \qquad X' = \begin{bmatrix} x' \\ y' \end{bmatrix}.$$

(b) Prove that if X, A, and X' are defined as in part (a), then

$$A^{-1} = \begin{bmatrix} \cos\theta & \sin\theta \\ -\sin\theta & \cos\theta \end{bmatrix} \quad \text{and}$$

$$X' = A^{-1}X.$$

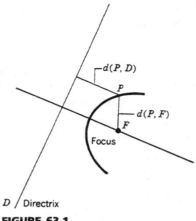

FIGURE 63.1

Let D be a fixed line (the **directrix**) and F a fixed point (the **focus**) not on D. For each point P in the plane of D and F, let $d(P, D)$ and $d(P, F)$ denote the distances of P from D and from F, respectively (Figure 63.1). Let e denote a positive constant (the **eccentricity**). Then the set of all P such that

$$\frac{d(P, F)}{d(P, D)} = e \qquad\qquad (63.1)$$

is

an ellipse if $0 < e < 1$,

a parabola if $e = 1$, and

a hyperbola if $e > 1$.

Proof. Choose the Cartesian coordinate system with the origin at F and the line $x = -d$ coincident with the line D (Figure 63.2). Then $P(x, y)$ satisfies the conditions of (63.1) iff

$$\frac{d(P, F)}{d(P, D)} = e, \quad \text{or} \quad \frac{\sqrt{x^2 + y^2}}{x + d} = e. \qquad\qquad (63.2)$$

If we square both sides of the last equation and simplify, we get

$$x^2 + y^2 = e^2x^2 + 2de^2x + d^2e^2$$
$$(1 - e^2)x^2 - 2de^2x + y^2 = d^2e^2. \qquad\qquad (63.3)$$

Review Exercises for Chapter XV

Draw the graph of each equation in Exercises 1–14.

1. $y^2 = 2x$
2. $x^2 + 4y^2 - 36 = 0$
3. $9x^2 - y^2 + 1 = 0$
4. $x^2 + 3y = 0$
5. $x^2 - 4y^2 = 0$
6. $x^2 + y^2 - 2x + 8y - 8 = 0$
7. $25x^2 + 9y^2 + 100x - 116 = 0$
8. $3x^2 + 2y^2 - 6x + 4y - 1 = 0$
9. $2(x - 5)^2 = y$
10. $x^2 + y^2 + 1 = 0$
11. $4x^2 - y^2 + 4y - 8 = 0$
12. $x^2 + 4x - y + 6 = 0$
13. $x^2 - y^2 - 2x + 2 = 0$
14. $4x^2 - 9 = 0$

In each of Exercises 15–20 find an equation of the conic section satisfying the given conditions.

15. Parabola with focus $(0, -5)$ and directrix $y = 5$.
16. Ellipse with endpoints of minor axis $(-2, 0)$ and $(2, 0)$ and major axis of length 10.
17. Hyperbola with foci $(-2, 0)$ and $(-2, 6)$, and vertices $(-2, 1)$ and $(-2, 5)$.
18. Parabola with vertex $(2, 0)$ and focus $(-1, 0)$.
19. Ellipse with foci $(-1, -2)$ and $(-1, 2)$, and the sum of the distances from the foci to each point on the ellipse equal to 8.
20. Hyperbola with vertex $(3, 0)$ and asymptotes $y = \pm 2x$.

In Exercises 21–24, rotate the axes to eliminate the cross product term, and then draw the graph.

21. $3x^2 + 2\sqrt{3}xy + y^2 + 2x - 2\sqrt{3}y = 0$
22. $3x^2 - 10xy + 3y^2 + 4 = 0$
23. $241x^2 - 576xy + 409y^2 - 625 = 0$
24. $52x^2 + 72xy + 73y^2 - 100 = 0$

Use the discriminant to classify the graph of each equation in Exercises 25 and 26.

25. $3x^2 + 5xy + 2y^2 - x + 12 = 0$
26. $3x^2 - 6xy + 3y^2 = 0$

Draw the graph of each equation in Exercises 27–30.

27. $r = \dfrac{6}{1 - 3\sin\theta}$
28. $r = \dfrac{4}{1 + \frac{1}{2}\cos\theta}$
29. $r = \dfrac{9}{2 - 6\cos\theta}$
30. $r = \dfrac{6}{4 + 4\sin\theta}$

31. Find the polar equation of the conic section with eccentricity $\frac{3}{2}$, one focus at the origin, and center $[4, \pi]$.

32. Find the polar equation of the conic section with eccentricity $\frac{1}{2}$, one focus at the origin, and horizontal directrix 3 units above the origin.

In Exercises 33–36, eliminate the parameter and then draw the graph.

33. $x = t + 2, y = 1 - 3t$
34. $x = \sqrt{3t}, y = 2 - 3t$
35. $x = 5\sin\theta, y = 2\cos\theta$
36. $x = 2\cos 2\theta, y = \cos\theta$

Math 45B

Chapter 8

Trigonometric Functions

5.1 INTRODUCTION TO TRIGONOMETRIC FUNCTIONS

The World's Largest Ferris Wheel

To celebrate the new millennium, British Airways announced its plans to fund construction of the world's largest ferris wheel.[1] The wheel, to be located on the south bank of the river Thames, in London, England, will measure 500 feet in diameter and will carry up to 1400 passengers in 60 capsules. It will turn continuously, completing a single rotation once every 20 minutes. This will be slow enough for people to hop on and off while it turns.

Suppose you decide to ride this ferris wheel for two full turns, and that you hop on at time $t = 0$. Let $h(t)$ be your height above the ground, measured in feet. Remember that the notation $h(t)$ means your height is a function of t, the number of minutes you have been riding.

Ferris Wheel Height as a Function of Time

We can figure out values of $h(t)$ for the times shown in Table 5.1. Since you are going to ride the wheel for two full turns, we show values of t from 0 minutes to 40 minutes.

TABLE 5.1   *We will determine values for h(t), your height above the ground (in feet) t minutes after boarding the wheel.*

t (in minutes)	0	5	10	15	20	25	30	35	40
$h(t)$ (in feet)	0								

Let's imagine that the wheel is turning in the counterclockwise direction. At time $t = 0$ you have just boarded the wheel, and so your height is 0 ft above the ground (not counting the height of your seat). This means that $h(0) = 0$. Since the wheel turns all the way around once every 20 minutes, we see that after 5 minutes, the wheel has turned one-quarter of the way around. Thinking of the wheel as a giant clock, this means you have been carried from the 6 o'clock position to the 3 o'clock position, as shown in Figure 5.1. You are now halfway up the wheel, or 250 feet above the ground, and so $h(5) = 250$.

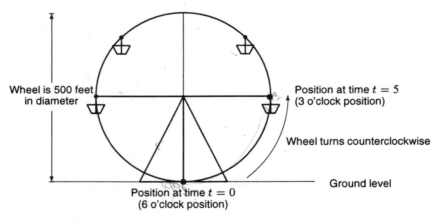

Figure 5.1: The world's largest ferris wheel is 500 ft in diameter and turns around once every 20 minutes. Seats not drawn to scale

---
[1] *The New York Times*, April 16, 1996

After 10 minutes, the wheel has turned halfway around, and so you will now be at the very top, in the 12 o'clock position. This means that $h(10) = 500$. And after 15 minutes, the wheel has turned three quarters of the way around, bringing you into the 9 o'clock position. This means that you have descended from the top of the wheel halfway down to the ground, and so you are once again 250 feet above the ground. Thus, $h(15) = 250$. (See Figures 5.2 and 5.3.) Finally, after 20 minutes, the wheel has turned all the way around, bringing you back to ground level. This means that $h(20) = 0$.

Figure 5.2: At time $t = 10$, the wheel has turned halfway around

Figure 5.3: At time $t = 15$, the wheel has turned three quarters of the way around

The Second Time Around On the Wheel

Since the wheel turns without stopping, at time $t = 20$ it begins its second turn. This means that at time $t = 25$, wheel has again turned one quarter of the way around, and so $h(25) = 250$. Similarly, at time $t = 30$ the wheel has again turned halfway around, bringing you back up to the very top. Likewise, at time $t = 35$, the wheel has carried you halfway back down to the ground. This means that $h(30) = 500$ and $h(35) = 250$. Finally, at time $t = 40$, the wheel has completed its second full turn, and so you are back at ground level. This means that $h(40) = 0$. All of these values of $h(t)$ have been recorded in Table 5.2.

TABLE 5.2 *Selected values of the function $h(t)$ for $0 \le t \le 80$*

t (in minutes)	0	5	10	15	20	25	30	35	
$h(t)$ (in feet)	0	250	500	250	0	250	500	250	
t (in minutes)	40	45	50	55	60	65	70	75	80
$h(t)$ (in feet)	0	250	500	250	0	250	500	250	0

The Repeating Values of the Ferris Wheel Function

Notice that the values of h begin repeating after 20 minutes. This is because the second turn is just like the first turn, except that it happens 20 minutes later in time. In fact, if you continued to ride the wheel for more full turns, the values of $h(t)$ would continue to repeat on 20-minute intervals. This is because every 20 minutes, the wheel begins a new full turn.

Table 5.2 gives values of $h(t)$ for values of t between 0 minutes and 80 minutes. Although you probably wouldn't want to ride the wheel this long, it is worth thinking about what the function h would look like if you did. During the 80-minute time period described by Table 5.2, we see that the values of h repeat themselves four times.

Graphing the Ferris Wheel Function

The data from Table 5.2 have been plotted in Figure 5.4. The graph begins at $h = 0$ (ground level), rises to $h = 250$ (halfway up the wheel) and then on up to $h = 500$ (the very top of the wheel). The graph then falls down to $h = 250$ and then down to $h = 0$. This cycle then repeats itself three more times, once for each rotation of the wheel.

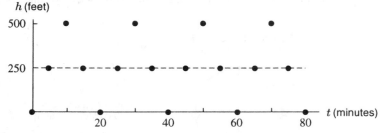

Figure 5.4: A graph of $h(t)$, the ferris wheel height function, for selected values of 5 minute intervals for $0 \le t \le 80$

Filling in the Graph of The Ferris Wheel Function

You may be tempted to connect the points in Figure 5.4 with straight lines, but this would be incorrect. Consider the first five minutes of your ride, starting at the six o'clock position and ending at the three o'clock position. (See Figure 5.5). Halfway through this part of the ride, the wheel has turned halfway from the six o'clock to the three o'clock position. However, as is clear from Figure 5.5, your seat rises less than half the vertical distance from $h = 0$ to $h = 250$. At the same time, the seat glides more than half the horizontal distance. If the points in Figure 5.4 were connected with straight lines, $h(2.5)$ would have to be halfway between $h(0)$ and $h(5)$, which would be incorrect.

Figure 5.5: As the wheel turns half the way from 6 o'clock to 3 o'clock, the seat rises less than half the vertical distance but glides more than half the horizontal distance

As you can see, the graph of $h(t)$ is a smooth, wave-shaped curve. The curve repeats itself in the sense that it looks the same from $t = 0$ to $t = 20$ as it does from $t = 20$ to $t = 40$, or from $t = 40$ to $t = 60$, or from $t = 60$ to $t = 80$.

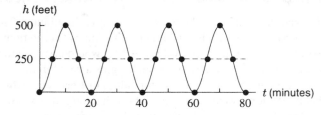

Figure 5.6: The graph of $h(t)$ is a smooth wave-shaped curve

Trigonometric Functions

The ferris wheel function h is an example of a simple *trigonometric function*, called a sinusoidal function. We will define several new terms in the context of the ferris wheel function h.

The Period

The length of the smallest time interval over which the function h completes one full cycle is called the *period* of h. We see that the period of h is 20 minutes. In Figure 5.7, the period of h is represented as a horizontal distance, indicating elapsed time. Functions like h with values that repeat on regular intervals are called *periodic functions*. While all sinusoidal functions are periodic, not all periodic functions are sinusoidal.

We can also think about the period in terms of horizontal shifts. If the graph of h is shifted to the left by 20 units, the resulting graph looks exactly the same. That is,

$$\underbrace{\text{graph of } f \text{ shifted}}_{h(t+20)} \text{ is the same as } \underbrace{\text{original graph,}}_{h(t)}$$
$$\overset{\text{left by 20 units}}{}$$

and so

$$h(t + 20) = h(t).$$

Note that this equation holds for all values of t.

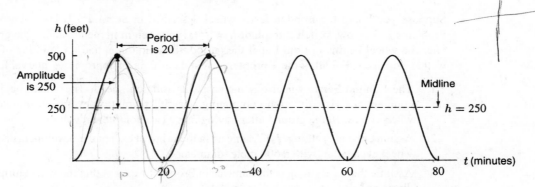

Figure 5.7: The graph of $h(t)$ showing the amplitude, period, and midline

In general:

A function f is **periodic** if its values repeat on regular intervals. Graphically, this means that if the graph of f is shifted horizontally by c units, for some constant c, the new graph is identical to the original. In function notation, periodic means

$$f(t + c) = f(t)$$

for all t in the domain of f. The smallest value of c for which this relationship holds for all values of t is called the **period** of f.

The Midline and the Amplitude

In Figure 5.7, the dashed horizontal line is called the *midline* of the graph of h. The midline of a trigonometric function is the horizontal line halfway between the function's maximum and minimum values. For the ferris wheel function, the equation of the midline is $h = 250$; this corresponds to a height midway between a minimum of 0 feet and a maximum of 500 feet.

The *amplitude* of a sinusoidal function is the distance between its maximum and the midline (or the distance between the midline and the minimum). Thus the amplitude of h is 250 because the ferris wheel's maximum height is 500 feet and its midline is at 250 feet. The amplitude is represented graphically as a vertical distance. (See Figure 5.7.)

In general:

The **midline** of a trigonometric function is the horizontal line midway between the function's maximum and minimum values. The **amplitude** is the distance between the function's maximum (or minimum) value and the midline.

Problems for Section 5.1

Suppose you board the London ferris wheel described in Section 5.1. For each of the stories in Problems 1–3 below, sketch a graph of $h = f(t)$, your height in meters above the ground t minutes after the wheel begins to turn. Label the period, the amplitude, and the midline of each graph, as well as both axes. For all of these problems, first determine an appropriate interval for t, with $t \geq 0$.

1. The London Ferris wheel has increased its rotation speed. The wheel begins to turn in a counterclockwise direction completing one full revolution every ten minutes. You get off when you reach the ground after having made two complete revolutions.

2. Assume that everything is the same as in the original except the developers decide to build the wheel even taller, with a 600 meter diameter.

3. Assume that everything is the same as in Problem 1 except that the wheel turns in a *clockwise* direction.

Problems 4–6 involve different ferris wheels. For each of them, draw a graph of $h = f(t)$. Label the period, the amplitude, and the midline for each graph. For all of these problems, first determine an appropriate interval for t, $t \geq 0$.

4. A ferris wheel is 50 meters in diameter and must be boarded from a platform that is 5 meters above the ground. Assume the six o'clock position on the ferris wheel is level with the loading platform. The wheel turns in the counterclockwise direction, completing one full revolution every 8 minutes. Suppose that at $t = 0$ you are at the loading platform.

5. A ferris wheel is 20 meters in diameter and must be boarded from a platform that is 4 meters above the ground. Assume the six o'clock position on the ferris wheel is level with the loading platform. The wheel turns in the *clockwise* direction, completing one full revolution every 2 minutes. Suppose that at $t = 0$ you are in the twelve o'clock position. From time $t = 0$ you will make two complete revolutions and then any additional part of a revolution needed to return to the boarding platform.

6. A ferris wheel is 35 meters in diameter, and can be boarded at ground level. The wheel turns in a counterclockwise direction, completing one full revolution every 5 minutes. Suppose that at $t = 0$ you are in the three o'clock position.

The graphs in Problems 7–10 describe your height $h = f(t)$ above the ground in meters, where t is the time elapsed in minutes on different ferris wheels. For each graph, determine the following: your initial position at $t = 0$, how long it takes the wheel to complete one full revolution, the diameter of the wheel, at what height above the ground you board the wheel, and the length of time you ride the wheel. Assume the boarding platform is level with the bottom of the wheel.

7.

Figure 5.8: This ferris wheel turns in a counterclockwise direction

8.

Figure 5.9: This ferris wheel turns in a clockwise direction

9.

Figure 5.10: This ferris wheel turns in a counterclockwise direction

10.

Figure 5.11: This ferris wheel turns in a clockwise direction

A weight is suspended from the ceiling by a spring. (See Figure 5.12.) Let d be the distance in centimeters from the ceiling to the weight. When the weight is motionless, $d = 10$. However, if the weight is disturbed, it will begin to bob up and down (or *oscillate*.) We will assume that the weight does not sway back and forth but undergoes vertical motion only. The weight's distance from the ceiling, d, will then be a function of t, the elapsed time in seconds, and we can write $d = f(t)$. Problems 11–14 concern the function $d = f(t)$, which models the motion of the weight attached to the spring.

Figure 5.12: A weight suspended from the ceiling by a spring

11. Figure 5.13 shows a graph of $d = f(t)$ for $0 \le t \le 3$. Determine the midline, the period, the amplitude, and the minimum and maximum values of f. Interpret these quantities physically; that is, use them to describe the motion of the weight for $0 \le t \le 3$.

Figure 5.13: Graph of $d = f(t)$ for $0 \le t \le 3$

12. A new experiment with the same weight and spring is modeled by Figure 5.14 which gives the graph of $d = f(t)$ for $0 \le t \le 3$. Compare Figure 5.14 to Figure 5.13. How do the oscillations differ? For both figures, the weight was disturbed at time $t = -0.25$ and then left alone to move naturally; determine the nature of the initial disturbances.

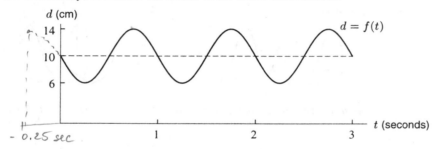

Figure 5.14: Graph of $d = f(t)$ for $0 \le t \le 3$

13. Suppose that the weight described by Figure 5.13 is gently pulled down to a distance of 14 cm away from the ceiling and at $t = 0$, released. Sketch a graph of the motion of the weight for $0 \le t \le 3$.

14. Figures 5.15 and 5.16 describe the motion of two different weights, A and B, attached to two different springs (similar to the spring described in Figure 5.12 on page 263). Based on these graphs, answer the following questions.

Figure 5.15: Weight A

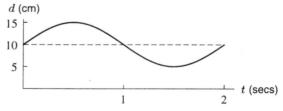

Figure 5.16: Weight B

(a) Which weight, when not in motion, is closest to the ceiling?
(b) Which weight makes the largest oscillations?
(c) Which weight makes the fastest oscillations?

15. A certain chemical reaction occurs most efficiently if the temperature oscillates between a low of 30°C and a high of 110°C. The temperature is at its lowest point when $t = 0$ and completes one cycle over a five-hour period.

    (a) Sketch a graph of the temperature T against the elapsed time t over a ten-hour period.
    (b) Find the period, the amplitude, and the midline of the graph you drew in part (a).

16. Table 5.3 gives data from a vibrating string experiment, with time t in seconds, and height $h(t)$ in centimeters. Find the midline, amplitude and period of the function $h(t)$ given in the table.

TABLE 5.3

t	0	0.1	0.2	0.3	0.4	0.5	0.6	0.7	0.8	0.9	1
$h(t)$	2	2.588	2.951	2.951	2.588	2	1.412	1.049	1.049	1.412	2

17. Table 5.4 gives the height in feet of a weight on a spring where t is the time in seconds. Find the midline, amplitude and period of the function $h = f(t)$ given in the table.

TABLE 5.4

t	0	1	2	3	4	5	6	7
$h = f(t)$	4.0	5.25	6.165	6.5	6.167	5.25	4.0	2.75

t	8	9	10	11	12	13	14	15
$h = f(t)$	1.835	1.5	1.8348	2.75	4.0	5.22	6.16	6.5

18. Data of U.S. imports of petroleum for the years 1973–1992 is shown in Table 5.5.

TABLE 5.5

Year	BTU (quadrillion)	Year	BTU (quadrillion)
1973	14.2	1983	13
1974	14.5	1984	15
1975	14	1985	12
1976	16.5	1986	14
1977	18	1987	16
1978	17	1988	17
1979	17	1989	18
1980	16	1990	17
1981	15	1991	16
1982	14	1992	16

(a) Graph this data for the period shown.
(b) What trends in U.S. oil imports do you notice?
(c) Determine an approximate midline, amplitude and period.

Chapter 8/   9

19. In the US, household electric service is provided in the form of *alternating current* (AC), at 110 volts and 60 hertz. This means that the voltage cycles between −110 volts and +110 volts, and that 60 cycles occur each second. Suppose that at $t = 0$ the voltage at a given outlet is at 0 volts.

    (a) Sketch a graph of $V = f(t)$, the voltage as a function of time, for the first 0.1 seconds.
    (b) State the period, the amplitude, and the midline of the graph you made in part (a). Describe the physical significance of these quantities.

20. Five different oscillating quantities are below. Match each description with the graph that best describes the situation. The units have been left off the vertical axis.

    (a) The average daily water flow in a river, given in cubic feet per second, measured over a calendar year.
    (b) The internal temperature of an Alaskan house during a complete day.
    (c) The electroencephalograph of the human brain during one second of sleep.
    (d) For an angle, the amount of error incurred by using an estimate for an elliptical orbit
    (e) The tide in height of water (ft) of Boston Harbor.

21. The number of white blood cells in a patient with periodic chronic myelogenous leukemia is given in Table 5.6. Plot these data points and estimate the midline, amplitude and period.

    TABLE 5.6

Day	0	10	40	50	60	70	75	80	90
WBC ($\times 10^4$/mL)	0.9	1.2	10	9.2	7.0	3.0	0.9	0.8	0.4
Day	100	110	115	120	130	140	145	150	160
WBC ($\times 10^4$/mL)	1.5	2.0	5.7	10.7	9.5	5.0	2.7	0.6	1.0
Day	170	175	185	195	210	225	230	240	255
WBC ($\times 10^4$/mL)	2.0	6.0	9.5	8.2	4.5	1.8	2.5	6.0	10.0

5.2 MEASURING POSITION IN TERMS OF ANGLES

In Section 5.1, we defined the function $h(t)$ as a person's height above the ground, in feet, t minutes after boarding a ferris wheel. We saw that the graph of h is wave-shaped, and we said that h is an example of a trigonometric function.

There are a number of different ways to describe positions on the ferris wheel. In Section 5.1, we spoke in terms of the hour hand of a clock. We said that time $t = 5$ corresponds to the three o'clock position, time $t = 10$ corresponds to a twelve o'clock position, and so on.

A more convenient way to describe a position on a wheel or a circle is by using angles. For this reason, angles are important in the study of trigonometric functions. Two different units are commonly used to measure angles: *degrees* and *radians*. Using degrees, one full turn around a circle is 360°, while in radians, the full turn is 2π rads. Degrees are convenient for studying geometry, but radians are more useful in calculus. We will discuss radians in more detail later in this section.

Describing a Position on the Ferris Wheel Using Angles

Imagine a ray, or directed half-line, that starts at the ferris wheel's center and goes horizontally to the right. We call this the initial ray of the angle. Wherever your seat is on the wheel, we can measure the angle that it makes with the initial ray. For example, Figure 5.17 shows the seat in two different positions on the wheel. The first position is at 1 o'clock, which corresponds to a 60° angle. The second position is at 10 o'clock, and it corresponds to a 150° angle. A point right at the 3 o'clock position corresponds to a 0° angle. By convention, angles are measured with respect to the initial ray, in the *counterclockwise* direction.

Figure 5.17: The 1 o'clock position forms a 60° angle with the indicated horizontal ray, and the 10 o'clock position forms a 150° angle

The Unit Circle

Many definitions in trigonometry are made with respect to a special circle called the *unit circle*. The unit circle is the circle of radius one unit that is centered at the origin in the coordinate plane. (See Figure 5.18.)

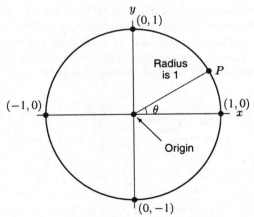

Figure 5.18: The unit circle

Describing Points on the Unit Circle Using Angles in Degrees

We can locate points on the unit circle in the same way that we locate positions on the ferris wheel, i.e., with angles.

Example 1   Figure 5.19 shows the point P determined by $\theta = 90°$. The coordinates of this point are $(0, 1)$. Figure 5.20 shows the point Q determined by the angle $\phi = 210°$. Later in the text we will see how to find the coordinates of point Q. Greek letters θ, pronounced *theta*, and ϕ, pronounced *phi*, are often used for the names of angles. Other letters from the Greek alphabet are also sometimes used.

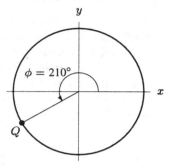

Figure 5.19: The angle $\theta = 90°$ specifes the point $P = (0, 1)$ on the unit circle

Figure 5.20: The angle $\phi = 210°$ specifes the points on the unit circle

Notice that if an angle is between $0°$ and $180°$, it specifies a point on the unit circle that lies *above* the x-axis, like point P in Figure 5.19. Similarly, if an angle is between $180°$ and $360°$, like point Q in Figure 5.20, it specifies a point that lies *below* the x-axis.

Negative Angles and Very Large Angles

Any position on a circle can be described by an angle between $0°$ and $360°$. But we will also sometimes need to use negative angles and angles larger than $360°$. It is easiest to think about such angles as displacements from the $0°$ position. For instance, if the ferris wheel turns through an angle of $360°$, then it carries you around one time and brings you back to where you started. But if it turns through an angle of $720°$, then it turns around two times, and if it turns through an angle of $1080°$, it turns around three times. So all the angles $0°$, $360°$, $720°$, $1080°$ indicate ending up at the same position (the starting position), but they each represent different displacements. Figure 5.21 shows these different situations. As is customary, angles larger than $360°$ are drawn so that they wrap around the circle more than once. (Notice that in the figure we assume your ride starts in the 3 o'clock position $= 0°$ position, instead of at ground level.)

Figure 5.21: The angles $0°$, $360°$, $720°$ and $1080°$ all specify the same position on the ferris wheel, but when thought of as displacements they are different

What about negative angles? For instance, what does a −90° angle mean? A glance at the number line suggests the correct way to think about negative angles. On the number line, positive numbers are (by convention) placed to the right of zero, while negative numbers are placed to the left. Similarly, 90° is one-quarter of a turn away from 0° on the unit circle in the counterclockwise direction, while −90° is one-quarter of a turn away from 0° in the *clockwise* direction.

Thus, on the ferris wheel, an angle of −90° indicates the 6 o'clock position. A 270° angle also indicates the 6 o'clock position. But in terms of displacements, a turn through −90° is a one-quarter turn in the clockwise direction, while a turn through 270° is a three-quarter turn in the counterclockwise direction. We see that these two angles specify the same position on the wheel even though they represent different displacements. (See Figure 5.22.)

270° is a three quarter turn in the counterclockwise direction

−90° is a one quarter turn in the clockwise direction

Figure 5.22: The angles −90° and 270°

> Any position on the unit circle may be uniquely described by an angle that is greater than or equal to 0° and less than 360°. Angles not between 0° and 360° may also be used to describe positions at the circle, when thought of as displacements:
> - Negative angles represent clockwise rotations.
> - Angles (either positive or negative) that are larger in magnitude than 360° represent rotations of more than one full turn.

Example 2   A hotel revolving door has three glass panels. Each panel is one meter in width and separates the door into three compartments of the same size. (See Figure 5.23. Note that A, B, C, D, E, and F are equally spaced points on a circle of radius one meter)

(a)   What is the measure of the angle θ?

(b)   What is the angle swept out as a panel moves from C to D in a counterclockwise direction (when viewed from above)? a clockwise direction?

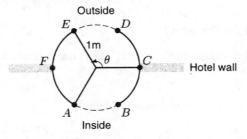

Outside

1m

Hotel wall

Inside

Figure 5.23: A three panel revolving door.

(c)   A child playing in the hotel lobby pushes the door from C through an angle of 3900° before his father stops him. Describe the motion of the door in words.

Chapter 8/   13

Solution   (a)   Since there are 360° in a circle and since the angles between each panel are equal,

$$\theta = \frac{360°}{3} = 120°.$$

(b)   The angle θ between C and E is 120°. The counterclockwise angle from C to D will be one half of this, or 60°. Turning clockwise, though, the angle is −300°.

(c)   The door completes ten full rotations (3600°), and then turns an additional 300°. Thus the panel the child was pushing comes to rest at B.

Radians

When we measure an angle in degrees, we divide the circumference of the unit circle into 360 equal pieces and count the number of pieces that are spanned by the angle. But there is another way to measure an angle: Instead of counting the number of pieces it spans, we can measure the length of the arc it spans. This is the idea behind radians.

Arc Length

For a given circle, the length of the arc spanned by an angle is proportional to the size of the angle. In other words, the larger the angle, the longer the arc. For instance, if the angle spans 90°, then the arc is one-quarter of the circle's circumference. If the angle spans 180°, then the arc is one-half of the circle's circumference. In general,

Arc length = (fraction of 360° made by angle) × (circumference of circle).

Since the fraction of 360° made by the angle θ is $\theta/360°$, and since the circumference is $2\pi r$, this means

$$l = \frac{\theta}{360°} \cdot 2\pi r = \theta \cdot \frac{\pi}{180°} \cdot r,$$

where l is the arc length. In words, we have

Arc length   =   angle in degrees   × $\dfrac{\pi}{180°}$ ×   radius.

Example 3   How long an arc does a 45° angle describe on a circle of radius 12 cm?

Solution   Using our formula, we have

$$l = 45° \cdot \frac{\pi}{180°} \cdot 12 \text{ cm} = 3\pi \text{ cm},$$

or about 9.4 cm. To see that this answer is reasonable, notice that the circle's circumference is 24π, and that a 45° angle spans one-eighth of the entire circumference, or 3π.

What is a Radian?

The unit circle has radius $r = 1$, and so our formula for arc length becomes

$$l = \frac{\pi}{180°} \cdot \theta.$$

Thus, a 45° angle spans an arc of length

$$l = \frac{\pi}{180°} \cdot 45° = \frac{\pi}{4} \approx 0.7854,$$

and a 90° angle spans an arc of length

$$l = \frac{\pi}{180°} \cdot 90° = \frac{\pi}{2} \approx 1.5708,$$

Chapter 8/   14

and so on. Notice in particular that a 60° angle spans an arc of length

$$l = \frac{\pi}{180°} \cdot 60° = \frac{\pi}{3} \approx 1.0472,$$

or almost exactly 1 unit. This raises the following question: Is there an angle t
the unit circle that is exactly 1 unit long? The answer is *yes*. Letting $l = 1$, we ha

$$1 = \frac{\pi}{180°} \cdot \theta,$$

and so

$$\theta = \frac{180°}{\pi} \approx 57.3°.$$

This special angle is called a *radian*.

Converting Between Degrees and Radians

Note that radians are just a different unit of measurement for angles than degrees. We can use either radians or degrees to measure angles. For instance, a 60° angle is a little larger than a radian, a 120° angle is a little larger than 2 radians, and a 180° angle is a little larger than 3 radians. To be more precise, notice that

$$1 \text{ radian} = \frac{180°}{\pi} = 57.3°$$

$$2 \text{ radians} = 2 \cdot \frac{180°}{\pi} = 114.6°$$

$$3 \text{ radians} = 3 \cdot \frac{180°}{\pi} = 171.9°,$$

and so on, giving us the following useful formula:

$$\text{Angle in degrees} = \text{angle in radians} \times \frac{180°}{\pi}.$$

Multiplying both sides of this equation by $\frac{\pi}{180°}$ gives us another useful formula:

$$\text{Angle in radians} = \text{angle in degrees} \times \frac{\pi}{180°}.$$

Arc Length and Radians

For angles measured in degrees, we have shown that a formula for arc length is

$$\text{Arc length} = \text{angle in degrees} \times \frac{\pi}{180°} \times \text{radius}.$$

But we have also shown that

$$\text{Angle in degrees} \times \frac{\pi}{180°} = \text{angle in radians}.$$

Thus, we can rewrite our arc length formula as follows:

$$\text{Arc length} = \underbrace{\text{angle in degrees} \times \frac{\pi}{180°}}_{\text{angle in radians}} \times \text{radius}$$

$$= \text{angle in radians} \times \text{radius}.$$

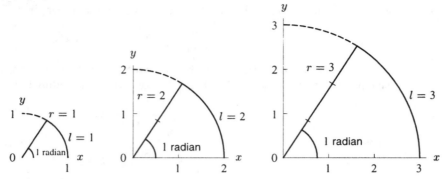

Figure 5.24: On a circle of radius 1, a radian (57.3°) spans an arc of length 1. On a circle of radius 2, it spans an arc of length 2, and on a circle of radius 3, it spans an arc of length 3

More simply,

$$l = r \cdot \theta,$$

where θ is in radians. This formula is more concise than the formula for degrees. This is one reason that radians are so useful—many mathematical formulas, not just the one for arc length, are simpler when angles are measured in radians rather than degrees.

Notice that the $l = r \cdot \theta$ formula means one radian on the unit circle spans an arc of length 1, one radian on a circle of radius 2 spans an arc of length 2, one radian on a circle of radius 3 spans an arc of length 3, etc. (See Figure 5.24.) In general, an angle of one radian spans an arc that is one radius long. Thus, it makes sense that the word *radian* suggests both the word radius and the word angle.

In summary, we have the following:

Converting Between Degrees and Radians
- Angle in radians = Angle in degrees $\cdot \dfrac{\pi}{180°}$
- Angle in degrees = Angle in radians $\cdot \dfrac{180°}{\pi}$

Arc Length
For a circle of radius r, the length l for arc determined by an angle θ is given by
- $l = r\theta \cdot \dfrac{\pi}{180°}$, if θ is in degrees,
- $l = r\theta$, if θ is in radians.

Problems for Section 5.2 ━━━━━━━━━━━━━━━━━━━━━━━━━━━━

1. Describe the angles $\phi = 420°$ and $\theta = -150°$ in terms of a displacement on the ferris wheel, assuming the car of the ferris wheel starts in the 3 o'clock position. What position on the wheel do these angles indicate?

2. Indicate the position of the following angles on a single unit circle:

    (a) 100°   (b) 200°   (c) −200°   (d) −45°   (e) 1000°   (f) −720°

For Problems 3–6, indicate the position on the unit circle of the following points:

3. S is at 225°, T is at 270°, and U is at 330°.

4. A is at 390°, B is at 495°, and C is at 690°.

5. D is at −90°, E is at −135°, and F is at −225°.

6. P is at 540°, Q is at −180°, and R is at 450°.

7. Convert the degree measure to a radian measure for each lettered point in Problems 3–6.

8. If you have the wrong degree/radian mode set on your calculator, you can get unexpected results.

    (a) If you intend to enter an angle of 30 degrees but you are in radian mode, the angle value would be considered 30 radians. How many degrees is a 30 radian angle?

    (b) If you intend to enter an angle of $\pi/6$ radians but you are in degree mode, the angle value would be considered $\pi/6$ degrees. How many radians is a $\pi/6°$ angle?

9. A revolving door at the entrance to a hotel moves in a *counterclockwise* direction. It has three equally spaced panels as shown in Figure 5.25. Points A, B, C, D, E, F are six equally spaced fixed points on a circle surrounding the door.

Figure 5.25

For parts (a) through (d) answer in both radians and degrees.

    (a) What is the angle between adjacent panels?

    (b) What is the angle created by a panel swinging from B to A?

    (c) When the door is as shown in Figure 5.25, a person going outside rotates the door from E to B. What is this angle?

    (d) When the door is initially as shown in Figure 5.25, a person coming inside rotates the outward-pointing panel to B and continues counterclockwise until this panel reaches E. What is this entire angle of rotation of the door?

    (e) Given that the door is in the position shown in Figure 5.25, where will the panel that began at C be after three people enter and then one person exits? Assume that people going in and going out do so in the manner described in parts (d) and (c). Also assume that each person goes completely through the door before the next one enters.

10. Suppose a revolving door which moves in a counterclockwise direction has four equally spaced panels, as shown in Figure 5.26. For parts (a)–(d) answer in both radians and degrees.

    (a) What is the angle between two adjacent panels?

(b) What is the angle created by a panel swinging from B to A?

(c) When the door is as shown in Figure 5.26, a person going outside rotates the door from D to B. What is this angle?

(d) If the door is initially as shown in Figure 5.26, a person coming inside rotates the door from B to D. What is this angle of rotation?

(e) Given that the door is in the position shown in Figure 5.26, where will the panel that began at A be after three people enter and five people exit? Assume that people going in and going out do so in the manner described in parts (d) and (c). Also assume that each person goes completely through the door before the next enters.

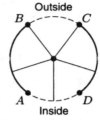

Figure 5.26   *Figure 5.27*

11. Suppose a revolving door (which moves in a counterclockwise direction) for the entrance to the Pentagon was designed with five equally spaced panels, as shown in Figure 5.27. Assume BC and AD are equal arcs. Answer the following questions in both radians and degrees.

(a) What is the angle between two adjacent panels?

(b) What is the angle of rotation created as a Four Star General enters by pushing on the panel at point B, and leaves the panel at point D?

(c) With the door in the position above, suppose an Admiral leaves the Pentagon by pushing the panel between A and D to point B. What was the angle of rotation?

12. An art student wants to make a string collage by connecting equally spaced points on the circumference of a circle to its center. What would be the radian and degree measure of the angle between two adjacent pieces of string if there were

(a) 6 points   (b) 12 points

(c) 24 points   (d) 48 points

13. Explain in your own words how to determine the radian measure of an angle given in degrees, and why this method works.

14. Recall that one radian is defined to be the angle at the center of a circle which cuts off an arc of length equal to the radius of the circle. This is because the arc length formula in radians, $l = r \cdot \theta$, becomes just $l = r$ when $\theta = 1$. Figure 5.28 gives two circles, having radii 2 cm and 3 cm.

Figure 5.28: Two circles, one of radius 2 cm and one of radius 3 cm

(a) Does the angle 1 radian appear to be the same in both circles?

(b) Estimate the number of arcs of length 2 cm that will fit in the circumference of the circle of radius 2 cm.

15. If a weight hanging on a string of length 3 feet swings through 5° on either side of the vertical, how long is the arc through which the weight moves from one high point to the other?

16. How far does the tip of the minute hand of a clock move in 35 minutes if the hand is 6 inches long?

17. How far does the tip of the minute hand of a clock move in 1 hour and 27 minutes if the hand is 2 inches long?

18. A circle has diameter 38 cm.

(a) What is the length l of the arc on this circle spanned by θ when $\theta = 3.83$ radians?

(b) Find the angle φ in radians which spans an arc length of 3.83 cm on the circumference of the circle.

19. Using a weight on a string called a *plumb bob*, it is possible to erect a pole that is exactly vertical, which means pointed directly at the center of the Earth. Two such poles are erected one hundred miles apart. It is determined that if the poles were extended they would meet at the center of the Earth, forming an angle of 1.4333°. Compute the radius of the Earth.

20. A weather satellite orbits the earth in a circular orbit 500 miles above the earth's surface. What is the radian measure of the angle (measured from the center of the earth) through which the satellite moves in traveling 600 miles along its circular orbit? (Assume the radius of the earth is 3960 miles.)

21. How many miles on the surface of the earth correspond to one degree of latitude? (Assume the radius of the earth is 3960 miles.)

22. A person on earth is observing the moon which is 238,860 miles away. If the moon has a diameter of 2160 miles, what is the angle in degrees spanned by the moon in the eye of the beholder?

23. In order to measure angles, the ancient Babylonians divided the circumference of a circle into 360 equal parts, so that an angle measuring one degree spans an arc equal to one 360th of the circle's circumference. Since the more modern metric system is based on powers of ten, write a proposal to create a new metric system for measuring angles. (Use a different subdivision of the circle.)

24. A compact disc is 12 cm in diameter and rotates at 100 rpm (revolutions per minute) when being played. The hole in the center is 1.5 cm in diameter. Find the speed in cm/min of a point on the outer edge of the disc and the speed of a point on the inner edge.

5.3 THE TRIGONOMETRIC FUNCTIONS

In this section, we define two important trigonometric functions, the *sine* and *cosine* functions. These functions can be used to model many periodic phenomena.

Definition of Sine and Cosine

If P is a point on the unit circle specified by the angle θ, and if the coordinates of P are (x, y), then we define the functions, *cosine* of θ, or $\cos\theta$, and the *sine* of θ, or $\sin\theta$, by the formulas

$$\cos\theta = x \quad \text{and} \quad \sin\theta = y.$$

Chapter 8/ 19

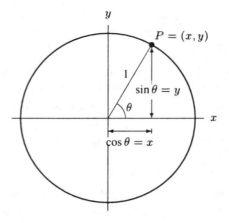

Figure 5.29: $\sin\theta$ is the y-coordinate and $\cos\theta$ is the x-coordinate of point P

In other words, $\cos\theta$ is the x-coordinate of the point on the unit circle specified by the angle θ and $\sin\theta$ is the y-coordinate. (See Figure 5.29.)

From Figure 5.29, we see that the sine of an angle is an oriented vertical distance on the xy-plane and the cosine is an oriented horizontal distance. (By *oriented distance* we mean that the distance is said to be positive or negative depending on which side of the x- or y-axis it is.) Thus, the sine function will be negative for points lying below the x-axis because these points have negative y-coordinates. Similarly, the cosine function will be negative for points lying to the left of the y-axis.

Finding Values of the Sine and Cosine Functions

In principle, we can find values of $\sin\theta$ and $\cos\theta$ for any value of θ. In practice, this is done using tables, calculators, or computers. (The method a computer uses is based on calculus.) However, we can determine some values of $\sin\theta$ and $\cos\theta$ on our own.

Example 1   Evaluate $\sin\theta$ and $\cos\theta$ for $\theta = 0°, 90°, 180°, 270°$, and $360°$.

Solution   Figure 5.30 gives the coordinates of the points on the unit circle specified by $0°, 90°, 180°, 270°$, and $360°$. We will use these coordinates to evaluate the sines and cosines of these five angles.

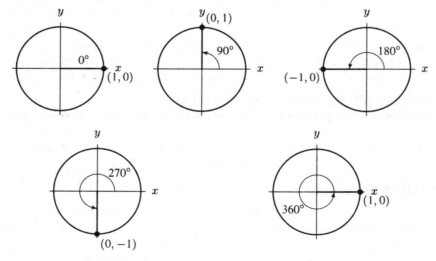

Figure 5.30: The coordinates of the points on the unit circle specified by the angles $0°, 90°, 180°, 270°$, and $360°$

The definition of the sine function tells us that $\sin 0°$ is the y-coordinate o
circle specified by the angle $0°$. Since the y-coordinate of this point is $y = 0$, w

$$\sin 0° = 0.$$

Similarly, the x-coordinate of the point $(1, 0)$ is $x = 1$ which gives

$$\cos 0° = 1.$$

From Figure 5.30 we see that the coordinates of the remaining points are, respectively, (0
$(-1, 0)$, $(0, -1)$, and $(1, 0)$. This gives us

$$\sin 90° = 1, \qquad \cos 90° = 0,$$
$$\sin 180° = 0, \qquad \cos 180° = -1,$$
$$\sin 270° = -1, \qquad \cos 270° = 0,$$
$$\sin 360° = 0, \qquad \cos 360° = 1.$$

In the previous example we found the sine and cosine of multiples of $90°$. The sine and cosine of some other special angles, $30°$, $45°$, and $60°$, are computed in the next two examples.

Example 2   Figure 5.31 shows the point $P = (x, y)$ specified by the angle $45°$ on the unit circle. A right triangle has also been drawn in. Notice that the triangle is isosceles, that is, it has two equal angles (both $45°$) and two equal sides. Thus, $x = y$. Combining $x = y$ with the Pythogorean theorem $x^2 + y^2 = 1$ gives

$$x^2 + x^2 = 1$$
$$2x^2 = 1$$
$$x^2 = \frac{1}{2}$$
$$x = \sqrt{\frac{1}{2}}.$$

We know that x is positive because P is in the first quadrant. This quantity is often rewritten as

$$\sqrt{\frac{1}{2}} = \sqrt{\frac{1}{2} \cdot \frac{2}{2}} = \sqrt{\frac{2}{4}} = \frac{\sqrt{2}}{2}.$$

Since $x = y$, we see that $y = \frac{\sqrt{2}}{2}$ as well. Thus, since x and y are the coordinates of P, we have $\cos 45° = \frac{\sqrt{2}}{2}$ and $\sin 45° = \frac{\sqrt{2}}{2}$.

Figure 5.31: This triangle has 2 equal angles and 2 equal sides, so $x = y$

ie point $Q = (x, y)$, determined by the angle 30° on the unit circle. A right
vn in, and a mirror image of this triangle is shown below the x-axis. Together
rm the triangle $\triangle OQA$. This triangle has 3 equal 60° angles and thus has 3
of length 1. The length of side $\overline{QA}$ can also be written as $2y$, and so we have
he Pythagorean theorem,

$$x^2 + y^2 = 1$$

$$x^2 + \left(\frac{1}{2}\right)^2 = 1$$

$$x^2 = \frac{3}{4}$$

$$x = \sqrt{\frac{3}{4}} = \frac{\sqrt{3}}{2}.$$

.. positive because Q is in the first quadrant. Since x and y are the coordinates of Q, this
means that $\cos 30° = \frac{\sqrt{3}}{2}$ and $\sin 30° = \frac{1}{2}$.

Using a similar argument, we can show that $\cos 60° = \frac{1}{2}$ and $\sin 60° = \frac{\sqrt{3}}{2}$. Naturally, these
conclusions hold for radians too. Using $30° = \pi/6$, $45° = \pi/4$, and $60° = \pi/3$, we have

$$\sin \frac{\pi}{6} = \frac{1}{2}, \qquad \cos \frac{\pi}{6} = \frac{\sqrt{3}}{2},$$

$$\sin \frac{\pi}{4} = \frac{\sqrt{2}}{2}, \qquad \cos \frac{\pi}{4} = \frac{\sqrt{2}}{2},$$

$$\sin \frac{\pi}{3} = \frac{\sqrt{3}}{2}, \qquad \cos \frac{\pi}{3} = \frac{1}{2}.$$

It is well worth memorizing the values of sine and cosine for these special angles.

Other Values for Sine and Cosine

Using a calculator or computer, we can find values of $\sin \theta$ and $\cos \theta$ for any angle on the unit circle.

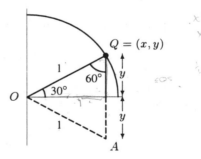

Figure 5.32: The triangle $\triangle OQA$ has 3 equal angles and 3 equal sides, so $2y = 1$

Example 4 In Figure 5.33, point P is determined by the angle $\theta = 65°$. What are the coordinates of point P
correct to two decimal places?

Solution Using a calculator and rounding to two decimal places, we find that $\cos 65° = 0.42$ and $\sin 65° = 0.91$. Thus, $P = (0.42, 0.91)$.

Most calculators can be set for units of degrees or radians. Make sure the calculator is set for the correct type of units in a given problem. Not being careful of degrees versus radians can result in errors. For instance, the sine of 10° is 0.1736, but the sine of 10 radians is −0.5440.

Reference Angles

We can determine the sine and cosine of any angle on the unit circle by refering to an angle in the first quadrant. To do this, we take advantage of the unit circle's symmetry.

Example 5   We know from Example 4 that $\sin 65° = 0.91$ and $\cos 65° = 0.42$. Use this fact to find the sine and cosine of $−65°, 245°$, and $785°$.

Solution   Let $P = (0.42, 0.91)$ be the point on the unit circle specified by the angle 65°. In Figure 5.33, we see that −65° specifies a point labeled Q that is the reflection of P across the x-axis. Thus, the y-coordinate of Q is the opposite of the y-coordinate of P, and so $Q = (0.42, −0.91)$. This means that

$$\sin(−65°) = −0.91 \quad \text{and} \quad \cos(−65°) = 0.42.$$

Also in Figure 5.33, we see that $245° = 180° + 65°$ specifies a point labeled R that is diametrically opposite the point P. The coordinates of R are the negatives of the coordinates of P, and so $R = (−0.42, −0.91)$. Thus,

$$\sin 245° = −0.91 \quad \text{and} \quad \cos 245° = −0.42.$$

Finally, we see that $785° = 720° + 65°$, and so this angle specifies the same point as 65° does. This means that

$$\sin 785° = 0.42 \quad \text{and} \quad \cos 785° = 0.91.$$

Figure 5.33: The angles $65°, −65°, 245°$, and $785°$ on a unit circle

Because we can find the sine and cosine of any angle by referring to an angle in the first quadrant, angles between 0° and 90° (or 0 and $\pi/2$ radians) are called *reference angles*.

Graphs of the Sine and Cosine Functions

Figure 5.34 gives graphs for the sine and cosine functions. Note that here the angle θ and the θ-axis are measured in radians. The viewing window is $−2\pi \leq \theta \leq 4\pi, −1 \leq y \leq 1$.

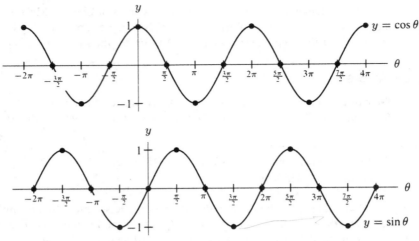

Figure 5.34: The graphs of $\sin\theta$ and $\cos\theta$ for $-2\pi \leq \theta \leq 4\pi$

TABLE 5.7   *A table of values for* $\sin\theta$ *and* $\cos\theta$.

θ (degrees)	0°	90°	180°	270°	360°	450°	540°	630°	720°	$\cdots$
θ (radians)	0	$\pi/2$	π	$3\pi/2$	2π	$\frac{5\pi}{2}$	3π	$\frac{7\pi}{2}$	4π	$\cdots$
$\sin\theta$	0	1	0	-1	0	1	0	-1	0	$\cdots$
$\cos\theta$	1	0	-1	0	1	0	-1	0	1	$\cdots$

The Domain and Range of the Sine and Cosine Functions

Since outputs of the sine function are y-coordinates of points on the unit circle, they must lie between -1 and 1. Similarly, since outputs of the cosine function are x-coordinates of points on the unit circle, they must also lie between -1 and 1. Thus, the range of these functions is given by

$$-1 \leq \sin\theta \leq 1, \quad \text{and} \quad -1 \leq \cos\theta \leq 1.$$

As for the domain, the input of the sine function is an angle that specifies a point on the unit circle. As we saw in Section 5.2, such angles can be either positive or negative, and they can be as large or small as we like. Thus, the domain of the sine function is any value of θ. The same is true for the cosine function.

The Periodic Nature of the Sine and Cosine Functions

We already know that adding multiples of 360° to an angle does not change the point on the unit circle that the angle satisfies. For example, $-325°$, $35°$, and $395°$ all specify the same point on the unit circle. Consequently, the values of $\sin\theta$ will repeat with a period of 360°. That is, no matter what the value of θ, we know that $\sin\theta = \sin(\theta + 360°) = \sin(\theta + 720°)$ and so on. The same is true for $\cos\theta$.

Similar statements hold if our angles are measured in radians. However, $\sin\theta$ and $\cos\theta$ repeat with a period of 2π radians. This is because 2π radians = 360°.

The Period, Amplitude, and Midline of the Sine and Cosine Functions

As we have seen, the sine and cosine functions both have periods of 2π radians (or 360°). Judging from Figure 5.34, we see that the midline of both their graphs is $y = 0$, and that the amplitudes of each is 1. A *sinusoidal* function is one that can be expressed as a transformation of $y = \sin\theta$.

The Tangent Function

We define the *tangent* of θ, written $\tan \theta$, by

$$\tan \theta = \frac{\sin \theta}{\cos \theta}.$$

Since we cannot divide by 0, the tangent of θ is only defined when $\cos \theta \neq 0$. We have seen that $\sin \theta$ and $\cos \theta$ are represented on the unit circle by oriented distances. Since the tangent of an angle is the ratio of a vertical distance to a horizontal distance, its graphical interpretation is not a distance but a *slope*. If P is a point on the unit circle specified by the angle θ, then the slope of the line passing from the origin through P is given by

$$m = \frac{\Delta y}{\Delta x} = \frac{y - 0}{x - 0} = \frac{y}{x}.$$

But since $y = \sin \theta$ and $x = \cos \theta$, this means that

$$m = \frac{\sin \theta}{\cos \theta} = \tan \theta.$$

In words, the tangent of the angle θ is the slope of the line passing through the origin and through point P. (See Figure 5.35.)

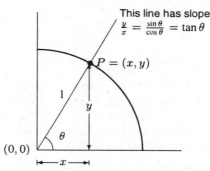

Figure 5.35: The slope of the line passing through the origin and point P is $\dfrac{\sin \theta}{\cos \theta} = \tan \theta$

Example 6   Using a computer or calculator, sketch a graph of $\tan \theta$ for $-2\pi \leq \theta \leq 2\pi$. Describe the graph in words.

Solution   The graph of $\tan \theta$ for $-2\pi \leq \theta \leq 2\pi$ is shown in Figure 5.36.

Figure 5.36: The graph of $y = \tan \theta$, for $-2\pi \leq \theta \leq 2\pi$

We see that the tangent function has a period of π. This is different from the sine and cosine functions, which have a period of 2π. We can also see that the tangent function is increasing everywhere it is defined. The graph has vertical asymptotes where $\cos t = 0$. Even though the tangent function is periodic, it does not have an amplitude or a midline because it does not have a maximum or a minimum value.

The Connection Between the Unit Circle and the Graph of Tangent

Figure 5.37 illustrates the connection between an angle θ on the unit circle and the graph of the tangent function.

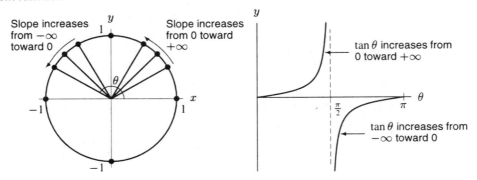

Figure 5.37: The connection between the unit circle and the graph of tangent

As the angle θ opens from $0°$ to $90°$, the slope of the line (and therefore the tangent of θ) increases from 0 toward $+\infty$. At $\theta = 90°$, this line is vertical, and its slope is undefined. Thus, $\tan 90°$ is also undefined. As θ moves past $90°$, the slope becomes negative, and so does the tangent function. The line becomes less steep as θ approachs $180°$, where it becomes horizontal. Thus, $\tan \theta$ becomes less negative and gets close to 0.

Note the tangent of $45°$ is 1, since $\tan 45° = \frac{\sin 45°}{\cos 45°} = \frac{\sqrt{2}/2}{\sqrt{2}/2} = 1$. This makes sense since an angle of $45°$ describes a ray halfway between the x and y axes. This ray has slope 1 since the ratio of the rise to the run is 1.

Example 7   Find the equation of line l shown in Figure 5.38.

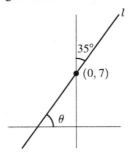

Figure 5.38: Line l makes a $35°$ angle with the y-axis

Solution   We know that the equation of l is $y = mx + 7$, where m is the slope. We see that $\theta = 90° - 35° = 55°$, and so this line makes a $55°$ angle with the x-axis. Thus, its slope is $m = \tan 55°$, and so its equation is $y = 7 + x \tan 55°$. A calculator gives $\tan 55° = 1.43$. So $y = 1.43x + 7$ is the equation of l.

The Reciprocals of the Trigonometric Functions

The reciprocals of the trigonometric functions are given special names. Th
sionally used to simplify the appearance of trigonometric expressions. Wher
not equal zero, we have

$$\text{secant } \theta = \sec \theta = \frac{1}{\cos \theta}.$$

$$\text{cosecant } \theta = \csc \theta = \frac{1}{\sin \theta}.$$

$$\text{cotangent } \theta = \cot \theta = \frac{1}{\tan \theta} = \frac{\cos \theta}{\sin \theta}.$$

Problems for Section 5.3

1. (a) Evaluate $\sin \theta$, $\cos \theta$ and $\tan \theta$, for the angle θ given on the unit circle in Figure 5.39
   (b) Evaluate $\sin \theta$, $\cos \theta$ and $\tan \theta$, for the angle θ given on the unit circle in Figure 5.40

$\sin \theta = 0.6$
$\cos \theta = -0.8$

$\tan \theta = -\frac{0.6}{0.8}$

$(-0.8, 0.6)$

$(-0.6, 0.8)$

$\sin \theta = 0.8$
$\cos \theta = -0.6$

$\tan \theta = -\frac{0.8}{0.6}$

Figure 5.39

Figure 5.40

2. Suppose an ant starts at the point $(1,0)$ on the unit circle, and walks counterclockwise a distance of 3 units around the circle. Find the x and y coordinates of the final location of the ant. Your answer should be accurate to 2 decimal places.

$(1,0)$
3 units

$\theta = \frac{s}{n} = \frac{3}{1}$

$\theta = 3$

$(\cos 3, \sin 3)$

3. Evaluate the following expressions:
   (a) $\sin 0°$ (b) $\cos 90°$ (c) $\tan 90°$
   (d) $\cos 540°$ (e) $\tan 540°$

4. Evaluate the following expressions, making use of reference angles if applicable:
   (a) $\sin 30°$ (b) $\sin 150°$ (c) $\cos 150°$
   (d) $\cos 300°$ (e) $\tan 300°$

5. Compare the values of $\sqrt{\frac{1}{2}}$ and $\frac{\sqrt{2}}{2}$ using your calculator.

6. Compare the values of $\sqrt{\frac{3}{4}}$ and $\frac{\sqrt{3}}{2}$ using your calculator.

7. In which quadrants do the following statements hold?
   (a) $\sin \theta > 0$ and $\cos \theta > 0$ (b) $\tan \theta > 0$ (c) $\tan \theta < 0$
   (d) $\sin \theta < 0$ and $\cos \theta > 0$ (e) $\cos \theta < 0$ and $\tan \theta > 0$

8. Make a table of exact values of $\sin\theta$ and $\cos\theta$ for $0°$, $30°$, $45°$, $60°$, and $90°$. Extend the table to include all angles $0° \leq \theta < 360°$ which have $0°$, $30°$, $45°$, $60°$, or $90°$ as their reference angle.

9. Let θ be an angle in the first quadrant, and suppose $\sin\theta = a$. Evaluate the following expressions in terms of a. (See Figure 5.41.)

    (a) $\sin(\theta + 360°)$ a (b) $\sin(\theta + 180°)$ $-a$ (c) $\cos(90° - \theta)$ $= a$

    (d) $\sin(180° - \theta)$ a (e) $\sin(360° - \theta)$ $-a$ (f) $\cos(270° - \theta)$ $-a$

Figure 5.41

10. Using the same scale on both axes, sketch a graph of $y = \sin t$ on the interval $-\pi \leq t \leq 3\pi$.

    (a) Indicate the interval(s) on which the function is

        (i) positive   (ii) increasing   (iii) concave up

    (b) Estimate the t values at which the function is increasing most rapidly.

11. (a) Using what you know about the graph of $y = \sin x$, make predictions about the graph of $y = (\sin x)^2$. Compare your predictions to the actual graph.

    (b) Using a computer or a graphing calculator, graph $g(x) = (\sin x)^2$, $h(x) = (\cos x)^2$ and $f(x) = g(x) + h(x)$, on the interval $-2\pi \leq x \leq 2\pi$. Given your result from part (a), does the graph of $f(x)$ make sense? Why or why not?

12. Sketch the following functions of x in the domain $-2\pi \leq x \leq 2\pi$.

    (a) $f(x) = \sin x$ (b) $g(x) = |\sin x|$ (c) $h(x) = \sin|x|$ (d) $i(x) = |\sin|x||$

    (e) Do any two of these functions have identical graphs? If so, explain why this makes sense.

13. A four panel revolving door is shown in Figure 5.42. Each of the four panels is one meter wide. What is d, the width of the opening straight across from B to C?

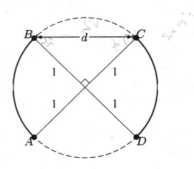

Figure 5.42: A four-panel revolving door

14. What would the width of the opening be if each panel in the revolving door in Problem 13 were two meters wide?

15. Suppose that a revolving door has three panels of length one which make equal angles with each other, as in Figure 5.43. What is the width w of the opening between A and B?

Figure 5.43: A revolving door with three panels

Figure 5.44

16. A stationary sensor S is mounted on the wall containing a revolving door with 1 meter panels as shown in Figure 5.44. Suppose that a second, moving sensor M is mounted at the tip of a panel in such a way that it continually sends a beam perpendicular to the wall line.

   (a) How far is the intersection point of the two beams from the sensor S when the panels are as shown in Figure 5.44?

   (b) How far is the intersection point of the two beams from the wall sensor after the door has been rotated counterclockwise 75° from its position in Figure 5.44?

17. Find an equation for line l in terms of x_0, y_0, and θ.

18. For each angle in the set $\{0°, 15°, 30°, \cdots, 330°, 345°, 360°\}$, list the reference angle.

19. Explain in your own words the definition of $\sin\theta$ on the unit circle (θ in degrees).

20. Graph $y = \tan\theta, 0 \le \theta \le 2\pi$. Describe the graph in words. Relate your description to an interpretation of $\tan\theta$ given in the text: $\tan\theta$ is the slope of a line passing through the origin at an angle of θ to the x-axis. Is this interpretation consistent with the appearance of your graph?

21. Graph $y = \sec\theta$, $y = \csc\theta$ and $y = \cot\theta$ for $-\pi \le \theta \le \pi$. Describe the graphs in words.

22. Graph $y = \cos x \cdot \tan x$. Is this function exactly the same as $y = \sin x$? Why or why not?

23. Graph $y = \sin\theta$ and $y = \tan\theta$, for $-20° \le \theta \le 20°$. Explain any similarities or differences between the two graphs.

24. Describe the similarities and differences between the graphs of $y = \sin(1/x)$ and $y = 1/\sin x$.

25. Let f be a function defined for all real numbers.
    (a) Is $f(\sin t)$ a periodic function? Justify your answer.
    (b) Is $\sin(f(t))$ a periodic function? Justify your answer.

26. A ferris wheel is 20 meters in diameter and makes one revolution every 4 minutes. For how many minutes of any revolution will your seat be above 15 meters?

27. Suppose a bug is crawling around the Cartesian plane. Let t represent time, let $x = f(t)$ be the function denoting the x-coordinate of the bug's position as a function of time, and let $y = g(t)$ be the y-coordinate of the bug's position.
    (a) Suppose $f(t) = t$ and $g(t) = t$. What path does the bug follow?
    (b) Now let $f(t) = \cos t$, and $g(t) = \sin t$. What path does the bug follow? What is its starting point? (i.e. where is the bug when $t = 0$?) When does the bug get back to its starting point?
    (c) Now let $f(t) = \cos t$ and $g(t) = 2 \sin t$. What path does the bug follow? What is its starting point? (i.e. where is the bug when $t = 0$?) When does the bug get back to its starting point?

28. Define $f(\theta)$ as the y-coordinate of the point P in Figure 5.45.

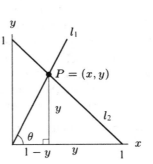

Figure 5.45: The point
$P = (x, y)$

    (a) Find a formula for y in terms of θ alone, where $0 < \theta < \frac{\pi}{2}$. (Hint: Use the equation for line l_2.)
    (b) Graph $y = f(\theta)$ on the interval $-\pi \le \theta \le \pi$.
    (c) Analyze how the graph describes the y-value as θ changes. Discuss whether $y = f(\theta)$ is periodic or not.

5.4 FINDING A FORMULA FOR THE FERRIS WHEEL FUNCTION

The function $h(t)$ from Section 5.1 gives height (in feet) above ground t minutes after boarding a ferris wheel. Let's find a formula for this function. Based on the wave-like graph of $h(t)$ in Figure 5.7 on page 261, we might expect the formula to involve a sine or cosine function.

In Figure 5.46, let the point $P = (x, y)$ indicate position t minutes after boarding the wheel. Here x and y are measured with respect to the center of the wheel, which has been labeled $(0, 0)$.

Figure 5.46: The point $P = (x, y)$ indicates your position on the wheel with respect to the wheel's center, labeled $(0, 0)$

From Figure 5.46, we see that

$$\text{Height above ground} = 250 + y.$$

In Figure 5.46, the angle corresponding to point P has been labeled θ. Figure 5.47 compares this angle to the same angle on the unit circle. The two triangles in Figure 5.47 are similar triangles, and the ratio of side opposite θ to hypotenuse length is the same for both:

$$\frac{y}{250} = \frac{\sin \theta}{1}.$$

This means that

$$y = 250 \sin \theta$$

and so

$$\text{Height above ground} = 250 + 250 \sin \theta.$$

The Ferris Wheel   The Unit Circle

Figure 5.47: Comparing the ferris wheel to the unit circle, we see that the height y is related to $\sin \theta$. (Note: pictures are not drawn to scale)

We have determined the height above the ground in terms of θ, but we want to get height as a function of time, t. We know that the wheel is turning at a steady rate. The position at time $t = 0$ (ground level) corresponds to the 6 o'clock position, at an angle $\theta = -\frac{\pi}{2}$. After 5 minutes, the position corresponds to the 3 o'clock position where $\theta = 0$. At "12 o'clock," 10 minutes into the ride, the position corresponds to $\theta = \frac{\pi}{2}$, and so on. Table 5.8 gives values of the angle θ for different values of t.

TABLE 5.8   *Values of θ for different values of t*

t, minutes	0	5	10	15	20	25
θ, radians	$-\frac{\pi}{2}$	0	$\frac{\pi}{2}$	π	$\frac{3\pi}{2}$	2π

From Table 5.8, we see that θ is a linear function of t. We see that θ increases by $\pi/2$ every 5 minutes, so that

$$\begin{array}{c}\text{Rate of change of } \theta \\ \text{with respect to } t\end{array} = \frac{\Delta \theta}{\Delta t} = \frac{\pi/2}{5} = \frac{\pi}{10}.$$

Since at time $t = 0$ the starting value of θ is $-\frac{\pi}{2}$, we see that a formula for θ is

$$\theta = \underbrace{\text{starting value}}_{-\pi/2} + \underbrace{\text{rate of change}}_{\pi/10} \times \quad t$$

$$= -\frac{\pi}{2} + \frac{\pi}{10}t.$$

Now that we know θ in terms of t, we can get the height at time t:

$$h(t) = \text{height at time } t = 250 \quad + \quad 250\sin\theta$$

$$= 250 \quad + \quad 250\sin\underbrace{\left(\frac{\pi}{10}t - \frac{\pi}{2}\right)}_{\theta}.$$

This formula can be checked at some particular time values. For example, when $t = 0$, we have $h(0) = 250 + 250\sin(0 - \frac{\pi}{2}) = 250 - 250 = 0$, which is the correct starting height above the ground.

Example 1   According to our formula, what is your height above ground 3 minutes after boarding the wheel? 11 minutes after boarding the wheel? Are these values reasonable?

Solution   We have

$$h(3) = 250 + 250\sin\left(\frac{\pi}{10}\cdot 3 - \frac{\pi}{2}\right) = 103.1 \text{ ft}$$

$$\text{and} \quad h(11) = 250 + 250\sin\left(\frac{\pi}{10}\cdot 11 - \frac{\pi}{2}\right) = 487.8 \text{ ft}.$$

These answers seem reasonable. Three minutes after boarding the wheel, you will have climbed less than halfway up, or less than 250 feet. Eleven minutes after boarding the wheel, you will have just passed the highest point at 500 feet, and have begun your descent.

Comparing the Graphs of the Sine Function and the Ferris Wheel Function

The formula for the ferris wheel function involves the sine function, and so it is not surprising that the graphs of these two functions are related. In fact, the graph of the ferris wheel function can be thought of in terms of shifting and stretching the graph of the sine function.

To see how this works, let's break the formula for the ferris wheel function into smaller pieces. These pieces are graphed in Figure 5.48.

Figure 5.48: The sequence of transformations that relate the sine function to the ferris wheel function

The first piece we will consider is shown below:

Ferris wheel function: $h(t) = 250 + 250 \underbrace{\sin\left(\frac{\pi}{10}t - \frac{\pi}{2}\right)}_{\text{first piece}}$

First piece we will consider: $g(t) = \sin\left(\frac{\pi}{10}t - \frac{\pi}{2}\right).$

Here, we have given the name $g(t)$ to this smaller piece. This allows us to write the height function, $h(t)$, as:

$$h(t) = 250 + 250g(t).$$

Thinking about the new function g, we see that it involves two inside changes to the sine function: an inside shift and an inside stretch. To understand how these inside changes go together, we can rewrite the formula for g by factoring:

$$g(t) = \sin\left(\frac{\pi}{10}t - \frac{\pi}{2}\right)$$
$$= \sin\left(\frac{\pi}{10}(t - 5)\right).$$

This means that the graph of g resembles the graph of $\sin\frac{\pi}{10}t$ shifted to the right by 5 units. To see this, notice that if we let $f(t) = \sin\frac{\pi}{10}t$, then g and f are the same except for an input shift of 5:

$$\text{if}\quad g(t) = \sin\left(\frac{\pi}{10}(t - 5)\right)$$
$$\text{and if}\quad f(t) = \sin\left(\frac{\pi}{10}t\right),$$
$$\text{then}\quad g(t) = f(t - 5).$$

The function $f(t) = \sin(\frac{\pi}{10}t)$ is the second piece of the ferris wheel function that we will consider. Its graph is a horizontally stretched version of the graph of $\sin t$. But how stretched out is the graph of f compared to the regular sine graph? Notice that

$$f(0) = \sin\left(\frac{\pi}{10} \cdot 0\right) = \sin 0 = 0$$
$$f(5) = \sin\left(\frac{\pi}{10} \cdot 5\right) = \sin\frac{\pi}{2} = 1$$
$$f(10) = \sin\left(\frac{\pi}{10} \cdot 10\right) = \sin \pi = 0$$
$$f(15) = \sin\left(\frac{\pi}{10} \cdot 15\right) = \sin\frac{3\pi}{2} = -1$$
$$f(20) = \sin\left(\frac{\pi}{10} \cdot 20\right) = \sin 2\pi = 0$$
$$f(25) = \sin\left(\frac{\pi}{10} \cdot 25\right) = \sin\frac{5\pi}{2} = 1$$
$$\vdots$$

We see that the function f begins repeating after $t = 20$. This stands to reason, because it takes the ferris wheel 20 minutes to complete one full turn. We say that the *period* of f is 20, which is about 3 times as long as the period of the sine function ($2\pi \approx 6$). This makes sense because $\sin(\frac{\pi}{10}t) \approx \sin(\frac{1}{3}t)$, representing a horizontal stretch by a factor of roughly 3.

Therefore, the graph of f resembles the graph of $\sin t$, except that its period is 20 instead of 2π.

The graph of g resembles the graph of f shifted to the right by 5, or by one-fourth of a period. Some values of g are:

$$g(0) = f(0 - 5) = f(-5) = -1$$
$$g(5) = f(5 - 5) = f(0) = 0$$
$$g(10) = f(10 - 5) = f(5) = 1$$
$$g(15) = f(15 - 5) = f(10) = 0$$
$$\vdots$$

Finally, since

$$h(t) = 250 + 250g(t),$$

we see that the graph of h resembles the graph of g stretched vertically by a factor of 250 and then shifted vertically by 250. Some values of h are

$$h(0) = 250 + 250g(0) = 250 + 250 \cdot -1 = 0$$
$$h(5) = 250 + 250g(5) = 250 + 250 \cdot 0 = 250$$
$$h(10) = 250 + 250g(10) = 250 + 250 \cdot 1 = 500$$
$$h(15) = 250 + 250g(15) = 250 + 250 \cdot 0 = 250$$
$$\vdots$$

Thus, we have seen that the ferris wheel function is in the family of sinusoidal functions. It can be derived from the basic sine function by suitable shifts and stretches.

Problems for Section 5.4

In Problems 1–3, find a formula (using the sine function) for your height above ground after t minutes on the London ferris wheel described. Graph the function to check that it is correct.

1. The London ferris wheel has increased its rotation speed. The wheel begins to turn in a counterclockwise direction completing one full revolution every ten minutes.

2. The London ferris wheel is built as planned but with the wheel only 300 meters high.

3. The developers of the London ferris wheel build a loading tower of height 250 meters. So leading is done at the 3 o'clock position, but unloading still is done on the ground level.

Problems 4–6 involve different ferris wheels. Find a formula, using the sine function for your height above ground after t minutes on the ferris wheeel. Graph the function to check that it is correct.

4. A ferris wheel is 35 meters in diameter, and can be boarded at ground level. The wheel turns in a counterclockwise direction, completing one full revolution every 5 minutes. Suppose that at $t = 0$ you are in the three o'clock position.

5. A ferris wheel is 20 meters in diameter and must be boarded from a platform that is 4 meters above the ground. Assume the six o'clock position on the ferris wheel is level with the loading platform. The wheel turns in the *clockwise* direction, completing one full revolution every 2 minutes. Suppose that at $t = 0$ you are in the twelve o'clock position.

6. A ferris wheel is 50 meters in diameter and must be boarded from a platform that is 5 meters above the ground. Assume the six o'clock position on the ferris wheel is level with the loading platform. The wheel turns in the counterclockwise direction, completing one full revolution every 8 minutes. Suppose that at $t = 0$ you are at the loading platform.

In Problems 7–9 a graph shows your height above ground after t minutes on three different ferris wheels. Find an equation (using the sine function) for your height above ground after t minutes on each ferris wheel. Graph your function to see that it is identical to the graph shown.

Figure 5.49

Figure 5.50

Figure 5.51

In Problems 10–11 a table gives data about a vibrating string that can be modeled by a sine function. Find a formula for the string's displacement as a function of time. Graph your function to see that it passes through the data points.

10.   Table 5.9 gives theoretical values from a vibrating string experiment, with time t in seconds, and height $h = f(t)$ in centimeters.

TABLE 5.9

t	0	0.1	0.2	0.3	0.4	0.5	0.6	0.7	0.8	0.9	1
$h = f(t)$	2	2.588	2.951	2.951	2.588	2	1.412	1.049	1.049	1.412	2

11.   Table 5.10 gives the height in feet of a weight on a spring where t is the time in seconds.

TABLE 5.10

t	0	1	2	3	4	5	6	7
$h = f(t)$	4.0	5.25	6.165	6.5	6.167	5.25	4.0	2.75
t	8	9	10	11	12	13	14	15
$h = f(t)$	1.835	1.5	1.8348	2.75	4.0	5.22	6.16	6.5

5.5   A GENERAL FORMULA FOR TRIGONOMETRIC FUNCTIONS

In Section 5.4, we saw how to find a formula for the ferris wheel function h in terms of the sine function, and how to graph $h(t)$ by shifting and stretching the graph of $\sin t$. In this section we will investigate some modifications of the general sine and cosine functions. These modifications are based on the same kinds of shifts and stretches that we used for the ferris wheel function. These modifications of sine and cosine are sometimes called general sine and cosine functions.

Before we continue, it will be useful to recall the following definitions from Section 5.1:

- The **period** of a trigonometric function $f(t)$ is the smallest positive number c such that $f(t) = f(c + t)$ for all t. More concisely, the period c is the length of the repeated interval in the graph of $f(t)$.

- The **midline** is the horizontal line midway between the function's minimum and maximum values.

- The **amplitude** is the distance between the function's midline and maximum value (or between its midline and minimum value).

The General Formula for Sine Functions

The graph of a general sine function resembles the graph of $y = \sin t$, but it may also be shifted, flipped, and stretched. This may change the period, amplitude, midline, and the value of the sine function at $t = 0$. The *general formula for sine functions* is given by

$$y = A \sin(Bt + C) + D,$$

where A, B, C, and D are constants that affect the shape of the graph. Specifically,

- $|A|$ is the amplitude. Note that the value of A can be positive or negative, but the amplitude itself is always positive.

- B is a positive constant related to the period P by the formula $P = 2\pi/B$.

- C is a constant that is related to the the horizontal shift, S, to the left by the formula $S = C/B$.

- $y = D$ is the midline.

Example 1   From Figure 5.7 on page 261, we see that the graph of the ferris wheel function $f(t)$ resembles the graph of $\sin t$ except that its period is 20, its amplitude is 250, its midline is $h = 250$, and it has been shifted to the right a distance of 5 units. Using the general formula $h(t) = A \sin(Bt + C) + D$, we know from the amplitude and midline that $A = 250$ and $D = 250$. To find B we use the fact that the period is $P = 20$:

$$P = \frac{2\pi}{B}$$
$$20 = \frac{2\pi}{B}$$
$$B = \frac{\pi}{10}.$$

To find C, we use the fact that the horizontal shift is $S = -5$, where the value of S is negative because the shift is to the right. This gives

$$\frac{C}{B} = S$$
$$\frac{C}{\pi/10} = -5$$
$$C = -\frac{\pi}{2}.$$

Thus, a formula for this function is

$$h(t) = 250 \sin\left(\frac{\pi}{10}t - \frac{\pi}{2}\right) + 250,$$

which is the same as the formula we found in the last section by using a different approach.

Example 2   Figure 5.52 shows the graph of $y = p(t)$, an example of a sinusoidal function. This function resembles the graph of of $y = \sin t$, except that its period is 8 instead of 2π, its midline is $y = 20$ instead of the t-axis, and its amplitude is 12 instead of 1.

Notice $C = 0$ because the graph starts at the midline, so a formula for this function is $y = A \sin(Bt) + D$. Here, $A = 12$ because the amplitude of this function is 12. Since the period of this function is 8, we have

$$8 = \frac{2\pi}{B}$$
$$B = \frac{\pi}{4}.$$

Finally, $D = 20$ because the midline of this graph is $y = 20$. Thus, our formula is $y = 12 \sin\left(\frac{\pi}{4}t\right) + 20$.

Figure 5.52: A sine function with a period of 8, a midline of $y = 20$, and an amplitude of 12

Example 3   Sketch a graph of $y = 12 \sin\left(\frac{\pi}{4}t - \frac{\pi}{5}\right) + 20$.

Solution   This function is similar to the one in Example 2 except that it has been shifted to the right a distance of 0.8:

$$h = \frac{C}{B} = \frac{-\pi/5}{\pi/4} = -\frac{4}{5} = -0.8.$$

Notice that since the period of this function is $P = 8$, this is a shift through one-tenth of the period, because $\frac{1}{10} \cdot 8 = 0.8$. See Figure 5.53.

Figure 5.53: A graph of $y = 12 \sin\left(\frac{\pi}{4}t - \frac{\pi}{5}\right) + 20$

Example 4   A faint electric signal is detected by sensitive instruments. The strength of the signal (in volts) is given by $V = 0.03 \sin(200\pi t) - 0.08$, where t is time in seconds. Sketch a graph of this function and describe the signal in words.

Solution   The midline of the signal is -0.08 volts. The amplitude of this signal is $A = 0.03$. The period is given by

$$P = \frac{2\pi}{B} = \frac{2\pi}{200\pi} = \frac{1}{100}.$$

See Figure 5.54. In words, the signal varies around an average of -0.08 volts, climbing to as high as -0.05 volts and falling to as low as -0.11 volts and oscillates with a period of $P = 0.01$. In other words, the signal oscillates every hundredth of a second for a total of 100 oscillations per second.

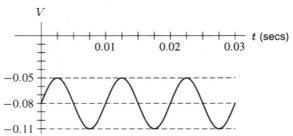

Figure 5.54: The strength of an electric signal in volts

Why The General Formula Works

We can think about transformations to see why the general formula $y = A \sin(Bt + C) + D$ works. Thinking first about the midline, we see that the graph of $y = \sin t + D$ resembles the graph of $y = \sin t$ shifted vertically by D units. Since the midline of $y = \sin t$ is $y = 0$, the midline of $y = \sin t + D$ is $y = D$. Thinking next about amplitude, we see that the graph of $y = A \sin t$ resembles the graph of $y = \sin t$ except that it has been stretched vertically by a factor of A. Since the amplitude of $y = \sin t$ is 1, the amplitude of $y = A \sin t$ is A. Notice that if A is negative, then $y = A \sin t$ is also flipped vertically across the t-axis when compared to $y = \sin t$, since $y = A \sin t$ is negative when $\sin t$ is positive, and vice versa.

As for the period, we see that the graph of $y = \sin(Bt)$ resembles the graph of $y = \sin t$ compressed horizontally by a factor of B. For instance, since the function $y = \sin t$ has a period of 2π, the function $\sin 2t$ has a period of $\frac{2\pi}{2} = \pi$, the function $\sin 4t$ has a period of $\frac{2\pi}{4} = \frac{\pi}{2}$, and so on. Generally, the period is

$$P = \frac{2\pi}{B}.$$

Finally, to understand the horizontal shift, we can factor the general formula so that it reads

$$y = \sin(Bt + C) = \sin\left[B\left(t + \frac{C}{B}\right)\right].$$

This function resembles the function $y = \sin Bt$ shifted horizontally by $h = C/B$ units, to the left if C is positive and to the right if C is negative.

The General Formula for Cosine Functions

The *general formula for cosine functions* is the same as the general formula for sine functions, except that it involves transformations of $y = \cos t$ instead of $y = \sin t$:

$$y = A \cos(Bt + C) + D.$$

The constants A, B, C, and D have the same meaning for cosine functions as they do for sine functions.

Example 5   Describe the function $y = 300 \cos(0.2\pi t) + 600$ in words and sketch its graph.

Solution   This function resembles $y = \cos t$ except that it has an amplitude of 300, a midline of $y = 600$, and a period of $P = 2\pi/0.2\pi = 10$. Figure 5.55 gives a graph of this function.

Figure 5.55: The function $y = 300 \cos(0.2\pi t) + 600$

If the Parameter A is Negative

In the equation $y = A \sin t$, if the value of A is negative, the resulting graph resembles the graph of $y = \sin t$ except that it is flipped vertically across the t-axis and it is vertically stretched or flattened by a factor of $|A|$. Thus, the amplitude of $A \sin t$ is $|A|$, and the orientation of $A \sin t$ is like that of an "upside-down" sine function. A similar statement holds for $y = A \cos t$.

Example 6   Suppose the temperature, T, in °C, of the surface water in a pond varies according to the graph in Figure 5.56. If t is the number of hours since sunrise at 6 am, find a possible formula for T.

Figure 5.56: A graph of T, the surface-water temperature in °C of a pond t hours after 6 am

Solution   The graph of T resembles a sine function with amplitude $|A| = 3$, period $P = 24$ and midline $D = 20$. One way to think about this function is that, compared to $y = \cos t$, there is no horizontal shift but the graph has been reflected across the midline, and so A will be negative. We have

$$24 = \frac{2\pi}{B},$$
$$B = \frac{2\pi}{24} = \frac{\pi}{12}.$$

Putting all this together gives the following formula for T (there are other possible formulas):

$$T(t) = -3 \cos\left(\frac{\pi}{12}t\right) + 20.$$

It is worth checking a few convenient values of t for this formula. For example, $T(6) = -3 \cos(\frac{\pi}{12}6) + 20 = (-3)(0) + 20 = 20$. This corresponds to the value of $T(t)$ for $t = 6$ on the graph in Figure 5.56.

Example 7 A rabbit population in a national park rises and falls each year. It reaches its minimum of 5000 rabbits in January. By July, as the weather warms up and food grows more abundant, the population triples in size. By the following January, the population again falls to 5000 rabbits, completing the annual cycle. If R gives the size of the rabbit population as a function of t, the number of months since January, find a possible formula for $R = f(t)$ using a trigonometric function.

Solution To find a formula for R, we can begin with a table and a graph. We will call January month 0, and so July is month 6. The five points given in Table 5.11 have been plotted in Figure 5.57, and a curve has been drawn in. This curve has period $P = 12$, midline $R = 10,000$, and amplitude $|A| = 5000$. It resembles a cosine function reflected across the horizontal axis. Thus, a possible formula for this curve is

$$R = -5000\cos\left(\frac{\pi}{6}t\right) + 10000.$$

There are other possible formulas.

TABLE 5.11 *Rabbit population for a two-year period*

t	R
0	5000
6	15000
12	5000
18	15000
24	5000

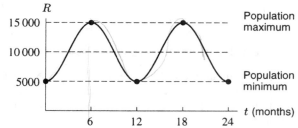

Figure 5.57: The number of rabbits, R, as a function of time in months, t, for $0 \leq t \leq 24$

Phase Shift

The constant C in the general formula $A\cos(Bt + C)$ is related to the horizontal shift of the graph and is known as the *phase shift*. The phase shift tells us the fraction of a full period that the curve is shifted. For instance, if $C = \pi/10$, the fraction of a period that the curve shifts is

$$\frac{\pi/10}{2\pi} \quad = \quad \frac{1}{20} \quad = \quad \text{one-twentieth of a full period,}$$

no matter what the period is. Similarly, if $C = \pi/4$, the fraction of a period that the curve shifts is

$$\frac{\pi/4}{2\pi} \quad = \quad \frac{1}{8} \quad = \quad \text{one-eighth of a full period.}$$

The point is that the graphs of cosine functions with the same amplitude, midline, and phase shift will have a similar appearance even if their periods are different. The same is true for sine functions.

Example 8 Compare the graphs of $y = \sin(t + \pi/4)$, $y = \sin(6t + \pi/4)$, and $y = \sin(\frac{\pi}{8}t + \pi/4)$.

Solution The function $y = \sin(t + \pi/4)$ has a period of 2π and it is shifted horizontally to the left by $\pi/4$. This is one-eighth of its period because $\frac{1}{8} \cdot 2\pi = \frac{\pi}{4}$. Similarly, the function $y = \sin(6t + \pi/4)$ has a period of $\pi/3$ and is shifted to the left by $\pi/24$. This is one-eighth of its period, because $\frac{1}{8} \cdot \frac{\pi}{3} = \frac{\pi}{24}$. Finally, the function $y = \sin(\frac{\pi}{8}t + \pi/4)$ has a period of 16 and it is shifted to the left by 2, which is one-eighth of its period because $\frac{1}{8} \cdot 16 = 2$.

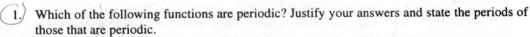

Figure 5.58: Three functions with different periods but the same phase shift.
Note: the horizontal scales are different

From Figure 5.58, we see that the appearance of these three functions is very similar, even though they have different periods and have been shifted horizontally by different amounts. They all cross the y-axis at the same point and are increasing as they cross at $t = 0$. The phase shift for all three functions is $\pi/4$.

Summary of Transformations

If
$$y = A\sin(Bt + C) + D \quad \text{or} \quad y = A\cos(Bt + C) + D,$$

then

- $|A|$ is the **amplitude**
- C is the **phase shift**
- $y = D$ is the **midline**.

- $P = 2\pi/|B|$ is the **period**
- C/B is the **horizontal shift**

Functions that can be expressed in this form are called sinusoidal functions.

Problems for Section 5.5

1. Which of the following functions are periodic? Justify your answers and state the periods of those that are periodic.
   (a) $y = \sin(-t)$ (b) $y = 4\cos(\pi t)$ (c) $y = \sin(t) + t$ (d) $y = \sin(\frac{t}{2}) + 1$

2. Graph one full period for each of the following functions.
   (a) $y = \sin(\frac{1}{2}t)$ (b) $y = 4\cos(t + \frac{\pi}{4})$
   (c) $y = 5 - \sin t$ (d) $y = \cos(2t) + 4$

3. Compare the graph of $y = \sin\theta$ to the graphs of $y = 2\sin\theta$ and $y = -0.5\sin\theta$ for $0 \le \theta \le 2\pi$. How are these graphs similar? How are they different?

4. Find possible formulas for the trigonometric functions in Figures 5.59–5.61.

(a)

Figure 5.59: $y = f(t)$

(b)

Figure 5.60: $y = g(t)$

(c)

Figure 5.61: $y = h(t)$

Chapter 8/ 41

5. Find possible formulas for the trigonometric functions in Figure 5.62.

(a)

(b)

(c)

Figure 5.62

6. Find formulas for the trigonometric functions in Figure 5.63.

(a)

(b)

(c)

Figure 5.63

7. State the amplitude, period, phase shift, and horizontal shifts for each of the following functions and graph each of them on the given interval.

(a) $y = \cos(\frac{t}{4} - \frac{\pi}{4})$, $0 \le t \le 2\pi$ (b) $y = -4\sin t$, $-2\pi \le t \le 2\pi$

(c) $y = 3\sin(4\pi t + 6\pi)$, $-\frac{3}{2} \le t \le \frac{1}{2}$ (d) $y = \cos(2t + \frac{\pi}{2})$, $-\pi \le t \le 2\pi$

(e) $y = -20\cos(4\pi t)$, $-\frac{3}{4} \le t \le 1$

8. The following formulas give animal populations as functions of t = time, in years. Describe these populations in words.

(a) $P = 1500 + 200t$ (b) $P = 2700 - 80t$ (c) $P = 1800(1.03)^t$

(d) $P = 800e^{-0.04t}$ (e) $P = 230\sin\left(\frac{2\pi}{7}t\right) + 3800$

9. Compare the graph of $y = \sin\theta$ to the graphs of $y = 2\sin\theta$ and $y = -0.5\sin\theta$, $0 \le \theta \le 2\pi$. How are these graphs similar? How are they different?

10. Draw the graph of $y = (\sin x)^2$. Use the graph to find values of A, B, C, and D so that $y = A\cos(Bx + C) + D$.

11. A population of animals varies sinusoidally over a year between a low of 700 on January 1 and a high of 900 on July 1. It returns to a low of 700 on the following January 1.

(a) Graph the population as a function of time for a period of one year.
(b) Find a formula for the population as a function of t = time, measured in months since the start of the year.

12. A population of animals oscillates between a low of 1300 on January 1 ($t = 0$) to a high of 2200 on July 1 ($t = 6$) back to a low of 1300 the following January ($t = 12$).

(a) Find a formula for the population P in terms of the time t (in months).
(b) Interpret the amplitude, period, and midline of the function $P = f(t)$.
(c) Use a graph to estimate when $P = 1500$ during the year.

13. Find a possible formula for the trigonometric function given in Table 5.12.

TABLE 5.12

x	0	0.1	0.2	0.3	0.4	0.5	0.6	0.7	0.8	0.9	1
$g(x)$	2	2.588	2.951	2.951	2.588	2	1.412	1.049	1.049	1.412	2

Chapter 8/ 42

14. Find a formula for the function $h(t)$ that fits (approximately) the data in Table 5.13.

   TABLE 5.13

t	0	1	2	3	4	5	6	7
$h(t)$	4.0	5.25	6.165	6.5	6.167	5.25	4.0	2.75
t	8	9	10	11	12	13	14	15
$h(t)$	1.835	1.5	1.8348	2.75	4.0	5.22	6.16	6.5

15. Let $f(x) = \sin(2\pi x)$ and $g(x) = \cos(2\pi x)$. State the periods, amplitudes, and midlines of f and g.

16. Let $f(x) = \sin(2\pi x)$ and $g(x) = \cos(2\pi x)$. Sketch graphs of the following on the interval $0 \le x \le 3$. (Hint: Use what you know about graph transformations.)

   (a) $y = 2f(x)$ (b) $y = -\frac{1}{2}g(x)$ (c) $y = 3 + 2f(x)$

   (d) $y = g(2x)$ (e) $y = f(\frac{1}{3}x)$ (f) $y = 2f(3x)$

17. Let $f(x) = \sin(2\pi x)$ and $g(x) = \cos(2\pi x)$. Find possible formulas in terms of f and g for the graphs below. (Assume x is in radians.)

   (a)
   (b)
   (c)
   (d)

18. Household electrical service in the US is usually provided in the form of *alternating currents* (AC). Typically the voltage alternates smoothly between +110 volts and -110 volts, doing so 60 times per second. Use a cosine function to model a standard household alternating current.

19. Let $f(t) = A\sin(Bt)$ be a trigonometric function. Several values of f are given in Table 5.14.

   TABLE 5.14 *Several values of a trigonometric function*

t	0	2	4	6	8	10
$f(t)$	0	3	0	-3	0	3

   (a) Find a possible formula for $f(t)$.
   (b) Is it possible that more than one trigonometric function could be represented by Table 5.14? If so, find a formula of another such function.

20. A company sells $S(t)$ thousand electric blankets in month t (with $t = 0$ being January). An approximation of this function is given by

$$S(t) \approx 72.25 + 41.5\sin\left(\frac{\pi t}{6} + \frac{\pi}{2}\right).$$

Sketch the graph of this function over one year. Determine the period and amplitude of its graph and explain the practical significance of these quantities.

Chapter 8/ 43

[Handwritten margin notes:]

freq varies 5 times/hr.

low 90   high 230

period: $\frac{1}{5}(60)=12$

$\frac{90+230}{2}=160$

$\frac{2\pi}{B}=12$ $B=\pi/6$

$P=160-70\cos\left(\pi/6\,t\right)$

$115=160-70\cos\left(\pi/6\,t\right)$

$\cos\left(\frac{\pi}{6}\,t\right)=45/70$

$\frac{\pi}{6}\,t=\cos^{-1}(45/70)$

$t=\frac{6}{\pi}\cos^{-1}(45/70)$

$t=1.66$

21. The pressure P (in lbs/ft^2) in a certain pipe varies over time. Five times an hour, the pressure oscillates between a low of 90 to a high of 230 and then back to a low 90. The pressure at $t=0$ is 90.

    (a) Sketch the graph of $P=f(t)$, where t is time in minutes. Label your axes.

    (b) Find a possible formula for $P=f(t)$.

    (c) By graphing $P=f(t)$ for $0\leq t\leq 2$, t in minutes, on a graphing calculator, estimate when the pressure first equals 115 lbs/ft^2.

22. The population of Somerville, Massachusetts from 1920 to 1990 as reported by the U.S. census is given in Table 5.15:

TABLE 5.15

Years since 1920	0	10	20	30	40	50	60	70
Population (in thousands)	93	104	102	102	95	89	77	76

    (a) Graph the population data given in Table 5.15, with time in years on the horizontal axis.

    (b) Based on the data, a researcher decides the population varies in an approximately periodic way with time. Do you agree?

    (c) On your graph, sketch in a sine curve that fits your data as closely as possible. Your sketch should capture the overall trend of the data but need not pass through all the data points. (Hint: Start by choosing a midline.)

    (d) Find a formula for the curve you drew in part (c).

    (e) According to the U.S. census, the population of Somerville in 1910 was 77,236. How well does this agree with your formula?

23. Table 5.16 shows the average daily maximum temperature in degrees Fahrenheit in Boston each month.

    (a) Plot the average daily maximum temperature as a function of the number of months past January.

    (b) What is the amplitude of the function? What is the period?

    (c) Find a trigonometric approximation of this function.

    (d) Use your formula to estimate the daily maximum temperature for October. How well does this answer agree with the data?

Normal Daily Maximum Temperature for Boston,
TABLE 5.16   *Source: Statistical Abstract of the United States*

Month	Jan	Feb	Mar	Apr	May	Jun
Temperature	36.4	37.7	45.0	56.6	67.0	76.6

Month	Jul	Aug	Sep	Oct	Nov	Dec
Temperature	81.8	79.8	72.3	62.5	47.6	35.4

24. Table 5.17 lists the average monthly temperatures in degrees Fahrenheit for the city of Fairbanks, Alaska. The table gives y, the average monthly temperature, as a function of t, the month, where $t=0$ indicates January.

TABLE 5.17   *Average monthly temperature for Fairbanks*

	Jan	Feb	Mar	Apr	May	Jun	Jul	Aug	Sep	Oct	Nov	Dec
t	0	1	2	3	4	5	6	7	8	9	10	11
y	−11.5	−9.5	0.5	18.0	36.9	53.1	61.3	59.9	48.8	31.7	12.2	−3.3

(a)   Plot the data points. On the same graph, draw a curve which fits the data.
(b)   What kind of a function best fits the data? Be specific.
(c)   Find a formula for a function that models the temperature data. Explain how you found your formula. [Note: There are many correct answers.]
(d)   In the southern hemisphere, the times at which summer and winter occur are reversed, relative to the northern hemisphere. Modify your formula from part (c) so that it represents the average monthly temperature for a southern-hemisphere city whose summer and winter temperatures are similar to Fairbanks.

25.   U.S. petroleum imports for the years 1973–1992 are shown in Table 5.18.

TABLE 5.18

Year	BTU's (quadrillion)	Year	BTU's (quadrillion)
1973	14.2	1983	13
1974	14.5	1984	15
1975	14	1985	12
1976	16.5	1986	14
1977	18	1987	16
1978	17	1988	17
1979	17	1989	18
1980	16	1990	17
1981	15	1991	16
1982	14	1992	16

Plot the data on the inteval $73 \leq t \leq 92$ and find a trigonometric function $f(t)$ that approximates the behavior for this data, where t is the number of years since 1900.

26.   A circle of radius 5 is centered at the point $(-6, 7)$. Define $f(\theta)$ as the x-coordinate of the point $P = (x, y)$ on the circle specified by the angle θ (see Figure 5.64). Find a formula for $f(\theta)$.

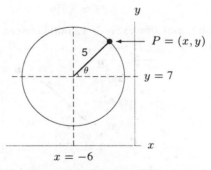

Figure 5.64: The function $f(\theta)$ is defined as the x-coordinate of the point P

27. A flight from La Guardia Airport in New York City to Logan Airport in Boston has to circle Boston several times before landing. Figure 5.65 shows the graph of the distance of the plane from La Guardia as a function of time. Construct a function $f(t)$ whose graph looks like this one. Do this by defining $f(t)$ using different formulas on the intervals $0 \le t \le 1$ and $1 \le t \le 2$.

Figure 5.65: Graph of the distance of the plane from La Guardia

5.6 TRIGONOMETRIC EQUATIONS AND THEIR INVERSES

Solving Trigonometric Equations Graphically

A *trigonometric equation* is an equation that involves trigonometric functions. Using a graphing calculator, we can find approximate solutions to trigonometric equations.

Example 1   Let R be the rabbit population function from Example 7 on page 296. During what months will R exceed 12,000?

Solution   From Figure 5.66, we see that the graph of $R = f(t)$ is above the line $R = 12,000$ between times t_1 and t_2. To find these values, we need to solve the inequality $R > 12,000$. Our approach will be to first solve the equation

$$-5000\cos\left(\frac{\pi}{6}t\right) + 10000 = 12000 \quad \text{for } 0 \le t < 12$$

by looking at a graph.

The first solution, t_1, occurs between the 3rd and 6th months, or between April and July (remember that January is month $t = 0$). The second solution, t_2, occurs somewhere between the 6th and 9th months, or between July and October. Using a computer or a graphing calculator, we can zoom in to give better approximations of t_1 and t_2:

$$t_1 \approx 3.79 \quad \text{and} \quad t_2 \approx 8.21.$$

Thus the rabbit population exceeds 12,000 between late April (month $t = 3$) and early September (month $t = 8$).

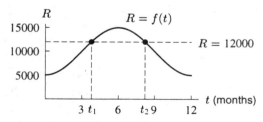

Figure 5.66: The graph of $R = f(t)$, for $0 \le t < 12$, and the line $R = 12,000$

Solving Trigonometric Equations Algebraically

We can try to solve the equation from Example 1 algebraically. Keeping in mind that $0 \le t \le 12$, we have

$$-5000 \cos\left(\frac{\pi}{6}t\right) + 10000 = 12000$$

$$-5000 \cos\left(\frac{\pi}{6}t\right) = 2000$$

$$\cos\left(\frac{\pi}{6}t\right) = -0.4.$$

In order to solve for t, we need to find an angle whose cosine is -0.4. If we could find such an angle, we could write

$$\frac{\pi}{6}t = \text{angle whose cosine is } (-0.4).$$

This means

$$t = \frac{6}{\pi} \cdot [\text{angle whose cosine is } (-0.4)].$$

Thus, in order to complete our solution, we need a way to find angles given cosines. Until we can do this, we will not be able to solve trigonometric equations using algebra alone.

The Inverse Cosine Function

In general, knowing the cosine of an angle is not enough to tell us what the angle is. For example, given the equation

$$\cos\theta = \frac{1}{2}, \quad -2\pi \le \theta \le 2\pi,$$

we see from Figure 5.67 that $\theta = \pi/3$, $\theta = 5\pi/3$, $\theta = -\pi/3$, and $\theta = -5\pi/3$ are all solutions. This means that the cosine function does not have a unique input value for a given output.

Figure 5.67: This function has many input values for each output value

However, if we know one of the angles whose cosine is given, we can find all the others by using reference angles ot the symmetry of the cosine curve. Therefore, we will define a new function that assigns just one angle to each output value of cosine. By convention, we choose these angles from the interval $0 \le t \le \pi$. Thus, our new function has as its inputs values of y between -1 and 1 inclusive (all possible values of $\cos t$), and as outputs it has angles in radians between 0 and π. You can see in Figure 5.68 that these angles are sufficient to account for all values in the range of $\cos t$.

Figure 5.68: The solid portion of this graph represents a function that has only one input value for each output value

This new function "undoes" the effect of the cosine function, so we call it the arc cosine, or inverse cosine, denoted by $\arccos(y)$ or $\cos^{-1}(y)$. We interpret the values of the function $\cos^{-1}(y)$ as "the angle between 0 and π whose cosine is y." Thus, for example,

$$\cos^{-1}\left(\frac{1}{2}\right) = \frac{\pi}{3} \qquad \text{because } \cos\left(\frac{\pi}{3}\right) = \frac{1}{2}, \quad \text{and}$$

$$\cos^{-1}(1) = 0 \qquad \text{because } \cos(0) = 1.$$

Most scientific and graphing calculators have an inverse cosine button that gives the output angle. For example. if you use your calculator (in radian mode) to evaluate $\cos^{-1}(1/2)$, you will find

$$\cos^{-1}\left(\frac{1}{2}\right) \approx 1.047,$$

which is an approximation for $\pi/3$.

We summarize the properties of this new function below.

The **arc cosine function**, also called the **inverse cosine function**, is written either **arccos y** or **cos⁻¹y**. We have

$$\theta = \arccos y \quad \text{provided that} \quad y = \cos\theta \quad \text{and} \quad 0 \le \theta \le \pi.$$

In other words, if $\theta = \arccos y$, then θ is the angle between 0 and π whose cosine is y. Two results of this definition are that $\cos(\cos^{-1} y) = y$ for all values of y between -1 and 1, and that $\cos^{-1}(\cos\theta) = \theta$ for all values of θ between 0 and π.

It is critically important to realize that the notation $\cos^{-1} y$ does not mean the same thing as $(\cos y)^{-1}$. This is because

$$(\cos y)^{-1} = \frac{1}{\cos y},$$

which is not at all the same as the inverse cosine function. The notation $\cos^{-1} y$ is perplexing, especially because it is quite acceptable to write $\cos^2\theta$ when one means $(\cos\theta)^2$.

Using Inverse Cosine To Solve Trigonometric Equations

We now return to the equation $\cos\left(\frac{\pi}{6}t\right) = -0.4$ from page 303. Applying the inverse cosine to both sides of the equation gives

$$\cos^{-1}\left(\cos\left(\frac{\pi}{6}t\right)\right) = \cos^{-1}(-0.4).$$

By definition, $\cos^{-1}(\cos(\frac{\pi}{6}t))$ will equal $\frac{\pi}{6}t$ provided that $\frac{\pi}{6}t$ is between 0 and π. Thus, one solution to this equation is

$$\frac{\pi}{6}t = \cos^{-1}(-0.4) \qquad \text{for } 0 \le \frac{\pi}{6}t \le \pi$$

$$t = \frac{6}{\pi}\cos^{-1}(-0.4),$$

and this is an exact solution. Using a calculator to evaluate $\cos^{-1}(-0.4)$ we see that $t \approx 3.79$. This agrees with the value for t_1 we found graphically. (See Figure 5.66.) But how do we find the second solution, t_2? Notice that the graph of f is symmetric about the line $t = 6$. Figure 5.69 shows that $t_2 = 12 - t_1$. This means that

$$t_2 = 12 - \frac{6}{\pi} \cos^{-1}(-0.4) \approx 8.21.$$

This also agrees with our earlier result.

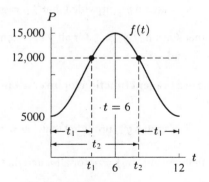

Figure 5.69: By the symmetry of f about the line $t = 6$, we see that $t_2 = 12 - t_1$

Trigonometric Equations May Have Many Solutions

The previous example illustrates an important point: Using the inverse cosine function to solve a trigonometric equation may not give us every possible solution; in fact, it may not give a solution at all. For instance, the equation $P = f(t) = 12{,}000$ has two solutions on the interval $0 \le t \le 12$ but only one of them is given by the inverse cosine function.

The situation is similar to using square roots to solve equations. The equation $x^2 = 9$ has two solutions because 9 has two square roots, 3 and -3. However, using the square root button on our calculator will only provide one of these solutions: $x = \sqrt{9} = +3$. We don't expect the square root button to return both solutions at once. If it did, it would not represent a function.

The Inverse Sine And Inverse Tangent Functions

Having defined the inverse cosine function, we now define the *inverse sine* and *inverse tangent* functions. We face the same difficulty we faced with the inverse cosine function: No periodic function has a unique input value for a given output. Therefore, we use the same technique we used for the inverse cosine function and look for ways to restrict the domains of the sine and tangent so that they become invertible.

For $y = \sin t$, we see that we cannot choose the same interval that we chose for $\cos \theta$, which was $0 \le t \le \pi$. However, the interval $-\pi/2 \le t \le \pi/2$ includes a unique angle for each value of $\sin t$ between -1 and 1, as you can see in Figure 5.70. The interval $-\pi/2 \le t \le \pi/2$ also works for $y = \tan t$, as illustrated in Figure 5.71.

Figure 5.70: The graph of $y = \sin \theta$, $-\frac{\pi}{2} \le \theta \le \frac{\pi}{2}$

Figure 5.71: The graph of $y = \tan \theta$, $-\frac{\pi}{2} < \theta < \frac{\pi}{2}$

We define the **arc sine function** (or **inverse sine function**), written **arcsin** y or **sin^{-1}y**, as follows:

$$\theta = \arcsin y \quad \text{provided that} \quad y = \sin\theta \quad \text{and} \quad -\frac{\pi}{2} \leq \theta \leq \frac{\pi}{2}.$$

This means that $\sin(\sin^{-1} y) = y$ for all y between -1 and 1, and that $\sin^{-1}(\sin\theta) = \theta$ for all θ between $-\frac{\pi}{2}$ and $\frac{\pi}{2}$.

We define the **arc tangent function** (or **inverse tangent function**), written **arctan** y or **tan^{-1}y**, as follows:

$$\theta = \arctan y \quad \text{provided that} \quad y = \tan\theta \quad \text{and} \quad -\frac{\pi}{2} < \theta < \frac{\pi}{2}.$$

This means that $\tan(\tan^{-1} y) = y$ for all y and that $\tan^{-1}(\tan\theta) = \theta$ for all θ between $-\frac{\pi}{2}$ and $\frac{\pi}{2}$.

Example 2   Evaluate $\arctan(-1)$.

Solution   By definition, $\arctan(-1)$ is the angle between $-\pi/2$ and $\pi/2$ whose tangent is -1. Thinking of tangent in terms of slope, we need to find an angle between $-\pi/2$ and $\pi/2$ corresponding to a slope of $m = -1$. The line $y = -x$ has this slope, and it makes a $-45°$ angle with the x-axis or, in radians, an angle of $-\pi/4$. Thus, $\tan(-\pi/4) = -1$, and since $-\pi/4$ is between $-\pi/2$ and $\pi/2$, we have $\arctan(-1) = -\pi/4$.

Example 3   While riding the ferris wheel, how much time do you spend during the first turn at a height of 400 feet or more?

Solution   Since your first turn takes 20 minutes, and since your height is given by $f(t) = 250 + 250\sin\left(\frac{\pi}{10}t - \frac{\pi}{2}\right)$, we must solve the inequality

$$250 + 250\sin\left(\frac{\pi}{10}t - \frac{\pi}{2}\right) \geq 400 \qquad \text{for } 0 \leq t \leq 20.$$

This can be simplified as follows:

$$250\sin\left(\frac{\pi}{10}t - \frac{\pi}{2}\right) \geq 150$$

$$\sin\left(\frac{\pi}{10}t - \frac{\pi}{2}\right) \geq \frac{3}{5}.$$

From Figure 5.72, we see that the equation $\sin\left(\frac{\pi}{10}t - \frac{\pi}{2}\right) = \frac{3}{5}$ has two solutions on the interval $0 \leq t \leq 20$. One of them can be found by using the arcsine function:

$$\frac{\pi}{10}t - \frac{\pi}{2} = \arcsin\frac{3}{5}$$

$$\frac{\pi}{10}t = \frac{\pi}{2} + \arcsin\frac{3}{5}$$

$$t = \frac{10}{\pi}\left(\frac{\pi}{2} + \arcsin\frac{3}{5}\right) \approx 7.05.$$

The other solution can be found by symmetry to be $20 - 7.05 = 12.95$ minutes. Thus, you spend $12.95 - 7.05 = 5.9$ minutes at a height of 400 feet or more.

Figure 5.72: The ferris wheel at $t = 7.05$ minutes and $t = 12.95$ minutes

---

Problems for Section 5.6

1. A biologist is studying the fox population in the national park where the rabbit population was described by Example 1 on page 302. She finds that F, the number of foxes in the park, is a function of t, the number of months elapsed since January. Her data indicates that

    $$F = g(t) = 350 - 200 \sin\left(\frac{\pi t}{6}\right).$$

    (a) Prepare a graph of $F = g(t)$ for a two-year period. Interpret the meaning of the period, the amplitude, and the midline of your graph.

    (b) The biologist believes that the park's rabbit population supplies the fox population with its principal source of food. Compare the graph of fox population to the graph of rabbit population from Example 1 on page 302. Are these graphs consistent with her theory? Discuss.

2. Approximate the x-coordinates of points P and Q shown in Figure 5.73, assuming that the curve is a sine curve. (Hint: find a formula for the curve.)

Figure 5.73

3. A company's sales are seasonal with the peak in mid-December and the lowest point in mid-June. The company makes \$100,000 in sales in December, and only \$20,000 in June.

    (a) Find a trigonometric equation for $s = f(t)$, the dollar sales at any time t months after mid-January.

    (b) What would you expect the sales to be for mid-April?

    (c) Find the t value for which $s(t) = 60,000$. Interpret your answer.

4. In a tidal river, the time between high tide and low tide is 6.2 hours. At high tide the depth of the water is 17.2 feet, while at low tide the depth is 5.6 feet. Assuming the water depth is a trigonometric function of time,

    (a) Sketch a graph of the depth of the water over time if there is a high tide at 12:00 noon. Label your graph, indicating the high and low tide.
    (b) Write an equation for the curve you drew in part (a).
    (c) If a boat requires a depth of 8 feet to sail, and is docked at 12:00 noon, what is the latest time in the afternoon it can set sail? Your answer should be accurate to the nearest minute.

5. Evaluate the following expressions in radians:

    (a) arcsin(0.5)   (b) arccos(−1)   (c) arcsin(0.1)

6. In your own words explain what each of the following expressions means, and evaluate each expression for $x = 0.5$.

    (a) $\sin^{-1} x$ (b) $\sin(x^{-1})$ (c) $(\sin x)^{-1}$.

7. Let
$$f(t) = 3 - 5\sin(4t), \qquad 0 \le t < \frac{\pi}{2}.$$

    (a) Approximate the zero(s) of f graphically.
    (b) Using the arcsin function, write a solution(s) of $3 - 5\sin 4t = 0$ on the interval $0 \le t \le \pi/2$.

8. Solve $5\sin(2t + 1) = 3$ on the interval $0 \le t \le \pi$.
9. For what value(s) of θ does $\sin\theta = \frac{3}{4}, 0 \le \theta \le \pi$?
10. Solve the first equation exactly on the indicated interval. For the second equation give an approximate solution in degrees correct to 3 decimal places.

    (a) $\tan\theta = 1, -\frac{\pi}{2} < \theta < \frac{\pi}{2}$
    (b) $\sin\theta = 0.95, -360° \le \theta \le 0°$

11. Solve the inequality $\sin(2x) \le 0.3$ with $-1 \le x \le 3$.
12. One of the following statements is always true; the other can be true sometimes and false sometimes. Which is which? Justify your answer with an example.

    I. $\arcsin(\sin t) = t$ II. $\sin(\arcsin y) = y$

13. Solve the following equations for t, assuming that t is between 0 and 2π. First obtain approximate answers from a graph, and then find exact answers.

    (a) $\cos(2t) = \frac{1}{2}$ (b) $\tan t = \frac{1}{\tan t}$
    (c) $2\sin t \cos t - \cos t = 0$ (d) $3\cos^2 t = \sin^2 t$

14. Suppose that a is a number with $0 \le a \le \pi/2$. Suppose $b = \pi + a$.

    (a) What is $\arccos(\cos a)$?   (b) What is $\arccos(\cos b)$?

15. Use your calculator to find $\cos^{-1}(\cos x)$ for $x = 1, 2, 3, 4, 5, 6, 7$ radians. Explain your results.

16. Mark each of the following statements true or false.

    (a) For all angles θ in radians, $\arccos(\cos\theta) = \theta$.
    (b) For all values of x between -1 and 1, $\cos(\arccos x) = x$.

(c) If $\tan A = \tan B$, then $\dfrac{A-B}{\pi}$ is an integer.

(d) $\cos A = \cos B$ implies that $\sin A = \sin B$.

17. For each of the following statements, write *true* if the statement must be true, *false* otherwise.

(a) One solution of $3e^t \sin t - 2e^t \cos t = 0$ is $t = \arctan(\frac{2}{3})$.

(b) $0 \le \cos^{-1}(\sin(\cos^{-1} x)) \le \frac{\pi}{2}$ for all x in the domain of $\cos^{-1} x$.

(c) If $a > b > 0$, then the domain of $f(t) = \ln(a + b \sin t)$ is all real numbers t.

(d) For all $t \le 0$, $\cos(e^t) + \sin(e^t) \le \sin 1$.

18. The planet Betagorp travels around its sun, Trigosol, in an elliptical orbit. The distance of Betagorp from Trigosol at time θ is given by

$$r = \frac{5.35 \times 10^7}{1 - 0.234 \cos \theta}.$$

Find the least positive θ (in decimal degrees to 3 significant digits) so that Betagorp is 5.12×10^7 miles from Trigosol.

19. Let k be a positive constant, and t be an angle measured in radians.

(a) Explain why any solution to the equation

$$k \sin t = t^2$$

must be between $-\sqrt{k}$ and $\sqrt{k}$ (inclusive).

(b) Approximate every solution to the above equation when $k = 2$.

(c) Explain why the equation has more solutions for larger values of k than it does for small values.

(d) Approximate the least value of k, if any, for which the above equation has a negative solution.

5.7 TRIGONOMETRIC IDENTITIES

Equations Versus Identities

Consider the equation and solve for x:

$$(x - 1)^2 = x^2 - 1$$
$$x^2 - 2x + 1 = x^2 - 1$$
$$x = 1$$

This equation is not true for all x and is only true for $x = 1$. Now consider the equation

$$(x - 1)^2 = x^2 - 2x + 1$$
$$x^2 - 2x + 1 = x^2 - 2x + 1.$$

Since the left and right sides of the equation are identical, we can see that the equation is true for all x.

An equation that is true for all values of x is called an *identity*. By graphing $f(x) = (x - 1)^2$ and $g(x) = x^2 - 1$ from the first equation, we would see the graphs intersect in one point and not in others. In the second equation letting the right-hand side be $h(x) = x^2 - 2x + 1$, and graphing $f(x)$ and $h(x)$, we would see that the graphs are identical.

There are many identities involving trigonometric functions. For example; from Figure 5.74 we see that by shifting the graph of $y = \cos t$ to the right by $\frac{\pi}{2}$ units, we obtain the graph of $y = \sin t$. This means that

$$\sin t = \cos\left(t - \frac{\pi}{2}\right) \qquad \text{for all } t.$$

Similarly, by shifting the graph of $\sin t$ to the left by $\frac{\pi}{2}$, we obtain the graph of $y = \cos t$. Thus,

$$\cos t = \sin\left(t + \frac{\pi}{2}\right) \qquad \text{for all } t.$$

These two equations are examples of trigonometric identities because they hold true for all values of t.

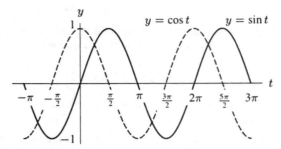

Figure 5.74: The graph of $y = \sin(t)$ (solid line) can be obtained by shifting the graph of $y = \cos t$ (dashed line) $\frac{\pi}{2}$ to the right

Negative-Angle Identities

Because the cosine is an even function whose graph is symmetric across the y-axis, $\cos(-t) = \cos t$. Similarly, because the sine and tangent are odd functions whose graphs are symmetric across the origin, $\sin(-t) = -\sin t$ and $\tan(-t) = -\tan t$. These formulas are called the *negative-angle identities*.

The Pythagorean Identity

We will now derive the most important identity in all of trigonometry, the *Pythagorean Identity*. By definition of sine and cosine, we have

$$\sin\theta = y \qquad \text{and} \qquad \cos\theta = x,$$

where x and y are the coordinates of the point on the unit circle specified by the angle θ. (See Figure 5.75.) Thinking of x and y as the legs of a right triangle which has a hypotenuse of length 1, the Pythagorean theorem tells us that

$$x^2 + y^2 = 1.$$

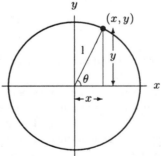

Figure 5.75: By definition, $\sin\theta = y$ and $\cos\theta = x$

Example 1   But since $x = \cos\theta$ and $y = \sin\theta$, this gives us

$$(\cos\theta)^2 + (\sin\theta)^2 = 1.$$

This is the Pythagorean Identity. By convention, we write $\cos^2\theta$ for $(\cos\theta)^2$ and $\sin^2\theta$ for $(\sin\theta)^2$. Using this notation, the Pythagorean identity becomes

$$\cos^2\theta + \sin^2\theta = 1.$$

Suppose t is an angle in the third quadrant and that $\cos(t) = -0.21$. What is $\sin t$? What is $\tan t$?

Solution   We have

$$\sin^2 t + \cos^2 t = 1$$
$$\sin^2 t + (-0.21)^2 = 1$$
$$(\sin t)^2 = 0.96$$
$$\sin t = -0.98$$

Notice that since t is in the third quadrant, the value of $\sin t$ is negative. We also have

$$\tan t = \frac{\sin t}{\cos t} = \frac{-0.98}{-0.21} = 4.67.$$

Example 2   The expression $\cos^2(\arcsin t)$ occurs during an important derivation in calculus. Simplify this expression.

Solution   Letting $z = \arcsin t$, this expression becomes $\cos^2 z$. We know that

$$\sin^2 z + \cos^2 z = 1,$$

and so we have

$$\cos^2 z = 1 - \sin^2 z.$$

Substituting back in for z gives

$$\cos^2(\arcsin t) = 1 - \sin^2(\arcsin t),$$

which can be rewritten as

$$\cos^2(\arcsin t) = 1 - [\sin(\arcsin t)]^2.$$

But we know that $\sin(\arcsin t) = t$, and so

$$\cos^2(\arcsin t) = 1 - t^2.$$

Other Ways of Writing The Pythagorean Identity

The Pythagorean identity can take many different forms. For example, assuming $\cos t \neq 0$, we can divide both sides of the identity by $\cos^2 t$, giving

$$\frac{\sin^2 t + \cos^2 t}{\cos^2 t} = \frac{1}{\cos^2 t}.$$

We can simplify this by writing

$$\frac{\sin^2 t}{\cos^2 t} + \frac{\cos^2 t}{\cos^2 t} = \frac{1}{\cos^2 t}$$

$$\left(\frac{\sin t}{\cos t}\right)^2 + 1 = \left(\frac{1}{\cos t}\right)^2 \quad (\text{for } \cos t \neq 0).$$

Since $\tan t = \frac{\sin t}{\cos t}$, we can write

$$\tan^2 t + 1 = \frac{1}{\cos^2 t} \quad (\text{for } \cos t \neq 0).$$

Similarly, dividing the initial identity by $\sin^2 t$, we get,

$$1 + \cot^2 t = \frac{1}{\sin^2 t} \quad (\text{for } \sin t \neq 0).$$

Although this is a new identity, it follows directly from the initial statement $\cos^2 t + \sin^2 t = 1$.

Double-Angle Formulas

The Double-Angle Formula for Sine

We will now find a formula for $\sin 2\theta$ in terms of $\sin \theta$ and $\cos \theta$. First, note that $\sin 2\theta$ is not the same as $2 \sin \theta$. For one thing, the graph of $y = \sin 2\theta$ has a different period and amplitude than the graph of $y = 2 \sin \theta$.

Figure 5.76 gives the unit circle together with the angles θ and 2θ. It also gives the triangle EOB. In Figure 5.77 consider the triangles $\triangle AOC$ and $\triangle DOB$, which are both isosceles with two sides equal to 1 and an angle of 2θ at the origin. They are congruent and thus have equal areas.

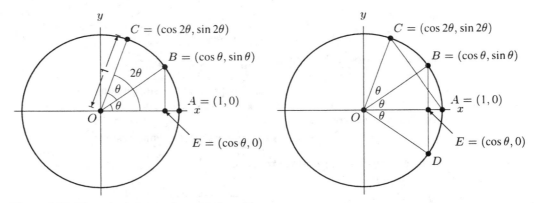

Figure 5.76: The unit circle together with the angles θ and 2θ

Figure 5.77

Figure 5.76 shows that triangle EOB has base $\cos\theta$ and height $\sin\theta$. Thus, its area is $\frac{1}{2}\sin\theta\cos\theta$. The area of ΔDOB is twice the area of ΔEOB so its area is $\sin\theta\cos\theta$. Thus, the area of ΔAOC is also $\sin\theta\cos\theta$. But, since the y-coordinate of point C is $\sin2\theta$, the height of ΔAOC is $\sin2\theta$, and so its area is $\frac{1}{2}(1)(\sin2\theta)$ (since its base has length 1). This means that the area of ΔAOC can be written in two different ways: $\frac{1}{2}\sin2\theta$ and $\sin\theta\cos\theta$. Thus

$$\frac{1}{2}\sin2\theta = \sin\theta\cos\theta$$

so

$$\sin2\theta = 2\sin\theta\cos\theta.$$

This identity is known as the *double-angle formula for sine*.

The Double-Angle Formula for Cosine

There is also a *double-angle formula for cosine*. By the Pythagorean identity, we have $(\cos2t)^2 + (\sin2t)^2 = 1$. Thus,

$$(\cos2t)^2 = 1 - (\sin2t)^2.$$

If we apply the double-angle formula for sine, we obtain

$$(\cos2t)^2 = 1 - (2\sin t\cos t)^2 = 1 - 4\sin^2 t\cos^2 t \quad \text{(because } \sin 2t = 2\sin t\cos t\text{).}$$

But by the Pythagorean identity we have $\cos^2 t = 1 - \sin^2 t$, and so

$$\begin{aligned}
(\cos2t)^2 &= 1 - 4\sin^2 t(1 - \sin^2 t)\\
&= 1 - 4\sin^2 t + 4\sin^4 t\\
&= (1 - 2\sin^2 t)^2 \quad \text{(after factoring).}
\end{aligned}$$

Taking the square root of both sides and checking for the correct sign, we get

$$\cos2t = 1 - 2\sin^2 t.$$

We can find two other ways to write $\cos2t$. We know that

$$\begin{aligned}
\cos2t &= 1 - 2\sin^2 t\\
&= 1 - 2(1 - \cos^2 t) \quad \text{(by the Pythagorean Identity)}\\
&= 2\cos^2 t - 1.
\end{aligned}$$

Similarly,

$$\begin{aligned}
\cos2t &= 1 - 2\sin^2 t\\
&= (\sin^2 t + \cos^2 t) - 2\sin^2 t \quad \text{(by the Pythagorean Identity)}\\
&= \cos^2 t - \sin^2 t.
\end{aligned}$$

The **double-angle formula for sine** is

$$\sin2t = 2\sin t\cos t.$$

The **double-angle formula for cosine** is usually written in one of three different ways:

$$\begin{aligned}
\cos2t &= \cos^2 t - \sin^2 t\\
&= 2\cos^2 t - 1\\
&= 1 - 2\sin^2 t.
\end{aligned}$$

Using Identities to Solve Trigonometric Equations

Sometimes we can use trigonometric identities to solve equations.

Example 3   Find all solutions to

$$\sin 2t = \sin t, \text{ for } 0 \le t \le 2\pi.$$

Solution   Writing $\sin 2t$ as $2 \sin t \cos t$, we have

$$2 \sin t \cos t = \sin t$$
$$2 \sin t \cos t - \sin t = 0$$
$$\sin t (2 \cos t - 1) = 0 \qquad \text{(factoring out } \sin t \text{)}.$$

Thus,

$$\sin t = 0 \quad \text{or} \quad 2 \cos t - 1 = 0.$$

Now, $\sin t = 0$ for $t = 0$, π, and 2π. We can solve the second equation by writing

$$2 \cos t - 1 = 0$$
$$2 \cos t = 1$$
$$\cos t = \frac{1}{2}.$$

We know that $\cos t = \frac{1}{2}$ for $t = \frac{\pi}{3}$ and $t = \frac{5\pi}{3}$. Thus there are five solutions to the original equation on the interval $0 \le t \le 2\pi$: They are $t = 0, \pi/3, \pi, 5\pi/3$, and 2π. Figure 5.78 illustrates these solutions graphically as the points where the graphs of $\sin(2t)$ and $\sin t$ intersect.

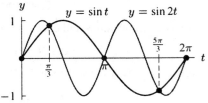

Figure 5.78: There are five solutions to the equation $\sin 2t = \sin t$, for $0 \le t \le 2\pi$

Example 4   Solve $3 \sin^2 t = 5 - 5 \cos t$ for $0 \le t \le \pi$.

Solution   To solve this equation algebraically, we want to write it entirely in terms of $\sin t$ or entirely in terms of $\cos t$. Since $\sin^2 t = 1 - \cos^2 t$, we convert to $\cos t$, giving

$$3(1 - \cos^2 t) = 5 - 5 \cos t$$
$$3 - 3 \cos^2 t = 5 - 5 \cos t$$
$$3 \cos^2 t - 5 \cos t + 2 = 0.$$

The left-hand side can be factored to give

$$(3 \cos t - 2)(\cos t - 1) = 0,$$

and so we have $3 \cos t - 2 = 0$ or $\cos t - 1 = 0$. This gives $\cos t = 1$, which is true for $t = 0$, and $\cos t = \frac{2}{3}$, which is true for $t = \cos^{-1} \frac{2}{3}$. Note that both solutions fall on the interval $0 \le t \le \pi$. We could also solve the equation by graphing $y = 3(\sin t)^2$ and $y = 5 - 5 \cos t$ and finding the points of intersection for $0 \le t \le \pi$.

A summary of the identities in this section:

- The **Pythagorean Identity** (expressed in three different ways):

$$\sin^2 t + \cos^2 t = 1$$

$$\tan^2 t + 1 = \frac{1}{\cos^2 t} \quad \text{for } \cos t \neq 0$$

$$\cot^2 t + 1 = \frac{1}{\sin^2 t} \quad \text{for } \sin t \neq 0$$

- The **double-angle formula for sine**:

$$\sin 2t = 2 \sin t \cos t$$

- The **double-angle formula for cosine** (expressed in three different ways):

$$\cos 2t = 1 - 2 \sin^2 t$$
$$\cos 2t = 2 \cos^2 t - 1$$
$$\cos 2t = \cos^2 t - \sin^2 t$$

- **Negative angle identities**:

$$\sin(-t) = -\sin t$$
$$\cos(-t) = \cos t$$
$$\tan(-t) = -\tan t$$

- **Identities relating sine and cosine**:

$$\sin t = \cos(t - \frac{\pi}{2})$$
$$\cos t = \sin(t + \frac{\pi}{2})$$

Problems for Section 5.7

1. Use a trigonometric identity to find all the exact solutions to the following equations on the indicated intervals.

   (a) $\cos 2\theta + \cos \theta = 0, \quad 0 \leq \theta < 360°$
   (b) $2 \cos^2 \theta = 3 \sin \theta + 3, \quad 0 \leq \theta \leq 2\pi$

2. Which of the following expressions are algebraically identical?

   (a) $2 \cos^2 t + \sin t + 1$ (b) $\cos^2 t$ (c) $\dfrac{\left(\dfrac{1}{\cos t} - 1\right)}{1 - \cos t}$

   (d) $\dfrac{1 + \cos(2t)}{2}$ (e) $2 \sin t \cos t$ (f) $\cos^2 t - \sin^2 t$

   (g) $\sin(2t)$ (h) $\sin(3t)$ (i) $-2 \sin^2 t + \sin t + 3$

   (j) $\dfrac{1 - \sin t}{\sin t}$ (k) $1 - 2 \sin^2 t$ (l) $\cos(2t)$

   (m) $\sin(2t) \cos t + \cos(2t) \sin t$

16
3
$4\sqrt{3}$

3. Verify the following identities.

   (a) $\dfrac{\sin t}{1 - \cos t} = \dfrac{1 + \cos t}{\sin t}$

   (b) $\dfrac{\cos x}{1 - \sin x} - \tan x = \dfrac{1}{\cos x}$

   (c) $\dfrac{\sin x \cos y + \cos x \sin y}{\cos x \cos y - \sin x \sin y} = \dfrac{\tan x + \tan y}{1 - \tan x \tan y}$

4. Complete the following table, using exact values where possible. State the trigonometric identities that relate the quantities in the table, and verify these identities numerically.

θ in rad.	$\sin^2 \theta$	$\cos^2 \theta$	$\sin 2\theta$	$\cos 2\theta$
1				
$\pi/2$				
2				
$5\pi/6$				

5. Describe the similarities and differences between $y = \cos(2x)$ and $y = \cos(x^2)$.

6. Write a memo to a classmate describing what your graphing calculator draws for each of the following:

   (a) $y = \sin x^2$ (b) $y = (\sin x)^2$ (c) $y = \sin^2 x$

7. Simplify the expression
$$(\cos(2\theta))^2 + (\sin(2\theta))^2.$$

8. Suppose $\sin \theta = \frac{1}{7}$ for $\frac{\pi}{2} < \theta < \pi$.

   (a) Use the Pythagorean identity to find $\cos \theta$.

   (b) What is θ?

9. Find an identity for $\cos(4\theta)$ in terms of $\cos \theta$. (You need not simplify your answer.)

10. Use trigonometric identities to find an identity for $\sin(4\theta)$ in terms of $\sin \theta$ and $\cos \theta$.

11. Use the identity $\cos 2x = 2 \cos^2 x - 1$ to find an expression for $\cos(\frac{\theta}{2})$, assuming $0 \le \theta \le \frac{\pi}{2}$. Do this by letting $x = \frac{\theta}{2}$, and then finding an expression for $\cos x$ in terms of $\cos(2x)$.

12. Let x be the side adjacent to the angle θ, $0 < \theta < \frac{\pi}{4}$, in a right triangle whose hypotenuse is 1. (See Figure 5.79.) Express the following functions in terms of x.

    (a) $\cos \theta$ (b) $\cos(\frac{\pi}{2} - \theta)$ (c) $\tan^2 \theta$

    (d) $\sin(2\theta)$ (e) $\cos(4\theta)$ (f) $\sin(\cos^{-1} x)$

Figure 5.79: Triangle for Problem 12

13. Find the range for each of the following functions.

(a) $y = \arccos x$

(b) $y = \dfrac{3}{2 - \cos x}$

(c) $y = \sin\left(\dfrac{1}{1 + x^2}\right)$

(d) $y = 4 \sin x \cos x$

(e) $y = 3^{3+\sin x}$

14. The identity $\sin^2 x + \cos^2 x = 1$ can be used to eliminate radicals from algebraic expressions. For example, suppose the function $f(x) = \sqrt{4 - x^2}$ appears in an application. We can transform the formula $f(x)$ by making the substitution $x = 2 \sin u$. Begin by observing that

$$4 - x^2 = 4 - (2 \sin u)^2 = 4 - 4\sin^2 u = 4(1 - \sin^2 u) = 4\cos^2 u.$$

This means that

$$f(x) = \sqrt{4 - x^2} = \sqrt{4\cos^2 u} = 2|\cos u| = 2\left|\cos\left(\sin^{-1}\left(\frac{x}{2}\right)\right)\right|,$$

since $u = \sin^{-1}\left(\dfrac{x}{2}\right)$. Notice that the choice of 2 in $x = 2\sin u$ comes from $2 = \sqrt{4}$.

(a) Rewrite $f(x) = \sqrt{9 - x^2}$ in a form which does not use a radical.

(b) Rewrite $g(x) = \sqrt{5 - x^2}$ in a form which does not use a radical.

5.8 MODELS INVOLVING TRIGONOMETRIC FUNCTIONS

Sums Of Trigonometric Functions

In this section we will consider models involving trigonometric functions. The first model we consider involves sums of trigonometric functions.

Example 1   A utility company serves two different cities. Let P_1 be the power requirements in megawatts (MW) for city 1, and P_2 be the requirements for city 2. Both P_1 and P_2 are functions of t, the number of hours elapsed since midnight. Suppose P_1 and P_2 are described by the following formulas:

$$P_1 = f_1(t) = 40 - 15\cos\left(\frac{\pi}{12}t\right)$$

$$P_2 = f_2(t) = 50 + 10\sin\left(\frac{\pi}{12}t\right).$$

(a) Describe the power requirements of both cities in words.

(b) What is the maximum total power the utility company must be prepared to provide?

Solution   (a) The power requirements of city 1 are at a minimum of $40 - 15 = 25$ MW at $t = 0$, or midnight. They rise to a maximum of $40 + 15 = 55$ MW by noon and then fall back to a minimum of 25 MW by the following midnight. The power requirements of city 2 are at a maximum of 60 MW at 6 am. They fall to a minimum of 40 MW by 6 pm but by the following morning have climbed back to 60 MW, again at 6 am. Figure 5.80 gives graphs of P_1 and P_2 over a two-day period.

Figure 5.80: Power requirements in megawatts for cities 1 and 2 over a 48 hour period

Figure 5.81: Total power demand for a 48 hour period

(b)   The utility company must provide enough power at any given time to satisfy the needs of both cities. The total power required by both cities, we have

$$T = g(t) = f_1(t) + f_2(t).$$

Figure 5.81 gives a graph of g for $0 \le t \le 48$. From the graph, g appears to be a periodic function. In fact, it appears to be a trigonometric function. It varies between about 108 MW and 72 MW, giving it an amplitude of roughly 18 MW. A formula for T in terms of t is given by

$$T = P_1 + P_2$$
$$= 90 + 10 \sin\left(\frac{\pi}{12}t\right) - 15 \cos\left(\frac{\pi}{12}t\right).$$

Since the maximum value of T is about 108, the utility company must be prepared to provide at least this much power at all times.

Since the maximum value of P_1 is 55 and the maximum value of P_2 is 60, you might expect that the maximum value of T would be $55 + 60 = 115$. The reason that this isn't true is that the maximum values of P_1 and P_2 occur at different times. However, the midline of T appears to be a horizontal line at 90, which does equal the height of the midline of P_1 plus the height of the midline of P_2. Finally, the period of T is 24 hours because the values of both P_1 and P_2 begin repeating after 24 hours so their sum repeats that frequently as well.

It is not always true that a sum of sine or cosine functions will appear to be a simple trigonometric function, as we see in the next example.

Example 2   Sketch and describe the graph of $y = \sin 2x + \sin 3x$.

Solution   From Figure 5.82, we can see that the function $y = \sin 2x + \sin 3x$ is not a simple trigonometric function. It is, however, a periodic function. Its period seems to be 2π as it repeats twice on the interval shown.

This function has a period of 2π because the period of $\sin 2x$ is π and the period of $\sin 3x$ is $\frac{2\pi}{3}$. Thus, on any interval of length 2π, the function $y = \sin 2x$ will complete 2 cycles and the function $y = \sin 3x$ will complete 3 cycles. Both functions will be at the beginning of a new cycle after an interval of 2π so their sum will begin to repeat at this point. (See Figure 5.83.) Notice one more thing: even though the maximum value of each of the functions $\sin 2x$ and $\sin 3x$ is 1, the maximum value of their sum is not 2; it is a little less than 2. This is because $\sin 2x$ and $\sin 3x$ achieve their maximum values for different x values.

Figure 5.82: A graph of $y = \sin 2x + \sin 3x$,
$0 \le x \le 4\pi$

Figure 5.83: The graphs of $y = \sin 2x$ and
$y = \sin 3x$ on an interval of 2π

Damped Oscillation

In Problems 11–14 in Section 5.1, we considered the motion of a weight attached to the ceiling by a spring. We imagined that if the weight were disturbed, it would begin bobbing up and down, and we modeled the weight's motion using a trigonometric function.

Figure 5.84 shows a weight at rest suspended from the ceiling by a spring. Suppose d is the displacement in centimeters from the weight's at-rest position. For instance, if $d = 5$ then the weight is 5 cm above its at-rest position; if $d = -5$, then the weight is 5 cm below its at-rest position.

Imagine that you raised the weight 5 cm above its at-rest position and released it at time $t = 0$. Suppose the weight bobbed up and down once every second for the first few seconds. We could model this behavior with the function given by the formula

$$d = f(t) = 5\cos(2\pi t)$$

where t is in seconds. One full cycle is completed each second, so the period P is 1, and the amplitude is 5. Figure 5.85 gives a graph of d for the first 3 seconds of the weight's motion.

Our trigonometric model of the spring's motion is flawed, however, because it predicts that the weight will bob up and down forever. In fact, we know that as time passes, the "amplitude" of the bobbing will diminish and that eventually the weight will come to rest. How can we fix our formula so that it models this kind of behavior? Our formula $d = f(t) = 5\cos(2\pi t)$ does get one thing right — the weight's position oscillates over time, once every second. Whatever we do, we do not want to change the formula in a way that removes the oscillatory behavior. What we would like to have is a formula which models the oscillations but with an amplitude which decreases over time in a realistic way.

For example, we might imagine that the amplitude of our spring's motion decreases at a constant rate, so that after 5 seconds, the weight stops moving. In other words, we could imagine that the amplitude is a decreasing linear function of time. Using A to represent the amplitude, this would mean that $A = 5$ at $t = 0$, and that $A = 0$ at $t = 5$. Thus, $A(t) = 5 - t$, as you can check for yourself. Instead of writing

Figure 5.84: The quantity d measures the weight's displacement from its at-rest position $d = 0$

Figure 5.85: The predicted motion of the weight for the first 3 seconds

$$d = f(t) = \underbrace{\text{constant amplitude}}_{5} \cos 2\pi t,$$

we could write

$$d = f(t) = \underbrace{\text{decreasing amplitude}}_{(5-t)} \cos 2\pi t$$

so that our formula becomes

$$d = f(t) = (5 - t) \cdot \cos 2\pi t.$$

A graph of this function is given in Figure 5.86.

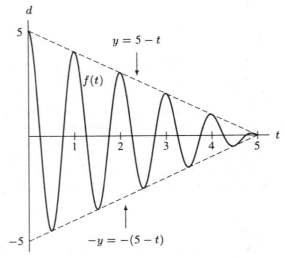

Figure 5.86: A graph of the weight's displacement
assuming that the amplitude is a decreasing linear function
of time

While the function $d = f(t) = (5 - t) \cos 2\pi t$ provides a better model for the behavior of the spring for $0 \le t \le 5$, Figure 5.87 shows that this model does not work for $t > 5$. The breakdown in the model occurs because $A(t) = 5 - t$ starts to *increase* in magnitude when t grows larger than 5.

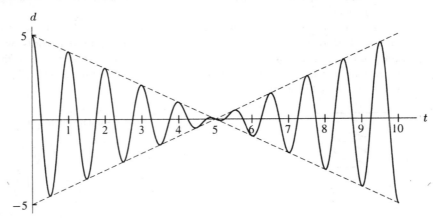

Figure 5.87: The formula $d = f(t) = (5 - t) \cos 2\pi t$ makes inaccurate predictions for
values of t larger than 5

To improve our model, we would like to keep the idea of representing the amplitude as a decreasing function of time, but be more selective about which decreasing function we pick. The problem with our linear function $A(t) = 5 - t$ is two-fold. It approaches zero too abruptly, and, once attaining zero, it becomes increasingly negative. Therefore, we would like to represent our amplitude by a function that approaches zero gradually and does not become negative.

Let's try using a decreasing exponential function. To do this, let's suppose that we carefully measure the amplitude of the spring's motion and find that it is halved each second. Since at $t = 0$ the amplitude is 5, the amplitude at time t would be given by

$$A(t) = 5\left(\frac{1}{2}\right)^t.$$

Thus, a formula for the spring's motion would be

$$d = f(t) = \underbrace{5\left(\frac{1}{2}\right)^t}_{\text{decreasing amplitude}} \cos 2\pi t.$$

Figure 5.88 gives a graph of this formula. The dashed curves in Figure 5.88 show the decreasing exponential function used to represent the amplitude. (There are two curves, $y = 5(\frac{1}{2})^t$ and $y = -5(\frac{1}{2})^t$, because the amplitude measures distance either above or below the midline.)

Figure 5.88 predicts that the weight's oscillations will diminish gradually, so that at time $t = 5$ the weight will still be oscillating slightly. To see this, consider Figure 5.89 which gives a graph of $d = f(t)$ between 5 seconds and 10 seconds. As you can see, the weight continues to make small oscillations long after 5 seconds have elapsed.

In general, a function of the form

$$y = A_0 e^{-kt} \cos(Bt) + C$$

or

$$y = A_0 e^{-kt} \sin(Bt) + C$$

can be used to model an oscillating quantity whose amplitude decreases exponentially. Note A_0, B, and C are constants. Here, A_0 is the initial amplitude, and the amplitude changes with time according to $A(t) = A_0 e^{-kt}$. Notice that in general equations the exponential function would be expressed using e as the base.

Figure 5.88: A graph of the weight's displacement assuming that the amplitude is a decreasing exponential function of time

Figure 5.89: This graph shows that the weight is still oscillating for $t \geq 5$, but with extremely small oscillations. Note the reduced scale on the d-axis

Oscillation With A Rising Midline

In the next example, we consider an oscillating quantity which does not have a horizontal midline, but whose amplitude of oscillation is in some sense constant.

Example 3   In Section 5.5, Example 7 we considered a rabbit population which was undergoing seasonal size fluctuations. We modeled this population by the function

$$P = f(t) = 10{,}000 - 5{,}000\cos\left(\frac{\pi}{6}t\right),$$

where $P(t)$ is the size of the rabbit population t months after January. Figure 5.90 gives a graph of the rabbit population over a five–year period. We see that the rabbit population varies periodically about the midline $y = 10{,}000$. We can say that the average number of rabbits is 10,000, but that, depending on the time of year, the actual number might be above or below this average. We can also think of this average as being represented by the midline, in the sense that the population fluctuates equally above and below this line.

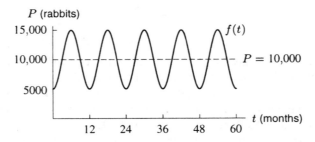

Figure 5.90: A graph of the rabbit population on a 5-year (60 month) period

This suggests the following way of thinking about the formula for P:

$$P = f(t) = \underbrace{10{,}000}_{\text{average value of population}} \underbrace{-5000\cos\left(\frac{\pi}{6}t\right)}_{\text{seasonal variation in population}}.$$

Notice that we can't say the average or midline value of the rabbit population is 10,000 unless we look at the population in at least year-long units. For example, if we looked at the population over the first two months, an interval on which it is never above 10,000, then the average would certainly not be 10,000.

But what if the average, even over long periods of time, does not remain constant? For example, suppose that due to conservation efforts, the overall ecology of the area has been improving over a ten-year period. Further, suppose this improvement has caused a steady increase of 50 rabbits per month in the average rabbit population. Thus, instead of writing

$$P = f(t) = \underbrace{10{,}000}_{\substack{\text{constant midline}\\\text{population}}} \underbrace{-5000\cos\left(\frac{\pi}{6}t\right)}_{\text{seasonal variation}},$$

we can write

$$P = f(t) = \underbrace{10{,}000 + 50t}_{\substack{\text{midline population increasing}\\\text{by 50 every month}}} -5000\cos\left(\frac{\pi}{6}t\right).$$

Figure 5.91 gives a graph of this new function over a five-year period.

Figure 5.91: A graph of the gradually increasing rabbit population

The population now oscillates above and below the line $P = 10,000 + 50t$. How can we think about what is "average"? Consider Figure 5.92, which gives a graph of the gradually increasing rabbit population over a 1-year period. On this interval, it is clear that although the population varies in a regular manner about a diagonal midline, its average value can still be indicated by a horizontal line.

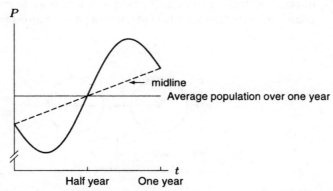

Figure 5.92: Although the rabbit population varies in a regular manner about its midline, the average population over a one-year period is not given by the midline

Problems for Section 5.8

1. A power company serves two different cities, City A and City B. The power requirements of both cities vary in a predictable fashion over the course of a typical day.

   (a) At midnight, the power requirement of City A is at a minimum of 40 megawatts. (A megawatt is a unit of power.) By noon the city has reached its maximum power consumption of 90 megawatts and by midnight it once again requires only 40 megawatts. Let $f(t)$ be the power, in megawatts, required by City A as a function of t, the number of hours elapsed since midnight. Assuming f is a simple trigonometric function, find a possible formula for $f(t)$.

   (b) The power requirements of City B differ from those of City A. Let $g(t)$ be the power in megawatts required by City B as a function of t, the number of hours elapsed since midnight. Suppose

   $$g(t) = 80 - 30\sin\left(\frac{\pi}{12}t\right).$$

State the amplitude and the period of $g(t)$, and give physical interpretations of these quantities.

(c) Graph and find all t such that

$$f(t) = g(t), \qquad 0 \le t < 24,$$

and interpret your solution(s) in terms of power usage.

(d) The power company is interested in the maximum value of the function

$$h(t) = f(t) + g(t), \qquad 0 \le t < 24,$$

Why should the power company be interested in the function s? What is the approximate maximum of this function, and approximately when does it attain this maximum?

2. A certain amusement park has a giant double ferris wheel as in Figure 5.93. The double ferris wheel has a 30-meter rotating arm attached at its center to a 25-meter main support. The arm rotates in the counterclockwise direction. At each end of the rotating arm is attached a ferris wheel measuring 20 meters in diameter. Each ferris wheel rotates in the counterclockwise direction as well. It takes the rotating arm 6 minutes to complete one full revolution, and it takes 4 minutes for each wheel to complete a revolution about that wheel's hub.

Figure 5.93

Suppose that at time $t = 0$ the rotating arm is parallel to the ground, and that your seat is at the 3 o'clock position of the rightmost wheel.

(a) Find a formula for $h = f(t)$, your height above the ground in meters, as a function of time elapsed in minutes. (Hint: Your height above ground equals the height of your wheel hub above ground plus or minus your height above that hub.)

(b) Sketch the graph of $f(t)$. Is $f(t)$ a periodic function? If so, what is its period?

(c) Approximate the least value of t such that h is at a maximum value. What is this maximum value?

3. Graph the function $f(x) = e^{-x}(2\cos x + \sin x)$ on the interval $[0, 12]$. What is the maximum value of the function? What is the minimum value?

4. Sketch graphs of each of the following functions for $0 \le x \le 2\pi$.
   (a) $y = x \sin x$ (b) $y = (1/x)\sin x$ (c) $y = \sin(x^2)$
   (d) $y = (\sin x)^2$ (e) $y = |\sin x|$ (f) $y = e^x \sin x$

5. Graph $y = t + 5\sin t$ and $y = t$ on $0 \le t \le 2\pi$. Where do the two graphs intersect if t is not restricted to $0 \le t \le 2\pi$?

Chapter 8/ 68

6. John wants to develop a mathematical model for predicting the value of a certain stock traded on the New York Stock Exchange. He has made two observations from the past behavior of the stock: 1) its value seems to have a cyclical component which increases for the first three months of each year, falls for the next six and then rises again for the last three; 2) inflation adds a linear component to the stock's price. For these reasons John is seeking a model of the form

$$f(t) = mt + b + A \sin \frac{\pi t}{6},$$

where t represents the time in months after Jan. 1, 1990. He has the following data:

TABLE 5.19

Date	Stock Price
1/1/90	$20.00
4/1/90	$37.50
7/1/90	$35.00
10/1/90	$32.50
1/1/91	$50.00

(a) Find values of m, b, and A so that f fits the data.

(b) During which month(s) does this stock appreciate the most?

(c) During what period each year is this stock actually losing value?

7. Let $f(x) = \sin \left(\dfrac{1}{x} \right)$ for $x > 0$, x in radians.

(a) $f(x)$ has a horizontal asymptote as $x \to \infty$. Find the equation for the asymptote and explain carefully why $f(x)$ has this asymptote.

(b) Describe the behavior of $f(x)$ as $x \to 0$. Explain why $f(x)$ behaves in this way.

(c) Is $f(x)$ a periodic function?

(d) Let z_1 be the greatest zero of $f(x)$. Find the exact value of z_1.

(e) How many zeros do you think the function $f(x)$ has?

(f) Suppose a is a zero of f. Find a formula for b, the largest zero of f less than a.

8. A rigid metal bar of length l_0 is tapped sharply on one end at time $t = 0$. The bar begins to ring, which means that it is oscillating very rapidly along its length. Let Δl be the initial change in the bar's length, so that $l_0 - \Delta l$ is the length of the contracted bar at time $t = 0$. (See Figure 5.94.) Suppose that the bar rings at a frequency of 250 Hertz, or 250 cycles per second, and that after 1 second the amplitude of the ringing has diminished by a factor of 10,000. It continues to decrease by this factor each second. Find a formula for $l(t)$, the length of the bar as a function of time, t, in seconds.

Figure 5.94: As the bar oscillates, its length $l(t)$ alternately contracts and expands, so that $l(t)$ is a periodic function of time.

Chapter 8/ 69

9. In the July 1993 issue of *Standard and Poors Industry Surveys* (**PL51**) the editors state:

> The strength (of sales) of video games, seven years after the current fad began, is amazing . . . . What will happen next year is anything but clear. While video sales ended on a strong note last year, the toy industry is nothing if not cyclical.

The graph for this industry is shown in Figure 5.95.

retail sales of games and
cartridges (in billions of dollars)

year (after 1900)

Figure 5.95: Video game roller coaster [2]

(a) Why might sales of video games be cyclical?

(b) Would $s(t) = a\sin(bt)$, where t is time, serve as a reasonable model for this sales graph? What about $s(t) = a\cos(bt)$?

(c) Think of a way to modify your choice in part (b) to provide for the higher amplitude in the years 1985–1992 as compared to 1979–1982.

(d) Graph the function created in part (c) and compare your results to the graph provided. Make modifications to your function and see how close you can make your graph approximate the given graph.

(e) Use your function to predict sales for 1993.

10. Let $f(t) = \cos(e^t)$, where t is measured in radians.

(a) Note f has a horizontal asymptote as $t \to -\infty$. Find its equation, and explain why f has this asymptote.

(b) Describe the behavior of f as $t \to \infty$. Explain why f behaves this way.

(c) Find the vertical intercept of f.

(d) Let t_1 be the least zero of f. Find t_1 exactly. [Hint: What is the smallest positive zero of the cosine function?]

(e) Find a formula for t_2, the least zero of f greater than t_1.

11. Imagine a rope with one free end. If we give the free end a small upward shake, a wiggle travels down the length of the rope. Suppose that we repeatedly shake the free end so that a periodic series of wiggles travels down the rope. This situation can be described by a wave function:

$$y(x,t) = A\sin(k \cdot x - \omega \cdot t).$$

Here, x is the distance along the rope in meters; y is the displacement distance perpendicular to the rope; t is time; A is the amplitude; $\dfrac{2\pi}{k}$ = wavelength (λ), the distance from peak to peak; and $\dfrac{2\pi}{\omega}$ = time for one wavelength to pass by. Suppose $A = 0.06$, $k = 2\pi$, and $\omega = 4\pi$.

(a) What is the wavelength of the motion?

(b) How many peaks of the wave pass by a given point each second?

(c) Construct the graph of this wave from $x = 0$ to $x = 1.5$ m when t is fixed at 0.

(d) What other values of t would give the same graph as the one found in part (d)?

---

[2] Source: Nintendo of America

9.5 USING TRIGONOMETRIC IDENTITIES

In this section we will apply the identity found in Section 9.4

$$\sin(\theta + \phi) = \sin\theta\cos\phi + \sin\phi\cos\theta.$$

Chapter 8/ 72

Figure 9.26: A graph of $f(t) = \sin t + \cos t$

Figure 9.26 shows a graph of the function $f(t) = \sin t + \cos t$. This graph looks remarkably like the graph of the sine function itself, having the same period but a larger amplitude (somewhere between 1 and 2). It also seems to have a phase shift of about $\pi/4$. Despite these differences, it is surprising that this graph looks so much like the sine graph.

We would like to determine if f is actually sinusoidal, that is, if f can be written in the form $f(t) = A\sin(Bt + C) + D$. If so, it would seem that $D = 0$ and that $B = 1$, but what about the values of A and C?

From Figure 9.26, it looks like the phase shift, C, is $\frac{\pi}{4}$. So let us use our new identity $\sin(\theta+\phi) = \sin\theta\cos\phi + \sin\phi\cos\theta$ to study $\sin(t + \frac{\pi}{4})$. With $\phi = \frac{\pi}{4}$, we have

$$\sin\left(t + \frac{\pi}{4}\right) = \sin t \cos\frac{\pi}{4} + \sin\frac{\pi}{4}\cos t$$

[handwritten: $\sin(\theta + \phi) = \sin\theta\cos\phi + \cos\theta\sin\phi$; $\sin\phi\cos\theta$]

$$= \frac{\sqrt{2}}{2}\sin t + \frac{\sqrt{2}}{2}\cos t.$$

Multiplying both sides of this equation by $\sqrt{2}$ gives

$$\sqrt{2}\sin\left(t + \frac{\pi}{4}\right) = \sqrt{2}\left(\frac{\sqrt{2}}{2}\sin t + \frac{\sqrt{2}}{2}\cos t\right)$$

$$= \sin t + \cos t.$$

Thus,

$$f(t) = \sqrt{2}\sin\left(t + \frac{\pi}{4}\right).$$

We see that f is indeed a sine function with period 2π, amplitude $A = \sqrt{2} \approx 1.4$, and phase shift $C = \pi/4$. These values fit the graph in Figure 9.26.

Sums Involving Sine and Cosine

We have just seen that the function $f(t) = \sin t + \cos t$ can be written as a single sine function. We will now show that this statement can be extended: The sum of any two cosine and sine functions having the same period and phase shift can be written as a single sine function.[2] We start with

$$y = a_1\sin(Bt) + a_2\cos(Bt),$$

where a_1, a_2, and B are constants. We want to show that this sum can be written as a single sine function of the form $y = A\sin(Bt + \phi)$. To do this we will again use the identity $\sin(\theta + \phi) = \sin\theta\cos\phi + \sin\phi\cos\theta$. Using this identity with $\theta = Bt$ and multiplying by A, we have

---

[2]The sum of a sine and a cosine can also be written as a single cosine function.

$$A \sin(Bt + \phi) = A \sin(Bt) \cos \phi + A \sin \phi \cos(Bt)$$
$$= A \cos \phi \sin(Bt) + A \sin \phi \cos(Bt).$$

This looks very much like $y = a_1 \sin(Bt) + a_2 \cos(Bt)$, if we let $a_1 = A \cos \phi$ and $a_2 = A \sin \phi$. If we divide by A, the relationships we want for the constants a_1, a_2, A, and ϕ are given by

$$\cos \phi = \frac{a_1}{A} \quad \text{and} \quad \sin \phi = \frac{a_2}{A}.$$

Recall from triangle trigonometry that these relationships are true. See Figure 9.27.

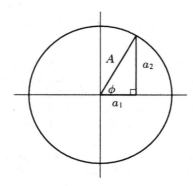

Figure 9.27: A right triangle with legs a_1 and a_2

Applying the Pythagorean theorem to the triangle in the figure gives

$$\left(\frac{a_1}{A}\right)^2 + \left(\frac{a_2}{A}\right)^2 = 1,$$

$$a_1^2 + a_2^2 = A^2$$

or

$$A = \sqrt{a_1^2 + a_2^2}.$$

Also, since $\tan \phi = \frac{\sin \phi}{\cos \phi}$, we have

$$\tan \phi = \frac{a_2}{a_1}.$$

These formulas allow A and ϕ to be determined from a_1 and a_2. We apply this to the previous example $y = \sin x + \cos x$. Here $a_1 = 1$ and $a_2 = 1$, so $A = \sqrt{2}$ and $\tan \phi = 1$, so $\phi = \frac{\pi}{4}$.

In summary:

Provided their periods are equal, the sum of a sine function and a cosine function can be written as a single sine function. We have

$$a_1 \sin(Bt) + a_2 \sin(Bt) = A \cos(Bt + \phi)$$

where

$$A = \sqrt{a_1^2 + a_2^2} \quad \text{and} \quad \tan \phi = \frac{a_2}{a_1}.$$

Example 1   If $g(t) = 2\sin 3t + 5\cos 3t$, express the formula for g as a single sine function.

Solution   We have $a_1 = 2$, $a_2 = 5$, and $B = 3$. Thus,

$$A = \sqrt{2^2 + 5^2} = \sqrt{29} \qquad \text{and} \qquad \tan\phi = \frac{2}{5}$$

One possible value for ϕ is $\arctan(2/5) = 0.38$. Therefore,

$$g(t) = \sqrt{29}\sin(3t + 0.38).$$

Sums and Differences of Angles

The identity $\sin(\theta + \phi) = \sin\theta\cos\phi + \sin\phi\cos\theta$ can be used to derive other important identities. We will now use this identity to derive a similar identity for $\cos(\theta + \phi)$. From Chapter 5, recall that

$$\sin\left(x + \frac{\pi}{2}\right) = \cos x \qquad \text{and} \qquad \cos\left(x + \frac{\pi}{2}\right) = -\sin x.$$

If we look back at Figure 5.7 on page 310, we notice that taking the cosine of $x + \frac{\pi}{2}$ yields $-\sin x$. These relations can be understood in terms of horizontal shifts: Shifting the graph $y = \sin x$ to the left by $\pi/2$ gives $y = \cos x$, and shifting the graph $y = \cos x$ to the left by $\pi/2$ gives $y = -\sin x$. Thus,

$$\sin\left[(\theta + \phi) + \frac{\pi}{2}\right] = \cos(\theta + \phi).$$

However, it is also true that

$$\sin\left[(\theta + \phi) + \frac{\pi}{2}\right] = \sin\left[\theta + \left(\phi + \frac{\pi}{2}\right)\right]$$

$$= \sin\theta\underbrace{\cos\left(\phi + \frac{\pi}{2}\right)}_{-\sin\phi} + \underbrace{\sin\left(\phi + \frac{\pi}{2}\right)}_{\cos\phi}\cos\theta$$

$$= -\sin\theta\sin\phi + \cos\theta\cos\phi.$$

Therefore,

$$\cos(\theta + \phi) = \cos\theta\cos\phi - \sin\theta\sin\phi.$$

Now we determine identities involving the difference of angles. Given the fact that $\cos(-\theta) = \cos\theta$ (because cosine is even) and $\sin(-\theta) = -\sin\theta$ (because sine is odd), we have

$$\sin(\theta - \phi) = \sin\left(\theta + (-\phi)\right)$$
$$= \sin\theta\cos(-\phi) + \sin(-\phi)\cos\theta$$
$$= \sin\theta\cos\phi - \sin\phi\cos\theta.$$

A similar argument shows that

$$\cos(\theta - \phi) = \cos\theta\cos\phi + \sin\theta\sin\phi.$$

In summary:

The **sum-of-angle** and **difference-of-angle** formulas for sine and cosine are given by

$$\sin(\theta + \phi) = \sin\theta\cos\phi + \sin\phi\cos\theta$$

$$\sin(\theta - \phi) = \sin\theta\cos\phi - \sin\phi\cos\theta$$

and

$$\cos(\theta + \phi) = \cos\theta\cos\phi - \sin\theta\sin\phi$$

$$\cos(\theta - \phi) = \cos\theta\cos\phi + \sin\theta\sin\phi$$

Example 2 A utility company serves two different cities. Let P_1 be the power requirements in megawatts (MW) for city 1, and P_2 be the requirements for city 2. Both P_1 and P_2 are functions of t, the number of hours elapsed since midnight. Suppose P_1 and P_2 are described by the following formulas:

$$P_1 = f_1(t) = 40 - 15\cos\left(\frac{\pi}{12}t\right)$$
$$P_2 = f_2(t) = 50 + 10\sin\left(\frac{\pi}{12}t\right).$$

(a) Describe the power requirements of both cities in words.
(b) What is the maximum total power the utility company must be prepared to provide?

Solution (a) The power requirements of city 1 are at a minimum of $40 - 15 = 25$ MW at $t = 0$, or midnight. They rise to a maximum of $40 + 15 = 55$ MW by noon and then fall back to a minimum of 25 MW by the following midnight. The power requirements of city 2 are at a maximum of 60 MW at 6 am. They fall to a minimum of 40 MW by 6 pm but by the following morning have climbed back to 60 MW, again at 6 am. Figure 9.28 gives graphs of P_1 and P_2 over a two-day period.

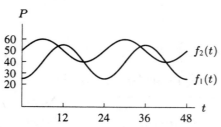

Figure 9.28: Power requirements in megawatts for cities 1 and 2 over a 48 hour period

Figure 9.29: Total power demand for a 48 hour period

(b) The utility company must provide enough power at any given time to satisfy the needs of both cities. The total power required by both cities, we have

$$T = g(t) = f_1(t) + f_2(t).$$

Figure 9.29 gives a graph of g for $0 \le t \le 48$. From the graph, g appears to be a periodic function. In fact, it appears to be a trigonometric function. It varies between about 108 MW and 72 MW, giving it an amplitude of roughly 18 MW. A formula for T in terms of t is given by

$$T = P_1 + P_2$$
$$= 90 + 10\sin\left(\frac{\pi}{12}t\right) - 15\cos\left(\frac{\pi}{12}t\right).$$

Since the maximum value of T is about 108, the utility company must be prepared to provide at least this much power at all times.

To find the exact function $T(t)$, we begin by taking the square root of the sum of the squares of the coefficients 10 and 15. This yields $A = \sqrt{10^2 + 15^2} \approx 18.03$. This means that $\sqrt{\left(\frac{10}{18.03}\right)^2 + \left(\frac{15}{18.03}\right)^2} = 1$, and so we have the following right triangle in the unit circle:

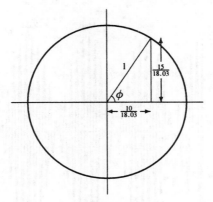

Figure 9.30

Thus, $\cos \phi = \frac{10}{18.03}$ and $\sin \phi = \frac{15}{18.03}$. This means that $\phi = 0.983$. We can now use the difference-of-angle identity from page 539:

$$\sin \left(\frac{\pi}{12}t - \phi \right) = \cos \phi \sin \left(\frac{\pi}{12}t \right) - \sin \phi \cos \left(\frac{\pi}{12}t \right).$$

This means

$$T(t) = 90 + 10 \sin \left(\frac{\pi}{12}t \right) - 15 \cos \left(\frac{\pi}{12}t \right)$$

$$= 90 + 18.03 \left[\frac{10}{18.03} \sin \left(\frac{\pi}{12}t \right) - \frac{15}{18.03} \cos \left(\frac{\pi}{12} \right) \right]$$

$$= 90 + 18.03 \sin \left(\frac{\pi}{12}t - 0.983 \right).$$

Indeed, the amplitude is roughly 18.03, and the maximum and minimum values are about 108 and 72.

Acoustic Beats

On a perfectly tuned piano, the A above middle C has (by international agreement) a frequency of 440 cycles per second, also written 440 hertz (Hz). The lowest-pitched note on the piano (the key at the left-most end) is also an A and is four octaves lower. Its frequency is 55 hertz (representing a decrease by a factor of 1/2 for each octave). Suppose this low A is struck together with a note on an out-of-tune piano, and that the out-of-tune note has a frequency of 61 hertz. The intensities of these two separate tones can be modeled using the functions

$$I_1 = \cos(2\pi f_1 t) \qquad \text{and} \qquad I_2 = \cos(2\pi f_2 t),$$

where $f_1 = 55$, and $f_2 = 61$, and where t is in seconds. If both tones are sounded at the same time, then their combined intensity is modeled as the sum of their separate intensities:

$$I = I_1 + I_2 = \cos(2\pi f_1 t) + \cos(2\pi f_2 t).$$

Figure 9.31 gives a graph of this function on the interval $0 \leq t \leq 1, -2 \leq I \leq 2$. From Figure 9.31, we see that this function resembles a rapidly varying sinusoidal function except that its amplitude

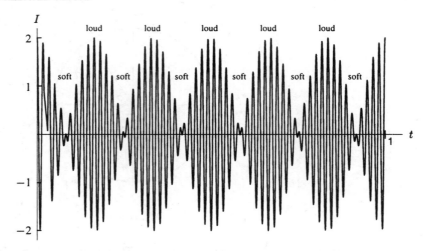

Figure 9.31: A graph of $I = \cos(2\pi f_1 t) + \cos(2\pi f_2 t)$

goes up and down. The ear perceives this variation in amplitude as a variation in loudness, and so the tone appears to waver (or *beat*) in a regular way. This is an example of the phenomenon known as *acoustic beats*.

How can we explain the graph in Figure 9.31 in terms of what we know about the cosine function? We will approach this problem by deriving a new identity that relates the sum of two different cosine functions—such as $\cos(2\pi f_1 t)$ and $\cos(2\pi f_2 t)$—to the product of two new cosine functions. We begin with the fact that

$$\cos(\theta + \phi) = \cos\theta\cos\phi - \sin\theta\sin\phi$$

$$\text{and} \qquad \cos(\theta - \phi) = \cos\theta\cos\phi + \sin\theta\sin\phi.$$

Notice that if we add these two equations, the terms involving the sine function cancel out, leaving only cosines:

$$\cos(\theta + \phi) + \cos(\theta - \phi) = 2\cos\theta\cos\phi.$$

The left-hand side of this equation can be rewritten by making the substitutions

$$u = \theta + \phi \qquad \text{and} \qquad v = \theta - \phi.$$

This gives

$$\cos\underbrace{(\theta + \phi)}_{u} + \cos\underbrace{(\theta - \phi)}_{v} = 2\cos\theta\cos\phi$$

$$\cos u + \cos v = 2\cos\theta\cos\phi.$$

The right-hand side of the equation can also be rewritten in terms of u and v. To do this, notice that $u + v = 2\theta$ and $u - v = 2\phi$, so that

$$\theta = \frac{u + v}{2} \qquad \text{and} \qquad \phi = \frac{u - v}{2}.$$

With these substitutions, we have

$$\cos u + \cos v = 2\cos\frac{u + v}{2}\cos\frac{u - v}{2}.$$

This identity relates the sum of two cosine functions to the product of two new cosine functions. For instance, our function $I = \cos(2\pi f_1 t) + \cos(2\pi f_2 t)$ can be rewritten as

$$I = \cos(2\pi f_2 t) + \cos(2\pi f_1 t) = 2\cos\frac{2\pi f_2 t + 2\pi f_1 t}{2}\cos\frac{2\pi f_2 t - 2\pi f_1 t}{2}$$
$$= 2\cos\frac{2\pi \cdot (61+55)t}{2}\cos\frac{2\pi \cdot (61-55)t}{2}$$
$$= 2\cos(2\pi \cdot 58t)\cos(2\pi \cdot 3t).$$

We can rewrite this formula in the following way:

$$I = 2\cos(2\pi \cdot 3t)\cdot\cos(2\pi \cdot 58t)$$
$$= A(t)p(t),$$

where $A(t) = 2\cos(2\pi \cdot 3t)$ gives a (slowly) changing amplitude (or loudness) and where $p(t) = \cos(2\pi \cdot 58t)$ gives a pure tone of 58 Hz. Thus, we can think of the tone described by I as having a pitch of 58 Hz, which is midway between the tones sounded by the two pianos. As the amplitude rises and falls, the tone grows louder and softer, but its pitch remains a constant 58 Hz. (See Figure 9.32.)

Notice from Figure 9.32 that the function $A(t)$ completes 3 full cycles on the interval $0 \le t \le 1$. The tone will be loudest whenever $A(t) = 1$ or $A(t) = -1$. Since both of these values occur once per cycle, the tone grows loud *six* times every second. In addition to the formula we found for the sum of two cosine functions, there are similar formulas for the sum of two sine functions, and the difference between sine functions and cosine functions. Derivations of some of these identities are left to the exercises, but we will summarize them here:

$$\cos u + \cos v = 2\cos\frac{u+v}{2}\cos\frac{u-v}{2}$$
$$\sin u + \sin v = 2\sin\frac{u+v}{2}\cos\frac{u-v}{2}$$
$$\cos u - \cos v = -2\sin\frac{u+v}{2}\sin\frac{u-v}{2}$$
$$\sin u - \sin v = 2\cos\frac{u+v}{2}\sin\frac{u-v}{2}$$

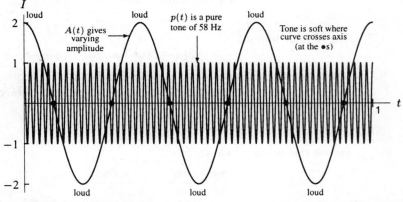

Figure 9.32: The function $A(t) = 2\cos(2\pi \cdot 3t)$ gives a varying amplitude while the function $p(t) = \cos(2\pi \cdot 58t)$ gives a pure tone of 58 Hz.

Chapter 8/ 79

Problems for Section 9.5 ━━━━━━━━━━━━━━━━━━━━━━━━━━━━━

1. Test each identity by first evaluating both sides to see that they are numerically equal when $u = 15°$ and $v = 42°$. Then let $u = x$ and $v = 20°$ and compare the graphs of each side of the identity as functions of x.

    (a) $\sin(u + v) = \sin u \cos v + \sin v \cos u$
    (b) $\sin(u - v) = \sin u \cos v - \sin v \cos u$
    (c) $\cos(u + v) = \cos u \cos v - \sin v \sin u$
    (d) $\cos(u - v) = \cos u \cos v + \sin v \sin u$

2. Test each identity by first evaluating both sides to see that they are numerically equal when $u = 35°$ and $v = 40°$. Then let $u = x$ and $v = 25°$ and compare the graphs of each side of the identity as functions of x.

    (a) $\cos u + \cos v = 2\cos\left(\dfrac{u + v}{2}\right)\cos\left(\dfrac{u - v}{2}\right)$
    (b) $\cos u - \cos v = -2\cos\left(\dfrac{u + v}{2}\right)\cos\left(\dfrac{u - v}{2}\right)$
    (c) $\sin u + \sin v = 2\sin\left(\dfrac{u + v}{2}\right)\cos\left(\dfrac{u - v}{2}\right)$
    (d) $\sin u - \sin v = 2\cos\left(\dfrac{u + v}{2}\right)\sin\left(\dfrac{u - v}{2}\right)$

3. Recall that we could write exact values of $\sin\theta$ and $\cos\theta$ when θ had a reference angle of 0, 30, 45, 60, and 90 degrees. Explain how you can now find exact values for $\theta = 15°$ and $\theta = 75°$.

4. Solve the equation $\sin 4x + \sin x = 0$ for values of x in the interval $0 < x < 2\pi$ by applying an identity to the left side of the equation.

5. Prove
$$\cos u - \cos v = -2\sin\left(\frac{u + v}{2}\right)\sin\left(\frac{u - v}{2}\right).$$

6. Prove
$$\sin u + \sin v = 2\sin\left(\frac{u + v}{2}\right)\cos\left(\frac{u - v}{2}\right).$$

7. The addition formula
$$\sin(u + v) = \sin u \cos v + \sin v \cos u$$

    lets us transform expressions involving the sum of two angles. One situation where this transformation is useful occurs when we are looking at an average rate of change:
$$\frac{\Delta y}{\Delta x} = \frac{f(x + h) - f(x)}{h}.$$

    For the sine function this is
$$\frac{\Delta y}{\Delta x} = \frac{\sin(x + h) - \sin x}{h}$$
$$= = \sin x\left(\frac{\cos h - 1}{h}\right) + \cos x\left(\frac{\sin h}{h}\right).$$

Chapter 8/   80

5.9 TRIANGLES

How does a surveyor measure the distance across a river or the height of a tall building? The answers to this kind of question can be found by using the properties of triangles and trigonometric functions. The word *trigonometry* means, literally, the measurement of triangles, and in this section we will explore its applications.

Right Triangles

If θ is an angle in a right triangle (other than the right angle), then the sine, cosine and tangent of θ can be expressed in terms of lengths of the triangle's sides. This is not surprising, since we have defined $\sin \theta$ and $\cos \theta$ using a right triangle inscribed in the unit circle.

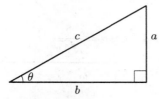

Figure 5.96: A right triangle with legs a and b, and hypotenuse c

Figure 5.97: A similar right triangle shown with the unit circle

Figure 5.96 gives a right triangle with legs of length a and b and hypotenuse of length c. Figure 5.97 shows a similar triangle on the unit circle and a point $P = (x, y)$ determined by θ. Since ratios of side lengths are the same for similar triangles, we have

$$\frac{a}{c} = \frac{y}{1} = y.$$

Since $\sin \theta$ is defined to be y, this means

$$\sin \theta = \frac{a}{c}.$$

Similarly,

$$\cos \theta = x = \frac{x}{1} = \frac{b}{c}.$$

Side a is directly across from the angle θ and is commonly referred to as the *opposite* side. Side b is called the *adjacent* side, and side c is the hypotenuse. Thus, we can write formulas for trigonometric functions in geometric terms:

If θ is an angle in a right triangle (other than the right angle),

$$\sin \theta = \frac{\text{opposite}}{\text{hypotenuse}} \qquad \cos \theta = \frac{\text{adjacent}}{\text{hypotenuse}}$$

Example 1   Let θ be the angle shown in Figure 5.98. Evaluate the sine and cosine of θ.

Figure 5.98   **Figure 5.99:** Measuring the width of a river

Solution   Let c be the length of the hypotenuse. Using the Pythagorean theorem,

$$c^2 = 4^2 + 5^2 = 41.$$

Thus $c = \sqrt{41}$ and

$$\sin \theta = \frac{4}{\sqrt{41}}, \quad \text{and} \quad \cos \theta = \frac{5}{\sqrt{41}}.$$

The Tangent Function

For the triangle in Figure 5.96, we know that $\sin \theta = a/c$ and $\cos \theta = b/c$. Since $\tan \theta = \frac{\sin \theta}{\cos \theta}$, this gives

$$\tan \theta = \frac{a/c}{b/c} = \frac{a}{b}.$$

In words,

$$\tan \theta = \frac{\text{opposite}}{\text{adjacent}}.$$

Example 2   A surveyor must measure the distance between the two banks of a straight river. (See Figure 5.99.) She sights a tree at point T on the opposite bank of the river and drives a stake into the ground (at point P) directly across from the tree. Then she walks 50 yards upstream and places a stake at point Q. She measures angle PQT and finds that it is $58°$. Find the width of the river.

Solution   Figure 5.99 illustrates this situation. Since the tangent of an angle in a right triangle is the ratio of its opposite leg to its adjacent leg,

$$\tan 58° = \frac{d}{50}$$
$$d = 50 \tan 58° \approx 80.$$

The width of the river is about 80 yards.

Non-Right Triangles

The sine and cosine functions are useful because they allow us to relate the angles of a triangle to its sides. Such relationships exist for all triangles, not just right triangles. However, the rules are somewhat more complicated for non-right triangles.

The Law of Cosines

The Pythagorean theorem relates the three sides of a triangle, but it only works for right triangles. The *Law of Cosines* relates the three sides of *any* triangle, not just right triangles.

Figure 5.100: We can derive the Law of Cosines by referring to this figure

---

Law of Cosines:
$$c^2 = a^2 + b^2 - 2ab\cos C$$
for a triangle with sides a, b, c and angle C opposite side c.

We can refer to the triangle in Figure 5.100 to derive the Law of Cosines. In the figure, h has been drawn at a right angle to side a, and it divides this side into two pieces, one of length x and one of length $a - x$.

Based on the figure, the Pythagorean theorem tells us that
$$(a - x)^2 + h^2 = c^2$$
$$a^2 - 2ax + x^2 + h^2 = c^2.$$

Also from the Pythagorean theorem, we see that $x^2 + h^2 = b^2$. Thus,
$$a^2 - 2ax + \underbrace{x^2 + h^2}_{b^2} = c^2$$
$$a^2 + b^2 - 2ax = c^2.$$

But $\cos C = \frac{x}{b}$, and so $x = b\cos C$. This gives
$$a^2 + b^2 - 2ab\cos C = c^2$$

which is the Law of Cosines.

Notice that if C happens to be a right angle, that is, if $C = 90°$, then $\cos C = 0$. In this right angle case, the Law of Cosines becomes
$$a^2 + b^2 - 2ab \cdot 0 = c^2$$
$$a^2 + b^2 = c^2,$$

which is the Pythagorean theorem. Therefore, the Law of Cosines is in some sense a version of the Pythagorean theorem that works for any triangle, not just right triangles. Notice also that in Figure 5.100 we assumed that angle C is acute, that is, less than $90°$. However, we can give a similar derivation for the case where $90° < C \le 180°$. This is left for the exercises.

The Law of Cosines is useful when two sides of a triangle and the angle between them are known.

Example 3   A person leaves her home and walks 5 miles due east and then 3 miles northeast. How far has she walked? How far away from home is she?

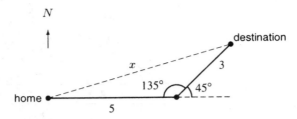

Figure 5.101: A person walks 5 miles east and then 3 miles northeast

Solution   One side of the triangle in Figure 5.101 is 5 units long, while the second side is 3 units long and at an angle of 45° to the first. This is because when the person turns northeast, she turns through an angle of 45°. Thus, we know two sides of this triangle, 5 and 3, and the angle between them, which is 135°. The length of the third side, x, can be found by applying the Law of Cosines:

$$x^2 = 5^2 + 3^2 - 2 \cdot 5 \cdot 3 \cos 135°$$
$$= 34 - 30\left(-\frac{\sqrt{2}}{2}\right)$$
$$= 55.2.$$

This gives $x = \sqrt{55.2} = 7.43$ miles. Notice that this is less than her total distance walked, which is $5 + 3 = 8$ miles.

The Law of Cosines can also be useful if all three sides of a triangle are known.

Example 4   At what angle must the person from Example 3 face if she wants to walk directly home?

Solution   According to Figure 5.102, if the person faces due west and then turns south through an angle of θ she can head directly home. Recall that this angle θ is then the same as the angle opposite the side of length 3 in the triangle. We see from the Law of Cosines that

$$3^2 + 7.43^2 - 2(3)(7.43)\cos\theta = 5^2$$
$$-44.6\cos\theta = -39.2$$
$$\cos\theta = 0.8789$$
$$\theta = \arccos(0.8789) = 28.5°.$$

Figure 5.102: The person must face $\theta°$ to the south of due west in order to head directly home

In the last two examples, notice how we used the Law of Cosines in two different ways for the same triangle. To keep track of which sides go with which angles, remember that angle C should always go between sides a and b, which means opposite side c. In words, the Law of Cosines reads

$(1^{st} \text{ side})^2 + (2^{nd} \text{ side})^2 - 2 \cdot (1^{st} \text{ side}) \cdot (2^{nd} \text{ side}) \cdot \cos(\text{angle between them}) = (3^{rd} \text{ side})^2.$

$a^2 \qquad\qquad b^2 \qquad - \quad 2ab \cdot \cos\theta = c^2$

The Law of Sines

Figure 5.103 shows the same triangle as in Figure 5.100. We will use this figure to derive the Law of Sines:

Law of Sines:

$$\frac{\sin A}{a} = \frac{\sin B}{b} = \frac{\sin C}{c}$$

for a triangle with sides a, b, c and angles A, B, C opposite these sides, respectively.

Notice from the figure that $\sin C = \frac{h}{b}$ and that $\sin B = \frac{h}{c}$. Thus, we can write h as $h = b \sin C$ or as $h = c \sin B$. This means that

$$b \sin C = c \sin B$$

and so

$$\frac{\sin B}{b} = \frac{\sin C}{c}.$$

A similar argument shows that

$$a \sin B = b \sin A,$$

which leads to the Law of Sines:

$$\frac{\sin A}{a} = \frac{\sin B}{b} = \frac{\sin C}{c}.$$

The Law of Sines is sometimes useful in cases where the Law of Cosines does not apply.

Figure 5.103: We can use this triangle to derive the Law of Sines

---

Example 5   Suppose an aerial tram starts at a point one half mile from the base of a mountain whose face has a 60° angle of elevation. (See Figure 5.104.) The tram ascends at an angle of 20°. What is the length of the cable needed to span the distance from T to A?

Figure 5.104

Solution   The Law of Cosines will not help us here because we only know the length of one side of the triangle. We do however know two angles in this diagram. Thus, we can use the Law of Sines. We have:

$$\frac{\sin A}{a} = \frac{\sin C}{c}$$

$$\frac{\sin 40°}{0.5} = \frac{\sin 120°}{c}$$

so $c = 0.5 \left(\dfrac{\sin 120°}{\sin 40°} \right) \approx 0.6736$. Therefore, the cable spans approximately 0.6736 miles.

The Ambiguous Case

There is a drawback to using the Law of Sines for finding angles. The drawback is that the Law of Sines does not tell us the angle directly, but rather its sine. The problem with this is that there are always two angles between 0° and 180° corresponding to a given sine. For example, we may know that the sine of an angle in a triangle is $\frac{1}{2}$. However, without further information we can't be sure whether this angle is 30° or 150°.

Example 6   Solve the following triangles for θ and ϕ.

(a)

(b)

Figure 5.105   **Figure 5.106**

Solution   (a)

$$\frac{\sin \theta}{8} = \frac{\sin 40°}{7}$$

$$\sin \theta = \frac{8}{7} \sin 40°$$

$$\theta = \sin^{-1} \left(\frac{8}{7} \sin 40° \right) \approx 47.3°.$$

(b)

$$\frac{\sin \phi}{8} = \frac{\sin 40°}{7}$$

$$\sin \phi = \frac{8}{7} \sin 40°.$$

This is the same equation we found for part (a). However, judging from the figures, ϕ appears to be larger than θ. To resolve this apparent paradox, recall that knowing the sine of an angle is not enough to tell us what the angle is. In fact, there are *two* angles between 0° and 180° whose sine is given by the number $\frac{8}{7} \sin 40°$. One of them is $\theta = \sin^{-1} \left(\frac{8}{7} \sin 40° \right) \approx 47.3°$, and the other is $\phi = 180° - \theta \approx 132.7°$.

Problems for Section 5.9

1. Consider the angle θ in the triangle in Figure 5.107: Evaluate the following expressions:
   (a) $\tan\theta$ (b) $\sin\theta$ (c) $\cos\theta$

2. Find the values of the sine, cosine and tangent for the angles of the right triangle in Figure 5.108.

Figure 5.107

Figure 5.108: Triangle with three known sides

3. Find the lengths of the sides of the triangle in Figure 5.109.

Figure 5.109

4. A kite flyer wondered how high her kite was flying. She used a protractor to measure an angle of 38° from level ground to the kite string. If she used a full 100 yard spool of string, how high, in feet, was the kite? (Disregard the string sag and the height of the string reel above the ground.)

5. The top of a 200-foot vertical tower is to be anchored by cables that make an angle of 30° with the ground. How long must the cables be? How far from the base of the tower should anchors be placed?

6. A tree 50 feet tall casts a shadow 60 feet long. Find the angle of elevation θ of the sun.

7. A staircase is to rise 17.3 feet over a horizontal distance of 10 feet. At approximately what angle with respect to the floor should it be built?

8. You have been asked to build a ramp for Dan's Daredevil Motorcycle Jump. The dimensions you are given are indicated in Figure 5.110. Complete the figure by finding all the other dimensions. Make sure you clearly indicate how you obtained each answer.

Figure 5.110

9. Suppose that $y = \sin\theta$ for $0° < \theta < 90°$. Evaluate $\cos\theta$ in terms of y.

10. Simplify the expression $\sin\left(2\cos^{-1}\left(\dfrac{5}{13}\right)\right)$ to a rational number.

11. Refer to Figure 5.111 and evaluate the following expressions in terms of θ.

(a) $1 + y^2$ (b) $\cos\varphi$

(c) y (d) The triangle's area

Figure 5.111

12. Find $\tan\theta$ if $\sin\theta = -\frac{3}{5}$, and θ is in the fourth quadrant.

13. Find approximately the acute angle formed by the line $y = -2x + 5$ and the x-axis.

14. You see a friend, whose height you know is 5 feet 10 inches, some distance away. Using a surveying device called a transit, you determine the angle between the top of your friend's head and ground level to be 8°. You want to find the distance d between you and your friend.

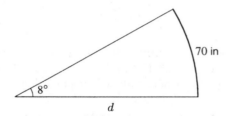

Figure 5.112: Arc of 70 in with 8° angle

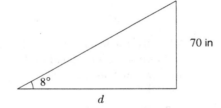

Figure 5.113: Triangle with side 70 in and angle 8°

(a) First assume you cannot find your calculator to evaluate trigonometric functions. Find d by approximating the arc length of an 8° angle with your friend's height. (See Figure 5.112.)

(b) Now assume that you have a calculator. Use it to find the distance d. (See Figure 5.113.)

(c) Would the difference between these two values for d increase or decrease if the angle were smaller?

15. Use Figure 5.114 to help you answer the following questions about parasailing:

(a) After taking off behind a parasailing boat on a rope that is 125 feet long you stabilize at a height that forms a 45° angle with the water. What is that height?

(b) After enjoying the scenery, you encounter a strong wind that blows you down to a height that forms a 30° angle with the water. At what height are you now?

(c) Find the distance c, i.e. the horizontal distance between you and the boat, in case (a).

(d) Find the distance d, i.e. the horizontal distance between you and the boat, in case (b).

16. A bridge over a river was damaged in an earthquake and you are called in to determine the length of the steel beam needed to fill the gap. (See Figure 5.115.) You cannot be on the bridge, but you are able to drop a line from T, the beginning of the bridge, and measure a distance of 50ft to the vantage point P. Also, from P you find the angles of elevation to the two ends of the gap to be 42° and 35°. How wide is the gap?

Figure 5.114

Figure 5.115: Gap in damaged bridge

17. Solve for x in Figure 5.116.
18. Solve for x in Figure 5.117.

Figure 5.116

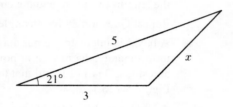

Figure 5.117

19. In Figure 5.118:
    (a) Find $\sin \theta$. (b) Solve for θ.

Figure 5.118

20. Find all the sides and angles of the triangle in Problem 19.
21. (a) Find an expression for $\sin \theta$ (from Figure 5.119) and $\sin \phi$ (in Figure 5.120.)
    (b) Explain how you can find θ and ϕ by using the inverse sine function. In what way does the method used for θ differ from the method used for ϕ?

Figure 5.119: Find $\sin \theta$

Figure 5.120: Find $\sin \phi$

22. Give a derivation of the Law of Cosines for the case when the angle C is obtuse, as in Figure 5.121

23. Use Figure 5.122 to show that $\frac{\sin A}{a} = \frac{\sin B}{b}$.

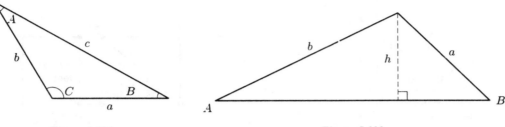

Figure 5.121   **Figure 5.122**

24. Consider a central angle of 2 degrees in a circle of radius 5 feet. To six decimal places, find the lengths of the arc and the chord determined by this angle.

25. Repeat Question 24 for an angle of 30 degrees.

26. A buyer is interested in purchasing the triangular lot with vertices LOT in Figure 5.123, but unfortunately, the marker at point L has been lost. The deed indicates that side TO is 435 ft and side LO is 112 ft and that the angle at L is 82.6°. What is the distance from L to T? (See Figure 5.123.)

27. A UFO is first sighted due east from an observer at an angle of 25° from the ground and at an altitude (vertical distance above ground) of 200 m. (See point P_1 in Figure 5.124.) The UFO is next sighted due east at an angle of 50° and an altitude of 400 m. (See point P_2.) How far did the UFO travel from P_1 to P_2?

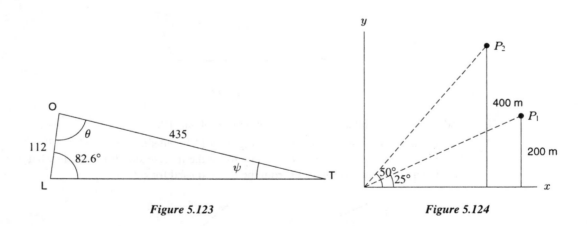

Figure 5.123   **Figure 5.124**

28. Find all sides and angles of the triangles in Figures 5.125–5.130. (Sides and angles are not necessarily drawn to scale.)

Chapter 8/ 90

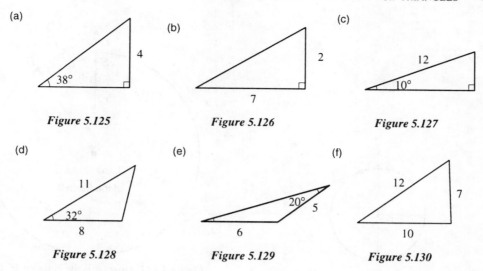

Figure 5.125   Figure 5.126   Figure 5.127

Figure 5.128   Figure 5.129   Figure 5.130

29. Find all sides and angles of the triangles in Figure 5.131.

Figure 5.131

30. Solve each triangle described below. Sketch each triangle. If there is more than one possible triangle, solve and sketch both. Note α is the angle opposite side a, β is the angle opposite side b and γ is the angle opposite side c.

 (a) $b = 510.0$ ft, $c = 259.0$ ft, $\gamma = 30.0°$
 (b) $a = 16.0$ m, $b = 24.0$ m, $c = 20.0$ m
 (c) $a = 18.7$ cm, $c = 21.0$ cm, $\beta = 22°$
 (d) $a = 2.00$ m, $\alpha = 25.80°$, $\beta = 10.50°$

31. Every triangle has three sides and three angles. Make a chart showing the set of all possible triangle configurations where three of these six measures are known, and the other three measures can be deduced (or partially deduced) from the three known measures.

32. A triangle has the following angles: 27°, 32°, and 121°. The length of the side opposite the 121° angle is 8.

 (a) Find the lengths of the two remaining sides.
 (b) Write an expression for the area of the triangle.

33. The line in Figure 5.132 has a y-intercept of 4, makes a 22° angle with the x-axis, and is tangent to the given circle at point P. Find the coordinates of P. [Hint: The tangent line is perpendicular to the radius of the circle at point P.]

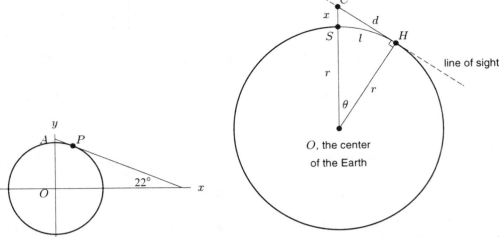

Figure 5.133: How far is the horizon, H, from the crow's
nest, C?

Figure 5.132

If you perched in the crow's nest atop the mast of a ship x meters above the surface of the ocean, how far could you see? That is, how far away is the horizon, H? How far is your ship's current position, S, from the horizon, H? See Figure 5.133. Let r be the radius of the earth. In Problems 34–35, you will answer these questions.

34. Find formulas for d, the distance you can see to the horizon, and l, the distance to the horizon along the earth's surface, in terms of x, the height of the ship's mast, and r, the radius of the earth.

35. The radius r of the earth is 6,370,000 meters. How far is the horizon when viewed from the top of a 50-meter mast? How far is the horizon from the ship's position on the ocean?

36. Using a protractor and a ruler, construct a right triangle with hypotenuse 4 inches and one angle 0.4 radian. Measure the two legs and the remaining angle. The three angles (in radians) should add up to what? Do they? Do the three sides satisfy the Pythagorean theorem?

37. Let y be the leg opposite from the angle θ in a right triangle whose hypotenuse is 1. (See Figure 5.134.) Find a formula in terms of y for each of the following expressions.

Figure 5.134: Use this
triangle to answer
Problem 37.

(a) $\cos\theta$ (b) $\tan\theta$ (c) $\cos(2\theta)$

(d) $\sin(\pi - \theta)$ (e) $\sin^2(\cos^{-1}(y))$

REVIEW PROBLEMS FOR CHAPTER FIVE

1. Make a paper airplane and unfold it so all the fold lines are flat and visible. Measure all the angles formed by fold lines and edges.

2. Consider the equation $\sin t = k$ for $-\pi \le t \le \pi$. Using graphs, explain why this equation:

   (a) Has one solution when $k = 1$.   (b) Has two solutions when $k = -1/2$.

   (c) Has three solutions when $k = 0$.   (d) Has no solution when $k = 2$.

3. Graph $y = \sin\theta$ for $0 \le \theta \le 360$ where θ is in degrees and put ticks marks on the x-axis at $\{0, 90, 180, 270, 360\}$. Use this graph to explain the sign of the sine function as θ goes through each of the four quadrants.

4. Graph $y = \sin(t)$ where $-6 \le t \le 6$, assuming

   (a) t is in degrees.   (b) t is in radians.

5. (a) Evaluate and compare the following four pairs of values: $\cos\left(\frac{\pi}{6}\right)$ and $\cos\left(-\frac{\pi}{6}\right)$, $\cos\left(\frac{3\pi}{4}\right)$ and $\cos\left(-\frac{3\pi}{4}\right)$, $\cos\left(\frac{7\pi}{6}\right)$ and $\cos\left(-\frac{7\pi}{6}\right)$, $\cos\left(\frac{11\pi}{6}\right)$ and $\cos\left(-\frac{11\pi}{6}\right)$. What do you observe?

   (b) Compare the following pairs of values: $\sin\left(\frac{\pi}{6}\right)$ and $\sin\left(-\frac{\pi}{6}\right)$, $\sin\left(\frac{3\pi}{4}\right)$ and $\sin\left(-\frac{3\pi}{4}\right)$, $\sin\left(\frac{7\pi}{6}\right)$ and $\sin\left(-\frac{7\pi}{6}\right)$, $\sin\left(\frac{11\pi}{6}\right)$ and $\sin\left(-\frac{11\pi}{6}\right)$. What do you observe?

   (c) Based on parts (a) and (b) what can you say about $\tan(x)$ and $\tan(-x)$?

6. Computers and calculators often show algebraically simple values in their decimal approximation forms. Without using a calculator you should be able to recognize the following set of common values in their decimal approximation form. Match the exact form to the decimal approximation.

   (a) $\pi/3$ (b) $\sqrt{2}/2$ (c) $\pi/6$

   (d) $\pi/4$ (e) $\sqrt{3}/2$ (f) $\pi/2$

   0.5235987756   1.570796327   1.047197551

   0.7853981634   0.7071067812   0.8660254038

7. Match the graph to the function:

   (a) $y = \sin(2t)$ (b) $y = (\sin t) + 2$ (c) $y = 2\sin t$ (d) $y = \sin(t + 2)$

Figure 5.135

8. Find a possible formula for the following trigonometric function:

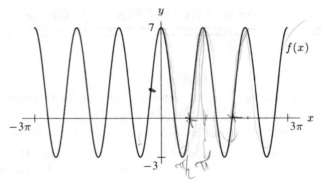

Figure 5.136

9. In a physics lab you collected the following data on the height above the floor of a weight bobbing on a spring attached to the ceiling.

    TABLE 5.20

secs	0.0	0.1	0.2	0.3	0.4	0.5
cm	120	136	165	180	166	133
secs	0.6	0.7	0.8	0.9	1.0	1.1
cm	120	135	164	179	165	133

    Find a sine function to model this data.

10. Table 5.21 shows the temperature in degrees Fahrenheit in Tucson, Arizona, every hour during a day in September.[3]

    TABLE 5.21

Time (am)	1:00	2:00	3:00	4:00	5:00	6:00
Temperature °F	69	67	66	65	65	65
Time (am)	7:00	8:00	9:00	10:00	11:00	Noon
Temperature °F	66	72	77	83	87	89
Time (pm)	1:00	2:00	3:00	4:00	5:00	6:00
Temperature °F	91	92	92	92	90	88
Time (pm)	7:00	8:00	9:00	10:00	11:00	Midnight
Temperature °F	81	78	76	76	74	72

    (a) Plot this data. (Draw a smooth curve fitting this data.)
    (b) Find the average temperature during the 24-hour period rounded to the nearest whole degree.
    (c) Suppose you want to model the temperature, H, by a trigonometric function of the form

    $$H = f(t) = A \sin \left(B(t - C) \right) + D$$

    where t is the time in hours since midnight. Use the graph to find reasonable values for A, B, C, and D.

    ---
    [3] Data from *The Tucson Citizen*, September 16, 1993

Chapter 8/ 94

11. An animal population increases from a low of 1200 in year $t = 0$, to a high of 3000 just four years later and then the population decreases back to 1200 in the next four years. Model this behavior by writing a sinusoidal function.

12. Suppose the angle θ is in the first quadrant, and that $\tan \theta = \dfrac{3}{4}$. Since $\tan \theta = \dfrac{\sin \theta}{\cos \theta}$, does this mean that $\sin \theta = 3$ and $\cos \theta = 4$?

$\vec{O} =$

13. For $f(t) = \tan(t)$ are there any limitations on
     (a) The input values of $f(t)$?   (b) The output values of $f(t)$?

14. If possible, find one exact zero of
     (a) $f(t) = \cos(t+2)$ (b) $f(t) = 2\cos(t)$ (c) $f(t) = \cos(2t)$ (d) $f(t) = \cos(t)+2$

15. In climates that require central heating, the setting of a household thermostat indicates the temperature at which the furnace will turn on. Water is boiled, and steam is forced into various radiators that then warm the house. Once the household temperature reaches the thermostat setting, the furnace shuts off. However, the radiators remain hot for some time, and so the household temperature continues rising for a while before it starts to drop. Once it drops back to the thermostat setting, the furnace relights and the cycle begins anew. As it takes some time for the radiators to reheat, the house will continue to cool even after the furnace has turned back on.

     (a) Suppose the household temperature, T, can be modeled by a trigonometric function. (See Figure 5.137.) Given the graph, what must be the setting on the thermostat? (Assume the furnace spends as much time on as it does off).
     (b) According to the graph, describe what is happening at $t = 0, 0.25, 0.5, 0.75, 1$.
     (c) Give a formula for $T = f(t)$, the temperature in terms of t (hours).
     (d) Describe the physical significance of the period, the amplitude, and the midline.
     (e) The house described in this exercise takes as much time to heat up as it does to cool down. Suppose another house takes 15 minutes to heat up but 45 minutes to cool. Sketch (roughly) its temperature over one hour. Label any significant points (such as times the furnace turns on or off). Is this the graph of a trigonometric function?

16. Which line segment in Figure 5.138 has length representing the value of the following expressions:

     (a) $\sin \theta$ (b) $\cos \theta$ (c) $\tan \theta$
     (d) $\dfrac{1}{\sin \theta}$ (e) $\dfrac{1}{\cos \theta}$ (f) $\dfrac{1}{\tan \theta}$

Figure 5.137   *Figure 5.138*

17. State all exact zeroes of the function $f(x) = 3\sin(\pi x - 1) + 1$.

18. Graph the following functions, labeling your axes, state the domain and range.
    (a) $f(x) = 2\cos^{-1}(x)$
    (b) $g(x) = \sin^{-1}(\pi x)$

19. Evaluate the following:
    (a) $\cos^{-1}\left(\frac{1}{2}\right)$ (b) $\cos^{-1}\left(-\frac{1}{2}\right)$
    (c) $\cos\left(\cos^{-1}\left(\frac{1}{2}\right)\right)$ (d) $\cos^{-1}\left(\cos\left(\frac{5\pi}{3}\right)\right)$

20. One student maintained that $\sin 2\theta \neq 2\sin\theta$, but another student said let $\theta = \pi$ and then $\sin 2\theta = 2\sin\theta$. Who is right?

21. Graph the two functions $f(t) = \cos t$ and $g(t) = \sin(t + \frac{\pi}{2})$. Describe.

22.

To check the calibration of their transit, two student surveyors used the carefully measured set-up shown (in meters). What angles in degrees for α and β should they get if their transit is accurate?

23. Two surveyors want to check their transit and have the test angle (in degrees) come out to an integer value. What triangle could they set up?

24. Knowing the height of the Columbia Tower in Seattle, determine the height of the Sea First Tower and the distance between them.

25. (a) Find expressions in terms of $a, b,$ and c for the sine, the cosine, and the tangent of the angle ϕ in Figure 5.139.
    (b) Based on your answers in part (a), show that $\sin\phi = \cos\theta$ and $\cos\phi = \sin\theta$.

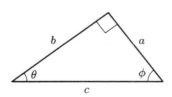

Figure 5.139

26. Find the value of the angle θ shown in Figure 5.140.

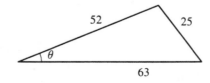

Figure 5.140: Find the value of θ

27. Figure 5.141 gives a right triangle ABC with sides a, b, and c.

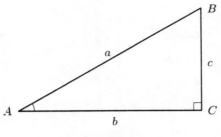

Figure 5.141

(a) If angle $A = 30°$ and $b = 2\sqrt{3}$, find the lengths of the other sides and find the other angles of triangle ABC.

(b) Repeat part (a), this time assuming that $a = 25$ and $c = 24$.

28. Find the angles of the triangle in Figure 5.142.

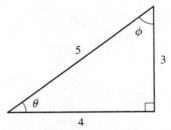

Figure 5.142: Triangle with three known sides

29. This problem outlines another approach to prove the Law of Cosines.

(a) Using Figure 5.143 as a guide, apply the Pythagorean theorem twice, as well as the definition of $\cos C$, to prove the Law of Cosines.

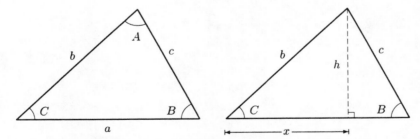

Figure 5.143: Use these diagrams to derive the Law of Cosines

(b) In Figure 5.143, we assumed that the angle C was acute — that is, less than 90°. Give a derivation similar to the one in part (b) assuming that C is obtuse, or greater than 90°.

Chapter 9

Polar Coordinates, Polar Equations of Conics, Parametric Equations, Defined Curves, Complex Numbers and Hyperbolic Functions

8.5 POLAR COORDINATES

Points in the plane are usually labeled with *Cartesian coordinates* (x, y). Here x is the horizontal distance from the origin, and y is the vertical distance, as shown in Figure 8.30. However, there is an alternative way of describing the location of a point. We can specify the length r and angle θ of the position vector directed from the origin to the point. As usual, θ is the angle measured counterclockwise from the positive x-axis to the line joining P to the origin. The labels r and θ are called the *polar coordinates* of point P. When using polar coordinates, we measure θ in *radians*.

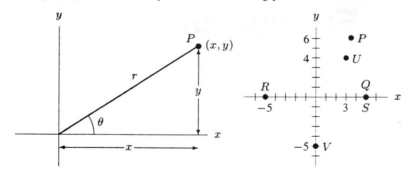

Figure 8.30: Cartesian and polar coordinates   ***Figure 8.31***

---

[4] Adapted from Cavalli-Sforza and Edwards, "Models and Estimation Procedures," Am J. Hum. Genet., Vol. 19 (1967), pp. 223-57.

Relation Between Cartesian and Polar Coordinates

By applying trigonometry to the right triangle in Figure 8.30, we see that

- $x = r \cos \theta$ and $y = r \sin \theta$
- $r = \sqrt{x^2 + y^2}$
- $\tan \theta = \dfrac{y}{x}, x \neq 0$

Example 1 (a) Give the Cartesian coordinates of the points with polar coordinates (r, θ) given by $P = (7, \pi/3)$, $Q = (5, 0)$, $R = (5, \pi)$, and $S = (-5, \pi)$.

(b) Give the polar coordinates of the points with Cartesian coordinates (x, y) given by $U = (3, 4)$ and $V = (0, -5)$.

Solution The points are shown in Figure 8.31

(a) Point P is located by a position vector of length 7 directed at an angle of $\pi/3$ radians (60°) to the positive x-axis. We see that the Cartesian coordinates of P are given by

$$x = r \cos \theta = 7 \cos \frac{\pi}{3} = \frac{7}{2} \quad \text{and} \quad y = r \sin \theta = 7 \sin \frac{\pi}{3} = \frac{7\sqrt{3}}{2}.$$

Point Q is located by a position vector of length 5 units that points along the positive x-axis. The Cartesian coordinates of point P are the same as its polar coordinates: $(x, y) = (5, 0)$. To confirm this, we have

$$x = r \cos \theta = 5 \cos 0 = 5 \quad \text{and} \quad y = r \sin \theta = 5 \sin 0 = 0.$$

Now for point R:

$$x = r \cos \theta = 5 \cos \pi = -5 \quad \text{and} \quad y = r \sin \theta = 5 \sin \pi = 0.$$

(b) For $U = (3, 4)$, we see that $r = \sqrt{3^2 + 4^2} = 5$ and that $\tan \theta = 4/3$. One possible value for θ is $\theta = \arctan 4/3 = 0.93$ radians or about 53.1°. There are other possibilities, because the angle θ can be allowed to wrap around more than once. But this is the most straightforward answer. Similarly, since the point $V = (0, -5)$ falls on the y-axis, we can choose $r = 5$, $\theta = 3\pi/2$, or instead $r = 5$, $\theta = -\pi/2$. But the most straightforward choice is the one with θ between 0 and 2π. Notice that for point V we cannot use our conversion formulas to find θ, because the tangent of any angle parallel to the y-axis is undefined:

$$\tan \theta = \frac{y}{x} = \frac{-5}{0}, \quad \text{so } \tan \theta \text{ is undefined.}$$

Graphing Equations in Polar Coordinates

The equations for certain graphs are much simpler when expressed in polar coordinates than in Cartesian coordinates. On the other hand, some graphs that have simple equations in Cartesian coordinates have complicated equations in polar coordinates.

Example 2 (a) Describe in words the graphs of the equation $y = 1$ (in Cartesian coordinates) and the equation $r = 1$ (in polar coordinates).

(b) Write the equation $y = 1$ using Cartesian coordinates. Write the equation $y = 1$ using polar coordinates.

Solution (a) The equation $y = 1$ describes a horizontal line. Every point on this line has y-coordinate 1. Notice that since the equation $y = 1$ places no restrictions on the value of x, it describes (by default) *every* point having a y-value of 1, no matter what the value of its x-coordinate. Similarly, the equation $r = 1$ places no restrictions on the value of θ. Thus, it describes *every* point having an r-value of 1, no matter what the point's value of θ. This set of points is the unit circle, because every point on this circle is 1 unit from the origin. See Figure 8.32.

(b) Since $r = \sqrt{x^2 + y^2}$, we can rewrite the equation $r = 1$ using Cartesian coordinates as $\sqrt{x^2 + y^2} = 1$, or, squaring both sides, as $x^2 + y^2 = 1$. We see that the equation for the unit circle is simpler in polar coordinates than it is in Cartesian coordinates.

On the other hand, since $y = r \sin \theta$, we can rewrite the equation $y = 1$ in polar coordinates as $r \sin \theta = 1$, or, dividing both sides by $\sin \theta$, as $r = 1 / \sin \theta$. We see that the equation for this horizontal line is simpler in Cartesian coordinates than it is in polar coordinates.

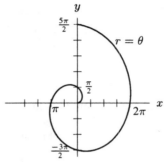

Figure 8.32: The graph of the equation $r = 1$ is the unit circle because $r = 1$ for every point regardless of the value of θ. The graph of $y = 1$ is a horizontal line since $y = 1$ for any x

Figure 8.33: A graph of the Archimedean spiral $r = \theta$

Example 3   The graph of the equation $r = \theta$ in polar coordinates is quite interesting. It is called an *Archimedean spiral* after the ancient Greek mathematician Archimedes who described its properties (although not by using polar coordinates). To visualize what this graph looks like, we can construct a table of values, as in Table 8.2. To help us think about the shape of the spiral, let's write the angles in Table 8.2 using degrees and the r-values using decimals. This has been done in Table 8.3.

TABLE 8.2   *Points on the Archimedean spiral $r = \theta$, with θ in radians*

θ	0	$\frac{\pi}{6}$	$\frac{\pi}{3}$	$\frac{\pi}{2}$	$\frac{2\pi}{3}$	$\frac{5\pi}{6}$	π	$\frac{7\pi}{6}$	$\frac{4\pi}{3}$	$\frac{3\pi}{2}$
r	0	$\frac{\pi}{6}$	$\frac{\pi}{3}$	$\frac{\pi}{2}$	$\frac{2\pi}{3}$	$\frac{5\pi}{6}$	π	$\frac{7\pi}{6}$	$\frac{4\pi}{3}$	$\frac{3\pi}{2}$

TABLE 8.3   *Points on the Archimedean spiral $r = \theta$, with θ in degrees*

θ	0	30°	60°	90°	120°	150°	180°	210°	240°	270°
r	0.00	0.52	1.05	1.57	2.09	2.62	3.14	3.67	4.19	4.71

Notice that as the angle θ increases, points on the curve move farther from the origin. At 0°, the point is at the origin. At 30°, it is 0.52 units away from the origin, at 60° it is 1.05 units away, and at 90° it is 1.57 units away. We can see why the graph of this equation is in fact a spiral: As the angle winds around, the point traces out a curve that moves steadily away from the origin. In fact, as the angle θ increases past 2π (360°), the spiral will continue to wind around the origin at an ever increasing distance, forming more circuits of the spiral. (See Figure 8.33.) Again we note the simplicity of the equation for such a complex curve.

Problems for Section 8.5

1. Suppose the origin is at the center of a clock, with the positive x-axis going through 3 and the positive y-axis going through 12. Suppose the hour hand is 3 cm long and the minute hand is 4 cm long. What are the coordinates and polar coordinates, H and M, of the tips of the hour hand and minute hand at the following times?

(a) 12 noon (b) 3 pm (c) 9 am
(d) 11 am (e) 1:30 pm (f) 7 am
(g) 3:30 pm (h) 9:15 am

2. Describe the following regions in polar coordinates: (what r and θ values are allowed?)

Figure 8.34

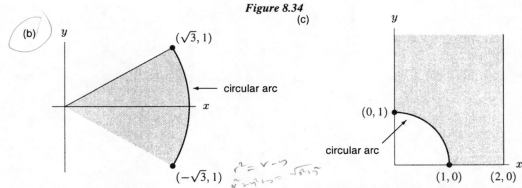

Figure 8.35

Figure 8.36: Note: Region extends indefinitely in the y-direction

3. (a) Graph the equation $r = 1 - \sin\theta$ on a set of r, θ-axes. Mark the points $\theta = 0, \pi/3, \pi/2, 2\pi/3, \pi, \cdots$.
   (b) Now use the marked points to help graph the equation $r = 1 - \sin\theta$ in the x, y-plane. (Hint: this curve is called a *cardioid*.)
   (c) At what point(s) does the cardioid $r = 1 - \sin\theta$ intersect a circle of radius 1/2 centered at the origin?
   (d) Graph the curve $r = 1 - \sin 2\theta$ in the x, y-plane, and compare this graph to the cardioid $r = 1 - \sin\theta$.

Chapter 9/   5

SECTION 63

POLAR EQUATIONS OF CONICS

A. Focus-Directrix Property

The definition of parabola in Section 59 made use of a focus and a directrix. The following result shows that ellipses and hyperbolas can be characterized in the same way.

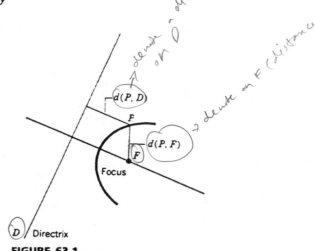

FIGURE 63.1

Let D be a fixed line (the **directrix**) and F a fixed point (the **focus**) not on D. For each point P in the plane of D and F, let $d(P, D)$ and $d(P, F)$ denote the distances of P from D and from F, respectively (Figure 63.1). Let e denote a positive constant (the **eccentricity**). Then the set of all P such that

$$\frac{d(P, F)}{d(P, D)} = e \qquad (63.1)$$

is

an ellipse if $0 < e < 1$,

a parabola if $e = 1$, and

a hyperbola if $e > 1$.

Proof. Choose the Cartesian coordinate system with the origin at F and the line $x = -d$ coincident with the line D (Figure 63.2). Then $P(x, y)$ satisfies the conditions of (63.1) iff

$$\frac{d(P, F)}{d(P, D)} = e, \quad \text{or} \quad \frac{\sqrt{x^2 + y^2}}{x + d} = e. \qquad (63.2)$$

If we square both sides of the last equation and simplify, we get

$$x^2 + y^2 = e^2x^2 + 2de^2x + d^2e^2$$
$$(1 - e^2)x^2 - 2de^2x + y^2 = d^2e^2. \qquad (63.3)$$

Chapter 9/   8

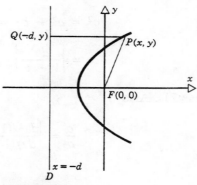

FIGURE 63.2

Suppose $e = 1$. In this case, the equations in (63.2) correspond directly to the definition of a parabola. Alternatively, Equation (63.3) can be rewritten as

$$y^2 = 4 \cdot \frac{d}{2}\left(x + \frac{d}{2}\right).$$

By (59.7), this represents a parabola with directrix $x = -d$, focus $(0, 0)$, vertex $(-d/2, 0)$, and axis $y = 0$.

Suppose $e \neq 0$. Then $1 - e^2 \neq 0$, so Equation (63.3) can be rewritten as

$$x^2 - \frac{2de^2}{1 - e^2}x + \frac{y^2}{1 - e^2} = \frac{d^2e^2}{1 - e^2}.$$

We can complete the square on the x terms by adding $[de^2/(1 - e^2)]^2$ to both sides. If we then simplify the right side and divide both sides by $d^2e^2/(1 - e^2)^2$, the result is

$$\frac{\left(x - \dfrac{de^2}{1 - e^2}\right)^2}{\dfrac{d^2e^2}{(1 - e^2)^2}} + \frac{y^2}{\dfrac{d^2e^2}{1 - e^2}} = 1. \tag{63.4}$$

If $0 < e < 1$, then the expression beneath y^2 is positive and the graph of Equation (63.4) is an ellipse. If $e > 1$, the expression beneath y^2 is negative and the graph is a hyperbola. $\square$

Equation (63.4) shows that, in the notation of Section 60,

$$a^2 = \frac{d^2e^2}{(1 - e^2)^2} \quad \text{and} \quad b^2 = \frac{d^2e^2}{1 - e^2}.$$

It follows that

$$c^2 = a^2 - b^2 = \frac{d^2 e^4}{(1 - e^2)^2}, \quad \text{and}$$

$$c = \left| \frac{de^2}{1 - e^2} \right| \tag{63.5}$$

(Exercise 21). Also

$$\frac{c}{a} = \left| \frac{de^2/(1 - e^2)}{de/(1 - e^2)} \right| = e,$$

so

$$e = c/a. \tag{63.6}$$

(Since $a > 0$, $c > 0$, and $e > 0$, we have $e = c/a$ rather than $e = -c/a$.) Thus, for ellipses, the eccentricity defined here is the same as in Section 60C.

The conclusion of (63.1) shows that the condition in (63.1) always produces a conic section. It can be proved that, conversely, every conic section can be defined using the focus-directrix property in (63.1), with the following exceptions: circles, points, lines, and pairs of intersecting lines. For the case of circles, notice that Equation (63.4) would produce a circle iff $0 < e < 1$ and the two denominators were equal; but the two denominators are equal only for $e = 0$, so a circle is not possible.

B. Polar Equations

Polar coordinates and polar equations were studied in Section 43. The polar equations of conic sections can be derived easily using Statement (63.1). First, assume that the focus is at the origin of a polar coordinate system and that the directrix is perpendicular to the polar axis and d units to the left of the origin (Figure 63.3). Then $P[r, \theta]$ is on the conic section D defined by (63.1) iff

$$\frac{d(P, F)}{d(P, D)} = e$$

$$\frac{r}{d + r \cos \theta} = e$$

$$r = e(d + r \cos \theta)$$

$$r = \frac{de}{1 - e \cos \theta}. \tag{63.7}$$

With the focus at the origin, and the directrix d units from the focus and either parallel to or perpendicular to the polar axis, the three possibilities other than that in Figure 63.3 are these: directrix d units to the right of F, d units

FIGURE 63.3

below F, or d units above F. The corresponding conics have the following equations, respectively.

$$r = \frac{de}{1 + e \cos \theta} \tag{63.8}$$

$$r = \frac{de}{1 - e \sin \theta} \tag{63.9}$$

$$r = \frac{de}{1 + e \sin \theta} \tag{63.10}$$

Figure 63.4 illustrates the possibilities in (63.7)–(63.10). The derivations for (63.8)–(63.10) are similar to that for (63.7). (See Exercises 22–24.) We call the equations in (63.7)–(63.10) the **standard forms** for the polar equations of the graphs they represent. A key in each case is that the constant term in the denominator must be 1.

FIGURE 63.4

Example 63.1 Draw the graph of $r = \dfrac{6}{2 - \sin \theta}$.

Solution This equation will have the form of Equation (63.9) if we divide both the numerator and denominator of the right side by 2.

$$r = \frac{3}{1 - \frac{1}{2}\sin\theta}$$

The coefficient of $\sin\theta$ is $\frac{1}{2}$, so $e = \frac{1}{2}$ and the graph is an ellipse $(0 < e < 1)$. The major axis is along the line $\theta = \pi/2$ [Figure 63.4c], so the vertices (endpoints of the major axis) correspond to $\theta = \pi/2$ and $\theta = 3\pi/2$. Thus the vertices are $[6, \pi/2]$ and $[2, 3\pi/2]$ (Figure 63.5). The center is $[2, \pi/2]$, the midpoint of the major axis. Because the length of the semimajor axis is a (Section 60), we have $a = 4$. Therefore, $c = ea = \frac{1}{2}(4) = 2$ and $b^2 = a^2 - c^2 = 16 - 4 = 12$, so the length of the semiminor axis is $\sqrt{12}$. Points on the graph other than the endpoints of the major and minor axes can be found by assigning values to θ, as in Section 43. As usual, the number of coordinate pairs to be computed depends on the accuracy required. Figure 63.5 shows the graph in this case.

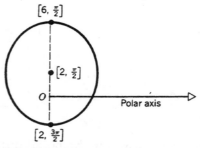

FIGURE 63.5

Example 63.2   Find the polar equation of the hyperbola with one focus at the origin and with vertices at $[1, \pi]$ and $[5, \pi]$.

Solution   The center is at $[3, \pi]$, the midpoint of the segment joining the vertices. Also, the transverse axis is along the line $\theta = \pi$. The distance between the center and a vertex is a, so $a = 2$ in this case (Figure 61.3). The distance between the center and a focus is c, so $c = 3$. Therefore, $e = c/a = \frac{3}{2}$.

We can now compute d from Equation (63.5).

$$d = \frac{|c(1 - e^2)|}{e^2} = \frac{|3\left[1 - \left(\frac{3}{2}\right)^2\right]|}{\left(\frac{3}{2}\right)^2} = \frac{5}{3}$$

Because a vertex is to the left of the origin, the appropriate standard form is (63.7). With $d = \frac{5}{3}$ and $e = \frac{3}{2}$, we get

$$r = \frac{\frac{5}{2}}{1 - \frac{3}{2}\cos\theta}, \quad \text{or} \quad r = \frac{5}{2 - 3\cos\theta}.$$

Exercises for Section 63

Draw the graph of each equation in Exercises 1-12.

1. $r = \dfrac{4}{1 + \sin \theta}$

2. $r = \dfrac{6}{1 - 2 \sin \theta}$

3. $r = \dfrac{2}{1 + \frac{1}{2} \cos \theta}$

4. $r = \dfrac{8}{1 - \frac{3}{2} \cos \theta}$

5. $r = \dfrac{8}{1 - \frac{1}{4} \sin \theta}$

6. $r = \dfrac{5}{1 + \cos \theta}$

7. $r = \dfrac{4}{4 + 3 \cos \theta}$

8. $r = \dfrac{5}{2 + 2 \sin \theta}$

9. $r = \dfrac{6}{3 - 5 \sin \theta}$

10. $r = \dfrac{10}{3 - 3 \sin \theta}$

11. $r = \dfrac{10}{5 + 3 \cos \theta}$

12. $r = \dfrac{6}{3 - 2 \cos \theta}$

In Exercises 13-18, find the polar equation of the conic section satisfying the given conditions and with a focus at the origin.

13. Eccentricity 3/4 and vertical directrix 3 units to the left of the origin.

14. Eccentricity 5/4 and center at $[3, 3\pi/2]$.

15. Parabola with vertex at $[10, \pi/2]$.

16. Eccentricity 2 and the other focus at $[6, 0]$.

17. Eccentricity 1 and horizontal directrix 2 units below the origin.

18. Ellipse with vertices at $[1, \pi/2]$ and $[8, 3\pi/2]$.

19. If $e > 1$, then the graph of Equation (63.7) is a hyperbola. What are the polar coordinates of its vertices?

20. If $e < 1$, then the graph of Equation (63.9) is an ellipse. Find the lengths of its major and minor axes.

21. Use the values of a^2 and b^2 preceding Equation (63.5) to compute the value of c^2, and then simplify to get c as in (63.5).

Exercises 22-24 are similar to the derivation of Equation (63.7). In each case the focus is at the origin and d units from the directrix.

22. Derive Equation (63.8) for a conic section with directrix to the right of the focus.

23. Derive Equation (63.9) for a conic section with directrix below the focus.

24. Derive Equation (63.10) for a conic section with directrix above the focus.

9.2 PARAMETRIC EQUATIONS

Robots on Mars

Recent fossil evidence of microbial life on Mars has kindled interest in sending spacecraft to that planet for further investigation. Such missions may include the use of unmanned robots that can move around the Martian landscape collecting samples and taking pictures.

How is such a robot to be controlled? In other words, how can we tell it where it should go, how fast, and when? Imagine that the robot is moving around on the xy-plane. Clearly, the surface of Mars is not so flat as the xy-plane, but this will make for a useful first approximation. If we then choose the origin $(0,0)$ to be the spot where the robot's spacecraft lands, we can direct its motion by giving it (x, y) coordinates to which it should travel.

For instance, suppose we select the positive y-axis so that it points north (that is, towards the northern pole of Mars) and the positive x-axis so that it points east. Suppose also that our units of measurement are in meters, so that (for instance) the coordinates $(3, 8)$ indicate a point that is 3 m to the east and 8 m to the north of the landing site.

Now imagine that we program the robot to move to the following coordinates immediately after it lands:

$$(0,0) \quad \rightarrow \quad (1,1) \quad \rightarrow \quad (2,2) \quad \rightarrow \quad (2,3) \quad \rightarrow \quad (2,4).$$

These points have been plotted in Figure 9.2. From the figure, we see that the robot first heads northeast until it arrives at the point $(2, 2)$. It then heads due north until it arrives at the point $(2, 4)$, where it stops.

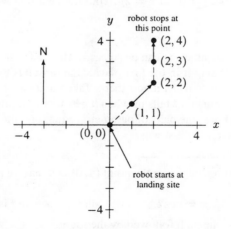

Figure 9.2: The robot is programmed to move along this path

Programming the Robot Using a Parameter

A more efficient way to program the robot's path is to use a *parameter*. To do this, we need two equations: one for the robot's x-coordinate, given by $x = f(t)$, and one for its y-coordinate, given by $y = g(t)$. The equation for x describes the robot's east-west motion, and the equation for y describes its north-south motion. The two equations for x and y are called *parametric equations* with *parameter t*.

Example 1   Suppose we program the robot to follow a path defined by

$$x = 2t, \qquad y = t \qquad \text{for} \quad 0 \le t \le 5,$$

where t is time in minutes. Describe the path followed by the robot.

Solution   At time $t = 0$, the robot's position is given by

$$x = 2 \cdot 0 = 0, \qquad y = 0,$$

so it starts at the point $(0, 0)$. One minute later, at $t = 1$, its position is given by

$$x = 2 \cdot 1 = 2, \qquad y = 1,$$

so it has moved to the point $(2, 1)$. At time $t = 2$, its position is given by

$$x = 2 \cdot 2 = 4, \qquad y = 2,$$

so it has moved to the point $(4, 2)$. Continuing in this fashion, we see that the path followed by the robot is given by

$$(0, 0) \quad \to \quad (2, 1) \quad \to \quad (4, 2) \quad \to \quad (6, 3) \quad \to \quad (8, 4) \quad \to \quad (10, 5).$$

At time $t = 5$, the robot stops at the point $(10, 5)$. This is because we have restricted the values of t to the interval $0 \le t \le 5$—in other words, we have told the robot to stop moving after 5 minutes. Figure 9.3 shows the path followed by the robot. We see from the figure that the graph is a straight line.

In the previous example, notice that we can use substitution to rewrite our formula for x in terms of y: $x = 2t$, but $t = y$, so $x = 2y$. Thus the path followed by the robot is given by the equation

$$y = \frac{1}{2}x.$$

Since the parameter t can be so easily eliminated from our equations, you may wonder why we should bother using it in the first place. One reason is that it can be useful to know not only *where* the robot is but also *when* it gets there. Taken together, the values of x and y tell us where the robot is, while the parameter t tells us when it gets there. Another reason for introducing the parameter t is less obvious: For some pairs of parametric equations, the parameter t cannot be so easily eliminated, as the next example illustrates.

Example 2   Suppose the robot begins at the point $(1, 0)$ and that we program it to follow the path defined by the equations

$$x = \cos t, \qquad y = \sin t \qquad \text{where } t \text{ is in minutes,} \quad 0 \le t \le 6.$$

(a)   Describe the path followed by the robot.
(b)   What happens when you try to eliminate the parameter t from these equations?

Figure 9.3: The path followed by the robot if
$x = 2t, y = t$ for $0 \le t \le 5$

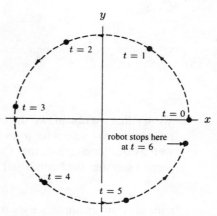

Figure 9.4: The path followed by the robot
if $x = \cos t, y = \sin t$ for $0 \le t \le 6$

Solution   (a)   At time $t = 0$, the robot's position is given by

$$x = \cos 0 = 1, \qquad y = \sin 0 = 0$$

so it starts at the point $(1, 0)$, as required. After one minute, that is, at time $t = 1$, its position is given by

$$x = \cos 1 = 0.54, \qquad y = \sin 1 = 0.84.$$

Thus, it has moved somewhat west and north. At time $t = 2$ its position is given by

$$x = \cos 2 = -0.42, \qquad y = \sin 2 = 0.91.$$

Now it is even farther west and (slightly) farther north. Continuing, we see that the path followed by the robot is given by

$$(1, 0) \rightarrow (0.54, 0.84) \quad \rightarrow \quad (-0.42, 0.91) \quad \rightarrow \quad (-0.99, 0.14)$$
$$\rightarrow (-0.65, -0.76) \quad \rightarrow \quad (0.28, -0.96) \quad \rightarrow \quad (0.96, -0.28).$$

Figure 9.4 shows the path followed by the robot. We see from the figure that the path is circular with a radius of one meter. We also see that at the end of 6 minutes the robot has not quite returned to its starting point at $(1, 0)$.

(b)   Instead of requiring that $0 \le t \le 6$, let's assume that t can take on any value. One way to eliminate t from this pair of equations is to use the Pythagorean identity,

$$\cos^2 t + \sin^2 t = 1.$$

Since $x = \cos t$ and $y = \sin t$, we can substitute x and y into this equation:

$$(\underbrace{\cos t}_{x})^2 + (\underbrace{\sin t}_{y})^2 = 1$$

$$x^2 + y^2 = 1.$$

We have successfully eliminated t, but can we solve for y in terms of x? Attempting to do so, we obtain

$$x^2 + y^2 = 1$$
$$y^2 = 1 - x^2$$
$$y = \begin{cases} +\sqrt{1 - x^2} \\ -\sqrt{1 - x^2} \end{cases}$$

We see that we obtain two different equations for y in terms of x. The first, $y = +\sqrt{1 - x^2}$, returns positive values for y (as well as 0), while the second returns negative values for y (as well as 0). We conclude that the first equation specifies the top half of the circle, while the second specifies the bottom half.

In the previous example, we see that y is not a function of x, because for all x-values (other than 1 and -1) there are two possible y values. But this merely confirms what we already knew, because the graph in Figure 9.4 fails the vertical line test.

Different Motions Along the Same Path

It is possible to parameterize the same curve (or a part of it) in more than one way, as the next example illustrates.

Example 3   Describe the motion of the robot if it follows the path given by

$$x = \cos \frac{1}{2}t, \qquad y = \sin \frac{1}{2}t \qquad \text{for} \quad 0 \le t \le 6.$$

Solution   At time $t = 0$, the robot's position is given by

$$x = \cos\left(\frac{1}{2} \cdot 0\right) = 1, \qquad y = \sin\left(\frac{1}{2} \cdot 0\right) = 0$$

so it starts at the point $(1, 0)$, as before. After one minute, that is, at time $t = 1$, its position (rounded to thousandths) is given by

$$x = \cos\left(\frac{1}{2} \cdot 1\right) = 0.878, \qquad y = \sin\left(\frac{1}{2} \cdot 1\right) = 0.479.$$

At time $t = 2$ its position is given by

$$x = \cos\left(\frac{1}{2} \cdot 2\right) = 0.540, \qquad y = \sin\left(\frac{1}{2} \cdot 2\right) = 0.841.$$

Continuing, we see that the path followed by the robot is given by

$$(1,0) \to (0.878, 0.479) \to (0.540, 0.841) \to (0.071, 0.997)$$
$$\to (-0.416, 0.909) \to (-0.801, 0.598) \to (-0.990, 0.141).$$

Figure 9.5 shows the path described by these parametric equations. We see from the figure that the path is again circular with a radius of one meter. However, at the end of 6 minutes the robot has not even made it half way around the circle. In fact, because we have multiplied the parameter t by a factor of $1/2$, the robot moves at half its original rate.

Figure 9.5: The path followed by the robot if $x = \cos\frac{1}{2}t$, $y = \sin\frac{1}{2}t$ for $0 \leq t \leq 6$

Example 4   Describe the motion of the robot if it follows the path given by:

(a) $x = \cos(-t)$, $y = \sin(-t)$ for $0 \leq t \leq 6$
(b) $x = \cos t$, $y = \sin t$ for $0 \leq t \leq 10$

Solution   (a) Figure 9.6 shows the path followed by the robot. In this case, the robot travels around the circle in the clockwise direction, which is the opposite of what it did in Example 2 and 3.

(b) Figure 9.7 shows the path followed by the robot. In this case, the robot travels around the circle more than once but less than twice, coming to a stop somewhere roughly southwest of the landing site.

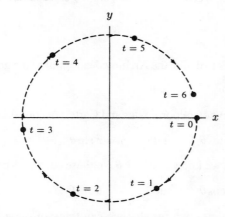

Figure 9.6: The path followed by the robot if $x = \cos(-t)$, $y = \sin(-t)$ for $0 \leq t \leq 6$

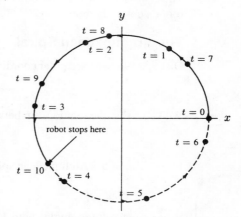

Figure 9.7: $x = \cos t$, $y = \sin t$ for $0 \leq t \leq 10$

Other Types of Parametric Curves

Using parametric equations, it is possible to describe extremely complicated motions. For instance, suppose we want our robot to follow a rambling path in order to cover a greater variety of terrain. The parametric equations

$$x = 20\cos t + 4\cos(4\sqrt{5}t)$$
$$y = 20\sin t + 4\sin(4\sqrt{8}t),$$

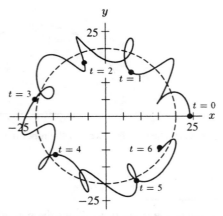

Figure 9.8: An unusual parametrically
defined curve

describe such a path, as we can see from Figure 9.8. Notice that the path is vaguely circular and that the robot moves in (more or less) a counterclockwise direction. In fact, the dashed-in circle shown in Figure 9.8 is given by the parametric equations

$$x = 20\cos t, \qquad y = 20\sin t \qquad \text{for } 0 \le t \le 2\pi.$$

Thus, we see that it is the other terms, $4\cos(4\sqrt{5}t)$ and $4\sin(4\sqrt{8}t)$, that are responsible for the robot's unsteady motion.

The Archimedean Spiral

On page 496, we used polar coordinates to define the Archimedean spiral as the graph of the equation

$$r = \theta.$$

We know that the relationship between polar coordinates and Cartesian coordinates is given by

$$x = r\cos\theta \qquad \text{and} \qquad y = r\sin\theta.$$

In the case of the Archimedean spiral, we know that $r = \theta$, so these equations can be written as

$$x = \theta\cos\theta \qquad \text{and} \qquad y = \theta\sin\theta.$$

If we replace θ (an angle) with t (a time), we see that we can think of these equations as being parametric equations for the spiral:

$$x = t\cos t$$
$$y = t\sin t.$$

This curve is shown in Figure 9.9 for $0 \le t \le 4\pi$. The value of t has been labeled at several points along the curve. Notice that as t increases, the curve is traced out in the counter-clockwise direction.

Lissajous Figures

Some parametrically defined functions are quite beautiful and have a high degree of symmetry. One example is given by the equations

$$x = \cos 3t, \qquad y = \sin 5t \qquad \text{for } 0 \le t \le 2\pi.$$

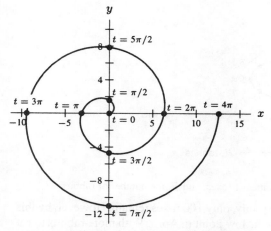

Figure 9.9: The Archimedean spiral given by
$x = t \cos t, y = t \sin t, 0 \le t \le 4\pi$

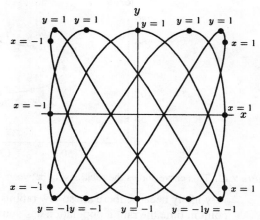

Figure 9.10: A Lissajous figure: $x = \cos 3t$,
$y = \sin 5t, 0 \le t \le 2\pi$

A graph of this curve is shown in Figure 9.10. It is an example of a *Lissajous figure*.

To understand why this Lissajous figure looks the way it does, consider the fact that $y = \sin 5t$ completes 5 full oscillations on the interval $0 \le t \le 2\pi$. Thus, since the amplitude of $y = \sin 5t$ is 1, y will reach a maximum value of 1 at five different values of t. (These t-values are $t = \pi/10$, $5\pi/10, 9\pi/10, 13\pi/10$, and $17\pi/10$, as you can check for yourself.) Similarly, the value of y will be -1 at another five different values of t. The curve must climb to a high point at $y = 1$ for a total of five times and fall to a low point of $y = -1$ for a total of five times. As you can see from Figure 9.10, this is exactly what happens.

Meanwhile, since $x = \cos 3t$, the value of x will oscillate between 1 and -1 a total of 3 times on the interval $0 \le t \le 2\pi$. Thus, the curve must move to its right-most boundary at $x = 1$ for a total of 3 times and to its left-most boundary at $x = -1$ for a total of 3 times. Consulting Figure 9.10, we see that this is indeed the case.

Foxes and Rabbits

In a certain national park there is a population of foxes that prey on a population of rabbits. Suppose that F gives the number of foxes and R gives the number of rabbits and that

$$R = 1000 - 500 \sin \frac{\pi}{6} t \qquad \text{and} \qquad F = 150 + 50 \cos \frac{\pi}{6} t$$

where t is the number of months since January 1.

Taken together, these two equations parametrically define the curve shown in Figure 9.11. We see that F is not a function of R is because this curve fails the vertical line test.

Even though R and F are functions of t and not of each other, we can still use the curve to analyze the relationship between the rabbit population and the fox population. In January there are 1000 rabbits but they are beginning to die off rapidly, so that by April only 500 rabbits remain. However, by July the rabbit population has rebounded to 1000 rabbits, and by October it has soared to 1500 rabbits. At this point the rabbit population begins to fall again, so that by the following April there are once more only 500 rabbits.

As the rabbit population rises and falls, so does the fox population. However, the two populations do not always rise or fall at the same time of year. In January, the fox population is at its greatest, numbering 200 foxes. By April, it has fallen to 150 foxes. By this point the rabbit population is at its minimum and is slowly beginning to recover. Even so, the fox population continues to fall quite fast,

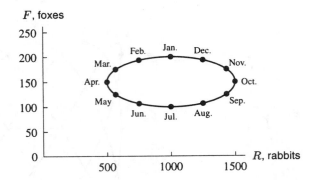

Figure 9.11: This curve shows the relationship between F, the number of foxes, and R, the number of rabbits

very likely because there are so few rabbits to eat. By July, only 100 foxes remain. However, by this point in time the rabbit population has doubled from its low point in April. With more rabbits to eat (and fewer foxes to share them with), the fox population begins to stage a comeback. By October, when the rabbit population is at its largest, the fox population is growing rapidly, so that by January it has returned to its maximum size of 200 foxes. By this point, though, the rabbit population is already dropping rapidly, no doubt because there are so many hungry foxes around. We see that the cycle begins to repeat.

Using Graphs to Parameterize a Curve

Example 5   Figure 9.12 shows the graphs of two functions, $f(t)$ and $g(t)$. Describe the motion of the particle whose coordinates at time t are $x = f(t), y = g(t)$.

Figure 9.12: Graphs of $x = f(t)$ and $y = g(t)$ used to trace out the path $(f(t), g(t))$ in Figure 9.13

Solution   Between times $t = 0$ and $t = 1$, the x-coordinate increases from 0 to 1, while the y-coordinate stays fixed at 0. The particle moves along the x-axis from $(0, 0)$ to $(1, 0)$. Then, between times $t = 1$ and $t = 2$, the x-coordinate stays fixed at $x = 1$, while the y-coordinate increases from 0 to 1. Thus, the particle moves along the vertical line from $(1, 0)$ to $(1, 1)$. Between times $t = 2$ and $t = 3$, it moves horizontally backward to $(0, 1)$, and between times $t = 3$ and $t = 4$ it moves down the y-axis to $(0, 0)$. Thus, it traces out the square in Figure 9.13.

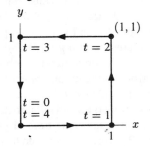

Figure 9.13: The square parameterized by $(f(t), g(t))$

Problems for Section 9.2

For Problems 1–4, describe the motion of a particle whose position at time t is $x = f(t)$, $y = g(t)$, where the graphs of f and g are as shown.

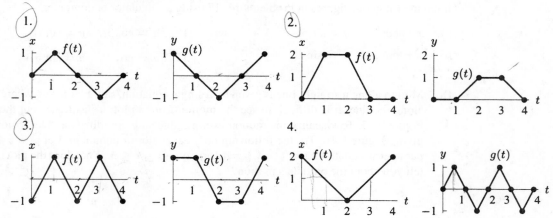

Problems 5–8 give parameterizations of the unit circle or a part of it. In each case, describe in words how the circle is traced out, including when and where the particle is moving clockwise and when and where the particle is moving counterclockwise.

5. $x = \cos t$, $\quad y = -\sin t$

6. $x = \sin t$, $\quad y = \cos t$

7. $x = \cos(t^2)$, $\quad y = \sin(t^2)$

8. $x = \cos(\ln t)$, $\quad y = \sin(\ln t)$

9. Describe the similarities and differences among the motions in the plane given by the following three pairs of parametric equations:
   (a) $x = t$, $\quad y = t^2$ (b) $x = t^2$, $\quad y = t^4$ (c) $x = t^3$, $\quad y = t^6$.

10. As t varies, the following parametric equations trace out a line in the plane

$$x = 2 + 3t, \quad y = 4 + 7t.$$

   (a) What part of the line is obtained by restricting t to nonnegative numbers?
   (b) What part of the line is obtained if t is restricted to $-1 \le t \le 0$?
   (c) How should t be restricted to give the part of the line to the left of the y-axis?

11. Suppose $a, b, c, d, m, n, p, q > 0$. Match each pair of parametric equations below with one of the lines l_1, l_2, l_3, l_4 in Figure 9.14.

   I. $\begin{cases} x = a + ct, \\ y = -b + dt. \end{cases}$ II. $\begin{cases} x = m + pt, \\ y = n - qt. \end{cases}$

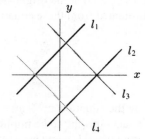

Figure 9.14

Write a parameterization for each of the curves in the xy-plane in Problems 12–13.

12. A vertical line through the point $(-2, -3)$.

13. The line through the points $(2, -1)$ and $(1, 3)$.

Graph the Lissajous figures in Problems 14–17 using a calculator or computer.

14. $x = \cos 2t, \quad y = \sin 5t$

15. $x = \cos 3t, \quad y = \sin 7t$

16. $x = \cos 2t, \quad y = \sin 4t$

17. $x = \cos 2t, \quad y = \sin \sqrt{3}t$

18. Motion along a straight line is given by a single equation, say, $x = t^3 - t$ where x is distance along the line. It is difficult to see the motion from a plot; it just traces out the x-line, as in Figure 9.15. To visualize the motion, we introduce a y-coordinate and let it slowly increase, giving Figure 9.16. Try the following on a calculator or computer. Let $y = t$. Now plot the parametric equations $x = t^3 - t, y = t$ for, say, $-3 \leq t \leq 3$. What does the plot in Figure 9.16 tell you about the particle's motion?

Figure 9.15   Figure 9.16

For Problems 19–20, plot the motion along the x-line by introducing a y-coordinate. What does the plot tell you about the particle's motion?

19. $x = \cos t, \quad -10 \leq t \leq 10$

20. $x = t^4 - 2t^2 + 3t - 7, \quad -3 \leq t \leq 2$

9.3 IMPLICITLY DEFINED CURVES

In Example 2 on page 514, we saw that the parametrically defined curve

$$x = \cos t, \qquad y = \sin t \qquad \text{for} \quad 0 \leq t \leq 2\pi$$

is the circle of radius 1 centered at the origin—in other words, the unit circle. We also saw that the parameter t can be eliminated from these equations by using the Pythagorean identity:

$$\underbrace{(\cos t)}_{x}^{2} + \underbrace{(\sin t)}_{y}^{2} = 1$$

$$x^2 + y^2 = 1.$$

The circle described by the equation $x^2 + y^2 = 1$ is an example of an *implicitly defined* curve. To be explicit is to state a fact outright; to be implicit is to make a statement in a round-about way. If a curve is defined by stating that y is some particular function of x, such as $y = f(x)$, then we say that

y is an *explicit* function of x and that the curve has been explicitly defined. In this case, though, the equation $x^2 + y^2 = 1$ does not explicitly state that y depends on x. Rather, this dependence is only implied by the equation. In fact, if we try to solve for y in terms of x, we do not obtain a function. Rather, we obtain *two* functions, one for the top half of the unit circle and one for the bottom half:

$$y = \begin{cases} +\sqrt{1 - x^2} \\ -\sqrt{1 - x^2} \end{cases}$$

Example 1   Sketch a graph of $|y| = |x|$. Can you find an explicit formula for y in terms of x?

Solution   The equation $|y| = |x|$ is implicit because it does not tell us what y equals: Rather, it tells us what $|y|$ equals. Let's attack this problem by considering specific values of x and y. For instance, suppose $x = 2$. What values can y equal? We see from our equation that

$$|y| = |2| = 2.$$

Therefore, y can equal either 2 or -2, because for either of these numbers $|y| = 2$. Similarly, if $x = 3$, we see that y can equal either 3 or -3, because for either of these numbers $|y| = 3$. What if x is negative? If for instance $x = -2$, we have

$$|y| = |-2| = 2.$$

This means that if $x = -2$ then y can equal either 2 or -2, because (as we have already seen) these are the solutions to $|y| = 2$.

It seems that for almost all x-values, there are two y-values, one given by $y = +|x|$ and one by $y = -|x|$. The only exception is at $x = 0$, because the only solution to the equation $|y| = 0$ is $y = 0$. Thus, we see that the graph of $|y| = |x|$ has two parts. They are given by

$$y = \begin{cases} +|x| \\ -|x| \end{cases}$$

We know that the graph of $y = -|x|$ is an upside-down version of the graph of $y = |x|$. Thus, when both parts of the graph of $|y| = |x|$ are plotted together, the resulting graph looks like an X. (See Figure 9.17.)

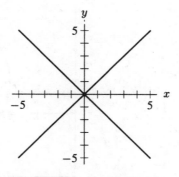

Figure 9.17: A graph of $|y| = |x|$

Conic Sections

The curves known as *conic sections* include two we are already familiar with: circles and parabolas. They also include two other curves called *ellipses* and *hyperbolas*. An ellipse is a flattened circle; an example is given by Figure 9.11 on page 520, which shows the relationship between a population of foxes and a population of rabbits. The function $y = 1/x$ is a special type of hyperbola known as a *rectangular hyperbola*.

Conic sections are so-called because, as was demonstrated by the ancient Greeks, they can be constructed by slicing (or *sectioning*) a cone. We will not consider this highly geometrical aspect of these curves, but instead will study them in terms of parametric and implicit equations.

Conic sections are extremely important in physics, where it can be shown that a body orbiting the sun (or any other object) will follow a path that traces out a conic section. Since we have already studied parabolas (as the graphs of quadratic functions) and rectangular hyperbolas (as graphs of the power function $y = k/x$), we will focus in this section on circles and ellipses.

Circles

Example 2   Consider the pair of parametric equations

$$x = 5 + 2\cos t \qquad \text{and} \qquad y = 3 + 2\sin t.$$

Based on what we know about trigonometric functions, we see that x varies between 3 and 7 with a midline of 5 while y varies between 1 and 5 with a midline of 3. Figure 9.18 gives a graph of this function. It appears to be a circle of radius 2 centered at the point $(5, 3)$.

Compare Figure 9.18 with Figure 9.19 which shows a circle of radius r centered at the point (h, k). A point $P = (x, y)$ on the circle has been labeled, as has θ, the angle formed with respect to the x axis. From the diagram, we see that

$$x = h + r\cos\theta \qquad \text{and} \qquad y = k + r\sin\theta.$$

If we replace θ (an angle) with t (a generic parameter), we can think of these equations as parametric equations. Thus, the equations graphed in Figure 9.18 are an example of a class of parametric equations for circles.

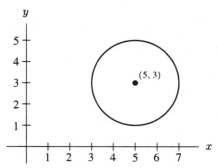

Figure 9.18: The circle defined by
$x = 5 + 2\cos t, y = 3 + 2\sin t, 0 \le t \le 2\pi$

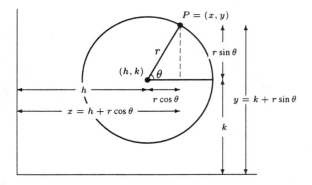

Figure 9.19: A circle of radius r centered at the point (h, k)

The parametric equations

$$x = h + r \cos t \qquad 0 \le t \le 2\pi$$
$$y = k + r \sin t$$

describe a circle of radius r centered at the point (h, k).

Eliminating the Parameter t in the Equations for a Circle

We can eliminate the parameter t from our parametric equations for a circle. To do this, we will apply the Pythagorean identity. Notice that we can rewrite our defining equations as

$$x - h = r \cos t$$
$$(x - h)^2 = r^2 \cos^2 t \qquad \text{squaring both sides}$$

and

$$y - k = r \sin t$$
$$(y - k)^2 = r^2 \sin^2 t \qquad \text{squaring both sides}$$

Adding these two equations gives

$$(x - h)^2 + (y - k)^2 = r^2 \cos^2 t + r^2 \sin^2 t$$
$$= r^2 (\cos^2 t + \sin^2 t) \qquad \text{factoring}$$
$$= r^2 \qquad \text{because } \cos^2 t + \sin^2 t = 1$$

This gives us an implicitly defined equation for the circle of radius r centered at the point (h, k):

$$(x - h)^2 + (y - k)^2 = r^2.$$

Example 3   For the unit circle, we have $h = 0$, $k = 0$, and $r = 1$. This gives

$$(x - 0)^2 + (y - 0)^2 = 1^2,$$

which reduces to $x^2 + y^2 = 1$, the equation we found earlier. For the circle in Example 2, we have $h = 5$, $k = 3$, and $r = 2$. This gives

$$(x - 5)^2 + (y - 3)^2 = 2^2 = 4.$$

If we expand the equation for the circle in Example 2, we get

$$x^2 - 10x + 25 + y^2 - 6y + 9 = 4,$$

or

$$x^2 + y^2 - 10x - 6y + 30 = 0,$$

a quadratic equation in two variables. Note that the coefficients of x^2 and y^2 (1, in this case) are equal. Such equations often describe circles, and we can put the equation into standard form by completing the square.

Example 4   Describe in words the curve defined by the equation

$$x^2 + 10x + 20 = 4y - y^2.$$

Solution   Rearranging terms gives

$$x^2 + 10x + y^2 - 4y = -20.$$

We complete the square for the terms involving x and (separately) for the terms involving y. This gives

$$\underbrace{(x^2 + 10x + 25)}_{(x+5)^2} + \underbrace{(y^2 - 4y + 4)}_{(y-2)^2} \quad \underbrace{-25 - 4}_{\substack{\text{compensating}\\\text{terms}}} \quad = -20$$

$$(x + 5)^2 + (y - 2)^2 - 29 = -20$$
$$(x + 5)^2 + (y - 2)^2 = 9.$$

Thus, this is a circle of radius $r = 3$ with center $(h, k) = (-5, 2)$.

Ellipses

The curves defined by the parametric equations

$$x = h + a\cos t \qquad 0 \le t \le 2\pi$$
$$y = k + b\sin t$$

are called *ellipses*. In the special case where $a = b$, we see that these equations are the same as the parametric equations of a circle of radius $r = a$. Thus, a circle is a special kind of ellipse. In general, however, not all ellipses are circles.

Example 5   Figure 9.20 shows the ellipse given by

$$x = 7 + 5\cos t, \qquad y = 4 + 2\sin t, \qquad 0 \le t \le 2\pi.$$

Here, $(h, k) = (7, 4)$ is the center of the ellipse. We see that $a = 5$ determines the horizontal "radius" of the ellipse, while $b = 2$ determines the vertical "radius". This seems reasonable, given what we know about parametric equations. For instance, we know that x varies from a maximum of 12 to a minimum of 2 about the midline of $x = 7$. Looking at the ellipse, we see that it extends horizontally to the right as far as $x = 12$ and to the left as far as $x = 2$ and is centered on (symmetric about) the vertical line $x = 7$. Similarly, the parameter y varies from a maximum of 6 to a minimum of 2 about the midline $y = 4$. This corresponds to the fact that the ellipse extends vertically from $y = 2$ to $y = 6$ and is centered on the horizontal line $y = 4$.

In general, the horizontal axis of an ellipse has length $2a$, and the vertical axis has length $2b$. This is similar to the situation with a circle, which has a diameter $2r$. The difference here is that the diameter of a circle is the same no matter where on the circle it is drawn, while the "diameter" of an ellipse will be between a minimum and maximum value depending on where it is drawn.

The longer axis of an ellipse is called the *major* axis, and the shorter axis is called the *minor* axis. Either the horizontal or the vertical axis can be the longer axis, as the next example shows.

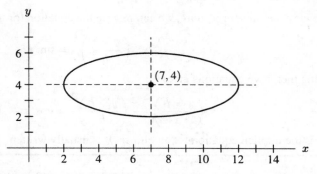

Figure 9.20: The ellipse given by $x = 7 + 5\cos t$, $y = 4 + 2\sin t$, $0 \leq t \leq 2\pi$

Example 6   Consider the ellipse given by

$$x = 7 + 2\cos t, \qquad y = 4 + 5\sin t.$$

How is this ellipse similar to the one in Example 5? How is it different?

Solution   For this ellipse, we have $(h, k) = (7, 4)$, so it has the same center as the ellipse in Example 5. However, as we can see from Figure 9.21, the vertical axis of this ellipse is the longer one (the major), and the horizontal axis is the shorter (the minor). This is the opposite of the situation in Example 5. Figure 9.21 gives a graph of this ellipse.

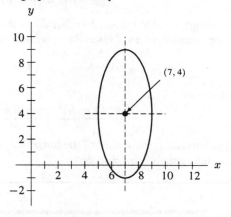

Figure 9.21: $x = 7 + 2\cos t$, $y = 4 + 5\sin t$, $0 \leq t \leq 2\pi$

Eliminating the Parameter t in the Equations for an Ellipse

As with circles, we can eliminate t from our parametric equations for an ellipse. We first rewrite the equation for x as follows:

$$x = h + a\cos t$$
$$x - h = a\cos t$$
$$\frac{x - h}{a} = \cos t$$
$$\left(\frac{x - h}{a}\right)^2 = \cos^2 t.$$

Chapter 9/ 29

Following the same procedure, we can rewrite the equation for y as

$$\left(\frac{y-k}{b}\right)^2 = \sin^2 t.$$

Adding these two equations gives

$$\left(\frac{x-h}{a}\right)^2 + \left(\frac{y-k}{b}\right)^2 = \cos^2 t + \sin^2 t = 1.$$

This is the implicit equation for an ellipse. It is usually written

$$\frac{(x-h)^2}{a^2} + \frac{(y-k)^2}{b^2} = 1.$$

Summary of Circles and Ellipses

The equation of a circle can be written parametrically as

$$x = h + r\cos t, \qquad y = k + r\sin t, \quad 0 \le t \le 2\pi$$

or implicitly as

$$(x-h)^2 + (y-k)^2 = r^2.$$

In both equations, r is the radius, $2r$ is the diameter, and (h, k) is the center of the circle. Similarly, the equation of an ellipse can be written parametrically as

$$x = h + a\cos t, \qquad y = k + b\sin t, \quad 0 \le t \le 2\pi$$

or implicitly as

$$\frac{(x-h)^2}{a^2} + \frac{(y-k)^2}{b^2} = 1.$$

In both equations, $2a$ is the length of the horizontal axis, $2b$ is the length of the vertical axis, and (h, k) is the center of the ellipse.

Problems for Section 9.3

Write a parameterization for each of the curves in the xy-plane in Problems 1–7.

1. A circle of radius 3 centered at the origin and traced out clockwise.
2. A circle of radius 5 centered at the point $(2, 1)$ and traced out counterclockwise.
3. A circle of radius 2 centered at the origin traced clockwise starting from $(-2, 0)$ when $t = 0$.
4. The circle of radius 2 centered at the origin starting at the point $(0, 2)$ when $t = 0$.
5. The circle of radius 4 centered at the point $(4, 4)$ starting on the x-axis when $t = 0$.
6. An ellipse centered at the origin and crossing the x-axis at ± 5 and the y-axis at ± 7.
7. An ellipse centered at the origin, crossing the x-axis at ± 3 and the y-axis at ± 7. Start at the point $(-3, 0)$ and trace out the ellipse counterclockwise.

Chapter 9/ 30

8. What can you say about the values of a, b and k if the equations

$$x = a + k\cos t, \quad y = b + k\sin t, \quad 0 \le t \le 2\pi,$$

trace out each of the circles in Figure 9.22? (a) C_1 (b) C_2 (c) C_3

Figure 9.22

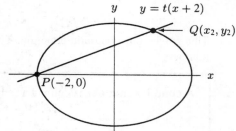

Figure 9.23: The ellipse $2x^2 + 3y^2 = 8$ and an intersecting line

What curves do the parametric equations in Problems 9–11 trace out? Find an implicit or explicit equation for each curve.

9. $x = 2 + \cos t, \ y = 2 - \sin t$ 10. $x = 2 + \cos t, \ y = 2 - \cos t$

11. $x = 2 + \cos t, \ y = \cos^2 t$

State whether the equations in Problems 12–14 represent a curve parametrically, implicitly, or explicitly. Give the two other types of representations for the same curve.

12. $xy = 1$ for $x > 0$ 13. $x^2 - 2x + y^2 = 0$ for $y < 0$

14. $x = e^t, \ y = e^{2t}$ for all t

15. An ant, starting at the origin, moves at 2 units/sec along the x-axis to the point $(1, 0)$. The ant then moves counterclockwise along the unit circle to $(0, 1)$ at a speed of $3\pi/2$ units/sec, then straight down to the origin at a speed of 2 units/sec along the y-axis.

    (a) Express the ant's coordinates as a function of time, t, in secs.

    (b) Express the reverse path as a function of time.

16. (a) The ellipse $2x^2 + 3y^2 = 8$ intersects the line of slope t through the point $P = (-2, 0)$ in two points, one of which is P. Compute the coordinate of the other point Q. See Figure 9.23.

    (b) Give a parameterization of the ellipse $2x^2 + 3y^2 = 8$ by rational functions.

9.4 COMPLEX NUMBERS

The quadratic equation

$$x^2 - 2x + 2 = 0$$

is not satisfied by any real number x. If you try applying the quadratic formula, you get

$$x = \frac{2 \pm \sqrt{4 - 8}}{2} = 1 \pm \frac{\sqrt{-4}}{2}.$$

Apparently, you need to take a square root of -4. But -4 doesn't have a square root, at least, not one which is a real number.

To overcome this problem, we define the imaginary number i to be a number such that

$$i^2 = -1.$$

Using this i, we see that $(2i)^2 = -4$. Now returning to our solution of the quadratic:

$$x = 1 \pm \frac{\sqrt{-4}}{2} = 1 \pm \frac{2i}{2} = 1 \pm i.$$

This solves our quadratic equation. The two numbers $1 + i$ and $1 - i$ are examples of complex numbers.

A **complex number** is defined as any number that can be written in the form

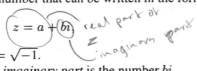

$$z = a + bi$$

where a and b are real numbers and $i = \sqrt{-1}$.
The *real part* of z is the number a; the *imaginary part* is the number bi.

Calling the number i imaginary makes it sound like i doesn't exist in the same way that real numbers exist. In some cases, it is useful to make such a distinction between real and imaginary numbers. If we measure mass or position, we want our answers to be real numbers. But the imaginary numbers are just as legitimate mathematically as the real numbers are. For example, complex numbers are used in studying wave motion in electric circuits.

Algebra of Complex Numbers

Numbers such as 0, 1, $\frac{1}{2}$, π, e and $\sqrt{2}$ are called *purely real*, because they contain no imaginary components. Numbers such as i, $2i$, and $\sqrt{2}i$ are called *purely imaginary*, because they contain only the number i multiplied by a nonzero real coefficient.

Two complex numbers are called *conjugates* if their real parts are equal and if their imaginary parts differ only in sign. The complex conjugate of the complex number $z = a + bi$ is denoted $\bar{z}$, so

$$\bar{z} = a - bi.$$

(Note that z is real if and only if $z = \bar{z}$.)

- Adding two complex numbers is done by adding real and imaginary parts separately:
  $(a + bi) + (c + di) = (a + c) + (b + d)i.$
- Subtracting is similar: $(a + bi) - (c + di) = (a - c) + (b - d)i.$
- Multiplication works just like for polynomials, using $i^2 = -1$:

$$(a + bi)(c + di) = a(c + di) + bi(c + di) = ac + adi + bci + bdi^2$$
$$= ac + adi + bci - bd = (ac - bd) + (ad + bc)i.$$

- Powers of i: We know that $i^2 = -1$; then, $i^3 = i \cdot i^2 = -i$, and $i^4 = (i^2)^2 = (-1)^2 = 1$. Then $i^5 = i \cdot i^4 = i$, and so on. Thus we have

$$i^n = \begin{cases} i & \text{for } n = 1, 5, 9, 13, \ldots \\ -1 & \text{for } n = 2, 6, 10, 14, \ldots \\ -i & \text{for } n = 3, 7, 11, 15, \ldots \\ 1 & \text{for } n = 4, 8, 12, 16, \ldots \end{cases}$$

- The product of a number and its conjugate is always real and nonnegative:

$$z \cdot \bar{z} = (a + bi)(a - bi) = a^2 - abi + abi - b^2 i^2 = a^2 + b^2.$$

- Dividing is done by multiplying the denominator by its conjugate, thereby making the denominator real:

$$\frac{a + bi}{c + di} = \frac{a + bi}{c + di} \cdot \frac{c - di}{c - di} = \frac{ac - adi + bci - bdi^2}{c^2 + d^2} = \frac{ac + bd}{c^2 + d^2} + \frac{bc - ad}{c^2 + d^2}i.$$

conjugate

Example 1   Write $(2 + 7i)(4 - 6i) - i$ as a single complex number

Solution $(2 + 7i)(4 - 6i) - i = 8 + 28i - 12i - 42i^2 - i = 8 + 15i + 42 = 50 + 15i.$

Example 2   Compute $\dfrac{2 + 7i}{4 - 6i}$.

Solution $\dfrac{2 + 7i}{4 - 6i} = \dfrac{2 + 7i}{4 - 6i} \cdot \dfrac{4 + 6i}{4 + 6i} = \dfrac{8 + 12i + 28i + 42i^2}{4^2 + 6^2} = \dfrac{-34 + 40i}{52} = \dfrac{-17}{26} + \dfrac{10}{13}i.$

The Complex Plane and Polar Coordinates

It is often useful to picture a complex number $z = x + iy$ in the plane, with x along the horizontal axis and y along the vertical. The xy-plane is then called the *complex plane*. Figure 9.24 shows the complex numbers $3i$, $-2 + 3i$, -3, $-2i$, 2, and $1 + i$.

Figure 9.24: Points in the complex plane

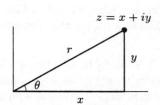

Figure 9.25: The point $z = x + iy$ in the complex plane, showing polar coordinates

The triangle in Figure 9.25 shows that a complex number can be written using polar coordinates as follows:

$$\boxed{z = x + iy = r\cos\theta + ir\sin\theta.}$$

Example 3   Express $z = -2i$ and $z = -2 + 3i$ using polar coordinates. (See Figure 9.24.)

Solution   For $z = -2i$, the distance of z from the origin is 2. Thus $r = 2$. Also, one value for θ is $\theta = 3\pi/2$. Thus, using polar coordinates, $-2i = 2\cos(3\pi/2) + i\,2(\sin 3\pi/2)$.

For $z = -2 + 3i$, we have $x = -2, y = 3$, so $r = \sqrt{(-2)^2 + 3^2} \approx 3.61$ and $\tan\theta = 3/(-2)$, so, for example, $\theta \approx 2.16$. Thus using polar coordinates, $-2 + 3i \approx 3.61\cos(2.16) + i\,3.61\sin(2.16)$.

Example 4   Consider the point with polar coordinates $r = 5$ and $\theta = 3\pi/4$. What complex number does this point represent?

Solution   Since $x = r\cos\theta$ and $y = r\sin\theta$ we see that $x = 5\cos 3\pi/4 = -5/\sqrt{2}$, and $y = 5\sin 3\pi/4 = 5/\sqrt{2}$, so $z = -5/\sqrt{2} + i\,5/\sqrt{2}$.

Euler's Formula

Based on what we have seen so far, we have no reason to expect that there is any connection between the exponential function e^x and the trigonometric functions $\sin x$ and $\cos x$. However, in the eighteenth century, the Swiss mathematician Leonhard Euler discovered a surprising connection between these functions that involves complex numbers. This result, called *Euler's formula*, states that

$$e^{i\theta} = \cos\theta + i\sin\theta$$

provided θ is measured in radians.

Example 5   Evaluate $e^{i\pi}$.

Solution   Using Euler's formula,

$$e^{i\pi} = \cos\pi + i\sin\pi$$
$$= -1 + i\cdot 0$$
$$= -1.$$

This statement, known as *Euler's identity*, is sometimes written $e^{i\pi} + 1 = 0$. It is famous because it relates five of the most fundamental constants in mathematics: $0, 1, e, \pi$, and i.

You may be wondering what it means to raise a number to an imaginary power. Euler's formula doesn't really tell us what complex powers mean, but it does provide a way for us to evaluate complex powers that is consistent with the other facts we know about arithmetic.

In this regard, complex exponents are similar to other types of exponents we have seen, such as fractional and negative exponents. When we first learn about exponents, they serve to collect repeated multiplications: For instance, $4 \times 4 \times 4 \times 4 \times 4$ is more easily written as 4^5. But this fact doesn't help us to understand what, for instance, $4^{1/2}$ means. It isn't until we learn more about exponent rules that we are able to interpret $4^{1/2}$ as $\sqrt{4}$. Similarly, knowing that $4 \times 4 \times 4 \times 4 \times 4 = 4^5$ doesn't help us to understand what 4^i means. It isn't until we learn Euler's formula that we are able to evaluate this expression:

$$4^i = \left(e^{\ln 4}\right)^i \qquad \text{because } e^{\ln 4} = 4$$
$$= e^{i(\ln 4)} \qquad \text{using an exponent rule}$$
$$= \cos(\ln 4) + i\sin(\ln 4) \qquad \text{using Euler's formula}$$
$$= 0.183 + 0.983i \qquad \text{using a calculator.}$$

Example 6   We know that $\sqrt{-1} = i$, but what about $\sqrt{i}$? Is this expression defined? If not, explain why not; if so, find a possible value for it.

Solution   From Example 5, we know that

$$e^{i\pi} = -1.$$

Taking the square root of both sides gives

$$\sqrt{e^{i\pi}} = \sqrt{-1}$$
$$\left(e^{i\pi}\right)^{1/2} = i$$
$$e^{i\pi/2} = i \qquad \text{using an exponent rule}$$

We can now find $\sqrt{i}$. Taking the square root of both sides of this equation, we have

$$\sqrt{e^{i\pi/2}} = \sqrt{i}$$
$$\left(e^{i\pi/2}\right)^{1/2} = \sqrt{i}$$
$$e^{i\pi/4} = \sqrt{i}.$$

Thus, $\sqrt{i} = e^{i\pi/4}$. We can write this number in the form $a + bi$ by using Euler's formula:

$$e^{i\pi/4} = \cos\frac{\pi}{4} + i\sin\frac{\pi}{4}$$
$$= \frac{\sqrt{2}}{2} + i\frac{\sqrt{2}}{2}.$$

Thus, we see that

$$\sqrt{i} = \frac{\sqrt{2}}{2} + i\frac{\sqrt{2}}{2}.$$

To see that this value for $\sqrt{i}$ is reasonable, we can square it (multiply it by itself) to see if we get i:

$$\left(\frac{\sqrt{2}}{2} + i\frac{\sqrt{2}}{2}\right)^2 = \left(\frac{\sqrt{2}}{2} + i\frac{\sqrt{2}}{2}\right)\left(\frac{\sqrt{2}}{2} + i\frac{\sqrt{2}}{2}\right)$$
$$= \left(\frac{\sqrt{2}}{2}\right)^2 + \frac{\sqrt{2}}{2}\left(i\frac{\sqrt{2}}{2}\right) + i\frac{\sqrt{2}}{2}\left(\frac{\sqrt{2}}{2}\right) + \left(i\frac{\sqrt{2}}{2}\right)^2$$
$$= \frac{1}{2} + \frac{1}{2}i + \frac{1}{2}i - \frac{1}{2}$$
$$= i.$$

Note that we have *not* shown that this is the only number whose square is i. In fact, another square root of i is given by $z = -\frac{\sqrt{2}}{2} - i\frac{\sqrt{2}}{2}$, as you can check for yourself.

The last example is significant for the following reason: Having introduced i as $\sqrt{-1}$, it would be inconvenient (to say the least) if we needed a new symbol for $\sqrt{i}$, and another new symbol for the square root of $\sqrt{i}$, and so on. However, it turns out that no new numbers other than i are needed. By including i, the so-called *complex number system* is "closed" in the sense that no algebraic operation leads us to numbers not in the system (other than division by 0).

Polar Form of a Complex Number

Euler's formula allows us to write the complex number represented by the point with polar coordinates (r, θ) in the following form:

$$z = r(\cos\theta + i\sin\theta) = re^{i\theta}.$$

Similarly, since $\cos(-\theta) = \cos\theta$ and $\sin(-\theta) = -\sin\theta$, we have

$$re^{-i\theta} = r\left(\cos(-\theta) + i\sin(-\theta)\right) = r(\cos\theta - i\sin\theta).$$

The expression $re^{i\theta}$ is called the *polar form* of the complex number z.

Example 7 Express the complex number represented by the point with polar coordinates $r = 8$ and $\theta = 3\pi/4$, in Cartesian form $a + bi$ and in polar form, $z = re^{i\theta}$.

Solution Using Cartesian coordinates, the complex number is

$$z = 8\left(\cos\left(\frac{3\pi}{4}\right) + i\sin\left(\frac{3\pi}{4}\right)\right) = \frac{-8}{\sqrt{2}} + i\frac{8}{\sqrt{2}}.$$

Knowing the polar coordinates we write the polar form as

$$z = 8e^{i\,3\pi/4}.$$

Among its many benefits, the polar form of complex numbers makes finding powers and roots of complex numbers much easier. Using the polar form, $z = re^{i\theta}$, for a complex number, we may find any power of z as follows:

$$z^p = (re^{i\theta})^p = r^p e^{ip\theta}.$$

To find roots, we let p be a fraction, as in the following example.

Example 8 Find a cube root of the complex number represented by the point with polar coordinates $(8, 3\pi/4)$.

Solution In Example 7, we saw that this complex number could be written as $z = 8e^{i3\pi/4}$. Thus,

$$\sqrt[3]{z} = \left(8e^{i\,3\pi/4}\right)^{1/3} = 8^{1/3}e^{i(3\pi/4)\cdot(1/3)} = 2e^{\pi i/4} = 2\left(\cos(\pi/4) + i\sin(\pi/4)\right)$$
$$= 2\left(1/\sqrt{2} + i/\sqrt{2}\right) = 2/\sqrt{2} + i2/\sqrt{2}.$$

Euler's Formula and Trigonometric Identities

We can use Euler's formula to derive many of the trigonometric identities we are familiar with.

Example 9   Derive the Pythagorean identity using Euler's formula.

Solution   According to the usual exponent rules, we have

$$e^{i\theta} \cdot e^{-i\theta} = e^{i\theta - i\theta} = e^0 = 1.$$

Using Euler's formula, we can rewrite this as

$$\underbrace{(\cos\theta + i\sin\theta)}_{e^{i\theta}}\underbrace{(\cos\theta - i\sin\theta)}_{e^{-i\theta}} = 1.$$

Multiplying out the left-hand side gives

$$(\cos\theta + i\sin\theta)(\cos\theta - i\sin\theta) = \cos^2\theta - i\sin\theta\cos\theta + i\sin\theta\cos\theta - i^2\sin^2\theta$$
$$= \cos^2\theta + \sin^2\theta,$$

and so $\cos^2\theta + \sin^2\theta = 1$.

Example 10   Find identities for $\cos(\theta + \phi)$ and $\sin(\theta + \phi)$.

Solution   According to the usual exponent rules, we see from Euler's formula that

$$e^{i(\theta + \phi)} = e^{i\theta} \cdot e^{i\phi}$$
$$= (\cos\theta + i\sin\theta)(\cos\phi + i\sin\phi)$$
$$= \cos\theta\cos\phi + \underbrace{i\cos\theta\sin\phi + i\sin\theta\cos\phi}_{i(\cos\theta\sin\phi + \sin\theta\cos\phi)} + \underbrace{i^2\sin\theta\sin\phi}_{-\sin\theta\sin\phi}$$
$$= \underbrace{\cos\theta\cos\phi - \sin\theta\sin\phi}_{\text{real part}} + \underbrace{i(\cos\theta\sin\phi + \sin\theta\cos\phi)}_{\text{imaginary part}}.$$

But it is also true that

$$e^{i(\theta + \phi)} = \underbrace{\cos(\theta + \phi)}_{\text{real part}} + \underbrace{i\sin(\theta + \phi)}_{\text{imaginary part}}.$$

Setting real parts equal gives

$$\cos(\theta + \phi) = \cos\theta\cos\phi - \sin\theta\sin\phi.$$

Setting imaginary parts equal gives

$$\sin(\theta + \phi) = \cos\theta\sin\phi + \sin\theta\cos\phi.$$

This last identity is usually written in the following way:

$$\sin(\theta + \phi) = \sin\theta\cos\phi + \sin\phi\cos\theta.$$

Problems for Section 9.4

For Problems 1–6, express the given complex number in polar form, $z = re^{i\theta}$.

1. $2i$
2. -5
3. $-3 - 4i$
4. 0
5. $-i$
6. $-1 + 3i$

For Problems 7–14, perform the indicated calculations. Give your answer in Cartesian form, $z = x + iy$.

7. $(2 + 3i) + (-5 - 7i)$

8. $(2 + 3i)(5 + 7i)$

9. $(2 + 3i)^2$

10. $(0.5 - i)(1 - i/4)$

11. $(2i)^3 - (2i)^2 + 2i - 1$

12. $(e^{i\pi/3})^2$

13. $\sqrt{e^{i\pi/3}}$

14. $\sqrt[4]{10e^{i\pi/2}}$

By writing the complex numbers in polar form, $z = re^{i\theta}$, find a value for the quantities in Problems 15–22. Give your answer in Cartesian form, $z = x + iy$.

15. $\sqrt{i}$

16. $\sqrt{-i}$

17. $\sqrt[3]{i}$

18. $\sqrt{7i}$

19. $(1 + i)^{2/3}$

20. $(\sqrt{3} + i)^{1/2}$

21. $(\sqrt{3} + i)^{-1/2}$

22. $(\sqrt{5} + 2i)^{\sqrt{2}}$

Solve the simultaneous equations in Problems 23–24 for the complex numbers A_1 and A_2.

23. $A_1 + A_2 = 2$
$(1 - i)A_1 + (1 + i)A_2 = 0$

24. $A_1 + A_2 = i$
$iA_1 - A_2 = 3$

25. Let $z_1 = -3 - i\sqrt{3}$ and $z_2 = -1 + i\sqrt{3}$.
   (a) Find z_1z_2 and z_1/z_2. Give your answer in Cartesian form, $z = x + iy$.
   (b) Put z_1 and z_2 into polar form, $z = re^{i\theta}$. Find z_1z_2 and z_1/z_2 using the polar form, and verify that you get the same answer as in part (a).

26. If the roots of the equation $x^2 + 2bx + c = 0$ are the complex numbers $p \pm iq$, find expressions for p and q in terms of a and b.

Are the statements in Problems 27–32 true or false? Explain your answer.

27. Every nonnegative real number has a real square root.

28. For any complex number z, the product $z \cdot \bar{z}$ is a real number.

29. The square of any complex number is a real number.

30. If f is a polynomial, and $f(z) = i$, then $f(\bar{z}) = i$.

31. Every nonzero complex number z can be written in the form $z = e^w$, where w is another complex number.

32. If $z = x + iy$, where x and y are positive, then $z^2 = a + ib$ has a and b positive.

For Problems 33–34, use Euler's formula to derive the following relationships. (Note that if a, b, c, d are real numbers, $a + bi = c + di$ means that $a = c$ and $b = d$.)

33. $\sin 2\theta = 2 \sin \theta \cos \theta$

34. $\cos 2\theta = \cos^2 \theta - \sin^2 \theta$

9.6 HYPERBOLIC FUNCTIONS

There are two combinations of the functions e^x and e^{-x} used so often in engineering that they are given their own names. They are the hyperbolic sine, abbreviated sinh and pronounced "cinch", and hyperbolic cosine, abbreviated cosh, (rhymes with "gosh") which are defined as follows:

Hyperbolic Functions

$$\cosh x = \frac{e^x + e^{-x}}{2} \qquad \sinh x = \frac{e^x - e^{-x}}{2}$$

Properties of Hyperbolic Functions

The graphs of the $\cosh x$ and $\sinh x$ are given in Figures 9.34 and 9.35 together with the graphs of multiples of e^x and e^{-x}.

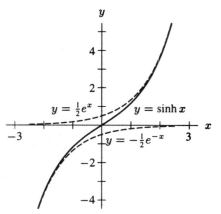

Figure 9.34: Graph of $y = \cosh x$ with multiples of e^x and e^{-x}

Figure 9.35: Graph of $y = \sinh x$ with multiples of e^x and e^{-x}

The graphs suggest that

$$\cosh 0 = 1 \qquad \sinh 0 = 0$$
$$\cosh(-x) = \cosh x \qquad \sinh(-x) = -\sinh x$$

To show that the hyperbolic functions really do have these properties, we can use their formulas.

Example 1   Show that

(a) $\cosh(0) = 1$

(b) $\cosh(-x) = \cosh x$

Solution   (a)   Substituting $x = 0$ into the formula for $\cosh x$ gives

$$\cosh 0 = \frac{e^0 + e^{-0}}{2} = \frac{1 + 1}{2} = 1.$$

(b)   Substituting $-x$ for x gives

$$\cosh(-x) = \frac{e^{-x} + e^{-(-x)}}{2} = \frac{e^{-x} + e^x}{2} = \cosh x.$$

Thus, we know that $\cosh x$ is an even function.

Example 2   Describe and explain the behavior of $\cosh x$ as $x \to \infty$ and then as $x \to -\infty$.

Solution   From Figure 9.34, we see that as $x \to \infty$, the graph of $\cosh x$ resembles the graph of $\frac{1}{2}e^x$. Similarly, as $x \to -\infty$, the graph of $\cosh x$ resembles the graph of $\frac{1}{2}e^{-x}$. Using the formula for $\cosh x$, and the facts that $e^{-x} \to 0$ as $x \to \infty$ and $e^x \to 0$ as $x \to -\infty$, we can predict the same result algebraically:

$$\text{As } x \to \infty, \qquad \cosh x = \frac{e^x + e^{-x}}{2} \to \frac{1}{2}e^x \to \infty.$$

$$\text{As } x \to -\infty, \qquad \cosh x = \frac{e^x + e^{-x}}{2} \to \frac{1}{2}e^{-x} \to \infty.$$

Chapter 9/ 40

Identities Involving cosh x and sinh x

The hyperbolic functions have names that remind us of the trigonometric functions because they have some properties that are similar to those of the trigonometric functions. Consider the expression

$$(\cosh x)^2 - (\sinh x)^2.$$

This can be simplified using the formulas and the fact the $e^x \cdot e^{-x} = 1$:

$$
\begin{aligned}
(\cosh x)^2 - (\sinh x)^2 &= \left(\frac{e^x + e^{-x}}{2}\right)^2 - \left(\frac{e^x - e^{-x}}{2}\right)^2 \\
&= \frac{e^{2x} + 2e^x \cdot e^{-x} + e^{-2x}}{4} - \frac{e^{2x} - 2e^x \cdot e^{-x} + e^{-2x}}{4} \\
&= \frac{e^{2x} + 2 + e^{-2x} - e^{2x} + 2 - e^{-2x}}{4} \\
&= 1.
\end{aligned}
$$

Thus, writing $\cosh^2 x$ for $(\cosh x)^2$ and $\sinh^2 x$ for $(\sinh x)^2$, we have the identity

$$\boxed{\cosh^2 x - \sinh^2 x = 1}$$

This identity is reminiscent of the Pythagorean identity $\cos^2 x + \sin^2 x = 1$. Extending the analogy, we define

$$\boxed{\tanh x = \frac{\sinh x}{\cosh x}}$$

Notice that since

$$\cosh x - \sinh x = e^{-x},$$

the difference between $\cosh x$ and $\sinh x$ is positive for all x, because e^{-x} is positive for all x. This tells us that

$$\cosh x > \sinh x \quad \text{for all } x.$$

This fact will be useful in our discussion below.

Parameterizing the Hyperbola

Consider the curve parameterized by the equations

$$x = \cosh t, \quad y = \sinh t, \quad -\infty < t < \infty.$$

At $t = 0$, we have $(x, y) = (\cosh 0, \sinh 0) = (1, 0)$, so the curve passes through the point $(1, 0)$. As $t \to \infty$, we know that both $\cosh t$ and $\sinh t$ approach $(1/2)e^t$, so for large values of t we see that $\cosh t \approx \sinh t$. Thus, as t increases the curve will draw close to the diagonal line $y = x$. Even though this line is not horizontal or vertical, we refer to it as an asymptote to the curve. Additionally, since $\sinh x < \cosh x$ for all x, we know that $y < x$, so the curve will approach this asymptote from below.

Similarly, as $t \to -\infty$, we know that $x \to e^{-t}/2$ and $y \to -e^{-t}/2$, which means that $y \approx -x$. Thus, as $t \to -\infty$, the curve draws close to the asymptote $y = -x$. In this case, though, the curve approaches the asymptote from above, because the y-coordinate will be slightly larger (less negative) than the x-coordinate.

Figure 9.36 shows a graph of this curve, known as a *hyperbola*. Hyperbolas are a type of conic section. (We have studied three other types of conic section: parabolas, circles, and ellipses.) Notice from the figure that this hyperbola passes through the point (1,0), as predicted, and that it has asymptotes $y = x$ and $y = -x$.

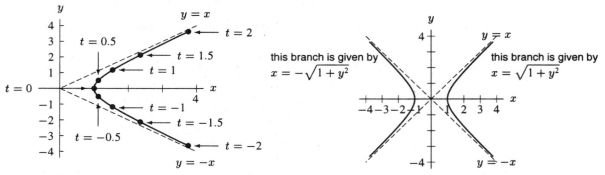

Figure 9.36: A graph of the hyperbola parameterized by $x = \cosh t$, $y = \sinh t$, $-\infty < t < \infty$

Figure 9.37: A graph of the hyperbola defined implicitly by $x^2 - y^2 = 1$

The Implicit Formula for a Hyperbola

The parameter t in the equations for the hyperbola can be eliminated using the identity $\cosh^2 t - \sinh^2 t = 1$:

$$x^2 - y^2 = \underbrace{\cosh^2 t}_{x^2} - \underbrace{\sinh^2 t}_{y^2}$$
$$= 1.$$

This gives us the following implicit equation:

$$\boxed{\text{Hyperbola:} \qquad x^2 - y^2 = 1}$$

The graph of this equation is not exactly the same as the graph in Figure 9.36. This is because, in solving the equation for x, we obtain *two* values of x for every value of y:

$$x^2 - y^2 = 1$$
$$x^2 = 1 + y^2$$
$$x = \pm\sqrt{1 + y^2}.$$

The graph of $x = \sqrt{1 + y^2}$ appears in Figure 9.36. The equation $x = -\sqrt{1 + y^2}$ is a reflection across the y-axis of the graph of $x = \sqrt{1 + y^2}$. Figure 9.37 shows both of these graphs. The two branches are usually considered to be part of a single hyperbola.

Relating Trigonometric and Hyperbolic Functions

Provided x is real, we know from Euler's formula that

$$e^{ix} = \cos x + i \sin x.$$

Since cosine is an even function ($\cos(-x) = \cos x$) and sine is an odd function ($\sin(-x) = -\sin x$), we have

$$e^{-ix} = e^{i(-x)} = \cos(-x) + i \sin(-x) = \cos x - i \sin x.$$

Then

$$e^{ix} + e^{-ix} = (\cos x + i \sin x) + (\cos x - i \sin x)$$
$$= 2 \cos x,$$

so

$$\cos x = \frac{e^{ix} + e^{-ix}}{2}.$$

The expression on the right looks like the formula for the hyperbolic cosine function, except it involves imaginary exponents. Extending the definition of $\cosh x$ to imaginary values of the input, we can write

$$\cosh(ix) = \frac{e^{ix} + e^{-ix}}{2}.$$

Thus, we have the following relationship between the cosine function and the hyperbolic cosine function:

$$\boxed{\cosh(ix) = \cos x}$$

In Problem 7, we derive the analogous formula

$$\boxed{\sinh(ix) = i \sin x}$$

Problems for Section 9.6

1. Show that $\sinh 0 = 0$.
2. Show that $\sinh(-x) = -\sinh(x)$.
3. Describe and explain the behavior of $\sinh x$ as $x \to \infty$ and as $x \to -\infty$.
4. Is there an identity analogous to $\sin 2x = 2 \sin x \cos x$ for the hyperbolic functions? Explain.
5. Is there an identity analogous to $\cos 2x = \cos^2 x - \sin^2 x$ for the hyperbolic functions? Explain.
6. Consider the family of functions $y = a \cosh(x/a)$ for $a > 0$. Sketch graphs for $a = 1, 2, 3$. Describe in words the effect of increasing a.
7. Show that $\sinh(ix) = i \sin x$.
8. Find an expression for $\cos(ix)$ in terms of $\cosh x$.

REVIEW PROBLEMS FOR CHAPTER NINE

In Problems 1–2, decide which of the following are geometric series. For those which are, give the first term and the ratio between successive terms. For those which are not, explain why not.

1. $1 - y^2 + y^4 - y^6 + \cdots$ 2. $1 + 2z + (2z)^2 + (2z)^3 + \cdots$

3. Find the sum of the series in Problem 1.
4. Find the sum of the series in Problem 2.

5. A ball is dropped from a height of 10 feet and bounces. Each bounce is 3/4 of the height of the bounce before. Thus after the ball hits the floor for the first time, the ball rises to a height of $10(3/4) = 7.5$ feet, and after it hits the floor for the second time, it rises to a height of $7.5(3/4) = 10(3/4)^2 = 5.625$ feet.

    (a) Find an expression for the height to which the ball rises after it hits the floor for the nth time.
    (b) Find an expression for the total vertical distance the ball has traveled when it hits the floor for the first, second, third, and fourth times.
    (c) Find an expression for the total vertical distance the ball has traveled when it hits the floor for the nth time. Express your answer in closed-form.

6. You might think that the ball in Problem 5 keeps bouncing forever since it takes infinitely many bounces. This is not true! It can be shown that a ball dropped from a height of h feet reaches the ground in $\frac{1}{4}\sqrt{h}$ seconds. It is also true that it takes a bouncing ball the same amount of time to rise h feet. Use these facts to show that the ball in Problem 5 stops bouncing after

$$\frac{1}{4}\sqrt{10} + \frac{1}{2}\sqrt{10}\sqrt{\frac{3}{4}}\left(\frac{1}{1 - \sqrt{3/4}}\right)$$

seconds, or approximately 11 seconds.

Problems 7–7 are about *bonds*, which are issued by a government to raise money. An individual who buys a $1000 bond gives the government $1000 and in return receives a fixed sum of money, called the *coupon*, every six months or every year for the life of the bond. At the time of the last coupon, the individual also gets the $1000, or *principal*, back.

7. (a) What is the present value of a $1000 bond which pays $50 a year for 10 years, starting one year from now? Assume the interest rate is 5% per year, compounded annually.
    (b) Since $50 is 5% of $1000, this bond is often called a 5% bond. What does your answer to part (a) tell you about the relationship between the principal and the present value of this bond when the interest rate is 5%?
    (c) If the interest rate is more than 5% per year, compounded annually, which one is larger: the principal or the value of the bond? Why do you think the bond is then described as *trading at discount*?
    (d) If the interest rate is less than 5% per year, compounded annually, why is the bond described as *trading at a premium*?

8. This problem illustrates how banks create credit and can thereby lend out more money than has been deposited. Suppose that initially $100 is deposited in a bank. Experience has shown bankers that on average only 8% of the money deposited is withdrawn by the owner at any time. Consequently, bankers feel free to lend out 92% of their deposits. Thus $92 of the original $100 is loaned out to other customers (to start a business, for example). This $92 will become someone else's income and, sooner or later, will be redeposited in the bank. Then 92% of $92, or $92(0.92) = $84.64, is loaned out again and eventually redeposited. Of the $84.64, the bank again loans out 92%, and so on.

    (a) Find the total amount of money deposited in the bank.
    (b) The total amount of money deposited divided by the original deposit is called the *credit multiplier*. Calculate the credit multiplier for this example and explain what this number tells us.

Chapter 9/ 44

9. Let x be the position of a particle moving along a horizontal line. Plot the motion $x = t \ln t$, $0.01 \leq t \leq 10$ by introducing a y-coordinate. What does the plot tell you about the particle's motion?

Write a parameterization for each of the curves in Problems 10–11.

10. The horizontal line through the point $(0, 5)$.

11. The circle of radius 1 in the xy-plane centered at the origin, traversed counterclockwise when viewed from above.

12. On a graphing calculator or a computer, plot $x = 2t/(t^2 + 1)$, $y = (t^2 - 1)/(t^2 + 1)$, first for $-50 \leq t \leq 50$ then for $-5 \leq t \leq 5$. Explain what you see. Is the curve really a circle?

13. Plot the Lissajous figure given by $x = \cos 2t$, $y = \sin t$ using a graphing calculator or computer. Explain why it looks like part of a parabola. [Hint: Use a double angle identity from trigonometry.]

14. Suppose that a planet P in the xy-plane orbits the star S counterclockwise in a circle of radius 10 units, completing one orbit in 2π units of time. Suppose in addition a moon M orbits the planet P counterclockwise in a circle of radius 3 units, completing one orbit in $2\pi/8$ units of time. The star S is fixed at the origin $x = 0$, $y = 0$, and at time $t = 0$ the planet P is at the point $(10, 0)$ and the moon M is at the point $(13, 0)$.

    (a) Find parametric equations for the x- and y-coordinates of the planet at time t.
    (b) Find parametric equations for the x- and y-coordinates of the moon at time t. [Hint: For the moon's position at time t, take a vector from the sun to the planet at time t and add a vector from the planet to the moon].
    (c) Plot the path of the moon in the xy-plane, using a graphing calculator or computer.

15. A wheel of radius 1 meter rests on the x-axis with its center on the y-axis. There is a spot on the rim at the point $(1, 1)$. See Figure 9.38. At time $t = 0$ the wheel starts rolling on the x-axis in the direction shown at a rate of 1 radian per second.

    (a) Find parametric equations describing the motion of the center of the wheel.
    (b) Find parametric equations describing the motion of the spot on the rim. Plot its path.

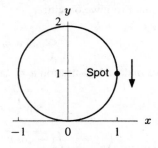

Figure 9.38

For Problems 16–17, express the given complex number in polar form, $z = re^{i\theta}$.

16. $1 + i$ 17. $5 - 12i$

For Problems 18–19, perform the indicated calculations. Give your answer in Cartesian form, $z = x + iy$.

18. $(1 + i)^2 + (1 + i)$ 19. $(5e^{i7\pi/6})^3$

By writing the complex numbers in polar form, $z = re^{i\theta}$, find a value for the quantities in Problems 20–21. Give your answer in Cartesian form, $z = x + iy$.

20. $(1 + i)^{100}$

21. $(-4 + 4i)^{2/3}$

For Problems 22–22, use Euler's formula to derive the following relationships. (Note that if a, b, c, d are real numbers, $a + bi = c + di$ means that $a = c$ and $b = d$.)

22. $\sin^2 \theta + \cos^2 \theta = 1$

23. Prove
$$\sin u - \sin v = 2 \cos\left(\frac{u + v}{2}\right) \sin\left(\frac{u - v}{2}\right).$$

24. The addition formula
$$\cos(u + v) = \cos u \cos v - \sin u \sin v$$
lets us transform expressions involving the sum of two angles. One situation where this transformation is useful occurs when we are looking at an average rate of change:
$$\frac{\Delta y}{\Delta x} = \frac{f(x + h) - f(x)}{h}.$$
For the cosine function this is
$$\frac{\Delta y}{\Delta x} = \cos x \left(\frac{\cos h - 1}{h}\right) - \sin x \left(\frac{\sin h}{h}\right).$$
Use the sum formula and basic algebra to verify this equation.

25. We can obtain formulas to transform expressions involving half-angles by using the double angle formulas. To find an expression for $\sin \frac{1}{2} x$ in terms of full angles we first use the cosine double angle formula, $\cos 2u = 1 - 2 \sin^2 u$. Writing this relationship in terms of $\cos 2u$ we get
$$\sin^2 u = \frac{1 - \cos 2u}{2}.$$
Taking the square root we obtain:
$$\sin u = \pm\sqrt{\frac{1 - \cos 2u}{2}},$$
and finally we make a substitution $u = \frac{1}{2} v$ to get:
$$\sin \frac{1}{2} v = \pm\sqrt{\frac{1 - \cos v}{2}}.$$

(a) Show that $\cos \frac{1}{2} v = \pm\sqrt{\dfrac{1 + \cos v}{2}}$.

(b) Show that $\tan \frac{1}{2} v = \pm\sqrt{\dfrac{1 - \cos v}{1 + \cos v}}$.

The sign in these formulas depends on the measure of $\frac{v}{2}$. If $\frac{v}{2}$ is in quadrant I then the sign of $\sin \frac{v}{2}$ is +, the sign of $\cos \frac{v}{2}$ is +, and the sign of $\tan \frac{v}{2}$ is +.

(c) If $\frac{v}{2}$ is in quadrant II find the signs for $\sin \frac{v}{2}$, for $\cos \frac{v}{2}$ and for $\tan \frac{v}{2}$.

(d) If $\frac{v}{2}$ is in quadrant III find the signs for $\sin \frac{v}{2}$, for $\cos \frac{v}{2}$ and for $\tan \frac{v}{2}$.

(e) If $\frac{v}{2}$ is in quadrant IV find the signs for $\sin \frac{v}{2}$, for $\cos \frac{v}{2}$ and for $\tan \frac{v}{2}$.

26. Find an expression for $\sin(ix)$ in terms of $\sinh x$.

Draw the graph of each equation in Exercises 27–30.

27. $r = \dfrac{6}{1 - 3 \sin \theta}$

28. $r = \dfrac{4}{1 + \frac{1}{2} \cos \theta}$

29. $r = \dfrac{9}{2 - 6 \cos \theta}$

30. $r = \dfrac{6}{4 + 4 \sin \theta}$

31. Find the polar equation of the conic section with eccentricity $\frac{3}{2}$, one focus at the origin, and center $[4, \pi]$.

32. Find the polar equation of the conic section with eccentricity $\frac{1}{2}$, one focus at the origin, and horizontal directrix 3 units above the origin.

In Exercises 33–36, eliminate the parameter and then draw the graph.

33. $x = t + 2,\ y = 1 - 3t$

34. $x = \sqrt{3t},\ y = 2 - 3t$

35. $x = 5 \sin \theta,\ y = 2 \cos \theta$

36. $x = 2 \cos 2\theta,\ y = \cos \theta$

Chapter 10

Partial Fractions, Systems Equations, Matrices and Determinants

SECTION **20**

PARTIAL FRACTIONS

A. Introduction

To add rational functions we convert to common denominators, add, and then simplify. For example,

$$\frac{3}{x + 1} - \frac{x}{x^2 - x + 2} = \frac{3(x^2 - x + 2) - x(x + 1)}{(x + 1)(x^2 - x + 2)}$$

$$= \frac{2x^2 - 4x + 6}{x^3 + x + 2}. \qquad (20.1)$$

In this section we consider how to reverse that process—how to begin with an expression like that on the right in (20.1) and end with an expression like that on the left. This reversed process is needed in calculus, for example.

The method we use rests on the following fact, whose proof is omitted: With real coefficients, every polynomial can be written as a product of linear and irreducible quadratic factors. That fact, together with the division algorithm for polynomials, can be used to justify the following statement.

Every rational function can be written uniquely as a sum of a polynomial (which may be identically zero) and fractions of the form

$$\frac{A}{(ax + b)^m} \quad \text{and} \quad \frac{Bx + C}{(ax^2 + bx + c)^n}$$

where $ax^2 + bx + c$ is irreducible.

The resulting form is called the **partial fraction decomposition** of the original rational function. The linear $(ax + b)$ and quadratic $(ax^2 + bx + c)$ factors in the decomposition are the irreducible factors of the original denominator. The first step is always to factor the original denominator into powers of irreducible factors. Remember that a quadratic factor is irreducible iff its discriminant is negative.)

B. Distinct Linear Factors

We call an irreducible factor of the denominator *distinct* (as opposed to *repeated*) if it occurs only with exponent one when we factor the denominator.

Each distinct linear factor $ax + b$ contributes a term of the form

$$\frac{A}{ax + b}$$

to the decomposition.

Example .1 Decompose $\dfrac{x + 12}{(x - 2)(x + 5)}$ into partial fractions.

Solution The factors $x - 2$ and $x + 5$ will contribute terms

$$\frac{A}{x - 2} \quad \text{and} \quad \frac{B}{x + 5}$$

respectly. If

$$\frac{x + 12}{(x - 2)(x + 5)} = \frac{A}{x - 2} + \frac{B}{x + 5} \tag{20.2}$$

then on multiplying by $(x - 2)(x + 5)$ to clear the denominators, we obtain

$$x + 12 = A(x + 5) + B(x - 2). \tag{20.3}$$

The last equation must be true for all values of x, so in particular it must be true for $x = -5$ and $x = 2$, the zeros of the two linear factors. By substituting these in turn we can determine A and B.

Use $x = -5$ in (20.3):

$$-5 + 12 = A(0) + B(-7)$$
$$B = -1.$$

Use $x = 2$ in (20.3):

$$2 + 12 = A(7) + B(0)$$
$$A = 2.$$

With $A = 2$ and $B = -1$, Equation (20.2) gives the answer:

$$\frac{x + 12}{(x - 2)(x + 5)} = \frac{2}{x - 2} \frac{1}{x + 5}.$$

To check the answer perform the subtraction incated on the right and show that the result simplifies to the expression on the left.

C. Repeated Linear Factors

Each repeated linear factor $(ax + b)^m$ contributes a sum of the form

$$\frac{A_1}{ax + b} + \frac{A_2}{(ax + b)^2} + \cdots + \frac{A_m}{(x + b)^m}$$

to the decomposition.

Example 20.2 Decompose $\dfrac{x^2 - 5x - 2}{x^3 + 2x^2 + x}$ into partial fractions.

Solution First, factor the denominator completely

$$x^3 + 2x^2 + x = x(x^2 + 2x + 1) = x(x + 1)^2$$

The distinct factor x contributes

$$\frac{A}{x}.$$

The repeated linear factor $(x + 1)^2$ contributes

$$\frac{B}{x + 1} + \frac{C}{(x + 1)^2}.$$

If

$$\frac{x^2 - 5x - 2}{x(x + 1)^2} = \frac{A}{x} + \frac{B}{x + 1} + \frac{C}{(x + 1)^2} \tag{20.4}$$

then

$$x^2 - 5x - 2 = A(x + 1)^2 + Bx(x + 1) + Cx. \tag{20.5}$$

With $x = 0$ in (20.5) we will get $A = -2$. With $x = -1$ in (20.5) we will get $C = -4$. Now we use any other value of x in (20.5), along with $A = -2$ and $C = -4$, to get B. With $x = 1$ we will get $B = 3$.

If we use $A = -2$, $B = 3$, and $C = -4$ in Equation (20.5), and revert to the original form of the denominator on the left, we get

$$\frac{x^2 - 5x - 2}{x^3 + 2x^2 + x} = -\frac{2}{x} + \frac{3}{x + 1} - \frac{4}{(x + 1)^2}.$$

D. Distinct Quadratic Factors

Each distinct quadratic factor $ax^2 + bx + c$ contributes a term of the form

$$\frac{Ax + B}{ax^2 + bx + c}$$

to the decomposition.

Example 20.3 Decompose $\dfrac{3x^2 + 2x}{(x + 1)(x^2 + x + 1)}$ into partial fractions.

Chapter 10/ 5

Solution The factor $x^2 + x + 1$ is irreducible. The factors $x + 1$ and $x^2 + x + 1$ contribute terms

$$\frac{A}{x + 1} \quad \text{and} \quad \frac{Bx + C}{x^2 + x + 1}$$

respectively. If

$$\frac{3x^2 + 2x}{(x + 1)(x^2 + x + 1)} = \frac{A}{x + 1} + \frac{Bx + C}{x^2 + x + 1} \qquad (20.6)$$

then

$$3x^2 + 2x = A(x^2 + x + 1) + (Bx + C)(x + 1). \qquad (20.7)$$

With $x = -1$ in (20.7) we will get $A = 1$. With $x = 0$ and $A = 1$ in (20.7) we will get $C = -1$. With $x = 1$, $A = 1$, and $C = -1$ in (20.7) we will get $B = 2$. Thus

$$\frac{3x^2 + 2x}{(x + 1)(x^2 + x + 1)} = \frac{1}{x + 1} + \frac{2x - 1}{x^2 + x + 1}.$$

E. Repeated Quadratic Factors

Each repeated quadratic factor $(ax^2 + bx + c)^n$ contributes a sum of the form

$$\frac{A_1 x + B_1}{ax^2 + bx + c} + \frac{A_2 x + B_2}{(ax^2 + bx + c)^2} + \cdots + \frac{A_n x + B_n}{(ax^2 + bx + c)^n}$$

to the decomposition.

In the previous examples the coefficients in the partial fraction decompositions have been determined by substituting appropriate numbers for x. The next example uses a method based on the fact that a polynomial in x is identically zero (that is, zero for every value of x) iff each of its coefficients is zero. (This will be proved in Section 46.)

Example 20.4 Decompose $\dfrac{1}{x(x^2 + 2)^2}$ into partial fractions.

Solution The factors x and $(x^2 + 2)^2$ contribute

$$\frac{A}{x} \quad \text{and} \quad \frac{Bx + C}{x^2 + 2} + \frac{Dx + E}{(x^2 + 2)^2}$$

respectively. If

$$\frac{1}{x(x^2 + 2)^2} = \frac{A}{x} + \frac{Bx + C}{x^2 + 2} + \frac{Dx + E}{(x^2 + 2)^2} \tag{20.8}$$

then

$$1 = A(x^2 + 2)^2 + (Bx + C)x(x^2 + 2) + (Dx + E)x$$

$$1 = A(x^4 + 4x^2 + 4) + B(x^4 + 2x^2) + C(x^3 + 2x)$$
$$+ Dx^2 + Ex$$

$$(A + B)x^4 + Cx^3 + (4A + 2B + D)x^2 + (2C + E)x + 4A - 1 = 0. \tag{20.9}$$

Since Equation (20.9) is to be satisfied for every value of x, each of the coefficients must be zero. (See the remark preceding this example.)

$$x^4: \quad A + B = 0 \qquad\qquad x^3: \quad C = 0$$

$$x^2: \quad 4A + 2B + D = 0 \qquad x: \quad 2C + E = 0$$

$$x^0: \quad 4A - 1 = 0$$

The equation for x^0 yields $A = \frac{1}{4}$. The equation for x^4 then yields $B = -\frac{1}{4}$. The equation for x^3 yields $C = 0$. The equation for x then yields $E = 0$. With $A = \frac{1}{4}$ and $B = -\frac{1}{4}$, the equation for x^2 yields $D = -\frac{1}{2}$. With these values for A, B, C, D, and E, Equation (20.8) becomes

$$\frac{1}{x(x^2 + 2)^2} = \frac{1}{4x} - \frac{x}{4(x^2 + 2)} - \frac{x}{2(x^2 + 2)^2}.$$

F. Improper Fractions

A rational function is called a **proper fraction** if the degree of the numerator is less than the degree of the denominator; otherwise it is called an **improper fraction**. By division, an improper fraction can be written as a sum of a polynomial and a proper fraction. The preceding methods can then be applied to decompose the proper fraction into partial fractions.

Example 20.5 Decompose

$$f(x) = \frac{x^4 + 3x^3 - 11x^2 - 2x + 22}{x^2 + 3x - 10}$$

into partial fractions.

Solution   Division yields

$$f(x) = x^2 - 1 + \frac{x + 12}{x^2 + 3x - 10}.$$

The proper fraction on the right is the same as the fraction in Example 20.1. Therefore, using the solution of that example, we have

$$f(x) = x^2 - 1 + \frac{2}{x - 2} - \frac{1}{x + 5}.$$

Exercises for Section 20

Decompose into partial fractions.

1. $\dfrac{x - 8}{(x + 1)(x - 2)}$

2. $\dfrac{3x + 3}{x(x - 3)}$

3. $\dfrac{6x - 18}{(x + 2)(x - 4)}$

4. $\dfrac{2}{3x^2 + 4x}$

5. $\dfrac{-1}{2x^2 + x - 1}$

6. $\dfrac{8x + 3}{6x^2 + 2x}$

7. $\dfrac{3x - 4}{(x - 1)^2}$

8. $\dfrac{4x + 5}{(2x + 1)^2}$

9. $\dfrac{-4x + 11}{(2x - 3)^2}$

10. $\dfrac{-x^2 + 2x + 4}{x^3 + x^2}$

11. $\dfrac{2x^2 - 2x + 3}{x^3 - 2x^2 + x}$

12. $\dfrac{7x^2 - 9x}{(x + 1)(x - 1)^2}$

13. $\dfrac{4x^2 + x + 4}{x^3 + x^2 + x}$

14. $\dfrac{2x^2 + 5x + 2}{x^3 + x}$

15. $\dfrac{-3x^2 + 4x - 6}{x^3 + 2x}$

16. $\dfrac{7x^2 + 13}{(x^2 + 1)(x^2 + 2)}$

17. $\dfrac{x^2 - 2}{x^4 + x^2}$

18. $\dfrac{-x^2}{(x^2 + 1)(x^2 + 3)}$

19. $\dfrac{x^3 - x + 1}{(x^2 + 1)^2}$

20. $\dfrac{3x^2 + 4x + 5}{(x^2 + 2)^2}$

21. $\dfrac{2x^3 + x^2 + 4x - 1}{(x^2 + x + 1)^2}$

22. $\dfrac{-2x^2 + 2x + 3}{x^4 + x^3}$

23. $\dfrac{4x^2 - 11x + 8}{(x - 1)^3}$

24. $\dfrac{-2x^3 + x^2 + 2x + 4}{(x^2 + 1)^3}$

25. $\dfrac{3x^3 + 2x^2 - 2x + 1}{x^2 + x}$

26. $\dfrac{x^4 - 2x^3 - x^2 + 6x - 5}{(x - 1)^2}$

27. $\dfrac{2x^5 - x^4 + 5x^3 - 3x^2 + x - 2}{(x^2 + 1)^2}$

SECTION 47

SYSTEMS OF LINEAR EQUATIONS

A. Introduction

The idea of a linear equation in two variables extends in a natural way to more than two variables. For example, a **linear equation** in the variables x, y, and z is an equation that can be written in the form

$$ax + by + cz = d$$

for some constant real numbers a, b, c, and d, with a, b, and c not all 0. In this section we consider systems of such linear equations.

A **solution** of a system such as

$$
\begin{aligned}
a_1x + b_1y + c_1z &= d_1 \\
a_2x + b_2y + c_2z &= d_2 \\
a_3x + b_3y + c_3z &= d_3
\end{aligned}
\qquad (47.1)
$$

is an ordered triple (a, b, c) of real numbers that satisfies each of the equations in the system. If necessary, we can be more explicit and write a solution in the form $x = a$, $y = b$, and $z = c$. The definition of a *solution* of a system with more variables or different variables, or with nonlinear equations, is defined in the same way.

Example 47.1 The triple $(4, 0, -3)$ is a solution of the system

$$
\begin{aligned}
x + 3y - z &= 7 \\
2x - y + 3z &= -1 \\
-x + 5y - 2z &= 2.
\end{aligned}
$$

If we substitute $x = 4$, $y = 0$, and $z = -3$ in the second equation, for instance, the result is

$$
\begin{aligned}
2(4) - (0) + 3(-3) &\stackrel{?}{=} -1 \\
-1 &= -1.
\end{aligned}
$$

You can check the first and third equations in the same way.

We concentrate primarily on three linear equations with three variables, but the method we use will carry over to systems with more linear equations and variables. As with systems of two linear equations with two variables, any system of linear equations will have either one solution, infinitely many solutions, or no solution. If a system has at least one solution, then the system is said to be **consistent**. If there is no solution, then the system is said to be **inconsistent**.

For linear systems with three variables, the solutions have a geometrical interpretation similar to that in the case of two variables. It can be shown that relative to a three-dimensional coordinate system, each linear equation in x, y, and z is represented by a plane. A solution for a system corresponds to a point of intersection of the planes that represent the system. If there is a unique point of intersection, then the system has a unique solution. If the planes intersect in a line or a plane, then there are infinitely many solutions. If the planes have no point in common, then there is no solution.

B. Solution by Elimination

One system of equations is **equivalent** to another if the two systems have the same solutions. In the method of **elimination** we solve a system by replacing it by a succession of equivalent systems until we arrive at a system for which the solutions are obvious. This method depends on the fact that we arrive at an equivalent system if we perform any combination of the following operations on a given system:

 I. Interchange the equations.
 II. Multiply an equation by a nonzero constant.
 III. Add a constant multiple of one of the equations to the other equation.

In II, to multiply an equation by a constant means to multiply both sides of the equation by the constant. Operations I–III can be used to try to arrive at equations with only one variable each; that is, equations from which all but one variable has been *eliminated*. Before we look at an example, let us see why operations I–III produce equivalent systems. For simplicity, we consider two equations with two variables.

It is obvious that operation I will not change the solutions of a system. Operation II will not change the solutions because if $k \neq 0$, then

$$ax + by = c \text{ iff } k(ax + by) = kc.$$

Finally, operation III will not change the solutions because if

$$a_1x + b_1y = c_1 \quad \text{and} \quad a_2x + b_2y = c_2 \tag{47.2}$$

and k is a real number, then

$$a_1x + b_1y = c_1 \quad \text{and} \quad k(a_1x + b_1y) + a_2x + b_2y = kc_1 + c_2; \tag{47.3}$$

and, conversely, if (47.3) is true, then (47.2) is true [add $-k$ times the first equation in (47.3) to the second equation in (47.3) to produce the second equation in (47.2)].

Example 47.2 Solve the system

$$4x + y = 5$$
$$x + 2y = -4$$

by elimination.

Solution First we replace the system by an equivalent system in which the coefficient of the first variable in the first equation is 1. This is not an essential step, but it fits a systematic pattern that will arise later when we consider systems with more equations and more variables. Interchange the two equations.

$$x + 2y = -4$$
$$4x + y = 5$$

Add -4 times the first equation to the second equation. This will eliminate x from the second equation.

$$x + 2y = -4$$
$$- 7y = 21$$

Multiply the second equation by $-\frac{1}{7}$, so that the coefficient on y will be 1.

$$x + 2y = -4$$
$$y = -3$$

Add -2 times the second equation to the first equation. This will eliminate y from the first equation.

$$x \quad = 2$$
$$y = -3$$

Thus the solution is $(2, -3)$.

The method of elimination will uncover dependent and inconsistent systems in the same way as the method of substitution (Section 9B): a dependent system will lead to the equaton $0 = 0$, and an inconsistent system will lead to a contradiction.

C. Gaussian Elimination

We have solved linear systems by two methods, substitution and elimination. The method we use in this section is a combination of the two; we begin with elimination and then complete the process by substitution. This method is called **Gaussian elimination** [after Karl Friedrich Gauss (1777–1855)]. Operations I–III (Subsection B) are used for all but the last two steps in the following outline; the last two steps use substitution.

Outline of Gaussian Elimination

*The goal of the step on the left is to produce the form on the right, where each * denotes an unspecified constant.*

Obtain an equivalent system with 1 as the coefficient of x in the first equation. This may require no change or it may require the use of I and II.	$x + {*}y + {*}z = {*}$ ${*}x + {*}y + {*}z = {*}$ ${*}x + {*}y + {*}z = {*}$
Eliminate x from the second and third equations by adding appropriate multiples of the first equation to the second and third equations.	$x + {*}y + {*}z = {*}$ ${*}y + {*}z = {*}$ ${*}y + {*}z = {*}$
Obtain an equivalent system with 1 as the coefficient of y in the second equation, without changing the first equation.	$x + {*}y + {*}z = {*}$ $y + {*}z = {*}$ ${*}y + {*}z = {*}$
Eliminate y from the third equation by adding an appropriate multiple of the second equation to the third equation.	$x + {*}y + {*}z = {*}$ $y + {*}z = {*}$ ${*}z = {*}$
Obtain an equivalent system with 1 as the coefficient of z in the third equation, without changing the first two equations. The value of z will now be obvious.	$x + {*}y + {*}z = {*}$ $y + {*}z = {*}$ $z = {*}$
Substitute the value of z into the second equation and solve for y.	$x + {*}y + {*}z = {*}$ $y \quad\quad = {*}$ $z = {*}$
Substitute the values of y and z into the first equation and solve for x.	$x \quad\quad\quad = {*}$ $y \quad\quad = {*}$ $z = {*}$

Gaussian elimination can also be used for more than three variables and equations. For four linear equations in w, x, y, and z, for example, work for the form

$$w + {}^*x + {}^*y + {}^*z = {}^* \quad \text{and then} \quad w \qquad\qquad = {}^*$$
$$x + {}^*y + {}^*z = {}^* \qquad\qquad x \qquad = {}^*$$
$$y + {}^*z = {}^* \qquad\qquad y \quad = {}^*$$
$$z = {}^* \qquad\qquad z = {}^*.$$

The steps listed should be thought of as an outline that can be varied whenever it is convenient or necessary. For example, if a system is inconsistent, a contradiction will arise somewhere along the way, and then we simply stop. Or, for a system with infinitely many solutions the equation $0 = 0$ will arise somewhere along the way; Example 47.5 will show how to handle that.

Example 47.3 Solve the system

$$3x - y - 2z = 8$$
$$x + 2y - z = -1$$
$$-2x - 5y + z = -1.$$

Solution We follow the plan outlined above, with a variation where noted. Interchange the first two equations.

$$x + 2y - z = -1$$
$$3x - y - 2z = 8$$
$$-2x - 5y + z = -1$$

Add -3 times the first equation to the second equation.
Add 2 times the first equation to the third equation.

$$x + 2y - z = -1$$
$$-7y + z = 11$$
$$-y - z = -3$$

We could now multiply the second equation by $-\frac{1}{7}$ so that the coefficient on y would be 1. But that would introduce fractions, which can be avoided in this problem as follows. (Fractions cannot always be avoided, however.) Multiply the third equation by -1 to make 1 the coefficient of y; then interchange the second and third equations.

$$x + 2y - z = -1$$
$$y + z = 3$$
$$-7y + z = 11$$

Add 7 times the second equation to the third equation.

$$x + 2y - z = -1$$
$$y + z = 3$$
$$8z = 32$$

Multiply the third equation by $\frac{1}{8}$.

$$x + 2y - z = -1$$
$$y + z = 3$$
$$z = 4$$

Thus $z = 4$. With $z = 4$ the second equation becomes $y + 4 = 3$, so that $y = -1$. Finally, with $y = -1$ and $z = 4$ the first equation becomes $x + 2(-1) - 4 = -1$, so that $x = 5$. Therefore, the solution of the system is $(5, -1, 4)$.

Example 47.4 Solve the system

$$x - 2y + 4z = 9$$
$$2x + y + 3z = 3$$
$$-x - 4y + 2z = 4.$$

Solution Again we follow the plan preceding Example 47.3. The first step there requires no change in this problem.

Add -2 times the first equation to the second equation.
Add the first equation to the third equation.

$$x - 2y + 4z = 9$$
$$5y - 5z = -15$$
$$-6y + 6z = 13$$

Multiply the second equation by $\frac{1}{5}$.

$$x - 2y + 4z = 9$$
$$y - z = -3$$
$$-6y + 6z = 13$$

Add 6 times the second equation to the third equation.

$$x - 2y + 4z = 9$$
$$y - z = -3$$
$$0 = -5$$

The equation $0 = -5$ is a contradiction, so the system is inconsistent.

Example 47.5   Solve the system

$$x - y + 3z = 0$$
$$2x - y + 4z = 1$$
$$5x - 3y + 11z = 2.$$

Solution   Add -2 times the first equation to the second equation. Add -5 times the first equation to the third equation.

$$x - y + 3z = 0$$
$$y - 2z = 1$$
$$2y - 4z = 2$$

Add -2 times the second equation to the third equation.

$$x - y + 3z = 0$$
$$y - 2z = 1$$
$$0 = 0.$$

The last set of equations shows that if t is any real number then we get a solution with

$$z = t$$
$$y = 2t + 1 \quad \text{(from the second equation)}$$
$$x = y - 3z$$
$$ = (2t + 1) - 3t$$
$$ = -t + 1 \quad \text{(from the first equation)}.$$

For example, $t = 0$ gives the solution $(1, 1, 0)$. And $t = -2$ gives the solution $(3, -3, -2)$. In set-builder notation, the set of all solutions is

$$\{(-t + 1, 2t + 1, t): \quad t \text{ is a real number}\}.$$

D. Applications

Example 47.6 A farmer needs 1000 pounds of fertilizer that is 50% nitrogen, 15% phosphorous, and 35% potassium. He can draw from mixtures *A*, *B*, and *C*, whose compositions are shown in Table 47.1. How many pounds of each mixture should he use?

TABLE 47.1

	Nitrogen	Phosphorus	Potassium
A	40%	20%	40%
B	60%		40%
C	50%	20%	30%

Solution Let *x*, *y*, and *z* denote the required number of pounds of mixtures *A*, *B*, and *C*, respectively. We can write one equation for each nutrient. For example, the total amount of nitrogen, which is 50% of 1000 pounds, or 500 pounds, must equal the sum of the amounts from mixture *A* (40% of *x*, or 0.4*x*), mixture *B* (60% of *y*, or 0.6*y*), and mixture *C* (50% of *z*, or 0.5*z*). The equations that arise in this way are

$$0.4x + 0.6y + 0.5z = 500 \quad \text{nitrogen}$$
$$0.2x + 0.2z = 150 \quad \text{phosphorus}$$
$$0.4x + 0.4y + 0.3z = 350 \quad \text{potassium.}$$

The solution of this system is $x = 250$, $y = 250$, and $z = 500$, so the farmer should use 250 pounds each of mixtures *A* and *B*, and 500 pounds of mixture *C*.

If two points are in a Cartesian plane but are not on the same vertical line, they determine a unique *linear* function—the function whose graph passes through the two points (Section 11). In the same way, if three noncollinear points are in a Cartesian plane but no two are on the same vertical line, they determine a unique *quadratic* function—the function whose graph passes through the three points. The following example shows how to find the quadratic function from the coordinates of the three points.

Example 47.7 There is a unique quadratic function

$$f(x) = ax^2 + bx + c$$

such that $f(-1) = 0$, $f(1) = 2$, and $f(2) = 9$. What is it? [Geometrically, the problem asks for the equation of the parabola through $(-1, 0)$, $(1, 2)$, and $(2, 9)$. See Figure 47.1.]

Solution If $f(-1) = 0$ then

$$0 = a(-1)^2 + b(-1) + c \text{ so that } a - b + c = 0.$$

Similarly, $f(1) = 2$ implies $a + b + c = 2$, and $f(2) = 9$ implies $4a + 2b + c = 9$. Therefore, a, b, and c must satisfy each of the following equations.

$$a - b + c = 0$$
$$a + b + c = 2$$
$$4a + 2b + c = 9$$

The solution of this system is $a = 2$, $b = 1$, and $c = -1$, so the function is

$$f(x) = 2x^2 + x - 1.$$

Example 47.7 is related to the following general fact: If $b_1, b_2, \ldots, b_{n+1}$ are any real numbers and $a_1, a_2, \ldots, a_{n+1}$ are any distinct real numbers, then there is a unique polynomial function of degree not exceeding n such that $f(a_i) = b_i$ for $1 \le i \le n + 1$. Exercise 31 gives an illustration with $n = 3$.

Exercises for Section 47

Solve each system by Gaussian elimination. If there are infinitely many solutions, give the answer in set-builder notation. If a system is inconsistent, so state.

1.
$$x + 2y + z = 1$$
$$y + 3z = -7$$
$$4x + 8y + 3z = 6$$

$(5, -1, 2)$

2.
$$x + 5y - 2z = -5$$
$$-3x + 2y - 4z = 2$$
$$y + z = 4$$

3.
$$x + 2y - 2z = -2$$
$$x - 4y + z = 4$$
$$2x + 4y - z = 5$$

4.
$$x - 3y + 2z = 1$$
$$2x - 5y + 6z = 3$$
$$4x - 11y + 10z = 5$$

Chapter 10/18

5. $2u + 7u + 4w = 2$
$u + 4v + 3w = 1$
$u + 5v + 5w = 1$

6. $2r \quad\;\; + 6t = -7$
$s + 2t = 2$
$r + s + 5t = 1$

7. $3p + q + 14r = 10$
$q - 4r = -12$
$p + q + 2r = 1$

8. $-x + 3y - 3z = 2$
$y - z = 1$
$2x - y + 2z = 7$

9. $5x + 2y - z = 0$
$y + 2z = -10$
$x - y - 3z = 14$

10. $2a + 3b - c \quad\;\; = 0$
$a + 2b + c - 7 = 0$
$5a + 8b - c - 7 = 0$

11. $2a \quad\quad + 36c = 7$
$4a + 6b + 3c = -1$
$a + 2b - 5c = 2$

12. $p + 9q + 3r - 5 = 0$
$p \quad\quad + 6r - 6 = 0$
$3p + 9q + 15r - 17 = 0$

13. $x + 4y - z = 2$
$-2x + 3y + z = 0$
$4x + 5y - 3z = 4$

14. $x + y - 2z - 2 = 0$
$4x + 3y - 4z - 7 = 0$
$6x - y + 4z - 2 = 0$

$$\begin{array}{ccc|c} 1 & 1 & -2 & +2 \\ 4 & 3 & -4 & 7 \\ 6 & 1 & 4 & 2 \end{array}$$

15. $-x + 4y + 2z = -1$
$3x + 2y - 2z = 2$
$9x - 8y - 10z = 6$

16. $9x - y + 5z = 2$
$4x + 2y + 3z = 2$
$-2x + 3y + z = 1$

17. $2x + 2y - 2z = 3$
$-3x + y + 2z = 1$
$7x + 3y - 6z = 5$

18. $2x - y + 2z = 3$
$-3x + 2y - z = -3$
$4x + 2y - z = -1$

19. $x + y + 2z - w = 1$
$y - z + w = 8$
$2x \quad\quad + 2w = 10$
$x - y \quad\; + w = 1$

20. $w - 2x + 3y \quad\;\; = 4$
$w - 3x + 4y - z = 0$
$4x - 3y \quad\;\; = 2$
$5w - 4x + 11y - 2z = 16$

21. $y - 2z + w = 3$
$x - y - 3z - w = 1$
$2x + 4y \quad\; + 2w = 5$
$4x + 3y - 8z + w = 9$

22. Suppose the farmer in Example 47.6 needs 1000 pounds of fertilizer that is 53% nitrogen, 10% phosphorous, and 37% potassium. How many pounds of each mixture (*A*, *B*, and *C*) should he use?

23. Suppose the farmer in Example 47.6 has the same requirements as in the example, except that he must draw from mixtures *A* and *B* (as in the example) and a mixture *D* that is 40% nitrogen, 30% phosphorous, and 30% potassium. How many pounds of each mixture (*A*, *B*, and *D*) should he use?

24. A total of $1000 is divided into three accounts, which pay 6%, 7%, and 9% simple annual interest respectively. The total interest earned in 1 year is $75. The sum of the amounts in the 6% and 9% accounts is $100 more than the amount in the 7% account. How much is invested in each account?

25. In the 50 years from 1926 through 1975, National League teams won the World Series one more time than the Yankees (an American League team), and the Yankees won eight more times than the other American League teams combined. Determine how many times the Series was won by National League teams, by the Yankees, and by American League teams other than the Yankees.

(It is irrelevant to the solution of this problem, but during 1926–1975 the Yankees lost the series seven times.)

26. Of the 50 states in the U.S., the number entering the Union from 1800 through 1850 was one less than the number entering before 1800, one more than the number entering from 1851 through 1900, and three times the number entering after 1900. How many entered in each of the four periods: before 1800, 1800–1850, 1851–1900, and after 1900?

27. The normal annual precipitation amounts in Cleveland, Phoenix, and Mobile satisfy these relationships: the amount in Cleveland is five times the amount in Phoenix, the amount in Mobile is just three inches less than ten times the amount in Phoenix, and the total amount in the three cities is 109 inches. Find the amount in each city.

28 There is a unique quadratic function f such that $f(-1) = 0$, $f(1) = 1$, and $f(4) = 0$. What is it?

29. Find the equation of the parabola through the points $(-2, 6)$, $(1, 3)$, and $(2, 10)$.

30. Find the equation of the parabola that passes through the points $(0, 4)$ and $(1, \frac{3}{2})$ and is symmetric with respect to the y-axis.

31. There is a unique polynomial function f of degree three such that $f(-1) = -2$, $f(1) = 2$, $f(2) = 4$, and $f(3) = 14$. What is it?

32. Prove that there is no quadratic function f such that $f(0) = -3$, $f(2) = 1$, and $f(3) = 3$. (Suggestion: The method of Example 47.7 will lead to $a = 0$.)

33. A small rocket is to be fired upward near the earth's surface with initial velocity v_0 feet per second and initial height s_0 feet, in such a way that its maximum altitude will be 225 feet and it will reach the ground 4.5 seconds after it is fired. Determine what v_0 and s_0 should be. (See Example 12.5. Use $g = 32$.)

SECTION 48

LINEAR SYSTEMS AND ROW-EQUIVALENT MATRICES

A. Augmented Matrices

The essential information from the system

$$a_1 x + b_1 y + c_1 z = d_1$$
$$a_2 x + b_2 y + c_2 z = d_2$$
$$a_3 x + b_3 y + c_3 z = d_3$$

is contained in the rectangular array

$$\text{Row } 1 \rightarrow \begin{bmatrix} a_1 & b_1 & c_1 & d_1 \\ a_2 & b_2 & c_2 & d_2 \\ a_3 & b_3 & c_3 & d_3 \end{bmatrix}, \tag{48.1}$$

$$\uparrow$$
$$\text{Column } 4$$

which is called the **augmented matrix** of the system. In general, the term *matrix* is used to describe any rectangular array of numbers. Any matrix consists of (horizontal) **rows** and (vertical) **columns**, numbered respectively from top to bottom and from left to right as suggested in (48.1).

Example 48.1   The augmented matrix of the system

$$2x + y - 8z = 7$$
$$y - 2z = 2$$
$$x - 2y + 6z = 1$$

is

$$\begin{bmatrix} 2 & 1 & -8 & 7 \\ 0 & 1 & -2 & 2 \\ 1 & -2 & 6 & 1 \end{bmatrix}.$$

The 0 in the second row and first column is the coefficient of the missing x in the second equation.

Augmented matrices for linear systems with more variables or different variables are defined in a similar way. Just remember that before writing the augmented matrix the variables must be in the same order in all of the equations. Also, the constant terms are to be on the right of the equality signs.

B. Linear Systems and Row-Equivalence

Rather than writing out all of the equations at each step in solving a system, we can simply write the corresponding augmented matrix. Each of the three types of operations used to solve a system by elimination produces a corresponding operation on the augmented matrix. If we interchange the first and third equations, for example, then we correspondingly interchange the first and third rows of the augmented matrix. The operations on matrices that can arise in this way are called **elementary row operations**. They are of three types (compare I, II, and III in Section 47B).

  I. Interchange two rows.
 II. Multiply a row by a nonzero constant.
III. Add a constant multiple of one row to another row.

To solve systems in this section we use I–III on the augmented matrix until the solution is obvious. This amounts to modifying Gaussian elimination so that substitution is not used. If possible, transform the augmented matrix as follows (for the case of three equations with three variables; other cases are similar).

$$
\begin{bmatrix} * & * & * & * \\ * & * & * & * \\ * & * & * & * \end{bmatrix} \rightarrow
\begin{bmatrix} 1 & * & * & * \\ * & * & * & * \\ * & * & * & * \end{bmatrix} \rightarrow
\begin{bmatrix} 1 & * & * & * \\ 0 & * & * & * \\ 0 & * & * & * \end{bmatrix} \rightarrow
\begin{bmatrix} 1 & * & * & * \\ 0 & 1 & * & * \\ 0 & * & * & * \end{bmatrix}
$$

$$
\rightarrow \begin{bmatrix} 1 & 0 & * & * \\ 0 & 1 & * & * \\ 0 & 0 & * & * \end{bmatrix} \rightarrow
\begin{bmatrix} 1 & 0 & * & * \\ 0 & 1 & * & * \\ 0 & 0 & 1 & * \end{bmatrix} \rightarrow
\begin{bmatrix} 1 & 0 & 0 & * \\ 0 & 1 & 0 & * \\ 0 & 0 & 1 & * \end{bmatrix}
$$

In some cases the final form will necessarily be different, as Examples 48.3 and 48.4 will show. To keep track of the operations we use abbreviations like these:

(Row 1) ↔ (Row 2) will mean to interchange Rows 1 and 2.

5(Row 1) will mean to multiply each element of Row 1 by 5.

(Row 3) − 6(Row 1) will mean to add −6 times Row 1 to Row 3.

Example 48.2 Use augmented matrices to solve the system in Example 48.1.

Solution

$$
\begin{bmatrix} 2 & 1 & -8 & 7 \\ 0 & 1 & -2 & 2 \\ 1 & -2 & 6 & 1 \end{bmatrix}
\xrightarrow{\text{(Row 1) ↔ (Row 3)}}
\begin{bmatrix} 1 & -2 & 6 & 1 \\ 0 & 1 & -2 & 2 \\ 2 & 1 & -8 & 7 \end{bmatrix}
$$

$$
\xrightarrow{\text{(Row 3) − 2(Row 1)}}
\begin{bmatrix} 1 & -2 & 6 & 1 \\ 0 & 1 & -2 & 2 \\ 0 & 5 & -20 & 5 \end{bmatrix}
$$

$$
\xrightarrow[\text{(Row 3) − 5(Row 2)}]{\text{(Row 1) + 2(Row 2)}}
\begin{bmatrix} 1 & 0 & 2 & 5 \\ 0 & 1 & -2 & 2 \\ 0 & 0 & -10 & -5 \end{bmatrix}
$$

$$
\xrightarrow{-\frac{1}{10}\text{(Row 3)}}
\begin{bmatrix} 1 & 0 & 2 & 5 \\ 0 & 1 & -2 & 2 \\ 0 & 0 & 1 & \frac{1}{2} \end{bmatrix}
$$

$$
\xrightarrow[\text{(Row 2) + 2(Row 3)}]{\text{(Row 1) − 2(Row 3)}}
\begin{bmatrix} 1 & 0 & 0 & 4 \\ 0 & 1 & 0 & 3 \\ 0 & 0 & 1 & \frac{1}{2} \end{bmatrix}
$$

The last matrix is the augmented matrix of

$$x \qquad\qquad = 4$$
$$y \qquad = 3$$
$$z = \tfrac{1}{2}.$$

Thus the solution is $(4, 3, \tfrac{1}{2})$.

Example 48.3 Use augmented matrices to solve the system

$$x - 3y - 5z = 2$$
$$2x - 5y + z = 3$$
$$x - 2y + 6z = 2.$$

Solution

$$\begin{bmatrix} 1 & -3 & -5 & 2 \\ 2 & -5 & 1 & 3 \\ 1 & -2 & 6 & 2 \end{bmatrix} \xrightarrow[\text{(Row 3) } - \text{ (Row 1)}]{\text{(Row 2) } - 2\text{(Row 1)}} \begin{bmatrix} 1 & -3 & -5 & 2 \\ 0 & 1 & 11 & -1 \\ 0 & 1 & 11 & 0 \end{bmatrix}$$

$$\xrightarrow[\text{(Row 3) } - \text{ (Row 2)}]{\text{(Row 1) } + 3\text{(Row 2)}} \begin{bmatrix} 1 & 0 & 28 & -1 \\ 0 & 1 & 11 & -1 \\ 0 & 0 & 0 & 1 \end{bmatrix}$$

The third row of the last matrix corresponds to the equation $0x + 0y + 0z = 1$, which implies $0 = 1$, an impossibility. Therefore, the system is inconsistent.

Example 48.4 Use augmented matrices to solve the system

$$x - 2y + z = 4$$
$$2x - 4y + 3z = 14$$
$$-x + 2y \qquad = 2.$$

Solution

$$\begin{bmatrix} 1 & -2 & 1 & 4 \\ 2 & -4 & 3 & 14 \\ -1 & 2 & 0 & 2 \end{bmatrix} \xrightarrow[\text{(Row 3) } + \text{ (Row 1)}]{\text{(Row 2) } - 2\text{(Row 1)}} \begin{bmatrix} 1 & -2 & 1 & 4 \\ 0 & 0 & 1 & 6 \\ 0 & 0 & 1 & 6 \end{bmatrix}$$

No row operation will transform the last matrix to the form

$$\begin{bmatrix} 1 & * & * & * \\ 0 & 1 & * & * \\ 0 & * & * & * \end{bmatrix}.$$

But we can get the form

$$\begin{bmatrix} 1 & * & * & * \\ 0 & 0 & 1 & * \\ 0 & 0 & 0 & 0 \end{bmatrix}.$$

$$\begin{bmatrix} 1 & -2 & 1 & 4 \\ 0 & 0 & 1 & 6 \\ 0 & 0 & 1 & 6 \end{bmatrix} \xrightarrow[\text{(Row 3)} - \text{(Row 2)}]{\text{(Row 1)} - \text{(Row 2)}} \begin{bmatrix} 1 & -2 & 0 & -2 \\ 0 & 0 & 1 & 6 \\ 0 & 0 & 0 & 0 \end{bmatrix}$$

The last matrix translates to

$$x - 2y \quad\;\; = -2$$
$$z = 6.$$

The first equation will give a value of x for each value of y. The second equation dictates $z = 6$. Therefore, the complete solution is

$$\{(2t - 2, t, 6): \quad t \text{ is a real number}\}.$$

The ideas in the preceding examples can be summarized as follows. If one matrix can be obtaind from another by a finite sequence of elementary row operations, then the two matrices are said to be **row equivalent**. It follows that two systems of linear equations are equivalent iff their augmented matrices are row equivalent. Therefore, we can solve a system by transforming its augmented matrix by a sequence of elementary row operations until the solutions become obvious. An appropriate form is given in the following statement, which is presented here without proof.

Each matrix is row equivalent to a unique matrix in **reduced echelon form**, which is, by definition, a matrix such that

1. the first nonzero entry (the **leading entry**) of each row is 1;
2. the other entries in any column containing such a leading entry are 0;
3. the leading entry in each row is to the right of the leading entry in each preceding row; and
4. rows containing only 0's are below rows with nonzero entries.

Example 48.5

(a) For the reasons indicated, these matrices are not in reduced echelon form.

$$\begin{bmatrix} 1 & 0 & 4 & 3 \\ 0 & 2 & -4 & 0 \\ 0 & 0 & 0 & 0 \end{bmatrix} \quad \begin{bmatrix} 1 & 0 & 5 \\ 1 & 0 & 10 \end{bmatrix} \quad \begin{bmatrix} 1 & 0 & 0 & 8 \\ 0 & 0 & 1 & 4 \\ 0 & 1 & 0 & -7 \end{bmatrix} \quad \begin{bmatrix} 1 & 0 & 0 & 0 & -9 \\ 0 & 0 & 0 & 0 & 0 \\ 0 & 0 & 1 & 0 & 6 \\ 0 & 0 & 0 & 0 & 0 \end{bmatrix}$$

Violates 1   Violates 2   Violates 3   Violates 4

(b) Each of these matrices is in reduced echelon form and is equivalent to the corresponding matrix in part (a).

$$\begin{bmatrix} 1 & 0 & 4 & 3 \\ 0 & 1 & -2 & 0 \\ 0 & 0 & 0 & 0 \end{bmatrix} \quad \begin{bmatrix} 1 & 0 & 5 \\ 0 & 0 & 1 \end{bmatrix} \quad \begin{bmatrix} 1 & 0 & 0 & 8 \\ 0 & 1 & 0 & -7 \\ 0 & 0 & 1 & 4 \end{bmatrix} \quad \begin{bmatrix} 1 & 0 & 0 & 0 & -9 \\ 0 & 0 & 1 & 0 & 6 \\ 0 & 0 & 0 & 0 & 0 \\ 0 & 0 & 0 & 0 & 0 \end{bmatrix}$$

C. More Examples

Linear systems with two variables or with more than three variables can also be solved by the method of this section. The method applies as well when the number of equations is different from the number of variables, as illustrated by the following examples.

Example 48.6 Solve

$$\begin{aligned} 2x \quad\quad + 5z &= 6 \\ 3y \quad\quad &= -1 \\ 4x - 3y + z &= 4 \\ 2x + 3y + z &= 1. \end{aligned}$$

Solution The augmented matrix

$$\begin{bmatrix} 2 & 0 & 5 & 6 \\ 0 & 3 & 0 & -1 \\ 4 & -3 & 1 & 4 \\ 2 & 3 & 1 & 1 \end{bmatrix}$$

is row equivalent to the reduced echelon matrix

$$\begin{bmatrix} 1 & 0 & 0 & \frac{1}{2} \\ 0 & 1 & 0 & -\frac{1}{3} \\ 0 & 0 & 1 & 1 \\ 0 & 0 & 0 & 0 \end{bmatrix}$$

Therefore, the solution is $(\frac{1}{2}, -\frac{1}{3}, 1)$.

Example 48.7 Solve

$$w + 2x + 7y \quad\quad - 1 = 0$$
$$x + 2y \quad\quad - 1 = 0$$
$$-w + x - y + 5z - 6 = 0.$$

Solution The augmented matrix

$$\begin{bmatrix} 1 & 2 & 7 & 0 & 1 \\ 0 & 1 & 2 & 0 & 1 \\ -1 & 1 & -1 & 5 & 6 \end{bmatrix}$$

is row equivalent to the reduced echelon matrix

$$\begin{bmatrix} 1 & 0 & 3 & 0 & -1 \\ 0 & 1 & 2 & 0 & 1 \\ 0 & 0 & 0 & 1 & \frac{4}{5} \end{bmatrix}.$$

The last row gives $z = \frac{4}{5}$. No leading coefficient occurs in the third column, so y can be assigned arbitrarily. If $y = t$, then the first and second rows give

$$w + 3t = -1 \quad \text{and} \quad x + 2t = 1.$$

Therefore,

$$w = -3t - 1 \quad \text{and} \quad x = -2t + 1,$$

so that

$$w = -3t - 1, \quad x = -2t + 1, \quad y = t, \quad \text{and } z = \frac{4}{5}$$

is a solution for each real number t. Or, the set of all solutions is

$$\{(-3t - 1, \, -2t + 1, \, t, \, \tfrac{4}{5}): \quad t \text{ is a real number}\}.$$

The following statements can be proved about a system of m linear equations with n unknown variables. If $m > n$, then the system may have one solution, infinitely many solutions, or no solution, depending on the system. If $m < n$ then the system may have infinitely many solutions or no solution, depending on the system; there will never be just one solution in this case.

Exercises for Section 48

Each matrix in Exercises 1–9 is the reduced echelon matrix for a system with variables w, x, y and z (in that order). Write the solution or solutions, or indicate that the system is inconsistent.

1. $\begin{bmatrix} 1 & 0 & 0 & 0 & -5 \\ 0 & 1 & 0 & 0 & 0 \\ 0 & 0 & 1 & 0 & 6 \\ 0 & 0 & 0 & 0 & 1 \end{bmatrix}$ *inconsistant*

2. $\begin{bmatrix} 1 & 0 & 0 & 0 & 0 \\ 0 & 1 & 0 & 0 & 8 \\ 0 & 0 & 1 & 0 & -3 \\ 0 & 0 & 0 & 1 & 12 \end{bmatrix}$

3. $\begin{bmatrix} 1 & 0 & 0 & 0 & 4 \\ 0 & 1 & 0 & 3 & -1 \\ 0 & 0 & 1 & 2 & 7 \\ 0 & 0 & 0 & 0 & 0 \end{bmatrix}$

4. $\begin{bmatrix} 1 & 0 & 0 & 0 & -1 \\ 0 & 1 & 8 & 0 & -2 \\ 0 & 0 & 0 & 1 & 23 \\ 0 & 0 & 0 & 0 & 0 \end{bmatrix}$

5. $\begin{bmatrix} 1 & 0 & 0 & 0 & 13 \\ 0 & 1 & 0 & 0 & 4 \\ 0 & 0 & 0 & 0 & 1 \\ 0 & 0 & 0 & 0 & 0 \end{bmatrix}$ *inconsistr*

6. $\begin{bmatrix} 1 & 0 & 0 & 0 & 8 \\ 0 & 1 & 0 & 0 & -9 \\ 0 & 0 & 1 & 0 & 7 \\ 0 & 0 & 0 & 1 & 23 \end{bmatrix}$

7. $\begin{bmatrix} 1 & 0 & 0 & 0 & -3 \\ 0 & 1 & 0 & 0 & 8 \\ 0 & 0 & 1 & 0 & 6 \\ 0 & 0 & 0 & 1 & 6 \end{bmatrix}$

8. $\begin{bmatrix} 1 & 4 & 0 & 0 & 7 \\ 0 & 0 & 1 & 0 & 4 \\ 0 & 0 & 0 & 1 & -3 \\ 0 & 0 & 0 & 0 & 0 \end{bmatrix}$

9. $\begin{bmatrix} 1 & 2 & 0 & 0 & 11 \\ 0 & 0 & 1 & 0 & -2 \\ 0 & 0 & 0 & 0 & 1 \\ 0 & 0 & 0 & 0 & 0 \end{bmatrix}$

In Exercises 10–30 solve each system by reducing the augmented matrix to reduced echelon form.

10. $x - 3y = -6$
     $3x + 2y = 26$

11. $2x + y = -2$
     $3x + 2y = 0$

12. $x + 5y = -2$
     $4x + 2y = -1$

13. $x - 7y + 2z = -6$
     $5x - 5y + 3z = 2$ $(0, 2, 4)$
     $-2x + y - z = -2$

14. $x + y + z = 3$
     $x - y - z = -1$
     $2x + 3y = 4$

15. $x + 5y + 10z = 2$
     $-3x + 15z = 4$
     $-x + 10y + 35z = 8$

16. $-a - 2b = 3$
     $2a + 5b - c = -4$
     $-3a - 5b - c = 12$

17. $p - 4q + r = 0$
     $3p - 11q + 4r = 1$
     $2p - 7q + 3r = -2$

18. $-t + 4u - v = 2$
     $3t - u + 2v = 1$
     $-4t + u - v = -1$

19. $2x + y - z - 2 = 0$
     $-5x + y + 3z = 0$
     $3x + 5y - z - 8 = 0$

20. $3x - 3y + z - 6 = 0$
     $2x + 2z - 5 = 0$
     $-4x + 6y + 7 = 0$

21. $5x - 2y + z - 2 = 0$
     $2x + y - z - 2 = 0$
     $3x + 6y - 5z + 6 = 0$

22.
$$w - 2x + 3y + 7z = 8$$
$$x \quad + z = -3$$
$$w \quad y + 3z = 2$$
$$w + x + y + 4z = -1$$

23.
$$w + 2x - y \quad = -6$$
$$w + 3x \quad + 3z = -1$$
$$-2x + y \quad = 2$$
$$2w \quad - 2y + 5z = -7$$

24.
$$w \quad + 2y \quad = 1$$
$$x \quad + z = -2$$
$$w + 2x + 2y + 2z = 0$$
$$-w + x - 2y \quad = 0$$

25.
$$x + 5y = 8$$
$$2x + 4y = 7$$
$$-x + 3y = 4$$

26.
$$2x - y = 5$$
$$x + 2y = 4$$
$$-x + 8y = 3$$

27.
$$x - y = 4$$
$$-2x + 2y = -8$$
$$5x - 10y = 20$$

28.
$$p - q + 2r - 4 = 0$$
$$-2p + 2q - 4r + 7 = 0$$

29.
$$t \quad - v \quad = -3$$
$$u + 2v \quad = 1$$
$$w = 2$$
$$2t + u \quad = -5$$

30.
$$2a + b + 2c \quad = 0$$
$$b + 2c \quad = 1$$
$$2a + b + 2c - 3d = -1$$
$$2a + 2b + 4c \quad = 1$$

Solve each exercise by writing a system of equations and then solving the system with augmented matrices.

31. The perimeter of a triangle is 45 centimeters. The length of the longest side is 3 centimeters less than the sum of the lengths of the other two sides. The longest side is 3 times as long as the shortest side. Find the length of each side.

32. The sum of three numbers is 85. The sum of 10% of the first, 20% of the second, and 25% of the third is 17. The sum of 25% of the first, 40% of the second, and 90% of the third is 51. Find the three numbers.

33. The sum of three real numbers is 3, the largest of the three is 5 times the smallest of the three, and the remaining number is 3 times the smallest of the three. Find the numbers.

34. The three largest lakes in the world, by area, are the Caspian Sea, Lake Superior, and Lake Victoria. The area of the Caspian Sea is 16 thousand square miles more than 4 times the area of Lake Superior and 9 thousand square miles more than 5 times the area of Lake Victoria. The area of Lake Superior is 5 thousand square miles more than the area of Lake Victoria. Find the area of each lake. (All areas are rounded to the nearest thousand square miles. The Caspian Sea is a saltwater lake; Superior and Victoria are both freshwater lakes.)

35. In the 50 years from 1926 through 1975, the number of seven-game World Series was four more than twice the number of four-game Series, the number of seven-game Series was six more than twice the number of six-game Series, and the number of Series that lasted either four or five games was two-thirds the number that lasted either six or seven games. Find the number of Series of each length. (A World Series lasts either four, five, six, or seven games.)

36. The population of the U.S. in 1950 was 1 million less than twice the population in 1900. The population east of the Mississippi River increased by 45 million from 1900 to 1950, and the population west of the river increased by 30 million from 1900 to 1950. In 1950 the population east of the river was 2 million less than twice the population west of the river. Determine the population both east and west of the river in 1900, and both east and west of the river in 1950. Then determine the percentage increases both east and west of the river between 1900 and 1950. (All populations are rounded to the nearest million.)

37. There is a unique polynomial function f of degree three such that $f(-2) = 10$, $f(-1) = 4$, $f(1) = 4$, and $f(2) = -2$. What is it?

$$y = a_n x^n + a_{n-1} x^{n-1} + \cdots + a_1 x + a_0$$

38. There is exactly one circle that passes through the three points $(1, 3)$, $(3, -1)$, and $(4, 2)$. Find its equation. [Compare Example 47.7. Begin with Equation (7.5), $x^2 + y^2 + ax + by + c = 0$, and determine a, b, and c.]

39. Prove that there is no circle that passes through the three points $(-3, 2)$, $(-2, 1)$, and $(1, -2)$. (The method suggested in Exercise 38 will lead to an inconsistent system.)

SECTION 49

SYSTEMS OF INEQUALITIES

A. Graphs of Inequalities

The next section will show that applications can involve systems of inequalities as well as systems of equations. Before looking at such applications, however, we need more facts about inequalities that contain variables.

A **solution** of an inequality in variables x and y is an ordered pair (a, b) of numbers that satisfies the inequality; that is, such that a true statement results if x is replaced by a and y is replaced by b.

Example 49.1 Consider the inequality $2x - 3y < 6$.

(a) The pair $(0, 0)$ is a solution because $2(0) - 3(0) < 6$.

(b) The pair $(2, -1)$ is not a solution because $2(2) - 3(-1) \not< 6$.

The **graph** of an inequality in x and y is the set of all points in the Cartesian plane whose coordinates are solutions of the inequality. To graph an inequality we make use of the equation that results when the inequality sign ($<$, $>$, $\leq$, or $\geq$) is replaced by an equality sign; we call this equation the **associated equation** of the inequality. Thus the associated equation of $2x - 3y < 6$ is $2x - 3y = 6$. An inequality is said to be **linear** if its associated equation is linear; otherwise the inequality is **nonlinear**.

The first step in graphing an inequality is to graph its associated equation. If the sign in the inequality is either $<$ or $>$, then the points on the graph of the associated equation *will not* belong to the graph of the inequality; we indicate

FIGURE 49.1

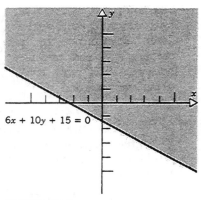

FIGURE 49.2

this by graphing the associated equation as a *dashed* line or curve (as in Figure 49.1). If the sign in the inequality is either ≤ or ≥, then the points on the graph of the associated equation *will* belong to the graph of the inequality; in this case we graph the associated equation as a *solid* line or curve (as in Figure 49.2).

Example 49.2   Draw the graph of $2x - 3y < 6$.

Solution   The graph of the associated equation is the dashed line in Figure 49.1. To graph the inequality we first solve it for y:

$$-3y < 6 - 2x$$
$$y > (6 - 2x)/-3$$
$$y > (2x - 6)/3.$$

For each x, a point with coordinates (x, y) will be

on the dashed line if $y = (2x - 6)/3$

and

above the dashed line if $y > (2x - 6)/3$.

Therefore, the graph of the inequality is the shaded region consisting of all of the points above the dashed line.

Any line in a plane divides the points of the plane into three sets: the points on one side of the line, the points on the other side of the line, and the points on the dividing line itself. Each of the first two sets is called an **open half-plane**. The graph of any linear inequality with < or > (like Figure 49.1) will be an open half-plane. An open half-plane together with the points on the dividing line is called a **closed half-plane**. The graph of any linear inequality with ≤ and ≥ (like Example 49.3, which follows) will be a closed half-plane.

The graph of any linear inequality can be drawn quickly with the following two steps.

Step I   Draw the graph of the associated equation, making the appropriate choice of a dashed line or a solid line.

Step II   Choose any point (a, b) not on the graph of the associated equation. If (a, b) *satisfies* the inequality, then the graph is the half-plane *containing* (a, b) (open or closed, as appropriate). If (a, b) *does not satisfy* the inequality, then the graph is the half-plane *not containing* (a, b) (again, open or closed, as appropriate).

For Step I, recall that the quickest way to graph most linear equations is to use the intercepts, but the important thing is to use points that are reasonably far apart. For Step II, the easiest point to check will be $(0, 0)$; if $(0, 0)$ satisfies the associated equation, then we must use some other point to help decide which half-plane to use.

Example 49.3   Draw the graph of $6x + 10y + 15 \geq 0$.

Solution   The y-intercept of the associated equation is $(0, -1.5)$. The x-intercept is $(-2.5, 0)$. Draw the solid line through these points (Figure 49.2). The pair $(0, 0)$ satisfies the inequality, so the graph is the closed half-plane containing the origin, as shown.

The two-step method given for graphing linear inequalities can be modified to handle many nonlinear inequalities, especially when the graph of the associated equation divides the other points of the plane into two easily identifiable parts. This includes most of the cases where the associated equation can be written as either $y = f(x)$ or $x = g(y)$ for a function f or g. Here is an example.

Example 49.4   Draw the graph of $x^2 + y < 0$.

Solution   This can be rewritten as $y < -x^2$. The graph of the associated equation is the dashed parabola in Figure 49.3, which divides the plane into

FIGURE 49.3

two parts. It is clear that the points for which $y < -x^2$ are those below the parabola; thus they make up the graph of the inequality. We could also determine which of the two parts of the plane to use by testing a pair such as $(1, 1)$; since this pair does not satisfy $y < -x^2$, the graph is the part of the plane not containing $(1, 1)$.

B. Systems of Inequalities

A **solution** of a system of inequalities in x and y is an ordered pair of numbers that satisfies every inequality in the system. The set of all solutions of such a system is called the **solution set** of the system.

In many cases this solution set can be described most easily with a graph. An element is in the **intersection** of a collection of sets iff it is in every set of the collection (Appendix C). It follows that the graph of the solution set of a system of inequalities is the intersection of the graphs of all of the inequalities in the system.

Example 49.5   Graph the solution set of the system

$$x^2 + y^2 < 21$$

$$4x - y^2 \geq 0.$$

Solution   The graph of $x^2 + y^2 = 21$ is the dashed circle in Figure 49.4. The graph of $x^2 + y^2 < 21$ is the set of all points inside that circle.

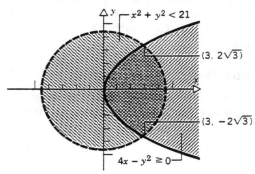

FIGURE 49.4

The graph of $4x = y^2$ is the parabola in Figure 49.4. The parabola divides the other points of the plane into two parts; the graph of $4x - y^2 \geq 0$ includes the part to the right of the parabola, as can be seen by verifying that the pair $(1, 0)$ satisfies the inequality.

The graph of the solution set of the system is the intersection of the graphs of the two inequalities.

The coordinates of the points where the circle and the parabola intersect can be found by the methods of Section 9. Addition of the associated equations gives

$$x^2 + 4x = 21$$
$$x^2 + 4x - 21 = 0$$
$$(x + 7)(x - 3) = 0$$
$$x = -7 \quad \text{or} \quad x = 3.$$

If $x = -7$, then $4x - y^2 = 0$ implies $y^2 = -28$, which has no real solution. If $x = 3$, then $4x - y^2 = 0$ implies $y^2 = 12$, or $y = \pm 2\sqrt{3}$. Thus the points of intersection are $(3, 2\sqrt{3})$ and $(3, -2\sqrt{3})$, as shown in the figure.

Example 49.6   Graph the solution set of the system

$$x \geq 0, \quad y \geq 0, \quad x + 2y \leq 4.$$

Solution   The graph of $x \geq 0$ is the closed half-plane of all points on or to the right of the *y*-axis. The graph of $y \geq 0$ is the closed half-plane of all points on or above the *x*-axis. The graph of $x + 2y \leq 4$ is the closed half-plane of all points on or below the line $x + 2y = 4$. The intersection of these graphs is the triangular region in Figure 49.5.

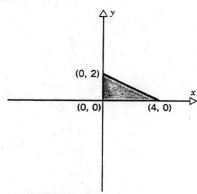

FIGURE 49.5

Exercises for Section 49

Draw the graph of each inequality.

1. $5x + 2y \geq 10$
2. $3x - 4y > 12$
3. $x - 2y \leq 4$
4. $-x + 2y < 6$
5. $2x + 2y \leq 5$
6. $4x + 3y > 8$
7. $x^2 + y^2 < 4$
8. $y - 2x^2 \geq 0$
9. $y + x^2 < 1$
10. $y \geq |x|$
11. $y < -|x|$
12. $x \geq |y|$

Graph the solution set of each system. Show the coordinates of the points where the graphs of the associated equations intersect.

13. $y - x^2 \geq 0$
    $y < 2$

14. $x^2 + y^2 < 9$
    $x \geq 0$

15. $x^2 + y^2 \leq 25$
    $y - x \geq 0$

16. $5x - 6y > -3$
    $y > 0$
    $x \leq 0$

17. $-x + y \geq -2$
    $x > 0$
    $y < 0$

18. $x + y < 3$
    $y > 1$
    $x \geq 0$

19. $x^2 + y^2 > 2$
    $-3 \leq x \leq 3$
    $-3 \leq y \leq 3$

20. $y < -x^2 + 2$
    $y > x^2 - 2$

21. $y - x^2 \geq 0$
    $x - y^2 \geq 0$

22. $y + 2x \geq 4$
    $x \geq 0$
    $y \geq 0$

23. $y - x^2 > 0$
    $x - y \geq -2$

24. $x^2 + y^2 > 4$
    $x^2 + y^2 < 9$
    $y \geq 0$

25. $y - x < 2$
    $y + x < 2$
    $y - x > -2$
    $y + x > -2$

26. $2y + 3x \geq 6$
    $4y + x \geq 4$
    $4y + 3x \leq 12$

27. $2x + 5y \geq 10$
    $6x + 2y \geq 12$
    $x \geq 0$
    $y \geq 0$

28. $3x - y \geq 0$
    $x + 3y \geq 0$
    $x + y < 2$

29. $y < |x|$
    $y > |x| - 2$
    $|x| \leq 1$

30. $|y - x| \leq 1$
    $xy \leq 0$

In each of Exercises 31–36, write a system of inequalities having the given set as its solution set. (The points on the x- and y-axes are not in any quadrant.)

31. The points in the first quadrant.

32. The points in the second quadrant.

33. The points in the fourth quadrant.

34. The points in the third quadrant that are more than 10 units from the origin.

35. The points above the x-axis that are within 5 units of the origin.

36. The points that are closer to the x-axis than to the y-axis.

SECTION 51

MATRIX ALGEBRA

A. Terminology

In Section 48 we used matrices merely as a convenience—to avoid writing variables, +'s, and ='s in solving systems of linear equations. In many other applications matrices are more than a mere convenience. The most significant applications depend on combining matrices through the operations of *addition* and *multiplication,* which will be studied in this section. We begin with some general terminology.

A matrix having m rows and n columns is said to be **m × n** (read "*m* by *n*"). We also say the matrix has **size** $m \times n$. The number in the ith row and jth column of a matrix A is called its (i, j)-entry and is denoted a_{ij}. Thus, if A is an $m \times n$ matrix, then

$$A = \begin{bmatrix} a_{11} & a_{12} & \cdots & a_{1n} \\ a_{21} & a_{22} & \cdots & a_{2n} \\ \vdots & \vdots & & \vdots \\ a_{m1} & a_{m2} & \cdots & a_{mn} \end{bmatrix}.$$

This is often abbreviated $A = [a_{ij}]$. In this book matrix entries will be real numbers.

Two matrices A and B are said to be **equal** if they have the same size (same number of rows and columns) and all of their corresponding entries are equal—that is, if $a_{ij} = b_{ij}$ for all i and j.

Example 51.1 Let

$$A = \begin{bmatrix} 3 & 7 \\ -1 & 0 \end{bmatrix}, \quad B = \begin{bmatrix} 3 & 7 & -4 \\ -1 & 0 & 5 \end{bmatrix}, \quad C = \begin{bmatrix} c_{11} & c_{12} \\ -1 & 0 \end{bmatrix}.$$

Then $A \neq B$ and $B \neq C$ because the sizes are different in each case. And

$$A = C \text{ iff } c_{11} = 3 \text{ and } c_{12} = 7.$$

B. Matrix Addition

DEFINITION The **sum** of two $m \times n$ matrices A and B, denoted $A + B$, is the $m \times n$ matrix whose (i, j)-entry is $a_{ij} + b_{ij}$.

In other words, matrices of the same size are added by adding their corresponding entries. Matrices can be added only if they have the same size.

Example 51.2

$$\begin{bmatrix} 3 & 0 \\ 6 & 2 \\ -8 & 4 \end{bmatrix} + \begin{bmatrix} 1 & 8 \\ -1 & 3 \\ 1 & -5 \end{bmatrix} = \begin{bmatrix} 3+1 & 0+8 \\ 6+(-1) & 2+3 \\ -8+1 & 4+(-5) \end{bmatrix} = \begin{bmatrix} 4 & 8 \\ 5 & 5 \\ -7 & -1 \end{bmatrix}$$

Matrix addition satisfies many of the properties of addition of real numbers. Here are the first two such properties.

Commutative law for matrix addition. If A and B are $m \times n$ matrices, then

$$A + B = B + A.$$

Associative law for matrix addition. If A, B, and C are $m \times n$ matrices, then

$$A + (B + C) = (A + B) + C.$$

Partial Proof. The (i, j)-entry of $A + B$ is $a_{ij} + b_{ij}$. The (i, j)-entry of $B + A$ is $b_{ij} + a_{ij}$. These entries are equal because $a_{ij} + b_{ij} = b_{ij} + a_{ij}$ for all a_{ij} and b_{ij} by the commutative law for addition of real numbers (Section 1). The proof of the associative law is similar. □

For each pair (m, n), the $m \times n$ matrix whose entries are all 0's is called the $m \times n$ **zero matrix.** For example, the 2×3 zero matrix is

$$\begin{bmatrix} 0 & 0 & 0 \\ 0 & 0 & 0 \end{bmatrix}.$$

Each zero matrix will be denoted by 0; if there is a chance of confusion about which zero matrix is meant, the $m \times n$ zero matrix can be denoted $0_{m \times n}$. The following property of zero matrices is obvious.

If A is any $m \times n$ matrix and 0 is the $m \times n$ zero matrix, then

$$A + 0 = A \quad \text{and} \quad 0 + A = A.$$

The **negative** of a matrix $A = [a_{ij}]$ is the matrix whose (i, j)-entry is $-a_{ij}$ for all i and j. The negative of A is denoted $-A$.

Example 51.3

$$\text{If } A = \begin{bmatrix} \pi & 0 \\ -1 & \sqrt{2} \end{bmatrix}, \text{ then } -A = \begin{bmatrix} -\pi & 0 \\ 1 & -\sqrt{2} \end{bmatrix}.$$

> If A is any $m \times n$ matrix, then
>
> $$A + (-A) = (-A) + A = 0_{m \times n}$$
>
> and
>
> $$-(-A) = A.$$

> The **difference** $A - B$ of two $m \times n$ matrices is defined by
>
> $$A - B = A + (-B).$$

We now know enough about matrix addition to be able to solve any matrix equation of the form $A + X = B$ (provided A and B have the same size; otherwise the equation is impossible). By subtracting $-A$ from both sides of $A + X = B$, we can conclude that if there is a solution, then it must be $X = (-A) + B$. Substitution shows that $(-A) + B$ is indeed a solution:

$$A + X = B$$
$$A + [(-A) + B] \overset{?}{=} B \qquad \text{Substitution.}$$
$$[A + (-A)] + B \overset{?}{=} B \qquad \text{Associative law.}$$
$$0 + B \overset{?}{=} B \qquad A + (-A) = 0.$$
$$B = B \qquad 0 + B = B.$$

Example 51.4 Solve $A + X = B$ if

$$A = \begin{bmatrix} 0.06 & 0.18 \\ -0.1 & 0.4 \end{bmatrix} \text{ and } B = \begin{bmatrix} 2 & -1 \\ 3 & 2 \end{bmatrix}.$$

Solution The solution is

$$X = (-A) + B = \begin{bmatrix} -0.06 & -0.18 \\ 0.1 & -0.4 \end{bmatrix} + \begin{bmatrix} 2 & -1 \\ 3 & 2 \end{bmatrix} = \begin{bmatrix} 1.94 & -1.18 \\ 3.1 & 1.6 \end{bmatrix}.$$

C. Matrix Multiplication

Two matrices can be added if they have the same size. In contrast, we shall see that the *product* of two matrices is defined iff the number of columns in the first matrix is equal to the number of rows in the second matrix. When the matrix product AB is defined, its size will satisfy the following pattern.

$$\begin{array}{ccc} A & B & = & C \\ m \times n & n \times p & & m \times p \end{array}$$

These must be equal.

Number of rows in A.

Number of columns in B.

Example 51.5
(a) If A is 3×2 and B is 2×4, then AB will be 3×4 and BA will be undefined.
(b) If A is 3×2 and B is 3×4, then neither AB nor BA will be defined.
(c) If A is 2×2 and B is 2×2, then both AB and BA will be 2×2.

In the definition of the product AB, which follows, we shall see that the (i, j)-entry of AB depends only on the *ith row* of A and the *jth column* of B.

jth column
$$\downarrow$$

$$ith\ row \rightarrow \begin{bmatrix} a_{11} & a_{12} & \cdots & a_{1n} \\ \vdots & \vdots & & \vdots \\ a_{i1} & a_{i2} & \cdots & a_{in} \\ \vdots & \vdots & & \vdots \\ a_{m1} & a_{m2} & \cdots & a_{mn} \end{bmatrix} \begin{bmatrix} b_{11} & \cdots & b_{1j} & \cdots & b_{1p} \\ b_{21} & \cdots & b_{2j} & \cdots & b_{2p} \\ \vdots & & \vdots & & \vdots \\ b_{n1} & \cdots & b_{nj} & \cdots & b_{np} \end{bmatrix}$$

DEFINITION   Assume that A is an $m \times n$ matrix and that B is an $n \times p$ matrix. The **product** of A and B, denoted AB, is the $m \times p$ matrix whose (i, j)-entry is

$$a_{i1}b_{1j} + a_{i2}b_{2j} + \cdots + a_{in}b_{nj}.$$

Example 51.6   Assume that A is 4×3, B is 3×2, and $AB = C$. Then C will be 4×2, and, for example,

$$c_{21} = a_{21}b_{11} + a_{22}b_{21} + a_{23}b_{31}.$$

That is, to compute the $(2, 1)$-entry of the product AB, use the second row of A and the first column of B: form the products of the pairs of entries that are connected in Figure 51.1, and then add the results.

FIGURE 51.1

Example 51.7 If

$$\begin{bmatrix} 2 & 0 & -5 \\ 3 & 7 & 9 \end{bmatrix} \begin{bmatrix} 4 & 8 \\ 2 & -3 \\ -1 & 5 \end{bmatrix} = \begin{bmatrix} c_{11} & c_{12} \\ c_{21} & c_{22} \end{bmatrix}$$

then

$$c_{11} = 2 \cdot 4 + 0 \cdot 2 + (-5) \cdot (-1) = 13$$
$$c_{12} = 2 \cdot 8 + 0 \cdot (-3) + (-5) \cdot (5) = -9$$
$$c_{21} = 3 \cdot 4 + 7 \cdot 2 + 9 \cdot (-1) = 17$$
$$c_{22} = 3 \cdot 8 + 7 \cdot (-3) + 9 \cdot 5 = 48.$$

Therefore,

$$\begin{bmatrix} 2 & 0 & -5 \\ 3 & 7 & 9 \end{bmatrix} \begin{bmatrix} 4 & 8 \\ 2 & -3 \\ -1 & 5 \end{bmatrix} = \begin{bmatrix} 13 & -9 \\ 17 & 48 \end{bmatrix}.$$

The commutative law for addition states that $A + B = B + A$ whenever both sums are defined (that is, whenever A and B have the same size). The corresponding law for multiplication, $AB = BA$, is *not* universally true, even if both AB and BA are defined. For one thing, both AB and BA may be defined and yet have different sizes: for example, if A is 2×3 and B is 3×2, then AB will be 2×2 but BA will be 3×3. But even if AB and BA are both defined and of the same size, they may be unequal, as in the next example.

Example 51.8 This example shows that the commutative law is not true for matrix multiplication:

$$\begin{bmatrix} 2 & -4 \\ 1 & -2 \end{bmatrix} \begin{bmatrix} 1 & -2 \\ -3 & 6 \end{bmatrix} = \begin{bmatrix} 14 & -28 \\ 7 & -14 \end{bmatrix}$$

but

$$\begin{bmatrix} 1 & -2 \\ -3 & 6 \end{bmatrix} \begin{bmatrix} 2 & -4 \\ 1 & -2 \end{bmatrix} = \begin{bmatrix} 0 & 0 \\ 0 & 0 \end{bmatrix}.$$

The preceding equation also shows that the product of two matrices may be the zero matrix even though neither of the two matrices is the zero matrix. This contrasts with the property of real numbers that guarantees $ab = 0$ iff $a = 0$ or $b = 0$.

The associative law for matrix multiplication, stated below, is true even though the commutative law is not. Exercise 34 asks you to prove it in the special case where A, B, and C are all 2×2 matrices; the proof for all cases can be found in books on matrices or linear algebra.

Associative law for matrix multiplication.   If A, B, and C are matrices such that both $A(BC)$ and $(AB)C$ are defined, then

$$A(BC) = (AB)C.$$

A **square matrix** is one in which the number of rows equals the number of columns. The **main diagonal** of an $n \times n$ (square) matrix consists of the elements $a_{11}, a_{22}, \ldots, a_{nn}$. For each n, the $n \times n$ matrix that contains all 1's on the main diagonal and all 0's elsewhere is called the $n \times n$ **identity matrix**. For example, the 3×3 identity matrix is

$$\begin{bmatrix} 1 & 0 & 0 \\ 0 & 1 & 0 \\ 0 & 0 & 1 \end{bmatrix}.$$

Each identity matrix will be denoted by I. If there is a chance of confusion about which identity matrix is meant, the $n \times n$ identity matrix can be denoted I_n.

The next property shows that identity matrices are to matrix multiplication what the number 1 is to multiplication of real numbers.

If A is an $m \times n$ matrix, then

$$I_m A = A \quad \text{and} \quad A I_n = A.$$

Chapter 10/41

Exercise 35 asks you to prove the preceding statement for $m = n = 2$. Exercises 36 and 37 ask you to prove special cases of the following distributive laws.

Distributive laws. Each of the following equations is true for all matrices A, B, and C for which the sums and products in the equations are defined.

$$A(B + C) = AB + AC$$
$$(A + B)C = AC + BC.$$

If c is a real number and $A = [a_{ij}]$ is a matrix, then cA is defined to be the matrix whose (i, j)-entry is ca_{ij}.

Example 51.9 If $A = \begin{bmatrix} \sqrt{2} & 4 \\ -1 & 0 \end{bmatrix}$,

then

$$3A = \begin{bmatrix} 3\sqrt{2} & 12 \\ -3 & 0 \end{bmatrix}, \quad 0A = \begin{bmatrix} 0 & 0 \\ 0 & 0 \end{bmatrix}, \quad \text{and} \quad (-1)A = \begin{bmatrix} -\sqrt{2} & -4 \\ 1 & 0 \end{bmatrix}.$$

The last equation illustrates the general property that $(-1)A = -A$ for every matrix A. Other properties of the operation cA are stated in the exercises.

Further properties of matrix multiplication, along with an application, will be discussed in the next section.

Exercises for Section 51

Determine the variables in each case so that the matrices are equal.

1. $\begin{bmatrix} 7 & -5 \\ -4 & 3 \end{bmatrix} = \begin{bmatrix} 7 & x \\ y & 3 \end{bmatrix}$

2. $\begin{bmatrix} 4 & a & -1 \\ 6 & -9 & b \end{bmatrix} = \begin{bmatrix} x & 2 & -1 \\ y & z & 8 \end{bmatrix}$

3. $\begin{bmatrix} 1 & 2 \\ c & -\frac{1}{2} \\ \frac{7}{8} & d \end{bmatrix} = \begin{bmatrix} x & 2 \\ \frac{3}{4} & y \\ z & 7 \end{bmatrix}$

Perform the indicated operations.

4. $\begin{bmatrix} 0 & -9 \\ 3 & 8 \end{bmatrix} + \begin{bmatrix} 4 & 5 \\ -3 & 4 \end{bmatrix}$

5. $\begin{bmatrix} 5 & 27 \\ 14 & -13 \end{bmatrix} + \begin{bmatrix} -6 & 1 \\ 0 & 5 \end{bmatrix}$

6. $\begin{bmatrix} 7 & \frac{4}{5} \\ \frac{1}{4} & -5 \\ 0 & 2 \end{bmatrix} + \begin{bmatrix} -7 & \frac{2}{3} \\ -\frac{1}{3} & 5 \\ \frac{1}{8} & -6 \end{bmatrix}$

7. $\begin{bmatrix} 9 & 5 & -3 \\ 2 & 0 & 17 \end{bmatrix} - \begin{bmatrix} 7 & -1 & 9 \\ 6 & 4 & 1 \end{bmatrix}$

8. $[7 \quad 12 \quad -4] - [8 \quad 9 \quad -1]$

9. $\begin{bmatrix} 6 \\ 13 \\ -7 \end{bmatrix} - \begin{bmatrix} -7 \\ 10 \\ -2 \end{bmatrix}$

Solve for X in each case.

10. $\begin{bmatrix} 9 & -6 \\ 0 & 2 \end{bmatrix} + X = \begin{bmatrix} 3 & 12 \\ -11 & 10 \end{bmatrix}$

11. $X + [4 \quad 0 \quad -7] = [14 \quad 1 \quad 8]$

12. $\begin{bmatrix} -2 & 5 & 6 \\ 9 & 7 & 11 \end{bmatrix} + X = \begin{bmatrix} 12 & 9 & -3 \\ -5 & -1 & 0 \end{bmatrix}$

13. If A is 3×5 and B is 5×1, what are the dimensions of AB?

14. If A is 3×1, B is $m \times 4$, and AB is defined, what is m and what are the dimensions of AB?

15. If A is $m \times 3$, B is $3 \times p$, and AB is 6×7, what are m and p?

Compute the matrices indicated in Exercises 16–33 with A, B, C, D, E, and F defined as follows.

$$A = \begin{bmatrix} 3 & 6 \\ 1 & -4 \end{bmatrix} \quad B = \begin{bmatrix} -8 & 1 \\ 1 & 6 \end{bmatrix}$$

$$C = \begin{bmatrix} 6 & 5 & -2 \\ 3 & 0 & -1 \\ 2 & 1 & 2 \end{bmatrix} \quad D = \begin{bmatrix} 0 & 1 & 4 \\ -7 & 1 & 2 \\ 3 & -2 & 0 \end{bmatrix}$$

$$E = \begin{bmatrix} 7 & 5 \\ 0 & 0 \\ -5 & 6 \end{bmatrix} \quad F = \begin{bmatrix} 2 & 9 & -5 \\ 0 & 3 & -6 \end{bmatrix}$$

16. AB
17. BA
18. AF
19. BF
20. EA
21. EB
22. FC
23. CD
24. DC
25. CE
26. FE
27. DE
28. $2A$
29. $-2E$
30. $3F$
31. $E(A + B)$
$\begin{bmatrix} -14 & -10 \\ 0 & \end{bmatrix}$
32. $(A + B)F$
33. $F(C + D)$

In Exercises 34–42, use

$$A = \begin{bmatrix} a_{11} & a_{12} \\ a_{21} & a_{22} \end{bmatrix}, \quad B = \begin{bmatrix} b_{11} & b_{12} \\ b_{21} & b_{22} \end{bmatrix},$$

$$C = \begin{bmatrix} c_{11} & c_{12} \\ c_{21} & c_{22} \end{bmatrix}.$$

34. Prove that $A(BC) = (AB)C$.
35. Prove that $AI_2 = A$ and $I_2A = A$.
36. Prove that $A(B + C) = AB + AC$.
37. Prove that $(A + B)C = AC + BC$.
38. It can be proved that if A is any matrix and 0 is an appropriately sized zero matrix in each case, then $A0 = 0$ and $0A = 0$. Write a proof for the special cases where A is 2×2.
39. Prove that $(-A)B = A(-B) = -(AB)$.
40. Prove that $(-A)(-B) = AB$.
41. Prove that $A(B - C) = AB - AC$.
42. Prove that $(A - B)C = AC - BC$.
43. For real numbers, $(a + b)^2 = a^2 + 2ab + b^2$. This exercise examines the analogous relationship for matrices.
    (a) Show that $(A + B)^2 \neq A^2 + 2AB + B^2$ for the matrices A and B preceding Exercise 16.
    (b) Prove that if A and B are $n \times n$ matrices, then $(A + B)^2 = A^2 + AB + BA + B^2$. (Suggestion: Use the distributive laws.)
44. For real numbers, $(a + b)(a - b) = a^2 - b^2$.
    (a) Show that $(A + B)(A - B) \neq A^2 - B^2$ for the matrices A and B preceding Exercise 16.
    (b) Prove that if A and B are $n \times n$ matrices, then $(A + B)(A - B) = A^2 - AB + BA - B^2$.
45. For real numbers, if $ab = ac$ and $a \neq 0$, then $b = c$. Show that the analogous fact does not hold for matrices, by finding 2×2 matrices A, B, and C such that $AB = AC$ and $A \neq 0$ but $B \neq C$. (Suggestion: Let A and B be the two matrices on the left in the second equation of Example 51.8, and let C be the zero matrix.)

SECTION **52**

THE INVERSE OF A MATRIX.
APPLICATION TO LINEAR SYSTEMS

A. The Inverse of a Matrix

We know that identity matrices have the following similarity with the real number 1:

$$I_m A = A = A I_n \quad \text{for every } m \times n \text{ matrix } A$$

just as

$$1a = a = a1 \quad \text{for every real number } a.$$

Real numbers have the further property that if $a \neq 0$, then a has an inverse (reciprocal), a^{-1}, such that

$$aa^{-1} = 1 = a^{-1}a.$$

Some nonzero matrices do not have an inverse in this sense, however. Those matrices that do are singled out by the following definition. Notice that the definition applies only to square matrices.

DEFINITION   An $n \times n$ matrix A is said to be **invertible** if there is an $n \times n$ matrix B such that

$$AB = I_n = BA.$$

The matrix B is called an **inverse** of A in this case.

It can be proved that if a matrix is invertible, then its inverse is unique (see Exercise 28). Therefore, we can refer to *the* inverse of an invertible matrix A; this unique inverse is denoted A^{-1}.

Example 52.1   The matrix $\begin{bmatrix} 2 & -3 \\ 3 & -4 \end{bmatrix}$ is the inverse of $\begin{bmatrix} -4 & 3 \\ -3 & 2 \end{bmatrix}$, because

$$\begin{bmatrix} -4 & 3 \\ -3 & 2 \end{bmatrix} \begin{bmatrix} 2 & -3 \\ 3 & -4 \end{bmatrix} = \begin{bmatrix} 1 & 0 \\ 0 & 1 \end{bmatrix}$$

and

$$\begin{bmatrix} 2 & -3 \\ 3 & -4 \end{bmatrix} \begin{bmatrix} -4 & 3 \\ -3 & 2 \end{bmatrix} = \begin{bmatrix} 1 & 0 \\ 0 & 1 \end{bmatrix}.$$

Example 52.2 Prove that the matrix $A = \begin{bmatrix} 0 & 1 \\ 0 & 0 \end{bmatrix}$ is not invertible.

Solution If $AB = I$, then

$$\begin{bmatrix} 0 & 1 \\ 0 & 0 \end{bmatrix} \begin{bmatrix} b_{11} & b_{12} \\ b_{21} & b_{22} \end{bmatrix} = \begin{bmatrix} 1 & 0 \\ 0 & 1 \end{bmatrix}$$

and thus

$$\begin{bmatrix} b_{21} & b_{22} \\ 0 & 0 \end{bmatrix} = \begin{bmatrix} 1 & 0 \\ 0 & 1 \end{bmatrix}.$$

The last equation is impossible since the (2, 2)-entries, 0 and 1, are unequal. Thus there is no matrix B such that $AB = I$, and A is not invertible.

The last example points up the general fact that a matrix A is not invertible if either $AB = I$ is impossible or $BA = I$ is impossible. It can be proved that, in fact, for square matrices the two equations $AB = I$ and $BA = I$ are equivalent, in the sense that if either one is true, then the other is also true. This means that to show that B is the inverse of A we need to check only one of the two equations, $AB = I$ or $BA = I$. (Most books on matrices or linear algebra give a proof.)

B. Computing Inverses: The 2 × 2 Case by Determinants

Following is an easy-to-use criterion for determining whether a 2×2 matrix is invertible, together with a formula for the inverse if the matrix *is* invertible.

> A matrix $A = \begin{bmatrix} a & b \\ c & d \end{bmatrix}$ is invertible if $ad - bc \neq 0$. If $ad - bc \neq 0$, then
>
> $$A^{-1} = \frac{1}{ad - bc} \begin{bmatrix} d & -b \\ -c & a \end{bmatrix}.$$
> (52.1)

The number $ad - bc$ in the denominator in (52.1) is called the **determinant** of the matrix A; notice that it is the product of the two elements on the main diagonal minus the product of the two elements on the other diagonal. The matrix shown in (52.1) results from interchanging the two entries on the main diagonal of A and changing the signs of the other two entries of A.

Proof If $AB = I$ with $B = \begin{bmatrix} w & x \\ y & z \end{bmatrix}$, then

$$\begin{bmatrix} aw + by & ax + bz \\ cw + dy & cx + dz \end{bmatrix} = \begin{bmatrix} 1 & 0 \\ 0 & 1 \end{bmatrix}. \tag{52.2}$$

The equality of corresponding entries in the first columns in (52.2) dictates that

$$aw + by = 1 \quad \text{and} \quad cw + dy = 0. \tag{52.3}$$

The equality of the entries in the second columns in (52.2) dictates that

$$ax + bz = 0 \quad \text{and} \quad cx + dz = 1. \tag{52.4}$$

Since the matrix A is given, we think of w, x, y, and z as unknowns in the Systems (52.3) and (52.4).

To solve System (52.3) for y, compute a times the second equation minus c times the first equation; this eliminates w and leads to

$$(ad - bc)y = -c,$$

from which

$$y = \frac{-c}{ad - bc} \text{ if } ad - bc \neq 0.$$

Moreover, if $ad - bc = 0$, then there is no solution for y and A has no inverse.

To solve System (52.3) for w, compute d times the first equation minus b times the second equation; this eliminates y and leads to

$$(ad - bc)w = d,$$

from which

$$w = \frac{d}{ad - bc} \text{ if } ad - bc \neq 0.$$

The system (52.4) can be solved in the same way, giving

$$x = \frac{-b}{ad - bc} \text{ if } ad - bc \neq 0$$

and

$$z = \frac{a}{ad - bc} \text{ if } ad - bc \neq 0.$$

Substitution in B of these solutions for w, x, y, and z will give A^{-1} in Equation (52.1). Exercise 29 asks you to verify that $A^{-1}A = I$ and $AA^{-1} = I$ for A^{-1} as in (52.1).   □

As pointed out in the proof, if $ad - bc = 0$, then A is *not* invertible. Thus we can make the following statement.

> A 2×2 matrix is invertible
> iff
> its determinant is nonzero.

The next two sections will consider determinants of larger square matrices and will give a generalization of the preceding statement.

Example 52.3 Determine whether $A = \begin{bmatrix} 5 & 1 \\ 6 & -3 \end{bmatrix}$ is invertible, and if it is invertible compute its inverse.

Solution The determinant of A is $(5)(-3) - (1)(6) = -21$, which is nonzero; therefore, A is invertible. To compute the inverse, apply (52.1):

$$A^{-1} = \begin{bmatrix} 5 & 1 \\ 6 & -3 \end{bmatrix}^{-1} = \frac{1}{-21}\begin{bmatrix} -3 & -1 \\ -6 & 5 \end{bmatrix} = \begin{bmatrix} \frac{1}{7} & \frac{1}{21} \\ \frac{2}{7} & -\frac{5}{21} \end{bmatrix}.$$

To check this answer, you can verify directly that $AA^{-1} = I$.

C. Computing Inverses by Elementary Row Operations

We now consider a method that can be used to compute the inverse of an invertible matrix of any size. The method uses *elementary row operations* and *reduced echelon form*, which you may want to review from Section 48B.

It can be proved that if A is an $n \times n$ invertible matrix, then there is a sequence of elementary row operations that will transform A into I_n; moreover, the same sequence of operations will transform I_n into A^{-1}. We can apply this as follows.

To compute the inverse of an $n \times n$ invertible matrix A, form the $n \times 2n$ matrix

$$[A \mid I_n].$$

Use elementary row operations on this $n \times 2n$ matrix to transform A, the left half, into I_n. Then the result in the right half, which was originally I_n, will be A^{-1}.

Example 52.4 The matrix $A = \begin{bmatrix} 1 & 0 & 3 \\ 2 & -5 & 4 \\ 1 & -2 & 2 \end{bmatrix}$ is invertible. Use elementary row operations to compute A^{-1}.

Solution Begin with $[A \mid I_3]$.

$$\begin{bmatrix} 1 & 0 & 3 & 1 & 0 & 0 \\ 2 & -5 & 4 & 0 & 1 & 0 \\ 1 & -2 & 2 & 0 & 0 & 1 \end{bmatrix}$$

$$\xrightarrow[\text{(Row 3) } - \text{ (Row 1)}]{\text{(Row 2) } - 2(\text{Row 1})} \begin{bmatrix} 1 & 0 & 3 & 1 & 0 & 0 \\ 0 & -5 & -2 & -2 & 1 & 0 \\ 0 & -2 & -1 & -1 & 0 & 1 \end{bmatrix}$$

$$\xrightarrow{-\frac{1}{5}(\text{Row 2})} \begin{bmatrix} 1 & 0 & 3 & 1 & 0 & 0 \\ 0 & 1 & \frac{2}{5} & \frac{2}{5} & -\frac{1}{5} & 0 \\ 0 & -2 & -1 & -1 & 0 & 1 \end{bmatrix}$$

$$\xrightarrow{(\text{Row 3}) + 2(\text{Row 2})} \begin{bmatrix} 1 & 0 & 3 & 1 & 0 & 0 \\ 0 & 1 & \frac{2}{5} & \frac{2}{5} & -\frac{1}{5} & 0 \\ 0 & 0 & -\frac{1}{5} & -\frac{1}{5} & -\frac{2}{5} & 1 \end{bmatrix}$$

$$\xrightarrow{-5(\text{Row 3})} \begin{bmatrix} 1 & 0 & 3 & 1 & 0 & 0 \\ 0 & 1 & \frac{2}{5} & \frac{2}{5} & -\frac{1}{5} & 0 \\ 0 & 0 & 1 & 1 & 2 & -5 \end{bmatrix}$$

$$\xrightarrow[\text{(Row 2) } - \frac{2}{5}(\text{Row 3})]{\text{(Row 1) } - 3(\text{Row 3})} \begin{bmatrix} 1 & 0 & 0 & -2 & -6 & 15 \\ 0 & 1 & 0 & 0 & -1 & 2 \\ 0 & 0 & 1 & 1 & 2 & -5 \end{bmatrix}$$

The result is $[I_3 \mid A^{-1}]$. Check:

$$AA^{-1} = \begin{bmatrix} 1 & 0 & 3 \\ 2 & -5 & 4 \\ 1 & -2 & 2 \end{bmatrix} \begin{bmatrix} -2 & -6 & 15 \\ 0 & -1 & 2 \\ 1 & 2 & -5 \end{bmatrix} = \begin{bmatrix} 1 & 0 & 0 \\ 0 & 1 & 0 \\ 0 & 0 & 1 \end{bmatrix} = I_3.$$

No sequence of elementary row operations will transform a *noninvert* matrix into an identity matrix. If the method in Example 52.4 is attempte with a matrix A that is not invertible, then A will be transformed into a matrix with a row of 0's. When that happens we can simply stop.

Example 52.5 Use elementary row operations to determine whether $A = \begin{bmatrix} 1 & 1 & 2 \\ 0 & 1 & -4 \\ 3 & 1 & 14 \end{bmatrix}$ is invertible.

Solution

$$\begin{bmatrix} 1 & 1 & 2 & | & 1 & 0 & 0 \\ 0 & 1 & -4 & | & 0 & 1 & 0 \\ 3 & 1 & 14 & | & 0 & 0 & 1 \end{bmatrix}$$

$$\xrightarrow{\text{(Row 3)} - 3\text{(Row 1)}} \begin{bmatrix} 1 & 1 & 2 & | & 1 & 0 & 0 \\ 0 & 1 & -4 & | & 0 & 1 & 0 \\ 0 & -2 & 8 & | & -3 & 0 & 1 \end{bmatrix}$$

$$\xrightarrow[\text{(Row 3)} + 2\text{(Row 2)}]{\text{(Row 1)} - \text{(Row 2)}} \begin{bmatrix} 1 & 0 & 6 & | & 1 & -1 & 0 \\ 0 & 1 & -4 & | & 0 & 1 & 0 \\ 0 & 0 & 0 & | & -3 & 2 & 1 \end{bmatrix}$$

The left half of the third row contains only 0's, so A is not invertible.

D. Application to Linear Systems of Equations

A linear system

$$\begin{aligned} a_1 x + b_1 y + c_1 z &= d_1 \\ a_2 x + b_2 y + c_2 z &= d_2 \\ a_3 x + b_3 y + c_3 z &= d_3 \end{aligned} \tag{52.5}$$

can be represented in matrix form as

$$AX = B, \tag{52.6}$$

$$A = \begin{bmatrix} a_1 & b_1 & c_1 \\ a_2 & b_2 & c_2 \\ a_3 & b_3 & c_3 \end{bmatrix}, \quad X = \begin{bmatrix} x \\ y \\ z \end{bmatrix}, \quad \text{and} \quad B = \begin{bmatrix} d_1 \\ d_2 \\ d_3 \end{bmatrix}.$$

ι (52.6) is the matrix product, and the equality in (52.6) is
ιe matrix A is called the **coefficient matrix** of the system.
variables can be represented similarly.

ριε 52.6 The matrix form of the system

$$\begin{aligned} x \quad\quad + 3z &= -2 \\ 2x - 5y + 4z &= 4 \\ x - 2y + 2z &= 1 \end{aligned}$$

is

$$AX = B,$$

where

$$A = \begin{bmatrix} 1 & 0 & 3 \\ 2 & -5 & 4 \\ 1 & -2 & 2 \end{bmatrix}, \quad X = \begin{bmatrix} x \\ y \\ z \end{bmatrix}, \quad \text{and} \quad B = \begin{bmatrix} -2 \\ 4 \\ 1 \end{bmatrix}.$$

If the coefficient matrix in Equation (52.6) is invertible, then we can multiply both sides of the equation on the left by A^{-1} to obtain

$$A^{-1}(AX) = A^{-1}B$$
$$(A^{-1}A)X = A^{-1}B$$
$$IX = A^{-1}B$$
$$X = A^{-1}B. \tag{52.7}$$

Thus, by computing A^{-1} and then $A^{-1}B$ we can solve System (52.5). [*Important*: In general, $A^{-1}B \neq BA^{-1}$. Equation (52.7) requires $A^{-1}B$.]

Example 52.7 The inverse of the coefficient matrix for Example 52.6 was computed in Example 52.4:

$$A^{-1} = \begin{bmatrix} -2 & -6 & 15 \\ 0 & -1 & 2 \\ 1 & 2 & -5 \end{bmatrix}.$$

Therefore, the solution of the system in Example 52.6 is given by

$$X = A^{-1}B = \begin{bmatrix} -2 & -6 & 15 \\ 0 & -1 & 2 \\ 1 & 2 & -5 \end{bmatrix} \begin{bmatrix} -2 \\ 4 \\ 1 \end{bmatrix} = \begin{bmatrix} -5 \\ -2 \\ 1 \end{bmatrix}.$$

That is, the solution is $x = -5, y = -2, z = 1$.

If the coefficient matrix of System (52.5) is not invertible, then the system does not have a unique solution; it may have no solution or infinitely many solutions.

Exercises for Section 52

Verify that $B = A^{-1}$ in each case by computing AB.

1. $A = \begin{bmatrix} 2 & 3 \\ -3 & -5 \end{bmatrix} \quad B = \begin{bmatrix} 5 & 3 \\ -3 & -2 \end{bmatrix}$

2. $A = \begin{bmatrix} 2 & -4 \\ 3 & -7 \end{bmatrix} \quad B = \frac{1}{2}\begin{bmatrix} 7 & -4 \\ 3 & -2 \end{bmatrix}$

3. $A = \begin{bmatrix} 5 & -5 & -5 \\ -4 & 3 & 6 \\ 2 & 1 & -3 \end{bmatrix} \quad B = \frac{1}{5}\begin{bmatrix} 3 & 4 & 3 \\ 0 & 1 & 2 \\ 2 & 3 & 1 \end{bmatrix}$

Determine whether each matrix is invertible by computing its determinant. If the matrix is invertible, compute its inverse by using Equation (52.1). Check each inverse by computing its product with the given matrix.

4. $\begin{bmatrix} 6 & -3 \\ -3 & 2 \end{bmatrix}$

5. $\begin{bmatrix} 5 & 7 \\ 2 & 2 \end{bmatrix}$

6. $\begin{bmatrix} 15 & 2 \\ -30 & -4 \end{bmatrix}$

7. $\begin{bmatrix} \frac{1}{2} & \frac{1}{4} \\ \frac{1}{3} & \frac{1}{3} \end{bmatrix}$

8. $\begin{bmatrix} \frac{3}{2} & -\frac{1}{5} \\ -3 & \frac{2}{5} \end{bmatrix}$

9. $\begin{bmatrix} 1.7 & -0.5 \\ -10 & 3 \end{bmatrix}$

10. $\begin{bmatrix} 0.5 & -4 \\ -1.5 & 12 \end{bmatrix}$

11. $\begin{bmatrix} 14 & -2 \\ 35 & 5 \end{bmatrix}$

12. $\begin{bmatrix} \sqrt{2} & \sqrt{3} \\ 3\sqrt{3} & -2\sqrt{2} \end{bmatrix}$

Use elementary row operations to determine whether each matrix is invertible, and if the matrix is invertible give its inverse.

13. $\begin{bmatrix} 1 & 0 & 1 \\ 5 & -2 & 2 \\ 1 & 3 & 4 \end{bmatrix}$

14. $\begin{bmatrix} 1 & 3 & -5 \\ 4 & 10 & 3 \\ 2 & 0 & 2 \end{bmatrix}$

15. $\begin{bmatrix} -1 & 2 & 3 \\ 1 & 9 & 3 \\ 5 & 1 & 8 \end{bmatrix}$

16. $\begin{bmatrix} 2 & 2 & -1 \\ 6 & -1 & 7 \\ 3 & 0 & -1 \end{bmatrix}$

17. $\begin{bmatrix} 5 & -3 & 6 \\ 1 & 0 & 7 \\ -1 & -2 & 9 \end{bmatrix}$

18. $\begin{bmatrix} 1 & 5 & 2 \\ 4 & -2 & -2 \\ 1 & 3 & 8 \end{bmatrix}$

19. $\begin{bmatrix} 1 & 0 & 4 & 0 \\ 0 & -2 & -3 & -1 \\ -2 & 1 & -10 & 1 \\ 1 & 0 & 5 & 2 \end{bmatrix}$

20. $\begin{bmatrix} 1 & -2 & 4 & 1 \\ 3 & -5 & 13 & 1 \\ 1 & -2 & 5 & 1 \\ 1 & -2 & 4 & 2 \end{bmatrix}$

21. $\begin{bmatrix} 1 & -1 & 2 & -1 \\ 2 & 1 & -2 & 1 \\ -5 & -2 & 4 & -2 \\ 3 & 1 & -2 & 1 \end{bmatrix}$

Solve each system by first computing the inverse of the coefficient matrix, as in Example 52.7.

22. $\begin{aligned} 2x - 3y &= 1 \\ x + y &= 5 \end{aligned}$ **23.** $\begin{aligned} -x - y &= 3 \\ 4x + 2y &= 7 \end{aligned}$

24. $\begin{aligned} 5x + y &= 3 \\ 7x - 2y &= 0 \end{aligned}$ **25.** $\begin{aligned} x + y + z &= 1 \\ 2x - y - z &= 3 \\ 5y + z &= 0 \end{aligned}$

26. $\begin{aligned} 2x - 2y + 3z &= 0 \\ x - y + 2z &= 5 \\ 2x + 2y - 3z &= 1 \end{aligned}$

27. $\begin{aligned} x + 2y &= 1 \\ -3x + z &= 1 \\ 4x - y &= 3 \end{aligned}$

28. To prove that each invertible matrix has a *unique* inverse, suppose that $AB = I$ and $BA = I$ (so that B is an inverse of A) and that $AC = I$ and $CA = I$ (so that C is an inverse of A). Now give a reason for each equality that follows; together, they prove that $B = C$: $B = BI = B(AC) = (BA)C = IC = C$.

29. Verify by direct multiplication that $AA^{-1} = I$ and $A^{-1}A = I$ for A^{-1} as in Equation (52.1) and for A as in the same display.

30. If A is an invertible matrix, then A^{-1} is also invertible. What is the inverse of A^{-1}? Justify your answer.

In Exercises 31–33, first write a linear system of equations and then solve the system by the method of Subsection D.

31. The total world gold production in 1975 was estimated to be 39 million ounces. The production in South Africa was 9 million ounces less than twice the production outside of South Africa. Find the production in South Africa and outside of South Africa. (All figures are given to the nearest million ounces.)

32. The Consumer Price Index increased 27 points from 1960 to 1970 and then increased 113 more points from 1970 to 1980. The index for 1980 was 42 points more than the sum of the indices for 1960 and 1970. Find the index in each of the three years, 1960, 1970, and 1980. (Indices have been rounded to the nearest point for simplicity.) Compute the percentage increases from 1960 to 1970 and from 1970 to 1980.

33. Energy use in the United States in 1980 was 78 quads (quadrillion BTU's). Coal and imported oil provided equal amounts of this energy, and natural gas and domestic oil also provided equal amounts. Natural gas and domestic oil together provided 10 quads more than coal and imported oil together. Nuclear and other sources provided 6 quads. Let C, G, D, and I denote the number of quads provided by coal, natural gas, domestic oil, and imported oil, respectively. Determine C, G, D, and I. (Begin by writing four linear equations in C, G, D, and I. All figures are approximate and adjusted slightly for simplicity.)

SECTION 53

DETERMINANTS

A. Second- and Third-order Determinants

Associated with each square matrix A is a real number called the *determinant* of A, which we denote by either *det A* or $|A|$. In the language of functions, *det* is a function whose domain is the set of square matrices and whose range is the set of real numbers. This section introduces determinants of 2×2 and 3×3 matrices. Determinants of larger matrices are introduced in the section that follows.

DEFINITION

$$\det \begin{bmatrix} a_{11} & a_{12} \\ a_{21} & a_{22} \end{bmatrix} = \begin{vmatrix} a_{11} & a_{12} \\ a_{21} & a_{22} \end{vmatrix} = a_{11}a_{22} - a_{12}a_{21}$$

Example 53.1

$$\begin{vmatrix} 12 & 4 \\ 5 & -1 \end{vmatrix} = (12)(-1) - (4)(5) = -12 - 20 = -32$$

To define determinants of 3×3 matrices we use *minors* and *cofactors*, which are defined as follows.

DEFINITION The (i, j)-**minor** of a 3×3 matrix A, denoted M_{ij}, is the determinant of the 2×2 matrix that remains when the ith row and jth column of A have been deleted.

Example 53.2 Assume $A = \begin{bmatrix} 2 & -7 & 0 \\ 3 & -3 & -5 \\ -2 & 6 & 1 \end{bmatrix}$.

(a) To compute M_{11} we first delete the first row and first column of A:

$$\begin{bmatrix} 2 & -7 & 0 \\ 3 & -3 & -5 \\ -2 & 6 & 1 \end{bmatrix}.$$

Thus

$$M_{11} = \begin{vmatrix} -3 & -5 \\ 6 & 1 \end{vmatrix} = (-3)(1) - (-5)(6) = 27.$$

(b) To compute M_{32} we first delete the third row and second column of A:

$$\begin{bmatrix} 2 & -7 & 0 \\ 3 & -3 & -5 \\ -2 & 6 & 1 \end{bmatrix}.$$

Thus

$$M_{32} = \begin{vmatrix} 2 & 0 \\ 3 & -5 \end{vmatrix} = (2)(-5) - (0)(3) = -10.$$

DEFINITION The **(i, j)-cofactor** of a 3×3 matrix A, denoted C_{ij}, is defined by $C_{ij} = (-1)^{i+j}M_{ij}$.

Since $(-1)^{i+j}$ is $+1$ if $i + j$ is even and -1 if $i + j$ is odd, it follows that either $C_{ij} = M_{ij}$ or $C_{ij} = -M_{ij}$, depending on whether $i + j$ is even or odd, respectively. Here is an easy way to determine the appropriate sign: the minor and cofactor that result from deleting a given row and column will have the same or opposite signs depending on whether there is a + or a − at the intersection for the given row and column in the following matrix.

$$\begin{bmatrix} + & - & + \\ - & + & - \\ + & - & + \end{bmatrix}$$

Example 53.3

(a) The (1, 1)-cofactor of the matrix in Example 53.2 is

$$C_{11} = +M_{11} = 27.$$

(b) The (3, 2)-cofactor of the matrix in Example 53.2 is

$$C_{32} = -M_{32} = -(-10) = 10.$$

DEFINITION

$$\det \begin{bmatrix} a_{11} & a_{12} & a_{13} \\ a_{21} & a_{22} & a_{23} \\ a_{31} & a_{32} & a_{33} \end{bmatrix} = \begin{vmatrix} a_{11} & a_{12} & a_{13} \\ a_{21} & a_{22} & a_{23} \\ a_{31} & a_{32} & a_{33} \end{vmatrix}.$$

$$= a_{11}C_{11} + a_{12}C_{12} + a_{13}C_{13} \quad (53.1)$$

In words: To compute the determinant of a 3 × 3
entry in the first row of the matrix by the corresponding co
the results. Using minors in place of cofactors, the determina

$$a_{11}M_{11} - a_{12}M_{12} + a_{13}M_{13}.$$

Example 53.4

$$\begin{vmatrix} 2 & -7 & 0 \\ 3 & -3 & -5 \\ -2 & 6 & 1 \end{vmatrix} = 2\begin{vmatrix} -3 & -5 \\ 6 & 1 \end{vmatrix} - (-7)\begin{vmatrix} 3 & -5 \\ -2 & 1 \end{vmatrix} + 0\begin{vmatrix} 3 & -3 \\ -2 & 6 \end{vmatrix}$$

$$= 2(27) - (-7)(-7) + 0(12)$$

$$= 5$$

It can be proved that the determinant of a 3 × 3 matrix can also be obtained by using the idea in (53.1) with any other row or column in place of the first row. Specifically:

To compute the determinant of a 3 × 3 matrix, multiply each entry in any row or column by the corresponding cofactor and then add the results.

Using the second column rather than the first row, for example, (53.1) becomes

$$\begin{vmatrix} a_{11} & a_{12} & a_{13} \\ a_{21} & a_{22} & a_{23} \\ a_{31} & a_{32} & a_{33} \end{vmatrix} = a_{12}C_{12} + a_{22}C_{22} + a_{32}C_{32}.$$

This is called *the expansion of the determinant by the second column*. A similar expression is used for the expansion by any other row or column.

If a 3 × 3 matrix has only 0's in some row or column, then we can expand the determinant by using that row or column and the final result will obviously be 0 regardless of the cofactors.

B. Cramer's Rule

We now look at an application of determinants in solving systems of linear equations. We begin with systems having two equations and two variables.

With the system

$$a_1x + b_1y = c_1$$
$$a_2x + b_2y = c_2$$

(53.2)

ɛ determinants:

$$= \begin{vmatrix} a_1 & b_1 \\ a_2 & b_2 \end{vmatrix}, \quad D_x = \begin{vmatrix} c_1 & b_1 \\ c_2 & b_2 \end{vmatrix}, \quad D_y = \begin{vmatrix} a_1 & c_1 \\ a_2 & c_2 \end{vmatrix}. \tag{53.3}$$

ː the determinant of the coefficient matrix, that D_x is obtained
ːacing the coefficients of x (a_1 and a_2) by the constant terms
ː that D_y is obtained from D by replacing the coefficients of y by
ːrms. Exercise 37 indicates how to prove the following result.

le (2 × 2 Case)

.53.3), then the system (53.2) has the unique solution

$$x = \frac{D_x}{D}, \quad y = \frac{D_y}{D}.$$

Example 53.5 Use Cramer's Rule to solve the system

$$-2x + y = 5$$
$$x + 3y = 7.$$

replace
rov D_x

D_x D_y D

Solution   *cd − bc*

$$D = \begin{vmatrix} -2 & 1 \\ 1 & 3 \end{vmatrix} = -7, \quad D_x = \begin{vmatrix} 5 & 1 \\ 7 & 3 \end{vmatrix} = 8, \quad D_y = \begin{vmatrix} -2 & 5 \\ 1 & 7 \end{vmatrix} = -19.$$

−6 − 1

Therefore, the solution is

$$x = \frac{8}{-7} = -\frac{8}{7}, \quad y = \frac{-19}{-7} = \frac{19}{7}.$$

Cramer's Rule extends to three equations with three variables as follows.
With the system

$$a_1x + b_1y + c_1z = d_1$$
$$a_2x + b_2y + c_2z = d_2 \tag{53.4}$$
$$a_3x + b_3y + c_3z = d_3$$

we associate four determinants: the determinant of the coefficient matrix,

$$D = \begin{vmatrix} a_1 & b_1 & c_1 \\ a_2 & b_2 & c_2 \\ a_3 & b_3 & c_3 \end{vmatrix}, \tag{53.5}$$

and the three determinants D_x, D_y, and D_z, where D_x is obtained from D by replacing the coefficients of x by the constant terms, and D_y and D_z are obtained similarly.

Cramer's Rule (3 × 3 Case)

If $D \neq 0$ in (53.5), then the system (53.4) has the unique solution

$$x = \frac{D_x}{D}, \quad y = \frac{D_y}{D}, \quad z = \frac{D_z}{D}.$$

Example 53.6 Use Cramer's Rule to solve the system

$$
\begin{aligned}
2x - 7y &= 1 \\
3x - 3y - 5z &= -2 \\
-2x + 6y + z &= 0.
\end{aligned}
$$

Solution . The determinant D was evaluated in Example 53.4. The computations for D_x, D_y, and D_z can be carried out in the same way.

$$
D = \begin{vmatrix} 2 & -7 & 0 \\ 3 & -3 & -5 \\ -2 & 6 & 1 \end{vmatrix} = 5, \quad D_x = \begin{vmatrix} 1 & -7 & 0 \\ -2 & -3 & -5 \\ 0 & 6 & 1 \end{vmatrix} = 13,
$$

$$
D_y = \begin{vmatrix} 2 & 1 & 0 \\ 3 & -2 & -5 \\ -2 & 0 & 1 \end{vmatrix} = 3, \quad D_z = \begin{vmatrix} 2 & -7 & 1 \\ 3 & -3 & -2 \\ -2 & 6 & 0 \end{vmatrix} = 8.
$$

Therefore, the solution is

$$x = \tfrac{13}{5}, \quad y = \tfrac{3}{5}, \quad z = \tfrac{8}{5}.$$

For a proof of Cramer's Rule in the 3 × 3 case, as well as the statements that follow, see a book on matrices or linear algebra.

In both the 2 × 2 and 3 × 3 cases Cramer's Rule covers all cases where $D \neq 0$. The cases where $D = 0$ are covered by the following statement.

Assume $D = 0$.

(a) If D_x and D_y (and D_z in the 3 × 3 case) all equal zero, then the system is dependent (has infinitely many solutions).

(b) If one or more of D_x, D_y, and D_z is nonzero, then the system is inconsistent (has no solution).

(53.6)

A linear system in which the constant terms are all 0 is said to be **homogeneous**. For a homogeneous system each of the determinants D_x and D_y (and D_z in the 3 × 3 case) will contain a column of 0's and will, therefore, have the value 0. It follows, using Cramer's Rule, that if $D \neq 0$ for a homogeneous system, then the only solution of the system is the one in which each variable equals 0. And, using (a) above, if $D = 0$ for a homogeneous system, then the system is dependent. Hence for $D = 0$ the homogeneous system has nontrivial solutions, that is, solutions in which some of the variables are not 0.

Example 53.7 For the homogeneous system

$$2x - y = 0$$
$$-7x + 2y = 0,$$

$$D = \begin{vmatrix} 2 & -1 \\ -7 & 2 \end{vmatrix} = -3, \quad D_x = \begin{vmatrix} 0 & -1 \\ 0 & 2 \end{vmatrix} = 0, \quad D_y = \begin{vmatrix} 2 & 0 \\ -7 & 0 \end{vmatrix} = 0.$$

Thus (0, 0) is the unique solution.

Exercises for Section 53

Compute the indicated minors and cofactors for the matrix

$$\begin{bmatrix} 2 & 8 & -6 \\ 4 & 1 & 5 \\ 0 & 2 & -2 \end{bmatrix}.$$

1. M_{21}
2. M_{33}
3. M_{13}
4. C_{21}
5. C_{33}
6. C_{13}
7. C_{22}
8. C_{31}
9. C_{12}

Evaluate by expanding by the first row [Equation (53.1)].

10. $\begin{vmatrix} 2 & -1 & 3 \\ 6 & 2 & -5 \\ 0 & 2 & 1 \end{vmatrix}$

11. $\begin{vmatrix} 2 & 1 & 0 \\ -5 & 4 & 2 \\ 1 & 0 & 6 \end{vmatrix}$

12. $\begin{vmatrix} 3 & 0 & 7 \\ -6 & -3 & -3 \\ 4 & 1 & 2 \end{vmatrix}$

13. $\begin{vmatrix} 1 & 4 & 9 \\ 6 & -1 & 2 \\ 2 & 3 & -1 \end{vmatrix}$

14. $\begin{vmatrix} 2 & 1 & 2 \\ 3 & -5 & -1 \\ -2 & 0 & 4 \end{vmatrix}$

15. $\begin{vmatrix} -2 & 8 & 3 \\ -7 & 1 & 3 \\ 0 & 3 & -4 \end{vmatrix}$

Evaluate by expanding by the second column.

16. $\begin{vmatrix} 1 & 4 & 1 \\ 3 & -1 & 5 \\ -2 & 6 & 0 \end{vmatrix}$

17. $\begin{vmatrix} -3 & 4 & 2 \\ 4 & -1 & 2 \\ 9 & 5 & -6 \end{vmatrix}$

18. $\begin{vmatrix} -9 & 2 & 0 \\ 7 & 1 & -5 \\ 7 & 3 & 4 \end{vmatrix}$

Evaluate by expanding by the row or column with the most 0's.

19. $\begin{vmatrix} -1 & 0 & \frac{4}{3} \\ 0 & 7 & 0 \\ 6 & \frac{1}{2} & 2 \end{vmatrix}$

20. $\begin{vmatrix} 4 & \frac{1}{5} & 0 \\ \frac{3}{5} & 0 & 2 \\ 3 & 0 & -1 \end{vmatrix}$

21. $\begin{vmatrix} 0 & -6 & 2 \\ -5 & \frac{1}{8} & \frac{1}{3} \\ 7 & 0 & 0 \end{vmatrix}$

Solve each system using Cramer's Rule.

22. $x - 2y = 5$
    $3x + y = 1$

23. $3x + y = 0$
    $-x - 5y = 4$

24. $7x - y = 1$
    $-6x + y = 3$

25. $2u - 6v = 1$
    $8u - 13v = 5$

26. $8w + z = 5$
    $2w - z = 0$

27. $-r + 2s = 3$
    $5r - 3s = 2$

28. $x + y + z = 9$
    $2x - y - z = 1$
    $3x + z = 2$

29. $3y - z = 1$
    $x + z = 5$
    $2x - y = 6$

30. $x - y + z = 3$
    $2x + y + 5z = 0$
    $x - z = 7$

Each system is either dependent or inconsis-tent. Use determinants and (53.6) to deter-mine which in each case.

31. $4x - y = 5$
    $-8x + 2y = 1$

32. $6x - 4y = 10$
    $9x - 6y = 15$

33. $12x - 8y = 3$
    $-9x + 6y = 0$

34. $x - y - z = 1$
    $2x + 3y - z = -2$
    $2x - 7y - 3z = 6$

35. $5x + y + z = 2$
    $x - y + z = 1$
    $3x + 3y - z = -1$

36. $3x + y + z = 0$
    $4x - y - 2z = 1$
    $-2x - 3y - 4z = 1$

37. Prove the 2×2 case of Cramer's Rule by substitution. [That is, substitute D_x/D for x and D_y/D for y in the System (53.2).]

38. Verify that
$$\begin{vmatrix} 1 & a & a^2 \\ 1 & b & b^2 \\ 1 & c & c^2 \end{vmatrix} = (b - a)(c - a)(c - b).$$

39. Prove that the equation of the line through the points (x_1, y_1) and (x_2, y_2) is
$$\begin{vmatrix} x & y & 1 \\ x_1 & y_1 & 1 \\ x_2 & y_2 & 1 \end{vmatrix} = 0.$$

40. Bach, Beethoven, and Mozart lived a total of 157 years. Bach lived 9 years more than Beethoven, and Beethoven lived 20 years more than Mozart. How long did each live? (All ages are to the nearest year.)

41. The United States paid a total of $125 billion for imported oil in the years 1970, 1978, and 1980. The cost in 1978

was 14 times the cost in 1970, and the cost in 1980 was $4 billion less than twice the cost in 1978. Find the cost in each of the three years.

42. In the 50 years from 1927 through 1976, the Montreal Canadiens won the Stanley Cup six more times than the Toronto Maple Leafs, and the Canadiens and the Maple Leafs together won the Cup six more times than all other teams combined. How many times was the Cup won by the Canadiens, by the Maple Leafs, and by all other teams combined?

SECTION 54

MORE ABOUT DETERMINANTS (OPTIONAL)

A. General Definition

The definition of *determinant* for 3×3 matrices can be extended in an obvious way to obtain the definition for larger matrices. First, the **(i, j)-minor** of an $n \times n$ matrix A, denoted M_{ij}, is the determinant of the $(n-1) \times (n-1)$ matrix that remains when the ith row and jth column of A have been deleted. The **(i, j)-cofactor** is $C_{ij} = (-1)^{i+j}M_{ij}$. The pattern for the signs relating M_{ij} and C_{ij} is given by simply extending the pattern from the 3×3 case.

$$\begin{bmatrix} + & - & + & - & \cdots \\ - & + & - & + & \cdots \\ + & - & + & - & \cdots \\ - & + & - & + & \cdots \\ \vdots & \vdots & \vdots & \vdots & \ddots \end{bmatrix}$$

Example 54.1 If

$$A = \begin{bmatrix} 8 & -2 & 1 & -4 \\ -1 & 0 & 0 & 2 \\ 3 & -3 & 7 & -6 \\ 2 & 1 & -1 & 8 \end{bmatrix}$$

then

$$M_{14} = \begin{vmatrix} -1 & 0 & 0 \\ 3 & -3 & 7 \\ 2 & 1 & -1 \end{vmatrix} = -1\begin{vmatrix} -3 & 7 \\ 1 & -1 \end{vmatrix} - 0\begin{vmatrix} 3 & 7 \\ 2 & -1 \end{vmatrix} + 0\begin{vmatrix} 3 & -3 \\ 2 & 1 \end{vmatrix}$$
$$= -1(-4) = 4.$$

And

$$C_{14} = -M_{14} = -$$

DEFINITION   If A is an $n \times n$ matrix ($n \geq 2$), then

$$\det A = |A| = a_{11}C_{11} + a_{12}C$$

In terms of minors,

$$\det A = |A| = a_{11}M_{11} - a_{12}M_{1}$$

As in the 3×3 case, we can expand a determinant by using an, or column in place of the first row.

To compute the determinant of an $n \times n$ matrix ($n \geq 2$), multiply each entry in any row or column by the corresponding cofactor and then add the results.

Example 54.2   To compute $|A|$ for A as in Example 54.1, we can take advantage of the two zeros in the second row; by expanding by the second row in this example we need to compute only two 3×3 cofactors.

$$\begin{vmatrix} 8 & -2 & 1 & -4 \\ -1 & 0 & 0 & 2 \\ 3 & -3 & 7 & -6 \\ 2 & 1 & -1 & 8 \end{vmatrix} = -(-1)\begin{vmatrix} -2 & 1 & -4 \\ -3 & 7 & -6 \\ 1 & -1 & 8 \end{vmatrix} + 0\begin{vmatrix} 8 & 1 & -4 \\ 3 & 7 & -6 \\ 2 & -1 & 8 \end{vmatrix}$$

$$- 0\begin{vmatrix} 8 & -2 & -4 \\ 3 & -3 & -6 \\ 2 & 1 & 8 \end{vmatrix} + 2\begin{vmatrix} 8 & -2 & 1 \\ 3 & -3 & 7 \\ 2 & 1 & -1 \end{vmatrix}$$

$$= 1(-66) + 0 - 0 + 2(-57)$$

$$= -180$$

Exercise 26 asks you to verify that in the 2×2 case the definition in (54.1) agrees with the definition in Section 53.

B. Properties of Determinants

In each of the following properties A is assumed to be an $n \times n$ matrix for $n \geq 2$. The examples will indicate some of the proofs for 3×3 matrices. For general proofs consult a book on matrices or linear algebra.

Property I If any row or column of A contains only 0's, then $|A| = 0$.

Example 54.3 Suppose the second row of a 3×3 matrix A contains only 0's. If we expand $|A|$ by the second row, we get

$$\begin{vmatrix} a_{11} & a_{12} & a_{13} \\ 0 & 0 & 0 \\ a_{31} & a_{32} & a_{33} \end{vmatrix} = 0C_{21} + 0C_{22} + 0C_{23} = 0.$$

The operations in Properties II, III, and V are similar to the elementary row operations on matrices (Section 48B). Here, however, the operations are also applied to columns, and we must pay careful attention to the effect on the determinant.

Property II If B is obtained from A by multiplying each element of any row or column of A by the real number k, then $|B| = k|A|$.

Example 54.4 Suppose that each element of the third column of a 3×3 matrix A is multiplied by k to produce B. Using expansion by the third column, we have

$$|B| = \begin{vmatrix} a_{11} & a_{12} & ka_{13} \\ a_{21} & a_{22} & ka_{23} \\ a_{31} & a_{32} & ka_{33} \end{vmatrix}.$$

$$= ka_{13}C_{13} + ka_{23}C_{23} + ka_{33}C_{33}$$

$$= k(a_{13}C_{13} + a_{23}C_{23} + a_{33}C_{33})$$

$$= k|A|.$$

Example 54.5 Property II implies that a common factor of the elements of any row or column can be removed by placing it in front of the determinant. For example,

$$\begin{vmatrix} 0 & 4 & -3 \\ 2 & -6 & 1 \\ -7 & 2 & 5 \end{vmatrix} = \begin{vmatrix} 0 & 2(2) & -3 \\ 2 & 2(-3) & 1 \\ -7 & 2(1) & 5 \end{vmatrix} = 2 \begin{vmatrix} 0 & 2 & -3 \\ 2 & -3 & 1 \\ -7 & 1 & 5 \end{vmatrix}.$$

Property III If B is obtained from A by interchanging two rows (or two columns) of A, then $|B| = -|A|$.

Example 54.6 Exercises 27 and 28 ask you to verify these special cases.

$$\begin{vmatrix} a_1 & b_1 & c_1 \\ a_2 & b_2 & c_2 \\ a_3 & b_3 & c_3 \end{vmatrix} = - \begin{vmatrix} a_3 & b_3 & c_3 \\ a_2 & b_2 & c_2 \\ a_1 & b_1 & c_1 \end{vmatrix} \qquad \text{Interchange rows 1 and 3.}$$

$$\begin{vmatrix} a_1 & b_1 & c_1 \\ a_2 & b_2 & c_2 \\ a_3 & b_3 & c_3 \end{vmatrix} = - \begin{vmatrix} b_1 & a_1 & c_1 \\ b_2 & a_2 & c_2 \\ b_3 & a_3 & c_3 \end{vmatrix} \quad \text{Interchange columns 1 and 2.}$$

Property IV If two rows (or two columns) of A are identical, then $|A| = 0$.

Example 54.7 Exercise 29 asks you to verify that

$$\begin{vmatrix} a_1 & b_1 & c_1 \\ a_1 & b_1 & c_1 \\ a_3 & b_3 & c_3 \end{vmatrix} = 0.$$

Property V If B is obtained from A by adding k times one row (column) of A to another row (column) of A, then $|A| = |B|$.

Example 54.8 Exercise 30 asks you to use Properties II and IV to verify the following special case.

$$\begin{vmatrix} a_1 & b_1 & c_1 \\ a_2 & b_2 & c_2 \\ a_3 & b_3 & c_3 \end{vmatrix} = \begin{vmatrix} a_1 & b_1 + ka_1 & c_1 \\ a_2 & b_2 + ka_2 & c_2 \\ a_3 & b_3 + ka_3 & c_3 \end{vmatrix}$$

C. Cramer's Rule

Cramer's Rule, stated in Section 53 for systems with two or three variables, can also be extended to systems with more than three variables. For example, if D, the determinant of the coefficient matrix, is nonzero for the system

$$a_1 w + b_1 x + c_1 y + d_1 z = k_1$$
$$a_2 w + b_2 x + c_2 y + d_2 z = k_2$$
$$a_3 w + b_3 x + c_3 y + d_3 z = k_3$$
$$a_4 w + b_4 x + c_4 y + d_4 z = k_4,$$

then the system has a unique solution which is given by

$$w = \frac{D_w}{D}, \quad x = \frac{D_x}{D}, \quad y = \frac{D_y}{D}, \quad z = \frac{D_z}{D},$$

where D_w is obtained from D by replacing the coefficients of w by the constant terms, and D_x, D_y, and D_z are obtained similarly. In general this method of solving a system is not as efficient as the method using augmented matrices and elementary row operations (Section 48).

Exercises for Section 54

Compute the indicated minors and cofactors for the matrix

$$\begin{bmatrix} 8 & -2 & 3 & 7 \\ 1 & 6 & 1 & 0 \\ 5 & 0 & -1 & 0 \\ 4 & 1 & 9 & 5 \end{bmatrix}$$

1. M_{41}
2. M_{33}
3. M_{12}
4. C_{41}
5. C_{33}

6. C_{12}
7. C_{22}
8. C_{34}
9. C_{13}

Evaluate by expanding by a row or column with the maximum number of 0's.

10. $\begin{vmatrix} 4 & 0 & -1 & 2 \\ 0 & 3 & 1 & 0 \\ 5 & -2 & 6 & 7 \\ 1 & 2 & -1 & 1 \end{vmatrix}$

11. $\begin{vmatrix} 0 & -4 & 3 & 2 \\ 2 & -3 & 0 & 1 \\ 0 & 4 & 0 & 0 \\ 5 & 7 & 6 & -2 \end{vmatrix}$

12. $\begin{vmatrix} 4 & -1 & 7 & -3 \\ 0 & -1 & 6 & 4 \\ 0 & 3 & 7 & 2 \\ 1 & 2 & -2 & 5 \end{vmatrix}$

13. $\begin{vmatrix} 0 & -4 & 2 & 2 & 6 \\ 1 & 3 & -2 & 0 & 1 \\ 0 & 1 & 7 & 0 & 2 \\ 4 & -5 & -3 & 1 & 0 \\ 0 & 1 & 3 & -1 & 0 \end{vmatrix}$

14. $\begin{vmatrix} 1 & 0 & 0 & 2 & 3 \\ 4 & 5 & 0 & 0 & 6 \\ 7 & 8 & 9 & 0 & 0 \\ 0 & 0 & -6 & -5 & -4 \\ -3 & 0 & 0 & -2 & -1 \end{vmatrix}$

15. $\begin{vmatrix} 1 & 0 & -1 & 0 & 1 \\ 0 & -1 & 0 & -2 & 0 \\ -1 & 0 & 2 & 0 & -3 \\ 0 & 1 & 0 & 1 & 0 \\ 1 & 0 & 1 & 0 & 1 \end{vmatrix}$

Each equation in Exercises 16–21 is true because of one of the Properties I–V in Subsection B. Provide the reason in each case.

16. $\begin{vmatrix} 2 & 0 & 10 \\ 1 & -3 & 7 \\ 5 & 4 & -6 \end{vmatrix} = -\begin{vmatrix} 2 & 0 & 10 \\ 5 & 4 & -6 \\ 1 & -3 & 7 \end{vmatrix}$

17. $\begin{vmatrix} 12 & 0 & 6 \\ -7 & 4 & 11 \\ 12 & 0 & 6 \end{vmatrix} = 0$

18. $\begin{vmatrix} 6 & -1 & 0 \\ 3 & 2 & 0 \\ 4 & 1 & 1 \end{vmatrix} = \begin{vmatrix} 6 & -1 & 0 \\ 11 & 4 & 2 \\ 4 & 1 & 1 \end{vmatrix}$

19. $\begin{vmatrix} 19 & 7 & 4 \\ -1 & 1 & 1 \\ 0 & 0 & 0 \end{vmatrix} = 0$

20. $\begin{vmatrix} 4 & 7 & 0 \\ -6 & 2 & 5 \\ 10 & 8 & -3 \end{vmatrix} = 2\begin{vmatrix} 2 & 7 & 0 \\ -3 & 2 & 5 \\ 5 & 8 & -3 \end{vmatrix}$

21. $-3\begin{vmatrix} 1 & 0 & 2 \\ -1 & 4 & 2 \\ 7 & 8 & -3 \end{vmatrix} = \begin{vmatrix} 1 & 0 & 2 \\ 3 & -12 & -6 \\ 7 & 8 & -3 \end{vmatrix}$

Solve each system using Cramer's Rule.

22. $\begin{aligned} w - 3x + y &= 2 \\ w + 2y - 4z &= 2 \\ 6x + 2z &= 3 \\ 3w - 2y &= 4 \end{aligned}$

23. $\begin{aligned} w + x - 3y + 4z &= -5 \\ 3x - 2z &= 1 \\ 2w + 2x + 3y &= 0 \\ w - x + 2z &= -2 \end{aligned}$

24. $\begin{aligned} -s + 4t - 5u &= 4 \\ r + s - 8t &= -6 \\ -r + 10u &= 0 \\ 2s + 4t &= -1 \end{aligned}$

25. Show that

$$\begin{vmatrix} a_{11} & a_{12} & a_{13} & a_{14} \\ a_{21} & a_{22} & a_{23} & a_{24} \\ 0 & 0 & a_{33} & a_{34} \\ 0 & 0 & a_{43} & a_{44} \end{vmatrix} =$$

Review Exercises for Chapter XII

Use either substitution or elimination to determine all of the solutions of each system.

1. $x - 3y = 2$
    $-2x + 6y = -4$

2. $3x - y = 5$
    $x - 2y = -10$

3. $3x + 4y = -1$
    $6x - 2y = 3$

4. $-5x + 3y = 2$
    $15x - 9y = -5$

5. $4x - y - 1 = 0$
    $-8x + 2y - 3 = 0$

6. $12x - 6y - 9 = 0$
    $-4x + 2y + 3 = 0$

Use Gaussian elimination to determine all of the solutions of each system.

7. $x - 2y + z = 8$
    $-x \quad\quad - 2z = -8$
    $3x + 4y + 3z = 4$

8. $2x - 3y + z = 1$
    $2x + 2y + 2z = 3$
    $-2x - 4y + 4z = 1$

9. $x - y + z = 3$
    $2x + y - z = 1$
    $\quad\quad 3y - 3z = -5$

10. $3x - 2y - z = 4$
    $x + y + z = 18$
    $-2x + y + z = -5$

11. $2x - 3y + 4z - 10 = 0$
    $2x + y - 5z - 18 = 0$
    $-x + 4y + z \quad\quad = 0$

12. $x - y - 5z - 1 = 0$
    $2x + 5y + 4z - 6 = 0$
    $\quad\quad 7y + 14z - 3 = 0$

Solve each system by reducing the augmented matrix to reduced echelon form.

13. $x + y + z = 7$
    $x - 3y - z = 5$
    $3x \quad\quad + z = 17$

14. $x + y + 2z = 8$
$3x - y - z = -3$
$2x + 4y + z = 3$

15. $y - 9z = 5$
$3x + 2y + 3z = 1$
$x - 2z = 3$

16. $-x + 7y - 3z = 4$
$x + y - z = 2$
$2x - 2y = 1$

17. $4x - 2y + 3z - 2 = 0$
$y - 3z - 12 = 0$
$x + 3y + 10z - 3 = 0$

18. $2x - 3z - 4 = 0$
$-x + y + 2z - 9 = 0$
$x - 2y - z + 5 = 0$

Find the real solutions of each system.

19. $3x - y = -7$
$y = 3x^2 + 1$

20. $2x - y = -4$
$y = 2x^2$

21. $x^2 + y^2 = 25$
$x^2 + 9y^2 = 36$

22. $x^2 - y^2 = 5$
$x^2 + 4y^2 = 25$

Graph the solution set of each system.

23. $x + 2y \geq 10$
$x^2 + y^2 < 25$

24. $x < y^2$
$x^2 + 2y^2 \leq 24$

25. Determine the maximum and minimum values of $f(x, y) = 3x - 9y$ for (x, y) restricted to the feasible set $x \geq 0$, $y \geq 0$, $x + y \geq 1$, $x + 3y \leq 3$.

26. Determine the maximum and minimum values of $f(x, y) = x + 2y - 3$ for (x, y) restricted to the feasible set $y \leq 2x$, $3y \geq x$, $x + 2y \leq 5$.

Review Exercises for Chapter XIII

Perform the indicated operations.

1. $\begin{bmatrix} -3 & 14 \\ 0 & 5 \end{bmatrix} + \begin{bmatrix} 5 & 9 \\ -2 & -2 \end{bmatrix}$

2. $\begin{bmatrix} 0 & 6 \\ -5 & -2 \\ 9 & 11 \end{bmatrix} + \begin{bmatrix} 0 & -3 \\ 2 & 1 \\ 4 & 7 \end{bmatrix}$

3. $\begin{bmatrix} 4 & 1 & 0 \\ -1 & 3 & 5 \end{bmatrix} \begin{bmatrix} -1 & -2 \\ 5 & 6 \\ 8 & 7 \end{bmatrix}$

4. $\begin{bmatrix} 1 & -1 & 0 \\ 4 & 6 & 2 \\ -1 & -2 & 5 \end{bmatrix} \begin{bmatrix} 2 & -1 & 5 \\ 2 & 4 & -3 \\ 1 & -2 & 0 \end{bmatrix}$

Compute the inverse of each matrix by using the determinant [Equation (52.1)].

5. $\begin{bmatrix} 4 & 1 \\ -5 & 2 \end{bmatrix}$

6. $\begin{bmatrix} \frac{1}{2} & \frac{1}{3} \\ \frac{1}{4} & \frac{1}{5} \end{bmatrix}$

Use elementary row operations to determine whether each matrix is invertible, and if the matrix is invertible give its inverse.

7. $\begin{bmatrix} 1 & 0 & 2 \\ 3 & 2 & 7 \\ -1 & 2 & 6 \end{bmatrix}$

8. $\begin{bmatrix} 4 & 1 & 0 \\ -2 & 3 & 1 \\ 2 & -10 & 3 \end{bmatrix}$

9. $\begin{bmatrix} 3 & 1 & 3 \\ 4 & 0 & -2 \\ 1 & 3 & 13 \end{bmatrix}$

10. $\begin{bmatrix} 1 & 2 & 4 \\ 5 & 0 & -3 \\ -6 & 0 & -1 \end{bmatrix}$

Solve each system by first computing the inverse of the coefficient matrix (that is, use that the solution of $AX = B$ is $X = A^{-1}B$.)

11. $\begin{aligned} 0.5x + y &= 2 \\ -0.1x + 3y &= 1.5 \end{aligned}$

12. $\begin{aligned} 2x - y - z &= 0 \\ x + y + z &= 4 \\ x - y \phantom{{} + z} &= 1 \end{aligned}$

Evaluate each determinant.

13. $\begin{vmatrix} 2 & -5 & 1 \\ 4 & 0 & 2 \\ -7 & 1 & 5 \end{vmatrix}$

14. $\begin{vmatrix} -\frac{1}{2} & 1 & \frac{1}{2} \\ 2 & \frac{1}{4} & -2 \\ \frac{1}{3} & 1 & -\frac{1}{3} \end{vmatrix}$

15. $\begin{vmatrix} 0 & -1 & 1 & 0 \\ 2 & 5 & 0 & -3 \\ 1 & 0 & -2 & 1 \\ 0 & 2 & -1 & 1 \end{vmatrix}$

16. $\begin{vmatrix} a & 0 & b & 0 \\ 0 & b & 0 & c \\ b & 0 & c & 0 \\ 0 & c & 0 & d \end{vmatrix}$

Use determinants to determine whether each system has a unique solution, is dependent, or is inconsistent. If the system has a unique solution, find it using Cramer's Rule.

17. $4x + y = 3$
$-x + y = 1$

18. $x - 2y = 3$
$-2x + 4y = 6$

19. $x - y - z = 1$
$2x - 2y - z = 3$
$4x - 4y - 3z = 5$

20. $2x \quad + z = 0$
$x - y - z = 1$
$4x + y + z = 5$

Chapter 11

Mathematical Induction and Sequences + Series

SECTION 55

MATHEMATICAL INDUCTION

A. Sequences and Series

A collection of real numbers arranged so that there is a first, a second, a third, and so on, is called a **sequence** (or, if we need to be more precise, a **sequence of real numbers**). The successive numbers in the sequence are called its **terms**: the **first term**, the **second term**, the **third term**, and so on. A sequence with a last term is said to be **finite**; if there is no last term the sequence is said to be **infinite**.

Example 55.1

(a) 5, 10, 15, . . . , 100

(b) $\frac{1}{1}, \frac{1}{3}, \frac{1}{5}, \frac{1}{7}, \ldots$

(c) 1, -1, 1, -1, . . .

(d) 4, 4, 4, 4, . . .

Sequence (a) is finite. The other sequences are infinite. Sequences (c) and (d) make the point that different terms in the same sequence can be equal.

To represent general sequences we use notation like

$$a_1, a_2, \ldots, a_m \tag{55.1}$$

(for finite sequences) and

$$a_1, a_2, \ldots, a_n, \ldots \tag{55.2}$$

(for infinite sequences).

A sequence is actually a function. The sequence in (55.1), for example, can be thought of as a function whose domain is the set $\{1, 2, \ldots, m\}$; the output of the function for the input k is a_k. The sequence in (55.2) can be thought of as a function whose domain is the set of all positive integers; and again, the output is a_k for the input k.

For many sequences a rule or formula can be given for a_n. It is best to give such a rule or formula whenever possible; that eliminates the possibility of uncertainty or ambiguity about the terms that are not listed.

Example 55.2   Here are the sequences from Example 55.1 with the nth term specified in each case. If you replace n by 1 in the nth term, you will get the first term, and so on for $n = 2, 3, \ldots$.

(a) 5, 10, 15, . . . , 5n, . . . , 100

(b) $\dfrac{1}{1}, \dfrac{1}{3}, \dfrac{1}{5}, \cdots, \dfrac{1}{2n-1}, \cdots$

(c) 1, −1, 1, . . . , $(-1)^{n+1}$, . . .

(d) 4, 4, 4, . . . , 4, . . .

Part (b) illustrates that the nth positive odd integer is $2n - 1$. Part (c) illustrates that to introduce alternating signs we can use $(-1)^{n+1}$. [To alternate signs starting with −1, use $(-1)^n$.]

Example 55.3 Write the first seven terms of the sequence defined by

$$a_n = \begin{cases} n^2 & \text{if } n \text{ is odd} \\ 1 & \text{if } n \text{ is even.} \end{cases}$$

Solution   1, 1, 9, 1, 25, 1, 49.

Expressions like

$$a_1 + a_2 + a_3 + \cdots + a_n \tag{55.3}$$

and

$$a_1 + a_2 + a_3 + \cdots + a_n + \cdots, \tag{55.4}$$

obtained from adding the terms of a sequence, are called **series**. The series in this section will be **finite**, like (55.3). In Section 57 we shall also consider **infinite series**, like (55.4).

B. Principle of Mathematical Induction

In Example 55.4 we shall prove that if n is a positive integer, then

$$1 + 2 + 3 + \cdots + n = \frac{n(n+1)}{2}. \tag{55.5}$$

We can verify (55.5) for small values of n by direct computation. Here are two examples.

n = 5 case:

$$1 + 2 + 3 + 4 + 5 = 15 \quad \text{and} \quad \frac{5 \cdot 6}{2} = 15.$$

n = 10 case:

Chapter 11/ 3

$$1 + 2 + 3 + \cdots + 10 = 55 \quad \text{and} \quad \frac{10 \cdot 11}{2} = 55.$$

To prove (55.5) once and for all, for *every* value of n, we need a different idea. The Principle of Mathematical Induction provides such an idea; it applies not only to (55.5) but to a very broad class of similar statements.

Principle of Mathematical Induction

For each positive integer n, let P_n represent a statement depending on n. If

(a) P_1 is true, and

(b) the truth of P_k implies the truth of P_{k+1} for each positive integer k,

then P_n is true for every positive integer n.

The Principle of Mathematical Induction can be visualized in terms of an infinite sequence of dominoes, originally standing on edge (Figure 55.1): the fall of the nth domino corresponds to the truth of P_n. Part (a) guarantees that the first domino will fall, and part (b) guarantees that if any particular domino [the kth] falls, then the next one [the $(k + 1)$st] will also fall; it follows that every domino will fall.

To apply the Principle of Mathematical Induction we must verify both parts, (a) and (b). Notice that to verify (b) we must prove that *if* P_k is true, *then* P_{k+1} is true; that is, we must establish P_{k+1} based on the assumption of P_k.

 · · · · · ·

1   2   3 k $k+1$ $k+2$ $k+3$

FIGURE 55.1

C. Examples

Example 55.4 Prove that Equation (55.5) is true for every positive integer n.

Proof.   Let P_n represent Equation (55.5).

(a) P_1 is true because

$$1 = \frac{1 \cdot 2}{2}.$$

(b) Assume P_k, that is,

$$1 + 2 + 3 + \cdots + k = \frac{k(k + 1)}{2}. \qquad (55.6)$$

We must prove P_{k+1}, that is, (55.5) with $k + 1$ in place of n:

$$1 + 2 + 3 + \cdots + (k + 1) = \frac{(k + 1)(k + 2)}{2}. \qquad (55.7)$$

To emphasize the strategy involved, notice that we are to *prove* (55.7), and we may use (55.6) in the process. If we begin with (55.6) and add $k + 1$ to both sides, we obtain

$$1 + 2 + 3 + \cdots + k + (k + 1) = \frac{k(k + 1)}{2} + (k + 1)$$

$$1 + 2 + 3 + \cdots + k + (k + 1) = \frac{k(k + 1) + 2(k + 1)}{2}$$

$$1 + 2 + 3 + \cdots + k + (k + 1) = \frac{(k + 1)(k + 2)}{2}$$

[handwritten margin notes: original, add (k+1) to equation then this equation will equal the equation of replacing n+1; $k^2 + k + 2k + 2$]

The last equation is the same as (55.7), which is what we were to prove. $\square$

Example 55.5 Prove that

$$\frac{1}{1 \cdot 3} + \frac{1}{3 \cdot 5} + \frac{1}{5 \cdot 7} + \cdots + \frac{1}{(2n - 1)(2n + 1)} = \frac{n}{2n + 1} \qquad (55.8)$$

for every positive integer n.

Remark To help clarify the meaning of (55.8), here is the special case $n = 5$.

$$\frac{1}{1 \cdot 3} + \frac{1}{3 \cdot 5} + \frac{1}{5 \cdot 7} + \frac{1}{7 \cdot 9} + \frac{1}{9 \cdot 11} = \frac{5}{11}$$

(Even with a calculator the direct computation of the left-hand side would be tedious, and the answer would only be a decimal approximation of the exact sum $\frac{5}{11}$. More important, a calculator could not provide the general formula $n/(2n + 1)$ for the sum.)

Proof. Let P_n represent Equation (55.8).

(a) P_1 is true because

$$\frac{1}{1 \cdot 3} = \frac{1}{2 \cdot 1 + 1}.$$

[handwritten margin notes:
$n = \frac{n(n+1)}{2}$

as $n = 1$ $\quad 1 = \frac{1(2)}{2}$

$1 = 1$

as $n+1 = n$

$n+1 = \frac{(n+1)(n+2)}{2}$

now $n+1$ add to the first equation

$n + n+1 = \frac{n(n+1)}{2} + n+1$

$= \frac{n(n+1)}{2} + \frac{2(n+1)}{2}$

$= \frac{n^2 + n + 2n + 2}{2} = \frac{(n+1)(n+2)}{2}$ *]*

(b) Assume P_k, that is,

$$\frac{1}{1\cdot 3} + \frac{1}{3\cdot 5} + \frac{1}{5\cdot 7} + \cdots + \frac{1}{(2k-1)(2k+1)} = \frac{k}{2k+1}. \quad (55.9)$$

To find P_{k+1}, which is what we must prove from P_k, substitute $k+1$ for n in (55.8) and simplify; the result is

$$\frac{1}{1\cdot 3} + \frac{1}{3\cdot 5} + \frac{1}{5\cdot 7} + \cdots + \frac{1}{(2k+1)(2k+3)} = \frac{k+1}{2k+3}. \quad (55.10)$$

To repeat, (55.10) is what we are to prove, and we may use (55.9) in the process. We add

$$\overset{2k-1 \qquad\qquad 2k+3 \qquad\quad 4k+2}{\frac{1}{(2k-1)(2k+1)(2k+3)} + \frac{1}{(2k-1)(2k+1)(2k+3)}}$$

to both sides of (55.9) and simplify the right-hand side.

$$\frac{1}{1\cdot 3} + \frac{1}{3\cdot 5} + \frac{1}{5\cdot 7} + \cdots + \frac{1}{(2k+1)(2k+3)}$$

$$= \frac{k}{2k+1} + \frac{1}{(2k+1)(2k+3)}$$

$$= \frac{k(2k+3)+1}{(2k+1)(2k+3)}$$

$$= \frac{2k^2 + 3k + 1}{(2k+1)(2k+3)}$$

$$= \frac{(2k+1)(k+1)}{(2k+1)(2k+3)}$$

$$= \frac{k+1}{2k+3} \qquad\qquad \square$$

The next example illustrates a slight variation on the Principle of Mathematical Induction. In place of beginning with P_1 we begin with P_5. That is, we show that

(a) P_5 is true, and

(b) the truth of P_k implies the truth of P_{k+1} for each integer $k \geq 5$;

it will follow that P_n is true for every integer $n \geq 5$. (This corresponds to starting with the fifth domino rather than the first domino in Figure 55.1.) In other problems the same idea can be applied with 5 replaced by another appropriate starting number.

Example 55.6 Prove that $2^n > n^2$ for every integer n such that $n \geq 5$.

Proof. Let P_n represent $2^n > n^2$.

(a) P_5 is true because $2^5 > 5^2$, that is, $32 > 25$.

(b) Assume that $k \geq 5$ and that P_k is true, that is,

$$2^k > k^2. \tag{55.11}$$

We must prove P_{k+1}, that is,

$$2^{k+1} > (k + 1)^2. \tag{55.12}$$

If we multiply both sides of (55.11) by 2, we have

$$2^{k+1} > 2k^2.$$

To get (55.12), it will suffice to prove that

$$2k^2 > (k + 1)^2, \tag{55.13}$$

for then we shall have $2^{k+1} > 2k^2 > (k + 1)^2$, from which $2^{k+1} > (k + 1)^2$. Inequality (55.13) is equivalent to

$$2k^2 > k^2 + 2k + 1$$
$$k^2 - 2k > 1$$
$$k(k - 2) > 1. \tag{55.14}$$

The latter inequality is satisfied because $k \geq 5$. This completes the proof. $\square$

Remark Notice that (55.14) is true for $k \geq 3$. Thus in part (b) we have actually shown that P_k implies P_{k+1} for $k \geq 3$. However, that does not prove P_n for $n \geq 3$, because P_3 is not true (P_3 would say $2^3 > 3^2$, which is false). What about P_1? P_2? P_4?

The other sections of this chapter will give more proofs by mathematical induction.

Exercises for Section 55

Write the first five terms and the $(n + 1)$st term of the sequence whose nth term is a_n.

1. $a_n = 5n$
2. $a_n = n^3$
3. $a_n = n/(n + 1)$
4. $a_n = -2$

5. $a_n = (-2)^n$
6. $a_n = (-1)^{n+1}[1 + (1/n)]$

Use mathematical induction to prove each statement for every positive integer n or for those n satisfying the stated restriction.

7. $1 + 2 + 2^2 + \cdots + 2^n = 2^{n+1} - 1$

8. $1^2 + 2^2 + 3^2 + \cdots + n^2 =$
$$\frac{n(n + 1)(2n + 1)}{6}$$

9. $5 + 10 + 15 + \cdots + 5n =$
$$\frac{5n(n + 1)}{2}$$

10. $1 + 3 + 5 + \cdots + (2n + 1) = n^2$

11. $1^3 + 2^3 + \cdots + n^3 =$
$$\left(\frac{n(n + 1)}{2}\right)^2$$

12. $1^3 + 3^3 + \cdots + (2n - 1)^3 =$
$$n^2(2n^2 - 1)$$

13. $(1 \cdot 2) + (2 \cdot 3) + (3 \cdot 4) + \cdots +$
$$n(n + 1) = \frac{n(n + 1)(n + 2)}{3}$$

14. $\dfrac{1}{1 \cdot 2} + \dfrac{1}{2 \cdot 3} + \dfrac{1}{3 \cdot 4} + \cdots +$
$$\frac{1}{n(n + 1)} = \frac{n}{n + 1}$$

15. $\dfrac{1}{1 \cdot 2 \cdot 3} + \dfrac{1}{2 \cdot 3 \cdot 4} + \dfrac{1}{3 \cdot 4 \cdot 5} + \cdots +$
$$\frac{1}{n(n + 1)(n + 2)} = \frac{n(n + 3)}{4(n + 1)(n + 2)}$$

16. $\left(1 + \dfrac{1}{1}\right)\left(1 + \dfrac{1}{2}\right)\left(1 + \dfrac{1}{3}\right) \cdots \left(1 + \dfrac{1}{n}\right)$
$$= n + 1$$

17. $\left(1 - \dfrac{1}{4}\right)\left(1 - \dfrac{1}{9}\right)\left(1 - \dfrac{1}{16}\right) \cdots \left(1 - \dfrac{1}{n^2}\right)$
$$= \frac{n + 1}{2n}$$

18. $\dfrac{1}{2} + \dfrac{2}{2^2} + \dfrac{3}{2^3} + \cdots + \dfrac{n}{2^n} =$
$$2 - \frac{n + 2}{2^n}$$

19. $2n \leq 2^n$

20. $n^3 < 3^n$ for $n \geq 4$.

21. $(1 + \frac{1}{2})^n \geq 1 + (1/2^n)$

22. If $a > 1$, then $a^n > 1$.

23. If $0 < a < 1$, then $a^n < 1$.

24. $\log(a_1 a_2 \cdots a_n) = \log a_1 + \log a_2 + \cdots + \log a_n$

25. The sum of the interior angles of an n-sided convex polygon is $(n - 2) \cdot 180°$ ($n \geq 3$). (A polygon is *convex* if all of the points on a line segment are inside the polygon whenever the endpoints of the segment are inside the polygon. You may assume that the sum of the interior angles of a triangle is $180°$.)

26. The number of lines determined by n points, no three of which are collinear, is $\frac{1}{2}n(n - 1)$ ($n \geq 2$).

27. The number of diagonals of an n-sided convex polygon is $n(n - 3)/2$ for $n \geq 3$. (See Exercise 25 for the definition of a convex polygon.)

11.1 DEFINING FUNCTIONS USING SUMS

Landscape timbers are large beams of wood used to landscape gardens. To make the terrace in Figure 11.1, one timber is set into the slope, followed by a stack of two, then a stack of three, then a stack of four. The stacks are separated by earth.

The total number of timbers used is the sum of the number of timbers in each stack:

$$\text{Number of timbers} = 1 + 2 + 3 + 4 = 10.$$

For a larger terrace using 5 stacks of timbers, the total number is given by

$$\begin{array}{c}\text{Number of timbers} \\ \text{in 5 stacks}\end{array} = 1 + 2 + 3 + 4 + 5 = 15.$$

For an even larger terrace using 6 stacks, the total number is given by

$$\begin{array}{c}\text{Number of timbers} \\ \text{in 6 stacks}\end{array} = 1 + 2 + 3 + 4 + 5 + 6 = 21.$$

In general, for a terrace made from n stacks of landscape timbers, we see that

$$\begin{array}{c}\text{Number of timbers} \\ \text{in } n \text{ stacks}\end{array} = 1 + 2 + \cdots + n.$$

The $\cdots$ means that all the integers from 1 to n are included in the sum.

Letting T be the total number of timbers in a terrace made using n stacks of timbers, we see that T is a function of n, so

$$T = f(n) = 1 + 2 + \cdots + n.$$

In this section wee how to evaluate functions defined by sums.

Figure 11.1: A slope terraced for planting using landscape timbers

Arithmetic Sequences

Each stack of landscape timbers contains one more timber than the previous one. The list, or *sequence*, of numbers

$$1, 2, 3, 4, 5, \ldots$$

is an example of an *arithmetic sequence*.

Arithmetic Sequence

A **sequence** is a list of numbers. In an **arithmetic sequence**, the terms increase (or decrease) by adding (or subtracting) a fixed quantity.

The nth Term in an Arithmetic Sequence

The terms in an arithmetic sequence increase (or decrease) by a fixed number, d. If a_1 is the first term, a_2 the second, a_3 the third, we have

$$a_2 = a_1 + d$$
$$a_3 = a_2 + d = (a_1 + d) + d = a_1 + 2d$$
$$a_4 = a_3 + d = (a_1 + 2d) + d = a_1 + 3d,$$

and so on. In general:

A formula for a_n, the nth **term of an arithmetic sequence**, is given by

$$a_n = a_1 + \underbrace{d + d + \cdots + d}_{n-1 \text{ times}} = a_1 + (n-1)d.$$

Arithmetic Series

To find the total number of timbers in n stacks, we add the terms in our arithmetic sequence. Such a sum is called an *arithmetic series*.

Arithmetic Series

A **series** is a sum of the numbers in a list or sequence. An **arithmetic series** is the sum of terms in an arithmetic sequence.

The total number of landscape timbers is the arithmetic series consisting of the sum of the first n positive integers, written

$$S_n = 1 + 2 + \cdots + n.$$

A famous story concerning this series[1] is told about the great mathematician Carl Friedrich Gauss (1777–1855), who as a young boy was asked by his teacher to add the numbers from 1 to 100. He did so almost immediately:

$$S_{100} = 1 + 2 + 3 + \cdots + 100 = 5050.$$

Of course, no one really knows how Gauss accomplished this, but he probably did not perform the calculation directly, by adding 100 terms. He might have noticed that the terms in the sum can be regrouped into pairs, as follows:

$$S_{100} = 1 + 2 + \cdots + 99 + 100 = \underbrace{(1 + 100) + (2 + 99) + \cdots + (50 + 51)}_{50 \text{ pairs}}$$
$$= \underbrace{101 + 101 + \cdots + 101}_{50 \text{ terms}} \qquad \text{Each pair adds to 101}$$
$$= 50 \cdot 101 = 5050.$$

---

[1] As told by E.T. Bell in *The Men of Mathematics*, p.221 (New York: Simon and Schuster, 1937), the series involved was arithmetic, but more complicated than this one.

The approach of pairing numbers works for the sum from 1 to n, no matter how large n is. Provided n is an even number, we can write

$$S_n = 1 + 2 + \cdots + (n-1) + n = \underbrace{(1+n) + (2+(n-1)) + (3+(n-2)) + \cdots}_{\frac{1}{2}n \text{ pairs}}$$

$$= \underbrace{(1+n) + (1+n) + \cdots}_{\frac{1}{2}n \text{ pairs}} \quad \text{Each pair adds to } 1 + n$$

so we have the formula:

$$S_n = \frac{1}{2}n(n+1).$$

To check this formula, let $n = 100$:

$$S_{100} = 1 + 2 + \cdots + 100 = \frac{1}{2}(100)(100+1) = 50(101) = 5050.$$

A similar derivation shows that this formula for S_n also holds for odd values of n.

The Sum of an Arithmetic Series

To find a formula for the sum of a general arithmetic series, we begin by writing[2]

$$S_n = a_1 + a_2 + \cdots + a_n$$
$$= \underbrace{(a_1 + a_n) + (a_2 + a_{n-1}) + (a_3 + a_{n-2}) + \cdots}_{\frac{1}{2}n \text{ pairs}}.$$

We pair off the first term with the last term, the second term with the next to last term, and so on, just as Gauss may have done. Each pair of terms adds up to the same value, just as Gauss's pairs added to 101. Using the formula for the terms of an arithmetic sequences, $a_n = a_1 + (n-1)d$, the first pair, $a_1 + a_n$, can be written as

$$a_1 + a_n = a_1 + \underbrace{a_1 + (n-1)d}_{a_n} = 2a_1 + (n-1)d,$$

the second pair, $a_2 + a_{n-1}$, can be written as

$$a_2 + a_{n-1} = \underbrace{a_1 + d}_{a_2} + \underbrace{a_1 + (n-2)d}_{a_{n-1}} = 2a_1 + (n-1)d.$$

Both the first two pairs have the same sum: $2a_1 + (n-1)d$. The remaining pairs also all have the same sum, so

$$S_n = \underbrace{(a_1 + a_n) + (a_2 + a_{n-1}) + (a_3 + a_{n-2}) + \cdots}_{\frac{1}{2}n \text{ pairs}} = \frac{1}{2}n\left(2a_1 + (n-1)d\right).$$

---

[2]We assume that n is even, but a similar argument gives the same result for odd values.

Chapter 11/12

> The **sum**, S_n, of the first n terms of the **arithmetic series** with $a_n = a_1 + (n-1)d$ is
>
> $$S_n = \frac{1}{2}n(2a_1 + (n-1)d).$$

Example 1   Calculate the sum $1 + 2 + \cdots + 100$ using the formula for S_n.

Solution   Here, $a_1 = 1$, $n = 100$, and $d = 1$. We get the same answer as before:

$$S_{100} = \frac{1}{2}n\left(2a_1 + (n-1)d\right) = \frac{1}{2}(100)\left(2(1) + (100-1)(1)\right) = 50(101) = 5050,$$

Summation Notation

The symbol Σ is used to represent a sum such as $a_1 + a_2 + \cdots + a_n$. This symbol, pronounced as *sigma*, is the Greek capital letter for S, which stands for sum. Using this notation, we write

$$\sum_{i=1}^{n} a_i$$

to stand for the sum $a_1 + a_2 + \cdots + a_n$. The Σ tells us we are adding some numbers. The a_i tells us that the numbers we are adding are called a_1, a_2, and so on. The sum begins with a_1 and ends with a_n because the subscript i starts at $i = 1$ (at the bottom of the Σ sign) and ends at $i = n$ (at the top of the Σ sign):

This tells us that the sum ends at a_n

$$\sum_{i=1}^{n} a_i$$

This tells us that the numbers we are adding are called a_1, a_2, a_3, ...

This tells us that the sum starts at a_1

Example 2   Using sigma notation, write a formula for $T = f(n)$, the total number of landscape timbers in n stacks.

Solution   We have $T = f(n) = 1 + 2 + \cdots + n$. We are adding n numbers, starting at $i = 1$ and ending at $i = n$. This sum can be written

$$T = f(n) = \sum_{i=1}^{n} i.$$

Example 3   Use sigma notation to write the sum of the first 20 positive odd numbers. Evaluate this sum.

Solution   The odd numbers form an arithmetic sequence: 1, 3, 5, 7, ... with $a_1 = 1$ and $d = 2$. The ith odd number is

$$a_i = 1 + (i-1)2 = 2i - 1.$$

The sum of the first 20 odd numbers is given by

$$\text{Sum} = \sum_{i=1}^{20} a_i = \sum_{i=1}^{20} (2i - 1).$$

We evaluate the sum using $n = 20$, $a_1 = 1$, and $d = 2$:

$$\text{Sum} = \frac{1}{2}n\left(2a_1 + (n-1)d\right) = \frac{1}{2}(20)\left(2(1) + (20-1)(2)\right) = 400.$$

Falling Objects

A falling object travels 16 ft during the first second, 48 ft during the next, 80 ft during the next, and so on. These distances form the arithmetic sequence 16, 48, 80, ... In this sequence, $a_1 = 16$ and $d = 32$. The nth term is $a_n = a_1 + (n-1)d = 16 + 32(n-1) = 32n - 16$. For instance, the value of the fifth term is $a_5 = 32(5) - 16 = 144$. The value of $a_{10} = 32(10) - 16 = 304$.

Example 4   Calculate S_1, S_2, S_3, the distances fallen by an object in 1, 2, 3 seconds, respectively.

Solution   Since $a_1 = 16$ and $d = 32$,

$$S_1 = a_1 = 16 \text{ feet}$$
$$S_2 = a_1 + a_2 = a_1 + (a_1 + d) = 16 + 48 = 64 \text{ feet}$$
$$S_3 = a_1 + a_2 + a_3 = 16 + 48 + 80 = 144 \text{ feet}$$

Alternatively, the values of S_n can be calculated using the formula $S_n = \frac{1}{2}n\left(2a_1 + (n-1)d\right)$:

$$S_1 = \frac{1}{2} \cdot 1(2 \cdot 16 + 0 \cdot 32) = 16, \quad S_2 = \frac{1}{2} \cdot 2(2 \cdot 16 + 1 \cdot 32) = 64, \quad S_3 = \frac{1}{2} \cdot 3(2 \cdot 16 + 2 \cdot 32) = 144.$$

Example 5   An object falls from 1000 feet starting at time $t = 0$ seconds. What is its height, h, in feet above the ground at $t = 1, 2, 3$ seconds? Show these values on a graph of height against time.

Chapter 11/14

Solution   At time $t = 0$, the height $h = 1000$ feet. At time $t = 1$, the object has fallen 16 feet, so

$$h = 1000 - 16 = 984 \text{ feet.}$$

At time $t = 2$, the object has fallen a total distance of $S_2 = 64$ feet, so

$$h = 1000 - 64 = 936 \text{ feet.}$$

At time $t = 3$, the object has fallen a total distance of 144 feet, so

$$h = 1000 - 144 = 856 \text{ feet.}$$

These heights are marked on the graph in Figure 11.2.

Figure 11.2: Height of a falling object

Arithmetic Sequences and Linear Functions

You may have noticed that the arithmetic sequence for a falling object is like a linear function. The formula for the nth term, $a_n = 32n - 16$, is the same as the formula for a linear function with slope $m = 32$ and initial value $b = -16$. However, for a sequence we consider only positive integer values of n, whereas a linear function is defined for all values of n. We can think of an arithmetic sequence as a linear function whose domain has been restricted to the positive integers.

Problems for Section 11.1

In Problems 1–4, write each of the sums using sigma notation.

1. $3 + 6 + 9 + 12 + 15 + 18 + 21$

2. $10 + 13 + 16 + 19 + 22$

3. $1/2 + 1 + 3/2 + 2 + 5/2 + 3 + 7/2 + 4$

4. $30 + 25 + 20 + 15 + 10 + 5$

(handwritten annotations:)

$a_n = 3 + (n-1)3$
$= 3 + 3n - 3$

1. $\stackrel{7}{\underset{n=1}{\Sigma}}(3n)$

2. $a_n = 10 + (n-1)3$
$10 + 3n - 3$
$3n + 7$

3. $= \stackrel{8}{\underset{n=1}{\Sigma}}\frac{1}{2}n$
$a_n = 3 + (n-1)3$
$3 + 3n - 3$
$3n$
$a_n = \frac{1}{2} + (n-1)\frac{1}{2}$
$= \frac{1}{2} + \frac{1}{2}n - \frac{1}{2}$
$\frac{1}{2} + \frac{1}{2} = 1 + \frac{1}{2} =$

4. $\stackrel{6}{\underset{n=1}{\Sigma}}$
$a_n = 30 + (n-1) - 5$
$= 30 - 5n + 5$
$(35 - 5n)$
$\stackrel{5}{\underset{i=10}{\Sigma}} 3n + 7$

[handwritten: $a_9 = 7 + 8(7) = 63$]
[handwritten: $S_9 = \dfrac{9(7+63)}{2} = 315$]
[handwritten: $a_n = 7 + (n-1)d$]
[handwritten: $7 + 7n - 7$]

5. Find the sum of the first nine terms of the series: $7 + 14 + 21 + \cdots$.

[handwritten: $9 \quad 8(7)$]
[handwritten: $7 + 8(7)$]
[handwritten: 56]

6. Find the thirtieth positive multiple of 5 and the sum of the first thirty positive multiples of 5.

Without using a calculator, find the sum of the series in Problems 7–10.

[handwritten: $a_{50} = 3 + (49)(3) = 150$]
[handwritten: $a_n = 63$]

7. $\displaystyle\sum_{i=1}^{50} 3i$ 8. $\displaystyle\sum_{i=1}^{30} (5i+10)$ 9. $\displaystyle\sum_{n=0}^{15} \left(2 + \tfrac{1}{2}n\right)$ 10. $\displaystyle\sum_{n=0}^{10} (8 - 4n)$

[handwritten: $S_{50} = \dfrac{50(3+150)}{2} = 3825$]
[handwritten: $= 3 + 6 + 9 + 12 + \cdots$]
[handwritten: $+ 150$]
[handwritten: $2 + \tfrac{1}{2}\,,\; 3\,,\; \tfrac{7}{2}\,,\; 4 \cdots + \tfrac{19}{2}$]
[handwritten: $a_{15} = 2 + (14)\left(\tfrac{1}{2}\right) = 9$]
[handwritten: $S_{15} = \dfrac{15(2+9)}{2} = 82.5$]

Problems 11–14 refer the falling object of Example 4 on page 506.

11. Calculate the distance, S_{10}, fallen by the object in 10 seconds.

12. (a) Find the total distance fallen by the object in 4, 5, 6 seconds.
    (b) The object falls from 1000 feet at time $t = 0$. Calculate its height at $t = 4$, $t = 5$, $t = 6$ seconds. Explain how you can check your answer using Figure 11.2.

13. Find a formula for $f(n)$, the distance fallen by the object in n seconds.

14. If the object falls from 1000 feet, how long does it take to hit the ground?

15. A boy is dividing M&Ms between himself and his sister. He gives one to his sister and takes one for himself. He gives another to his sister and takes two for himself. He gives a third to his sister and takes three for himself, and so on.

    (a) On the nth round, how many M&Ms does the boy give his sister? How many does he take himself?
    (b) After n rounds, how many M&Ms does his sister have? How many does the boy have?

16. An auditorium has 30 seats in the first row, 34 seats in the second row, 38 seats in the third row, and so on. If there are twenty rows in the auditorium, how many seats are there in the last row? How many seats are there in the auditorium?

17. In a workshop, it costs $300 to make one piece of furniture. The second piece costs a bit less, $280. The third costs even less, $263, and the fourth costs only $249. The cost for each additional piece of furniture is known to economists as the *marginal cost* of production. These costs are recorded in Table 11.1. The table also shows the difference between each marginal cost—for instance, $280 - 300 = -20$. Notice that although the sequence of numbers 300, 280, 263, ..., is not arithmetic, the sequence of the differences is arithmetic: $-20, -17, -14, \ldots$.

TABLE 11.1

n, Number pieces furniture	1		2		3		4
c, Marginal cost ($)	300		280		263		249
Change in marginal cost ($)		-20		-17		-14	

   (a) Assume that the arithmetic sequence $-20, -17, -14, \ldots$, continues. Complete the table for $n = 5, 6, \ldots, 12$.
   (b) Find a formula for c_n, the marginal cost for producing the nth piece of furniture. Use the fact that c_n are found by adding the terms in an arithmetic sequence. Using your formula, find the cost for producing the 12th piece and the 50th piece of furniture.
   (c) A piece of furniture can be sold at a profit provided it costs less than $400 to make. How many pieces of furniture should the workshop make each day? Discuss.

11.2 GEOMETRIC SERIES

In the previous section, we studied *arithmetic series*. An arithmetic series is the sum of terms in a sequence in which each term is obtained by adding a constant to the preceeding term. In this section, we study another type of sum, a *geometric series*. In a geometric series, each term is a constant multiple of the preceeding term.

Saving Money

A person deposits $50 every year in an account that pays 6% interest per year, compounded annually. After the first deposit (but before any interest has been earned), the balance of this account is

$$B_1 = 50.$$

After 1 year has passed, the first deposit has earned interest, becoming $50(1.06)$ and the second deposit is made. The balance is then

$$B_2 = \underbrace{2^{nd} \text{ deposit}}_{50} + \underbrace{1^{st}\text{deposit with interest}}_{50(1.06)}$$
$$= 50 + 50(1.06).$$

After 2 years have passed, the third deposit is made, and the balance is

$$B_3 = \underbrace{3^{rd} \text{ deposit}}_{50} + \underbrace{2^{nd} \text{ dep. with 1 year interest}}_{50(1.06)} + \underbrace{1^{st} \text{ deposit with 2 years interest}}_{50(1.06)^2}$$
$$= 50 + 50(1.06) + 50(1.06)^2.$$

Continuing in this fashion, we see that

After 4 deposits $\quad B_4 = 50 + 50(1.06) + 50(1.06)^2 + 50(1.06)^3$

After 5 deposits $\quad B_5 = 50 + 50(1.06) + 50(1.06)^2 + 50(1.06)^3 + 50(1.06)^4$

$$\vdots$$

After n deposits $\quad B_n = 50 + 50(1.06) + 50(1.06)^2 + \cdots + 50(1.06)^{n-1}.$

Example 1   How much money is in this account after 5 years? After 25 years?

Solution   After 5 years, we have made 6 deposits. A calculator gives

$$B_6 = 50 + 50(1.06) + 50(1.06)^2 + \cdots + 50(1.06)^5$$
$$= \$348.77.$$

After 25 years, we have made 26 deposits. Even using a calculator, it would be tedious to evaluate B_{26} by adding 26 terms. Fortunately, there is a shortcut. We begin with the formula for B_{26}:

$$B_{26} = 50 + 50(1.06) + 50(1.06)^2 + \cdots + 50(1.06)^{25}.$$

Multiplying both sides of this equation by 1.06 and adding 50 gives

$$1.06 B_{26} + 50 = 1.06 \left(50 + 50(1.06) + 50(1.06)^2 + \cdots + 50(1.06)^{25}\right) + 50.$$

We can simplify the right-hand side to give

$$1.06 B_{26} + 50 = 50(1.06) + 50(1.06)^2 + \cdots + 50(1.06)^{25} + 50(1.06)^{26} + 50.$$

Notice that the right-hand side of this equation and the formula for B_{26} have almost every term in common. We can rewrite this equation as

$$1.06 B_{26} + 50 = \underbrace{50 + 50(1.06) + 50(1.06)^2 + \cdots + 50(1.06)^{25}}_{B_{26}} + 50(1.06)^{26}$$

$$= B_{26} + 50(1.06)^{26}.$$

Solving for B_{26} gives

$$1.06 B_{26} - B_{26} = 50(1.06)^{26} - 50$$
$$0.06 B_{26} = 50(1.06)^{26} - 50$$
$$B_{26} = \frac{50(1.06)^{26} - 50}{0.06}.$$

Using a calculator to evaluate this expression for B_{26}, we find that $B_{26} = \$2957.82$.

Geometric Series

The formula for the bank balance,

$$B_{26} = 50 + 50(1.06) + 50(1.06)^2 + \cdots + 50(1.06)^{25},$$

is an example of a *geometric series*. In general, a geometric series is a sum in which each term is a constant multiple of the preceding term.

A geometric series is a sum of the form

$$S_n = a + ax + ax^2 + \cdots + ax^{n-1}.$$

The reason we stop at an exponent of $n - 1$ in the definition of S_n is so that there is a total of n terms (including the first term, which is $a = ax^0$). For instance, there are 26 terms in the series

$$50 + 50(1.06) + 50(1.06)^2 + \cdots + 50(1.06)^{25},$$

so $n = 26$. For this series, $x = 1.06$ and $a = 50$.

Another Geometric Series: Drug Levels in The Body

Geometric series arise naturally in many different contexts. The following example illustrates a geometric series with decreasing terms.

Example 2   A patient is given a 20 mg injection of a therapeutic drug. Each day, the patient's body metabolizes 50% of the drug present, so that after 1 day only one-half of the original amount remains, after 2 days only one-fourth remains, and so on. The patient is given a 20 mg injection of the drug every day at the same time. Write a geometric series that gives the drug level in this patient's body after n days.

Solution   Immediately after the 1st injection, the drug level in the body is given by

$$Q_1 = 20.$$

One day later, the original 20 mg has fallen to $20 \cdot \frac{1}{2} = 10$ mg and the second 20 mg injection is given. Right after the second injection, the drug level is given by

$$Q_2 = \underbrace{2^{\text{nd}} \text{ injection}}_{20} + \underbrace{\text{Residue of } 1^{\text{st}} \text{ injection}}_{\frac{1}{2} \cdot 20}$$

$$= 20 + 20 \left(\frac{1}{2} \right).$$

Two days later, the original 20 mg has fallen to $(20 \cdot \frac{1}{2}) \cdot \frac{1}{2} = 20(\frac{1}{2})^2 = 5$ mg, the second 20 mg injection has fallen to $20 \cdot \frac{1}{2} = 10$ mg, and the third 20 mg injection is given. Right after the third injection, the drug level is given by

$$Q_3 = \underbrace{3^{\text{rd}} \text{ injection}}_{20} + \underbrace{\text{Residue of } 2^{\text{nd}} \text{ injection}}_{20 \cdot \frac{1}{2}} + \underbrace{\text{Residue of } 1^{\text{st}} \text{ injection}}_{20 \cdot \frac{1}{2} \cdot \frac{1}{2}}$$

$$= 20 + 20 \left(\frac{1}{2} \right) + 20 \left(\frac{1}{2} \right)^2.$$

Continuing, we see that

After 4th injection $Q_4 = 20 + 20 \left(\dfrac{1}{2} \right) + 20 \left(\dfrac{1}{2} \right)^2 + 20 \left(\dfrac{1}{2} \right)^3,$

After 5th injection $Q_5 = 20 + 20 \left(\dfrac{1}{2} \right) + 20 \left(\dfrac{1}{2} \right)^2 + \cdots + 20 \left(\dfrac{1}{2} \right)^4,$

$$\vdots$$

After n^{th} injection $Q_n = 20 + 20 \left(\dfrac{1}{2} \right) + 20 \left(\dfrac{1}{2} \right)^2 + \cdots + 20 \left(\dfrac{1}{2} \right)^{n-1}.$

This is another example of a geometric series. Here, $a = 20$ and $x = 1/2$ in the geometric series formula

$$Q_n = a + ax + ax^2 + \cdots + ax^{n-1}.$$

To calculate the drug level for large values of n, we use the same shortcut as in Example 1.

Example 3   What quantity of the drug remains in the patient's body after the 10th injection?

Solution After the 10th injection, the drug level in the patient's body is given by

$$Q_{10} = 20 + 20\left(\frac{1}{2}\right) + 20\left(\frac{1}{2}\right)^2 + \cdots + 20\left(\frac{1}{2}\right)^9.$$

Multiply both sides of this formula by 1/2 and add 20, giving

$$\frac{1}{2}Q_{10} + 20 = \frac{1}{2} \cdot \left(20 + 20\left(\frac{1}{2}\right) + 20\left(\frac{1}{2}\right)^2 + \cdots + 20\left(\frac{1}{2}\right)^9\right) + 20$$

$$= \underbrace{20 + 20\left(\frac{1}{2}\right) + 20\left(\frac{1}{2}\right)^2 + \cdots + 20\left(\frac{1}{2}\right)^9}_{Q_{10}} + 20\left(\frac{1}{2}\right)^{10}$$

$$= Q_{10} + 20\left(\frac{1}{2}\right)^{10}.$$

We now solve for Q_{10}. We have

$$\frac{1}{2}Q_{10} + 20 = Q_{10} + 20\left(\frac{1}{2}\right)^{10}$$

$$-\frac{1}{2}Q_{10} = 20\left(\frac{1}{2}\right)^{10} - 20$$

$$Q_{10} = -2\left(20\left(\frac{1}{2}\right)^{10} - 20\right)$$

$$\approx 39.96 \text{ mg}.$$

The Sum of a Geometric Series

The shortcut from Examples 1 and 3 can be used to find the sum of a general geometric series. Let S_n be the sum of a geometric series of n terms, so that

$$S_n = a + ax + ax^2 + \cdots + ax^{n-1}.$$

Multiply both sides of this equation by x and add a, giving

$$xS_n + a = x\left(a + ax + ax^2 + \cdots + ax^{n-1}\right) + a$$
$$= \left(ax + ax^2 + ax^3 + \cdots + ax^{n-1} + ax^n\right) + a.$$

The right-hand side can be rewritten as

$$xS_n + a = \underbrace{a + ax + ax^2 + \cdots + ax^{n-1}}_{S_n} + ax^n$$
$$= S_n + ax^n.$$

Chapter 11/20

Solving the equation $xS_n + a = S_n + ax^n$ for S_n gives

$$xS_n - S_n = ax^n - a$$
$$S_n(x-1) = ax^n - a \qquad \text{factoring out } S_n$$
$$S_n = \frac{ax^n - a}{x-1}$$
$$= \frac{a(x^n-1)}{x-1}.$$

By multiplying the numerator and denominator by -1, this formula can be rewritten as follows:

The sum of a **geometric series of n terms** is given by

$$S_n = a + ax + ax^2 + \cdots + ax^{n-1} = \frac{a(1-x^n)}{1-x}.$$

Example 4 Check the formula for the sum of a geometric series by using it to solve Examples 1 and 3.

Solution For Example 1, we need to find B_6 and B_{26} where

$$B_n = 50 + 50(1.06) + 50(1.06)^2 + \cdots + 50(1.06)^{n-1}.$$

Using the formula for S_n with $a = 50$ and $x = 1.06$, we get the same answers as before:

$$B_6 = \frac{50(1-(1.06)^6)}{1-1.06} = 348.77,$$
$$B_{26} = \frac{50(1-(1.06)^{26})}{1-1.06} = 2957.82.$$

For Example 3, we need to find Q_{10} where

$$Q_n = 20 + 20\left(\frac{1}{2}\right) + 20\left(\frac{1}{2}\right)^2 + \cdots + 20\left(\frac{1}{2}\right)^{n-1}.$$

Using the formula for S_n with $a = 20$ and $x = 1/2$, we get the same quantity as before:

$$Q_{10} = \frac{20(1-(\frac{1}{2})^{10})}{1-\frac{1}{2}} = 39.96.$$

What Happens to the Drug Level Over Time?

Suppose the patient from Example 2 receives injections over a long period of time. What happens to the drug level in the patient's body? To find out, we calculate the drug level after 10, 15, 20, 25 injections:

$$Q_{10} = \frac{20(1 - (\frac{1}{2})^{10})}{1 - \frac{1}{2}} = 39.960938 \text{ mg,}$$

$$Q_{15} = \frac{20(1 - (\frac{1}{2})^{15})}{1 - \frac{1}{2}} = 39.998779 \text{ mg,}$$

$$Q_{20} = \frac{20(1 - (\frac{1}{2})^{20})}{1 - \frac{1}{2}} = 39.999962 \text{ mg,}$$

$$Q_{25} = \frac{20(1 - (\frac{1}{2})^{25})}{1 - \frac{1}{2}} = 39.999999 \text{ mg.}$$

It appears that the drug level approaches 40 mg over time. To see why this happens, notice that if there is less than 40 mg of the drug in the body, then the amount metabolized in one day is less than 20 mg. Thus, after the next 20 mg injection, the drug level is *higher* than it was before. For instance, if there are currently 30 mg, then after one day, half of this has been metabolized, leaving 15 mg. At the next injection the level rises to 35 mg, or 5 mg higher than where it started.

Similarly, if there is more than 40 mg in the body, then the amount metabolized in one day is more than 20 mg. Thus, after the next 20 mg injection, the drug level is *lower* than it was before. For instance, if there are currently 50 mg, then after one day, half of this has been metabolized, leaving 25 mg. At the next injection the level rises to 45 mg, or 5 mg lower than where it started.

Finally, if there is *exactly* 40 mg of drug in the body, then after one day, half of this amount has been metabolized, leaving 20 mg. At the next 20 mg injection, the level returns to 40 mg. We say that the *equilibrium* drug level is 40 mg. Since the patient has less than 40 mg of the drug at the start, the drug level rises toward 40 mg, where it levels off.

Infinite Geometric Series

Another way to think about the patient's drug level over time is to consider an *infinite geometric series*. We know that after n injections, the drug level is given by

$$Q_n = 20 + 20\left(\frac{1}{2}\right) + 20\left(\frac{1}{2}\right)^2 + \cdots + 20\left(\frac{1}{2}\right)^{n-1} = \frac{20(1 - (\frac{1}{2})^n)}{1 - \frac{1}{2}}.$$

What happens to the value of this sum as the number of terms approaches infinity? It doesn't seem possible to add up an infinite number of terms. However, we can look at the *partial sums*, Q_n, to see what happens for large values of n. For large values of n, we see that $(1/2)^n$ is very small, so that

$$Q_n = \frac{20(1 - \text{Small number})}{1 - \frac{1}{2}}$$
$$= \frac{20(1 - \text{Small number})}{1/2}.$$

As n becomes arbitrarily large, that is, as $n \to \infty$, we know that $(1/2)^n \to 0$, so

$$Q_n \to \frac{20(1 - 0)}{1/2} = \frac{20}{1/2} = 40 \text{ mg.}$$

The Sum of an Infinite Geometric Series

Consider the geometric series $S_n = a + ax + ax^2 + \cdots + ax^{n-1}$. In general, if $|x| < 1$, then $x^n \to 0$ as $n \to \infty$, and

$$S_n = \frac{a(1-x^n)}{1-x} \to \frac{a(1-0)}{1-x} = \frac{a}{1-x} \text{ as } n \to \infty.$$

Thus, if $|x| < 1$, the partial sums S_n approache a finite value, S, as $n \to \infty$; we say that the series *converges* to S.

> For $|x| < 1$, the **sum of the infinite geometric series** is given by
>
> $$S = a + ax + ax^2 + \cdots + ax^n + \cdots = \frac{a}{1-x}.$$

On the other hand, if $|x| > 1$, then we say that the series does not converge. The terms in the series get larger and larger as $n \to \infty$, so adding infinitely many of them does not give a finite sum.

What happens when $x = \pm 1$? The formula for S_n does not apply in these cases, and in fact the infinite geometric series does not converge. (To see why, consider what happens to 1^n and $(-1)^n$ as n increases.)

Present Value of a Series of Payments

When basketball player Patrick Ewing was signed by the New York Knicks, he was given a contract for $30 million: $3 million a year for ten years. Of course, since much of the money was to be paid in the future, the team's owners did not have to have all $30 million available on the day of the signing. How much money would the owners have to deposit in a bank account on the day of the signing in order to cover all the future payments? Assuming the account was earning interest, the owners would have to deposit much less than $30 million. This smaller amount is called the *present value* of $30 million. We will calculate the present value of Ewing's contract on the day he signed.

Definition of Present Value

Let's consider a simplified version of this problem, with only one future payment: How much money would we need to deposit in a bank account today in order to have $3 million in one year? At an annual interest rate of 5%, compounded annually, the deposit would grow by a factor of 1.05. Thus,

$$\text{Required deposit} \times 1.05 = \$3 \text{ million,}$$
$$\text{Required deposit} = \frac{3{,}000{,}000}{1.05} = 2{,}857{,}142.86.$$

We would need to deposit $2,857,142.86. We say that this is the *present value* of the $3 million. Similarly, if we need $3 million in 2 years, the amount we would need to deposit is given by

$$\text{Required deposit} \times 1.05^2 = \$3 \text{ million,}$$
$$\text{Required deposit} = \frac{3{,}000{,}000}{1.05^2} = 2{,}721{,}088.44.$$

The $2,721,088.44 is the present value of $3 million payable two years from today. In general,

> The **present value**, P, of a future payment, B, is the amount which would have to be deposited (at some interest rate, r) in a bank account today to have exactly B in the account at the relevant time in the future.

If r is the annual interest rate (compounded annually) and if t is the number of years, then

$$B = P(1 + r)^n, \quad \text{or equivalently,} \quad P = \frac{B}{(1 + r)^n}.$$

Calculating the Present Value of Ewing's Contract

The present value of Ewing's contract represents what it was worth on the day it was signed. Suppose that he receives his money in 10 payments of \$3 million each, the first payment to be made on the day the contract was signed. We calculate the present values of all 10 payments assuming that interest is compounded annually at a rate of 5% per year. Since the first payment is made the day the contract is signed:

Present value of first payment, in millions of dollars $= 3$.

Since the second payment is made a year in the future:

Present value of second payment, in millions of dollars $= \frac{3}{(1.05)^1} = \frac{3}{1.05}$.

The third payment is made two years in the future:

Present value of third payment, in millions of dollars $= \frac{3}{(1.05)^2}$,

and so on. Similarly,

Present value of tenth payment, in millions of dollars $= \frac{3}{(1.05)^9}$.

Thus, in millions of dollars,

$$\text{Total present value} = 3 + \frac{3}{1.05} + \frac{3}{(1.05)^2} + \cdots + \frac{3}{(1.05)^9}.$$

Rewriting this expression, we see that it is a finite geometric series with $a = 3$ and $x = 1/1.05$:

$$\text{Total present value} = 3 + 3\left(\frac{1}{1.05}\right) + 3\left(\frac{1}{1.05}\right)^2 + \cdots + 3\left(\frac{1}{1.05}\right)^9,$$

The formula for the sum of a finite geometric series gives

$$\text{Total present value of contract in millions of dollars} = \frac{3\left(1 - \left(\frac{1}{1.05}\right)^{10}\right)}{1 - \frac{1}{1.05}} \approx 24.3.$$

Thus, the total present value of the contract is about \$24.3 million.

Example 5   Suppose Patrick Ewing's contract with the Knicks guaranteed him and his heirs an annual payment of $3 million *forever*. How much would the owners need to deposit in an account today in order to provide these payments?

Solution   At 5%, the total present value of an infinite series of payments is given by

$$\text{Total present value} = 3 + \frac{3}{1.05} + \frac{3}{(1.05)^2} + \cdots$$

$$= 3 + 3\left(\frac{1}{1.05}\right) + 3\left(\frac{1}{1.05}\right)^2 + \cdots.$$

The sum of this infinite geometric series can be found using the formula:

$$\text{Total present value} = \frac{3}{1 - \frac{1}{1.05}} = 63 \text{ million dollars.}$$

To see that this answer is reasonable, suppose that $63 million is deposited in an account today, and that a $3 million payment is immediately made to Patrick Ewing. Over the course of a year, the remaining $60 million earns 5% interest, which works out to $3 million, so the next year the account again has $63 million. Thus, it would have cost the New York Knicks only about $40 million more (than the $24.3 million) to pay Ewing and his heirs $3 million a year forever.

Summation Notation

In the last section, we saw how to write an arithmetic series using summation notation. We can also use summation notation for geometric series. For example, we write

$$\sum_{i=1}^{10} x^i = x^1 + x^2 + \cdots + x^{10}.$$

The Σ tells us we are adding some numbers. The x^i tells us that the quantities being added are x^1, x^2, and so on, up to x^{10}. The value of i starts at 1 because of the $i = 1$ at the bottom of the Σ sign and i stops at 10 because of the 10 at the top of the Σ sign.

Example 6   Evaluate $\displaystyle\sum_{i=0}^{5} 7\left(\frac{1}{2}\right)^i$.

Solution   The value of i starts at 0 and ends at 5. The quantities being added are $7(1/2)^0$, $7(1/2)^1$, ..., up to $7(1/2)^5$. Thus,

$$\sum_{i=0}^{5} 7\left(\frac{1}{2}\right)^i = 7 + 7\left(\frac{1}{2}\right) + 7\left(\frac{1}{2}\right)^2 + \cdots + 7\left(\frac{1}{2}\right)^5.$$

This is a geometric series of 6 terms with $a = 7$ and $x = 1/2$. Therefore, we have

$$\sum_{i=0}^{5} 7\left(\frac{1}{2}\right)^i = \frac{7(1 - (\frac{1}{2})^6)}{1 - \frac{1}{2}} = 13.78.$$

Summation notation provides a compact way of writing geometric series. Using this notation,

---

The general formula for a geometric series of n terms can be written

$$\sum_{i=0}^{n-1} ax^i = a + ax + ax^2 + \cdots + ax^{n-1}.$$

The general formula for an infinite geometric series can be written

$$\sum_{i=0}^{\infty} ax^2 = a + ax + ax^2 + \cdots.$$

Example 7   Represent the present value of Patrick Ewing's contract using summation notation.

Solution   We have

$$\text{Total present value} = 3 + \frac{3}{1.05} + \frac{3}{(1.05)^2} + \cdots + \frac{3}{(1.05)^9} = \sum_{i=0}^{9} 3 \left(\frac{1}{1.05} \right)^i.$$

Example 8   Find the sum of the geometric series $\sum_{i=0}^{17} 7(-z)^i$ and $\sum_{i=0}^{\infty} (-z)^i$ provided $|z| < 1$.

Solution   We have

$$\sum_{i=0}^{17} 7(-z)^i = 7 \cdot 1 + 7(-z)^1 + 7(-z)^2 + \cdots + 7(-z)^{17}.$$

This is a geometric series of 18 terms with $a = 7$ and $x = -z$. Thus, we have

$$\sum_{i=0}^{17} 7(-z)^1 = 7\frac{1 - (-z)^{18}}{1 - (-z)} = 7\frac{1 - z^{18}}{1 + z}.$$

As for $\sum_{i=0}^{\infty} (-z)^i$, this is an infinite geometric series. Since $|z| < 1$, we have

$$\sum_{i=0}^{\infty} (-z)^i = \frac{1}{1 - (-z)} = \frac{1}{1 + z}.$$

Problems for Section 11.2

In Problems 1–8, decide which of the following are geometric series. For those which are, give the first term and the ratio between successive terms. For those which are not, explain why not.

1. $2 + 1 + \frac{1}{2} + \frac{1}{4} + \frac{1}{8} + \cdots$ $\quad$ a. $r = \frac{1}{2}$

2. $1 - \frac{1}{2} + \frac{1}{4} - \frac{1}{8} + \frac{1}{16} + \cdots$

3. $1 + \frac{1}{2} + \frac{1}{3} + \frac{1}{4} + \frac{1}{5} + \cdots$

4. $5 - 10 + 20 - 40 + 80 - \cdots$

5. $1 - x + x^2 - x^3 + x^4 - \cdots$

6. $1 + x + 2x^2 + 3x^3 + 4x^4 + \cdots$

7. $y^2 + y^3 + y^4 + y^5 + \cdots$ $\quad$ $S = \frac{y^2}{1-y}$

8. $3 + 3z + 6z^2 + 9z^3 + 12z^4 + \cdots$ $\quad$ No Geometric.

9. Find the sum of the series in Problem 5.

10. Find the sum of the series in Problem 7.

Write each of the sums in Problems 11–14 in sigma notation. $\quad$ $a_n = 3(n-$

11. $1 + 4 + 16 + 64 + 256$

12. $3 - 9 + 27 - 81 + 243 - 729$

13. $2 + 10 + 50 + 250 + 1250 + 6250 + 31250$

14. $32 - 16 + 8 - 4 + 2 - 1$

15. Find the sum of the first seven terms of the series: $7 + 14 + 28 + \cdots$

16. Find the sum of the first ten terms of the series: $5/9 + 5/3 + 5 + \cdots$

Find the sum of the series in Problems 17–24.

17. $3 + \frac{3}{2} + \frac{3}{4} + \frac{3}{8} + \cdots + \frac{3}{2^{10}}$

18. $-2 + 1 - \frac{1}{2} + \frac{1}{4} - \frac{1}{8} + \frac{1}{16} - \cdots$ $\quad$ $r = -2$

19. $5 + 15 + 45 + 135 + \cdots + 5(3^{12})$

20. $1/125 + 1/25 + 1/5 + \cdots + 625$

21. $\displaystyle\sum_{i=4}^{\infty} \left(\frac{1}{3}\right)^i$

22. $\displaystyle\sum_{i=0}^{\infty} \frac{3^i + 5}{4^i}$ $\quad$ $\frac{1}{125} \cdot \frac{1}{20}$

23. $\displaystyle\sum_{n=1}^{10} 4(2^n)$

24. $\displaystyle\sum_{k=0}^{7} 2\left(\frac{3}{4}\right)^k$

25. A repeating decimal can always be expressed as a fraction. This problem shows how writing a repeating decimal as a geometric series enables you to find the fraction. Consider the decimal $0.232323\ldots$.

    (a) Use the fact that $0.232323\ldots = 0.23 + 0.0023 + 0.000023 + \cdots$ to write $0.232323\ldots$ as a geometric series.

    (b) Use the formula for the sum of a geometric series to show that $0.232323\ldots = 23/99$.

In Problems 26–31, use the method of Problem 25 to write each of the decimals as fractions.

26. $0.235235235\ldots$

27. $6.19191919\ldots$

28. $0.12222222\ldots$

29. $0.4788888\ldots$

30. $0.85656565656\ldots$

31. $0.7638383838\ldots$

.235 + .000235 + .000 000235

$\dfrac{.235}{1 - .0001}$ $\quad$ 6.19 .19 $\quad$ $= 0.232323$

Chapter 11/27

32. Figure 11.3 shows the quantity of the drug atenolol in the blood as a function of time, with the first dose at time $t = 0$. Atenolol is taken in 50 mg doses once a day to lower blood pressure.

   (a) If the half-life of atenolol in the blood is 6.3 hours, what percentage of the atenolol present at the start of a 24-hour period is still there at the end?

   (b) Find expressions for the quantities Q_0, Q_1, Q_2, Q_3, ..., and Q_n shown in Figure 32. Write the expression for Q_n in closed-form.

   (c) Find expressions for the quantities P_1, P_2, P_3, ..., and P_n shown in Figure 32. Write the expression for P_n in closed-form.

Figure 11.3

33. You have an ear infection and are told to take a 250 mg tablet of ampicillin (a common antibiotic) four times a day (every six hours). It is known that at the end of six hours, about 4% of the drug is still in the body. What quantity of the drug is in the body right after the third tablet? The fortieth? Assuming you continue taking tablets, what happens to the drug level in the long run?

34. In Problem 33 we found the quantity Q_n, the amount (in mg) of ampicillin left in the body right after the nth tablet is taken.

   (a) Make a similar calculation for P_n, the quantity of ampicillin (in mg) in the body right *before* the nth tablet is taken.

   (b) Find a simplified formula for P_n.

   (c) What happens to P_n in the long run? Is this the same as what happens to Q_n? Explain in practical terms why your answer makes sense.

35. Draw a graph like that in Figure 11.3 for 250 mg of ampicillin taken every 6 hours, starting at time $t = 0$. Put on the graph the values of Q_1, Q_2, Q_3, ... calculated in Problem 33 and the values of P_1, P_2, P_3, ... calculated in Problem 34.

36. Consider Patrick Ewing's contract described on page 516. Determine the present value of the contract if the interest rate is 7% per year, compounded continuously, for the entire 10-year period of the contract.

37. One way of valuing a company is to calculate the present value of all its future earnings. Suppose a farm expects to sell $1000 worth of Christmas trees once a year forever, with the first sale in the immediate future. What is the present value of this Christmas tree business? Assume that the interest rate is 4% per year, compounded continuously.

Problems 38–40 are about *bonds*, which are issued by a government to raise money. An individual who buys a $1000 bond gives the government $1000 and in return receives a fixed sum of money, called the *coupon*, every six months or every year for the life of the bond. At the time of the last coupon, the individual also gets the $1000, or *principal*, back.

38. What is the present value of a $1000 bond which pays $50 a year for 10 years, starting one year from now? Assume interest rate is 6% per year, compounded annually.

39. What is the present value of a $1000 bond which pays $50 a year for 10 years, starting one year from now? Assume the interest rate is 4% per year, compounded annually.

40. (a) What is the present value of a $1000 bond which pays $50 a year for 10 years, starting one year from now? Assume the interest rate is 5% per year, compounded annually.

   (b) Since $50 is 5% of $1000, this bond is often called a 5% bond. What does your answer to part (a) tell you about the relationship between the principal and the present value of this bond when the interest rate is 5%?

   (c) If the interest rate is more than 5% per year, compounded annually, which one is larger: the principal or the value of the bond? Why do you think the bond is then described as *trading at discount*?

   (d) If the interest rate is less than 5% per year, compounded annually, why is the bond described as *trading at a premium*?

SECTION 58

THE BINOMIAL THEOREM

A. Introduction. Factorial Notation

In this section we show how to extend the following list to include all higher integral powers of $a + b$.

$$(a + b)^0 = 1$$
$$(a + b)^1 = a + b$$
$$(a + b)^2 = a^2 + 2ab + b^2$$
$$(a + b)^3 = a^3 + 3a^2b + 3ab^2 + b^3$$

The theorem that gives $(a + b)^n$ in general is called the *Binomial Theorem*. Before stating and proving this theorem, however, we need some preliminary facts about *factorial notation* and *binomial coefficients*.

The notation $n!$ (read **n factorial**) is defined for positive integers as follows:

$$1! = 1$$
$$2! = 2 \cdot 1 = 2$$
$$3! = 3 \cdot 2 \cdot 1 = 6$$
$$4! = 4 \cdot 3 \cdot 2 \cdot 1 = 24$$

and, in general,

$$n! = n(n - 1)(n - 2) \cdots \cdot 2 \cdot 1.$$

You can easily verify that $5! = 120$. Fortunately, we will not need larger specific values like

$$20! = 2,432,902,008,176,640,000.$$

Notice that if n is any integer greater than 1, then $n! = n \cdot (n - 1)!$. With $n = 4$, for example, we have $4! = 4 \cdot 3! = 4 \cdot 3 \cdot 2 \cdot 1$. If we use $n = 1$ in $n! = n \cdot (n - 1)!$, we get $1! = 1 \cdot 0!$. Partly for this reason, and partly to make many formulas simpler, we *define* $0!$ by $0! = 1$.

B. Binomial Coefficients

The coefficients needed to expand $(a + b)^n$ are called **binomial coefficients** (remember from Section 2 that $a + b$ is called a *binomial*). For each pair of integers n and k such that $n \geq k \geq 0$, there is a binomial coefficient denoted by $\binom{n}{k}$ and defined by

$$\boxed{\binom{n}{k} = \frac{n!}{k!(n - k)!}.}$$

(58.1)

Example 58.1

(a) $\binom{5}{2} = \frac{5!}{2!3!} = \frac{5 \cdot 4 \cdot 3 \cdot 2 \cdot 1}{2 \cdot 1 \cdot 3 \cdot 2 \cdot 1} = 10$

(b) $\binom{10}{2} = \frac{10!}{2!8!} = \frac{10 \cdot 9 \cdot 8!}{2 \cdot 1 \cdot 8!} = 45$

(c) $\binom{12}{9} = \frac{12!}{9!3!} = \frac{12 \cdot 11 \cdot 10 \cdot 9!}{9! \cdot 3 \cdot 2 \cdot 1} = 220$

(d) $\binom{n}{0} = \frac{n!}{0!n!} = \frac{n!}{1 \cdot n!} = 1 \quad (n \geq 0)$

(e) $\binom{n}{n} = \frac{n!}{n!0!} = 1 \quad (n \geq 0)$

(f) $\binom{n}{1} = \frac{n!}{1!(n - 1)!} = \frac{n \cdot (n - 1)!}{1 \cdot (n - 1)!} = n \quad (n \geq 1)$

Following are two fundamental facts about binomial coefficients. They are valid whenever $n \geq k \geq 0$.

Chapter 11/31

$$\binom{n}{k} = \binom{n}{n-k} \qquad (58.2)$$

Proof.

$$\binom{n}{k} = \frac{n!}{k!(n-k)!}$$

$$= \frac{n!}{(n-k)!k!}$$

$$= \frac{n!}{(n-k)!(n-(n-k))!} = \binom{n}{n-k} \qquad \square$$

Example 58.2

(a) $\binom{20}{3} = \binom{20}{17}$ (b) $\binom{n}{1} = \binom{n}{n-1}$ (c) $\binom{n}{0} = \binom{n}{n}$

$$\binom{n+1}{k} = \binom{n}{k-1} + \binom{n}{k} \qquad (58.3)$$

Proof. We add the two terms on the right using a common denominator of $k!(n-k+1)!$. The result will turn out to be the term on the left.

$$\binom{n}{k-1} + \binom{n}{k} = \frac{n!}{(k-1)!(n-(k-1))!} + \frac{n!}{k!(n-k)!}$$

$$= \frac{k \cdot n!}{k \cdot (k-1)!(n-k+1)!} + \frac{n!(n-k+1)}{k!(n-k)!(n-k+1)}$$

$$= \frac{k \cdot n!}{k!(n-k+1)!} + \frac{(n-k+1) \cdot n!}{k!(n-k+1)!}$$

$$= \frac{(k+n-k+1) \cdot n!}{k!(n-k+1)!}$$

$$= \frac{(n+1)!}{k!(n-k+1)!}$$

$$= \binom{n+1}{k} \qquad \square$$

Equation (58.3) provides a convenient scheme for computing binomial coefficients for reasonably small n. This scheme is shown by the triangle in

FIGURE 58.1

Figure 58.1, named for the French mathematician Blaise Pascal (1623–1662) but known to the Chinese at least 300 years before his time. In Pascal's triangle $\binom{n}{k}$ stands at the intersection of the nth row and the kth diagonal. Equation (58.3) tells us that each entry can be obtained by adding the numbers immediately to the left and right in the row above it. Equation (58.2) is reflected in the left-right symmetry of the table. For example, the pair of 15's in the sixth row represent $\binom{6}{2}$ and $\binom{6}{4}$, which must be equal by (58.2).

Other notation used for the binomial coefficient $\binom{n}{k}$ includes $C(n, k)$, $_nC_k$, and C_k^n.

C. The Binomial Theorem

The Binomial Theorem

If n is any nonnegative integer then

$$(a + b)^n = \binom{n}{0}a^n + \binom{n}{1}a^{n-1}b + \binom{n}{2}a^{n-2}b^2 + \cdots$$

$$+ \binom{n}{k}a^{n-k}b^k + \cdots + \binom{n}{n}b^n. \tag{58.4}$$

The proof of the theorem will follow some observations and examples.

Observations

- The top entry in each binomial coefficient is n.
- The bottom entries in the binomial coefficients increase successively from 0 to n as we move to the right.
- In each term, the exponent on b is the same as the bottom entry of the term's binomial coefficient.

ponents on a decrease successively from n to 0 as we move to the
ınd the exponents on b increase successively from 0 to n.

h term, the sum of the exponents on a and b is n.

: are $n + 1$ terms in the expansion of $(a + b)^n$.

ıe 58.3

$$(a + b)^4 = \binom{4}{0}a^4 + \binom{4}{1}a^3b + \binom{4}{2}a^2b^2 + \binom{4}{3}ab^3 + \binom{4}{4}b^4$$

binomial coefficients needed here can be read from the fourth row of
cal's triangle: 1, 4, 6, 4, 1. Thus

$$(a + b)^4 = a^4 + 4a^3b + 6a^2b^2 + 4ab^3 + b^4.$$

Example 58.4 Expand $(x^2 - 2y)^5$.

Solution Use (58.4) with $a = x^2$, $b = -2y$, and $n = 5$. The binomial
coefficients can be read from the fifth row of Pascal's triangle. [You may want
to write out $(a + b)^5$ first and then substitute x^2 for a and $-2y$ for b.]

$$(x^2 - 2y)^5 = (x^2)^5 + 5(x^2)^4(-2y) + 10(x^2)^3(-2y)^2$$
$$+ 10(x^2)^2(-2y)^3 + 5(x^2)(-2y)^4 + (-2y)^5$$
$$= x^{10} - 10x^8y + 40x^6y^2 - 80x^4y^3$$
$$+ 80x^2y^4 - 32y^5$$

Example 58.5 Find the coefficient of a^4b^{16} in the expansion of $(a + b)^{20}$.

Solution Use (58.4) with $n = 20$. The coefficient of a^4b^{16} is

$$\binom{20}{16} = \frac{20!}{16!4!} = \frac{20 \cdot 19 \cdot 18 \cdot 17 \cdot 16!}{16! \cdot 4 \cdot 3 \cdot 2 \cdot 1} = 4845.$$

Example 58.6 Find the coefficient of u^6v^{12} in the expansion of $(2u^2 - v^3)^7$.

Solution Use (58.4) with $n = 7$ and with k chosen so that $(2u^2)^{7-k}(-v^3)^k$
involves v^{12}. This requires $k = 4$, and thus the term involving u^6v^{12} is

$$\binom{7}{4}(2u^2)^3(-v^3)^4 = \frac{7!}{4!3!} 8u^6(v^{12})$$
$$= 35 \cdot 8u^6v^{12}$$
$$= 280u^6v^{12}.$$

Therefore, the answer is 280.

Proof of the Binomial Theorem

Let P_n represent Equation (58.4) and use induction on n.

(a) P_1 is true because

$$(a + b)^1 = a + b = \binom{1}{0}a^1 + \binom{1}{1}b^1.$$

(b) We now show that P_m implies P_{m+1} for each positive integer m. (We are using m in place of k in the statement of the Principle of Mathematical Induction in Section 55.) Assume P_m, that is,

$$(a + b)^m = \binom{m}{0}a^m + \binom{m}{1}a^{m-1}b + \binom{m}{2}a^{m-2}b^2 + \cdots$$

$$+ \binom{m}{k}a^{m-k}b^k + \cdots + \binom{m}{m}b^m. \tag{58.5}$$

To prove P_{m+1} from (58.5), we multiply both sides of (58.5) by $a + b$. The result on the left will be $(a + b)^{m+1}$, as required. The result on the right will be

$$\left[\binom{m}{0}a^m + \binom{m}{1}a^{m-1}b + \cdots + \binom{m}{k}a^{m-k}b^k + \cdots + \binom{m}{m}b^m\right](a + b)$$

$$= \binom{m}{0}a^{m+1} + \binom{m}{1}a^m b + \cdots + \binom{m}{k}a^{m-k+1}b^k + \cdots$$

$$+ \binom{m}{m}ab^m + \binom{m}{0}a^m b + \binom{m}{1}a^{m-1}b^2 + \cdots$$

$$+ \binom{m}{k}a^{m-k}b^{k+1} + \cdots + \binom{m}{m}b^{m+1}$$

The term involving b^k in the last expansion is seen to be

$$\binom{m}{k}a^{m-k+1}b^k + \binom{m}{k-1}a^{m-k+1}b^k = \binom{m+1}{k}a^{m-k+1}b^k,$$

where we have used Equation (58.3). But $\binom{m+1}{k}a^{m-k+1}b^k$ is also the term involving b^k in P_{m+1}. Since the terms involving b^k are equal for all k ($0 \le k \le m + 1$), the proof is complete. $\square$

Exercises for Section 58

Compute

1. $\dbinom{10}{3}$ **4.** $\dbinom{50}{50}$

2. $\dbinom{12}{1}$ **5.** $\dbinom{20}{3}$

3. $\dbinom{9}{4}$ **6.** $\dbinom{14}{0}$

Simplify as much as possible.

7. $\dfrac{(n+2)!}{n!}$ **10.** $\dbinom{n}{0} + \dbinom{n}{n}$

8. $\dfrac{(n+1)!}{(n-1)!}$ **11.** $\dbinom{n}{1} + \dbinom{n}{n-1}$

9. $\dfrac{(n+1)!(n-1)!}{(n!)^2}$ **12.** $\dbinom{n}{2} + \dbinom{n}{n-2}$

13. Write rows 7 and 8 of Pascal's triangle.

14. Prove that

$$\binom{n}{k} = \frac{n}{k}\binom{n-1}{k-1}.$$

15. Prove that

$$\binom{n+2}{k} = \binom{n}{k-2} + 2\binom{n}{k-1} + \binom{n}{k}.$$

Expand and simplify.

16. $(x + y)^5$ **19.** $(a - b)^6$

17. $(u + v)^6$ **20.** $\left(x - \dfrac{2}{y}\right)^5$

18. $(a + 2)^4$ **21.** $(2u - v^2)^4$

22. Find and simplify the coefficient of $u^7 v^2$ in the expansion of $(u + v)^9$.

23. Find and simplify the coefficient of $x^{23}y^2$ in the expansion of $(x + y)^{25}$.

24. Find and simplify the coefficient of $a^3 b^9$ in the expansion of $(a + b)^{12}$.

25. Find and simplify the first four terms in the expansion of $(a^2 + 2b^3)^{10}$.

26. Find and simplify the first three terms in the expansion of $(2u - 5v)^{20}$.

27. Find and simplify the first four terms in the expansion of $(x + y)^{100}$.

28. Find and simplify the coefficient of $u^6 v^{15}$ in the expansion of $(2u^2 - v^3)^8$.

29. Find and simplify the coefficient of x^8 in $(x - \sqrt{x})^{10}$.

30. There is a constant term in the expansion of $[x - (1/x^2)]^{30}$. What is it?

31. The sum of the entries in the nth row of Pascal's triangle is 2^n. You can verify this for $1 \le n \le 6$ simply by addition and Figure 58.1. Prove it for every row. [Suggestion: Look at what (58.4) becomes when $a = b = 1$.]

32. The product of the first n positive even integers is $n!$ times a function of n. What is the function of n?

33. Show that if n is a positive integer, then

$$1 \cdot 3 \cdot 5 \cdot \,\cdots\, \cdot (2n - 1) = \frac{(2n)!}{2^n(n!)}.$$

1. Write the following using sigma notion $100 + 90 + 80 + 70 + \cdots + 0$.

2. (a) Write the sum $\displaystyle\sum_{i=1}^{5}(4i - 3)$ in expanded form.

   (b) Compute the sum.

3. Find the sum of the first eighteen terms of the series: $8 + 11 + 14 + \cdots$. What is the eighteenth term?

In Problems 4–5, decide which of the following are geometric series. For those which are, give the first term and the ratio between successive terms. For those which are not, explain why not.

4. $1 - y^2 + y^4 - y^6 + \cdots$

5. $1 + 2z + (2z)^2 + (2z)^3 + \cdots$

6. Find the sum of the series in Problem 4.

7. Find the sum of the series in Problem 5.

8. A store clerk has 108 cans to stack. He can fit 24 cans on the bottom row and can stack the cans 8 rows high. Use arithmetic series to determine how he can stack the cans so that each row contains fewer cans than the row beneath it and that the number of cans in each row decreases at a constant rate.

9. A ball is dropped from a height of 10 feet and bounces. Each bounce is 3/4 of the height of the bounce before. Thus after the ball hits the floor for the first time, the ball rises to a height of $10(3/4) = 7.5$ feet, and after it hits the floor for the second time, it rises to a height of $7.5(3/4) = 10(3/4)^2 = 5.625$ feet.

   (a) Find an expression for the height to which the ball rises after it hits the floor for the nth time.

   (b) Find an expression for the total vertical distance the ball has traveled when it hits the floor for the first, second, third, and fourth times.

   (c) Find an expression for the total vertical distance the ball has traveled when it hits the floor for the nth time. Express your answer in closed-form.

10. You might think that the ball in Problem 9 keeps bouncing forever since it takes infinitely many bounces. This is not true! It can be shown that a ball dropped from a height of h feet reaches the ground in $\frac{1}{4}\sqrt{h}$ seconds. It is also true that it takes a bouncing ball the same amount of time to rise h feet. Use these facts to show that the ball in Problem 9 stops bouncing after

$$\frac{1}{4}\sqrt{10} + \frac{1}{2}\sqrt{10}\sqrt{\frac{3}{4}}\left(\frac{1}{1 - \sqrt{3/4}}\right)$$

seconds, or approximately 11 seconds.

11. This problem illustrates how banks create credit and can thereby lend out more money than has been deposited. Suppose that initially $100 is deposited in a bank. Experience has shown bankers that on average only 8% of the money deposited is withdrawn by the owner at any time. Consequently, bankers feel free to lend out 92% of their deposits. Thus $92 of the original $100 is loaned out to other customers (to start a business, for example). This $92 will become someone else's income and, sooner or later, will be redeposited in the bank. Then 92% of $92, or $92(0.92) = $84.64, is loaned out again and eventually redeposited. Of the $84.64, the bank again loans out 92%, and so on.

    (a) Find the total amount of money deposited in the bank.
    (b) The total amount of money deposited divided by the original deposit is called the *credit multiplier*. Calculate the credit multiplier for this example and explain what this number tells us.

Review Exercises for Chapter XIV

1. Find and simplify the first four terms and the $(n + 1)$st term of the series

$$\sum_{k=2}^{\infty} 3^{k-1} \binom{k}{2}.$$

2. Represent the infinite series

$$1 - 20 + 300 - 4000 + \cdots$$

using summation (Σ) notation.

3. Use mathematical induction to prove that

$$3 + 7 + 11 + \cdots + (4n - 1) = n(2n + 1)$$

for every positive integer n.

4. Use mathematical induction to prove that

$$1^2 + 3^2 + 5^2 + \cdots + (2n - 1)^2 = \frac{n(2n - 1)(2n + 1)}{3}$$

for every positive integer n.

5. Find the sum of the first ten terms of the sequence $1, 1 - \pi, 1 - 2\pi, 1 - 3\pi, \ldots.$

6. Verify the equation in Review Exercise 3 by using a formula for the sum of an arithmetic sequence.

7. Write the first three terms and the tenth term of the geometric sequence having first term $2\sqrt{3}$ and common ratio $-\sqrt{3}$.

8. A geometric sequence has first term x and fifth term $0.0001xy^8$. What is the common ratio?

9. Find the sum of the first ten terms of the geometric series with first term 5 and common ratio -2.

10. Find the sum of the series

$$a + a^2b^2 + a^3b^4 + \cdots + a^nb^{2n-2}.$$

11. An infinite series has first term 1 and common ratio $5t$. Determine the values of t for which the series converges. Also find the sum of the series when it converges.

12. Find the sum of the series

$$4 + \tfrac{4}{3} + \tfrac{4}{9} + \tfrac{4}{27} + \cdots.$$

13. At the end of each month you place $25 in an account that pays interest at an annual rate of 6% compounded monthly. How much will be in the account at the end of the 40th month?

14. I plan to deposit a constant amount in an account at the end of each month, and I want $5000 in the account at the end of 5 years. The account will pay 6% (annual rate) compounded monthly. What is the minimum amount, rounded up to the nearest $5, that I should deposit each month?

15. Simplify as much as possible:

$$\binom{n + 1}{k} \Big/ \binom{n}{k - 1}.$$

16. Prove that

$$\binom{2n}{n} + \binom{2n}{n - 1} = \frac{1}{2}\binom{2n + 2}{n + 1}.$$

Expand and simplify.

17. $(a^2 - b)^5$ 18. $(10x + 0.1y)^6$

Chapter 12

Functions of Two Variables, Three Dimensional Space, Graphs, Contour Diagrams, and Vectors

11.1 FUNCTIONS OF TWO VARIABLES

Function Notation

Suppose you are planning to take out a five-year loan to buy a car and you need to calculate what your monthly payment will be; this depends on both the amount of money you borrow and the interest rate. These quantities can vary separately: the loan amount can change while the interest rate remains the same, or the interest rate can change while the loan amount remains the same. To calculate your monthly payment you need to know both. If the monthly payment is $$m$, the loan amount is $$L$, and the interest rate is $r\%$, then we express the fact that m is a function of L and r by writing:

$$m = f(L, r).$$

This is just like the function notation of one-variable calculus. The variable m is called the dependent variable, and the variables L and r are called the independent variables. The letter f stands for the *function* or rule that gives the value of m corresponding to given values of L and r.

A function of two variables can be represented graphically, numerically by a table of values, or algebraically by a formula. In this section we will give examples of each of these three ways of viewing a function.

Graphical Example: A Weather Map

Figure 11.1 shows a weather map from a newspaper. What information does it convey? It displays the predicted high temperature, T, in degrees Fahrenheit (°F), throughout the US on that day. The curves on the map, called *isotherms*, separate the country into zones, according to whether T is in the 60s, 70s, 80s, 90s, or 100s. (*Iso* means same and *therm* means heat.) Notice that the isotherm separating the 80s and 90s zones connects all the points where the temperature is exactly 90°F.

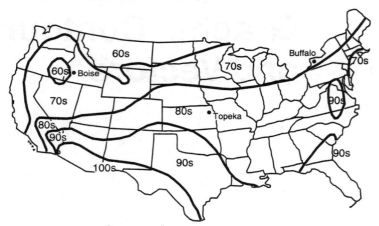

Figure 11.1: Weather map showing predicted high temperatures, T, on a summer day

---

Example 1   Estimate the predicted value of T in Boise, Idaho; Topeka, Kansas; and Buffalo, New York.

Solution   Boise and Buffalo are in the 70s region, and Topeka is in the 80s region. Thus, the predicted temperature in Boise and Buffalo is between 70 and 80 while the predicted temperature in Topeka is between 80 and 90.

In fact, we can say more. Although both Boise and Buffalo are in the 70s, Boise is quite close to the $T = 70$ isotherm, whereas Buffalo is quite close to the $T = 80$ isotherm. So we estimate that the temperature will be in the low 70s in Boise and the high 70s in Buffalo. Topeka is about halfway between the $T = 80$ isotherm and the $T = 90$ isotherm. Thus, we guess that the temperature in Topeka will be in the mid 80s. In fact, the actual high temperatures for that day were 71°F for Boise, 79°F for Buffalo, and 86°F for Topeka.

The predicted high temperature, T, illustrated by the weather map is a function of (that is, depends on) two variables, often longitude and latitude, or miles east-west and miles north-south of a fixed point, say, Topeka. The weather map in Figure 11.1 is called a *contour map* or *contour diagram* of that function. Section 11.3 shows another way of visualizing functions of two variables using surfaces; Section 11.4 looks at contour maps in detail.

Numerical Example: Beef Consumption

Suppose you are a beef producer and you want to know how much beef people will buy. This depends on how much money people have and on the price of beef. The consumption of beef, C (in pounds per week per household) is a function of household income, I (in thousands of dollars per year), and the price of beef, p (in dollars per pound). In function notation, we write:

$$C = f(I, p).$$

Table 11.1 contains values of this function. Values of p are shown across the top, values of I are down the left side, and corresponding values of $f(I,p)$ are given in the table.[1] For example, to find the value of $f(40, 3.50)$, we look in the row corresponding to $I = 40$ under $p = 3.50$, where we find the number 4.05. Thus,

$$f(40, 3.50) = 4.05.$$

This means that, on average, if a household's income is $40,000 a year and the price of beef is $3.50/lb, the family will buy 4.05 lbs of beef per week.

TABLE 11.1 *Quantity of beef bought (pounds/household/week)*

		Price of beef, p ($/lb)			
		3.00	3.50	4.00	4.50
Household income per year, I ($1000)	20	2.65	2.59	2.51	2.43
	40	4.14	4.05	3.94	3.88
	60	5.11	5.00	4.97	4.84
	80	5.35	5.29	5.19	5.07
	100	5.79	5.77	5.60	5.53

Notice how this differs from the table of values of a one-variable function, where one row or one column is enough to list the values of the function. Here many rows and columns are needed because the function has a value for every *pair* of values of the independent variables.

[1] Adapted from Richard G. Lipsey, *An Introduction to Positive Economics 3rd Ed.*, Weidenfeld and Nicolson, London, 1971

Algebraic Examples: Formulas

In both the weather map and beef consumption examples, there is no formula for the underlying function. That is usually the case for functions representing real-life data. On the other hand, for many idealized models in physics, engineering, or economics, there are exact formulas.

Example 2   Give a formula for the function $M = f(B, t)$ where M is the amount of money in a bank account t years after an initial investment of B dollars, if interest is accrued at a rate of 5% per year compounded (a) annually   (b) continuously.

Solution   (a) Annual compounding means that M increases by a factor of 1.05 every year, so

$$M = f(B, t) = B(1.05)^t.$$

(b) Continuous compounding means that M grows according to the exponential function e^{kt}, with $k = 0.05$, so

$$M = f(B, t) = Be^{0.05t}.$$

Example 3   A cylinder with closed ends has a radius r and a height h. If its volume is V and its surface area is A, find formulas for the functions $V = f(r, h)$ and $A = g(r, h)$.

Solution   Since the area of the circular base is πr^2, we have

$$V = f(r, h) = \text{Area of base} \cdot \text{Height} = \pi r^2 h.$$

The surface area of the side is the circumference of the bottom, $2\pi r$, times the height h, giving $2\pi rh$. Thus,

$$A = g(r, h) = 2 \cdot \text{Area of base} + \text{Area of side} = 2\pi r^2 + 2\pi rh.$$

Strategy to Investigate Functions of Two Variables: Vary One Variable at a Time

We can learn a great deal about functions of two or more variables by letting one variable vary at a time while holding the others fixed, thus obtaining a function of one variable.

The Wave

Suppose you are in a stadium where the audience is doing the wave. This is a ritual in which members of the audience stand up and sit down in such a way as to create a wave that moves around the stadium. Normally a single wave travels all the way around the stadium, but we assume there is a continuous sequence of waves. What sort of function will describe the motion of the audience? To keep things simple, we consider just one row of spectators. We consider the function which describes the motion of each individual in the row. This is a function of two variables: x (the seat number) and t (the time in seconds). For each value of x and t, we write $h(x, t)$ for the height (in feet) above the ground of the head of the spectator in seat number x at time t seconds. Suppose we are told that

$$h(x, t) = 5 + \cos(0.5x - t).$$

Example 4   (a) Explain the significance of $h(x, 5)$ in terms of the wave. Find the period of $h(x, 5)$. What does this period represent?

(b) Explain the significance of $h(2, t)$ in terms of the wave. Find the period of $h(2, t)$. What does this period represent?

Solution (a) Fixing $t = 5$ means we are taking a particular moment in time; letting x vary means we are looking along the whole row at that instant. Thus, the function $h(x,5) = 5 + \cos(0.5x - 5)$ gives the heights along the row at the instant $t = 5$. Figure 11.2 shows the graph of $h(x,5)$ which is a snapshot of the row at $t = 5$. The heights form a wave of period 4π, or about 12.6 seats. This period tells us that the length of the wave is about 13 seats.

(b) Fixing $x = 2$ means we are concentrating on the spectator in seat number 2; letting t vary means we are watching the motion of that spectator as time passes. Thus, the function $h(2,t)$ describes the motion of the spectator in seat 2 as a function of time. Figure 11.3 shows the graph of $h(2,t) = 5 + \cos(1 - t)$. Notice that the value of h varies between 4 feet and 6 feet as the spectator sits down and stands up. The period is 2π, or about 6.3 seconds. This period represents the time it takes for the spectator to stand up and sit down once.

Figure 11.2: The function $h(x,5)$ shows the shape of the wave at time $t = 5$

Figure 11.3: The function $h(2,t)$ shows the motion of the spectator in seat number 2

In general, the one-variable function $h(a,t)$ gives the motion of the spectator in seat a. Figure 11.3 shows the motion of the person in seat number 2. If we pick someone in another seat, we get a similar function, except that the graph may be shifted to the right or to the left.

Example 5 Show that the graph of $h(7,t)$ has the same shape as the graph of $h(2,t)$.

Solution The motion of the person in seat 7 is described by

$$h(7,t) = 5 + \cos(0.5(7) - t) = 5 + \cos(3.5 - t).$$

Since $h(2,t) = 5 + \cos(1 - t)$, we can rewrite $h(7,t)$ as

$$h(7,t) = 5 + \cos(1 + 2.5 - t) = 5 + \cos(1 - (t - 2.5)) = h(2, t - 2.5).$$

We see that $h(7,t)$ is the same function as $h(2,t)$, except that the t has been replaced by $t - 2.5$. Thus, the graph of $h(7,t)$ is the graph of $h(2,t)$ shifted 2.5 seconds to the right, which means 2.5 seconds later. This means the spectator in seat 7 stands up 2.5 seconds later than the person in seat 2. (See Figure 11.4.) This lag is what makes the wave travel around the stadium. If all the spectators stood up and sat down at the same time, there would be no wave.

Figure 11.4: Comparison of the motion of spectators in seats 2 and 7

Figure 11.5: The shape of the wave at $t = 5$ and $t = 6$

Example 6   Use the result of Example 5 to find the speed of the wave.

Solution   Since the spectator in seat 7 does the same thing as the spectator in seat 2 but 2.5 seconds later, the wave has moved 5 seats in 2.5 seconds. Thus, the speed is $5/2.5 = 2$ seats per second.

Example 7   Use the functions $h(x, 5)$ and $h(x, 6)$ to show that the speed of the wave is 2 seats per second.

Solution   Figure 11.5 shows graphs of $h(x, 5) = 5 + \cos(0.5x - 5)$ and $h(x, 6) = 5 + \cos(0.5x - 6)$, that is, snapshots of the wave at $t = 5$ and $t = 6$. The shape of the wave at $t = 6$ is the same as the shape at $t = 5$, only shifted to the right by about two seats. Thus, the wave is moving at a rate of about 2 seats per second. To confirm that the speed is exactly 2 seats per second, we must use algebra. When $t = 5$, the equation of the wave is

$$h(x, 5) = 5 + \cos(0.5x - 5),$$

which has a peak where

$$0.5x - 5 = 0,$$

so, at

$$x = 10,$$

that is, in the 10th seat. One second later, at $t = 6$, the equation of the wave is

$$h = 5 + \cos(0.5x - 6),$$

which has a peak where

$$0.5x - 6 = 0,$$

so, at

$$x = 12,$$

that is, in the 12th seat. Thus, the wave moved 2 seats in one second.

The Beef Data

For a function given by a table of values, such as the beef consumption data, we allow one variable to vary at a time by looking at one row or one column. For example, to fix the income at 40, we look at the row $I = 40$. This row gives values of the function $f(40, p)$. Since I is fixed, we now have a function of one variable that shows how much beef is bought at various prices by people who earn $40,000 a year. Table 11.2 shows that $f(40, p)$ decreases as p increases. The other rows tell the same story; for each income, I, the consumption of beef goes down as the price, p, increases.

TABLE 11.2   *Beef consumption by households making $40,000*

p	3.00	3.50	4.00	4.50
$f(40, p)$	4.14	4.05	3.94	3.88

Weather Map

What happens on the weather map in Figure 11.1 when we allow only one variable at a time to vary? Suppose x represents miles west-east of Topeka and y represents miles north-south, and suppose we move along the west-east line through Topeka. We keep y fixed at 0 and let x vary. Along this line, the high temperature T goes from the 60s along the west coast, to the 70s in Nevada and Utah, to the 80s in Topeka, to the 90s just before the east coast, then returns to the 80s. A possible graph is shown in Figure 11.6. Other graphs are possible because we don't know for sure how the temperature varies between contours.

Figure 11.6: Predicted high temperature on an east-west line through Topeka

Problems for Section 11.1

Problems 1–3 refer to the weather map in Figure 11.1 on page 2.

1. Give the range of daily high temperatures for
   (a) Pennsylvania   (b) North Dakota   (c) California.

2. Sketch the graph of the predicted high temperature T on a line north-south through Topeka.

3. Sketch the graphs of the predicted high temperature on a north-south line and an east-west line through Boise.

For Problems 4–8 refer to Table 11.1 on page 3, where p is the price of beef and I is annual household income.

4. Make a table showing the amount of money, M, that the average household spends on beef (in dollars per household per week) as a function of the price of beef and household income.

5. Give tables for beef consumption as a function of p, with I fixed at $I = 20$ and $I = 100$. Give tables for beef consumption as a function of I, with p fixed at $p = 3.00$ and $p = 4.00$. Comment on what you see in the tables.

6. How does beef consumption vary as a function of household income if the price of beef is held constant?

7. Make a table of the proportion, P, of household income spent on beef per week as a function of price and income. (Note that P is the fraction of income spent on beef.)

8. Express P, the proportion of household income spent on beef per week, in terms of the original function $f(I, p)$ which gave consumption as a function of p and I.

9. Sketch the graph of the bank account function f in Example 2(a) on page 4, holding B fixed at three different values and letting only t vary. Then sketch the graph of f, holding t fixed at three different values and letting only B vary. Explain what you see.

10. You are planning a long driving trip and your principal cost will be gasoline.
    (a) Make a table showing how the daily fuel cost varies as a function of the price of gasoline (in dollars per gallon) and the number of gallons you buy each day.
    (b) If your car goes 30 miles on each gallon of gasoline, make a table showing how your daily fuel cost varies as a function of your daily travel distance and the price of gas.

11. Consider the acceleration due to gravity, g, at a height h above the surface of a planet of mass m.
    (a) If m is held constant, is g an increasing or decreasing function of h? Why?
    (b) If h is held constant, is g an increasing or decreasing function of m? Why?

12. The *temperature adjusted for wind-chill* is a temperature which tells you how cold it feels, as a result of the combination of wind and temperature. Table 11.3 shows the temperature adjusted for wind-chill as a function of wind speed and temperature.

TABLE 11.3   *Temperature adjusted for wind-chill (°F)*

Wind Speed (mph)	Temperature (°F)							
	35	30	25	20	15	10	5	0
5	33	27	21	16	12	7	0	−5
10	22	16	10	3	−3	−9	−15	−22
15	16	9	2	−5	−11	−18	−25	−31
20	12	4	−3	−10	−17	−24	−31	−39
25	8	1	−7	−15	−22	−29	−36	−44

(a) If the temperature is 0°F and the wind speed is 15 mph, how cold does it feel?
(b) If the temperature is 35°F, what wind speed makes it feel like 22°F?
(c) If the temperature is 25°F, what wind speed makes it feel like 20°F?
(d) If the wind is blowing at 15 mph, what temperature feels like 0°F?

13. Using Table 11.3, make tables of the temperature adjusted for wind-chill as a function of wind speed for temperatures of 20°F and 0°F.

14. Using Table 11.3, make tables of the temperature adjusted for wind-chill as a function of temperature for wind speeds of 5 mph and 20 mph.

15. Suppose the function for the stadium wave on page 4 was given by $h(x,t) = 5 + \cos(x - 2t)$. How does this wave compare with the original wave? What is the speed of this wave (in seats per second)?

16. Suppose the stadium wave on page 4 was moving in the opposite direction, right-to-left instead of left-to-right. Give a possible formula for h.

Problems 17–20 concern a vibrating guitar string. Suppose you pluck a guitar string and watch it vibrate. Snapshots of the guitar string at millisecond intervals are shown in Figure 11.7.

Figure 11.7: A vibrating guitar string:
$f(x,t) = \cos t \sin x$ for four t values.

Think of the guitar string stretched tight along the x-axis from $x = 0$ to $x = \pi$. Each point on the string has an x-value, $0 \le x \le \pi$. As the string vibrates, each point on the string moves back and forth on either side of the x-axis. Let $y = f(x, t)$ be the displacement at time t of the point on the string located x units from the left end. Then a possible formula for $y = f(x, t)$ is

$$y = f(x, t) = \cos t \sin x, \quad 0 \leq x \leq \pi, \quad t \text{ in milliseconds.}$$

17. (a) Sketch graphs of y versus x for fixed t values, $t = 0, \pi/4, \pi/2, 3\pi/4, \pi$.
    (b) Use your graphs to explain why this function could represent a vibrating guitar string.

18. Explain what the functions $f(x, 0)$ and $f(x, 1)$ represent in terms of the vibrating string.

19. Explain what the functions $f(0, t)$ and $f(1, t)$ represent in terms of the vibrating string.

20. Describe the motion of the guitar strings whose displacements are given by the following:
    (a) $y = g(x, t) = \cos 2t \sin x$ (b) $y = h(x, t) = \cos t \sin 2x$

11.2 A TOUR OF THREE-DIMENSIONAL SPACE

Cartesian Coordinates in Three-Space

Imagine three coordinate axes meeting at the *origin*: a vertical axis, and two horizontal axes at right angles to each other. (See Figure 11.8.) Think of the xy-plane as being horizontal, while the z-axis extends vertically above and below the plane. The labels x, y, and z show which part of each axis is positive; the other side is negative. We generally use *right-handed axes* in which looking down the positive z-axis gives the usual view of the xy-plane. We specify a point in 3-space by giving its coordinates (x, y, z) with respect to these axes. Think of the coordinates as instructions telling you how to get to the point; start at the origin, go x units along the x-axis, then y units in the direction parallel to the y-axis and finally z units in the direction parallel to the z-axis. The coordinates can be positive, zero or negative; a zero coordinate means "don't move in this direction," and a negative coordinate means "go in the negative direction parallel to this axis." For example, the origin has coordinates $(0, 0, 0)$, since we get there from the origin by doing nothing at all.

Figure 11.8: Coordinate axes in three-dimensional space

Figure 11.9: The point $(1, 2, 3)$ in 3-space

Figure 11.10: The point $(0, 0, -1)$ in 3-space

Example 1   Describe the position of the points with coordinates $(1, 2, 3)$ and $(0, 0, -1)$.

Solution   We get to the point $(1, 2, 3)$ by starting at the origin, going 1 unit along the x-axis, 2 units in the direction parallel to the y-axis, and 3 units up in the direction parallel to the z-axis. (See Figure 11.9.)
To get to $(0, 0, -1)$, we don't move at all in the x and y directions, but move 1 unit in the negative z direction. So the point is on the negative z-axis. (See Figure 11.10.) You can check that the position of the point is independent of the order of the x, y, and z displacements.

Example 2   You start at the origin, go along the y-axis a distance of 2 units in the positive direction, and then move vertically upward a distance of 1 unit. What are the coordinates of your final position?

Solution   You started at the point $(0, 0, 0)$. When you went along the y-axis, your y-coordinate increased to 2. Moving vertically increased your z-coordinate to 1; your x-coordinate didn't change because you did not move in the x direction. So your final coordinates are $(0, 2, 1)$. (See Figure 11.11.)

Figure 11.11: The point $(0, 2, 1)$ is reached by moving 2 along the y-axis and 1 upward

It is often helpful to picture a three dimensional coordinate system in terms of a room. The origin is a corner at floor level where two walls meet the floor. The z-axis is the vertical intersection of the two walls; the x- and y-axes are the intersections of each wall with the floor. Points with negative coordinates lie behind a wall in the next room or below the floor.

Graphing Equations in Three-Dimensional Space

We can graph equations involving the variables x, y, and z in three-dimensional space.

Example 3   What do the graphs of the equations $z = 0$, $z = 3$, and $z = -1$ look like?

Solution   Graphing an equation means drawing the set of all points in space whose coordinates satisfy the equation. So to graph $z = 0$ we need to visualize the set of points whose z-coordinate is zero. If the z-coordinate is 0, then we must be at the same vertical level as the origin, that is, we are in the horizontal plane containing the origin. So the graph of $z = 0$ is the middle plane in Figure 11.12. The graph of $z = 3$ is a plane parallel to the graph of $z = 0$, but three units above it. The graph of $z = -1$ is a plane parallel to the graph of $z = 0$, but one unit below it.

Figure 11.12: The planes $z = -1$, $z = 0$, and $z = 3$

The plane $z = 0$ contains the x- and y-coordinate axes, and hence is called the xy-coordinate plane, or xy-plane for short. There are two other coordinate planes. The yz-plane contains both the y- and the z-axes, and the xz-plane contains the x- and z-axes. (See Figure 11.13.)

xy-plane   xz-plane   yz-plane

Figure 11.13: The three coordinate planes

Example 4   Which of the points $A = (1, -1, 0)$, $B = (0, 3, 4)$, $C = (2, 2, 1)$, and $D = (0, -4, 0)$ lies closest to the xz-plane? Which point lies on the y-axis?

Solution   The magnitude of the y-coordinate gives the distance to the xz-plane. The point A lies closest to that plane, because it has the smallest y-coordinate in magnitude. To get to a point on the y-axis, we move along the y-axis, but we don't move at all in the x or z directions. Thus, a point on the y-axis has both its x- and z-coordinates equal to zero. The only point of the four that satisfies this is D. (See Figure 11.14.)

In general, if a point has one of its coordinates equal to zero, it lies in one of the coordinate planes. If a point has two of its coordinates equal to zero, it lies on one of the coordinate axes.

Figure 11.14: Which point lies closest to the xz-plane? Which point lies on the y-axis?

Figure 11.15: The line $x = 0$, $z = -2$

Example 5   You are 2 units below the xy-plane and in the yz-plane. What are your coordinates?

Solution   Since you are 2 units below the xy-plane, your z-coordinate is -2. Since you are in the yz-plane, your x-coordinate is 0; your y-coordinate can be anything. Thus, you are at the point $(0, y, -2)$. The set of all such points forms a line parallel to the y-axis, 2 units below the xy-plane, and in the yz-plane. (See Figure 11.15.)

Example 6   You are standing at the point $(4, 5, 2)$, looking at the point $(0.5, 0, 3)$. Are you looking up or down?

Solution   The point you are standing at has z-coordinate 2, whereas the point you are looking at has z-coordinate 3; hence you are looking up.

Example 7   Imagine that the yz-plane in Figure 11.15 is a page of this book. Describe the region behind the page.

Solution   The positive part of the x-axis pokes out of the page; moving in the positive x direction brings you out in front of the page. The region behind the page corresponds to negative values of x, and so it is the set of all points in three-dimensional space satisfying the inequality $x < 0$.

Distance

In 2-space, the formula for the distance between two points (x, y) and (a, b) is given by

$$\text{Distance} = \sqrt{(x-a)^2 + (y-b)^2}.$$

The distance between two points (x, y, z) and (a, b, c) in 3-space is represented by PG in Figure 11.16. The side PE is parallel to the x-axis, EF is parallel to the y-axis, and FG is parallel to the z-axis.

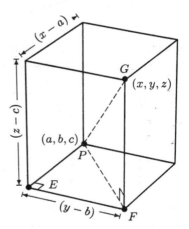

Figure 11.16: The diagonal PG gives the distance between the points (x, y, z) and (a, b, c)

Using Pythagoras' theorem twice gives

$$(PG)^2 = (PF)^2 + (FG)^2 = (PE)^2 + (EF)^2 + (FG)^2 = (x-a)^2 + (y-b)^2 + (z-c)^2.$$

Thus, a formula for the distance between the points (x, y, z) and (a, b, c) in 3-space is

$$\text{Distance} = \sqrt{(x-a)^2 + (y-b)^2 + (z-c)^2}.$$

$= \sqrt{(-3-1)^2 + (}$
$= \sqrt{18}$

14

Example 8 Find the distance between $(1, 2, 1)$ and $(-3, 1, 2)$.

Solution The formula gives
$$\text{Distance} = \sqrt{(-3-1)^2 + (1-2)^2 + (2-1)^2} = \sqrt{18} = 4.24.$$

Example 9 Find an expression for the distance from the origin to the point (x, y, z).

Solution The origin has coordinates $(0, 0, 0)$, so the distance from the origin to (x, y, z) is given by
$$\text{Distance} = \sqrt{(x-0)^2 + (y-0)^2 + (z-0)^2} = \sqrt{x^2 + y^2 + z^2}.$$

$0,0,0$
$\sqrt{x^2 + y^2 + z^2} = 1$

Example 10 Find the equation for a sphere of radius 1 with center at the origin.

Solution The sphere consists of all points (x, y, z) whose distance from the origin is 1, that is, which satisfy the equation
$$\sqrt{x^2 + y^2 + z^2} = 1.$$

This is an equation for the sphere. If we square both sides we get the equation in the form
$$x^2 + y^2 + z^2 = 1.$$

Note that this equation represents the *surface* of the sphere. The solid ball enclosed by the sphere is represented by the inequality $x^2 + y^2 + z^2 \le 1$.

Problems for Section 11.2

1. Which of the points $A = (1.3, -2.7, 0)$, $B = (0.9, 0, 3.2)$, $C = (2.5, 0.1, -0.3)$ is closest to the yz-plane? Which one lies on the xz-plane? Which one is farthest from the xy-plane?

2. Which of the points $A = (23, 92, 48)$, $B = (-60, 0, 0)$, $C = (60, 1, -92)$ is closest to the yz-plane? Which one lies on the xz-plane? Which one is farthest from the xy-plane?

3. You are at the point $(-1, -3, -3)$, standing upright and facing the yz-plane. You walk 2 units forward, turn left, and walk for another 2 units. What is your final position? From the point of view of an observer looking at the coordinate system in Figure 11.8 on page 9, are you in front of or behind the yz-plane? Are you to the left or to the right of the xz-plane? Are you above or below the xy-plane?

4. You are at the point $(3, 1, 1)$ facing the yz-plane. Assume you are standing upright. You walk 2 units forward, turn left, and walk for another 2 units. What is your final position? From the point of view of an observer looking at the coordinate system in Figure 11.8 on page 9, are you in front of or behind the yz-plane? Are you to the left of or to the right of the xz-plane? Are you above or below the xy-plane?

Sketch graphs of the equations in Problems 5–7 in 3-space.

5. $x = -3$

6. $y = 1$

7. $z = 2$ and $y = 4$

8. Find a formula for the shortest distance between a point (a, b, c) and the y-axis.

9. Describe the set of points whose distance from the x-axis is 2.

10. Describe the set of points whose distance from the x-axis equals the distance from the yz-plane.

$x = -3, z = 1$

11. Which of the points $P = (1, 2, 1)$ and $Q = (2, 0, 0)$ is closest to the origin?

12. Which two of the three points $P_1 = (1, 2, 3)$, $P_2 = (3, 2, 1)$ and $P_3 = (1, 1, 0)$ are closest to each other?

13. A cube is located such that its top four corners have the coordinates $(-1, -2, 2)$, $(-1, 3, 2)$, $(4, -2, 2)$ and $(4, 3, 2)$. Give the coordinates of the center of the cube.

14. A rectangular solid lies with its length parallel to the y-axis, and its top and bottom faces parallel to the plane $z = 0$. If the center of the object is at $(1, 1, -2)$ and it has a length of 13, a height of 5 and a width of 6, give the coordinates of all eight corners and draw the figure labeling the eight corners.

15. Which of the points $P_1 = (-3, 2, 15)$, $P_2 = (0, -10, 0)$, $P_3 = (-6, 5, 3)$ and $P_4 = (-4, 2, 7)$ is closest to $P = (6, 0, 4)$?

16. On a set of x, y, and z axes oriented as in Figure 11.8 on page 9, draw a straight line through the origin, lying in the xz-plane and such that if you move along the line with your x-coordinate increasing, your z-coordinate is decreasing.

17. On a set of x, y and z axes oriented as in Figure 11.8 on page 9, draw a straight line through the origin, lying in the yz-plane and such that if you move along the line with your y-coordinate increasing, your z-coordinate is increasing.

18. Find the equation of the sphere of radius 5 centered at the origin.

19. Find the equation of the sphere of radius 5 centered at $(1, 2, 3)$.

20. Given the sphere
$$(x - 1)^2 + (y + 3)^2 + (z - 2)^2 = 4,$$

    (a) Find the equations of the circles (if any) where the sphere intersects each coordinate plane.
    (b) Find the points (if any) where the sphere intersects each coordinate axis.

11.3 GRAPHS OF FUNCTIONS OF TWO VARIABLES

How do You Visualize a Function of Two Variables?

The weather map on page 2 is one way of visualizing a function of two variables. In this section we see how to visualize a function of two variables in another way, using a surface in 3-space.

The Graph of a Function and How to Plot One

For a function of one variable, $y = f(x)$, the graph of f is the set of all points (x, y) in 2-space such that $y = f(x)$. In general, these points lie on a curve in the plane. When a computer or calculator graphs f, it approximates by plotting points in the xy-plane and joining consecutive points by line segments. The more points, the better the approximation.

Now consider a function of two variables.

> The **graph** of a function of two variables, f, is the set of all points (x, y, z) such that $z = f(x, y)$. In general, the graph of a function of two variables is a surface in 3-space.

Plotting the Graph of the Function $f(x, y) = x^2 + y^2$

To sketch the graph of f we connect points as for a function of one variable. We first make a table of values of f, such as in Table 11.4.

TABLE 11.4 *Table of values of $f(x, y) = x^2 + y^2$*

		\multicolumn{7}{c}{y}
		-3	-2	-1	0	1	2	3
	-3	18	13	10	9	10	13	18
	-2	13	8	5	4	5	8	13
	-1	10	5	2	1	2	5	10
x	0	9	4	1	0	1	4	9
	1	10	5	2	1	2	5	10
	2	13	8	5	4	5	8	13
	3	18	13	10	9	10	13	18

Now we plot points. For example, we plot $(1, 2, 5)$ because $f(1, 2) = 5$ and we plot $(0, 2, 4)$ because $f(0, 2) = 4$. Then, we connect the points corresponding to the rows and columns in the table. The result is called a *wire-frame* picture of the graph. Filling in between the wires gives a surface. That is the way a computer drew the graphs in Figure 11.17 and 11.18. The more points that are plotted, the more the picture looks like the surface in Figure 11.19.

You should check to see if the sketches make sense. Notice that the graph goes through the origin since $(x, y, z) = (0, 0, 0)$ satisfies $z = x^2 + y^2$. Observe that if x is held fixed and y is allowed to vary, the graph dips down and then goes back up, just like the entries in the rows of Table 11.4. Similarly, if y is held fixed and x is allowed to vary, the graph dips down and then goes back up, just like the columns of Table 11.4.

Figure 11.17: Wire frame picture of $f(x, y) = x^2 + y^2$ for $-3 \le x \le 3$, $-3 \le y \le 3$

Figure 11.18: Wire frame picture of $f(x, y) = x^2 + y^2$ with more points plotted

Figure 11.19: Graph of $f(x, y) = x^2 + y^2$ for $-3 \le x \le 3$, $-3 \le y \le 3$

New Graphs from Old

We can use the graph of a function to visualize the graphs of related functions.

Example 1   Let $f(x, y) = x^2 + y^2$. Describe in words the graphs of the following functions:
(a) $g(x, y) = x^2 + y^2 + 3$,   (b) $h(x, y) = 5 - x^2 - y^2$,   (c) $k(x, y) = x^2 + (y - 1)^2$.

Solution We know from Figure 11.19 that the graph of f is a bowl with its vertex at the origin. From this we can work out what the graphs of g, h, and k will look like.

(a) The function $g(x, y) = x^2 + y^2 + 3 = f(x, y) + 3$, so the graph of g is the graph of f, but raised by 3 units. See Figure 11.20.

(b) Since $-x^2 - y^2$ is the negative of $x^2 + y^2$, the graph of $-x^2 - y^2$ is an upside down bowl. Thus, the graph of $h(x, y) = 5 - x^2 - y^2 = 5 - f(x, y)$ looks like an upside down bowl with vertex at $(0, 0, 5)$, as in Figure 11.21.

(c) The graph of $k(x, y) = x^2 + (y - 1)^2 = f(x, y - 1)$ is a bowl with vertex at $x = 0$, $y = 1$, since that is where $k(x, y) = 0$, as in Figure 11.22.

Figure 11.20: Graph of
$g(x, y) = x^2 + y^2 + 3$

Figure 11.21: Graph of
$h(x, y) = 5 - x^2 - y^2$

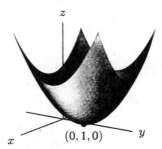

Figure 11.22: Graph of
$k(x, y) = x^2 + (y - 1)^2$

Example 2 Describe the graph of $G(x, y) = e^{-(x^2+y^2)}$. What symmetry does it have?

Solution Since the exponential function is always positive, the graph lies entirely above the xy-plane. From the graph of $x^2 + y^2$ we see that $x^2 + y^2$ is zero at the origin and gets larger as we move farther from the origin in any direction. Thus, $e^{-(x^2+y^2)}$ is 1 at the origin, and gets smaller as we move away from the origin in any direction. It can't go below the xy-plane; instead it flattens out, getting closer and closer to the plane. We say the surface is *asymptotic* to the xy-plane. (See Figure 11.23.)

Figure 11.23: Graph of
$G(x, y) = e^{-(x^2+y^2)}$

Now consider a point (x, y) on the circle $x^2 + y^2 = r^2$. Since

$$G(x, y) = e^{-(x^2+y^2)} = e^{-r^2},$$

the value of the function G is the same at all points on this circle. Thus, we say the graph of G has *circular symmetry*.

Chapter 12/ 16

Cross-Sections and the Graph of a Function

We have seen that a good way to analyze a function of two variables is to let one variable vary at a time while the other is kept fixed.

> For a function $f(x, y)$, the function we get by holding x fixed and letting y vary is called a **cross-section** of f with x fixed. The graph of the cross-section of $f(x, y)$ with $x = c$ is the curve, or cross-section, we get by intersecting the graph of f with the plane $x = c$. We define a cross-section of f with y fixed similarly.

For example, the cross-section of $f(x, y) = x^2 + y^2$ with $x = 2$ is $f(2, y) = 4 + y^2$. The graph of this cross-section is the curve we get by intersecting the graph of f with the plane perpendicular to the x-axis at $x = 2$. (See Figure 11.24.)

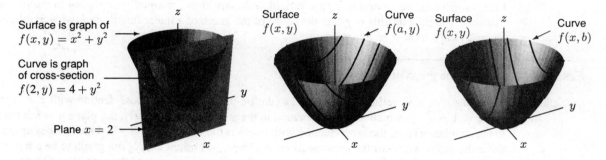

Surface is graph of $f(x, y) = x^2 + y^2$

Curve is graph of cross-section $f(2, y) = 4 + y^2$

Plane $x = 2$

Figure 11.24: Cross-section of the surface $z = f(x, y)$ by the plane $x = 2$

Figure 11.25: The curves $z = f(a, y)$ with a constant: cross-sections with x fixed

Figure 11.26: The curves $z = f(x, b)$ with b constant: cross-sections with y fixed

Figure 11.25 shows graphs of other cross-sections of f with x fixed; Figure 11.26 shows graphs of cross-sections with y fixed.

Example 3 Describe the cross-sections of the function $g(x, y) = x^2 - y^2$ with y fixed and then with x fixed. Use these cross-sections to describe the shape of the graph of g.

Solution The cross-sections with y fixed at $y = b$ are given by

$$z = g(x, b) = x^2 - b^2.$$

Thus, each cross-section with y fixed gives a parabola opening upwards, with minimum $z = -b^2$. The cross-sections with x fixed are of the form

$$z = g(a, y) = a^2 - y^2,$$

which are parabolas opening downwards with a maximum of $z = a^2$. (See Figures 11.27 and 11.28) The graph of g is shown in Figure 11.29. Notice the upward opening parabolas in the x-direction and the downward opening parabolas in the y-direction. We say that the surface is *saddle-shaped*.

Figure 11.27: Cross-sections of $g(x, y) = x^2 - y^2$ with y fixed

Figure 11.28: Cross-sections of $g(x, y) = x^2 - y^2$ with x fixed

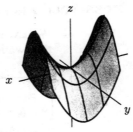

Figure 11.29: Graph of $g(x, y) = x^2 - y^2$ showing cross sections

Linear Functions

Linear functions are central to single variable calculus; they are equally important in multivariable calculus. You may be able to guess the shape of the graph of a linear function of two variables. (It's a plane.) Let's look at an example.

Example 4 Describe the graph of $f(x, y) = 1 + x - y$.

Solution The plane $x = a$ is vertical and parallel to the yz-plane. Thus, the cross-section with $x = a$ is the line $z = 1 + a - y$ which slopes downward in the y-direction. Similarly, the plane $y = b$ is parallel to the xz-plane. Thus, the cross-section with $y = b$ is the line $z = 1 + x - b$ which slopes upward in the x-direction. Since all the cross-sections are lines, you might expect the graph to be a flat plane, sloping down in the y-direction and up in the x-direction. This is indeed the case. (See Figure 11.30.)

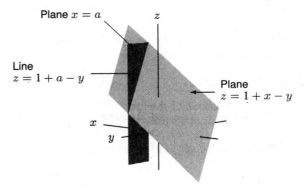

Figure 11.30: Graph of the plane $z = 1 + x - y$ showing cross-section with $x = a$

When One Variable is Missing: Cylinders

Suppose we graph an equation like $z = x^2$ which has one variable missing. What does the surface look like? Since y is missing from the equation, the cross-sections with y fixed are all the same parabola, $z = x^2$. Letting y vary up and down the y-axis, this parabola sweeps out the trough-shaped surface shown in Figure 11.31. The cross-sections with x fixed are horizontal lines, obtained by cutting the surface by a plane perpendicular to the x-axis.

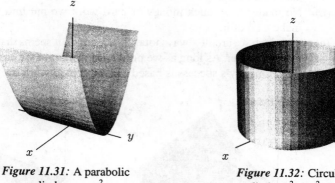

Figure 11.31: A parabolic
cylinder $z = x^2$

Figure 11.32: Circular
cylinder $x^2 + y^2 = 1$

This surface is called a *parabolic cylinder*, because it is formed from a parabola in the same way that an ordinary cylinder is formed from a circle; it has a parabolic cross-section instead of a circular one.

Example 5   Graph the equation $x^2 + y^2 = 1$ in 3-space.

Solution   Although the equation $x^2 + y^2 = 1$ does not represent a function, the surface representing it can be graphed by the method used for $z = x^2$. The graph of $x^2 + y^2 = 1$ in the xy-plane is a circle. Since z does not appear in the equation, the intersection of the surface with any horizontal plane will be the same circle $x^2 + y^2 = 1$. Thus, the surface is the cylinder shown in Figure 11.32.

Problems for Section 11.3

1. The surface in Figure 11.33 is the graph of the function $z = f(x, y)$ for positive x and y.

    (a) Suppose y is fixed and positive. Does z increase or decrease as x increases? Sketch a graph of z against x.

    (b) Suppose x is fixed and positive. Does z increase or decrease as y increases? Sketch a graph of z against y.

Figure 11.33

2. Match the following descriptions of a company's success with the graphs in Figure 11.34.
   (a) Our success is measured in dollars, plain and simple. More hard work won't hurt, but it also won't help. *II*
   (b) No matter how much money or hard work we put into the company, we just couldn't make a go of it. *I*
   (c) Although we aren't always totally successful, it seems that the amount of money invested doesn't matter. As long as we put hard work into the company our success will increase. *I*
   (d) The company's success is based on both hard work and investment. *IV*

 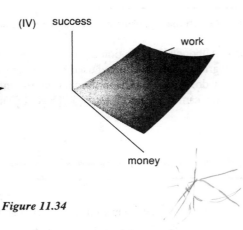

Figure 11.34

3. For each of the following functions, decide whether it could be a bowl, a plate, or neither. Consider a plate to be any fairly flat surface and a bowl to be anything that could hold water, assuming the positive z-axis is up.
   (a) $z = x^2 + y^2$ *bowl*   (b) $z = 1 - x^2 - y^2$ *neither bowl*   (c) $x + y + z = 1$ *a plate*
   (d) $z = -\sqrt{5 - x^2 - y^2}$ *bowl*   (e) $z = 3$ *a plate*

4. For each function in Problem 3 sketch cross-sections:
   (i) With x fixed at $x = 0$ and $x = 1$.
   (ii) With y fixed at $y = 0$ and $y = 1$.

5. Match the following functions with their graphs in Figure 11.35.
   (a) $z = \dfrac{1}{x^2 + y^2}$ (b) $z = -e^{-x^2-y^2}$ (c) $z = x + 2y + 3$ *IV*
   (d) $z = -y^2$ *II*   (e) $z = x^3 - \sin y$ *III*

(I) (II) (III)

(IV) (V)

Figure 11.35

6. You like pizza and you like cola. Which of the graphs in Figure 11.36 represents your happiness as a function of how many pizzas and how much cola you have if

    (a) There is no such thing as too many pizzas and too much cola?
    (b) There is such a thing as too many pizzas or too much cola?
    (c) There is such a thing as too much cola but no such thing as too many pizzas?

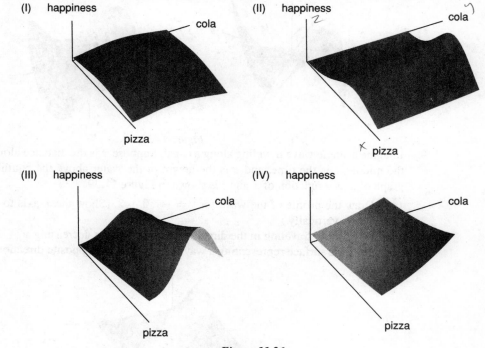

(I) happiness   (II) happiness

(III) happiness   (IV) happiness

Figure 11.36

7. For each of the graphs I-IV in Problem 6 draw:

    (a) Two cross-sections with pizza fixed   (b) Two cross-sections with cola fixed.

8. Figure 11.37 contains graphs of the parabolas $z = f(x, b)$ for $b = -2, -1, 0, 1, 2$. Which of the graphs of $z = f(x, y)$ in Figure 11.38 best fits this information?

Figure 11.37

(I)
(II)

(III)
(IV)

Figure 11.38

9. Imagine a single wave traveling along a canal. Suppose x is the distance along the canal from the middle, t is the time, and z is the height of the water above the equilibrium level. The graph of z as a function of x and t is shown in Figure 11.39.

   (a) Draw the profile of the wave for $t = -1, 0, 1, 2$. (Show the x-axis to the right and the z-axis vertically.)
   (b) Is the wave traveling in the direction of increasing or decreasing x?
   (c) Sketch a surface representing a wave traveling in the opposite direction.

Figure 11.39

10. Describe in words the cross-sections with t fixed and the cross-sections with x fixed of the vibrating guitar string function

$$f(x,t) = \cos t \sin x, \quad 0 \le x \le \pi, \quad 0 \le t \le 2\pi$$

on page 8. Explain the relation of these cross-sections to the graph of f.

11. Use a computer or calculator to draw the graph of the vibrating guitar string function:

$$g(x,t) = \cos t \sin 2x, \quad 0 \le x \le \pi, \quad 0 \le t \le 2\pi.$$

Relate the shape of the graph to the cross-sections with t fixed and those with x fixed.

12. Use a computer or a calculator to draw the graph of the traveling wave function:

$$h(x,t) = 3 + \cos(x - 0.5t), \quad 0 \le x \le 2\pi, \quad 0 \le t \le 2\pi.$$

Relate the shape of the graph to the cross-sections with t fixed and those with x fixed.

13. Consider the function f given by $f(x,y) = y^3 + xy$. Draw graphs of cross-sections with:
    (a) x fixed at $x = -1$, $x = 0$, and $x = 1$.   (b) y fixed at $y = -1$, $y = 0$, and $y = 1$.

14. A swinging pendulum consists of a mass at the end of a string. At one moment the string makes an angle x with the vertical and the mass has speed y. At that time, the energy, E, of the pendulum is given by the expression[2]

$$E = 1 - \cos x + \frac{y^2}{2}.$$

    (a) Consider the surface representing the energy. Sketch a cross-section of the surface:
    (i) Perpendicular to the x-axis at $x = c$.
    (ii) Perpendicular to the y-axis at $y = c$.
    (b) For each of the graphs in Figures 11.40 and 11.41 use your answer to part (a) to decide which is the x-axis and which is the y-axis and to put reasonable units on each one.

Figure 11.40   *Figure 11.41*

11.4 CONTOUR DIAGRAMS

The surface which represents a function of two variables often gives a good idea of the function's general behavior—for example, whether it is increasing or decreasing as one of the variables increases. However it is difficult to read numerical values off a surface and it can be hard to see all of the function's behavior from a surface. Thus, functions of two variables are often represented by contour diagrams like the weather map on page 2. Contour diagrams have the additional advantage that they can be extended to functions of three variables.

[2]Adapted from *Calculus in Context*, by James Callahan, Kenneth Hoffman, (New York: W.H. Freeman, 1995)

Topographical Maps

One of the most common examples of a contour diagram is a topographical map like that shown in Figure 11.42. It gives the elevation in the region and is a good way of getting an overall picture of the terrain: where the mountains are, where the flat areas are. Such topographical maps are frequently colored green at the lower elevations and brown, red, or white at the higher elevations.

Figure 11.42: A topographical map showing the region around South Hamilton, NY

The curves on a topographical map that separate lower elevations from higher elevations are called *contour lines* because they outline the contour or shape of the land.[3] Because every point along the same contour has the same elevation, contour lines are also called *level curves* or *level sets*. The more closely spaced the contours, the steeper the terrain; the more widely spaced the contours, the flatter the terrain. (Provided, of course, that the elevation between contours varies by a constant amount.) Certain features have distinctive characteristics. A mountain peak is typically surrounded by contour lines like those in Figure 11.43. A pass in a range of mountains may have contours that look like Figure 11.44. A long valley has parallel contour lines indicating the rising elevations on both sides of the valley (see Figure 11.45); a long ridge of mountains has the same type of contour lines, only the elevations decrease on both sides of the ridge. Notice that the elevation numbers on the contour lines are as important as the curves themselves.

Figure 11.43: Mountain peak

Figure 11.44: Pass between two mountains

Figure 11.45: Long valley

Figure 11.46: Impossible contour lines

There are some things contour lines cannot do. Two contours corresponding to different elevations cannot cross each other as shown in Figure 11.46. If they did, the point of intersection of the two curves would have two different elevations, which is impossible (assuming the terrain has no overhangs). We will often follow the convention of drawing contours for equally spaced values of z.

---

[3]In fact they are usually not straight lines, but curves. They may also be in disconnected pieces.

Corn Production

Contour maps can also be useful to display information about a function of two variables without reference to a surface. Consider how to represent the effect of different weather conditions on US corn production. What would happen if the average temperature were to increase (due to global warming, for example)? What would happen if the rainfall were to decrease (due to a drought)? One way of estimating the effect of these climatic changes is to use Figure 11.47. This is a contour diagram giving the corn production $f(R, T)$ in the United States as a function of the total rainfall, R, in inches, and average temperature, T, in degrees Fahrenheit, during the growing season.[4] Suppose at the present time, $R = 15$ inches and $T = 76°$F. Production is measured as a percentage of the present production; thus, the contour through $R = 15, T = 76$ has value 100, that is, $f(15, 76) = 100$.

Example 1   Use Figure 11.47 to estimate $f(18, 78)$ and $f(12, 76)$ and explain the answer in terms of corn production.

Figure 11.47: Corn production as a function of rainfall and temperature

Solution   The point with R-coordinate 18 and T-coordinate 78 is on the contour $C = 100$, so $f(18, 78) = 100$. This means that if the annual rainfall were 18 inches and the temperature were 78°F, the country would produce about the same amount of corn as at present, although it would be wetter and warmer than it is now.

The point with R-coordinate 12 and T-coordinate 76 is about halfway between the $C = 80$ and the $C = 90$ contours, so $f(12, 76) \approx 85$. This means that if the rainfall fell to 12 inches and the temperature stayed at 76°, then corn production would drop to about 85% of what it is now.

Example 2   Describe in words the cross-sections with T and R constant through the point representing present conditions. Give a common sense explanation of your answer.

Solution   To see what happens to corn production if the temperature stays fixed at 76°F but the rainfall changes, look along the horizontal line $T = 76$. Starting from the present and moving left along the line $T = 76$, the values on the contours decrease. In other words, if there is a drought, corn production decreases. Conversely, as rainfall increases, that is, as we move from the present to the right along the line $T = 76$, corn production increases, reaching a maximum of more than 110% when $R = 21$, and then decreases (too much rainfall floods the fields).

[4] Adapted from S. Beaty and R. Healy, *The Future of American Agriculture*, Scientific American, Vol. 248, No.2, February, 1983

If, instead, rainfall remains at the present value and temperature increases, we move up the vertical line $R = 15$. Under these circumstances corn production decreases; a $2°$ increase causes a 10% drop in production. This makes sense since hotter temperatures lead to greater evaporation and hence drier conditions, even with rainfall constant at 15 inches. Similarly, a decrease in temperature leads to a very slight increase in production, reaching a maximum of around 102% when $T = 74$, followed by a decrease (the corn won't grow if it is too cold).

Contour Diagrams and Graphs

Contour diagrams and graphs are two different ways of representing a function of two variables. How do we go from one to the other? In the case of the topographical map, the contour diagram was created by joining all the points at the same height on the surface and dropping the curve into the xy-plane.

How do we go the other way? Suppose we wanted to plot the surface representing the corn production function $C = f(R, T)$ given by the contour diagram in Figure 11.47. Along each contour the function has a constant value; if we take each contour and lift it above the plane to a height equal to this value, we get the surface in Figure 11.48.

Figure 11.48: Getting the graph of the corn yield function from the contour diagram

Notice that the raised contours are the curves we get by slicing the surface horizontally. In general, we have the following result:

> Contour lines, or level curves, are obtained from a surface by slicing it with horizontal planes.

Finding Contours Algebraically

Algebraic equations for the contours of a function f are easy to find if we have a formula for $f(x, y)$. Suppose the surface has equation

$$z = f(x, y).$$

A contour is obtained by slicing the surface with a horizontal plane with equation $z = c$. Thus, the equation for the contour at height c is given by:

$$f(x, y) = c.$$

Example 3   Find equations for the contours of $f(x, y) = x^2 + y^2$ and draw a contour diagram for f. Relate the contour diagram to the graph of f.

Solution   The contour at height c is given by

$$f(x,y) = x^2 + y^2 = c.$$

This is a contour only for $c \geq 0$, For $c > 0$ it is a circle of radius $\sqrt{c}$. For $c = 0$, it is a single point (the origin). Thus, the contours at an elevation of $c = 1, 2, 3, 4, \ldots$ are all circles centered at the origin of radius $1, \sqrt{2}, \sqrt{3}, 2, \ldots$. The contour diagram is shown in Figure 11.49. The bowl–shaped graph of f is shown in Figure 11.50. Notice that the graph of f gets steeper as we move further away from the origin. This is reflected in the fact that the contours become more closely packed as we move further from the origin; for example, the contours for $c = 6$ and $c = 8$ are closer together than the contours for $c = 2$ and $c = 4$.

Figure 11.49: Contour diagram for
$f(x,y) = x^2 + y^2$ (even values of c only)

Figure 11.50: The graph of $f(x,y) = x^2 + y^2$

Example 4   Draw a contour diagram for $f(x,y) = \sqrt{x^2 + y^2}$ and relate it to the graph of f.

Solution   The contour at level c is given by

$$f(x,y) = \sqrt{x^2 + y^2} = c$$

For $c > 0$ this is a circle, just as in the previous example, but here the radius is c instead of $\sqrt{c}$. For $c = 0$, it is the origin. Thus, if the level c increases by 1, the radius of the contour increases by 1. This means the contours are equally spaced concentric circles (see Figure 11.51) which do not become more closely packed further from the origin. Thus, the graph of f has the same constant slope as we move away from the origin (see Figure 11.52), making it a cone rather than a bowl.

Figure 11.51: A contour diagram for
$f(x,y) = \sqrt{x^2 + y^2}$

Figure 11.52: The graph of
$f(x,y) = \sqrt{x^2 + y^2}$

In both of the previous examples the level curves are concentric circles because the surfaces have circular symmetry. Any function of two variables which depends only on the quantity $(x^2 + y^2)$ has such symmetry: for example, $G(x, y) = e^{-(x^2+y^2)}$ or $H(x, y) = \sin(\sqrt{x^2 + y^2})$.

Example 5   Draw a contour diagram for $f(x, y) = 2x + 3y + 1$.

Solution   The contour at level c has equation $2x + 3y + 1 = c$. Rewriting this as $y = -(2/3)x + (c - 1)/3$, we see that the contours are parallel lines with slope $-2/3$. The y-intercept for the contour at level c is $(c - 1)/3$; each time c increases by 3, the y-intercept moves up by 1. The contour diagram is shown in Figure 11.53.

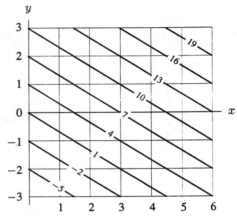

Figure 11.53: A contour diagram for
$f(x, y) = 2x + 3y + 1$

Contour Diagrams and Tables

Sometimes we can get an idea of what the contour diagram of a function looks like from its table.

Example 6   Relate the values of $f(x, y) = x^2 - y^2$ in Table 11.5 to its contour diagram in Figure 11.54.

TABLE 11.5   *Table of values of* $f(x, y) = x^2 - y^2$

	3	0	−5	−8	−9	−8	−5	0
	2	5	0	−3	−4	−3	0	5
	1	8	3	0	−1	0	3	8
y	0	9	4	1	0	1	4	9
	−1	8	3	0	−1	0	3	8
	−2	5	0	−3	−4	−3	0	5
	−3	0	−5	−8	−9	−8	−5	0
		−3	−2	−1	0	1	2	3
					x			

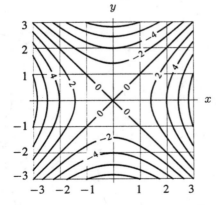

Figure 11.54: Contour map of $f(x, y) = x^2 - y^2$

Solution   One striking feature of the values in Table 11.5 is the zeros along the diagonals. This occurs because $x^2 - y^2 = 0$ along the lines $y = x$ and $y = -x$. So the $z = 0$ contour consists of these two lines. In the triangular region of the table that lies to the right of both diagonals, the entries are positive. To the left of both diagonals, the entries are also positive. Thus, in the contour diagram, the positive contours will lie in the triangular regions to the right and left of the lines $y = x$ and $y = -x$. Further, the table shows that the numbers on the left are the same as the numbers on the right; thus, each contour will have two pieces, one on the left and one on the right. See Figure 11.54. As we move away from the origin along the x-axis, we cross contours corresponding to successively larger values. On the saddle-shaped graph of $f(x, y) = x^2 - y^2$ shown in Figure 11.55, this corresponds to climbing out of the saddle along one of the ridges. Similarly, the negative contours occur in pairs in the top and bottom triangular regions; the values get more and more negative as we go out along the y-axis. This corresponds to descending from the saddle along the valleys that are submerged below the xy-plane in Figure 11.55. Notice that we could also get the contour diagram by graphing the family of hyperbolas $x^2 - y^2 = 0, \pm 2, \pm 4, \ldots$.

Figure 11.55: Graph of $f(x, y) = x^2 - y^2$
showing plane $z = 0$

Using Contour Diagrams: The Cobb-Douglas Production Function

Suppose you are running a small printing business, and decide to expand because you have more orders than you can handle. How should you expand? Should you start a night-shift and hire more workers? Should you buy more expensive but faster computers which will enable the current staff to keep up with the work? Or should you do some combination of the two?

Obviously, the way such a decision is made in practice involves many other considerations—such as whether you could get a suitably trained night shift, or whether there are any faster computers available. Nevertheless, you might model the quantity, P, of work produced by your business as a function of two variables: your total number, N, of workers, and the total value, V, of your equipment.

How would you expect such a production function to behave? In general, having more equipment and more workers enables you to produce more. However, increasing equipment without increasing the number of workers will increase production a bit, but not beyond a point. (If equipment is already lying idle, having more of it won't help.) Similarly, increasing the number of workers without increasing equipment will increase production, but not past the point where the equipment is fully utilized, as any new workers would have no equipment available to them.

Example 7   Explain why the contour diagram in Figure 11.56 does not model the behavior expected of the production function, whereas the contour diagram in Figure 11.57 does.

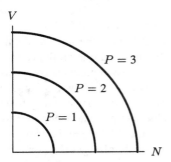

Figure 11.56: Incorrect contours
for printing production

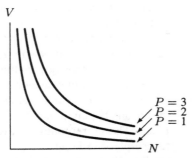

Figure 11.57: Correct contours for
printing production

Solution   Look at the contour diagram in Figure 11.56. Fixing V at a particular value and letting N increase means moving to the right on the contour diagram. As you do so, you cross contours with larger and larger P values, meaning that production increases indefinitely. On the other hand, in Figure 11.57, as you move in the same direction you find yourself moving nearly parallel to the contours, crossing them less and less frequently. Therefore, production increases more and more slowly as N increases while V is held fixed. Similarly, if you hold N fixed and let V increase, the contour diagram in Figure 11.56 shows production increasing at a steady rate, whereas Figure 11.57 shows production increasing, but at a decreasing rate. Thus, Figure 11.57 fits the expected behavior of the production function best.

Formula for a Production Function

Production functions with the qualitative behavior we want are often approximated by formulas of the form

$$P = f(N, V) = cN^{\alpha}V^{\beta}$$

where P is the total quantity produced and $c, \alpha,$ and β are positive constants with $0 < \alpha < 1$ and $0 < \beta < 1$.

Example 8   Show that the contours of the function $P = cN^{\alpha}V^{\beta}$ have approximately the shape of the contours in Figure 11.57.

Solution   The contours are the curves where P is equal to a constant value, say P_0, that is, where

$$cN^{\alpha}V^{\beta} = P_0.$$

Solving for V we get

$$V = \left(\frac{P_0}{c}\right)^{1/\beta} N^{-\alpha/\beta}.$$

Thus, V is a power function of N with a negative exponent, and hence its graph has the shape shown in Figure 11.57.

The Cobb-Douglas Production Model

In 1928, Cobb and Douglas used a similar function to model the production of the entire US economy in the first quarter of this century. Using government estimates of P, the total yearly production between 1899 and 1922, of K, the total capital investment over the same period, and of L, the total labor force, they found that P was well approximated by the *Cobb-Douglas production function*

$$P = 1.01L^{0.75}K^{0.25}.$$

This function turned out to model the US economy surprisingly well, both for the period on which it was based, and for some time afterwards.

Problems for Section 11.4

For the functions in Problems 1–9, sketch a contour diagram with at least four labeled contours. Describe in words the contours and how they are spaced.

1. $f(x,y) = x + y$
2. $f(x,y) = xy$
3. $f(x,y) = x^2 + y^2$
4. $f(x,y) = 3x + 3y$
5. $f(x,y) = -x^2 - y^2 + 1$
6. $f(x,y) = x^2 + 2y^2$
7. $f(x,y) = \sqrt{x^2 + 2y^2}$
8. $f(x,y) = y - x^2$
9. $f(x,y) = \cos\sqrt{x^2 + y^2}$

10. Figure 11.58 is a contour diagram of the monthly payment on a 5-year car loan as a function of the interest rate and the amount you borrow. Suppose that the interest rate is 13% and that you decide to borrow $6,000.

    (a) What is your monthly payment?
    (b) If interest rates drop to 11%, how much more can you borrow without increasing your monthly payment?
    (c) Make a table of how much you can borrow, without increasing your monthly payment, as a function of the interest rate.

Figure 11.58

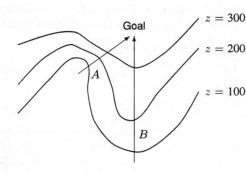

Figure 11.59

11. Figure 11.59 shows a contour map of a hill with two paths, A and B.

    (a) On which path, A or B, will you have to climb more steeply?
    (b) On which path, A or B, will you probably have a better view of the surrounding countryside? (Assuming trees do not block your view.)
    (c) Alongside which path is there more likely to be a stream?

12. Each of the contour diagrams in Figure 11.60 shows population density in a certain region. Choose the contour diagram that best corresponds to each of the following situations. Many different matchings are possible. Pick any reasonable one and justify your choice.

(a) The center of the diagram is a city.
(b) The center of the diagram is a lake.
(c) The center of the diagram is a power plant.

(I)   (II)   (III)

Figure 11.60

For each of the surfaces in Problems 13–15, sketch a possible contour diagram, marked with reasonable z-values. (Note: There are many possible answers.)

13.

Figure 11.61

14.

Figure 11.62

15.

Figure 11.63

16. Figure 11.64 shows the density of the fox population P (in foxes per square kilometer) for southern England. Draw two different cross-sections along a north-south line and two different cross-sections along an east-west line of the population density P.

Figure 11.64: Population density of foxes in southwestern England

17.   Use a computer or a calculator to sketch a contour diagram for the vibrating string function

$$f(x,t) = \cos t \sin 2x, \qquad 0 \le x \le \pi, \ 0 \le t \le \pi.$$

Use $c = -2/3, -1/3, 0, 1/3, 2/3$. (You will not be able to do this algebraically.)

18.   On page 4 we introduced the traveling wave function

$$h(x,t) = 5 + \cos(0.5x - t).$$

Draw a contour diagram using $c = 4, 4.5, 5, 5.5, 6$ for this function. Explain how your contour diagram relates to the cross-sections of h discussed on page 4. Where are the contours most closely spaced? Most widely spaced?

19.   Draw contour diagrams for each of the pizza-cola-happiness graphs given in Problem 6 on page 21.

20.   A manufacturer sells two goods, one at a price of $3000 a unit and the other at a price of $12000 a unit. Suppose a quantity q_1 of the first good and q_2 of the second good are sold at a total cost of $4000 to the manufacturer.

   (a)   Express the manufacturer's profit, π, as a function of q_1 and q_2.

   (b)   Sketch curves of constant profit in the $q_1 q_2$-plane for $\pi = 10000$, $\pi = 20000$, and $\pi = 30000$ and the break-even curve $\pi = 0$.

21.   The cornea is the front surface of the eye. Corneal specialists use a TMS, or Topographical Modeling System, to produce a "map" of the curvature of the eye's surface. A computer analyzes light reflected off the eye and draws level curves joining points of constant curvature. The regions between these curves are colored different colors.

        The first two pictures in Figure 11.65 are cross-sections of eyes with constant curvature, the smaller being about 38 units and the larger about 50 units. For contrast, the third eye has varying curvature.

   (a)   Describe in words how the TMS map of an eye of constant curvature will look.

   (b)   Draw the TMS map of an eye with the cross-section in Figure 11.66. Assume the eye is circular when viewed from the front, and the cross-section is the same in every direction. Put reasonable numeric labels on your level curves.

Large curvature   Small curvature   Small (or zero) curvature   Large curvature

Figure 11.65: Pictures of eyes with different curvature   *Figure 11.66*

22.   Match Tables 11.6–11.9 with the contour diagrams (I) - (IV) in Figure 11.67.

TABLE 11.6

$y\backslash x$	-1	0	1
-1	2	1	2
0	1	0	1
1	2	1	2

TABLE 11.7

$y\backslash x$	-1	0	1
-1	0	1	0
0	1	2	1
1	0	1	0

TABLE 11.8

$y\backslash x$	-1	0	1
-1	2	0	2
0	2	0	2
1	2	0	2

TABLE 11.9

$y\backslash x$	-1	0	1
-1	2	2	2
0	0	0	0
1	2	2	2

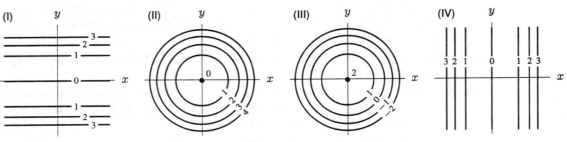

Figure 11.67

23.   Match the surfaces (a)–(e) in Figure 11.68 with the contour diagrams (I)–(V) in Figure 11.69.

Figure 11.68

Figure 11.69

24. The map in Figure 11.70 is from the undergraduate senior thesis of Professor Robert Cook, Director of Harvard's Arnold Arboretum. It shows level curves of the function giving the species density of breeding birds at each point in the US, Canada, and Mexico.

Figure 11.70

Using the map in Figure 11.70, decide if the the following statements are true or false. Explain your answers.

(a) Moving from south to north across Canada, the species density increases. F

(b) The species density in the area around Miami is over 100.

(c) In general, peninsulas (for example, Florida, Baja California, the Yucatan) have lower species densities than the areas around them. T

(d) The greatest rate of change in species density with distance is in Mexico. If you think this is true, mark the point and direction which give the maximum rate of change and explain why you picked the point and direction you did.

25. The temperature T (in °C) at any point in the region $-10 \le x \le 10$, $-10 \le y \le 10$ is given by the function

$$T(x, y) = 100 - x^2 - y^2.$$

(a) Sketch isothermal curves (curves of constant temperature) for $T = 100°C$, $T = 75°C$, $T = 50°C$, $T = 25°C$, and $T = 0°C$.

(b) Suppose a heat-seeking bug is put down at any point on the xy-plane. In which direction should it move to increase its temperature fastest? How is that direction related to the level curve through that point?

26.

Figure 11.71

Figure 11.71 shows the level curves of the temperature H in a room near a recently opened window. Label the three level curves with reasonable values of H if the house is in the following locations.

(a) Minnesota in winter (where winters are harsh).

(b) San Francisco in winter (where winters are mild).

(c) Houston in summer (where summers are hot).

(d) Oregon in summer (where summers are mild).

27. Match each Cobb-Douglas production function with the correct graph in Figure 11.72 and with the correct statements.

(a) $F(L, K) = L^{0.25} K^{0.25}$ (D) Tripling each input triples output.

(b) $F(L, K) = L^{0.5} K^{0.5}$ (E) Quadrupling each input doubles output.

(c) $F(L, K) = L^{0.75} K^{0.75}$ (G) Doubling each input almost triples output.

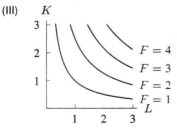

Figure 11.72

28. Consider the Cobb-Douglas production function $P = f(L, K) = 1.01L^{0.75}K^{0.25}$. What is the effect on production of doubling both labor and capital?

29. A general Cobb-Douglas production function has the form

$$P = cL^{\alpha}K^{\beta}.$$

An important economic question concerns what happens to production if labor and capital are both scaled up? For example, does production double if both labor and capital are doubled?
    Economists talk about

- *increasing returns to scale* if doubling L and K more than doubles P,
- *constant returns to scale* if doubling L and K exactly doubles P,
- *decreasing returns to scale* if doubling L and K less than doubles P.

What conditions on α and β lead to increasing, constant, or decreasing returns to scale?

30. Figure 11.73 shows the contours of the temperature along one wall of a heated room through one winter day, with time indicated as on a 24-hour clock. The room has a heater located at the left-most corner of the wall and one window in the wall. The heater is controlled by a thermostat about 2 feet from the window.

    (a) Where is the window?
    (b) When is the window open?
    (c) When is the heat on?
    (d) Draw graphs of the temperature along the wall of the room at 6 am, at 11 am, at 3 pm (15 hours) and at 5 pm (17 hours).
    (e) Draw a graph of the temperature as a function of time at the heater, at the window and midway between them.
    (f) The temperature at the window at 5 pm (17 hours) is less than at 11 am. Why do you think this might be?
    (g) To what temperature do you think the thermostat is set? How do you know?
    (h) Where is the thermostat?

Figure 11.73

REVIEW PROBLEMS FOR CHAPTER ELEVEN

1. Describe the set of points whose x coordinate is 2 and whose y coordinate is 1.
2. Find the center and radius of the sphere with equation $x^2 + 4x + y^2 - 6y + z^2 + 12z = 0$.
3. Find the equation of the plane through the points $(0, 0, 2), (0, 3, 0), (5, 0, 0)$.
4. Find a linear function whose graph is the plane that intersects the xy-plane along the line $y = 2x + 2$ and contains the point $(1, 2, 2)$.
5. Consider the function $f(r, h) = \pi r^2 h$ which gives the volume of a cylinder of radius r and height h. Sketch the cross-sections of f, first by keeping h fixed, then by keeping r fixed.
6. Consider the function $z = \cos \sqrt{x^2 + y^2}$.
   (a) Sketch the level curves of this function.
   (b) Sketch a cross-section through the surface $z = \cos \sqrt{x^2 + y^2}$ in the plane containing the x- and z-axes. Put units on your axes.
   (c) Sketch the cross-section through the surface $z = \cos \sqrt{x^2 + y^2}$ in the plane containing the z-axis and the line $y = x$ in the xy-plane.

For Problems 7–10, use a computer or calculator to sketch the graph of a function with the given shapes. Include the axes and the equation used to generate it in your sketch.

7. A cone of circular cross-section opening downward and with its vertex at the origin.

8. A bowl which opens upward and has its vertex at 5 on the z-axis.

9. A plane which has its x, y, and z intercepts all positive.

10. A parabolic cylinder opening upward from along the line $y = x$ in the xy-plane.

Decide if the statements in Problems 11–15 must be true, might be true, or could not be true. The function $z = f(x, y)$ is defined everywhere.

11. The level curves corresponding to $z = 1$ and $z = -1$ cross at the origin.

12. The level curve $z = 1$ consists of the circle $x^2 + y^2 = 2$ and the circle $x^2 + y^2 = 3$, but no other points.

13. The level curve $z = 1$ consists of two lines which intersect at the origin.

14. If $z = e^{-(x^2+y^2)}$, there is a level curve for every value of z.

15. If $z = e^{-(x^2+y^2)}$, there is a level curve through every point (x, y).

For each of the functions in Problems 16–19, make a contour plot in the region $-2 < x < 2$ and $-2 < y < 2$. In each case, what is the equation and the shape of the contour lines?

16. $z = \sin y$ 17. $z = 3x - 5y + 1$ 18. $z = 2x^2 + y^2$ 19. $z = e^{-2x^2 - y^2}$

20. Suppose you are in a room 30 feet long with a heater at one end. In the morning the room is 65°F. You turn on the heater, which quickly warms up to 85°F. Let $H(x, t)$ be the temperature x feet from the heater, t minutes after the heater is turned on. Figure 11.106 shows the contour diagram for H. How warm is it 10 feet from the heater 5 minutes after it was turned on? 10 minutes after it was turned on?

Figure 11.106

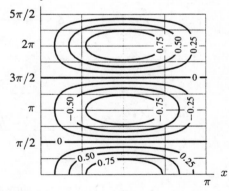

Figure 11.107

21. Using the contour diagram in Figure 11.106, sketch the graphs of the one-variable functions $H(x, 5)$ and $H(x, 20)$. Interpret the two graphs in practical terms, and explain the difference between them.

Chapter 12/ 39

22. Figure 11.107 shows the contour diagram for the vibrating string function from page 8:

$$f(x, t) = \cos t \sin x, \quad 0 \le x \le \pi.$$

Using the diagram, describe in words the cross-sections of f with t fixed and the cross-sections of f with x fixed. Explain what you see in terms of the behavior of the string.

Find equations for the linear functions with the contour diagrams in Problems 23–24.

23.

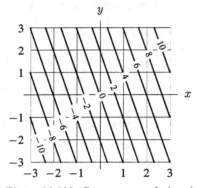

Figure 11.108: Contour map of $g(x, y)$

24.

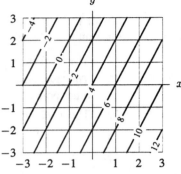

Figure 11.109: Contour map of $h(x, y)$

25. Figure 11.110 shows the contours of light intensity as a function of location and time in a microscopic wave-guide.

Figure 11.110

(a) Draw graphs showing intensity as a function of location at times 0, 2, 4, 6, 8, and 10 nanoseconds.

(b) If you could create an animation showing how the graph of intensity as a function of location varies as time passes, what would it look like?

(c) Draw a graph of intensity as a function of time at locations -5, 0 and 5 microns from center of wave-guide.

(d) Describe what the light beams are doing in this wave-guide.

In one-variable calculus we represented quantities such as velocity by numbers. However, to specify the velocity of a moving object in space, we need to say how fast it is moving and in what direction it is moving. In this chapter *vectors* are used to represent quantities that have direction as well as magnitude.

12.1 DISPLACEMENT VECTORS

Suppose you are a pilot planning a flight from Dallas to Pittsburgh. There are two things you must know: the distance to be traveled (so you have enough fuel to make it) and in what direction to go (so you don't miss Pittsburgh). Both these quantities together specify the displacement or *displacement vector* between the two cities.

> The **displacement vector** from one point to another is an arrow with its tail at the first point and its tip at the second. The **magnitude** (or length) of the displacement vector is the distance between the points, and is represented by the length of the arrow. The **direction** of the displacement vector is the direction of the arrow.

Figure 12.1 shows the displacement vectors from Dallas to Pittsburgh, from Albuquerque to Oshkosh, and from Los Angeles to Buffalo, SD. These displacement vectors have the same length and the same direction. We say that the displacement vectors between the corresponding cities are the same, even though they do not coincide. In other words

> Displacement vectors which point in the same direction and have the same magnitude are considered to be the same, even if they do not coincide.

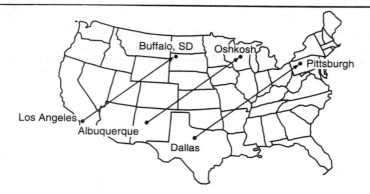

Figure 12.1: Displacement vectors between cities

Notation and Terminology

The displacement vector is our first example of a vector. Vectors have both magnitude and direction; in comparison, a quantity specified only by a number, but no direction, is called a *scalar*.[1] For instance, the time taken by the flight from Dallas to Pittsburgh is a scalar quantity. Displacement is a vector since it requires both distance and direction to specify it.

In this book, vectors are written with an arrow over them, $\vec{v}$, to distinguish them from scalars. Other books use a bold **v** to denote a vector. We use the notation $\overrightarrow{PQ}$ to denote the displacement vector from a point P to a point Q. The magnitude, or length, of a vector $\vec{v}$ is written $\|\vec{v}\|$.

Addition and Subtraction of Displacement Vectors

Suppose NASA commands a robot on Mars to move 75 meters in one direction and then 50 meters in another direction. (See Figure 12.2.) Where does the robot end up? Suppose the displacements are represented by the vectors $\vec{v}$ and $\vec{w}$, respectively. Then the sum $\vec{v} + \vec{w}$ gives the final position.

---

[1] So named by W. R. Hamilton because they are merely numbers on the *scale* from $-\infty$ to ∞.

The **sum**, $\vec{v} + \vec{w}$, of two vectors $\vec{v}$ and $\vec{w}$ is the combined displacement resulting from first applying $\vec{v}$ and then $\vec{w}$. (See Figure 12.3.) The sum $\vec{w} + \vec{v}$ gives the same displacement.

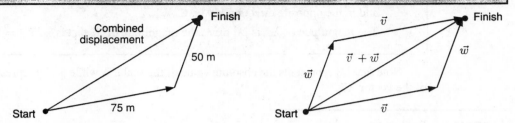

Figure 12.2: Sum of displacements of robots on Mars   *Figure 12.3:* The sum $\vec{v} + \vec{w} = \vec{w} + \vec{v}$

Suppose two different robots start from the same location. One moves along a displacement vector $\vec{v}$ and the second along a displacement vector $\vec{w}$. What is the displacement vector, $\vec{x}$, from the first robot to the second? (See Figure 12.4.) Since $\vec{v} + \vec{x} = \vec{w}$, we define $\vec{x}$ to be the difference $\vec{x} = \vec{w} - \vec{v}$. In other words, $\vec{w} - \vec{v}$ gets you from $\vec{v}$ to $\vec{w}$.

The **difference**, $\vec{w} - \vec{v}$, is the displacement vector which when added to $\vec{v}$ gives $\vec{w}$. That is, $\vec{w} = \vec{v} + (\vec{w} - \vec{v})$. (See Figure 12.4.)

Figure 12.4: The difference $\vec{w} - \vec{v}$

If the robot ends up where it started, then its total displacement vector is the *zero vector*, $\vec{0}$. The zero vector has no direction.

The **zero vector**, $\vec{0}$, is a displacement vector with zero length.

Scalar Multiplication of Displacement Vectors

If $\vec{v}$ represents a displacement vector, the vector $2\vec{v}$ represents a displacement of twice the magnitude in the same direction as $\vec{v}$. Similarly, $-2\vec{v}$ represents a displacement of twice the magnitude in the opposite direction. (See Figure 12.5.)

Figure 12.5: Scalar multiples of the vector $\vec{v}$

> If λ is a scalar and $\vec{v}$ is a displacement vector, the **scalar multiple of $\vec{v}$ by** λ, written $\lambda\vec{v}$, is the displacement vector with the following properties:
> - The displacement vector $\lambda\vec{v}$ is parallel to $\vec{v}$, pointing in the same direction if $\lambda > 0$, and in the opposite direction if $\lambda < 0$.
> - The magnitude of $\lambda\vec{v}$ is $|\lambda|$ times the magnitude of $\vec{v}$; that is, $\|\lambda\vec{v}\| = |\lambda|\,\|\vec{v}\|$.

Note that $|\lambda|$ represents the absolute value of the scalar λ while $\|\lambda\vec{v}\|$ represents the magnitude of the vector $\lambda\vec{v}$.

Example 1   Explain why $\vec{w} - \vec{v} = \vec{w} + (-1)\vec{v}$.

Solution   The vector $(-1)\vec{v}$ has the same magnitude as $\vec{v}$, but points in the opposite direction. Figure 12.6 shows that the combined displacement $\vec{w} + (-1)\vec{v}$ is the same as the displacement $\vec{w} - \vec{v}$.

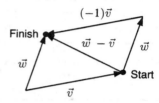

Figure 12.6: Explanation for why $\vec{w} - \vec{v} = \vec{w} + (-1)\vec{v}$

Parallel Vectors

Two vectors $\vec{v}$ and $\vec{w}$ are *parallel* if one is a scalar multiple of the other, that is, if $\vec{w} = \lambda\vec{v}$.

Components of Displacement Vectors: The Vectors $\vec{i}$, $\vec{j}$, and $\vec{k}$

Suppose that you live in a city with equally spaced streets running east-west and north-south and that you want to tell someone how to get from one place to another. You'd be likely to tell them how many blocks east-west and how many blocks north-south to go. For example, to get from P to Q in Figure 12.7, we go 4 blocks east and 1 block south. If $\vec{i}$ and $\vec{j}$ are as shown in Figure 12.7, then the displacement vector from P to Q is $4\vec{i} - \vec{j}$.

Figure 12.7: The displacement vector from P to Q is $4\vec{i} - \vec{j}$

We extend the same idea to 3-dimensions. First we choose a Cartesian system of coordinate axes. The three vectors of length 1 shown in Figure 12.8 are the vector $\vec{i}$, which points along the positive x-axis, the vector $\vec{j}$, along the positive y-axis, and the vector $\vec{k}$, along the positive z-axis.

Figure 12.8: The vectors $\vec{i}$, $\vec{j}$ and $\vec{k}$ in 3-space

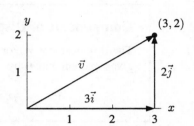

Figure 12.9: We resolve $\vec{v}$ into components by writing $\vec{v} = 3\vec{i} + 2\vec{j}$

Writing Displacement Vectors Using $\vec{i}$, $\vec{j}$, $\vec{k}$

Any displacement in 3-space or the plane can be expressed as a combination of displacements in the coordinate directions. For example, Figure 12.9 shows that the displacement vector $\vec{v}$ from the origin to the point $(3, 2)$ can be written as a sum of displacement vectors along the x and y-axes:

$$\vec{v} = 3\vec{i} + 2\vec{j}.$$

This is called *resolving $\vec{v}$ into components*. In general:

> We **resolve** $\vec{v}$ into components by writing $\vec{v}$ in the form
>
> $$\vec{v} = v_1\vec{i} + v_2\vec{j} + v_3\vec{k}.$$
>
> We call $v_1\vec{i}$, $v_2\vec{j}$, and $v_3\vec{k}$ the **components** of $\vec{v}$.

An Alternative Notation for Vectors

Many people write a vector in 3-dimensions as a string of three numbers, that is, as

$$\vec{v} = (v_1, v_2, v_3) \quad \text{instead of} \quad \vec{v} = v_1\vec{i} + v_2\vec{j} + v_3\vec{k}.$$

Since the first notation can be confused with a point and the second cannot, we usually use the second form.

Example 2 Resolve the displacement vector, $\vec{v}$, from the point $P_1 = (2, 4, 10)$ to the point $P_2 = (3, 7, 6)$ into components.

Solution To get from P_1 to P_2, we move 1 unit in the positive x-direction, 3 units in the positive y-direction, and 4 units in the negative z-direction. Hence $\vec{v} = \vec{i} + 3\vec{j} - 4\vec{k}$.

Example 3 Decide whether the vector $\vec{v} = 2\vec{i} + 3\vec{j} + 5\vec{k}$ is parallel to each of the following vectors:

$$\vec{w} = 4\vec{i} + 6\vec{j} + 10\vec{k}, \quad \vec{a} = -\vec{i} - 1.5\vec{j} - 2.5\vec{k}, \quad \vec{b} = 4\vec{i} + 6\vec{j} + 9\vec{k}$$

Solution Since $\vec{w} = 2\vec{v}$ and $\vec{a} = -0.5\vec{v}$, the vectors $\vec{v}$, $\vec{w}$, and $\vec{a}$ are parallel. However, $\vec{b}$ is not a multiple of $\vec{v}$ (since, for example, $4/2 \neq 9/5$), so $\vec{v}$ and $\vec{b}$ are not parallel.

In general, Figure 12.10 shows us how to express the displacement vector between two points in components:

Components of Displacement Vectors

The displacement vector from the point $P_1 = (x_1, y_1, z_1)$ to the point $P_2 = (x_2, y_2, z_2)$ is given in components by

$$\overrightarrow{P_1 P_2} = (x_2 - x_1)\vec{i} + (y_2 - y_1)\vec{j} + (z_2 - z_1)\vec{k}.$$

Position Vectors: Displacement of a Point from the Origin

A displacement vector whose tail is at the origin is called a *position vector*. Thus, any point (x_0, y_0, z_0) in space has associated with it the position vector $\vec{r}_0 = x_0\vec{i} + y_0\vec{j} + z_0\vec{k}$. (See Figure 12.11.) In general, a position vector gives the displacement of a point from the origin.

Figure 12.10: The displacement vector
$\overrightarrow{P_1 P_2} = (x_2 - x_1)\vec{i} + (y_2 - y_1)\vec{j} + (z_2 - z_1)\vec{k}$

Figure 12.11: The position vector
$\vec{r}_0 = x_0\vec{i} + y_0\vec{j} + z_0\vec{k}$

The Components of the Zero Vector

The zero displacement vector has magnitude equal to zero and is written $\vec{0}$. So $\vec{0} = 0\vec{i} + 0\vec{j} + 0\vec{k}$.

The Magnitude of a Vector in Components

For a vector, $\vec{v} = v_1\vec{i} + v_2\vec{j}$, the Pythagorean theorem is used to find its magnitude, $\|\vec{v}\|$. (See Figure 12.12.)

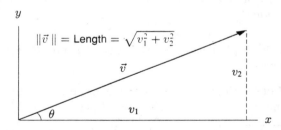

Figure 12.12: Magnitude, $\|\vec{v}\|$, of a 2-dimensional vector, $\vec{v}$

In 3-dimensions, for a vector $\vec{v} = v_1\vec{i} + v_2\vec{j} + v_3\vec{k}$, we have

---

Magnitude of $\vec{v}$ $= \|\vec{v}\| =$ Length of the arrow $= \sqrt{v_1^2 + v_2^2 + v_3^2}.$

For instance, if $\vec{v} = 3\vec{i} - 4\vec{j} + 5\vec{k}$, then $\|\vec{v}\| = \sqrt{3^2 + (-4)^2 + 5^2} = \sqrt{50}$.

Addition and Scalar Multiplication of Vectors in Components

Suppose the vectors $\vec{v}$ and $\vec{w}$ are given in components:

$$\vec{v} = v_1\vec{i} + v_2\vec{j} + v_3\vec{k} \quad \text{and} \quad \vec{w} = w_1\vec{i} + w_2\vec{j} + w_3\vec{k}.$$

Then

$$\vec{v} + \vec{w} = (v_1 + w_1)\vec{i} + (v_2 + w_2)\vec{j} + (v_3 + w_3)\vec{k},$$

and

$$\lambda\vec{v} = \lambda v_1\vec{i} + \lambda v_2\vec{j} + \lambda v_3\vec{k}.$$

Figures 12.13 and 12.14 illustrate these properties in two dimensions. Finally, $\vec{v} - \vec{w} = \vec{v} + (-1)\vec{w}$, so we can write $\vec{v} - \vec{w} = (v_1 - w_1)\vec{i} + (v_2 - w_2)\vec{j} + (v_3 - w_3)\vec{k}$.

Figure 12.13: Sum $\vec{v} + \vec{w}$ in components

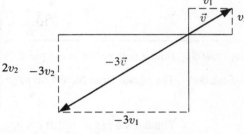

Figure 12.14: Scalar multiples of vectors showing $\vec{v}$, $2\vec{v}$, and $-3\vec{v}$

How to Resolve a Vector into Components

You may wonder how we find the components of a 2-dimensional vector, given its length and direction. Suppose the vector $\vec{v}$ has length v and makes an angle of θ with the x-axis, measured counterclockwise, as in Figure 12.15. If $\vec{v} = v_1\vec{i} + v_2\vec{j}$, Figure 12.15 shows that

$$v_1 = v\cos\theta \quad \text{and} \quad v_2 = v\sin\theta.$$

Thus, we resolve $\vec{v}$ into components by writing

$$\vec{v} = (v\cos\theta)\vec{i} + (v\sin\theta)\vec{j}.$$

Vectors in 3-space are resolved using direction cosines; see Problem 29 on page 95.

Figure 12.15: Resolving a vector:
$\vec{v} = (v\cos\theta)\vec{i} + (v\sin\theta)\vec{j}$

Example 4   Resolve $\vec{v}$ into components if $v = 2$ and $\theta = \pi/6$.

  Solution   We have $\vec{v} = 2\cos(\pi/6)\vec{i} + 2\sin(\pi/6)\vec{j} = 2(\sqrt{3}/2)\vec{i} + 2(1/2)\vec{j} = \sqrt{3}\vec{i} + \vec{j}$.

Unit Vectors

A *unit vector* is a vector whose magnitude is 1. The vectors $\vec{i}$, $\vec{j}$, and $\vec{k}$ are unit vectors in the directions of the coordinate axes. It is often helpful to find a unit vector in the same direction as a given vector $\vec{v}$. Suppose that $\|\vec{v}\| = 10$; a unit vector in the same direction as $\vec{v}$ is $\vec{v}/10$. In general, a unit vector in the direction of any nonzero vector $\vec{v}$ is

$$\vec{u} = \frac{\vec{v}}{\|\vec{v}\|}.$$

Example 5   Find a unit vector, $\vec{u}$, in the direction of the vector $\vec{v} = \vec{i} + 3\vec{j}$.

  Solution   If $\vec{v} = \vec{i} + 3\vec{j}$, then $\|\vec{v}\| = \sqrt{1^2 + 3^2} = \sqrt{10}$. Thus, a unit vector in the same direction is given by

$$\vec{u} = \frac{\vec{v}}{\sqrt{10}} = \frac{1}{\sqrt{10}}(\vec{i} + 3\vec{j}) = \frac{1}{\sqrt{10}}\vec{i} + \frac{3}{\sqrt{10}}\vec{j} \approx 0.32\vec{i} + 0.95\vec{j}.$$

Example 6   Find a unit vector at the point (x, y, z) that points radially outward away from the origin.

  Solution   The vector from the origin to (x, y, z) is the position vector

$$\vec{r} = x\vec{i} + y\vec{j} + z\vec{k}.$$

Thus, if we put its tail at (x, y, z) it will point away from the origin. Its magnitude is

$$\|\vec{r}\| = \sqrt{x^2 + y^2 + z^2},$$

so a unit vector pointing in the same direction is

$$\frac{\vec{r}}{\|\vec{r}\|} = \frac{x\vec{i} + y\vec{j} + z\vec{k}}{\sqrt{x^2 + y^2 + z^2}} = \frac{x}{\sqrt{x^2 + y^2 + z^2}}\vec{i} + \frac{y}{\sqrt{x^2 + y^2 + z^2}}\vec{j} + \frac{z}{\sqrt{x^2 + y^2 + z^2}}\vec{k}.$$

Problems for Section 12.1

1. The vectors $\vec{w}$ and $\vec{u}$ are in Figure 12.16. Match the vectors $\vec{p}, \vec{q}, \vec{r}, \vec{s}, \vec{t}$ with five of the following vectors: $\vec{u} + \vec{w}, \vec{u} - \vec{w}, \vec{w} - \vec{u}, 2\vec{w} - \vec{u}, \vec{u} - 2\vec{w}, 2\vec{w}, -2\vec{w}, 2\vec{u}, -2\vec{u}, -\vec{w}, -\vec{u}$.

Figure 12.16

Figure 12.17

2. Given the displacement vectors $\vec{v}$ and $\vec{w}$ in Figure 12.17, draw the following vectors:

    (a) $\vec{v} + \vec{w}$ (b) $\vec{v} - \vec{w}$ (c) $2\vec{v}$ (d) $2\vec{v} + \vec{w}$ (e) $\vec{v} - 2\vec{w}$.

For Problems 3–8, perform the indicated operations on the following vectors:

$$\vec{a} = 2\vec{j} + \vec{k}, \quad \vec{b} = -3\vec{i} + 5\vec{j} + 4\vec{k}, \quad \vec{c} = \vec{i} + 6\vec{j},$$

$$\vec{x} = -2\vec{i} + 9\vec{j}, \quad \vec{y} = 4\vec{i} - 7\vec{j}, \quad \vec{z} = \vec{i} - 3\vec{j} - \vec{k}.$$

what's ♡ ?

3. $\|\vec{z}\|$ $\sqrt{1 - 3^2 - 1^2} = \sqrt{1+9+1}$ 4. $\vec{a} + \vec{z} =$ 5. $5\vec{b} = -15\vec{i} + 25\vec{j} + 20\vec{k}$

6. $2\vec{c} + \vec{x} = 2\vec{i} + 12\vec{j} - 2\vec{i} + 9\vec{j} = 17\vec{j}$ 7. $\|\vec{y}\|$ (8.) $2\vec{a} + 7\vec{b} - 5\vec{z}$

For Problems 9–12, perform the indicated computation.

9. $(4\vec{i} + 2\vec{j}) - (3\vec{i} - \vec{j})$ 10. $(\vec{i} + 2\vec{j}) + (-3)(2\vec{i} + \vec{j})$

11. $-4(\vec{i} - 2\vec{j}) - 0.5(\vec{i} - \vec{k})$ 12. $2(0.45\vec{i} - 0.9\vec{j} - 0.01\vec{k}) - 0.5(1.2\vec{i} - 0.1\vec{k})$

Find the length of the vectors in Problems 13–16.

13. $\vec{v} = \vec{i} - \vec{j} + 3\vec{k}$ 14. $\vec{v} = \vec{i} - \vec{j} + 2\vec{k}$

15. $\vec{v} = 1.2\vec{i} - 3.6\vec{j} + 4.1\vec{k}$ 16. $\vec{v} = 7.2\vec{i} - 1.5\vec{j} + 2.1\vec{k}$

A cat is sitting on the ground at the point $(1, 4, 0)$ watching a squirrel at the top of a tree. The tree is one unit high and its base is at the point $(2, 4, 0)$. Find the displacement vectors in Problems 17–20.

17. From the origin to the cat.   18. From the bottom of the tree to the squirrel.

19. From the bottom of the tree to the cat.   20. From the cat to the squirrel.

21. On the graph of Figure 12.18, draw the vector $\vec{v} = 4\vec{i} + \vec{j}$ twice, once with its tail at the origin and once with its tail at the point $(3, 2)$.

Figure 12.18

Figure 12.19: Scale: 1 grid length = 0.25 inches

Resolve the vectors in Problems 22–26 into components.

22. The vector shown in Figure 12.19.

23. A vector starting at the point $P = (1, 2)$ and ending at the point $Q = (4, 6)$. $\vec{PQ} = 3\vec{i} + 4\vec{j}$

24. A vector starting at the point $Q = (4, 6)$ and ending at the point $P = (1, 2)$.

25.   26.

$\vec{a} = \vec{b} = \vec{c} = 3\vec{k}$

$\vec{d} = \vec{j}$

$\vec{e} = 2\vec{j}$

$\vec{d} = 2\vec{i} + 3\vec{k}$

$\vec{f} = -2\vec{i}$

$\vec{v} = \vec{i} + 2\vec{k}$

$\vec{u} = \vec{i} + \vec{k}$

$\vec{a} = 2$ $\vec{b} = 2$ $\vec{f} = 3$

$\vec{c} = 3$

$\vec{e} = 1$ $\vec{e} = 1\vec{i}$

              $\vec{a} = 2\vec{j}$

27. Find the length of the vectors $\vec{u}$ and $\vec{v}$ in Problem 26.

28. Find a vector that points in the same direction as $\vec{i} - \vec{j} + 2\vec{k}$, but has length 2.

29. (a) Find a unit vector from the point $P = (1, 2)$ and toward the point $Q = (4, 6)$.
    (b) Find a vector of length 10 pointing in the same direction.

30. Which of the following vectors are parallel?

$$\vec{u} = 2\vec{i} + 4\vec{j} - 2\vec{k}, \quad \vec{v} = \vec{i} - \vec{j} + 3\vec{k}, \quad \vec{w} = -\vec{i} - 2\vec{j} + \vec{k},$$
$$\vec{p} = \vec{i} + \vec{j} + \vec{k}, \quad \vec{q} = 4\vec{i} - 4\vec{j} + 12\vec{k}, \quad \vec{r} = \vec{i} - \vec{j} + \vec{k}.$$

31. Figure 12.20 shows a molecule with four atoms at O, A, B and C. Verify that every atom in the molecule is 2 units away from every other atom.

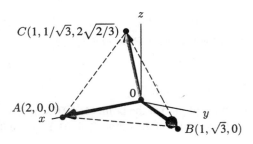

Figure 12.20

For Problems 32–33, consider the map in Figure 11.1 on page 2.

32. If you leave Topeka along the following vectors, does the temperature increase or decrease?
    (a) $\vec{u} = 3\vec{i} + 2\vec{j}$ (b) $\vec{v} = -\vec{i} - \vec{j}$ (c) $\vec{w} = -5\vec{i} - 5\vec{j}$.

33. Starting in Buffalo, sketch a vector pointing in the direction in which the temperature is increasing most rapidly. Starting in Boise, sketch a vector pointing in the direction in which the temperature is decreasing most rapidly.

34. A truck is traveling due north at 30 km/hr approaching a crossroad. On a perpendicular road a police car is traveling west toward the intersection at 40 km/hr. Suppose that both vehicles will reach the crossroad in exactly one hour. Find the vector currently representing the displacement of the truck with respect to the police car.

35. Show that the medians of a triangle intersect at a point 1/3 of the way along each median from the side it bisects.

36. Show that the lines joining the centroid (the intersection point of the medians) of a face of the tetrahedron and the opposite vertex meet at a point $\frac{1}{4}$ of the way from each centroid to its opposite vertex.

12.2   VECTORS IN GENERAL

Besides displacement, there are many quantities that have both magnitude and direction and are added and multiplied by scalars in the same way as displacements. Any such quantity is called a *vector* and is represented by an arrow in the same manner we represent displacements. The length of the arrow is the *magnitude* of the vector, and the direction of the arrow is the direction of the vector.

Velocity Versus Speed

The speed of a moving body tells us how fast it is moving, say 80 km/hr. The speed is just a number; it is therefore a scalar. The velocity, on the other hand, tells us both how fast the body is moving and the direction of motion; it is a vector. For instance, if a car is heading northeast at 80 km/hr, then its velocity is a vector of length 80 pointing northeast.

> The velocity vector of a moving object is a vector whose magnitude is the speed of the object and whose direction is the direction of its motion.

Example 1   A car is traveling north at a speed of 100 km/hr, while a plane above is flying horizontally south-west at a speed of 500 km/hr. Draw the velocity vectors of the car and the plane.

Solution   Figure 12.21 shows the velocity vectors. The plane's velocity vector is five times as long as the car's, because its speed is five times as great.

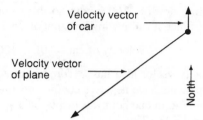

Figure 12.21: Velocity vector of the car is 100 km/hr north and of the plane is 500 km/hr south-west

The next example illustrates that the velocity vectors for two motions add to give the velocity vector for the combined motion, just as displacements do.

Example 2   A riverboat is moving with velocity $\vec{v}$ and a speed of 8 km/hr relative to the water. In addition, the river has a current $\vec{c}$ and a speed of 1 km/hr. (See Figure 12.22.) What is the physical significance of the vector $\vec{v} + \vec{c}$?

Figure 12.22: Boat's velocity relative to the river bed is the sum, $\vec{v} + \vec{c}$

Solution   The vector $\vec{v}$ shows how the boat is moving relative to the water, while $\vec{c}$ shows how the water is moving relative to the riverbed. During an hour, imagine that the boat first moves 8 km relative to the water, which remains still; this displacement is represented by $\vec{v}$. Then imagine the water moving 1 km while the boat remains stationary relative to the water; this displacement is represented by $\vec{c}$. The combined displacement is represented by $\vec{v} + \vec{c}$. Thus, the vector $\vec{v} + \vec{c}$ is the velocity of the boat relative to the riverbed.

Note that the effective speed of the boat is not necessarily 9 km/hr unless the boat is moving in the direction of the current. Although we add the velocity vectors, we do not necessarily add their lengths.

Chapter 12/51

Scalar multiplication also makes sense for velocity vectors. For example, if $\vec{v}$ is a velocity vector, then $-2\vec{v}$ represents a velocity of twice the magnitude in the opposite direction.

Example 3   A ball is moving with velocity $\vec{v}$ when it hits a wall at a right angle and bounces straight back, with its speed reduced by 20%. Express its new velocity in terms of the old one.

Solution   The new velocity is $-0.8\vec{v}$, where the negative sign expresses the fact that the new velocity is in the direction opposite to the old.

We can represent velocity vectors in components in the same way we did on page 65.

Example 4   Represent the velocity vectors of the car and the plane in Example 1 using components. Take north to be the positive y-axis, east to be the positive x-axis, and upward to be the positive z-axis.

Solution   The car is traveling north at 100 km/hr, so the y-component of its velocity is $100\vec{j}$ and the x-component is $0\vec{i}$. Since it is traveling horizontally, the z-component is $0\vec{k}$. So we have

$$\text{Velocity of car} = 0\vec{i} + 100\vec{j} + 0\vec{k} = 100\vec{j}.$$

The plane's velocity vector also has $\vec{k}$ component equal to zero. Since it is traveling southwest, its $\vec{i}$ and $\vec{j}$ components have negative coefficients (north and east are positive). Since the plane is traveling at 500 km/hr, in one hour it is displaced $500/\sqrt{2} \approx 354$ km to the west and 354 km to the south. (See Figure 12.23.) Thus,

$$\text{Velocity of plane} = -(500\cos 45°)\vec{i} - (500\sin 45°)\vec{j} \approx -354\vec{i} - 354\vec{j}.$$

Of course, if the car were climbing a hill or if the plane were descending for a landing, then the $\vec{k}$ component would not be zero.

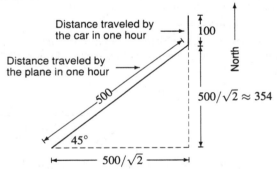

Figure 12.23: Distance traveled by the plane and car in one hour

Acceleration

Another example of a vector quantity is acceleration. Acceleration, like velocity, is specified by both a magnitude and a direction — for example, the acceleration due to gravity is 9.81 m/sec^2 vertically downward.

Force

Force is another example of a vector quantity. Suppose you push on an open door. The result depends both on how hard you push and in what direction. Thus, to specify a force we must give its magnitude (or strength) and the direction in which it is acting. For example, the gravitational force exerted on an object by the earth is a vector pointing from the object toward the center of the earth; its magnitude is the strength of the gravitational force.

Example 5   The earth travels around the sun in an ellipse. The gravitational force on the earth and the velocity of the earth are governed by the following laws:

Newton's Law of Gravitation: The magnitude of the gravitational attraction, F, between two masses m_1 and m_2 at a distance r apart is given by $F = Gm_1m_2/r^2$, where G is a constant. The force vector lies along the line between the masses.

Kepler's Second Law: The line joining a planet to the sun sweeps out equal areas in equal times.

(a)   Sketch vectors representing the gravitational force of the sun on the earth at two different positions in the earth's orbit.

(b)   Sketch the velocity vector of the earth at two points in its orbit.

Solution   (a)   Figure 12.24 shows the earth orbiting the sun. Note that the gravitational force vector always points toward the sun and is larger when the earth is closer to the sun because of the r^2 term in the denominator. (In fact, the real orbit looks much more like a circle than we have shown here.)

(b)   The velocity vector points in the direction of motion of the earth. Thus, the velocity vector is tangent to the ellipse. See Figure 12.25. Furthermore, the velocity vector is longer at points of the orbit where the planet is moving quickly, because the magnitude of the velocity vector is the speed. Kepler's Second Law enables us to determine when the earth is moving quickly and when it is moving slowly. Over a fixed period of time, say one month, the line joining the earth to the sun sweeps out a sector having a certain area. Figure 12.25 shows two sectors swept out in two different one-month time-intervals. Kepler's law says that the areas of the two sectors are the same. Thus, the earth must move farther in a month when it is close to the sun than when it is far from the sun. Therefore, the earth moves faster when it is closer to the sun and slower when it is farther away.

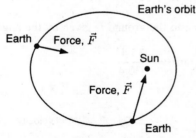

Figure 12.24: Gravitational force, $\vec{F}$, exerted by the sun on the earth: Greater magnitude closer to sun

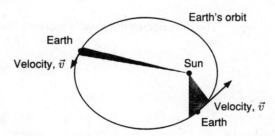

Figure 12.25: The velocity vector, $\vec{v}$, of the earth: Greater magnitude closer to the sun

Properties of Addition and Scalar Multiplication

In general, vectors add, subtract, and are multiplied by scalars in the same way as displacement vectors. Thus, for any vectors $\vec{u}, \vec{v}$, and $\vec{w}$ and any scalars α and β, we have the following properties:

Commutativity	**Associativity**
1. $\vec{v} + \vec{w} = \vec{w} + \vec{v}$	2. $(\vec{u} + \vec{v}) + \vec{w} = \vec{u} + (\vec{v} + \vec{w})$
	3. $\alpha(\beta\vec{v}) = (\alpha\beta)\vec{v}$
Distributivity	**Identity**
4. $(\alpha + \beta)\vec{v} = \alpha\vec{v} + \beta\vec{v}$	6. $1 \cdot \vec{v} = \vec{v}$ 8. $\vec{v} + \vec{0} = \vec{v}$
5. $\alpha(\vec{v} + \vec{w}) = \alpha\vec{v} + \alpha\vec{w}$	7. $0 \cdot \vec{v} = \vec{0}$ 9. $\vec{w} + (-1) \cdot \vec{v} = \vec{w} - \vec{v}$

Problems 16–23 at the end of this section ask for a justification of these results in terms of displacement vectors.

Using Components

Example 6   A plane, heading due east at an airspeed of 600 km/hr, experiences a wind of 50 km/hr blowing toward the northeast. Find the plane's direction and ground speed.

Solution   We choose a coordinate system with the x-axis pointing east and the y-axis pointing north. See Figure 12.26.

The airspeed tells us the speed of the plane relative to still air. Thus, the plane is moving due east with velocity $\vec{v} = 600\vec{i}$ relative to still air. In addition, the air is moving with a velocity $\vec{w}$. Writing $\vec{w}$ in components, we have

$$\vec{w} = (50\cos45°)\vec{i} + (50\sin45°)\vec{j} = 35.4\vec{i} + 35.4\vec{j}.$$

The vector $\vec{v} + \vec{w}$ represents the displacement of the plane in one hour relative to the ground. Therefore, $\vec{v} + \vec{w}$ is the velocity of the plane relative to the ground. In components, we have

$$\vec{v} + \vec{w} = 600\vec{i} + \left(35.4\vec{i} + 35.4\vec{j}\right) = 635.4\vec{i} + 35.4\vec{j}.$$

The direction of the plane's motion relative to the ground is given by the angle θ in Figure 12.26, where

$$\tan\theta = \frac{35.4}{635.4}$$

Figure 12.26: Plane's velocity relative to the ground is the sum $\vec{v} + \vec{w}$

so

$$\theta = \arctan\left(\frac{35.4}{635.4}\right) = 3.2°.$$

The ground speed is the speed of the plane relative to the ground, so

$$\text{Groundspeed} = \sqrt{635.4^2 + 35.4^2} = 636.4 \text{ km/hr}.$$

Thus, the speed of the plane relative to the ground has been increased slightly by the wind. (This is as we would expect, as the wind has a component in the direction in which the plane is traveling.) The angle θ shows how far the plane is blown off course by the wind.

Vectors in n Dimensions

Using the alternative notation $\vec{v} = (v_1, v_2, v_3)$ for a vector in 3-space, we can define a vector in n dimensions as a string of n numbers. Thus, a vector in n dimensions can be written as

$$\vec{c} = (c_1, c_2, \ldots, c_n).$$

Addition and scalar multiplication are defined by the formulas

$$\boxed{\vec{v} + \vec{w} = (v_1, v_2, \ldots, v_n) + (w_1, w_2, \ldots, w_n) = (v_1 + w_1, v_2 + w_2, \ldots, v_n + w_n)}$$

and

$$\boxed{\lambda\vec{v} = \lambda(v_1, v_2, \ldots, v_n) = (\lambda v_1, \lambda v_2, \ldots, \lambda v_n).}$$

Why Do We Want Vectors in n Dimensions?

Vectors in two and three dimensions can be used to model displacement, velocities, or forces. But what about vectors in n dimensions? There is another interpretation of 3-dimensional vectors (or 3-vectors) which is useful: they can be thought of as listing 3 different quantities — for example, the displacements parallel to the x, y, and z axes. Similarly, the n-vector

$$\vec{c} = (c_1, c_2, \ldots, c_n)$$

can be thought of as a way of keeping n different quantities organized. For example, a *population* vector $\vec{N}$ shows the number of children and adults in a population:

$$\vec{N} = (\text{Number of children, Number of adults}),$$

or, if we are interested in a more detailed breakdown of ages, we might give the number in each ten-year age bracket in the population (up to age 110) in the form

$$\vec{N} = (N_1, N_2, N_3, N_4, \ldots, N_{10}, N_{11}),$$

where N_1 is the population aged 0–9, and N_2 is the population aged 10–19, and so on.

A *consumption* vector ,

$$\vec{q} = (q_1, q_2, \ldots, q_n)$$

shows the quantities $q_1, q_2, \ldots, q_n$ consumed of each of n different goods. A *price* vector

$$\vec{p} = (p_1, p_2, \ldots, p_n)$$

contains the prices of n different items.

In 1907, Hermann Minkowski used vectors with four components when he introduced *space-time coordinates*, whereby each event is assigned a vector position $\vec{v}$ with four coordinates, three for its position in space and one for time:

$$\vec{v} = (x, y, z, t).$$

Example 7   Suppose the vector $\vec{I}$ represents the number of copies, in thousands, made by each of four copy centers in the month of December and $\vec{J}$ represents the number of copies made at the same four copy centers during the previous eleven months (the "year-to-date"). If $\vec{I} = (25, 211, 818, 642)$, and $\vec{J} = (331, 3227, 1377, 2570)$, compute $\vec{I} + \vec{J}$. What does this sum represent?

Solution   The sum is

$$\vec{I} + \vec{J} = (25 + 331, 211 + 3227, 818 + 1377, 642 + 2570) = (356, 3438, 2195, 3212).$$

Each term in $\vec{I} + \vec{J}$ represents the sum of the number of copies made in December plus those in the previous eleven months, that is, the total number of copies made during the entire year at that particular copy center.

Example 8   The price vector $\vec{p} = (p_1, p_2, p_3)$ represents the prices in dollars of three goods. Write a vector which gives the prices of the same goods in cents.

Solution   The prices in cents are $100p_1$, $100p_2$, and $100p_3$ respectively, so the new price vector is

$$(100p_1, 100p_2, 100p_3) = 100\vec{p}.$$

Problems for Section 12.2

In Problems 1–4, say whether the given quantity is a vector or a scalar.

1. The distance from Seattle to St. Louis.   scalar
2. The population of the US.   vectors
3. The magnetic field at a point on the earth's surface.   Vectors
4. The temperature at a point on the earth's surface.   scalar
5. A car is traveling at a speed of 50 km/hr. Assume the positive y-axis is north and the positive x-axis is east. Resolve the car's velocity vector (in 2-space) into components if the car is traveling in each of the following directions:
    (a) East   (b) South   (c) Southeast   (d) Northwest.
6. Which is traveling faster, a car whose velocity vector is $21\vec{i} + 35\vec{j}$, or a car whose velocity vector is $40\vec{i}$, assuming that the units are the same for both directions?
7. A moving object has velocity vector $50\vec{i} + 20\vec{j}$ in meters per second. Express the velocity in kilometers per hour.
8. A car drives clockwise around the track in Figure 12.27, slowing down at the curves and speeding up along the straight portions. Sketch velocity vectors at the points P, Q, and R.
9. A racing car drives clockwise around the track shown in Figure 12.27 at a constant speed. At what point on the track does the car have the longest acceleration vector, and in roughly what direction is it pointing? (Recall that acceleration is the rate of change of velocity.)

Figure 12.27

Figure 12.28

10. A particle moving with speed v hits a barrier at an angle of 60° and bounces off at an angle of 60° in the opposite direction with speed reduced by 20 percent, as shown in Figure 12.28. Find the velocity vector of the object after impact.

11. There are five students in a class. Their scores on the midterm (out of 100) are given by the vector $\vec{v} = (73, 80, 91, 65, 84)$. Their scores on the final (out of 100) are given by $\vec{w} = (82, 79, 88, 70, 92)$. If the final counts twice as much as the midterm, find a vector giving the total scores (as a percentage) of the students.

12. Shortly after taking off, a plane is climbing northwest through still air at an airspeed of 200 km/hr, and rising at a rate of 300 m/min. Resolve into components its velocity vector in a coordinate system in which the x-axis points east, the y-axis points north, and the z-axis points up.

13. An airplane is heading northeast at an airspeed of 700 km/hr, but there is a wind blowing from the west at 60 km/hr. In what direction does the plane end up flying? What is its speed relative to the ground?

14. An airplane is flying at an airspeed of 600 km/hr in a cross-wind that is blowing from the northeast at a speed of 50 km/hr. In what direction should the plane head to end up going due east?

15. A plane is heading due east and climbing at the rate of 80 km/hr. If its airspeed is 480 km/hr and there is a wind blowing 100 km/hr to the northeast, what is the ground speed of the plane?

Use the geometric definition of addition and scalar multiplication to explain each of the properties in Problems 16–23.

16. $\vec{w} + \vec{v} = \vec{v} + \vec{w}$

17. $(\alpha + \beta)\vec{v} = \alpha\vec{v} + \beta\vec{v}$

18. $\alpha(\vec{v} + \vec{w}) = \alpha\vec{v} + \alpha\vec{w}$

19. $(\vec{u} + \vec{v}) + \vec{w} = \vec{u} + (\vec{v} + \vec{w})$

20. $\alpha(\beta\vec{v}) = (\alpha\beta)\vec{v}$

21. $\vec{v} + \vec{0} = \vec{v}$

22. $1\vec{v} = \vec{v}$

23. $\vec{v} + (-1)\vec{w} = \vec{v} - \vec{w}$

12.3 THE DOT PRODUCT

We have seen how to add vectors; can we multiply two vectors together? In the next two sections we will see two different ways of doing so: the *scalar product* (or *dot product*) which produces a scalar, and the *vector product* (or *cross product*), which produces a vector.

Definition of the Dot Product

The dot product links geometry and algebra. We already know how to calculate the length of a vector from its components; the dot product gives us a way of computing the angle between two vectors. For any two vectors $\vec{v} = v_1\vec{i} + v_2\vec{j} + v_3\vec{k}$ and $\vec{w} = w_1\vec{i} + w_2\vec{j} + w_3\vec{k}$, shown in Figure 12.29, we define a scalar as follows:

> The following two definitions of the **dot product**, or **scalar product**, $\vec{v} \cdot \vec{w}$, are equivalent:
> - **Geometric definition**
> $\vec{v} \cdot \vec{w} = \|\vec{v}\|\|\vec{w}\|\cos\theta$ where θ is the angle between $\vec{v}$ and $\vec{w}$ and $0 \leq \theta \leq \pi$.
> - **Algebraic definition**
> $\vec{v} \cdot \vec{w} = v_1w_1 + v_2w_2 + v_3w_3$.
> Notice that the dot product of two vectors is a *number*.

Why don't we give just one definition of $\vec{v} \cdot \vec{w}$? The reason is that both definitions are equally important; the geometric definition gives us a picture of what the dot product means and the algebraic definition gives us a way of calculating it.

How do we know the two definitions are equivalent — that is, they really do define the same thing? First, we observe that the two definitions give the same result in a particular example. Then we show why they are equivalent in general.

Figure 12.29: The vectors $\vec{v}$ and $\vec{w}$

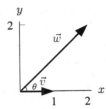

Figure 12.30: Calculating the dot product of the vectors $v = \vec{i}$ and $\vec{w} = 2\vec{i} + 2\vec{j}$ geometrically and algebraically gives the same result

Example 1   Suppose $\vec{v} = \vec{i}$ and $\vec{w} = 2\vec{i} + 2\vec{j}$. Compute $\vec{v} \cdot \vec{w}$ both geometrically and algebraically.

Solution   To use the geometric definition, see Figure 12.30. The angle between the vectors is $\pi/4$, or $45°$, and the lengths of the vectors are given by

$$\|\vec{v}\| = 1 \quad \text{and} \quad \|\vec{w}\| \doteq 2\sqrt{2}.$$

Thus,

$$\vec{v} \cdot \vec{w} = \|\vec{v}\|\|\vec{w}\| \cos\theta = 1 \cdot 2\sqrt{2}\cos\left(\frac{\pi}{4}\right) = 2.$$

Using the algebraic definition, we get the same result:

$$\vec{v} \cdot \vec{w} = 1 \cdot 2 + 0 \cdot 2 = 2.$$

Why the Two Definitions of the Dot Product Give the Same Result

In the previous example, the two definitions give the same value for the dot product. To show that the geometric and algebraic definitions of the dot product always give the same result, we must show that, for any vectors $\vec{v} = v_1\vec{i} + v_2\vec{j} + v_3\vec{k}$ and $\vec{u} = w_1\vec{i} + w_2\vec{j} + w_3\vec{k}$ with an angle θ between them:

$$\|\vec{v}\|\|\vec{w}\|\cos\theta = v_1 w_1 + v_2 w_2 + v_3 w_3.$$

One method follows; a method which does not use trigonometry is given in Problem 33 on page 85.

Using the Law of Cosines. Suppose that $0 < \theta < \pi$, so that the vectors $\vec{v}$ and $\vec{w}$ form a triangle. (See Figure 12.31.) By the Law of Cosines, we have

$$\|\vec{v} - \vec{w}\|^2 = \|\vec{v}\|^2 + \|\vec{w}\|^2 - 2\|\vec{v}\|\|\vec{w}\|\cos\theta.$$

This result is also true for $\theta = 0$ and $\theta = \pi$. We calculate the lengths using components:

$$\|\vec{v}\|^2 = v_1^2 + v_2^2 + v_3^2$$
$$\|\vec{w}\|^2 = w_1^2 + w_2^2 + w_3^2$$
$$\|\vec{v} - \vec{w}\|^2 = (v_1 - w_1)^2 + (v_2 - w_2)^2 + (v_3 - w_3)^2$$
$$= v_1^2 - 2v_1 w_1 + w_1^2 + v_2^2 - 2v_2 w_2 + w_2^2 + v_3^2 - 2v_3 w_3 + w_3^2.$$

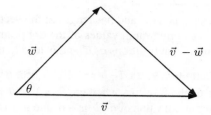

Figure 12.31: Triangle used in the justification of
$$\|\vec{v}\,\|\|\vec{w}\,\|\cos\theta = v_1 w_1 + v_2 w_2 + v_3 w_3$$

Substituting into the Law of Cosines and canceling, we see that

$$-2v_1 w_1 - 2v_2 w_2 - 2v_3 w_3 = -2\|\vec{v}\,\|\|\vec{w}\,\|\cos\theta.$$

Therefore we have the result we wanted, namely that:

$$v_1 w_1 + v_2 w_2 + v_3 w_3 = \|\vec{v}\,\|\|\vec{w}\,\|\cos\theta.$$

Properties of the Dot Product

The following properties of the dot product can be justified using the algebraic definition; see Problem 26 on page 84. For a geometric interpretation of Property 3, see Problem 30.

> **Properties of the Dot Product.** For any vectors $\vec{u}$, $\vec{v}$, and $\vec{w}$ and any scalar λ,
> 1. $\vec{v} \cdot \vec{w} = \vec{w} \cdot \vec{v}$
> 2. $\vec{v} \cdot (\lambda \vec{w}) = \lambda(\vec{v} \cdot \vec{w}) = (\lambda \vec{v}) \cdot \vec{w}$
> 3. $(\vec{v} + \vec{w}) \cdot \vec{u} = \vec{v} \cdot \vec{u} + \vec{w} \cdot \vec{u}$

Perpendicularity, Magnitude, and Dot Products

Two vectors are perpendicular if the angle between them is $\pi/2$ or $90°$. Since $\cos(\pi/2) = 0$, if $\vec{v}$ and $\vec{w}$ are perpendicular, then $\vec{v} \cdot \vec{w} = 0$. Conversely, provided that $\vec{v} \cdot \vec{w} = 0$, then $\cos\theta = 0$, so $\theta = \pi/2$ and the vectors are perpendicular. Thus, we have the following result:

> Two nonzero vectors $\vec{v}$ and $\vec{w}$ are **perpendicular**, or **orthogonal**, if and only if
>
> $$\vec{v} \cdot \vec{w} = 0.$$

For example: $\vec{i} \cdot \vec{j} = 0, \vec{j} \cdot \vec{k} = 0, \vec{i} \cdot \vec{k} = 0.$

If we take the dot product of a vector with itself, then $\theta = 0$ and $\cos\theta = 1$. For any vector $\vec{v}$:

> Magnitude and dot product are related as follows:
>
> $$\vec{v} \cdot \vec{v} = \|\vec{v}\,\|^2.$$

For example: $\vec{i} \cdot \vec{i} = 1, \vec{j} \cdot \vec{j} = 1, \vec{k} \cdot \vec{k} = 1.$

Using the Dot Product

Depending on the situation, one definition of the dot product may be more convenient to use than the other. In Example 2 which follows, the geometric definition is the only one which can be used because we are not given components. In Example 3, the algebraic definition is used.

Example 2   Suppose the vector $\vec{b}$ is fixed and has length 2; the vector $\vec{a}$ is free to rotate and has length 3. What are the maximum and minimum values of the dot product $\vec{a} \cdot \vec{b}$ as the vector $\vec{a}$ rotates through all possible positions? What positions of $\vec{a}$ and $\vec{b}$ lead to these values?

Solution   The geometric definition gives $\vec{a} \cdot \vec{b} = \|\vec{a}\|\|\vec{b}\| \cos\theta = 3 \cdot 2 \cos\theta = 6\cos\theta$. Thus, the maximum value of $\vec{a} \cdot \vec{b}$ is 6, and it occurs when $\cos\theta = 1$ so $\theta = 0$, that is, when $\vec{a}$ and $\vec{b}$ point in the same direction. The minimum value of $\vec{a} \cdot \vec{b}$ is -6, and it occurs when $\cos\theta = -1$ so $\theta = \pi$, that is, when $\vec{a}$ and $\vec{b}$ point in opposite directions. (See Figure 12.32.)

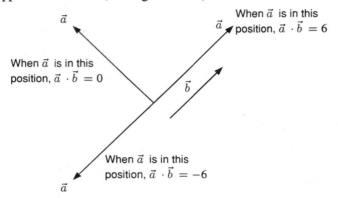

Figure 12.32: Maximum and minimum values of $\vec{a} \cdot \vec{b}$ obtained from a fixed vector $\vec{b}$ of length 2 and rotating vector $\vec{a}$ of length 3

Example 3   Which pairs from the following list of 3-dimensional vectors are perpendicular to one another?

$$\vec{u} = \vec{i} + \sqrt{3}\,\vec{k}, \quad \vec{v} = \vec{i} + \sqrt{3}\,\vec{j}, \quad \vec{w} = \sqrt{3}\,\vec{i} + \vec{j} - \vec{k}.$$

Solution   The geometric definition tells us that two vectors are perpendicular if and only if their dot product is zero. Since the vectors are given in components, we calculate dot products using the algebraic definition:

$$\vec{v} \cdot \vec{u} = (\vec{i} + \sqrt{3}\,\vec{j} + 0\vec{k}) \cdot (\vec{i} + 0\vec{j} + \sqrt{3}\,\vec{k}) = 1 \cdot 1 + \sqrt{3} \cdot 0 + 0 \cdot \sqrt{3} = 1,$$
$$\vec{v} \cdot \vec{w} = (\vec{i} + \sqrt{3}\,\vec{j} + 0\vec{k}) \cdot (\sqrt{3}\,\vec{i} + \vec{j} - \vec{k}) = 1 \cdot \sqrt{3} + \sqrt{3} \cdot 1 + 0(-1) = 2\sqrt{3},$$
$$\vec{w} \cdot \vec{u} = (\sqrt{3}\,\vec{i} + \vec{j} - \vec{k}) \cdot (\vec{i} + 0\vec{j} + \sqrt{3}\,\vec{k}) = \sqrt{3} \cdot 1 + 1 \cdot 0 + (-1) \cdot \sqrt{3} = 0.$$

So the only two vectors which are perpendicular are $\vec{w}$ and $\vec{u}$.

Normal Vectors and the Equation of a Plane

In Section 11.5 we wrote the equation of a plane given its x-slope, y-slope and z-intercept. Now we write the equation of a plane using a vector and a point lying on the plane. A *normal vector* to a plane is a vector that is perpendicular to the plane, that is, it is perpendicular to every displacement vector between any two points in the plane. Let $\vec{n} = a\vec{i} + b\vec{j} + c\vec{k}$ be a normal vector to the plane, let $P_0 = (x_0, y_0, z_0)$ be a fixed point in the plane, and let $P = (x, y, z)$ be any other point in the plane. Then $\overrightarrow{P_0P} = (x - x_0)\vec{i} + (y - y_0)\vec{j} + (z - z_0)\vec{k}$ is a vector whose head and tail both lie in the plane. (See Figure 12.33.) Thus, the vectors $\vec{n}$ and $\overrightarrow{P_0P}$ are perpendicular, so $\vec{n} \cdot \overrightarrow{P_0P} = 0$. The algebraic definition of the dot product gives $\vec{n} \cdot \overrightarrow{P_0P} = a(x - x_0) + b(y - y_0) + c(z - z_0)$, so we obtain the following result:

The **equation of the plane** with normal vector $\vec{n} = a\vec{i} + b\vec{j} + c\vec{k}$ and containing the point $P_0 = (x_0, y_0, z_0)$ is

$$a(x - x_0) + b(y - y_0) + c(z - z_0) = 0.$$

Letting $d = ax_0 + by_0 + cz_0$ (a constant), we can write the equation of the plane in the form

$$ax + by + cz = d.$$

Figure 12.33: Plane with normal $\vec{n}$ and containing a fixed point (x_0, y_0, z_0)

Example 4   Find the equation of the plane perpendicular to $-\vec{i} + 3\vec{j} + 2\vec{k}$ and passing through the point $(1, 0, 4)$.

Solution   The equation of the plane is

$$-(x - 1) + 3(y - 0) + 2(z - 4) = 0,$$

which simplifies to

$$-x + 3y + 2z = 7.$$

$-1(x-1) + 3(y-0) + 2(z-4)=0$

$-x+1 + 3y+2z - 8 = 0$

$-x + 3y +2z = 7$

Example 5   Find a normal vector to the plane with equation (a) $x - y + 2z = 5$ (b) $z = 0.5x + 1.2y$.

Solution   (a)   Since the coefficients of $\vec{i}$, $\vec{j}$, and $\vec{k}$ in a normal vector are the coefficients of x, y, z in the equation of the plane, a normal vector is $\vec{n} = \vec{i} - \vec{j} + 2\vec{k}$.
   (b)   Before we can find a normal vector, we rewrite the equation of the plane in the form

$$0.5x + 1.2y - z = 0.$$

Thus, a normal vector is $\vec{n} = 0.5\vec{i} + 1.2\vec{j} - \vec{k}$.

The Dot Product in n Dimensions

The algebraic definition of the dot product can be extended to vectors in higher dimensions.

If $\vec{u} = (u_1, \ldots, u_n)$ and $\vec{v} = (v_1, \ldots, v_n)$ then the dot product of $\vec{u}$ and $\vec{v}$ is the **scalar**

$$\vec{u} \cdot \vec{v} = u_1 v_1 + \ldots + u_n v_n.$$

Example 6   A video store sells videos, tapes, CD's, and computer games. We define the quantity vector $\vec{q} = (q_1, q_2, q_3, q_4)$, where q_1, q_2, q_3, q_4 denote the quantities sold of each of the items, and the price vector $\vec{p} = (p_1, p_2, p_3, p_4)$, where p_1, p_2, p_3, p_4 denote the price per unit of each item. What does the dot product $\vec{p} \cdot \vec{q}$ represent?

Solution   The dot product is $\vec{p} \cdot \vec{q} = p_1 q_1 + p_2 q_2 + p_3 q_3 + p_4 q_4$. The quantity $p_1 q_1$ represents the revenue received by the store for the videos, $p_2 q_2$ represents the revenue for the tapes, and so on. The dot product represents the total revenue received by the store for the sale of these four items.

Resolving a Vector into Components: Projections

In Section 12.1, we resolved a vector into components parallel to the axes. Now we see how to resolve a vector, $\vec{v}$, into components, called $\vec{v}_{\text{parallel}}$ and $\vec{v}_{\text{perp}}$, which are parallel and perpendicular, respectively, to a given nonzero vector, $\vec{u}$. (See Figure 12.34.)

The projection of $\vec{v}$ on $\vec{u}$, written $\vec{v}_{\text{parallel}}$, measures (in some sense) how much the vector $\vec{v}$ is aligned with the vector $\vec{u}$. The length of $\vec{v}_{\text{parallel}}$ is the length of the shadow cast by $\vec{v}$ on a line in the direction of $\vec{u}$.

To compute $\vec{v}_{\text{parallel}}$, we assume $\vec{u}$ is a unit vector. (If not, create one by dividing by its length.) Then Figure 12.34(a) shows that, if $0 \leq \theta \leq \pi/2$:

$$\|\vec{v}_{\text{parallel}}\| = \|\vec{v}\| \cos \theta = \vec{v} \cdot \vec{u} \qquad (\text{since } \|\vec{u}\| = 1).$$

Now $\vec{v}_{\text{parallel}}$ is a scalar multiple of $\vec{u}$, and since $\vec{u}$ is a unit vector,

$$\vec{v}_{\text{parallel}} = (\|\vec{v}\| \cos \theta)\vec{u} = (\vec{v} \cdot \vec{u})\vec{u}.$$

A similar argument shows that if $\pi/2 < \theta \leq \pi$, as in Figure 12.34(b), this formula for $\vec{v}_{\text{parallel}}$ still holds. The vector $\vec{v}_{\text{perp}}$ is specified by

$$\vec{v}_{\text{perp}} = \vec{v} - \vec{v}_{\text{parallel}}.$$

Thus, we have the following results:

Projection of $\vec{v}$ on the Line in the Direction of the Unit Vector $\vec{u}$

If $\vec{v}_{\text{parallel}}$ and $\vec{v}_{\text{perp}}$ are components of $\vec{v}$ which are parallel and perpendicular, respectively, to $\vec{u}$, then

$$\text{Projection of } \vec{v} \text{ on to } \vec{u} = \vec{v}_{\text{parallel}} = (\vec{v} \cdot \vec{u})\vec{u} \qquad \text{provided } \|\vec{u}\| = 1$$

and $\vec{v} = \vec{v}_{\text{parallel}} + \vec{v}_{\text{perp}}$ so $\vec{v}_{\text{perp}} = \vec{v} - \vec{v}_{\text{parallel}}.$

Figure 12.34: Resolving $\vec{v}$ into components parallel and perpendicular to $\vec{u}$
(a) $0 < \theta < \pi/2$ (b) $\pi/2 < \theta < \pi$

Example 7   Figure 12.35 shows the force the wind exerts on the sail of a sailboat. Find the component of the force in the direction in which the sailboat is traveling.

Figure 12.35: Wind moving a sailboat

Solution   Let $\vec{u}$ be a unit vector in the direction of travel. The force of the wind on the sail makes an angle of 30° with $\vec{u}$. Thus, the component of this force in the direction of $\vec{u}$ is

$$\vec{F}_{\text{parallel}} = (\vec{F} \cdot \vec{u})\vec{u} = \|\vec{F}\|(\cos 30°)\vec{u} = 0.87\|\vec{F}\|\vec{u}.$$

Thus, the boat is being pushed forward with about 87% of the total force due to the wind. (In fact, the interaction of wind and sail is much more complex than this model suggests.)

A Physical Interpretation of the Dot Product: Work

In physics, the word "work" has a slightly different meaning from its everyday meaning. In physics, when a force of magnitude F acts on an object through a distance d, we say the *work*, W, done by the force is

$$W = Fd,$$

provided the force and the displacement are in the same direction. For example, if a 1 kg body falls 10 meters under the force of gravity, which is 9.8 newtons, then the work done by gravity is

$$W = (9.8 \text{ newtons}) \cdot (10 \text{ meters}) = 98 \text{ joules.}$$

What if the force and the displacement are not in the same direction? Suppose a force $\vec{F}$ acts on an object as it moves along a displacement vector $\vec{d}$. Let θ be the angle between $\vec{F}$ and $\vec{d}$. First, we assume $0 \leq \theta \leq \pi/2$. Figure 12.36 shows how we can resolve $\vec{F}$ into components that are parallel and perpendicular to $\vec{d}$:

$$\vec{F} = \vec{F}_{\text{parallel}} + \vec{F}_{\text{perp}},$$

Figure 12.36: Resolving the force $\vec{F}$ into two forces, one parallel to $\vec{d}$, one perpendicular to $\vec{d}$

Then the work done by $\vec{F}$ is defined to be

$$W = \|\vec{F}_{\text{parallel}}\|\,\|\vec{d}\|.$$

We see from Figure 12.36 that $\vec{F}_{\text{parallel}}$ has magnitude $\|\vec{F}\|\cos\theta$. So the work is given by the dot product:

$$W = (\|\vec{F}\|\cos\theta)\|\vec{d}\| = \|\vec{F}\|\|\vec{d}\|\cos\theta = \vec{F}\cdot\vec{d}.$$

The formula $W = \vec{F}\cdot\vec{d}$ holds when $\pi/2 < \theta \leq \pi$ also. In that case, the work done by the force is negative and the object is moving against the force. Thus, we have the following definition:

> The **work**, W, done by a force $\vec{F}$ acting on an object through a displacement $\vec{d}$ is given by
>
> $$W = \vec{F}\cdot\vec{d}.$$

Notice that if the vectors $\vec{F}$ and $\vec{d}$ are parallel and in the same direction, with magnitudes F and d, then $\cos\theta = \cos 0 = 1$, so $W = \|\vec{F}\|\|\vec{d}\| = Fd$, which is the original definition. When the vectors are perpendicular, $\cos\theta = \cos\frac{\pi}{2} = 0$, so $W = 0$ and no work is done in the technical definition of the word. For example, if you carry a heavy box across the room at the same horizontal height, no work is done by gravity because the force of gravity is vertical but the motion is horizontal.

Problems for Section 12.3

For Problems 1–6, perform the following operations on the given 3-dimensional vectors.

$$\vec{a} = 2\vec{j}+\vec{k} \qquad \vec{b} = -3\vec{i}+5\vec{j}+4\vec{k} \qquad \vec{c} = \vec{i}+6\vec{j} \qquad \vec{y} = 4\vec{i}-7\vec{j} \qquad \vec{z} = \vec{i}-3\vec{j}-\vec{k}$$

1. $\vec{c}\cdot\vec{y}$
2. $\vec{a}\cdot\vec{z}$
3. $\vec{a}\cdot\vec{b}$
4. $(\vec{a}\cdot\vec{b})\vec{a}$
5. $(\vec{a}\cdot\vec{y})(\vec{c}\cdot\vec{z})$
6. $((\vec{c}\cdot\vec{c})\vec{a})\cdot\vec{a}$

7. Compute the angle between the vectors $\vec{i}+\vec{j}+\vec{k}$ and $\vec{i}-\vec{j}-\vec{k}$.

8. Which pairs of the vectors $\sqrt{3}\vec{i}+\vec{j}, 3\vec{i}+\sqrt{3}\vec{j}, \vec{i}-\sqrt{3}\vec{j}$ are parallel and which are perpendicular?

9. For what values of t are $\vec{u} = t\vec{i}-\vec{j}+\vec{k}$ and $\vec{v} = t\vec{i}+t\vec{j}-2\vec{k}$ perpendicular? Are there values of t for which $\vec{u}$ and $\vec{v}$ are parallel?

In Problems 10–12, find a normal vector to the given plane.

10. $2x+y-z = 5$
11. $z = 3x+4y-7$
12. $2(x-z) = 3(x+y)$

In Problems 13–17, find an equation of a plane that satisfies the given conditions.

13. Perpendicular to the vector $-\vec{i}+2\vec{j}+\vec{k}$ and passing through the point $(1,0,2)$.
14. Perpendicular to the vector $5\vec{i}+\vec{j}-2\vec{k}$ and passing through the point $(0,1,-1)$.
15. Perpendicular to the vector $2\vec{i}-3\vec{j}+7\vec{k}$ and passing through the point $(1,-1,2)$.
16. Parallel to the plane $2x+4y-3z = 1$ and through the point $(1,0,-1)$.
17. Through the point $(-2,3,2)$ and parallel to $3x+y+z = 4$.
18. Let S be the triangle with vertices $A = (2,2,2), B = (4,2,1)$, and $C = (2,3,1)$.
    - (a) Find the length of the shortest side of S.
    - (b) Find the cosine of the angle BAC at vertex A.

19. Write $\vec{a} = 3\vec{i} + 2\vec{j} - 6\vec{k}$ as the sum of two vectors, one parallel to $\vec{d} = 2\vec{i} - 4\vec{j} + \vec{k}$ and the other perpendicular to $\vec{d}$.

20. Find the points where the plane $z = 5x - 4y + 3$ intersects each of the coordinate axes. Then find the lengths of the sides and the angles of the triangle formed by these points.

21. Find the angle between the planes $5(x-1)+3(y+2)+2z = 0$ and $x+3(y-1)+2(z+4) = 0$.

22. A basketball gymnasium is 25 meters high, 80 meters wide and 200 meters long. For a half time stunt, the cheerleaders want to run two strings, one from each of the two corners above one basket to the diagonally opposite corners of the gym floor. What is the cosine of the angle made by the strings as they cross?

23. A consumption vector of three goods is defined by $\vec{x} = (x_1, x_2, x_3)$, where x_1, x_2 and x_3 are the quantities consumed of the three goods. Consider a budget constraint represented by the equation $\vec{p} \cdot \vec{x} = k$, where $\vec{p}$ is the price vector of the three goods and k is a constant. Show that the difference between two consumption vectors corresponding to points satisfying the same budget constraint is perpendicular to the price vector $\vec{p}$.

24. A 100-meter dash is run on a track in the direction of the vector $\vec{v} = 2\vec{i} + 6\vec{j}$. The wind velocity $\vec{w}$ is $5\vec{i} + \vec{j}$ km/h. The rules say that a legal wind speed measured in the direction of the dash must not exceed 5 km/h. Will the race results be disqualified due to an illegal wind? Justify your answer.

25. Recall that in 2 or 3 dimensions, if θ is the angle between $\vec{v}$ and $\vec{w}$, the dot product is given by

$$\vec{v} \cdot \vec{w} = \|\vec{v}\|\|\vec{w}\| \cos\theta.$$

We use this relationship to define the angle between two vectors in n-dimensions. If $\vec{v}$, $\vec{w}$ are n-vectors, then the dot product, $\vec{v} \cdot \vec{w} = v_1 w_1 + v_2 w_2 + \cdots + v_n w_n$, is used to define[2] the angle θ by

$$\cos\theta = \frac{\vec{v} \cdot \vec{w}}{\|\vec{v}\|\|\vec{w}\|} \qquad \text{provided } \|\vec{v}\|, \|\vec{w}\| \neq 0.$$

We now use this idea of angle to measure how close two populations are to one another genetically. Table 12.1 shows the relative frequencies of four alleles (variants of a gene) in four populations.

TABLE 12.1

Allele	Eskimo	Bantu	English	Korean
A_1	0.29	0.10	0.20	0.22
A_2	0.00	0.08	0.06	0.00
B	0.03	0.12	0.06	0.20
O	0.67	0.69	0.66	0.57

Let $\vec{a}_1$ be the 4-vector showing the relative frequencies in the Eskimo population;

$\vec{a}_2$ be the 4-vector showing the relative frequencies in the Bantu population;

$\vec{a}_3$ be the 4-vector showing the relative frequencies in the English population;

$\vec{a}_4$ be the 4-vector showing the relative frequencies in the Korean population.

---

[2]The result of Problem 34 shows that the quantity on the right-hand side of this equation is between -1 and 1, so this definition makes sense.

The genetic distance between two populations is defined as the angle between the corresponding vectors. Using this definition, is the English population closer genetically to the Bantus or to the Koreans? Explain.[3]

26. Show why each of the properties of the dot product in the box on page 77 follows from the algebraic definition of the dot product:

$$\vec{v} \cdot \vec{w} = v_1 w_1 + v_2 w_2 + v_3 w_3$$

27. What does Property 2 of the dot product in the box on page 77 say geometrically?

28. Show that the vectors $(\vec{b} \cdot \vec{c})\vec{a} - (\vec{a} \cdot \vec{c})\vec{b}$ and $\vec{c}$ are perpendicular.

29. Show that if $\vec{u}$ and $\vec{v}$ are two vectors such that

$$\vec{u} \cdot \vec{w} = \vec{v} \cdot \vec{w}$$

for every vector $\vec{w}$, then

$$\vec{u} = \vec{v}.$$

30. Figure 12.37 shows that, given three vectors $\vec{u}$, $\vec{v}$, and $\vec{w}$, the sum of the components of $\vec{v}$ and $\vec{w}$ in the direction of $\vec{u}$ is the component of $\vec{v} + \vec{w}$ in the direction of $\vec{u}$. (Although the figure is drawn in two dimensions, this result is also true in three dimensions.) Use this figure to explain why the geometric definition of the dot product satisfies $(\vec{v} + \vec{w}) \cdot \vec{u} = \vec{v} \cdot \vec{u} + \vec{w} \cdot \vec{u}$.

Figure 12.37: The component of $\vec{v} + \vec{w}$ in the direction of $\vec{u}$ is the sum of the components of $\vec{v}$ and $\vec{w}$ in that direction

31. (a) Using the geometric definition of the dot product, show that

$$\vec{u} \cdot (-\vec{v}) = -(\vec{u} \cdot \vec{v}).$$

[Hint: What happens to the angle when you multiply $\vec{v}$ by -1?]

(b) Using the geometric definition of the dot product, show that for any negative scalar λ

$$\vec{u} \cdot (\lambda\vec{v}) = \lambda(\vec{u} \cdot \vec{v})$$
$$(\lambda\vec{u}) \cdot \vec{v} = \lambda(\vec{u} \cdot \vec{v}).$$

32. The Law of Cosines for a triangle with side lengths a, b, and c, and with angle C opposite side c, says

$$c^2 = a^2 + b^2 - 2ab\cos C.$$

On page 76, we used the Law of Cosines to show that the two definitions of the dot product

[3]Adapted from Cavalli-Sforza and Edwards, "Models and Estimation Procedures," Am J. Hum. Genet., Vol. 19 (1967), pp. 223-57.

are equivalent. In this problem, you will use the geometric definition of the dot product and its properties in the box on page 77 to prove the Law of Cosines. [Hint: Let $\vec{u}$ and $\vec{v}$ be the displacement vectors from C to the other two vertices, and express c^2 in terms of $\vec{u}$ and $\vec{v}$.]

33. Use the following steps and the results of Problems 30–31 to show (without trigonometry) that the geometric and algebraic definitions of the dot product are equivalent.

    Follow these steps. Let $\vec{u} = u_1\vec{i} + u_2\vec{j} + u_3\vec{k}$ and $\vec{v} = v_1\vec{i} + v_2\vec{j} + v_3\vec{k}$ be any vectors. Write $(\vec{u} \cdot \vec{v})_{\text{geom}}$ for the result of the dot product computed geometrically. Substitute $\vec{u} = u_1\vec{i} + u_2\vec{j} + u_3\vec{k}$ and use Problems 30–31 to expand $(\vec{u} \cdot \vec{v})_{\text{geom}}$. Next substitute for $\vec{v}$ and expand. Finally, calculate geometrically the dot products $\vec{i} \cdot \vec{i}$, $\vec{i} \cdot \vec{j}$, etc.

34. Suppose that $\vec{v}$ and $\vec{w}$ are any two vectors. Consider the following function of t:

$$q(t) = (\vec{v} + t\vec{w}) \cdot (\vec{v} + t\vec{w})$$

    (a) Explain why $q(t) \geq 0$ for all real t.
    (b) Expand $q(t)$ as a quadratic polynomial in t using the properties on page 77.
    (c) Using the discriminant of the quadratic, show that,

$$|\vec{v} \cdot \vec{w}| \leq \|\vec{v}\|\|\vec{w}\|.$$

12.4   THE CROSS PRODUCT

In the previous section we combined two vectors to get a number, the dot product. In this section we see another way of combining two vectors, this time to get a vector, the *cross product*. Any two vectors in 3-space form a parallelogram. We define the cross product using this parallelogram.

The Area of a Parallelogram

Consider the parallelogram formed by the vectors $\vec{v}$ and $\vec{w}$ with an angle of θ between them. Then Figure 12.38 shows

$$\text{Area of parallelogram} = \text{Base} \cdot \text{Height} = \|\vec{v}\|\|\vec{w}\|\sin\theta.$$

How would we compute the area of the parallelogram if we were given $\vec{v}$ and $\vec{w}$ in components, $\vec{v} = v_1\vec{i} + v_2\vec{j} + v_3\vec{k}$ and $\vec{w} = w_1\vec{i} + w_2\vec{j} + w_3\vec{k}$? Problem 27 on page 92 shows that if $\vec{v}$ and $\vec{w}$ are in the xy-plane, so $v_3 = w_3 = 0$, then

$$\text{Area of parallelogram} = |v_1w_2 - v_2w_1|.$$

What if $\vec{v}$ and $\vec{w}$ do not lie in the xy-plane? The cross product will enable us to compute the area of the parallelogram formed by any two vectors.

Figure 12.38: Parallelogram formed by $\vec{v}$ and $\vec{w}$ has
Area $= \|\vec{v}\|\|\vec{w}\|\sin\theta$

Definition of the Cross Product

We define the cross product of the vectors $\vec{v}$ and $\vec{w}$, written $\vec{v} \times \vec{w}$, to be a vector perpendicular to both $\vec{v}$ and $\vec{w}$. The magnitude of this vector is the area of the parallelogram formed by the two vectors. The direction of $\vec{v} \times \vec{w}$ is given by the normal vector, $\vec{n}$, to the plane defined by $\vec{v}$ and $\vec{w}$. If we require that $\vec{n}$ be a unit vector, there are two choices for $\vec{n}$, pointing out of the plane in opposite directions. We pick one by the following rule (see Figure 12.39):

The right-hand rule: Place $\vec{v}$ and $\vec{w}$ so that their tails coincide and curl the fingers of your right hand through the smaller of the two angles from $\vec{v}$ to $\vec{w}$; your thumb points in the direction of the normal vector, $\vec{n}$.

Like the dot product, there are two equivalent definitions of the cross product:

The following two definitions of the **cross product** or **vector product** $\vec{v} \times \vec{w}$ are equivalent:
- **Geometric definition**
  If $\vec{v}$ and $\vec{w}$ are not parallel, then

$$\vec{v} \times \vec{w} = \left(\begin{array}{c} \text{Area of parallelogram} \\ \text{with edges } \vec{v} \text{ and } \vec{w} \end{array}\right) \vec{n} = (\|\vec{v}\|\|\vec{w}\|\sin\theta)\vec{n},$$

  where $0 \leq \theta \leq \pi$ is the angle between $\vec{v}$ and $\vec{w}$ and $\vec{n}$ is the unit vector perpendicular to $\vec{v}$ and $\vec{w}$ pointing in the direction given by the right-hand rule. If $\vec{v}$ and $\vec{w}$ are parallel, then $\vec{v} \times \vec{w} = \vec{0}$.
- **Algebraic definition**

$$\vec{v} \times \vec{w} = (v_2 w_3 - v_3 w_2)\vec{i} + (v_3 w_1 - v_1 w_3)\vec{j} + (v_1 w_2 - v_2 w_1)\vec{k}$$

  where $\vec{v} = v_1\vec{i} + v_2\vec{j} + v_3\vec{k}$ and $\vec{w} = w_1\vec{i} + w_2\vec{j} + w_3\vec{k}$.

Notice that the magnitude of the $\vec{k}$ component is the area of a 2-dimensional parallelogram and the other components have a similar form. Problems 25 and 26 at the end of this section show that the geometric and algebraic definitions of the cross product give the same result.

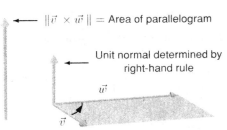

Figure 12.39: Area of parallelogram
$= \|\vec{v} \times \vec{w}\|$

Figure 12.40. The cross product $\vec{v} \times \vec{w}$

Unlike the dot product, the cross product is only defined for three-dimensional vectors. The geometric definition shows us that the cross product is *rotation invariant*. Imagine the two vectors $\vec{v}$ and $\vec{w}$ as two metal rods welded together. Attach a third rod whose direction and length correspond to $\vec{v} \times \vec{w}$. (See Figure 12.40.) Then, no matter how we turn this set of rods, the third will still be the cross product of the first two.

The algebraic definition is more easily remembered by writing it as a 3×3 determinant. (See Appendix C.)

$$\vec{v} \times \vec{w} = \begin{vmatrix} \vec{i} & \vec{j} & \vec{k} \\ v_1 & v_2 & v_3 \\ w_1 & w_2 & w_3 \end{vmatrix} = (v_2 w_3 - v_3 w_2)\vec{i} + (v_3 w_1 - v_1 w_3)\vec{j} + (v_1 w_2 - v_2 w_1)\vec{k}.$$

Example 1   Find $\vec{i} \times \vec{j}$ and $\vec{j} \times \vec{i}$.

Solution   The vectors $\vec{i}$ and $\vec{j}$ both have magnitude 1 and the angle between them is $\pi/2$. By the right-hand rule, the vector $\vec{i} \times \vec{j}$ is in the direction of $\vec{k}$, so $\vec{n} = \vec{k}$ and we have

$$\vec{i} \times \vec{j} = \left(\|\vec{i}\| \|\vec{j}\| \sin \frac{\pi}{2} \right) \vec{k} = \vec{k}.$$

Similarly, the right-hand rule says that the direction of $\vec{j} \times \vec{i}$ is $-\vec{k}$, so

$$\vec{j} \times \vec{i} = (\|\vec{j}\| \|\vec{i}\| \sin \frac{\pi}{2})(-\vec{k}) = -\vec{k}.$$

Similar calculations show that $\vec{j} \times \vec{k} = \vec{i}$ and $\vec{k} \times \vec{i} = \vec{j}$.

Example 2   For any vector $\vec{v}$, find $\vec{v} \times \vec{v}$.

Solution   Since $\vec{v}$ is parallel to itself, $\vec{v} \times \vec{v} = \vec{0}$.

Example 3   Find the cross product of $\vec{v} = 2\vec{i} + \vec{j} - 2\vec{k}$ and $\vec{w} = 3\vec{i} + \vec{k}$ and check that the cross product is perpendicular to both $\vec{v}$ and $\vec{w}$.

Solution   Writing $\vec{v} \times \vec{w}$ as a determinant and expanding it into three two-by-two determinants, we have

$$\vec{v} \times \vec{w} = \begin{vmatrix} \vec{i} & \vec{j} & \vec{k} \\ 2 & 1 & -2 \\ 3 & 0 & 1 \end{vmatrix} = \vec{i} \begin{vmatrix} 1 & -2 \\ 0 & 1 \end{vmatrix} - \vec{j} \begin{vmatrix} 2 & -2 \\ 3 & 1 \end{vmatrix} + \vec{k} \begin{vmatrix} 2 & 1 \\ 3 & 0 \end{vmatrix}$$

$$= \vec{i} \left(1(1) - 0(-2) \right) - \vec{j} \left(2(1) - 3(-2) \right) + \vec{k} \left(2(0) - 3(1) \right)$$

$$= \vec{i} - 8\vec{j} - 3\vec{k}.$$

To check that $\vec{v} \times \vec{w}$ is perpendicular to $\vec{v}$, we compute the dot product:

$$\vec{v} \cdot (\vec{v} \times \vec{w}) = (2\vec{i} + \vec{j} - 2\vec{k}) \cdot (\vec{i} - 8\vec{j} - 3\vec{k}) = 2 - 8 + 6 = 0.$$

Similarly,

$$\vec{w} \cdot (\vec{v} \times \vec{w}) = (3\vec{i} + 0\vec{j} + \vec{k}) \cdot (\vec{i} - 8\vec{j} - 3\vec{k}) = 3 + 0 - 3 = 0.$$

Thus, $\vec{v} \times \vec{w}$ is perpendicular to both $\vec{v}$ and $\vec{w}$.

Properties of the Cross Product

The right-hand rule tells us that $\vec{v} \times \vec{w}$ and $\vec{w} \times \vec{v}$ point in opposite directions. The magnitudes of $\vec{v} \times \vec{w}$ and $\vec{w} \times \vec{v}$ are the same, so $\vec{w} \times \vec{v} = -(\vec{v} \times \vec{w})$. (See Figure 12.41.)

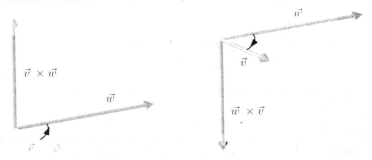

Figure 12.41: Diagram showing $\vec{v} \times \vec{w} = -(\vec{w} \times \vec{v})$

This explains the first of the following properties. The other two are derived in Problems 17, 21, and 25 at the end of this section.

Properties of the Cross Product

For vectors $\vec{u}, \vec{v}, \vec{w}$ and scalar λ
1. $\vec{w} \times \vec{v} = -(\vec{v} \times \vec{w})$
2. $(\lambda \vec{v}) \times \vec{w} = \lambda(\vec{v} \times \vec{w}) = \vec{v} \times (\lambda \vec{w})$
3. $\vec{u} \times (\vec{v} + \vec{w}) = \vec{u} \times \vec{v} + \vec{u} \times \vec{w}$.

The Equivalence of the Two Definitions of the Cross Product

Problems 22 and 25 on page 92 use geometric arguments to show that the cross product distributes over addition. Problem 26 then shows how the formula in the algebraic definition of the cross product can be derived from the geometric definition.

The Equation of a Plane Through Three Points

The equation of a plane is determined by a point $P_0 = (x_0, y_0, z_0)$ on the plane, and a normal vector, $\vec{n} = a\vec{i} + b\vec{j} + c\vec{k}$:

$$a(x - x_0) + b(y - y_0) + c(z - z_0) = 0.$$

However, a plane can also be determined by three points on it (provided they do not lie on a line). In that case we can find an equation of the plane by first determining two vectors in the plane and then finding a normal vector using the cross product, as in the following example.

Example 4   Find an equation of the plane containing the points $P = (1, 3, 0)$, $Q = (3, 4, -3)$, and $R = (3, 6, 2)$.

Solution   Since the points P and Q are in the plane, the displacement vector between them, $\overrightarrow{PQ}$, is in the plane, where

$$\overrightarrow{PQ} = (3-1)\vec{i} + (4-3)\vec{j} + (-3-0)\vec{k} = 2\vec{i} + \vec{j} - 3\vec{k}.$$

The displacement vector $\overrightarrow{PR}$ is also in the plane, where

$$\overrightarrow{PR} = (3-1)\vec{i} + (6-3)\vec{j} + (2-0)\vec{k} = 2\vec{i} + 3\vec{j} + 2\vec{k}.$$

Thus, a normal vector, $\vec{n}$, to the plane is given by

$$\vec{n} = \overrightarrow{PQ} \times \overrightarrow{PR} = \begin{vmatrix} \vec{i} & \vec{j} & \vec{k} \\ 2 & 1 & -3 \\ 2 & 3 & 2 \end{vmatrix} = 11\vec{i} - 10\vec{j} + 4\vec{k}.$$

Since the point $(1, 3, 0)$ is on the plane, the equation of the plane is

$$11(x - 1) - 10(y - 3) + 4(z - 0) = 0,$$

which simplifies to

$$11x - 10y + 4z = -19.$$

You should check that P, Q, and R satisfy the equation of the plane.

Areas and Volumes Using the Cross Product and Determinants

We can use the cross product to calculate the area of the parallelogram with sides $\vec{v}$ and $\vec{w}$. We say that $\vec{v} \times \vec{w}$ is the *area vector* of the parallelogram. The geometric definition of the cross product tells us that $\vec{v} \times \vec{w}$ is normal to the parallelogram and gives us the following result:

Area of a parallelogram with edges $\vec{v} = v_1\vec{i} + v_2\vec{j} + v_3\vec{k}$ and $\vec{w} = w_1\vec{i} + w_2\vec{j} + w_3\vec{k}$ is given by

$$\text{Area} = \|\vec{v} \times \vec{w}\|, \qquad \text{where} \quad \vec{v} \times \vec{w} = \begin{vmatrix} \vec{i} & \vec{j} & \vec{k} \\ v_1 & v_2 & v_3 \\ w_1 & w_2 & w_3 \end{vmatrix}.$$

Example 5   Find the area of the parallelogram with edges $\vec{v} = 2\vec{i} + \vec{j} - 3\vec{k}$ and $\vec{w} = \vec{i} + 3\vec{j} + 2\vec{k}$.

Solution   We calculate the cross product:

$$\vec{v} \times \vec{w} = \begin{vmatrix} \vec{i} & \vec{j} & \vec{k} \\ 2 & 1 & -3 \\ 1 & 3 & 2 \end{vmatrix} = (2 + 9)\vec{i} - (4 + 3)\vec{j} + (6 - 1)\vec{k} = 11\vec{i} - 7\vec{j} + 5\vec{k}.$$

The area of the parallelogram with edges $\vec{v}$ and $\vec{w}$ is the magnitude of the vector $\vec{v} \times \vec{w}$:

$$\text{Area} = \|\vec{v} \times \vec{w}\| = \sqrt{11^2 + (-7)^2 + 5^2} = \sqrt{195}.$$

Volume of a Parallelepiped

Consider the parallelepiped with sides formed by $\vec{a}$, $\vec{b}$, and $\vec{c}$. (See Figure 12.42.) Since the base is formed by the vectors $\vec{b}$ and $\vec{c}$, we have

$$\text{Area of base of parallelepiped} = \|\vec{b} \times \vec{c}\|.$$

Figure 12.42: Volume of a Parallelepiped   **Figure 12.43:** The vectors $\vec{a}$, $\vec{b}$, $\vec{c}$ are called a right-handed set   **Figure 12.44:** The vectors $\vec{a}$, $\vec{b}$, $\vec{c}$ are called a left-handed set

The vectors $\vec{a}$, $\vec{b}$, and $\vec{c}$ can be arranged either as in Figure 12.43 or as in Figure 12.44. In either case,

$$\text{Height of parallelepiped} = \|\vec{a}\|\cos\theta,$$

where θ is the angle between $\vec{a}$ and $\vec{b} \times \vec{c}$. In Figure 12.43 the angle θ is less than $\pi/2$, so the product, $(\vec{b} \times \vec{c}) \cdot \vec{a}$, called the *triple product*, is positive. Thus, in this case

$$\text{Volume of parallelepiped} = \text{Base} \cdot \text{Height} = \|\vec{b} \times \vec{c}\| \cdot \|\vec{a}\|\cos\theta = (\vec{b} \times \vec{c}) \cdot \vec{a}.$$

In Figure 12.44, the angle, $\pi - \theta$, between $\vec{a}$ and $\vec{b} \times \vec{c}$ is more than $\pi/2$, so the product $(\vec{b} \times \vec{c}) \cdot \vec{a}$ is negative. Thus, in this case we have

$$\text{Volume} = \text{Base} \cdot \text{Height} = \|\vec{b} \times \vec{c}\| \cdot \|\vec{a}\|\cos\theta = -\|\vec{b} \times \vec{c}\| \cdot \|\vec{a}\|\cos(\pi - \theta)$$
$$= -(\vec{b} \times \vec{c}) \cdot \vec{a} = \left|(\vec{b} \times \vec{c}) \cdot \vec{a}\right|.$$

Therefore, in both cases the volume is given by $\left|(\vec{b} \times \vec{c}) \cdot \vec{a}\right|$. Using determinants, we can write

---

Volume of a parallelepiped with edges $\vec{a}$, $\vec{b}$, $\vec{c}$ is given by

$$\text{Volume} = \left|(\vec{b} \times \vec{c}) \cdot \vec{a}\right| = \text{Absolute value of the determinant} \begin{vmatrix} a_1 & a_2 & a_3 \\ b_1 & b_2 & b_3 \\ c_1 & c_2 & c_3 \end{vmatrix}.$$

Problems for Section 12.4

1. Find $\vec{k} \times \vec{j}$.   scalar

2. Does $\vec{i} \times \vec{i} = \vec{i} \cdot \vec{i}$? Explain your answer.

In Problems 3–6, find $\vec{a} \times \vec{b}$.

3. $\vec{a} = \vec{i} + \vec{k}$ and $\vec{b} = \vec{i} + \vec{j}$.   4. $\vec{a} = -\vec{i}$ and $\vec{b} = \vec{j} + \vec{k}$.

5. $\vec{a} = \vec{i} + \vec{j} + \vec{k}$ and $\vec{b} = \vec{i} + \vec{j} + -\vec{k}$.   6. $\vec{a} = 2\vec{i} - 3\vec{j} + \vec{k}$ and $\vec{b} = \vec{i} + 2\vec{j} - \vec{k}$.

7. Given $\vec{a} = 3\vec{i} + \vec{j} - \vec{k}$ and $\vec{b} = \vec{i} - 4\vec{j} + 2\vec{k}$, find $\vec{a} \times \vec{b}$ and check that $\vec{a} \times \vec{b}$ is perpendicular to both $\vec{a}$ and $\vec{b}$.

8. If $\vec{v} \times \vec{w} = 2\vec{i} - 3\vec{j} + 5\vec{k}$, and $\vec{v} \cdot \vec{w} = 3$, find $\tan \theta$ where θ is the angle between $\vec{v}$ and $\vec{w}$.

9. Suppose $\vec{a}$ is a fixed vector of length 3 in the direction of the positive x-axis and the vector $\vec{b}$ of length 2 is free to rotate in the xy-plane. What are the maximum and minimum values of the magnitude of $\vec{a} \times \vec{b}$? In what direction is $\vec{a} \times \vec{b}$ as $\vec{b}$ rotates?

10. You are using a jet pilot dogfight simulator. Your monitor tells you that two missiles have honed in on your plane along the directions $3\vec{i} + 5\vec{j} + 2\vec{k}$ and $\vec{i} - 3\vec{j} - 2\vec{k}$. In what direction should you turn to have the maximum chance of avoiding both missiles?

Find an equation for the plane through the points in Problems 11–12.

11. $(1, 0, 0), (0, 1, 0), (0, 0, 1)$.   12. $(3, 4, 2), (-2, 1, 0), (0, 2, 1)$.

13. Given the points $P = (0, 1, 0)$, $Q = (-1, 1, 2)$, $R = (2, 1, -1)$, find
    (a) The area of the triangle PQR.
    (b) The equation for a plane that contains P, Q, and R.

14. Find a vector parallel to the intersection of the planes $2x - 3y + 5z = 2$ and $4x + y - 3z = 7$.

15. Find the equation of the plane through the origin which is perpendicular to the line of intersection of the planes in Problem 14.

16. Find the equation of the plane through the point $(4, 5, 6)$ which is perpendicular to the line of intersection of the planes in Problem 14.

17. Use the algebraic definition for the cross product to check that
$$\vec{a} \times (\vec{b} + \vec{c}) = (\vec{a} \times \vec{b}) + (\vec{a} \times \vec{c}).$$

18. In this problem, we arrive at the algebraic definition for the cross product by a different route. Let $\vec{a} = a_1\vec{i} + a_2\vec{j} + a_3\vec{k}$ and $\vec{b} = b_1\vec{i} + b_2\vec{j} + b_3\vec{k}$. We seek a vector $\vec{v} = x\vec{i} + y\vec{j} + z\vec{k}$ which is perpendicular to both $\vec{a}$ and $\vec{b}$. Use this requirement to construct two equations for x, y, and z. Eliminate x and solve for y in terms of z. Then eliminate y and solve for x in terms of z. Since z can be any value whatsoever (the direction of $\vec{v}$ is unaffected), select the value for z which eliminates the denominator in the equation you obtained. How does the resulting expression for $\vec{v}$ compare to the formula we derived on page 87?

19. Suppose $\vec{a}$ and $\vec{b}$ are vectors in the xy-plane, such that $\vec{a} = a_1\vec{i} + a_2\vec{j}$ and $\vec{b} = b_1\vec{i} + b_2\vec{j}$ with $0 < a_2 < a_1$ and $0 < b_1 < b_2$.
    (a) Sketch $\vec{a}$ and $\vec{b}$ and the vector $\vec{c} = -a_2\vec{i} + a_1\vec{j}$. Shade the parallelogram formed by $\vec{a}$ and $\vec{b}$.
    (b) What is the relation between $\vec{a}$ and $\vec{c}$? [Hint: Find $\vec{c} \cdot \vec{a}$ and $\vec{c} \cdot \vec{c}$.]
    (c) Find $\vec{c} \cdot \vec{b}$.
    (d) Explain why $\vec{c} \cdot \vec{b}$ gives the area of the parallelogram formed by $\vec{a}$ and $\vec{b}$.
    (e) Verify that in this case $\vec{a} \times \vec{b} = (a_1b_2 - a_2b_1)\vec{k}$.

20. If $\vec{a} + \vec{b} + \vec{c} = \vec{0}$, show that
$$\vec{a} \times \vec{b} = \vec{b} \times \vec{c} = \vec{c} \times \vec{a}.$$

Geometrically, what does this imply about $\vec{a}, \vec{b}$, and $\vec{c}$?

21. If $\vec{v}$ and $\vec{w}$ are nonzero vectors, use the geometric definition of the cross product to explain why
$$(\lambda\vec{v}) \times \vec{w} = \lambda(\vec{v} \times \vec{w}) = \vec{v} \times (\lambda\vec{w}).$$

Consider the cases $\lambda > 0$, and $\lambda = 0$, and $\lambda < 0$ separately.

22. Use a parallelepiped to show that $\vec{a} \cdot (\vec{b} \times \vec{c}) = (\vec{a} \times \vec{b}) \cdot \vec{c}$ for any vectors $\vec{a}$, $\vec{b}$, and $\vec{c}$.

23. Show that $\|\vec{a} \times \vec{b}\|^2 = \|\vec{a}\|^2\|\vec{b}\|^2 - (\vec{a} \cdot \vec{b})^2$.

24. For vectors $\vec{a}$ and $\vec{b}$, let $\vec{c} = \vec{a} \times (\vec{b} \times \vec{a})$.

    (a) Show that $\vec{c}$ lies in the plane containing $\vec{a}$ and $\vec{b}$.
    (b) Show that $\vec{a} \cdot \vec{c} = 0$ and $\vec{b} \cdot \vec{c} = \|\vec{a}\|^2\|\vec{b}\|^2 - (\vec{a} \cdot \vec{b})^2$. [Hint: Use Problems 22 and 23.]
    (c) Show that

    $$\vec{a} \times (\vec{b} \times \vec{a}) = \|\vec{a}\|^2\vec{b} - (\vec{a} \cdot \vec{b})\vec{a}.$$

25. Use the result of Problem 22 to show that the cross product distributes over addition. First, use distributivity for the dot product to show that for any vector $\vec{d}$,

    $$[(\vec{a} + \vec{b}) \times \vec{c}] \cdot \vec{d} = [(\vec{a} \times \vec{c}) + (\vec{b} \times \vec{c})] \cdot \vec{d}.$$

    Next, show that for any vector $\vec{d}$,

    $$[((\vec{a} + \vec{b}) \times \vec{c}) - (\vec{a} \times \vec{c}) - (\vec{b} \times \vec{c})] \cdot \vec{d} = 0.$$

    Finally, explain why you can conclude that

    $$(\vec{a} + \vec{b}) \times \vec{c} = (\vec{a} \times \vec{c}) + (\vec{b} \times \vec{c}).$$

26. Use the fact that $\vec{i} \times \vec{i} = \vec{0}, \vec{i} \times \vec{j} = \vec{k}, \vec{i} \times \vec{k} = -\vec{j}$, and so on, together with the properties of the cross product on page 88 to derive the algebraic definition for the cross product.

27. Let $\vec{a} = a_1\vec{i} + a_2\vec{j}$ and $\vec{b} = b_1\vec{i} + b_2\vec{j}$ be two nonparallel vectors in 2-space, as in Figure 12.45.

    (a) Use the identity $\sin(\beta - \alpha) = (\sin \beta \cos \alpha - \cos \beta \sin \alpha)$ to verify the formula for the area of the parallelogram formed by $\vec{a}$ and $\vec{b}$:

    $$\text{Area of parallelogram} = |a_1 b_2 - a_2 b_1|.$$

    (b) Show that $a_1 b_2 - a_2 b_1$ is positive when the rotation from $\vec{a}$ to $\vec{b}$ is counterclockwise, and negative when it is clockwise.

28. Consider the tetrahedron determined by three vectors $\vec{a}$, $\vec{b}$, $\vec{c}$ in Figure 12.46. The *area vector* of a face is a vector perpendicular to the face, pointing outward, whose magnitude is the area of the face. Show that the sum of the four outward pointing area vectors of the faces equals the zero vector.

Figure 12.45

Figure 12.46

REVIEW PROBLEMS FOR CHAPTER TWELVE

1. Given the displacement vectors $\vec{u}$ and $\vec{v}$ in Figure 12.47, draw the following vectors:
   (a) $(\vec{u} + \vec{v}) + \vec{u}$ (b) $\vec{v} + (\vec{v} + \vec{u})$ (c) $(\vec{u} + \vec{u}) + \vec{u}$.

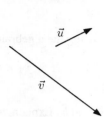

Figure 12.47

Figure 12.48

2. Figure 12.48 shows five points A, B, C, D, and E.
   (a) Read off the coordinates of the five points and thus resolve into components the following two vectors: $\vec{u} = (2.5)\overrightarrow{AB} + (-0.8)\overrightarrow{CD}$, $\vec{v} = (2.5)\overrightarrow{BA} - (-0.8)\overrightarrow{CD}$
   (b) What is the relation between $\vec{u}$ and $\vec{v}$? Why was this to be expected?

3. Find the components of a vector $\vec{p}$ which has the same direction as $\overrightarrow{EA}$ in Figure 12.48 and whose length equals two units.

4. For each of the four statements below, answer the following questions: Does the statement make sense? If yes, is it true for all possible choices of $\vec{a}$ and $\vec{b}$? If no, why not? Use complete sentences for your answers.
   (a) $\vec{a} + \vec{b} = \vec{b} + \vec{a}$ (b) $\vec{a} + \|\vec{b}\| = \|\vec{a} + \vec{b}\|$ (c) $\|\vec{b} + \vec{a}\| = \|\vec{a} + \vec{b}\|$
   (d) $\|\vec{a} + \vec{b}\| = \|\vec{a}\| + \|\vec{b}\|$.

5. Two adjacent sides of a regular hexagon are given as the vectors $\vec{u}$ and $\vec{v}$ in Figure 12.49. Label the remaining sides in terms of $\vec{u}$ and $\vec{v}$.

Figure 12.49

Figure 12.50

6. Figure 12.50 shows seven vectors $\vec{a}$, $\vec{b}$, $\vec{c}$, $\vec{d}$, $\vec{e}$, $\vec{f}$ and $\vec{g}$.
   (a) Are any of these two vectors equal? Write down all equal pairs.
   (b) Can you find a scalar x so that $\vec{a} = x\vec{g}$? If yes, find such an x; if no, explain why not.
   (c) Same question as in part (b), but for the equation $\vec{b} = x\vec{d}$.
   (d) Can you solve the equation $\vec{f} = u\vec{c} + v\vec{d}$ for the scalars u and v? If yes, find them; if no, explain why not.

7. For what values of t are the following pairs of vectors parallel?

    (a) $2\vec{i} + (t^2 + \frac{2}{3}t + 1)\vec{j} + t\vec{k}$, $6\vec{i} + 8\vec{j} + 3\vec{k}$

    (b) $t\vec{i} + \vec{j} + (t-1)\vec{k}$, $2\vec{i} - 4\vec{j} + \vec{k}$

    (c) $2t\vec{i} + t\vec{j} + t\vec{k}$, $6\vec{i} + 3\vec{j} + 3\vec{k}$.

Use the geometric definition to compute the cross products in Problems 8–9.

8. $2\vec{i} \times (\vec{i} + \vec{j})$

9. $(\vec{i} + \vec{j}) \times (\vec{i} - \vec{j})$

Compute the cross products for Problems 10–11, using the algebraic definition.

10. $\left((\vec{i} + \vec{j}) \times \vec{i}\right) \times \vec{j}$

11. $(\vec{i} + \vec{j}) \times (\vec{i} \times \vec{j})$

12. True or false? $\vec{a} \times \vec{b} = -(\vec{b} \times \vec{a})$ for all $\vec{a}$ and $\vec{b}$. Explain your answer.

13. Find the area of the triangle with vertices $P = (-2, 2, 0)$, $Q = (1, 3, -1)$, and $R = (-4, 2, 1)$ using the cross product.

14. Find the equation of the plane through the origin which is parallel to $z = 4x - 3y + 8$.

15. Find a vector normal to the plane $4(x - 1) + 6(z + 3) = 12$.

16. Find the equation of the plane through the points $(0, 0, 2), (0, 3, 0), (5, 0, 0)$.

17. Consider the plane $5x - y + 7z = 21$.

    (a) Find a point on the x-axis on this plane.

    (b) Find two other points on the plane.

    (c) Find a vector perpendicular to the plane.

    (d) Find a vector parallel to the plane.

18. Given the points $P = (1, 2, 3)$, $Q = (3, 5, 7)$, and $R = (2, 5, 3)$, find:

    (a) A unit vector perpendicular to a plane containing P, Q, R.

    (b) The angle between PQ and PR.

    (c) The area of the triangle PQR.

    (d) The distance from R to the line through P and Q.

19. Find all vectors $\vec{v}$ in the plane such that $\|\vec{v}\| = 1$ and $\|\vec{v} + \vec{i}\| = 1$.

20. Find all vectors $\vec{w}$ in 3-space such that $\|\vec{w}\| = 1$ and $\|\vec{w} + \vec{i}\| = 1$. Describe this set geometrically.

21. Is the collection of populations of each of the 50 states a vector or scalar quantity?

22. The price vector of beans, rice, and tofu is $(0.30, 0.20, 0.50)$ in dollars per pound. Express it in dollars per ounce.

23. An object is attached by an inelastic string to a fixed point and rotates 30 times per minute in a horizontal plane. Show that the speed of the object is constant but the velocity is not. What does this imply about the acceleration?

24. An object is moving counterclockwise at a constant speed around the circle $x^2 + y^2 = 1$, where x and y are measured in meters. It completes one revolution every minute.

    (a) What is its speed?

    (b) What is its velocity vector 30 seconds after it passes the point $(1, 0)$? Does your answer change if the object is moving clockwise? Explain.

25. In the game of laser tag, you shoot a harmless laser gun and try to hit a target worn at the waist by other players. Suppose you are standing at the origin of a three dimensional coordinate system and that the xy-plane is the floor. Suppose that waist-high is 3 feet above floor level and that eye level is 5 feet above the floor. Three of your friends are your opponents. One is standing so that his target is 30 feet along the x-axis, the other lying down so that his target is at the point $x = 20$, $y = 15$, and the third lying in ambush so that his target is at a point 8 feet above the point $x = 12$, $y = 30$.

  (a) If you aim with your gun at eye level, find the vector from your gun to each of the three targets.

  (b) If you shoot from waist height, with your gun one foot to the right of the center of your body as you face along the x-axis, find the vector from your gun to each of the three targets.

26. An airport is at the point $(200, 10, 0)$ and an approaching plane is at the point $(550, 60, 4)$. Assume that the xy-plane is horizontal, with the x-axis pointing eastward and the y-axis pointing northward. Also assume that the z-axis is upward and that all distances are measured in kilometers. The plane flies due west at a constant altitude at a speed of 500 km/h for half an hour. It then descends at 200 km/h, heading straight for the airport.

  (a) Find the velocity vector of the plane while it is flying at constant altitude.

  (b) Find the coordinates of the point at which the plane starts to descend.

  (c) Find a vector representing the velocity of the plane when it is descending.

27. A large ship is being towed by two tugs. The larger tug exerts a force which is 25% greater than the smaller tug and at an angle of 30 degrees north of east. Which direction must the smaller tug pull to ensure that the ship travels due east?

28. A man wishes to row the shortest possible distance from north to south across a river which is flowing at 4 km/hr from the east. He can row at 5 km/hr.

  (a) In which direction should he steer?

  (b) If there is a wind of 10 km/hr from the southwest, in which direction should he steer to try and go directly across the river? What happens?

29. (a) A vector $\vec{v}$ of magnitude v makes an angle α with the positive x-axis, angle β with the positive y-axis, and angle γ with the positive z-axis. Show that
$$\vec{v} = v \cos \alpha \vec{i} + v \cos \beta \vec{j} + v \cos \gamma \vec{k}.$$

  (b) Cos α, cos β, and cos γ are called *direction cosines*. Show that
$$\cos^2 \alpha + \cos^2 \beta + \cos^2 \gamma = 1.$$

30. Find the vector $\vec{v}$ with all of the following properties:

  (i) Magnitude 10

  (ii) Angle of $45°$ with positive x-axis

  (iii) Angle of $75°$ with positive y-axis

  (iv) Positive $\vec{k}$-component.

31. Using vectors, show that the perpendicular bisectors of a triangle intersect at a point.

32. Find the distance from the point $P = (2, -1, 3)$ to the plane $2x + 4y - z = -1$.

33. Find an equation of the plane passing through the three points $(1, 1, 1)$, $(1, 4, 5)$, $(-3, -2, 0)$. Find the distance from the origin to the plane.

34. Two lines in space are skew if they are not parallel and do not intersect. Determine the minimum distance between two such lines.

APPENDICES

Many of the skills you will need for calculus were covered in previous courses. However, it may have been a long time since you systematically practiced these skills. This appendix is designed as a review of some basic rules and definitions. As you work through the problems of the appendix, try to make both the vocabulary and the manipulations second nature so that you will be able to use them quickly and appropriately when you are studying calculus.

A EXPONENTS

Positive Integer Exponents

Repeated addition leads to multiplication. For example,

$$\underbrace{2 + 2 + 2 + 2 + 2}_{\text{5 terms in sum}} = 5 \times 2.$$

Similarly, repeated multiplication leads to *exponentiation*. For example,

$$\underbrace{2 \times 2 \times 2 \times 2 \times 2}_{\text{5 factors in product}} = 2^5.$$

Here, 5 is the *exponent* of 2, and 2 is called the *base*. Notice that 2^5 is not the same as 5^2, because $2^5 = 32$ and $5^2 = 25$.

In general, if a is a real number and n is a positive integer, then we define exponentiation as an abbreviation for multiplication:

$$\underbrace{a \cdot a \cdot a \cdots a}_{n \text{ factors}} = a^n.$$

It's worth noticing that $a^1 = a$, because here we have only 1 factor of a.

Exponent Rules

There are five basic facts, called exponent rules, which follow as a direct consequence of our definition of exponentiation. These rules are summarized in the following box, and explanations are given afterwards. If a and b are real numbers and m and n are positive integers, then the following five rules hold:

Five Exponent Rules:

1. $a^n \cdot a^m = a^{n+m}$ 2. $\dfrac{a^n}{a^m} = a^{n-m}$ 3. $(a^m)^n = a^{m \cdot n}$

4. $(ab)^n = a^n b^n$ 5. $\left(\dfrac{a}{b}\right)^n = \dfrac{a^n}{a^m}$

The explanation of all five rules are very straightforward. If you ever forget one of the rules, you should be able to immediately rederive it using the following logic.

For exponent rule 1, we have

$$a^n \cdot a^m = \underbrace{a \cdot a \cdot a \cdots a}_{n \text{ factors}} \underbrace{a \cdot a \cdot a \cdots a}_{m \text{ factors}} = \underbrace{a \cdot a \cdot a \cdots a}_{n + m \text{ factors}}$$
$$= a^{n+m}.$$

For example, $2^3 \cdot 2^5 = (2 \cdot 2 \cdot 2) \cdot (2 \cdot 2 \cdot 2 \cdot 2 \cdot 2) = 2^8$, and $8 = 3 + 5$.

For exponent rule 2, suppose that n and m are positive integers and $n > m$. Then the m factors of a in the denominator will cancel with some of the n factors of a in the numerator, leaving only $n - m$ factors of a:

$$\frac{a^n}{a^m} = \frac{\overbrace{a \cdot a \cdot a \cdot a \cdots a}^{n \text{ factors of } a}}{\underbrace{a \cdot a \cdots a}_{m \text{ factors of } a}} = \frac{\overbrace{\not{a} \cdot \not{a} \cdots \not{a}}^{m \text{ factors of } a \text{ cancel}} \cdot \overbrace{a \cdots a}^{n - m \text{ factors of } a \text{ are left after cancelling}}}{\underbrace{\not{a} \cdot \not{a} \cdots \not{a}}_{m \text{ factors of } a \text{ cancel}}} = \underbrace{a \cdot a \cdot a \cdots a}_{n - m \text{ factors}} = a^{n-m}$$

For example,

$$\frac{4^5}{4^3} = \frac{4 \cdot 4 \cdot 4 \cdot 4 \cdot 4}{4 \cdot 4 \cdot 4} = \frac{\not{4} \cdot \not{4} \cdot \not{4} \cdot 4 \cdot 4}{\not{4} \cdot \not{4} \cdot \not{4}} = 4 \cdot 4 = 4^2 = 4^{5-3},$$

For exponent rule 3,

$$(a^m)^n = (\underbrace{a \cdot a \cdot a \cdots a}_{m \text{ factors of } a})^n = \overbrace{(a \cdot a \cdot a \cdots a)\underbrace{(a \cdot a \cdot a \cdots a)}_{m \text{ factors of } a} \cdots \underbrace{(a \cdot a \cdot a \cdots a)}_{m \text{ factors of } a}}^{\substack{\text{the } m \text{ factors of } a \text{ are multiplied } n \text{ times,} \\ \text{giving a total of } m \cdot n \text{ factors of } a}} = a^{m \cdot n}.$$

For example,

$$(a^2)^3 = (\underbrace{a \cdot a}_{2 \text{ factors of } a})^3 = \underbrace{(a \cdot a)(a \cdot a)(a \cdot a)}_{3 \text{ times 2 factors of } a} = a^6.$$

An alternative explanation for rule 3 uses rule 1:

$$(a^m)^n = \underbrace{a^m \cdot a^m \cdots a^m}_{n \text{ factors of } a^m} = a^{\overbrace{m + m + \cdots + m}^{n \text{ terms in sum}}} = a^{m \cdot n}.$$

For example, $(2^5)^3 = 2^5 \cdot 2^5 \cdot 2^5 = 2^{5+5+5} = 2^{15}$, and $15 = 5 \cdot 3$.

To justify exponent rule 4, we use the commutative property of multiplication, which states that the order in which numbers are multiplied together does not affect the result. For example, $2 \cdot 9 \cdot 13 = 13 \cdot 2 \cdot 9 = 9 \cdot 13 \cdot 2 = 234$.

$$(a \cdot b)^n = \underbrace{(a \cdot b)(a \cdot b)(a \cdot b) \cdots (a \cdot b)}_{n \text{ factors of } (a \cdot b)} = \underbrace{\overbrace{(a \cdot a \cdot a \cdots a)}^{n \text{ factors of } a} \cdot \overbrace{(b \cdot b \cdot b \cdots b)}^{n \text{ factors of } b}}_{\substack{\text{since we can rearrange the order using the} \\ \text{commutative property of multiplication}}} = a^n \cdot b^n.$$

For example, $(5 \cdot 8)^2 = (5 \cdot 8)(5 \cdot 8) = (5 \cdot 5)(8 \cdot 8) = 5^2 \cdot 8^2 = 1600$.

For exponent rule 5,

$$\left(\frac{a}{b}\right)^n = \underbrace{\left(\frac{a}{b}\right) \cdot \left(\frac{a}{b}\right) \cdot \left(\frac{a}{b}\right) \cdots \left(\frac{a}{b}\right)}_{n \text{ factors of } \frac{a}{b}} = \frac{\overbrace{a \cdot a \cdot a \cdots a}^{n \text{ factors of } a}}{\underbrace{b \cdot b \cdot b \cdots b}_{n \text{ factors of } b}} = \frac{a^n}{b^n}.$$

For example, $\left(\dfrac{2}{7}\right)^3 = \left(\dfrac{2}{7}\right) \cdot \left(\dfrac{2}{7}\right) \cdot \left(\dfrac{2}{7}\right) = \dfrac{2 \cdot 2 \cdot 2}{7 \cdot 7 \cdot 7} = \dfrac{2^3}{7^3} = \dfrac{8}{343}.$

Appendix / 3

Be aware of the following notational conventions:

$$ab^n = a(b^n), \qquad \text{not } (ab)^n,$$
$$-b^n = -(b^n), \qquad \text{not } (-b)^n,$$
$$-ab^n = (-a)(b^n).$$

For example, $-2^4 = -(2^4) = -16$, but $(-2)^4 = (-2)(-2)(-2)(-2) = +16$. Also, be sure to realize that for values of n other than 0 and 1,

$$(a + b)^n \neq a^n + b^n \qquad \text{power of a sum} \neq \text{sum of powers.}$$

Rational Exponents

The natural definition for exponentiation as an abbreviation for multiplication holds for positive integers only. For example, 4^5 means 4 multiplied times itself 5 times, but it would be nonsense to try to make a similar definition for 4^0 or 4^{-1} or $4^{1/2}$. We have not yet defined what exponentiation means for exponents which are not positive integers.

Since there is no natural definition for 4^0 or 4^{-1} or $4^{1/2}$, it is up to mathematicians to create whichever unnatural definition they would like.

We have seen that the five exponent rules follow from the natural definition of exponentiation with positive integer exponents. Therefore, it makes sense to choose a definition for exponentiation with all real number exponents which is consistent with the five exponent rules.

The definitions of exponentiation for exponents which are not positive integers are summarized in the following box. After this summary, explanations are given which show why these particular choices of definition are consistent with the three exponent rules.

If a is a real number and m and n are positive integers, then the following definitions hold.

Definitions For Exponentiation

(i) $a^0 = 1$ (for $a \neq 0$)

(ii) $a^{-n} = \frac{1}{a^n}$ (for $a \neq 0$)

(iii) $a^{1/n} = \sqrt[n]{a}$ (if n is even, then $a \geq 0$.)

(iv) $a^{m/n} = \sqrt[n]{a^m} = (\sqrt[n]{a})^m$ (if n is even, then $a^m \geq 0$.)

If we would like to apply exponent rule 1 when one of the exponents is $m = 0$, then

$$a^n \cdot a^m = a^n \cdot a^0 = a^{n+0} = a^n, \quad \text{for } a \neq 0,$$
$$\text{or } a^n \cdot a^0 = a^n.$$

Notice that if we divide both sides of the equation by a^n, we get $a^0 = 1$. Therefore, if we want exponent rule 1 to hold for any exponent, including $m = 0$, we must define $a^0 = 1$, for $a \neq 0$. (We have not defined 0^0; this is left undefined.)

Suppose we apply exponent rule 2 when the exponent in the numerator is less than the exponent in the denominator. For example, we know that

$$\frac{a^2}{a^5} = \frac{a \cdot a}{a \cdot a \cdot a \cdot a \cdot a} = \frac{\not{a} \cdot \not{a}}{\not{a} \cdot \not{a} \cdot a \cdot a \cdot a} = \frac{1}{a^3}.$$

If we apply exponent rule 2, the result is a negative exponent:

$$\frac{a^2}{a^5} = a^{2-5} = a^{-3}.$$

Therefore, if we want exponent rule 2 to hold for any exponent, including negative numbers, we must define $a^{-3} = \frac{1}{a^3}$. In general, $a^{-n} = \frac{1}{a^n}$. Notice that, in particular, $a^{-1} = \frac{1}{a}$.

Example 1   Use the rules of exponents to simplify the following:

(a) $3b(2b)^3(b^{-1})$

(b) $\dfrac{y^4(x^3y^{-2})^2}{2x^{-1}}$

(c) $\left(\dfrac{2^{-3}}{L}\right)^{-2}$

(d) $\dfrac{5(2s+1)^4(s+3)^{-2}}{2s+1}$

Solution

(a) $3b(2b)^3\left(b^{-1}\right) = 3b^1(2^3b^3)b^{-1} = 3\cdot 8 \cdot b^1 b^3 b^{-1} = 3\cdot 8 \cdot b^{3+(-1)+1} = 24b^3$

(b) $\dfrac{y^4\left(x^3y^{-2}\right)^2}{2x^{-1}} = \dfrac{y^4 x^6 y^{-4}}{2x^{-1}} = \dfrac{y^{(4-4)}x^{(6-(-1))}}{2} = \dfrac{y^0 x^7}{2} = \dfrac{x^7}{2}$

(c) $\left(\dfrac{2^{-3}}{L}\right)^{-2} = \dfrac{2^{(-3)(-2)}}{L^{-2}} = \dfrac{2^6}{L^{-2}} = 64L^2$ (Note that $\dfrac{1}{L^{-2}} = \dfrac{L^0}{L^{-2}} = L^{0-(-2)} = L^2$.)

(d) $\dfrac{5(2s+1)^4(s+3)^{-2}}{(2s+1)} = \dfrac{5(2s+1)^{4-1}}{(s+3)^2} = \dfrac{5(2s+1)^3}{(s+3)^2}$

Before we explain definitions 3 and 4 for fractional exponents, we provide a brief review of notation:

- For $a \geq 0$,

  $\sqrt{a}$ is the positive number whose square is a.

  $\sqrt[n]{a}$ is the positive number whose nth power is a.

- For $a < 0$,

  If n is odd, $\sqrt[n]{a}$ is the negative number whose nth power is a.

  If n is even, $\sqrt[n]{a}$ is not a real number.

For example, $\sqrt{49} = 7$ because $7^2 = 49$. Likewise, $\sqrt[3]{125} = 5$ because $5^3 = 125$, and $\sqrt[5]{32} = 2$ because $2^5 = 32$. Similarly, $\sqrt[3]{-27} = -3$ because $(-3)^3 = -27$, and $\sqrt{-9}$ is not a real number, because the square of no real number is negative. When $\sqrt[n]{a}$ and $\sqrt[n]{b}$ are real numbers, the rules for radicals are as follows:

$$\sqrt[n]{ab} = \sqrt[n]{a}\,\sqrt[n]{b}, \qquad \sqrt[n]{\frac{a}{b}} = \frac{\sqrt[n]{a}}{\sqrt[n]{b}}$$

Example 2   Simplify the following radicals:

(a) $\sqrt{36}$ (b) $\sqrt[3]{-8x^6}$ (c) $\sqrt{\dfrac{16R^8}{25}}$

Solution (a) $\sqrt{36} = +6$ (Notice that the answer is the positive root, not ±6.)

(b) $\sqrt[3]{-8x^6} = \sqrt[3]{-8} \cdot \sqrt[3]{x^6} = -2x^2$

(c) $\sqrt{\dfrac{16R^8}{25}} = \dfrac{\sqrt{16R^8}}{\sqrt{25}} = \dfrac{\sqrt{16}\sqrt{R^8}}{\sqrt{25}} = \dfrac{4R^4}{5}$

Special case: n-th root of a^n

If n is odd,
$$\sqrt[n]{a^n} = a \qquad \text{by definition.}$$

If n is even,
$$\sqrt[n]{a^n} = |a| = \begin{cases} a & \text{if } a > 0 \\ -a & \text{if } a < 0 \end{cases}.$$

Example 3   Simplify:

(a) $\sqrt[4]{(-1)^4}$ (b) $\sqrt{9x^2}$

Solution (a) $\sqrt[4]{(-1)^4} = \sqrt[4]{1} = 1$ (Notice that in this case $\sqrt[n]{a^n} \neq a$.)

(b) $\sqrt{9x^2} = 3|x|$ (since x can be either positive or negative).

Suppose we would like to evaluate an expression with a fractional exponent, such as $(a^{1/2})^2$, for $a \geq 0$. If we apply exponent rule 3, we get

$$(a^{1/2})^2 = a^{\frac{1}{2} \cdot 2} = a^1 = a, \quad \text{or} \quad (a^{1/2})^2 = a.$$

Taking the square root of both sides results in $a^{1/2} = \sqrt{a}$. Therefore, if we want exponent rule 3 to hold for any exponent, including fractions, we must define $a^{1/2} = \sqrt{2}$. In general, $a^{1/n} = \sqrt[n]{a}$, and if n is even, then $a \geq 0$.

We can extend this explanation to an expression such as $(a^{1/3})^2$. We have just explained that $a^{1/3} = \sqrt[3]{a}$, therefore $(a^{1/3})^2 = (\sqrt[3]{a})^2$. Exponent rule 3 gives

$$(a^{\frac{1}{3}})^2 = a^{\frac{1}{3} \cdot 2} = a^{\frac{2}{3}}.$$

Therefore, if we want exponent rule 3 to hold for any exponent, including fractions, we must define $a^{2/3} = (\sqrt[3]{a})^2$. In general, $a^{m/n} = (\sqrt[n]{a})^m$. Because multiplication is commutative, we have

$$a^{\frac{m}{n}} = a^{m \cdot \frac{1}{n}} = a^{\frac{1}{n} \cdot m}$$
$$= (a^m)^{\frac{1}{n}} = (a^{\frac{1}{n}})^m$$
$$= \sqrt[n]{a^m} = (\sqrt[n]{a})^m.$$

We have chosen these definitions so that exponent rules 1–5 hold for any rational exponent.

Example 4   Find $(27)^{2/3}$.

Solution $(27)^{2/3} = \sqrt[3]{27^2} = \sqrt[3]{729} = 9$, or, equivalently, $(27)^{2/3} = \left(27^{\frac{1}{3}}\right)^2 = \left(\sqrt[3]{27}\right)^2 = 3^2 = 9$.

Example 5   Simplify:

(a) $\left(\dfrac{M^{1/5}}{3N^{-1/2}}\right)^2$ (b) $\dfrac{3u^2\sqrt{uw}}{w^{1/3}}$

Solution   (a) $\left(\dfrac{M^{1/5}}{3N^{-1/2}}\right)^2 = \dfrac{\left(M^{1/5}\right)^2}{\left(3N^{-1/2}\right)^2} = \dfrac{M^{2/5}}{3^2 N^{-1}} = \dfrac{M^{2/5}N}{9}$.

(b) $\dfrac{3u^2\sqrt{uw}}{w^{1/3}} = \dfrac{3u^2 u^{1/2}w}{w^{1/3}} = 3u^{(2+1/2)}w^{(1-1/3)} = 3u^{5/2}w^{2/3}$

Calculator Note

Most calculators will not compute $a^{m/n}$ for $m \neq 1$ when a is negative, even if n is odd. For example, though $(-1)^{2/3}$ is well defined, a calculator may display "error."

Example 6   Evaluate, if possible:

(a) $(-2197)^{2/3}$ (b) $(-256)^{3/4}$

Solution   (a) To find $(-2197)^{2/3}$ on a calculator, we can first evaluate $(-2197)^{1/3}$, and then square the result. This gives 169.

(b) $(-256)^{3/4}$ is not a real number since $(-256)^{1/4}$ is undefined.

Irrational and Variable Exponents

The rules for exponents given for integer and fractional exponents apply also when the exponent is an irrational number, as in $x^{\sqrt{3}}$, or a variable, as in 5^x.

Example 7   Simplify:

(a) $p^{\sqrt{2}} \cdot p^{\sqrt{8}}$ (b) $\sqrt{\dfrac{x^{3\pi}}{x^\pi}}$, $x > 0$

Solution   (a) $p^{\sqrt{2}} \cdot p^{\sqrt{8}} = p^{(\sqrt{2}+\sqrt{8})} = p^{(\sqrt{2}+2\sqrt{2})} = p^{3\sqrt{2}}$

(b) $\sqrt{\dfrac{x^{3\pi}}{x^\pi}} = \left(\dfrac{x^{3\pi}}{x^\pi}\right)^{1/2} = \left(x^{3\pi-\pi}\right)^{1/2} = \left(x^{2\pi}\right)^{1/2} = x^{2\pi(1/2)} = x^\pi$

Example 8   Simplify:

(a) $-3^x \cdot 3^{-x}$ (b) $\dfrac{4^x}{2^x}$ (c) $\dfrac{a^{2/3}(a^x)(a^x)}{a}$

Solution   (a) $-3^x \cdot 3^{-x} = -(3^x)(3^{-x}) = -(3^{x-x}) = -(3^0) = -1$

(b) $\dfrac{4^x}{2^x} = \left(\dfrac{4}{2}\right)^x = 2^x$

(c) $\dfrac{a^{2/3}(a^x)(a^x)}{a} = a^{2/3}(a^x)(a^x)(a^{-1}) = a^{(2/3+x+x-1)} = a^{2x-1/3}$

Problems for Section A

Evaluate mentally.

1. $\dfrac{1}{7^{-2}}$　　　　　　　　2. $\dfrac{2^7}{2^3}$　　　　　　　　3. $(-1)^{445}$

4. -11^2　　　　　　　　5. $(-2)\left(3^2\right)$　　　　　　6. $\left(5^0\right)^3$

7. $2.1\left(10^3\right)$　　　　　　8. $\sqrt[3]{-125}$　　　　　9. $\sqrt{(-4)^2}$

10. $(-1)^3\sqrt{36}$　　　　　11. $(0.04)^{1/2}$　　　　12. $(-8)^{2/3}$

13. $\left(\dfrac{1}{27}\right)^{-1/3}$　　　　14. $(0.125)^{1/3}$

Simplify and leave without radicals.

15. $(0.1)^2\left(4xy^2\right)^2$　　　16. $3\left(3^{x/2}\right)^2$　　　17. $\left(4L^{2/3}P\right)^{3/2}(P)^{-3/2}$

18. $7\left(5w^{1/2}\right)\left(2w^{1/3}\right)$　　19. $\left(S\sqrt{16xt^2}\right)^2$　　20. $\sqrt{e^{2x}}$

21. $(3AB)^{-1}\left(A^2B^{-1}\right)^2$　　22. $e^{kt}\cdot e^3\cdot e$　　　23. $\sqrt{M+2}(2+M)^{3/2}$

24. $\left(3x\sqrt{x^3}\right)^2$　　　25. $x^e\left(x^e\right)^2$　　　26. $\left(y^{-2}e^y\right)^2$

27. $\dfrac{4x^{(3\pi+1)}}{x^2}$　　　28. $\left(\dfrac{35(2b+1)^9}{7(2b+1)^{-1}}\right)^2$ (Do not　29. $\dfrac{a^{n+1}3^{n+1}}{a^n 3^n}$

　　　　　　　　　　　　expand $(2b+1)^9$.)

30. $\dfrac{12u^3}{3\left(uv^2w^4\right)^{-1}}$

Evaluate if possible. Check your answers with a calculator.

31. $(-32)^{3/5}$　　　　　32. $-32^{3/5}$　　　　　33. $-625^{3/4}$

34. $(-625)^{3/4}$　　　　35. $(-1728)^{4/3}$　　　36. $64^{-3/2}$

37. $-64^{3/2}$　　　　　38. $(-64)^{3/2}$

B MULTIPLYING ALGEBRAIC EXPRESSIONS

The *distributive property* for real numbers a, b, and c tells us that

$$a(b+c) = ab + ac,$$

and

$$(b+c)a = ba + ca.$$

We use the distributive property and the rules of exponents to multiply algebraic expressions involving parenthesis. This process is sometimes referred to as *expanding* the expression.

Example 1   Multiply the following and simplify.

(a) $3x^2 \left(x + \frac{1}{6}x^{-3} \right)$

(b) $((2t)^2 - 5)\sqrt{t}$

(c) $2^x(3^x + 2^{x-1})$

Solution (a) $3x^2 \left(x + \frac{1}{6}x^{-3} \right) = (3x^2)(x) + (3x^2)\left(\frac{1}{6}x^{-3} \right) = 3x^3 + \frac{1}{2}x^{-1}$

(b) $((2t)^2 - 5)\sqrt{t} = (2t)^2(\sqrt{t}) - 5\sqrt{t} = (4t^2)\left(t^{1/2} \right) - 5t^{1/2} = 4t^{5/2} - 5t^{1/2}$

(c) $2^x \left(3^x + 2^{x-1} \right) = (2^x)(3^x) + (2^x)\left(2^{x-1} \right) = (2 \cdot 3)^x + 2^{x+x-1} = 6^x + 2^{2x-1}$

If there are two terms in each factor, then there are four terms in the product:

$$(a + b)(c + d) = a(c + d) + b(c + d) = ac + ad + bc + bd.$$

The following special cases of the above product occur frequently. Learning to recognize their forms aids in factoring.

$$(a + b)(a - b) = a^2 - b^2$$
$$(a + b)^2 = a^2 + 2ab + b^2$$
$$(a - b)^2 = a^2 - 2ab + b^2$$

Example 2   Expand the following and simplify by gathering like terms.

(a) $(5x^2 + 2)(x - 4)$

(b) $(2\sqrt{r} + 2)(4\sqrt{r} - 3)$

(c) $(e^x + 1)(2x + e^{-x})$

(d) $\left(3 - \frac{1}{2}x \right)^2$

Solution (a) $(5x^2 + 2)(x - 4) = (5x^2)(x) + (5x^2)(-4) + (2)(x) + (2)(-4) = 5x^3 - 20x^2 + 2x - 8$

(b) $(2\sqrt{r}+2)(4\sqrt{r}-3) = (2)(4)(\sqrt{r})^2 + (2)(-3)(\sqrt{r}) + (2)(4)(\sqrt{r}) + (2)(-3) = 8r + 2\sqrt{r} - 6$

(c)

$$(e^x + 1)\left(2x + e^{-x} \right) = (e^x)(2x) + (e^x)\left(e^{-x} \right) + (1)(2x) + (1)(e^{-x})$$
$$= 2xe^x + e^{x-x} + 2x + e^{-x}$$
$$= 2xe^x + 1 + 2x + e^{-x}$$

(d) $\left(3 - \frac{1}{2}x \right)^2 = 3^2 - 2(3)\left(\frac{1}{2}x \right) + \left(-\frac{1}{2}x \right)^2 = 9 - 3x + \frac{1}{4}x^2$

Problems for Section B

Multiply and write without parentheses. Gather like terms.

1. $(3x - 2x^2)(4) + (5 + 4x)(3x - 4)$

2. $P(p - 3q)^2$

3. $(A^2 - B^2)^2$

4. $4(x - 3)^2 + 7$

5. $-\left(\sqrt{2x} + 1 \right)^2$

6. $(t^2 + 1)(50t) - (25t^2 + 125)(2t)$

7. $u\left(u^{-1} + 2^u \right)2^u$

8. $K(R - r)r^2$

9. $(x + 3)\left(\frac{24}{x} + 2 \right)$

10. $\left(\frac{e^x + e^{-x}}{2} \right)^2$

C FACTORING ALGEBRAIC EXPRESSIONS

If we want to write an expanded expression in factored form we "un-multiply" the expression. Some of the basic techniques used in factoring are given in this section. We can check factoring by remultiplying.

Removing a Common Factor

It is sometimes useful to factor out the same factor from each of the terms in an expression. This is basically the distributive law in reverse:

$$ab + ac = a(b + c).$$

One special case is removing a factor of -1, which gives

$$-a - b = -(a + b).$$

Another special case is

$$(a - b) = -(b - a).$$

Example 1   Factor the following:

(a) $\frac{2}{3}x^2y + \frac{4}{3}xy$ (b) $e^{2x} + xe^x$ (c) $(2p+1)p^3 - 3p(2p+1)$

Solution   (a) $\frac{2}{3}x^2y + \frac{4}{3}xy = \frac{2}{3}xy(x + 2)$
(b) $e^{2x} + xe^x = e^x \cdot e^x + xe^x = e^x(e^x + x)$
(c) $(2p + 1)p^3 - 3p(2p + 1) = (p^3 - 3p)(2p + 1) = p(p^2 - 3)(2p + 1)$
(Note that the expression $(2p + 1)$ was one of the factors common to both terms.)

Grouping Terms

Even though all the terms may not have a common factor, we can sometimes factor by first grouping the terms and then removing a common factor.

Example 2   Factor $x^2 - hx - x + h$.

Solution $x^2 - hx - x + h = (x^2 - hx) - (x - h) = x(x - h) - (x - h) = (x - h)(x - 1)$

Factoring Quadratics

One way to factor quadratics is to mentally multiply out the possibilities.

Example 3   Factor $t^2 - 4t - 12$.

Solution   If the quadratic factors nicely, it will be of the form

$$t^2 - 4t - 12 = (t + \_)(t + \_).$$

We are looking for two numbers whose product is -12 and whose sum is -4. By trying combinations in the blanks we find

$$t^2 - 4t - 12 = (t - 6)(t + 2).$$

Example 4   Factor $4 - 2M - 6M^2$.

Solution $4 - 2M - 6M^2 = (2 - 3M)(2 + 2M)$

Perfect Squares and the Difference of Squares

Recognition of the special products $(x+y)^2$, $(x-y)^2$ and $(x+y)(x-y)$ in expanded form is very useful in factoring. Reversing the equations from the last section, we have

$$a^2 + 2ab + b^2 = (a+b)^2,$$

$$a^2 - 2ab + b^2 = (a-b)^2,$$

$$a^2 - b^2 = (a-b)(a+b).$$

When we can see that terms in an expression we want to factor are squares, it often makes sense to look for one of these forms. The difference of squares identity (the third one listed above) is especially useful.

Example 5   Factor:

(a) $16y^2 - 24y + 9$ (b) $25S^2R^4 - T^6$ (c) $x^2(x-2) + 16(2-x)$

Solution   (a) $16y^2 - 24y + 9 = (4y-3)^2$
(b) $25S^2R^4 - T^6 = (5SR^2)^2 - (T^3)^2 = (5SR^2 - T^3)(5SR^2 + T^3)$
(c) $x^2(x-2) + 16(2-x) = x^2(x-2) - 16(x-2) = (x-2)(x^2 - 16) = (x-2)(x-4)(x+4)$

Problems for Section C

Factor completely (if possible).

1. $2x^2 - 10x + 12$

2. $\pi r^2 + 2\pi r h$

3. $B^2 - 10B + 24$

4. $x \sin x - \sin x$

5. $x^2 + y^2$

6. $a^4 - a^2 - 12$

7. $(t+3)^2 - 16$

8. $hx^2 + 12 - 4hx - 3x$

9. $r(r-s) - 2(s-r)$

10. $\cos^2 x - 2\cos x + 1$

11. $y^2 - 3xy + 2x^2$

12. $x^2 e^{-3x} + 2x e^{-3x}$

13. $e^{2x} + 2e^x + 1$

14. $P(1+r)^2 + P(1+r)^2 r$

D   WORKING WITH FRACTIONS

Algebraic fractions are combined in the same manner as numeric fractions–that is, according to the following rules:

$$\frac{a}{c} + \frac{b}{c} = \frac{a+b}{c} \qquad \text{add numerators when denominators are equal, or}$$

$$\frac{a}{b} + \frac{c}{d} = \frac{a(d)}{b(d)} + \frac{(b)c}{(b)d} = \frac{ad + bc}{bd} \qquad \text{find a common denominator}$$

$$\frac{a}{b} \cdot \frac{c}{d} = \frac{ac}{bd} \qquad \text{multiply numerators and denominators for a product}$$

$$\frac{a/b}{c/d} = \frac{a}{b} \cdot \frac{d}{c} = \frac{ad}{bc} \qquad \text{to divide by a fraction, multiply by its reciprocal}$$

(We assume that no denominators are zero.)

To expand the last case, where either the numerator or denominator of a fraction is itself a fraction, remember that

$$\frac{\frac{a}{b}}{c} = \frac{a}{b} \cdot \frac{1}{c} = \frac{a}{bc} \quad \text{and} \quad \frac{a}{\frac{b}{c}} = \frac{a}{1} \cdot \frac{c}{b} = \frac{ac}{b}.$$

In all cases, we cannot divide by zero—$(a/0)$ is not defined. Also the sign of a fraction is changed by changing the sign of the numerator or the denominator (but not both):

$$-\frac{a}{b} = \frac{-a}{b} = \frac{a}{-b}.$$

Example 1 Perform the indicated operations and express the answers as a single fraction.

(a) $\dfrac{4}{x^2 + 1} - \dfrac{1 - x}{x^2 + 1}$

(b) $\dfrac{M}{M^2 - 2M - 3} + \dfrac{1}{M^2 - 2M - 3}$

(c) $\dfrac{-H^2 P}{17} \cdot \dfrac{\left(PH^{1/3}\right)^2}{K^{-1}}$

(d) $\dfrac{2z/w}{w(w - 3z)}$

Solution (a) $\dfrac{4}{x^2 + 1} - \dfrac{1 - x}{x^2 + 1} = \dfrac{4 - (1 - x)}{x^2 + 1} = \dfrac{3 + x}{x^2 + 1}$

(b) $\dfrac{M}{M^2 - 2M - 3} + \dfrac{1}{M^2 - 2M - 3} = \dfrac{M + 1}{(M^2 - 2M - 3)} = \dfrac{M + 1}{(M + 1)(M - 3)} = \dfrac{1}{M - 3}$

(c) $\dfrac{-H^2 P}{17} \cdot \dfrac{\left(PH^{1/3}\right)^2}{K^{-1}} = \dfrac{-H^2 P \left(P^2 H^{2/3}\right)}{17K^{-1}} = -\dfrac{H^{8/3} P^3 K}{17}$

(d) $\dfrac{2z/w}{w(w - 3z)} = \dfrac{2z}{w} \cdot \dfrac{1}{w(w - 3z)} = \dfrac{2z}{w^2(w - 3z)}$

Example 2 Simplify the following expressions:

(a) $2x^{-1/2} + \dfrac{\sqrt{x}}{3}$

(b) $2\sqrt{t + 3} + \dfrac{1 - 2t}{\sqrt{t + 3}}$

Appendix / 12

Solution (a) $2x^{-\frac{1}{2}} + \dfrac{\sqrt{x}}{3} = \dfrac{2}{\sqrt{x}} + \dfrac{\sqrt{x}}{3} = \dfrac{2 \cdot 3 + \sqrt{x}\sqrt{x}}{3\sqrt{x}} = \dfrac{6 + x}{3\sqrt{x}} = \dfrac{6 + x}{3x^{1/2}}$

(b)

$$2\sqrt{t + 3} + \dfrac{1 - 2t}{\sqrt{t + 3}} = \dfrac{2\sqrt{t + 3}}{1} + \dfrac{1 - 2t}{\sqrt{t + 3}}$$

$$= \dfrac{2\sqrt{t + 3}\sqrt{t + 3} + 1 - 2t}{\sqrt{t + 3}}$$

$$= \dfrac{2(t + 3) + 1 - 2t}{\sqrt{t + 3}}$$

$$= \dfrac{7}{\sqrt{t + 3}}$$

$$= \dfrac{7}{(t + 3)^{1/2}}$$

Finding a Common Denominator

We can multiply (or divide) both the numerator and denominator of a fraction by the same non-zero number without changing the fraction's value. This is equivalent to multiplying by a factor of $+1$. We are using this rule when we add or subtract fractions with different denominators. For example, to add $\frac{x}{3a} + 1a$, we multiply $\frac{1}{a} \cdot \frac{3}{3} = \frac{3}{3a}$. Then $\frac{x}{3a} + \frac{1}{a} = \frac{x}{3a} + \frac{3}{3a} = \frac{x+3}{3a}$.

Example 3 Perform the indicated operations:

(a) $3 - \dfrac{1}{x - 1}$

(b) $\dfrac{2}{x^2 + x} + \dfrac{x}{x + 1}$

Solution (a) $3 - \dfrac{1}{x - 1} = 3\dfrac{(x - 1)}{(x - 1)} - \dfrac{1}{x - 1} = \dfrac{3(x - 1) - 1}{x - 1} = \dfrac{3x - 3 - 1}{x - 1} = \dfrac{3x - 4}{x - 1}$

(b) $\dfrac{2}{x^2 + x} + \dfrac{x}{x + 1} = \dfrac{2}{x(x + 1)} + \dfrac{x}{x + 1} = \dfrac{2}{x(x + 1)} + \dfrac{x(x)}{(x + 1)(x)} = \dfrac{2 + x^2}{x(x + 1)}$

Note: We can multiply (or divide) the numerator and denominator by the same non-zero number because this is the same as multiplying by a factor of $+1$, and multiplying by a factor of 1 does not change the value of the expression. However, we cannot perform any other operation that would change the value of the expression. For example, we cannnot *add* the same number to the numerator and denominator of a fraction *nor* can we square both, take the logarithm of both, etc., without changing the fraction.

Reducing Fractions (Canceling)

We can reduce a fraction when we have the same (non-zero) factor in both the numerator and the denominator. For example,

$$\dfrac{ac}{bc} = \dfrac{a}{b} \cdot \dfrac{c}{c} = \dfrac{a}{b} \cdot 1 = \dfrac{a}{b}.$$

Example 4 Reduce the following fractions (if possible).

(a) $\dfrac{2x}{4y}$

(b) $\dfrac{2+x}{2+y}$

(c) $\dfrac{5n-5}{1-n}$

(d) $\dfrac{x^2(4-2x)-(4x-x^2)(2x)}{x^4}$

Solution (a) $\dfrac{2x}{4y}=\dfrac{2}{2}\cdot\dfrac{x}{2y}=\dfrac{x}{2y}$

(b) $\dfrac{2+x}{2+y}$ cannot be reduced further.

(c) $\dfrac{5n-5}{1-n}=\dfrac{5(n-1)}{(-1)(n-1)}=-5$

(d)

$$\frac{x^2(4-2x)-\left(4x-x^2\right)(2x)}{x^4}=\frac{x^2(4-2x)-(4-x)(2x^2)}{x^4}$$

$$=\frac{[(4-2x)-2(4-x)]}{x^2}\left(\frac{x^2}{x^2}\right)$$

$$=\frac{4-2x-8+2x}{x^2}$$

$$=\frac{-4}{x^2}$$

Complex Fractions

A *complex fraction* is a fraction whose numerator or denominator (or both) contains one or more fractions. To simplify a complex fraction, we change the numerator and denominator to single fractions and then divide.

Example 5 Write the following as simple fractions in reduced form.

(a) $\dfrac{\frac{1}{x+h}-\frac{1}{x}}{h}$

(b) $\dfrac{a+b}{a^{-2}-b^{-2}}$

Solution (a) $\dfrac{\frac{1}{x+h}-\frac{1}{x}}{h}=\dfrac{\frac{x-(x+h)}{x(x+h)}}{h}=\dfrac{\frac{-h}{x(x+h)}}{\frac{h}{1}}=\dfrac{-h}{x(x+h)}\cdot\dfrac{1}{h}=\dfrac{-1}{x(x+h)}\dfrac{(h)}{(h)}=\dfrac{-1}{x(x+h)}$

(b) $\dfrac{a+b}{a^{-2}-b^{-2}}=\dfrac{a+b}{\frac{1}{a^2}-\frac{1}{b^2}}=\dfrac{a+b}{\frac{b^2-a^2}{a^2b^2}}=\dfrac{a+b}{1}\cdot\dfrac{a^2b^2}{b^2-a^2}=\dfrac{(a+b)(a^2b^2)}{(b+a)(b-a)}=\dfrac{a^2b^2}{b-a}$

Splitting Expressions

We can reverse the rule for adding fractions to split up an expression into two fractions,

$$\frac{a+b}{c}=\frac{a}{c}+\frac{b}{c}.$$

Appendix / 14

Example 6   Split $\dfrac{3x^2 + 2}{x^3}$ into two reduced fractions.

Solution

$$\frac{3x^2 + 2}{x^3} = \frac{3x^2}{x^3} + \frac{2}{x^3} = \frac{3}{x} + \frac{2}{x^3}$$

Sometimes we can alter the form of the fraction even further if we can create a duplicate of the denominator within the numerator. This technique is useful when graphing some rational functions. For example, we may rewrite the fraction $\dfrac{x + 3}{x + 1}$ by creating a factor of $(x - 1)$ within the numerator. To do this, we write

$$\frac{x + 3}{x - 1} = \frac{x - 1 + 1 + 3}{x - 1}$$

which can be written as

$$\frac{(x - 1) + 4}{x - 1}.$$

Then, splitting this fraction, we have

$$\frac{x + 3}{x - 1} = \frac{x - 1}{x - 1} + \frac{4}{x - 1} = 1 + \frac{4}{x - 1}.$$

Problems for Section D

Perform the following operations. Express answers in reduced form.

1. $\dfrac{3}{x - 4} - \dfrac{2}{x + 4}$

2. $\dfrac{x^2}{x - 1} - \dfrac{1}{1 - x}$

3. $\dfrac{1}{2r + 3} + \dfrac{3}{4r^2 + 6r}$

4. $u + a + \dfrac{u}{u + a}$

5. $\dfrac{1}{\sqrt{x}} - \dfrac{1}{(\sqrt{x})^3}$

6. $\dfrac{1}{e^{2x}} + \dfrac{1}{e^x}$

7. $\dfrac{a + b}{2} \cdot \dfrac{8x + 2}{b^2 - a^2}$

8. $\dfrac{0.07}{M} + \dfrac{3}{4} M^2$

9. $\dfrac{1}{r_1} + \dfrac{1}{r_2} + \dfrac{1}{r_3}$

10. $\dfrac{x^3}{x - 4} \Big/ \dfrac{x^2}{x^2 - 2x - 8}$

In Problems 11–20, simplify, if possible.

11. $\dfrac{\frac{1}{x+y}}{x + y}$

12. $\dfrac{\frac{w+2}{2}}{w + 2}$

13. $\dfrac{a^{-2} + b^{-2}}{a^2 + b^2}$

14. $\dfrac{a^2 - b^2}{a^2 + b^2}$

15. $p - \dfrac{q}{\frac{p}{q} + \frac{q}{p}}$

16. $\dfrac{[4 - (x + h)^2] - [4 - x^2]}{h}$

17. $\dfrac{2x(x^3+1)^2 - x^2(2)(x^3+1)(3x^2)}{[(x^3+1)^2]^2}$

18. $\dfrac{\frac{1}{2}(2x-1)^{-1/2}(2) - (2x-1)^{1/2}(2x)}{(x^2)^2}$

19. $\dfrac{\frac{1}{(x+h)^2} - \frac{1}{x^2}}{h}$

20. $\dfrac{\frac{1}{x}(3x^2) - (\ln x)(6x)}{(3x^2)^2}$

In Problems 21–26, split into a sum or difference of reduced fractions.

21. $\dfrac{26x+1}{2x^3}$

22. $\dfrac{\sqrt{x}+3}{3\sqrt{x}}$

23. $\dfrac{6l^2+3l-4}{3l^4}$

24. $\dfrac{7+p}{p^2+11}$

25. $\dfrac{\frac{1}{3}x-\frac{1}{2}}{2x}$

26. $\dfrac{t^{-1/2}+t^{1/2}}{t^2}$

In Problems 27–32, rewrite in the form $1+\frac{A}{B}$.

27. $\dfrac{x-2}{x+5}$

28. $\dfrac{q-1}{q-4}$

29. $\dfrac{R+1}{R}$

30. $\dfrac{3+2u}{2u+1}$

31. $\dfrac{\cos x + \sin x}{\cos x}$

32. $\dfrac{1+e^x}{e^x}$

E CHANGING THE FORM OF EXPRESSIONS

Rearranging Coefficients and Exponents

Often a simple change in the form of an expression can make the expression look quite different. As we work through a problem, changing forms can be useful at times. Consider the following cases of equivalent expressions:

- $\dfrac{x}{2} = \left(\dfrac{1}{2}\right)x$

- $\dfrac{3}{4(2r+1)^{10}} = \dfrac{3}{4}(2r+1)^{-10}$

- $2^{-n} = \left(\dfrac{1}{2}\right)^n$

- $2^{x+3} = 2^x \cdot 2^3 = 8(2^x)$

- $\dfrac{3x+\sqrt{2x}}{\sqrt{x}} = \dfrac{3x}{\sqrt{x}} + \dfrac{\sqrt{2x}}{\sqrt{x}} = \dfrac{3x}{\sqrt{x}} + \dfrac{\sqrt{2}\sqrt{x}}{\sqrt{x}} = 3x^{(1-\frac{1}{2})} + \sqrt{2} = 3x^{1/2} + \sqrt{2}$

Completing the Square

Another example of changing the form of an expression is the conversion of ax^2+bx+c into the form $a(x-h)^2+k$. We make this conversion by *completing the square*, a method for producing a "perfect square" within a quadratic expression. A perfect square is the square of a binomial,

$$(x+n)^2 = x^2 + 2nx + n^2$$

for some number n.

In order to complete the square in a given expression, we must find that number n. Observe that when a perfect square is multiplied out, the coefficient of x is 2 times the number n. Therefore, we can find n by dividing the coefficient of the x term by 2. Once we know n, then we know that the constant term in the perfect square must be n^2.

In summary:

To complete the square in the expression $x^2 + bx + c$, divide the coefficient of x by 2, giving $b/2$. Then add and subtract $(b/2)^2 = b^2/4$ and factor the perfect square:

$$x^2 + bx + c = \left(x + \frac{b}{2}\right)^2 - \frac{b^2}{4} + c.$$

To complete the square in the expression $ax^2 + bx + c$, factor out a first.

Example 1   Rewrite $x^2 - 10x + 4$ in the form $a(x - h)^2 + k$.

Solution   Notice that half of the coefficient of x is $\frac{1}{2}(-10) = -5$. Squaring -5 gives 25. We have

$$\begin{aligned}
x^2 - 10x + 4 &= x^2 - 10x + (25 - 25) + 4 \\
&= (x^2 - 10x + 25) - 25 + 4 \\
&= (x - 5)^2 - 21.
\end{aligned}$$

Thus, $a = +1$, $h = +5$, and $k = -21$.

Example 2   Complete the square in the formula $h(x) = 5x^2 + 30x - 10$.

Solution   We first factor out 5:

$$h(x) = 5(x^2 + 6x - 2).$$

Now we complete the square in the expression $x^2 + 6x - 2$.
Step 1: Divide the coefficient of x by 2, giving 3.
Step 2: Square the result: $3^2 = 9$.
Step 3: Add the result after the x term, then subtract it:

$$h(x) = 5(\underbrace{x^2 + 6x + 9}_{\text{a perfect square}} - 9 - 2).$$

Step 4: Factor the perfect square and simplify the rest:

$$h(x) = 5\left((x + 3)^2 - 11\right).$$

Now that we have completed the square, we can multiply by the 5:

$$h(x) = 5(x + 3)^2 - 55.$$

The Quadratic Formula

We will derive a general formula for the zeros of $q(x) = ax^2 + bx + c$ by completing the square.
To find the zeros, set $q(x) = 0$:

$$ax^2 + bx + c = 0.$$

Before we complete the square, we factor out the coefficient of x^2:

$$a\left(x^2 + \frac{b}{a}x + \frac{c}{a}\right) = 0.$$

Since $a \neq 0$, we can divide both sides by a:

$$x^2 + \frac{b}{a}x + \frac{c}{a} = 0.$$

To complete the square, we add and then subtract $\left((b/a)/2\right)^2 = b^2/(4a^2)$:

$$\underbrace{x^2 + \frac{b}{a}x + \frac{b^2}{4a^2}} - \frac{b^2}{4a^2} + \frac{c}{a} = 0.$$

a perfect square

We factor the perfect square and simplify the constant term, giving:

$$\left(x + \frac{b}{2a}\right)^2 - \left(\frac{b^2 - 4ac}{4a^2}\right) = 0 \quad \text{(since } \tfrac{-b^2}{4a^2} + \tfrac{c}{a} = \tfrac{-b^2}{4a^2} + \tfrac{4ac}{4a^2} = -\left(\tfrac{b^2-4ac}{4a^2}\right) \text{)}$$

$$\left(x + \frac{b}{2a}\right)^2 = \frac{b^2 - 4ac}{4a^2} \quad \text{(adding } \tfrac{b^2-4ac}{4a^2} \text{ to both sides)}$$

$$x + \frac{b}{2a} = \pm\sqrt{\frac{b^2 - 4ac}{4a^2}} = \frac{\pm\sqrt{b^2 - 4ac}}{2a} \quad \text{(taking the square root)}$$

$$x = \frac{-b}{2a} \pm \frac{\sqrt{b^2 - 4ac}}{2a} \quad \text{(subtracting } b/2a\text{)}$$

$$= \frac{-b \pm \sqrt{b^2 - 4ac}}{2a}.$$

Problems for Section E

In Problems 1–10, rewrite each expression as a sum of powers of the variable.

1. $3x^2\left(x^{-1}\right) + \dfrac{1}{2x} + x^2 + \dfrac{1}{5}$

2. $10\left(3q^2 - 1\right)(6q)$

3. $\left(y - 3y^{-2}\right)^2$

4. $x(x + x^{-1})^2$

5. $2P^2(P) + (9P)^{1/2}$

6. $\dfrac{(1 + 3\sqrt{t})^2}{2}$

7. $\dfrac{18 + x^2 - 3x}{-6}$

8. $\left(\dfrac{1}{N} - N\right)^2$

9. $\dfrac{-3(4x - x^2)}{7x}$

10. $\dfrac{x^4 + 2x + 1}{2\sqrt{x}}$

In Problems 11–16, rewrite each expression in the form $a(bx + c)^n$.

11. $\dfrac{12}{\sqrt{3x + 1}}$

12. $\dfrac{250\sqrt[3]{10 - s}}{0.25}$

13. $0.7(x - 1)^3(1 - x)$

14. $\dfrac{1}{2(x^2 + 1)^3}$

15. $4(6R + 2)^3(6)$

16. $\sqrt{\dfrac{28x^2 - 4\pi x}{x}}$

In Problems 17–26, rewrite each expression in the form ab^x.

17. $\dfrac{1^x}{2^x}$

18. $\dfrac{1}{2^x}$

19. $10,000(1 - 0.24)^t$

20. e^{2x+1}

21. $2 \cdot 3^{-x}$

22. $2^x \cdot 3^{x-1}$

23. $16^{t/2}$

24. $\dfrac{e^3}{e^{-x+4}}$

25. $\dfrac{5^x}{-3^x}$

26. $\dfrac{e \cdot e^x}{0.2}$

In Problems 27–30, rewrite each expression in the form $a(x - h)^2 + k$.

27. $x^2 - 2x - 3$

28. $10 - 6x + x^2$

29. $-x^2 + 6x - 2$

30. $3x^2 - 12x + 13$

In Problems 31–36, simplify and rewrite using positive exponents only.

31. $-3\left(x^2 + 7\right)^{-4}(2x)$

32. $-2\left(1 + 3^x\right)^{-3}(\ln 2)\left(2^x\right)$

33. $-(\sin(\pi t))^{-1}(-\cos(\pi t))\pi$

34. $-(\tan z)^{-2}\left(\dfrac{1}{\cos^2 z}\right)$

35. $\dfrac{-e^x\left(x^2\right) - e^{-x}2x}{\left(x^2\right)^2}$

36. $-x^{-2}(\ln x) + x^{-1}\left(\dfrac{1}{x}\right)$

In Problems 37–40, simplify and rewrite in radical form.

37. $\dfrac{1}{2}(x^2 + 16)^{-1/2}(2x)$

38. $\dfrac{1}{2}(x^2 + 10x + 1)^{-1/2}(2x + 10)$

39. $\dfrac{1}{2}(\sin(2x))^{-1/2}(2)\cos(2x)$

40. $\dfrac{2}{3}\left(x^2 - e^{3x}\right)^{-5/3}\left(3x^2 - e^{3x}(3)\right)$

F SOLVING EQUATIONS

Solving in your Head

When we first look at an equation, we see if we can guess the answer by mentally trying numbers. Consider the following equations and mental solutions.

$$\sqrt{x} - 4 = 0$$ "*I'm looking for a number whose square root is 4.*" $$\sqrt{16} - 4 = 0$$

$$2x - 3 = 0$$ "*What value can I use for x that will give 2x = 3?*" $$2\left(\frac{3}{2}\right) - 3 = 0$$

$$\frac{3}{x} + 1 = 0$$ "*Three divided by what number gives −1?*" $$\frac{3}{(-3)} + 1 = 0$$

$$e^x = 1$$ "*What exponent can I use with the base e to get 1?*" $$e^{(0)} = 1$$

$$x^2(x + 2) = 0$$ "*What number makes each factor zero?*" $$0^2 = 0 \text{ and } (-2) + 2 = 0$$

$$\frac{(x + 1)(3 - x)}{(1 - x)^2} = 0$$ "*What numbers make the numerator equal to 0?*" $$(-1) + 1 = 0 \text{ and } 3 - (3) = 0$$

$$1 - \sin x = 0$$ "*What numbers make the sine value equal 1?*" $$1 - \sin\left(\frac{\pi}{2}\right) = 0$$

Notice that the last equation, $\sin x = 1$, has many other solutions as well.

Operations on Equations

For more complicated equations, additional steps may be needed in order to find a solution.

Linear Equations

To solve a linear equation, we clear any parentheses and then isolate the variable.

Example 1 Solve $3 - [5.4 + 2(4.3 - x)] = 2 - (0.3x - 0.8)$ for x.

Solution We begin by clearing the innermost parentheses on each side. This gives

$$3 - [5.4 + 8.6 - 2x] = 2 - 0.3x + 0.8.$$

Then

$$3 - 14 + 2x = 2 - 0.3x + 0.8$$
$$2.3x = 13.8,$$
$$x = 6.$$

Example 2 Solve for q if $p^2q + r(-q - 1) = 4(p + r)$.

Solution

$$p^2q - rq - r = 4p + 4r$$
$$p^2q - rq = 4p + 5r$$
$$q(p^2 - r) = 4p + 5r$$
$$q = \frac{4p + 5r}{p^2 - r}$$

Appendix / 20

Solving by Factoring

Some equations can be put into factored form such that the product of the factors is zero. Then we solve by using the fact that if $a \cdot b = 0$ either a or b (or both) is zero.

Example 3   Solve $(x + 1)(x + 3) = 15$ for x.

Solution   Do not make the mistake of setting $x + 1 = 15$ and $x + 3 = 15$. It is not true that $a \cdot b = 15$ means that $a = 15$ or $b = 15$ (or both). This rule only works if $a \cdot b = 0$. So, we must expand the left-hand side and set the equation

$$x^2 + 4x + 3 = 15,$$
$$x^2 + 4x - 12 = 0.$$

Then, factoring gives

$$(x - 2)(x + 6) = 0.$$

Thus $x = 2$ and $x = -6$ are solutions.

Example 4   Solve $2(x + 3)^2 = 5(x + 3)$.

Solution   You might be tempted to divide both sides by x and 3. However, if you do this you will overlook one of the solutions. Instead, write

$$2(x + 3)^2 - 5(x + 3) = 0$$
$$(x + 3)\left(2(x + 3) - 5\right) = 0$$
$$(x + 3)(2x + 6 - 5) = 0$$
$$(x + 3)(2x + 1) = 0.$$

Thus, $x = -\frac{1}{2}$ and $x = -3$ are solutions.

Example 5   Solve $e^x + xe^x = 0$.

Solution   Factoring gives $e^x(1 + x) = 0$. Since e^x is never zero, $x = -1$ is the only solution.

Using the Quadratic Formula

If an equation is in the form $ax^2 + bx + c = 0$, we can use the quadratic formula to find the solutions,

$$x = \frac{-b + \sqrt{b^2 - 4ac}}{2a} \quad \text{or} \quad x = \frac{-b - \sqrt{b^2 - 4ac}}{2a}.$$

provided that $\sqrt{b^2 - 4ac}$ is a real number.

Example 6   Solve $11 + 2x = x^2$.

Solution

$$-x^2 + 2x + 11 = 0.$$

This does not factor using integers, so we use

$$x = \frac{-2 + \sqrt{4 - 4(-1)(11)}}{2(-1)} = \frac{-2 + \sqrt{48}}{-2} = \frac{-2 + \sqrt{16 \cdot 3}}{-2} = \frac{-2 + 4\sqrt{3}}{-2} = 1 - 2\sqrt{3},$$

$$x = \frac{-2 - \sqrt{4 - 4(-1)(11)}}{2(-1)} = \frac{-2 - \sqrt{48}}{-2} = \frac{-2 - \sqrt{16 \cdot 3}}{-2} = \frac{-2 - 4\sqrt{3}}{-2} = 1 + 2\sqrt{3}.$$

The solutions are $x = 1 - 2\sqrt{3}$ and $x = 1 + 2\sqrt{3}$.

Fractional Equations

If the equation involves fractions, we can eliminate the fractions by multiplying both sides of the equation by the least common denominator and then solving as before *if* we check for extraneous solutions in the end.

Example 7   Solve $\dfrac{2x}{x + 1} - 3 = \dfrac{2}{x^2 + x}$ for x.

Solution   To look for a common denominator, factor $x^2 + x$. Then we have

$$\frac{2x}{x + 1} - 3 = \frac{2}{x(x + 1)}.$$

Multiplying both sides by $x(x + 1)$ gives

$$x(x + 1)\left(\frac{2x}{x + 1} - 3\right) = 2$$
$$2x^2 - 3x(x + 1) = 2$$
$$2x^2 - 3x^2 - 3x = 2$$
$$-x^2 - 3x - 2 = 0,$$

or

$$x^2 + 3x + 2 = 0.$$

Factoring, we have

$$(x + 2)(x + 1) = 0,$$

so $x = -2$ and $x = -1$ are potential solutions. However, the original equation is not defined for $x = -1$, so the only solution is $x = -2$.

Example 8   Solve for P_2 if $\dfrac{1}{P_1} + \dfrac{1}{P_2} = \dfrac{1}{P_3}$.

Solution

$$P_2 P_3 + P_1 P_3 = P_1 P_2 \qquad \text{(multiplying by } P_1 P_2 P_3\text{)}$$

$$P_2 P_3 - P_1 P_2 = -P_1 P_3 \qquad \text{(moving all } P_2 \text{ terms to one side)}$$

$$P_2(P_3 - P_1) = -P_1 P_3 \qquad \text{(factoring out } P_2\text{)}$$

$$P_2 = \frac{-P_1 P_3}{P_3 - P_1} = \frac{P_1 P_3}{P_1 - P_3}.$$

Note that we assume that none of P_1, P_2, or $P_3 = 0$. Also, $P_3 \neq P_1$, since in this case the denominator of the solution is 0.

Radical Equations

We solve radical equations by raising both sides of the equation to the same power using the principle that if $a = b$, then $a^r = b^r$. Again, we must check for extraneous solutions.

Example 9   Solve $2\sqrt{x} = x - 3$.

Solution   Squaring both sides gives

$$(2\sqrt{x})^2 = (x - 3)^2$$
$$4x = x^2 - 6x + 9.$$

Then

$$x^2 - 10x + 9 = 0$$
$$(x - 1)(x - 9) = 0,$$

so $x = 1$ and $x = 9$ are potential solutions. Since $x = 1$ is not a solution of the original equation, the only solution is $x = 9$.

Example 10   Solve $4 = x^{-1/2}$.

Solution

$$(4)^{-2} = (x^{-1/2})^{-2}$$
$$(4)^{-2} = x,$$
$$x = \frac{1}{16}$$

Exponential Equations

When the variable we want to solve for is in the exponent, we again "do the same thing" to both sides of the equation. This time we take logarithms using the property that if $a = b$ then $\log a = \log b$, (provided $a, b > 0$). Note that we could also use the natural logarithm. We then use the rules of logarithms to simplify the equation.

Example 11   Solve $10^{2x+1} = 3$ for x.

Solution   Taking logs,

$$\log 10^{2x+1} = \log 3$$
$$2x + 1 = \log 3, \qquad \text{(since } \log 10^P = P\text{)}$$
$$x = \frac{(\log 3) - 1}{2}.$$

Example 12   Solve $2e^x = 12$.

Solution   We have

$$e^x = 6 \quad \text{(dividing both sides by 2)}$$
$$\ln e^x = \ln 6 \quad \text{(taking the natural log of both sides)}$$
$$x = \ln 6 \quad \text{(since } \ln e^P = P\text{)}.$$

Example 13   Solve $1.07 = 4^{-x}$.

Solution

$$\ln 1.07 = \ln(4^{-x})$$
$$\ln 1.07 = (-x)(\ln 4)$$
$$x = -\frac{\ln 1.07}{\ln 4}$$

When applying the logarithm function to both sides of an equation, we may use log base 10, log base e (the natural log), or indeed the log to *any* base b ($b > 0$). In Example 11, log base 10 is most convenient—as is the natural log for Example 12. The answers $x = \dfrac{(\log 3) - 1}{2}$ and $x = \ln 6$ are *exact* solutions. In order to compare answers in different forms or use these solutions in a numerical computation, we use a calculator to find a decimal approximation. Since a calculator will only compute logs base 10 or e, we must use one of these if we want an approximate decimal solution from the calculator.

Example 14   Solve for x in Examples 12 and 13 by taking the logarithm base 10 (rather than the natural logarithm) of both sides of the equations. Determine decimal approximations (to the accuracy of your calculator) for the solutions you find and for the solutions given in Examples 12 and 13. Are the answers equivalent?

Solution   In Example 12, we have

$$2e^x = 12$$
$$e^x = 6$$
$$\log e^x = \log 6$$
$$x \log e = \log 6$$
$$x = \frac{\log 6}{\log e} \approx 1.791759469.$$

The answer $x = \ln 6$ given in Example 12 is in a simpler form, but $\ln 6 \approx 1.791759469$. Yes, the answers agree (to at least nine decimal places)
In Example 13,

$$1.07 = 4^{-x}$$
$$\log 1.07 = \log 4^{-x}$$
$$\log 1.07 = -x \log 4$$
$$x = -\frac{\log 1.07}{\log 4} \approx -0.0488053983.$$

This agrees with $x = -\dfrac{\ln 1.07}{\ln 4} \approx -0.0488053983$.

Example 15 Solve for t in the equation $P = P_0 e^{kt}$.

Solution Dividing both sides by P_0, we have

$$\frac{P}{P_0} = e^{kt},$$

so

$$\ln \left(\frac{P}{P_0} \right) = \ln e^{kt},$$

$$\ln \left(\frac{P}{P_0} \right) = kt.$$

Thus, $t = \frac{1}{k} \ln \left(\frac{P}{P_0} \right)$.

Problems for Section F

Solve the following equations.

1. $\frac{5}{3}(y + 2) = \frac{1}{2} - y$

2. $3t - \frac{2(t - 1)}{3} = 4$

3. $B - 4[B - 3(1 - B)] = 42$

4. $1.06s - 0.01(248.4 - s) = 22.67s$

5. $8 + 2x - 3x^2 = 0$

6. $2p^3 + p^2 - 18p - 9 = 0$

7. $N^2 - 2N - 3 = 2N(N - 3)$

8. $\frac{1}{64}t^3 = t$

9. $x^2 - 1 = 2x$

10. $4x^2 - 13x - 12 = 0$

11. $60 = -16t^2 + 96t + 12$

12. $y^2 + 4y - 2 = 0$

13. $\frac{2}{z - 3} + \frac{7}{z^2 - 3z} = 0$

14. $\frac{x^2 + 1 - 2x^2}{(x^2 + 1)^2} = 0$

15. $4 - \frac{1}{L^2} = 0$

16. $2 + \frac{1}{q + 1} - \frac{1}{q - 1} = 0$

17. $\sqrt{r^2 + 24} = 7$

18. $\frac{1}{\sqrt[3]{x}} = -2$

19. $3\sqrt{x} = \frac{1}{2}x$

20. $10 = \sqrt{\frac{v}{7\pi}}$

For Problems 21–24, express answers in exact form *and* give a decimal approximation (to two decimal places).

21. $5000 = 2500(0.97)^t$

22. $280 = 40 + 30e^{2t}$

23. $\frac{1}{2}(2^x) = 16$

24. $1 + 10^{-x} = 4.3$

In Problems 25–32, solve for the indicated variable.

25. $T = 2\pi\sqrt{\dfrac{l}{g}}$. Solve for l.

26. $\left(\dfrac{1}{2}\right)^{t/1000} = e^{kt}$. Solve for k (to six decimal places).

27. $\dfrac{1}{2}P_0 = P_0(0.8)^x$. Solve for x (to three decimal places).

28. $y'y^2 + 2xyy' = 4y$. Solve for y'.

29. $l = l_0 + \dfrac{k}{2}w$. Solve for w.

30. $2x - (xy' + yy') + 2yy' = 0$. Solve for y'.

31. $by - d = ay + c$. Solve for y.

32. $u(v + 2) + w(v - 3) = z(v - 1)$. Solve for v.

G SYSTEMS OF EQUATIONS

To solve for two unknown values, we must have two equations— that is, two relationships between the unknowns. Similarly, three unknowns require three equations, and n unknowns (n an integer) require n equations. The group of equations is known as a *system* of equations. To solve the system, we find the *simultaneous* solutions to all equations in the system.

Example 1 Solve for x and y in the following system of equations.

$$\begin{cases} y + \frac{x}{2} = 3 \\ 2(x + y) = 1 - y \end{cases}$$

Solution Solving the first equation for y, we write $y = 3 - \frac{x}{2}$, and substituting for y in the second equation gives

$$2\left(x + \left(3 - \frac{x}{2}\right)\right) = 1 - \left(3 - \frac{x}{2}\right).$$

Then

$$2x + 6 - x = -2 + \frac{x}{2}$$
$$x + 6 = -2 + \frac{x}{2}$$
$$2x + 12 = -4 + x$$
$$x = -16.$$

Using $x = -16$ in the first equation to find the corresponding y, we have

$$y - \frac{16}{2} = 3$$
$$y = 3 + 8 = 11.$$

Thus, the solution that simultaneously solves both equations is $x = -16$, $y = 11$.

Example 2 Solve for x and y in the following system.

$$\begin{cases} y = x - 1 \\ x^2 + y^2 = 5 \end{cases}$$

Solution   We substitute the expression $(x - 1)$ for y in the second equation. Then

$$x^2 + (x - 1)^2 = 5$$
$$x^2 + x^2 - 2x + 1 = 5$$
$$2x^2 - 2x - 4 = 0$$
$$x^2 - x - 2 = 0.$$

Factoring gives $(x - 2)(x + 1) = 0$, so $x = 2$ or $x = -1$.

We then find the y-values which correspond to each x. If $x = 2$, $y = (2) - 1 = 1$, and if $x = -1$, $y = (-1) - 1 = -2$. The solutions to the system are $x = 2$ and $y = 1$ or $x = -1$ and $y = -2$.

Example 3   Solve for Q_0 and a in the system

$$\begin{cases} 90.7 = Q_0 a^{10} \\ 91 = Q_0 a^{13}. \end{cases}$$

Solution   Taking ratios,

$$\frac{Q_0 a^{13}}{Q_0 a^{10}} = \frac{91}{90.7}$$
$$a^3 = \frac{91}{90.7},$$
$$a = \sqrt[3]{\frac{91}{90.7}} \approx 1.0011.$$

To find Q_0,

$$90.7 = Q_0 (1.0011)^{10},$$
$$Q_0 = 89.7083.$$

The simultaneous solution is $a \approx 1.0011$ and $Q_0 \approx 89.7083$.

Graphically, the simultaneous solutions to a system of equations give us the coordinates of the point (or points) of intersection for the graphs of the equations in the system. For example, the solutions to Example 2 give the coordinates of the points where the line $y = x - 1$ intersects the circle centered at the origin with radius $\sqrt{5}$.

Example 4   Find the points of intersection for the graphs in Figure G.1.

Solution   We can solve $y = x^2 - 1$ and $y = x + 1$ simultaneously by setting the equations equal to one another. Then

$$x^2 - 1 = x + 1$$
$$x^2 - x - 2 = 0$$
$$(x + 1)(x - 2) = 0,$$

so $x = -1$ and $x = 2$ are solutions. To get the corresponding y-values, we use either equation to find $x = -1$ gives $y = 0$, and $x = 2$ gives $y = 3$. The graphs intersect at $(-1, 0)$ and $(2, 3)$.

For some systems of equations, it is impossible to find the simultaneous solution(s) using algebra. In this case, the only choice is to find the solution(s) by approximating the point(s) of intersection graphically.

Figure G.1

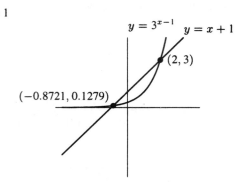

Figure G.2: The graphs reveal two intersection points

Example 5   Solve the system:

$$\begin{cases} y = x + 1 \\ y = 3^{x-1} \end{cases}$$

Solution   We are looking for the point or points of intersection of the line $y = x + 1$ and the exponential equation $y = 3^{x-1}$. Setting the expressions for y equal to one another gives

$$x + 1 = 3^{x-1}.$$

We cannot use the algebraic techniques of the previous section to solve this equation. We might try to guess a solution. Note that

$$2 + 1 = 3^{2-1}$$
$$3 = 3,$$

so $x = 2$, $y = 3$ is a solution to the system. If you were not able to guess this solution, you would be able to see it on the graph.

However, the graphs of the equations in Figure G.2 reveal that the system has two solutions. There is also a value of x such that $-1 < x < 0$ where the two graphs intersect. We find

$$x \approx -0.8721, y \approx 0.1279.$$

Thus, the solutions to the system are $x = 2$ and $y = 3$ or $x \approx -0.8721$ and $y \approx 0.1279$.

Simultaneous solutions to a system of equations in two variables can always be approximated by graphing, whereas it is only sometimes possible to find exact solutions using algebra.

Problems for Section G

Solve the following systems of equations.

1. $\begin{cases} 2x + 3y = 7 \\ y = -\frac{3}{5}x + 6 \end{cases}$

2. $\begin{cases} y = 2x - x^2 \\ y = -3 \end{cases}$

3. $\begin{cases} y = 4 - x^2 \\ y - 2x = 1 \end{cases}$

4. $\begin{cases} y = \frac{1}{x} \\ y = 4x \end{cases}$

Determine the points of intersection for Problems 5–8.

5.

Figure G.3

6.

Figure G.4

7.

Figure G.5

8. Fill in the missing coordinates and then write an equation of the line connecting the two points. Check your work by solving the system of two equations.

H SOLVING INEQUALITIES

Just as we can solve some simple equations mentally, we can solve some inequalities mentally. Consider the following examples.

To solve:	We think:	The solution is:
$x - 1 > 0$	*"If x is larger than +1, the left hand side is positive."*	$x > 1$
$x + 4 < 10$	*"As long as x stays smaller than +6, the left hand side will be less than the right hand side."*	$x < 6$
$3 - x < 0$	*"When x gets larger than +3, the left hand side will be negative."*	$x > 3$
$x - 2 \geq 0$	*"If x = 2 then x − 2 is 0. When x is larger than 2, then x − 2 is positive."*	$x \geq 2$
$x^2(x + 5) > 0$	*"The value of x^2 is always positive, so x + 5 needs to be positive."*	$x > -5$

More complicated inequalities may require additional work. We solve inequalities using some of the techniques used in solving equations. However, there are some important differences applications of these techniques to inequalities.

For a, b, and c real numbers, if $a < b$, then

$$a + c < b + c$$
$$a \cdot c < b \cdot c \qquad \text{if } c > 0$$
$$a \cdot c > b \cdot c \qquad \text{if } c < 0 \qquad \text{(inequality reverses direction).}$$

For a and b positive, when $a < b$, then

$$a^2 < b^2 \quad \text{, and} \quad \frac{1}{a} > \frac{1}{b} \qquad \text{(inequality reverses direction).}$$

Linear Inequalities

We solve linear inequalities with the same techniques we use to solve linear equations; however, the inequality is reversed whenever we multiply or divide both sides of the inequality by a negative number.

Example 1   Solve for x:

$$1 - \frac{3}{2}x \le 16.$$

Solution   We have

$$1 - \frac{3}{2}x - 1 \le 16 - 1$$

$$-\frac{3}{2}x \le 15$$

$$\left(-\frac{2}{3}\right)\left(-\frac{3}{2}x\right) \ge \left(-\frac{2}{3}\right)15$$

$$x \ge -10.$$

Example 2   Solve for x:

$$-6 < 4x - 7 < 5.$$

Solution   The solutions to this double inequality will be all values of x such that $4x - 7$ is between -6 and 5. We can operate on all three sections of the inequality at once (if we're careful). We start by adding 7 to each part which gives

$$-6 + 7 < 4x - 7 + 7 < 5 + 7.$$

$$1 < 4x < 12$$

$$\frac{1}{4} < x < 3.$$

The solution set includes all numbers between $\frac{1}{4}$ and 3.

Checking the Sign of an Expression

When an expression is a product or a quotient, we can determine the sign of the expression on an interval by looking at the sign of each factor over the interval.

Example 3   Determine the values of x which make the expression $(4 - x)^2 e^{-x}$ positive, negative, and zero respectively.

Solution   The expression e^{-x} is always positive, and $(4 - x)^2$ is positive for any value of x except $x = 4$, where it equals zero. Therefore, $(4 - x)^2 e^{-x} > 0$ for $x \ne 4$, and $(4 - x)^2 e^{-x} = 0$ if $x = 4$.

Example 4   Determine the values of x which make the expression $(x + 1)(x - 7)$ positive, negative, and zero respectively.

Solution   The expression will be zero if $x = -1$ or $x = +7$. The product has the potential for changing sign at $x = -1$ or $x = +7$. We can check the sign of the expression by looking at the sign of each factor over the intervals established by placing a flag at $x = -1$ and $x = +7$. The expression will be positive when both factors have the same sign.

$$\begin{array}{ccccc} \overline{}^{(-)(-)} & & {}^{(+)(-)} & & {}^{(+)(+)} \\ \text{positive} & -1 & \text{negative} & 7 & \text{positive} \end{array} \longrightarrow x$$

Thus,

$$(x + 1)(x - 7) = 0 \quad \text{for } x = -1 \text{ or } x = 7,$$
$$(x + 1)(x - 7) < 0 \quad \text{for } -1 < x < 7,$$
$$(x + 1)(x - 7) > 0 \quad \text{for } x < -1 \text{ or } x > 7.$$

Example 5   Determine the values of r for which the expression $\dfrac{2r + 5}{(r - 1)(r - 3)}$ is zero, positive, negative, or undefined.

Solution   A fraction is equal to 0 if the numerator is 0, so this expression equals 0 if $r = -\frac{5}{2}$. The values $r = 1$ and $r = 3$ make the expression undefined because here the denominator is zero. We divide the number line by flagging $-\frac{5}{2}$, 1, and 3, and we check the sign of each each factor on each interval. This gives

$$\begin{array}{ccccccc} \dfrac{(-)}{(-)(-)} & & \dfrac{(+)}{(-)(-)} & & \dfrac{(+)}{(+)(-)} & & \dfrac{(+)}{(+)(+)} \\ \text{negative} & -\frac{5}{2} & \text{positive} & 1 & \text{negative} & 3 & \text{positive} \end{array} \longrightarrow r$$

Therefore,

$$\frac{2r + 5}{(r - 1)(r - 3)} \quad \text{is not defined for } r = 1 \text{ or } r = 3.$$
$$\frac{2r + 5}{(r - 1)(r - 3)} = 0 \quad \text{for } r = -\frac{5}{2},$$
$$\frac{2r + 5}{(r - 1)(r - 3)} > 0 \quad \text{for } -\frac{5}{2} < r < 1 \text{ or } r > 3,$$
$$\frac{2r + 5}{(r - 1)(r - 3)} < 0 \quad \text{for } r < -\frac{5}{2} \text{ or } 1 < r < 3,$$

Example 6   Determine y-values which make the expression $\dfrac{\sqrt{y + 2}}{y^3}$ positive, negative, zero, or undefined.

Solution   The expression is zero if $y = -2$. It is not defined if y is less than -2 because we cannot take the square root of a negative number. Furthermore, the quotient is not defined if $y = 0$ because that gives a zero in the denominator. The radical is always positive (where defined), so the numerator will be positive. Because the cube of a negative number is negative, we can visualize signs in each interval.

$$\begin{array}{ccccc} & & \dfrac{(+)}{(-)} & & \dfrac{(+)}{(+)} \\ \text{undefined} & -2 & \text{negative} & 0 & \text{positive} \end{array} \longrightarrow y$$

Appendix / 31

So

$$\frac{\sqrt{y+2}}{y^3} \quad \text{is undefined for } y < -2 \text{ or } y = 0,$$

$$\frac{\sqrt{y+2}}{y^3} = 0 \quad \text{for } y = -2,$$

$$\frac{\sqrt{y+2}}{y^3} > 0 \quad \text{for } y > 0.$$

$$\frac{\sqrt{y+2}}{y^3} < 0 \quad \text{for } -2 < y < 0,$$

Solving Nonlinear Inequalities by Factoring and Checking Signs

We can often solve polynomial and rational inequalities by starting out the same way we would with an equation and then using a number line to find the intervals on which the inequality holds.

Example 7 Solve for x if

$$2x^2 + x^3 \le 3.$$

Solution We first set the inequality so that zero is on one side. Then

$$x^3 + 2x^2 - 3x \le 0,$$
$$x(x^2 + 2x - 3) \le 0,$$
$$x(x+3)(x-1) \le 0.$$

The left hand side equals 0 for $x = 0$, $x = -3$, and $x = 1$. To solve the inequality we want to select the x-values for which the left hand side is negative. We check signs over the four intervals created by flagging $x = 0, -3, +1$.

$$
\begin{array}{ccccc}
(-)(-)(-) & & (-)(+)(-) & & (+)(+)(-) \;\; (+)(+)(+) \\
\hline
\text{negative} \;\; -3 & & \text{positive} & & 0 \;\; \text{negative} \;\; 1 \;\; \text{positive}
\end{array} \quad x
$$

So $x^3 + 2x^2 - 3x < 0$ for $x < -3$ or $0 < x < 1$ and $x^3 + 2x^2 - 3x = 0$ at $x = 0$, $x = -3$, and $x = 1$. Therefore, $2x^2 + x^3 \le 3x$ for $x \le -3$ or $0 \le x \le 1$.

Example 8 Solve for q:

$$\frac{1}{2-q} > q.$$

Solution

$$\frac{1}{2-q} - q > 0,$$

$$\frac{1}{2-q} - q\frac{(2-q)}{(2-q)} > 0,$$

$$\frac{1 - q(2-q)}{2-q} > 0,$$

$$\frac{1 - 2q + q^2}{2-q} > 0.$$

We want this quotient to be positive, so the numerator and denominator must have the same sign. Notice that $q \neq 2$. Factoring the numerator, we have $\dfrac{(1-q)^2}{2-q} > 0$. The numerator is never negative, and the denominator will be positive if $2 - q > 0$ which gives $q < 2$. However, $(1-q)^2 = 0$ if $q = 1$, so $q = 1$ must be excluded in order to preserve the inequality. Therefore, $\dfrac{1}{2-q} > q$ for $q < 2$ and $q \neq 1$.

Radical inequalities

We can eliminate radicals by raising both sides to the same power if we check our answers.

Example 9   Solve for x:

$$\sqrt{x-6} < 2.$$

Solution   The expression $\sqrt{x-6}$ is not defined unless $x \geq 6$, so we can limit the x-values we need to consider. Also, $\sqrt{x-6} \geq 0$, and so we can square both sides giving

$$(\sqrt{x-6})^2 < 2^2,$$
$$x - 6 < 4,$$
$$x < 10.$$

However, we are only considering x-values which are 6 or larger, so $\sqrt{x-6} < 4$ for $6 \leq x < 10$.

Example 10   Solve for x given

$$\sqrt{2-x} > 3.$$

Solution   Squaring both sides gives

$$(\sqrt{2-x})^2 > 3^2,$$
$$2 - x > 9,$$
$$-x > 7,$$
$$x < -7.$$

In this case, the fact that the radical is only defined for $x \leq 2$ does not affect our solution because any number which is less than -7 is also less than 2.

Problems for Section H

Problems 1–10: Solve mentally.

1. $2(x-7) \geq 0$
2. $\sqrt{x} > 4$
3. $x^2 < 25$
4. $x - 3 > 2$
5. $1 + \sqrt{x+4} > 0$
6. $x^2 \geq 16$
7. $1 + x^2 > 0$
8. $5 - x < 0$
9. $2^{-x} > 0$
10. $2x^2 + 1 < 0$

Problems 11–16: Write as inequalities.

11. The x-values which are less than 0.001

12. The y-values between -1 and 1

13. All p-values except 5

14. All the positive values of k

15. All the r-values which are not negative

16. The t-values during or after the year 1995

In Problems 17–26, determine the real number values of the variable (if any) which will make each expression (a) undefined, (b) zero, (c) positive, (d) negative.

17. $3x^2 + 6x$

18. $(2x)e^x + x^2 e^x$

19. 2^{-x}

20. $6t^2 - 30t + 36$

21. $\dfrac{1}{3}x^{-2/3}$

22. $\dfrac{-24}{p^3}$

23. $\dfrac{1}{2\sqrt{x^2+1}}(2x)$

24. $\dfrac{\ln x}{x}$

25. $\dfrac{1 - 3u^2}{(u^2 + 1)^3}$

26. $-\dfrac{2x - 1}{\big(x(x - 1)\big)^2}$

Problems 27–36: Solve the inequalities.

27. $4 - x^2 > 0$

28. $-1 \le 4x - 3 \le 1$

29. $0 \le \frac{1}{2} - n < 11$

30. $\sqrt{3l} - \dfrac{1}{4} > 0$

31. $t^2 - 3t - 4 \ge 0$

32. $2(x - 1)(x + 4) + (x - 1)^2 > 0$

33. $2 + \dfrac{r}{r - 3} > 0$

34. $\dfrac{1}{x} > \dfrac{1}{x + 1}$

35. $\dfrac{2x^2 - (2x + 1)(2x)}{x^4} < 0$

36. $\dfrac{3(x + 2)^2 - 6x(x + 2)}{(x + 2)^4} > 0$

Answers to Odd-Numbered Problems

ANSWERS TO ODD NUMBERED PROBLEMS

Section 1.1

1 (a) 69°F
   (b) July 17th and 20th
   (c) Yes
   (d) No
5 (a) 36 seconds
   (c) 36 seconds, 7.5 lines
   (d) $T = 4n$
7 (a) (I), (III), (IV.), (V)
       (VII), (VIII)
   (b) (i) (V) and (VI)
       (ii) (VIII)
   (c) (III) and (IV)
13 $C = 1.06P$
15 (a) Yes
   (b) No
17 (a) Yes
   (b) No

Section 1.2

3 (b) 3
   (c) −8
   (d) 16
   (e) 6
5 (a) $P = (b, a)$
       $Q = (d, e)$
   (b) $f(b) = a$
   (c) $x = d$
   (d) $x = h$
   (e) $a = -e$
7 (a) 48 feet for both
   (b) 4 sec, 64 ft
9 (a) $s(2) = 146$
   (b) Solve $v(t) = 65$
   (c) At 3 hours
11 (a) $4871.25
   (b) $T(x) = 0.8x$
   (c) $L(x) = 0.063x - 483.75$
   (d) $4871.25
13 (c) 5050

Section 1.3

1 Domain: integers $0 \leq n \leq 200$
   Range: integers $0 \leq n \leq 800$
3 Domain: $x \geq 0$
   Range: $y \geq 0$
5 Domain: $x \leq 8$
   Range: $y \geq 0$
7 Domain: $x, x \neq 2$
   Range: $y > 0$
9 Domain: all real x
   Range: $y \geq 1$
11 Domain: all real x
   Range: $y \leq 9$
13 Domain: all real x
   Range: all real y
15 $y \geq 1$
17 $-4 \leq y \leq 5$
19 (a) $p(0) = 50$
       $p(10) \approx 131$
       $p(50) \approx 911$
   (c) $50 \leq p(t) < 1000$

Section 1.4

1 (a) (i) 248
       (ii) 142
       (iii) 4
       (iv) 12
       (v) 378
       (vi) −18
       (vii) 248
       (viii) 570
       (ix) 13
   (b) (i) $x = 2$
       (ii) $x = 8$
       (iii) $x = 7$
   (c) $x = 1, 4$
3 (a) −1
   (b) −3/2

587

   (d) 2/3
   (e) −1/3, −3/2
   (f) −4, −5/3
5 (a) $(-2, 2)$
   (b) $(-2\sqrt{2}, -2), (2\sqrt{2}, -2)$
   (c) −3
7 (a) Domain: $x \geq 4$
       Range: $f(x) \geq 0$
   (b) Domain: $4 \leq x \leq 20$
       Range: $0 \leq r(x) \leq 2$
   (c) Domain: all real numbers
       Range: $0 < g(x) \leq 1$
   (d) Domain: all real numbers
       Range: $h(x) \geq -16$
9 (a) (ii)
   (b) (iv)
   (c) (i)
   (d) (iii)
11 (a) $h(3) = 12$
   (b) $h(s + 1) = 4s + 4$
13 (a) $A = f(r) = \pi r^2$
   (b) $f(1.1r)$
   (c) 21%

Section 1.5

1 (a) $k = 4\pi/3$
   (b) $p = 3$
3 (a) $C(x) = kx$
   (b) $k = 9.5; C(x) = 9.5x$
   (c) $52.25
5 Direct; $k = 0.17, p = 1$
7 Direct; $k = -1/2, p = 1$
9 Direct; $k = 2\pi, p = 1$
11 Indirect; $k = 2/3, p = -1$
13 Yes; $k = 32, p = 5$
15 Yes; $k = 3, p = -5$
17 Yes; $k = -5, p = 4$
19 Yes; $k = 1/6$ and $p = -7$
21 No
23 No

Answers / 1

25 (b) 16 times greater

27 (a) $k = 2.823 \cdot 10^9$ pounds $\cdot$ miles^2

   (c) $f(5000) = 112.9$ pounds

29 $A = \pi d^2/4$

37 (b) $2.50

   (c) 7/8 mile

39 (b) Domain: $0 \le x \le 1000$
       Range: $0 \le y \le 274.5$
       or $624.5 < y \le 2180$
       Jump at $x = 150$

Section 1.6

3 Yes; No

7 24.5 degrees/minute

9 (a) 3, $-3/2$ hundred/yr

   (b) 5/3, $-5/6$ hundred/yr

   (c) 40/17, $-20/17$ hundred/yr

11 (a) 1/2

   (c) 1/4

13 (a) 5

   (b) 15, 15, 10, 20, 15, 15

   (c) No

15 Decreasing

17 (a) E, III

   (b) G, I

   (c) F, II

19 (c) Domain: $-\infty < x < \infty$
       Range: $-\infty < y < \infty$

   (d) Increasing: $-\infty < x < \infty$

   (e) Concave up: $0 < x < \infty$
       Cancave down: $-\infty < x < 0$

21 (c) Domain is all real numbers except 0
       Range: $0 < y < \infty$

   (d) Increasing: $-\infty < x < 0$
       Decreasing: $0 < x < \infty$

   (e) Concave up: $-\infty < x < 0$ and $0 < x < \infty$

23 (c) Domain: $-\infty < x < \infty$
       Range: $-\infty < y < \infty$

   (d) Increasing: $-\infty < x < \infty$

   (e) Concave up: $-\infty < x < 0$
       Cancave down: $0 < x < \infty$

25 (c) Horizontal: $y = 0$
       Vertical: $x = -2$

27 (c) Horizontal: $y = 2$
       Vertical: $x = -4$

29 (a) From A to F

   (b) From O to A

   (c) From D to E

   (d) From F to I

Chapter 1 Review

1 (a) No

   (b) No

   (c) Yes

3 (b) July

   (c) Increasing: Jan.–July
       Decreasing: July–Dec.

5 (a) Owens: 12 yards/sec.;
       horse: 20 yards/sec.

   (b) 6 seconds

7 (a) Yes

   (b) No

   (c) $y = 1, 2, 3, 4$

11 (a) Always increasing

   (c) Concave up months 4 to 5, then concave down

   (d) Greatest between months 4 and 5

   (e) About month 4

13 (a) $A = 2\pi r^2 + 710/r$

   (c) Domain: $r > 0$
       Approximate range: $A > 277.5$ cm^2

   (d) ≈ 277.5 cm^2
       $r \approx 3.83$ cm
       $h \approx 7.7$ cm

17 (a) 11,000

   (b) 16.064

   (c) 2,541,000

21 (a) Domain: all real numbers
       Range: all real numbers

   (b) Domain: all real numbers
       Range: $n(x) \le 9$

   (c) Domain: $x \ge 3$ or $x \le -3$
       Range: $q(x) \ge 0$

27 (a) Increasing until year 60, then decreasing

   (f) 1840; potato famine

29 (a) $1.01

   (b) $y = \begin{cases} 1 + x & \text{for} \ 0 < x < \\ 10x + x & \text{for} \ 0.1 < x \\ 5 + x & \text{for} \ x > 0.5 \end{cases}$

   (c) $4

Section 2.1

3 (c) 22 million

   (d) 0.3 million people/year

5 (a) Radius and circumference

   (c) 2π

7 (a) (i) -1.246

       (ii) -1.246

       (iii) -1.246

   (b) $f(x) = -0.367 - 1.246x$

9 $P = 18,310 + 58t$

11 $c = 4000 + 80r$

13 (a) $F = 2C + 30$

   (b) $-3°$, $-2°$, $1°$, and $4°$ respectively

   (c) $10°$C

15 (a) increasing function of x

   (b) $F(x) = 1.242x$

   (c) ≈ 3.7 pounds

17 No

21 Window: $0 \le d \le 20$ and $0 \le C \le 41.50$.

Section 2.2

1 (a) $y = 4 - \frac{3}{5}x$

   (b) $y = 180 - 10x$

   (c) $y = -0.3 + 5x$

   (d) $y = \frac{4}{5} - x$

   (e) $y = \frac{2}{3} + \frac{5}{3}x$

   (f) $y = 21 - x$

   (g) $y = -\frac{40}{3} - \frac{2}{3}x$

   (h) Not possible

3 $f(x) = 3 - 2x$

5 $f(t) = 2.2 - 1.22t$

9 (b) $p = 12 - s$

11 (a) Membership fee: \$55;
        Fixed price per meal:
        \$3.25

   (b) $C = 55 + 3.25m$

   (c) \$217.50

   (d) $m = (C - 55)/3.25$

   (e) 75 meals

13 $y = -4 + 4x$

15 (a) $y = -1250 + (9.50)x$

   (c) $x = 132$

   (d) $x = y/9.50 + 1250/9.50$

   (e) 2001

17 $y = f(0) + \frac{f(A) - f(0)}{A}x$

19 (a) y-intercept: c/q
        x-intercept: c/p

   (b) $-(p/q)$

21 (a) l_1

   (b) l_3

   (c) l_2

   (d) No match

Section 2.3

5 (a) (ii)

   (b) (iii)

   (c) (i)

7 (a) (V)

   (b) (IV)

   (c) (I)

   (d) (VI)

   (e) (II)

   (f) (III)

   (g) (VII)

9 (c) Yes, $y = 3 + 0x$

   (d) No

11 (a) $m_1 = m_2, b_1 \neq b_2$

   (b) $m_1 = m_2, b_1 = b_2$

   (c) $m_1 \neq m_2$

   (d) Not possible

13 $(1, 0)$

15 (a) 5 years

19 (a) Company A: $20 + 0.2x$
        Company B: $35 + 0.1x$

      Company C: 70

   (c) Slope: mileage rate
        Vertical intercept: fixed
        cost/day

   (d) A for $x < 150$
        B for $150 < x < 350$
        C for $x > 350$

21 (a) $y = -5484.1 + 2.84x$

   (b) 195.9 million tons.

Section 2.4

1 (c) $r \approx 1$

3 (c) $y = 15x - 80$

   (e) Yes, strong positive cor-
        relation.

5 (b) $r \approx -1/2$

   (c) $y = 27.5139 - 0.1674x$
        $r = -0.5389$

7 (c) $H = 37.26t - 39.85$,
        $r = 0.9995, r = 1$.

   (d) Slope is about 37.

Chapter 2 Review

1 (a) 162 calories

   (c) (i) Calories =
             $0.025 \times$ weight

        (ii) (0,0) is number of
              calories
              burned by a weight-
              less runner

        (iii) Domain $0 < w$;
              range $0 < c$

        (iv) 3.4

3 (a) $R = 0.95x$
        $C = 200 + 0.25x$
        $P = -200 + 0.70x$

5 \$10,500

7 $f(t) = 2.2 - 1.22t$

9 (c) 2.5 seconds

   (e) Moon: slope less nega-
        tive.
        Jupiter: slope more neg-
        ative.

11 (a) $x + y$

   (b) $0.15x + 0.18y$

   (c) $(15x + 18y)/(x + y)$

13 (a) $i(x) = 2.5x$

   (b) $i(0) = 0$

15 $y = -\frac{1}{5}x + \frac{7}{5}$

19 (a) Demand down to 100.

   (b) $D = 1100 - 200p$

   (c) \$5.25

23 (b) $0 \leq t \leq 4$

Section 3.1

3 (a) \$573.60 per month

   (b) \$440.40 per month

   (c) \$645.00 per month

   (d) \$12,852

   (e) \$55,296

5 $P = 70(1.019)^t$

7 (a) $f(0) = 1000$,
        $f(10) \approx 1480$

   (b) $0 \leq t \leq 10$,
        $0 \leq P \leq 1500$;
        $0 \leq t \leq 50$,
        $0 \leq P \leq 8000$

9 2015

11 (a) $N(r) = 64\left(\frac{1}{2}\right)^r$

   (b) 6

13 $L = 420(0.15)^n$

15 (a) 59 minutes

   (b) 58 minutes

17 (a) $P \approx 0.538$ millibars

   (b) $h \approx 0.784$ km

Section 3.2

3 (a) (ii)

   (b) (i)

   (c) (iv)

   (d) (ii)

   (e) (iii)

   (f) (i)

5 (a) $f(x)$ is exponential
        $g(x)$ is linear
        $h(x)$ is exponential
        $i(x)$ is linear

   (b) $f(x) = 12.5(1.1)^x$,
        $g(x) = 2x$

7 $a = 12. b \approx 0.841$.

9 $x < -1.7$ and $x > 2$

11 f

13 (a) $h(x) = 3(5)^x$
(b) $f(x) = -3(\frac{1}{2})^x$
(c) $g(x) = 2(4)^x$

15 $y = (1/2)^x$

17 $y = 1.2(2)^x$

19 (a) $P = 1154.23(1.2011)^t$
(b) $1154.23
(c) 20.1%

23 $\approx 8,587$ bacteria

25 (a) 600,000 people
(b) 926 bears
(c) 2029

27 (a) $p(n) = (5/6)^n$
(b) 4
(c) 13

Section 3.3

No short answers in section

Section 3.4

1 (a) 0
(b) -1
(c) 0
(d) 1/2
(e) 5
(f) 2
(g) $-1/2$
(h) 100
(i) 1
(j) 0.01

3 (a) $\log(A \cdot B) = \log A + \log B$;
$\log \frac{A}{B} = \log A - \log B$;
$\log A^B = B \log A$
(b) $p(\log A + \log B - \log C)$
$p \log \left(\dfrac{AB}{C} \right)$
$p(\log AB - \log C)$

5 (a) True
(b) False
(c) False
(d) True
(e) True
(f) False

7 (a) $x + y$
(b) $3x + \frac{1}{2}y$
(c) $\log(10^x - 10^y)$
(d) $\frac{x}{y}$
(e) $x - y$
(f) 10^{x+y}

9 (a) $2x$
(b) x^3
(c) $-3x$

11 1.4

13 (a) 0
(b) $\sqrt{2} - 1$
(c) $\frac{31}{30}$
(d) 27
(e) $\frac{1}{4}$
(f) 1

15 (a) $\frac{\log 3}{\log 1.04} \approx 28$
(b) $\frac{\log \frac{14}{3}}{\log 1.081} \approx 19.8$
(c) $\frac{\log(\frac{38}{84})}{\log 0.74} \approx 2.63$
(d) $\frac{\log(\frac{12}{5})}{3 \log 1.014} \approx 21$
(e) $\frac{\log(\frac{8}{5})}{\log(\frac{1.15}{1.07})} \approx 6.5$
(f) No solution

17 (a) $P = 3(\frac{100}{3})^{\frac{t}{3}}$
(b) 0.94 hours

19 (a) $x = \dfrac{\log 1.6}{\log 1.031} \approx 15.4$
(b) $x = \dfrac{\log(\frac{7}{4})}{\log(\frac{1.171}{1.088})} \approx 7.6$
(c) $x = 47$

21 (a) $W(t) = 50(1.029)^t$, $C(t) = 45(1.032)^t$
(b) 36.2 years
(c) 274 years

23 (b) No

Section 3.5

1 (a) $t(x)$
(b) $r(x)$
(c) $s(x)$

5 (a) $o(t) = 245 \cdot 1.03^t$
(b) $h(t) = 63 \cdot (2)^{\frac{t}{10}}$
(c) 34.2 years

7 (a) 10^{-2}, 10^{-4}, 10^{-7}
(b) Less

Section 3.6

1 (a) $1270.24
(b) $1271.01
(c) $1271.22
(d) $1271.25

3 $t = \dfrac{\log 1.5}{\log \left(1 + \frac{0.06}{365}\right)} \approx 2467$ days

5 32.5 years

7 5.39%

9 (a) Effective annual yield: 7.76%
(b) Nominal annual rate: 7.5%

11 (a) $18,655.38
(b) $18,532.00
(c) $18,520.84

13 18.55%

15 (a) Annually: 4.7%
(b) Monthly: 0.383%
(c) By the decade: 58.29%

17 (a) $P(t) = 22,000e^{0.071t}$
(b) $\approx 7.36\%$

19 (a) $Q(t) = 2e^{-0.04t}$
(b) 3.92%
(c) After 52 hours
(d) 55 hours after 2nd injection

21 From best to worst: C, A, B

23 (a) 2.708333333
(b) 2.718055556
(c) 2.718281828;
(d) 13 terms

25 $27,399.10

Section 3.7

1 (a) 1412 bacteria
(b) 10.0 hours
(c) 1 hour

3 (a) 4.73%
(b) 4.62%

5 23.4 years

7 (a) $P_0 = 14.85$; $k \approx 0.0385$
(b) 3.93%

$3 \left(\frac{100}{3}\right)^{\frac{1}{3}}$

9 (a) 3%
   (b) 5.3 million
   (c) 36.6 years
   (d) 516 years ago; No

11 (a) $t = \frac{\ln(18.5/16.3)}{\ln 1.072} \approx 1.821$
    (b) $t = \frac{1}{0.049}\ln\left(\frac{25}{13}\right) \approx 13.35$
    (c) $t = -6.2$ or $t = 61.9$

13 (a) 13.3%
    (b) 2.53%
    (c) 2.50%

15 (a) 2.03 volts
    (b) after 5.36 seconds
    (c) 25.9%

17 (b) $(0, 140)$;
    (c) 8 : 10 A.M.: $\approx 106°$; 9 A.M.: $\approx 67°$
    (d) Temp approaches $65°$; horizontal asymptote at $H = 65$.

19 (a) 7.0%
    (b) 0.7 years
    (c) 0.067

21 (a) $x = \ln 10 - 4$
    (b) $x = \frac{\ln 7 - 5}{1 - \ln 2}$
    (c) $x = -2, \frac{1}{3}$, or $-\frac{1}{3}$

23 12,146 years old

25 (a) $M(a) = M_0(0.98)^{(a-30)}$
    (b) 64.3 years old

27 About 5092 years ago

29 (a) $t = (1/0.48)\ln(99x/(100-x))$
    (b) $x = (100e^{0.48t - \ln 99})/(1 + e^{0.48t - \ln 99})$

Section 3.8

1 (b) Linear function
   (c) $f(x)$ is an exponential function;
        $g(x)$ is a linear function.
   (d) It is linear; yes

3 (b) Exponential function results
   (c) Linear function results

5 (a) $a \approx -7.786, b \approx 86.28$
   (c) 69,262 minutes $\approx$ 48 days
        0.18 minutes $\approx$ 11 seconds

7 (a) $y = 2237 + 2570x$
   (b) $\ln y = 8.227 + 0.2766x$
   (c) $y = 3740e^{0.2766x}$

9 (a) $y = 48 + 0.80x$;
        $r \approx 0.9996$
   (b) $y = 73(1.0048)^x$;
        $r \approx 0.9728$
   (c) $y = 8.1x^{0.62}$;
        $r \approx 0.9933$
   (d) Linear is best

11 (a) $y = -169 + 57.8x$;
         $r \approx 0.9914$
    (b) $y = 9.6(1.59)^x$;
         $r \approx 0.9773$
    (c) $y = 2.2x^{2.41}$;
         $r \approx 0.9707$
    (d) Power is best

13 (a) $y = -83 + 61.5x$; superb fit

15 (a) Negative
    (b) $y = b + px$
    (c) $(0, 244)$
    (d) No

Chapter 3 Review

1 (a) Linear, $Q(t) = 7 + 0.17t$
   (b) Exponential, $R(t) = 2.00(1.03)^t$
   (c) Neither

3 (a) A, D
   (b) C and E
   (c) D, E
   (d) B
   (e) F
   (f) (i) only

5 (a) 24.5%
   (b) 4.5%
   (c) $31

7 $-0.587 < x < 4.91$

9 $y = 2(3/2)^x$

11 $f(x) = 3\left(\frac{1}{9}\right)^x$

13 $f(x) = 0.0124 + 0.093x$
    $g(x) = 3.2(1.2)^x$

15 (c) Ratios $\to 1.618$
    (d) $f(n) \approx 0.447(1.618)^n$

17 (a) (i) $u - v$
         (ii) $-2u$
         (iii) $3u + v$
         (iv) $\frac{1}{2}(u + v)$
    (b) $\frac{1}{2}(u + 2v) = \log\sqrt{50} \approx \log 7$

19 (a) Starts at 15,000 and grows by 4% each year
    (b) $b = 1.003$; 0.3% monthly growth rate
    (c) 17.67; c is doubling time in years

21 35.97%

23 (a) $y = 2^x$
    (b) $b \approx 1.445$
    (c) $2.72 \approx e$
    (d) $b = e^{(1/e)}$

25 (a) $x = \ln 8 - 3 \approx -0.9206$
    (b) $x = \frac{\log 1.25}{\log 1.12} \approx 1.9690$
    (c) $-\frac{\ln 4}{0.13} \approx -10.6638$
    (d) $x = 105$
    (e) $x = \frac{1}{3}e^{\frac{3}{2}} \approx 1.4939$
    (f) $x = \frac{e^{\frac{1}{2}}}{e^{\frac{1}{2}} - 1} \approx 2.5415$
    (g) $x = -1.599$ or $x = 2.534$
    (h) $x = 2.478$ or $x = 3$
    (i) $x = 0.653$

27 (a) 5th week, 5 million
    (b) 2nd week, 5 million

29 (a) $k = 0.0583$
    (b) $b = 1.0747$

31 (a) 3%, 2.96%
    (b) 3.04%, 3%
    (c) Decay: 6%, 6.19%
    (d) Decay: 4.97%, 5.1%
    (e) 3.93%, 3.85%
    (f) Decay: 2.73%, 2.77%

33 (a) $y = \frac{3}{2}x$
    (b) $y = e^{x+2}$

(c) $y = e^{0.4x}$
(d) $y = e^{-1.7x}$
(e) $y = x^{\frac{3}{2}}$
(f) $y = e^2 x^{\frac{2}{3}}$

35 (a) $x = \dfrac{\log\left(\frac{Q_0}{P_0}\right)}{\log\left(\frac{a}{b}\right)}$
    (b) $x = 0$
    (c) x does not exist

Section 4.1

1 (a) Reduces temp by 2°F all day
   (b) Delay all changes by 2 hrs
   (c) $H(t)$, (70°F)
   (d) $H(t) - 2$

5 (a) $3^w - 3$
   (b) 3^{w-3}
   (c) $3^w + 1.8$
   (d) $3^{w+\sqrt{5}}$
   (e) $3^{w+2.1} - 1.3$
   (f) $3^{w-1.5} - 0.9$

7 (a) (vi)
   (b) (iii)
   (c) (ii)
   (d) (v)
   (e) (i)
   (f) (iv)

13 (a) $a(t) = g(t) + 0.5$
   (b) $b(t) = g(t + 1.5)$
   (c) $c(t) = g(t + 1.5) - 0.3$
   (d) $d(t) = g(t - 0.5)$
   (e) $e(t) = g(t - 0.5) + 1.2$

15 (a) $T(d) = S(d) + 1$
   (b) $P(d) = S(d - 1)$

19 (a) $t(x) = 5 + 3x$ for $x \geq 0$
   (b) $n(x) = t(x) + 1$ (vertical shift)
   (c) $p(x) = 10 + 3(x - 2)$ for $x \geq 2$, or $p(x) = t(x - 2) + 5$ for $x \geq 2$

21 $H(t) = 280(0.97)^t + 70$

Section 4.2

7 Flipped about y-axis.
9 (a) $f(-x) = \sqrt{4 - x^2}$

(c) Even

13 (a) $y = -x^3 + 2$
   (b) $y = -(x^3 + 2)$
   (c) No

15 (a) $y = |x - 1| + 2$
   (b) $y = (-x - 2)/(x + 1)$
   (c) $y = -(x + 1)^3 + 1$

21 (a) Symmetric about y-axis; even
   (b) Symmetric about origin; odd
   (c) Not symmetric
   (d) Not symmetric

27 If $f(x)$ is odd, then $f(0) = 0$

31 (a) Even if and only if $m = 0$
   (b) Odd if and only if $b = 0$
   (c) Both if and only if $m = 0, b = 0$

33 Yes, $f(x) = 0$

Section 4.3

3 (i) i
   (ii) c
   (iii) b
   (iv) g
   (v) d

9 (a) $y = f(-x) = 2^{-x}$
   (b) $y = -f(-x) = -2^{-x}$
   (c) $y = f(x) + 2 = 2^x + 1.5$
   (d) $y = 5f(x) = 5 \cdot 2^x$

13 (d) All three

Section 4.4

1 (a) Axis of symmetry: $x = 1$
       Vertex: $(1, 18)$
       Zeros: $x = -2, 4$
       y-intercept: $y = 16$
   (b) Axis of symmetry: y-axis
       Vertex: $(0, 3)$
       No zeros
       y-intercept: $y = 3$

5 $y = -2(x + 4)(x - 5)$
7 $y = -(x - 2)^2$

9 (a) Similar shape and end behavior, different intercepts
   (b) Differences in intercepts become less significant
   (c) Graphs look more like each other as the scale causes the distances between intercepts to decrease

11 Yes. $f(x) = -(x - 1)^2 + 4$

13 113% in 2002

15 $y = -(x - 3)^2$

19 (a) $-16t^2 + 23$
       $-16t^2 + 48t + 2$
   (d) 1.54 secs
       1.20 secs
   (e) 3.04 secs

21 $(x + 1.4)(x - 2.8)$

23 $(x - c)^2$

27 No

29 $y = 2(x + 3)^2 + 1$

31 Vertex is $(-11/2, -137/4)$
   Axis of symmetry is $t = -11/2$

33 Zeros are $x = -4 + \sqrt{11}, x = -4 - \sqrt{11}$

35 (a) $x \approx 0.06, x \approx 1.94$
   (b) No solutions

37 $x = 4m$

39 12.5 cm by 12.5 cm; $k/4$ by $k/4$

41 (b) $d \approx 39.2$ m
   (c) ≈ 7.35 m
   (d) ≈ 19.59 m

43 (a) $1631.25
       $1.25
   (b) $P(x - 2)$
       $3.25
   (c) $P(x) + 50$
       $1681.25

Section 4.5

3 (a) e
   (b) i
   (c) No Match

11 Not true

Chapter 4 Review

1 (a) 4
   (b) 1
   (c) 5
   (d) -2

5 (a) $f(10) = 6000$; 10 chairs for $6000
   (b) $f(30) = 7450$; 30 chairs for $7450
   (c) $z = 40$; 40 chairs for $8000
   (d) $f(0) = 5000$; fixed cost of production

7 (a) $d_1 = 650$, $d_2 = 550$, $d_3 = 500$

9 (b) $1.89 f(k)$

11 (a) $y = 3h(x)$
   (b) $y = -h(x - 1)$
   (c) $y = -h(2 - 2x)$

13 (b) $T(d) - 32$
   (c) $T(d + 7)$

17 (a) $f(t) = 12 - 0.25t$
   (b) $g(t) = 4\pi(12 - 0.25t)^2$
   (c) $0 \le t \le 40$
   (d) $t \approx 37$
   (e) Between $t = 0$ and $t = 10$
   (f) Graph (III)

Section 5.1

7 9 o'clock; 5 minutes; 40 meters; 0 meters; 11.25 minutes

9 3 o'clock; 4 minutes; 30 meters; 5 meters; 11 minutes

11 Midline: $y = 10$;
Period: 1;
Amplitude: 4;
Minimum: 6 cm;
Maximum: 14 cm

15 (b) Period: 5 hours;
Amplitude: 40°;
Midline: $T = 70$

17 Midline: $h = 4$ feet;
Amplitude: 2.5 feet;
Period: 12 seconds

19 (b) Period: 1/60 seconds;
Amplitude: 110 volts;
Midline: $V = 0$

21 Midline: $y = 5.55$;
Amplitude: 5.15 WBC $\times 10^4$/mL;
Period: 72 days

Section 5.2

7 S: $5\pi/4$; T: $3\pi/2$;
U: $11\pi/6$; A: $13\pi/6$;
B: $11\pi/4$; C: $23\pi/6$;
D: $-\pi/2$; E: $-3\pi/4$;
F: $-5\pi/4$; P: 3π;
Q: $-\pi$; R: $5\pi/2$

9 (a) 120° or $2\pi/3$ radians
   (b) 60° or $\pi/3$ radians
   (c) 180° or π radians
   (d) 240° or $4\pi/3$ radians
   (e) Panel initially at C will be at F

11 (a) 72° or $2\pi/5$ radians
   (b) 180° or π radians
   (c) 216° or $6\pi/5$ radians

15 $\pi/6$ feet

17 5.8π inches

19 ≈ 4000 miles

21 $l \approx 69.115$ miles

Section 5.3

1 (a) $\sin\theta = 0.6$;
$\cos\theta = -0.8$;
$\tan\theta = -0.75$
   (b) $\sin\theta = 0.8$;
$\cos\theta = -0.6$;
$\tan\theta = -4/3$

3 (a) 0
   (b) 0
   (c) Undefined
   (d) -1
   (e) 0

5 They are equal

7 (a) I
   (b) I and III

   (c) II and IV
   (d) IV
   (e) III

9 (a) a
   (b) $-a$
   (c) a.
   (d) a
   (e) $-a$
   (f) $-a$

11 (b) $g(x) + h(x) = 1$

13 $\sqrt{2}$ meters

15 $\sqrt{3}$ meters

17 $y = y_0 + (\tan\theta)(x - x_0)$

25 (a) Yes
   (b) No

27 (a) The line $y = x$
   (b) The path of a circle, with starting point $(1, 0)$ and period 2π
   (c) The path of an ellipse, with starting point $(1, 0)$ and period 2π

Section 5.4

1 $f(t) = 250 + 250\sin((\pi/5)t - \pi/2)$

3 $f(t) = 250 + 250\sin((\pi/10)t)$

5 $f(t) = 14 + 10\sin(\pi t + \pi/2)$

7 $f(t) = 20 + 20\sin((2\pi/5)t - \pi)$

9 $f(t) = 20 + 15\sin((\pi/2)t + \pi/2)$

11 $f(t) = 4 + 2.5\sin((\pi/6)t)$

Section 5.5

1 (a) Periodic, period 2π
   (b) Periodic, period 2
   (c) Not periodic
   (d) Periodic, period 4π

5 (a) $y = -2\sin(\pi\theta/6) + 2$
   (b) $y = 0.8\sin(28\theta)$
   (c) $y = \cos(2\pi\theta/13) - 4$

7 (a) Amplitude: 1;
Period: 8π;

Phase Shift: $-\pi/4$;
Horizontal Shift: $-\pi$

(b) $4; 2\pi; 0; 0$

(c) $3; 1/2; 6\pi; 3/2$

(d) $1; \pi; \pi/2; \pi/4$

(e) $20; 1/2; 0; 0$

11 (b) $P = 800 - 100\cos(\pi t/6)$

13 $g(x) = \sin(2\pi x) + 2$

15 f and g have periods $= 1$, amplitudes $= 1$, midlines $y = 0$.

17 (a) $y = 3f(x)$

(b) $y = -2g(x/2)$

(c) $y = -f(2x)$

(d) $y = 2g(x) - 3$

19 (a) $f(t) = 3\sin((\pi/4)t)$

(b) Yes

21 (b) $P = f(t) = -70\cos(\pi t/6) + 160$

(c) $t \approx 1.67$ min

23 (b) $23.2°$; 12 months

(c) $T = f(t) = -23.2\cos((\pi/6)t) + 58.6$

(d) $T = f(9) \approx 58.6°$

25 $f(t) = 3\sin((\pi/6)t - 38.75) + 15$

Section 5.6

3 (a) $s(t) = 40,000\cos\left(\frac{\pi}{6}t + \frac{\pi}{6}\right) + 60,000$

(b) $s(3) = \$40,000$

(c) Mid-March and mid-September

5 (a) $\pi/6$

(b) π

(c) ≈ 0.1

7 (a) The zeros are $t_1 \approx 0.16$ and $t_2 \approx 0.625$.

(b) $t_1 = \frac{\arcsin(3/5)}{4}$ and $t_2 = \frac{\pi}{4} - \frac{\arcsin(3/5)}{4}$

9 $\theta \approx 0.848$ and $\theta \approx 2.29$

11 $-1 \le x \le 0.1522$ and $1.4186 \le x \le 3$

13 (a) $t = \pi/6, 5\pi/6, 7\pi/6$, or $11\pi/6$

(b) $t = \pi/4, 3\pi/4, 5\pi/4$, or $7\pi/4$

(c) $t = \pi/2, 3\pi/2, \pi/6$, or $5\pi/6$

(d) $t = \pi/3, 4\pi/3, 5\pi/3$, or $2\pi/3$

15 $\cos^{-1}(\cos(1)) = 1$
$\cos^{-1}(\cos(2)) = 2$
$\cos^{-1}(\cos(3)) = 3$
$\cos^{-1}(\cos(4)) \approx 2.2832$
$\cos^{-1}(\cos(5)) \approx 1.2832$
$\cos^{-1}(\cos(6)) \approx 0.2832$
$\cos^{-1}(\cos(7)) \approx 0.7168$

17 (a) True

(b) True

(c) True

(d) False

19 (b) $t^2 = 2\sin t$ for $t = 0$ and $t \approx 1.40$

(d) $k \approx 20$

Section 5.7

1 (a) $\theta = 60°, 180°$, and $300°$

(b) $\theta = \frac{7\pi}{6}, \frac{3\pi}{2}, \frac{11\pi}{6}$

7 $(\cos(2\theta))^2 + (\sin(2\theta))^2 = 1$

9 $2(2\cos^2\theta - 1)^2 - 1$

11 $\cos\left(\frac{\theta}{2}\right) = \sqrt{\frac{1}{2}(1 + \cos\theta)}$

13 (a) $0 \le y \le \pi$

(b) $1 \le y \le 3$

(c) $0 < y < \sin(1) \approx 0.8415$

(d) $-2 \le y \le 2$

(e) $9 \le y \le 81$

Section 5.8

1 (a) $f(t) = 65 - 25\cos(\pi t/12)$

(b) Period: 24; Amplitude: 30

(c) $f(t) = g(t)$ at approximately 4 AM and 1 PM.

(d) At 3:20 PM

3 Maximum: 2; Minimum: ≈ -0.94

5 All multiples of π

7 (a) $y = 0$

(b) The function oscillates

more as $x \to 0$.

(c) No

(d) $z_1 = \frac{1}{\pi}$

(e) infinitely many

(f) If $a = 1/(k\pi)$ then $b = 1/((k+1)\pi)$

9 (b) No; no, but possibly for 1979-1989

(c) Multiply by an exponential function: $f(t) = (e^{0.05t})(-1.4\cos(\frac{2\pi}{6})t + 1.6)$

(e) 4.6 billion dollars

11 (a) 1 meter

(b) 2

(d) $t = k/2$ for any integer k

Section 5.9

1 (a) $\tan\theta = 2$

(b) $\sin\theta = 2/\sqrt{5}$

(c) $\cos\theta = 1/\sqrt{5}$

3 bottom side $= 4$, $x \approx 2.1268$, $h \approx 4.5305$

5 $h = 400$ feet; $x = 346.4$ feet

7 $\approx 60°$

9 $\cos\theta = \sqrt{1 - y^2}$

11 (a) $(1/\cos\theta)^2$ or $1 + \tan^2\theta$

(b) $\sin\theta$

(c) $\tan\theta$

(d) $(1/2)\tan\theta$

13 $\theta \approx 63.4°$

15 (a) $h \approx 88.39$ feet

(b) $h = 62.5$ feet

(c) $c \approx 88.39$ feet

(d) $d \approx 108.25$ feet

17 $x \approx 19.12$

19 (a) $\sin\theta = 0.282$

(b) $\theta \approx 16.38°$

21 (a) $\sin\theta = 3/7$
$\sin\phi = (15\sin(20°))/8$

25 Length of arc ≈ 2.617994 feet
Length of chord ≈ 2.588191 feet

27 $x \approx 220.7$m

29 (a) $x = 3, y \approx 5.83; \theta = 31°$
   (b) $x \approx 14.19, y \approx 9.83; \theta = 105°$
   (c) $x = 5; \theta \approx 67.38°, \psi \approx 22.62°$

33 $x = 1.39, y = 3.44$

35 $d = 25{,}239$ meters

37 (a) $\sqrt{1-y^2}$
   (b) $y/(\sqrt{1-y^2})$
   (c) $1 - 2y^2$
   (d) y
   (e) $1 - y^2$

Chapter 5 Review

5 (a) Equal, $y = \cos x$ is an even function
   (b) Negative, $\sin x$ is an odd function
   (c) $\tan(-x) = -\tan(x)$

7 (a) $C(t)$
   (b) $D(t)$
   (c) $A(t)$
   (d) $B(t)$

9 $H(t) = 30\sin((\frac{2\pi}{0.6})t - \frac{\pi}{2}) + 150$

11 $f(t) = -900\cos((\pi/4)t) + 2100.$

13 (a) Undefined for $\{\frac{\pi}{2}, \frac{\pi}{2} \pm \pi, \frac{\pi}{2} \pm 2\pi, ...\}$
   (b) No

15 (a) $70°$
   (c) $T = f(t) = 2\cos(2\pi t) + 70$

17 If k is $0, 1, 2, ...$, then $\frac{1+\arcsin(\frac{-1}{3})\pm 2\pi k}{\pi}$ and $\frac{1+\pi-\arcsin(\frac{-1}{3})\pm 2\pi k}{\pi}$ are solutions.

19 (a) $\pi/3$
   (b) $2\pi/3$
   (c) $1/2$
   (d) $\pi/3$

21 They are the same.

27 (a) $a = 4; c = 2; B = 60°$
   (b) $A \approx 73.7°; B \approx 16.3°; b = 7$

Section 6.1

1 $r(0) = 4, r(1) = 5, r(2) = 2, r(3) = 0, r(4) = 3, r(5)$ undefined.

5 (a) $\frac{x^2-6x+10}{x^2-6x+9}$
   (b) $\frac{1}{x^2-2}$
   (c) $x + 1$
   (d) $\sqrt{x^2+1}$
   (e) $\frac{x-3}{10-3x}$
   (f) $\frac{1}{x-2}$

7 $k(m(x)) = \left(\frac{1}{x-1}\right)^2$

9 $k(n(x)) = \frac{4x^4}{(x+1)^2}$

11 $m(n(x)) = \frac{x+1}{2x^2-x-1}$

13 $m(m(x)) = \frac{1-x}{x}$

15 $m(x^2) = \frac{1}{x^2-1}$

17 (a) $1/2$
   (b) $1/5$

19 $u(v(x))$ where
   (a) $u(x) = \sqrt{x}$
       $v(x) = x + 8$
   (b) $u(x) = \frac{1}{x}$
       $v(x) = x^2$
   (c) $u(x) = x^2 + x$
       $v(x) = x^2$
   (d) $u(x) = 1 - x$
       $v(x) = \sqrt{x}$
   (e) $u(x) = \sqrt{x}$
       $v(x) = 1 - x$
   (f) $u(x) = 2 + x$
       $v(x) = \frac{1}{x}$

21 $u(v(w(x)))$ where
   (a) $u(x) = \sqrt{x}$
       $v(x) = 1 - x$
       $w(x) = x^2$
   (b) $u(x) = \frac{1}{x}$
       $v(x) = 1 - x$
       $w(x) = 2x$
   (c) $u(x) = 1 - x$
       $v(x) = \sqrt{x}$
       $w(x) = x - 1$
   (d) $u(x) = x^{\frac{1}{3}}$
       $v(x) = 5 - x$
       $w(x) = \sqrt{x}$
   (e) $u(x) = x^2$
       $v(x) = 1 + x$
       $w(x) = \frac{1}{x}$

(f) $u(x) = \frac{1}{x}$
    $v(x) = 1 + x$
    $w(x) = \frac{1}{x+1}$

23 $j(t) = \frac{1}{t}$

25 $m(x) = \frac{1}{\sqrt{x}}$

29 (a) $r(x) = (x-1)/(x-2)$
   (b) $s(x) = x+1$ and $t(x) = 1/x$
   (c) $p(p(a)) = (2a+1)/(a+1)$

31 $u(x) = frac1x - 1, v(x) = x^2$

33 $d(a(x)) = 2x + 10$
   $a(d(x)) = 2x + 5$
   $d(a(x))$ is more profitable

Section 6.2

1 (a) $C(3.5) = \$6.25$
   (b) $C^{-1}(\$3.5) \approx 1.67$

3 (a) $A = f(r) = \pi r^2$
   (b) $f(0) = 0$
   (c) $f(r+1) = \pi(r+1)^2$
   (d) $f(r) + 1 = \pi r^2 + 1$
   (e) Centimeters

9 (a) 2
   (b) Unknown
   (c) 5
   (d) 2

11 (b), (d), and (e)

13 (a) $D(5) = 100$
   (b) $D(p) = 1100 - 200p$
   (c) $D^{-1}(5) \approx 5.48$
   (e) $\$3.50$
   (f) Yes, $100

15 (a) $f(t) = 7.11(1.08998)^t$
   (b) $f^{-1}(P) = \frac{\log(P/7.11)}{\log 1.08998}$
   (c) $f(25) = 61.17$
       $f^{-1}(25) = 14.59$

17 $h^{-1}(x) = \sqrt[3]{\frac{x}{12}}$

19 $k^{-1}(x) = \frac{2x+2}{x-1}$

21 $h^{-1}(x) = (x/(1-x))^2$

25 (a) If k is $0, 1, 2, ...$, then $x = \frac{1}{3}\arcsin\left(\frac{2}{7}\right) \pm$

$k\left(\frac{2\pi}{3}\right)$ and

$x = \pi - \frac{1}{3}\arcsin\left(\frac{2}{7}\right) \pm k\left(\frac{2\pi}{3}\right)$

are solutions.

(b) $x = (\ln 3/\ln 2) - 5$

(c) $x = 1.09^{1/1.05}$

(d) $x = e^{1.8} - 3$

(e) $x = -7/2$

(f) $x = (19 - \sqrt{37})/2$

Section 6.3

7 (a) $A = \pi r^2$

(c) $r \geq 0$

(d) $f^{-1}(A) = \sqrt{A/\pi}$

(e) Yes

9 (a) $C(0) = 99\%$

(b) $C(x) = \frac{99-x}{100-x}$

(c) $C^{-1}(y) = \frac{99-100y}{1-y}$

11 (a) $f^{-1}(x) = \log x$

(b) $g^{-1}(x) = \frac{1}{3}\ln(x-1)$

(c) $h^{-1}(x) = \frac{1}{2}(1 - 10^x)$

(d) $j^{-1}(x) = 1 + 10^{(x-2)}$

13 $B = (A^{2/3})/(2\pi(3\pi)^{2/3})$

15 (b) Domain: all $x \geq 0$;
Range: $f(x) \geq 0$

(d) $\$6000$

(e) $\$7000$

(f) Yes

17 (a) $f^{-1}(x) = \frac{2x-3}{5x+2}$

(b) $f^{-1}(x) = \frac{4x^2-4}{x^2-7}$

(c) $f^{-1}(x) = \left(9 - \frac{1}{x}\right)^2 + 4$

(d) $f^{-1}(x) = \left(\frac{11x-3}{1+x}\right)^2$

Section 6.4

5 (a) $h(x) = x^2 + x$, $h(3) = 12$

(b) $j(x) = x^2 - 2x - 3$, $j(3) = 0$

(c) $k(x) = x^3 + x^2 - x - 1$, $k(3) = 32$

(d) $m(x) = x - 1$ for $x \neq -1$, $m(3) = 2$

(e) $n(x) = 2x + 2$, $n(3) = 8$

7 (a) $P(t) = 4,017,857,143 \cdot$

$(1.023)^t$

(b) The population increases by 2.3%.

(c) $N(t) = 30,000 - 900t$

(d) $f(0) = 0.00000747$
$f(5) = 0.00000567$
$f(10) = 0.00000416$
$f(15) = 0.00000290$

(e) Neither

(f) It is the per capita number of warheads

9 (f) $f(x) = x^2 - 8x + 14$;
$g(x) = -x^2 + 4x + 4$;
$f(x) - g(x) = 2x^2 - 12x + 10$

11 (a) $f(x) = 2x + 4$, $g(x) = \frac{1}{3}x - 1$

13 $\$17.50$

15 False

17 40

Chapter 6 Review

1 (a) $f(2x) = 4x^2 + 2x$

(b) $g(x^2) = 2x^2 - 3$

(c) $h(1 - x) = \frac{1-x}{x}$

(d) $(f(x))^2 = (x^2 + x)^2$

(e) $g^{-1}(x) = \frac{x+3}{2}$

(f) $(h(x))^{-1} = \frac{1-x}{x}$

(g) $f(x)g(x) = (x^2 + x)(2x - 3)$

(h) $h(f(x)) = \frac{x^2+x}{1-x^2-x}$

3 (a) $g(f(23)) = 23$

(b) $f(g(5)) = 5$

5 Horizontal line $y = 4$

7 (a) $f(t) = 800 - 14t$ (gals.)

(b) (i) 800 gals

(ii) ≈ 57.1 days

(iii) ≈ 28.6 days

(iv) $14t$

9 (a) $P(t) = P_0(3)^{\frac{t}{7}}$

(b) 17%

(c) $P^{-1}(x) = \frac{7\log\frac{x}{P_0}}{\log 3}$

(d) 4.42 years

15 Ace estimates 2000 ft^2 of

office space costs $\$200,000$.

17 $f(2x) < 2f(x)$

19 Space estimates 1500 ft^2 of office space costs $\$200,000$

21 Ace seems to be a better value

23 (a) $g(x) = x + 1$, $h(x) = 2x$

(b) $g(x) = x^2$, $h(x) = x + 3$

(c) $g(x) = \sqrt{x}$, $h(x) = 1 + \sqrt{x}$

(d) $g(x) = x^2 + x$, $h(x) = 3x$

(e) $g(x) = \frac{1}{x^2}$, $h(x) = x + 4$

(f) $g(x) = \frac{1}{x^2+1}$, $h(x) = x + 4$

25 (a) $f^{-1}(x) = \frac{x+7}{3}$

(b) $g^{-1}(x) = \frac{1}{x+2}$

(c) $h^{-1}(x) = \frac{2x+1}{3x-2}$

(d) $j^{-1}(x) = (x^2 - 1)^2$

(e) $k^{-1}(x) = \left(\frac{3-2x}{x+1}\right)^2$

(f) $l^{-1}(x) = \frac{2x-1}{3x-2}$

27 $\frac{x}{1+x} + x + 1$

29 (a) $f^{-1}(x) = (\arccos x)^2$

(b) $g^{-1}(x) = \arcsin(\ln x/\ln 2)$

(c) $h^{-1}(x) = (\arcsin(2x))/4$

(d) $j^{-1}(x) = \arcsin(2x/(x+1))$

31 Always true: I, IV, V

33 (a) Increasing

(b) Decreasing

(c) Increasing

(d) Decreasing

(e) Can't tell

(f) Increasing

Section 7.1

1 (a) A - (iii)

(b) B - (ii)

(c) C - (iv)

(d) D - (i)

5 (a) $x^{-3} \to +\infty$, $x^{1/3} \to 0$

(b) $x^{-3} \to 0$, $x^{1/3} \to \infty$

7 (a) $h(x) = -2x^2$
(b) $j(x) = \frac{1}{4}x^2$

9 (a) 20 lbs; 1620 lbs
(b) 3/10

11 19.276 cm.

15 $g(x) = \frac{4}{(x+2)^2} + 2$

17 $A: kx^{5/7}; B: kx^{9/16};$
$C: kx^{3/8}; D: kx^{3/11}$

Section 7.2

3 $y = e^{-x}$

5 $m = 2, t = 4, k = \frac{1}{4}$

7 (a) $v = 40$
(b) $r(x) > t(x)$
(c) $t(x) > r(x)$

9 $g(x) = -\frac{1}{6}x^3$

11 (a) $f(x) = \frac{3}{2} \cdot x^{-2}$
(b) $g(x) = -\frac{1}{5}x^{-3}$

13 (a) $f(x) = 720x - 702$
(b) $f(x) = 2(9)^x$
(c) $f(x) = 18x^4$

15 (a) $f(x) = y = \frac{63}{4}x + \frac{33}{2}$
(b) $f(x) = 3 \cdot 4^x$
(c) $f(x) = \frac{3}{4}x^6$

17 (b) Exponential
(c) $g(x) = 19.98(11.36)^x$
(d) 20

19 (a) No
(b) No new deductions
(c) All points satisfying the equation $y = -3x^5$

21 (a) 147.6 million miles
(b) Yes

23 (a) $h(r) = b \cdot r^{5/4}$;
$g(r) = a \cdot r^{3/4}$
(b) $a \approx 8; b \approx 3$

Section 7.3

1 (a) Degree: 3;
Terms: 3;
$x \to -\infty: y \to -\infty$;
$x \to +\infty: y \to +\infty$
(b) Degree: 3;
Terms: 4;
$x \to -\infty: y \to +\infty$;

$x \to +\infty: y \to -\infty$
(c) Degree: 4;
Terms: 3;
$x \to \pm\infty: y \to -\infty$;

5 $x \approx 0.72, x \approx 1.70$.

9 -16.54

13 (a) 5
(b) May of 1908
(c) 790; February of 1907

17 Yes

Section 7.4

1 C

3 $f(x) = (x + 2)(x - 2)^3$

5 (a) $f(x) = \frac{1}{2}(x + \frac{1}{2})(x - 3)(x - 4)$
(b) $f(x) = -\frac{3}{2}(x + 4)(x + 2)(x - 2)$

7 $f(x) = -\frac{1}{16}(x+3)^2(x-3)x^2$

9 $f(x) = 4x(2x + 5)(x - 3)$;
Zeros: $0, \frac{-5}{2}, 3$.

11 (a) $f(x) = -\frac{1}{2}(x + 3)(x - 1)(x - 4)$
(b) $g(x) = -\frac{1}{15}(x-3)^2(x-5)(x + 1)$

13 (a) $V(x) = x(6 - 2x)(8 - 2x)$
(b) $0 < x < 3$
(d) ≈ 24.26 in^3

15 (a) Invertible
(b) Not invertible

17 (a) $x = -2$ or $x = -3$
(b) No solution
(c) $x = \pm\frac{1}{2}$
(d) No solution
(e) $x = \frac{3 \pm \sqrt{33}}{4}$
(f) $x \approx -0.143$

21 (a) $f(x) = \frac{2}{15}(x + 2)(x - 3)(x - 5)$
(b) $f(x) = -\frac{2}{75}(x+2)(x - 3)(x - 5)^2$
(c) $f(x) = \frac{1}{15}(x + 2)^2(x - 3)(x - 5)$

23 (a) $f(0) = 0$;
$f(1) = 1$;

$f(2) = 2$;
Pattern: $f(x) = x$;
Doesn't hold for other values
(b) $g(0) = 0$;
$g(1) = 1$;
$g(2) = 2$;
$g(3) = 3$;
Pattern: $g(x) = x$;
Doesn't hold for other values
(c) $h(x) = x(x - 1)(x - 2)(x - 3)(x - 4) + x$

Section 7.5

1 (a) (i) $C(1) = 5050$
(ii) $C(100) = 10,000$
(iii) $C(1000) = 55,000$
(iv) $C(10000) = 505,000$
(b) (i) $A(1) = 5050$
(ii) $A(100) = 100$
(iii) $A(1000) = 55$
(iv) $A(10000) = 50.5$
(c) $A(n)$ gets closer to $50

3 No

5 As $x \to \pm\infty, f(x) \to 1, g(x) \to x$, and $h(x) \to 0$.

7 (a) $y = -\frac{1}{x+2}$
(b) $y = -\frac{1}{x+2}$
(c) $(0, -\frac{1}{2})$

9 (a) $y = -\frac{1}{(x-3)^2}$
(b) $y = \frac{-1}{x^2-6x+9}$
(c) $(0, -\frac{1}{9})$

11 (a) $y = \frac{1}{x^2} + 2$
(b) $y = \frac{2x^2+1}{x^2}$
(c) None

13 (a) $\frac{1}{x^2}$
(b) $y = \frac{x^2-6x+10}{x^2-6x+9}$

15 (a) $\frac{1}{x^2}$
(b) $y = \frac{1+x^2}{x^2}$

Section 7.6

1 (a) Zero: $x = -3$;
Asymptote: $x = -5$;
$y \to 1$ as $x \to \pm\infty$

(b) Zero: $x = -3$;
Asymptote: $x = -5$;
$y \to 0$ as $x \to \pm\infty$

(c) Zeros: $x = 4$;
Asymptote: $x = \pm 3$;
$y \to 0$ as $x \to \pm\infty$

(d) Zeros: $x = \pm 2$;
Asymptote: $x = 9$;
Approaches $y = x$ as
$x \to \pm\infty$

3 (a) $f(x) = 2x + 3$

7 (c) Approaches 1
(d) About 3.75 weeks

9 (a) $y = \frac{1}{16}x^2(x+3)(x-2)$
(b) $y = -\left(\frac{x+1}{x-2}\right)$
(c) $y = \frac{(x+2)(x-3)}{(x-2)(x+1)}$

11 $f(x) = \frac{(x-3)(x+2)}{(x+1)(x-2)}$

13 (a) $\frac{1}{g(x)}$, or $\frac{f(x)}{g(x)^2}$
(b) $\frac{f(x)}{g(x)}$
(c) $\frac{1}{f(x)}$
(d) $\frac{g(x)}{f(x)}$
(e) $\frac{f(x)}{h(x)}$

17 (a) None
(b) $g(x)$
(c) None
(d) $f(x)$
(e) $j(x)$

Chapter 7 Review

1 (a) $y = 2\cos(\pi x) + 1$
(b) $y = \log_3 x$
(c) $y = 2(x^2 - 4)(x - 1)$
(d) $y = 3x^3$
(e) $y = \frac{1}{2}(5^x)$
(f) $y = 13 - 5x$

3 (a) $f(x) = -(x+1)(x-1)^2$.
(b) $g(x) = -\frac{1}{3}(x^2)(x+2)(x-2)$.
(c) $h(x) = \frac{1}{12}(x+2)(x+1)(x-1)^2(x-3)$.

7 $g(x) = \frac{1}{6}(x+1)(x-2)(x-4) + 4$

9 (a) $b = 0$

(b) $b = d = 0$

11 The radius of the planet can be no less than 27% of the radius of the Earth.

17 (a) $f^{-1}(x) = \frac{5x}{1-x}$
(b) $f^{-1}(0.2) = 1.25$
(c) $x = 0$
(d) $y = -5$

19 (a) Even
(b) Neither
(c) Odd
(d) Neither
(e) Neither
(f) Even
(g) Neither
(h) Even

21 (a) $p(x) = \frac{7}{1080}(x+3)(x-2)(x-5)(x-6)^2$
(b) $f(x) = \frac{(x+3)(x-2)}{(x+5)(x-7)}$
(c) $f(x) = \frac{-3(x-2)(x-3)}{(x-5)^2}$

23 (a) $f(x) = \frac{x+1}{x-1}$
(b) $g(x) = \frac{(x+1)^2}{(x-1)^2}$

25 (a) (iii)
(b) (i)
(c) (ii)
(d) (iv)
(e) (vi)
(f) (v)

27 (a) $f^{-1}(x) = \frac{2x}{2-3x}$
(b) $f^{-1}(x) = \frac{1}{2}(7 + 3^x)$
(c) $f^{-1}(x) = \frac{1}{3}\left(5 + \frac{\log x}{\log 2}\right)$
(d) $f^{-1}(x) = \ln\left(\frac{2x-4}{1+3x}\right)$
(e) $f^{-1}(x) = (x^2 - 3)^2$
(f) $f^{-1}(x) = \frac{1}{2}\sin^{-1}\left(\frac{1}{3}x - 4\right)$

29 (a) $f^{-1}(x) = \frac{x}{x-3}$
(b) $g^{-1}(x) = 3 + \sqrt{x-4}$
(c) $h^{-1}(x) = \frac{3x-5}{x-1}$
(d) $j^{-1}(x) = \sqrt[3]{\frac{x+1}{3x-2}}$
(e) $k^{-1}(x) = (\sqrt[3]{x} - 1)^2$
(f) $l^{-1}(x) = \sqrt{x+4} - 2$

31 (a) Table is linear
(b) $\Delta p(x) = 2x - 1$

35 (a) $I(x) = 0.01x$ (number infected);
$N(x) = 0.99x$ (number not infected)
(b) $T(x) = 0.0098x$
(c) $F(x) = 0.0297x$
(d) $P(x) = 0.0395x$
(e) $\frac{0.01x}{0.0395x} \approx 0.25$
(f) No

47 (b) $\approx 1.81, \approx 2.65$

Section 8.1

1 4.63 miles; 27.3° south of west

3 14,000 meters west with an angle of 17.82° from the horizontal

5 $\vec{p} = 2\vec{w}$
$\vec{q} = -\vec{u}$
$\vec{r} = \vec{u} + \vec{w}$
$\vec{s} = 2\vec{w} - \vec{u}$
$\vec{t} = \vec{u} - \vec{w}$

7 Scalar

9 Vector

Section 8.2

1 (a) $2\vec{i} + \vec{j}$
(b) $2\vec{i} - 2\vec{j}$
(c) $3\vec{i}$
(d) $-\vec{i} - 2\vec{j}$
(e) $\vec{i} + \vec{j}$
(f) $\vec{i} + 2\vec{j}$
(g) $\vec{i}$
(h) $\vec{j}$

3 90° or $\pi/2$

5 (a) $(3/5)\vec{i} + (4/5)\vec{j}$
(b) $6\vec{i} + 8\vec{j}$

7 $\vec{i} + 3\vec{j}$

9 $\vec{w} = -0.7\vec{i} + 1.0\vec{j}$

11 $-3\vec{i} - 4\vec{j}$

13 $-40\vec{i} - 30\vec{j}$

15 $-140.8\vec{i} + 140.8\vec{j} + 18\vec{k}$

17 (a) Yes
(b) No

19 $\sqrt{6}$

21 7.6

23 $\vec{k}$

25 $\vec{i} + \vec{k}$

Section 8.3

1 (a) $\vec{v} = 4.33\vec{i} + 2.5\vec{j}$
       For the second leg of his journey, $\vec{w} = x\vec{i}$
    (b) $x = 9.87$
    (c) 14.42

3 $\vec{q}_b = 3.20\vec{i} + 2.59\vec{j}$
   $\vec{q}_c = 2.13\vec{i} + 3.93\vec{j}$
   $\vec{q}_d = 0.49\vec{i} + 2.79\vec{j}$

5 48.3° east of north
   744 km/hr

Section 8.4

1 Parallel:
   $3\vec{i} + \sqrt{3}\vec{j}$ and $\sqrt{3}\vec{i} + \vec{j}$
   Perpendicular:
   $\sqrt{3}\vec{i} + \vec{j}$ and $\vec{i} - \sqrt{3}\vec{j}$
   $3\vec{i} + \sqrt{3}\vec{j}$ and $\vec{i} - \sqrt{3}\vec{j}$

3 No

7 (a) $\vec{a} = (1.5, 1, 2); \vec{c} = (c_b, c_e, c_m)$
       $1.5c_b + c_e + 2c_m = 20$, or $\vec{a} \cdot \vec{c} = 20$
    (c) The "freshness-adjusted" cost is cheaper at Beta

9 -38

11 14

13 238

15 1.91 radians (109.5°)

17 (a) $\sqrt{2}$
    (b) 0.32

Section 8.5

1 (a) $H : x = 0, y = 3, r = 3, \theta = \pi/2$
       $M : x = 0, y = 4, r = 4, \theta = \pi/2$
    (b) $H : x = 3, y = 0, r = 3, \theta = 0$ $M : x = 0, y = 4, r = 4, \theta = \pi/4$
    (c) $H : x = -3, y = $

$0, r = 3, \theta = \pi$ $M : x = 0, y = 4, r = 4, \theta = \pi/2$
    (d) $H : x = -3/2, y = 3\sqrt{3}/2, r = 3, \theta = 2\pi/3$ $M : x = 0, y = 4, r = 4, \theta = \pi/2$
    (e) $H : x = 2.12, y = 2.12, r = 3, \theta = \pi/4$ $M : x = 0, y = -4, r = 4, \theta = 3\pi/2$
    (f) $H : x = -1.5, y = -2.60, r = 3, \theta = 4\pi/3$ $M : x = 0, y = 4, r = 4, \theta = \pi/2$
    (g) $H : x = 2.24, y = -1.99, r = 3, \theta = 23\pi/13$ $M : x = 0, y = -4, r = 4, \theta = 3\pi/2$
    (h) $H : x = -2.97, y = 0.39, r = 3, \theta = 172.5\pi/180$ $M : x = 4, y = 0, r = 4, \theta = 0$

3 (c) $(x, y) = (\sqrt{3}/4, 1/4)$; $(-\sqrt{3}/4, 1/4)$

Chapter 8 Review

1 (a) 6π ft/sec
    (b) 6π ft/sec
    (d) Min: 0
         Max: 12π ft/sec

3 548.6 km/hr

5 $F = g \sin\theta$

9 (b) 12 o'clock $\rightarrow (x, y) = (1, 1)$ and $(r, \theta) = (\sqrt{2}, \pi/4)$,
       3 o'clock $\rightarrow (x, y) = (2, 0)$ and $(r, \theta) = (2, 0)$,
       6 o'clock $\rightarrow (x, y) = (1, -1)$ and $(r, \theta) = (\sqrt{2}, -\pi/4)$,
       9 o'clock $\rightarrow (x, y) = (0, 0)$ and $(r, \theta) = (0,$ any angle $)$

11 $0.3\vec{i} - 1.8\vec{j} + 0.03\vec{k}$

13 $\vec{u} = \vec{i} + \vec{j} + 2\vec{k}$
    $\vec{v} = -\vec{i} + 2\vec{k}$

15 $(2/\sqrt{6})\vec{i} - (2/\sqrt{6})\vec{j} + (4/\sqrt{6})\vec{k}$

17 (a) $\vec{AB} = 2\vec{i} - 2\vec{j} - 7\vec{k}$
       $\vec{AC} = -2\vec{i} + 2\vec{j} - 7\vec{k}$
    (b) $\theta = 44.00°$

Section 9.1

1 Yes, $a = 2$, ratio $= 1/2$.

3 No. Ratio between successive terms is not constant.

5 Yes, $a = 1$, ratio $= -x$.

7 Yes, $a = y^2$, ratio $= y$.

9 $1/(1 + x), |x| < 1$

11 $3(2^{11} - 1)/(2^{10})$

13 $1/54$

15 (a) $0.23 + 0.23(0.01) + 0.23(0.01)^2 + \ldots$
    (b) $0.23(1 - 0.01) = 23/99$

17 $Q_3 = 260.40$
    $Q_{40} = 260.417$
    $Q_n = 260.417$

21 \$25,503

23 \$926.40

Section 9.2

1 The particle moves on straight lines from $(0, 1)$ to $(1, 0)$ to $(0, -1)$ to $(-1, 0)$ and back to $(0, 1)$.

5 Clockwise for all t.

7 Clockwise: $t < 0$,
   Counter-clockwise: $t > 0$.

11 $(I) = l_2, (II) = l_3$.

13 $x = t, y = -4t + 7$

Section 9.3

1 $x = 3\cos t, y = -3\sin t, 0 \le t \le 2\pi$

3 $x = -2\cos t, y = 2\sin t, 0 \le t \le 2\pi$

5 $(4 + 4\cos(t - \pi/2), 4 + 4\sin(t - \pi/2))$

7 $x = -3\cos t, y = -7\sin t,$
$0 \le t \le 2\pi$

9 Circle:
$(x-2)^2 + (y-2)^2 = 1$

11 Parabola:
$y = (x-2)^2, 1 \le x \le 3$

13 Implicit:
$x^2 - 2x + y^2 = 0, y < 0,$
Explicit:
$y = -\sqrt{-x^2 + 2x},$
Parametric:
$x = 1 + \cos t, y = \sin t,$
with $\pi \le t \le 2\pi$

15 (a) $(2t, 0)$ when $0 \le t \le \frac{1}{2}$
$(\cos\frac{3\pi}{2}(t - \frac{1}{2}),$
$\sin\frac{3\pi}{2}(t - \frac{1}{2}))$
when $\frac{1}{2} < t \le \frac{5}{6}$
$(0, -2(t - \frac{4}{3}))$
when $\frac{5}{6} < t \le \frac{4}{3}$

(b) $(0, 2t)$ when $0 \le t \le \frac{1}{2}$
$(\sin\frac{3\pi}{2}(t - \frac{1}{2}),$
$\cos\frac{3\pi}{2}(t - \frac{1}{2}))$
when $\frac{1}{2} < t \le \frac{5}{6}$
$(-2(t - \frac{4}{3}), 0)$
when $\frac{5}{6} < t \le \frac{4}{3}$

Section 9.4

1 $2e^{\frac{i\pi}{2}}$

3 $5e^{i4.069}$

5 $e^{\frac{i3\pi}{2}}$

7 $-3 - 4i$

9 $-5 + 12i$

11 $3 - 6i$

13 $\frac{\sqrt{3}}{2} + \frac{i}{2}$

15 $\frac{\sqrt{2}}{2} + i\frac{\sqrt{2}}{2}$

17 $\frac{\sqrt{3}}{2} + \frac{i}{2}$

19 $\sqrt[3]{2} \cdot \frac{\sqrt{3}}{2} + i\sqrt[3]{2} \cdot \frac{1}{2}$

21 $\frac{1}{\sqrt{2}}\cos(\frac{-\pi}{12}) + i\frac{1}{\sqrt{2}}\sin(\frac{-\pi}{12})$

23 $A_1 = 1 - i, A_2 = 1 + i$

25 (a) $z_1 z_2 = 6 - i2\sqrt{3}$
$\frac{z_1}{z_2} = i\sqrt{3}$

(b) $z_1 = 2\sqrt{3}e^{i7\pi/6},$
$z_2 = 2e^{i2\pi/3}$

27 True

29 False

31 True

Section 9.5

1 (a) 0.839
(b) −0.454
(c) 0.544
(d) 0.891

3 $g\sin 15° = \cos 75° = (\sqrt{6} - \sqrt{2})/4$
$\cos 15° = \sin 75° = (\sqrt{6} + \sqrt{2})/4$

9 $\cos 3\theta = 4\cos^3\theta - 3\cos\theta$

Section 9.6

5 $\cosh 2x = \cosh^2 x + \sinh^2 x$

Chapter 9 Review

1 Yes, $a = 1$, ratio $= -y^2$.

3 $1/(1 + y^2), |y| < 1$

5 (a) $h_n = 10(3/4)^n$
(b) $D_1 = 10$ feet
$D_2 = h_0 + 2h_1 = 25$ feet
$D_3 = h_0 + 2h_1 + 2h_2 = 36.25$ feet
$D_4 = h_0 + 2h_1 + 2h_2 + 2h_3 \approx 44.69$ feet
(c) $D_n = 10 + 60\left(1 - (3/4)^{n-1}\right)$

7 (a) $1000
(b) When the interest rate is 5%, the present value equals the principal.
(c) The value of the bond.
(d) Because the present value is more than the principal.

11 $x = \cos t, y = \sin t$

13 The equation of the curve is $x = 1 - 2y^2, -1 \le y \le 1$.

15 (a) $(x, y) = (t, 1)$
(b) $(x, y) = (t + \cos t, 1 - \sin t)$

17 $13e^{i-1.176}$

19 $-125i$

21 $8i\sqrt[3]{2}$

25 (c) $+, -, -$
(d) $-, -, +$
(e) $-, +, -$

Appendix A

1 49

2 16

3 −1

4 −121

5 −18

6 1

7 2100

8 −5

9 4

10 −6

11 0.2

12 4

13 3

14 0.5

15 $0.16x^2 y^4$

16 3^{x+1}

17 $8L$

18 $70w^{5/6}$

19 $16S^2 x t^2$

20 e^x

21 $A^3/(3B^3)$

22 e^{kt+4}

23 $(M + 2)^2$

24 $9x^5$

25 x^{3e}

26 e^{2y}/y^4

27 $4x^{(3\pi - 1)}$

28 $25(2b + 1)^{20}$

29 $3a$

30 $4u^4 v^2 w^4$

31 -8

32 -8

33 -125

34 Not a real number

35 20,736

36 $1/512$

37 -512

38 Not a real number

Appendix B

1 $4x^2 + 11x - 20$

2 $Pp^2 - 6Ppq + 9Pq^2$

3 $A^4 - 2A^2B^2 + B^4$

4 $4x^2 - 24x + 43$

5 $-2x - 2\sqrt{2x} - 1$

6 $-200t$

7 $2^u + u2^{2u}$

8 $KRr^2 - Kr^3$

9 $30 + 72/x + 2x$

10 $(e^{2x} + 2 + e^{-2x})/4$

Appendix C

1 $2(x - 3)(x - 2)$

2 $\pi r(r + 2h)$

3 $(B - 6)(B - 4)$

4 $\sin x(x - 1)$

5 Cannot be factored.

6 $(a - 2)(a + 2)(a^2 + 3)$

7 $(t - 1)(t + 7)$

8 $(hx - 3)(x - 4)$

9 $(r + 2)(r - s)$

10 $(\cos x - 1)^2$

11 $(y - 2x)(y - x)$

12 $xe^{-3x}(x + 2)$

13 $(e^x + 1)^2$

14 $P(1 + r)^3$

Appendix D

1 $(x + 20)/(x^2 - 16)$

2 $(x^2 + 1)/(x - 1)$

3 $1/2r$

4 $((u + a)^2 + u)/(u + a)$

5 $\frac{x-1}{(\sqrt{x})^3} = x\sqrt{x} - \sqrt{x}/x^2$

6 $(1 + e^x)/e^{2x}$

7 $(4x + 1)/(b - a)$

8 $(0.28 + 3M^3)/(4M)$

9 $(r_2r_3 + r_1r_3 + r_1r_2)/(r_1r_2r_3)$

10 $x(x + 2)$

11 $1/(x + y)^2$

12 $1/2$

13 $1/(a^2b^2)$

14 Cannot be simplified further

15 $p^3/(p^2 + q^2)$

16 $-2x - h$

17 $(2x - 4x^4)/(x^3 + 1)^3$

18 $(-4x^2+2x+1)/(x^4\sqrt{2x-1})$

19 $(-2x - h)/\left(x^2(x + h)^2\right)$

20 $(1 - 2\ln x)/\left(3x^3\right)$

21 $13/x^2 + 1/(2x^3)$

22 $1/3 + 1/\sqrt{x}$

23 $1/3 + \sqrt{x}/x$

24 $7/(p^2 + 11) + p/(p^2 + 11)$

25 $1/6 - 1/(4x)$

26 $1/t^{5/2} + 1/t^{3/2}$

27 $1 - 7/(x + 5)$

28 $1 + 3/(q - 4)$

29 $1 + 1/R$

30 $1 + 2/(2u + 1)$

31 $1 + \sin x/\cos x$

32 $1 + 1/e^x$

Appendix E

1 $3x + (1/2)x^{-1} + x^2 + 1/5$

2 $180q^3 - 60q$

3 $y^2 - 6y^{-1} + 9y^{-4}$

4 $x^3 + 2x + x^{-1}$

5 $2P^3 + 3P^{1/2}$

6 $1/2 + 3t^{1/2} + (9/2)t$

7 $-3 - (1/6)x^2 + (1/2)x$

8 $N^{-2} - 2 + N^2$

9 $-12/7 + (3/7)x$

10 $(1/2)x^{7/2}+x^{1/2}+(1/2)x^{-1/2}$

11 $12(3x + 1)^{-1/2}$

12 $1000(10 - s)^{1/3}$

13 $-0.7(x - 1)^4$

14 $(1/2)(x^2 + 1)^{-3}$

15 $24(6R + 2)^3$

16 $2(7x - \pi)^{1/2}$

17 $(1/2)^x$

18 $(1/2)^x$

19 $10,000(0.76)^t$

20 $e\left(e^2\right)^x$

21 $2(1/3)^x$

22 $(1/3)6^x$

23 4^t

24 $(1/e)e^x$

25 $-(5/3)^x$

26 $5e(e^x)$

27 $(x - 1)^2 - 4$

28 $(x - 3)^2 + 1$

29 $-(x - 3)^2 + 7$

30 $3(x - 2)^2 + 1$

31 $-6x/(x^2 + 7)^4$

32 $(-2^{x+1}\ln 2)/(1 + 3^x)^3$

33 $\pi\cos(\pi t)/\sin(\pi t)$

34 $-1/\sin^2 z$

35 $-\left(xe^{2x} - 2\right)/x^3e^x$

36 $(1 - \ln x)/x^2$

37 $x/\sqrt{x^2 + 16}$

38 $(x + 5)/\sqrt{x^2 + 10x + 1}$

39 $\cos(2x)/\sqrt{\sin(2x)}$

40 $2/\left(\sqrt[3]{x^2 - e^{3x}}\right)^2$

Appendix F

1 $y = -17/16$

2 $t = 10/7$

3 $B = -2$

4 $s = -0.115$

5 $x = 2, x = -4/3$

6 $p = 3, p = -3, p = -1/2$

7 $N = 3, N = 1$

8 $t = 0, t = \pm 8$

9 $x = 1 \pm \sqrt{2}$

10 $x = 4, x = -3/4$

11 $t = 3 \pm \sqrt{6}$

12 $y = -2 \pm \sqrt{6}$

13 $z = -7/2$

14 $x = \pm 1$

15 $L = \pm 1/2$

16 $q = \pm \sqrt{2}$

17 $r = \pm 5$

18 $x = -1/8$

19 $x = 0, x = 36$

20 $v = 700\pi$

21 $t = \ln 2 / \ln 0.97 \approx -22.76$

22 $t = \ln 8 / 2 \approx 1.04$

23 $x = 5$

24 $x = -\log 3.3 \approx -0.52$

25 $l = gT^2 / 4\pi^2$

26 $k = \ln(1/2)/1000 \approx -0.000693$

27 $x = \ln(0.5)/\ln(0.8) \approx 3.106$

28 $y' = 4/(y + 2x)$

29 $w = (2/k)(l - l_0)$

30 $y' = 2x/(x - y)$

31 $y = (c + d)/(b - a)$

32 $v = (3w - 2u - z)/(u + w - z)$

Appendix G ———

1 $x = -55, y = 39$

2 $x = 3$ and $y = -3$, or $x = -1$ and $y = -3$

3 $x = -3$ and $y = -5$, or $x = 1$ and $y = 3$

4 $x = 1/2$ and $y = 2$, or

$x = -1/2$ and $y = -2$

5 $(3/2, 3/2)$

6 $(4, 3), (-3, -4)$

7 $(2, 4)$, or $(4, 16)$, $(-0.7667, 0.5878)$

8 $y = 13/x + 2/3.$

Appendix H ———

1 $x \geq 7$

2 $x > 16$

3 $-5 < x < 5$

4 $x > 5$

5 $x \geq -4$

6 $x \leq -4$ or $x \geq 4$

7 All real numbers

8 $x > 5$

9 All real numbers

10 No solution

11 $x < 0.001$

12 $-1 < y < 1$

13 $p \neq 5$

14 $k > 0$

15 $r \geq 0$

16 $t \geq 1995$

17 (a) None
    (b) $x = 0, x = -2$
    (c) $x > 0, x < -2$
    (d) $-2 < x < 0$

18 (a) None
    (b) $x = 0, x = -2$
    (c) $x > 0, x < -2$
    (d) $-2 < x < 0$

19 (a) None
    (b) None
    (c) All real numbers
    (d) None

20 (a) None

(b) $t = 2, t = 3$
(c) $t < 2, t > 3$
(d) $2 < t < 3$

21 (a) $x = 0$
    (b) None
    (c) $x \neq 0$
    (d) None

22 (a) $p = 0$
    (b) None
    (c) $p < 0$
    (d) $p > 0$

23 (a) None
    (b) $x = 0$
    (c) $x > 0$
    (d) $x < 0$

24 (a) $x \leq 0$
    (b) $x = 1$
    (c) $x > 1$
    (d) $0 < x < 1$

25 (a) None
    (b) $u = 1/\sqrt{3}, u = -1/\sqrt{3}, u^2 = 1/3$
    (c) $-1/\sqrt{3} < u < 1/\sqrt{3}$
    (d) $u < -1/\sqrt{3}, u > 1/\sqrt{3}$

26 (a) $x = 0, x = 1$
    (b) $x = 1/2$
    (c) $x < 1/2$ and $x \neq 0$
    (d) $x > 1/2$ and $x \neq 1$

27 $-2 < x < 2$

28 $1/2 \leq x \leq 1$

29 $1/2 \geq n > -21/2$

30 $l > 1/48$

31 $t \leq -1, t \geq 4$

32 $x < -7/3, x > 1$

33 $r < 2, r > 3$

34 $x < -1, x > 0$

35 $x < -1, x > 0$

36 $-2 < x < 2$

21. $\frac{1}{5}$

23. (a) $y = (2x - 1)/2$ (b) $x = (2y + 1)/2$

25. $r = I/(Pt)$ **27.** $V = k/P$

29. $L = (P - 2W)/2$ **31.** $V = Bn/(n - x)$

33. $r = (A - P)/Pt$ **35.** $a = bR/(b - R)$

37. $S = 4\pi r^2$ **39.** $V = \frac{1}{3}Bh$

41. $L < \frac{3}{10}S$ **43.** 1.5

45. 0.2 **47.** 82

49. $C = S/5$ **51.** 94 ft and 50 ft

53. 12 hrs **55.** $32

57. $30 **59.** $1000

61. $126.68 **63.** $670.05

65. $598.21 **67.** Use the suggestion.

69. $2117.13

Section 4

1. ± 6 **3.** ± 10 **5.** ± 1.5 **7.** No real solution.

9. No real solution. **11.** $\pm 3\sqrt{3}/A$ **13.** 0 **15.** $\pm \frac{2}{7}$

17. 0, 3 **19.** 1 **21.** 3 **23.** $-1, 4$ **25.** 0, 3

27. 0.5 **29.** $-2/3, 1$ **31.** ± 3.51 **33.** ± 6.94

35. $-3 \pm \sqrt{10}$ **37.** $-1, 1/3$ **39.** $(1 \pm \sqrt{6})/5$

41. $(-1 \pm \sqrt{37})/6$ **43.** Two. **45.** Two. **47.** None.

49. One. **51.** None. **53.** $(-1 \pm \sqrt{13})/6$ **55.** $-\frac{3}{2}, \frac{1}{4}$

57. $1 \pm \sqrt{5}$ **59.** $(-q \pm \sqrt{q^2 + 4q})/2$ **61.** 0, 7 **63.** $-\frac{1}{4}, 0$

65. $(-3 \pm \sqrt{5})/2$ **67.** ± 5 **69.** ± 0.1 **71.** $-\frac{3}{2}, 0$

73. -3 **75.** -5

77. $-2.17, 0.930$ **79.** $\pm \sqrt{3}s/2$

81. $(-\pi h \pm \sqrt{\pi^2 h^2 + 2\pi S})/2\pi$

83. $\sqrt{5/\pi} \approx 1.26$ cm

85. $C = 2\sqrt{\pi A}$ **87.** 55 mph

89. $\sqrt{S/P} - 1 \, (r > 0)$ **91.** $t = \sqrt{s}/4$

93. 78.4 m. 2 sec.

95. (a) $s = 16t^2 + 24t$ (b) 40 ft below where it was thrown.
(c) 0.5 sec

97. $\pi(R^2 - r^2) = 2\pi r^2$, so $R = \sqrt{3}r$.

99. 12 m $\times$ 5 m **101.** $\sqrt{4R^2 - t^2}/2$

103. $\pm 2\sqrt{2}$

105. $b^2 - 4ac = 0$ if $b = \pm 2\sqrt{ac}$

107. $\dfrac{-b + \sqrt{b^2 - 4ac}}{2a} \cdot \dfrac{-b - \sqrt{b^2 - 4ac}}{2a} = \dfrac{b^2 - (b^2 - 4ac)}{4a^2} = \dfrac{c}{a}$

Section 5

1. >   **3.** >   **5.** <   **7.** >   **9.** >   **11.** >

13. $\{x: \ x > -2\}$ **15.** $\{z: \ z < \frac{1}{6}\}$ **17.** $\{u: \ u > -7\}$

19. $\{v: \ v \geq -0.75\}$ **21.** $\{y: \ y \geq 3.5\}$

23. $[2, 3]$

25. $\varnothing$

27.   Not an interval.

29. $\varnothing$

31. $(-1, 5)$ **33.** $(-2, 4)$ **35.** $[-1, \frac{2}{3}]$

37. $(-\infty, -\frac{1}{2}) \cup (2, \infty)$ **39.** $(-\infty, -0.2) \cup (0.1, \infty)$

41. $[0, 1] \cup [2, \infty)$

43. $[-3, \infty)$ **45.** $(-\infty, 0)$

47. $(2, \infty)$

49. If $a > 0$ and $b > 0$, then $ab > 0$ and $(ab)/(ab)^2 = 1/(ab) > 0$. Therefore, $a > b > 0$ implies $a[1/(ab)] > b[1/(ab)]$, or $1/b > 1/a$.

51. $\{p: \ p < -6.25\}$

53. $\{p: \ 0 < p < 4\}$

55. Approximately $-16°$ C to $-6°$ C.

57. 2.5 in.^{3} to 5 in.^{3}

59. Those sets in which the smallest of the three integers is at least 11.

61. $(\sqrt{a} - \sqrt{b})^2 \geq 0$ implies $a - 2\sqrt{a}\sqrt{b} + b \geq 0$, which implies $(a + b)/2 \geq \sqrt{ab}$.

63. Show that $(x - a)^2 < (x - b)^2$ implies $2(b - a)x < (b + a)(b - a)$. Then use that $0 < b - a$.

Section 6

1. $\pm\frac{2}{3}$ **3.** -7

5. $\pm\sqrt{5}$ **7.** 0.24, 0.4

9. No solution.   **11.** $-2, (-1 \pm \sqrt{17})/4$

13. $-3, -\frac{21}{5}$

15. No solution. (The left-hand side is nonzero for all x because $2 + |x| \geq 2 > 0$ for all x and $||x| - 2| \geq 0$ for all x.)

17. $(-\infty, -7) \cup (7, \infty)$

19. $(-\infty, -\frac{1}{2}) \cup (\frac{1}{2}, \infty)$

21. $(-\infty, -2) \cup (2, \infty)$

23. $(-\infty, -2] \cup [\frac{4}{3}, \infty)$

25. $(-\infty, -1] \cup [5, \infty)$

27. $(-\infty, 1) \cup (2, \infty)$

29. $[-\frac{5}{2}, -\frac{1}{2}] \cup [\frac{1}{2}, \frac{3}{2}]$

31. $(-\infty, -3) \cup (-3, 2]$

33. $(-\infty, -7) \cup [7, \infty)$

35. 5.25, 10.5

37. (a) $|x - 5| < 2$ (b) $(3, 7)$

39. (a) $|x + 1| > 2|x - 2|$ (b) $(1, 5)$

41. Use the suggestion.

Chapter I Review

1. *Natural numbers:* $\sqrt{36}$. *Integers:* $0/\sqrt{2}$, $-12/\sqrt{9}$, $\sqrt{36}$, $-\sqrt{2}\,\sqrt{2}$. *Rational numbers:* $20.\overline{1}$, $0/\sqrt{2}$, $-12/\sqrt{9}$, $\sqrt{36}$, -3.14, $-\sqrt{2}\,\sqrt{2}$. *Irrational numbers:* 3π, $\sqrt{5}$.

2. See Section 1. **3.** 0.2 **4.** -0.88 **5.** -0.4

6. 0.4 **7.** 0.66 **8.** -0.43 **9.** -46

10. -21 **11.** $2a - 14b$ **12.** $3a - 4b$ **13.** $\frac{8}{15}$

14. $-\frac{2}{21}$ **15.** 4 **16.** $\frac{1}{4}$

17. 4 **18.** $-\frac{4}{3}$ **19.** 1.99 **20.** 10

21. 49 **22.** $-\frac{1}{1000}$ **23.** $-\frac{100}{9}$ **24.** -125

25. $x^3/(27y^3)$ **26.** $32a^{10}/b^5$ **27.** $1/(36a^2)$

28. $y^8/256$ **29.** $1000a^6b^3$ **30.** $125x^9y^{15}$

31. a^{6n}/b^{9n} **32.** $2^n u^{2n} v^{4n}/9^n$

33. $3|b|\sqrt{2a}$ **34.** $10|xy|\sqrt{10x}$

35. 7.72×10^8 **36.** 4.8×10^{-6}

37. $2x^3 + x^2 + x - 1$ **38.** $y^3 - y^2 - 8y + 6$

39. $a^2 - \frac{2}{3}a + \frac{1}{9}$ **40.** $b^2 + 0.4b + 0.04$

41. $a^3 + 6a^2b + 12ab^2 + 8b^3$ **42.** $c^6 - 3c^4d^2 + 3c^2d^4 - d^6$

43. $(t + 3)(t - 3)$ **44.** $(u - 11)^2$

45. $(v + 6)^2$ **46.** $(2w + 1)(2w - 1)$

47. $(5x + 2)(2x - 1)$ **48.** $(3y + 2)(3y - 1)$

49. $x(3x - 1)^2$ **50.** $y^2(y + 1)(y^2 - y + 1)$

51. $(5a - 2b)(3a + 2b)$

52. $(c^2 + d^2)(c + d)(c - d)$ **53.** $(m - n)^3$

54. $(u + v + 2)(u + v - 2)$

55. $(x + y)(x^n + y^n)(x^n - y^n)$

56. $(x^n - y^n)(x^{2n} + x^n y^n + y^{2n})$

57. $\frac{13}{11}$ **58.** $-\frac{9}{2}$ **59.** $(3y + 4)/4$ **60.** $(y - 9)/4$

61. -4 **62.** No solution.   **63.** $-\frac{1}{2}, \frac{7}{6}$ **64.** $\frac{7}{4}, \frac{5}{2}$ **65.** $-5, 2$ **66.** $-3/2, -1$

67. $(-3 \pm \sqrt{17})/4$ **68.** $(1 \pm \sqrt{13})/6$ **69.** $\pm\frac{11}{3}$

70. $(-p \pm \sqrt{p^2 - 4})/2$ **71.** $(3 \pm \sqrt{2})/7$ **72.** $\pm\frac{7}{5}$

73. Two.   **74.** Two.   **75.** None.   **76.** One.

77. $[-1, 2)$ **78.** $(-\pi, \sqrt{3}]$ **79.** $(-2, 7]$

80. $(-\infty, 6]$ **81.** $\{x: \ x > -9\}$ **82.** $\{y: \ y \ge 1/15\}$

83. $(-5, 7)$ **84.** $(-\infty, -2] \cup [\frac{1}{2}, \infty)$ **85.** $(-\infty, -2] \cup [\frac{6}{5}, \infty)$

86. $(-\frac{4}{3}, 2)$ **87.** $(-\infty, -3) \cup (0, 1)$ **88.** $[-2, \frac{1}{2}]$

89. 1.35   **90.** 147   **91.** $208.\overline{3}\%$

92. 6400   **93.** \$210   **94.** \$150

95. $\$2000(1.02)^{12} = \$2536.48$ **96.** $\$5000(1.005)^{30} = \$5807.00$

97. $\frac{4}{5}$ **98.** 20, 21, 22

99. $\frac{1}{2}\sqrt{4h^2 + x^2}$ **100.** First, show that $\overline{OD} = \sqrt{r^2 - (s/2)^2}$.

101. $\sqrt{10}/4 \approx 0.79$ sec   **102.** 3 sec

Section 7

1.

3.

5. $(2.5, -4)$ **7.** $(0, -4)$ **9.** $(0, 3.2)$

11. $(0, 2)$ and $(4, 2)$ are.   **13.** $(1, 1)$ and $(-2, 4)$ are.   **15.** None is.

17. Straight line parallel to and 1 unit below the x-axis.

19. Straight line parallel to and 1.5 units below the x-axis.

21. Straight line parallel to and 2 units to the left of the y-axis.

23. Circle centered at the origin wih radius 4.

25. Circle centered at $(1, 0)$ with radius $\sqrt{10}$.

27. Circle centered at $(-2, -1)$ with radius $\sqrt{12}$.

29. $y = -3$ 31. $x = 5$ 33. $y = 5$

35. $(x + 2)^2 + (y + 3)^2 = 2$ 37. $x^2 + y^2 = 25$

39. $(x + 3)^2 + (y - 1)^2 = 9$ 41. $\sqrt{34}$

43. $\sqrt{389}/20$ 45. $\sqrt{29}/2$

47. Circle centered at $(-6, 1)$ with radius $\sqrt{74}$.

49. The empty set.   51. The point $(10, 0)$.   53. The empty set.

55. Circle centered at $(\frac{5}{2}, 0)$ with radius 2.

57. Circle centered at $(-\frac{1}{2}, \frac{1}{2})$ with radius $\sqrt{6}$.

59. The set of all points in either the first or third quadrants.

61. The set of all points below the line $y = x$.

63. The set of all points inside or on the circle centered at the origin with radius 1.

65. The set of all points 4 units above the x-axis and with x-coordinate between 2 and 4.

67. $(-2, 0)$ and $(6, 0)$.

69. $(-2, -\sqrt{35})$, $(-2, \sqrt{35})$, $(2, \sqrt{11})$, $(2, -\sqrt{11})$

71. $6x - 4y - 13 = 0$

Section 8

1. -3 3. $\frac{1}{9}$ 5. 0   7. $x - 2y + 5 = 0$

9. $x - 4y = 0$ 11. $10x - 4y - 15 = 0$ 13. $2x - 5y + 8 = 0$

15. $x - y + 3 = 0$ 17. $6x - y - 5 = 0$ 19. $y = -x + 2$

21. $y = 2$ 23. $y = 0$ 25. $m = -2, b = 3$

27. $m = \frac{1}{2}, b = -\frac{3}{2}$ 29. $m = 1, b = 0$

31.

33.

35.

37.

39.

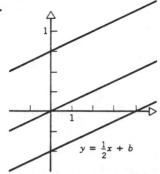

$y = \frac{1}{2}x + b$

41.

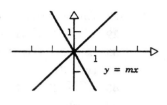

$y = mx$

43. $y = \frac{2}{3}x$ **45.** $x - y + 2 = 0$

47. $4x + 3y + 9 = 0$

49. Substitute m from (8.2) into (8.4).

51. $(\frac{1}{2}, \frac{9}{2})$

53. Substitute $x = 1$ and $y = 1$ into Equation (8.5), and then solve for m.

55. $2x - y - 7 = 0$

57. $3x + 4y - 25 = 0$

Section 9

1. $(2, 1)$ **3.** $(0, 3)$ **5.** $(-2, -3)$

7. $\{(x, 3x - 1): \ x \text{ is a real number}\}$

9. $\{(x, -\frac{1}{3}(x + 3)): \ x \text{ is a real number}\}$

11. If you add -2 times the second equation to 3 times the first equation, the result will be $-23 = 0$.

13. $(1, 2)$ **15.** $\{(x, 1 - 2x): \ x \text{ is a real number}\}$

17. $(\frac{4}{3}, \frac{1}{3})$ **19.** No intersection.   **21.** $(-12, 6)$

23. $(-3, 5)$ and $(5, 3)$

25. No intersection.

27. No intersection.

29. $(-\sqrt{7}/2, \frac{1}{2})$ and $(\sqrt{7}/2, \frac{1}{2})$

31. Use 0.5 liter of 20% alcohol and 1.5 liter of 60% alcohol.

33. 65 for children and 270 for adults.

35. Ground speed 290 mph, wind speed 10 mph.

37. Runner 10 mph, walker 5 mph.

39. 12 gm of 14-karat gold, 8 gm of 24-karat gold.

41. $\frac{27}{41}$

43. 2.5 and 1.5

45. 15 cm and 9 cm

23. $a^k < 1$ and $0 < a < 1$ imply $a^{k+1} < a < 1$, which implies $a^{k+1} < 1$.

25. By connecting appropriately chosen vertices, a $(k + 1)$-sided polygon can be divided into a k-sided polygon and a triangle. From this, the sum of the interior angles will be $(k - 2)180° + 180° = (k - 1)180°$.

27. Induction step: The number of diagonals of a $(k + 1)$-sided polygon is $\dfrac{k(k - 3)}{2} + (k - 1) = \dfrac{(k + 1)(k - 2)}{2}$.

Section 56

1. 5, 8, 11, 14, 17   **3.** 40, 28, 16, 4, -8 **5.** $\frac{3}{2}, \frac{7}{4}, 2, \ldots, \frac{15}{4}$

7. 1, 8, 15, 396   **9.** $\frac{1}{4}, \frac{3}{8}, \frac{1}{2}, \frac{115}{4}$ **11.** 120, 125, 130, 16,050

13. (a) $a_1 = a_n - (n - 1)d$ (b) 28

15. (a) $n = \dfrac{a_n - a_1}{d} 1$ (b) 351   **17.** -455

19. $b_1 + b_2 + b_3 + b_4 + b_5$ **21.** $4 + 5 + 6 + 7 + 8 + 9$

23. $\frac{1}{6} + \frac{1}{7} + \frac{1}{8} + \frac{1}{9} + \frac{1}{10} + \frac{1}{11}$ **25.** $\sum\limits_{k=1}^{10} 3^k$

27. $\sum\limits_{k=1}^{20} k \cdot 5^k$ **29.** $\dfrac{5n}{2}(3n + 1)$ **33.** $S_n = \dfrac{n}{2}(a_1 + a_n)$ **35.** 490

37. (a) 482.5 gal   (b) 47th day   **39.** $40

Section 57

1. $\frac{1}{2}$, 2, 8, 32, 128   **3.** 10^{-1}, $10b^{-4}$, 10^{-7}, 10^{-10}, 10^{-13}

5. 100, 10, 1, 10^{-7} **7.** $\dfrac{2^{k-1}}{5^{k-2}}$, $\dfrac{1031}{125}$

9. $3(-\sqrt{3})^{k-1}$, $39 - 12\sqrt{3}$ **11.** $(1 - \sqrt{2})(1 + \sqrt{2})^{k-1}$, $-1 - 2\sqrt{2}$

13. $\frac{665}{128}$ **15.** $1.5(1 - 0.6^{10}) \approx 1.49$ **17.** $22.\overline{2}$

19. (a) $a_1 = \dfrac{a_n}{r^{n-1}}$ (b) 486

21. (a) $a_1 = \dfrac{S_n(1 - r)}{(1 - r^n)}$ (b) $1 + \sqrt{2}$

23. $15,431.20   **25.** $7958.55   **27.** $19,124.88

29. $3000/32.38 \approx $92.94   **31.** $a_{k+1} = (a_1 r^{k-1})r = a_1 r^k$

35. $\dfrac{a_1 - a_1(-1)^n}{2}$. S_n alternates between 0 and a_1.

37. $\frac{31}{9}$ **39.** $\frac{697}{33}$ **41.** $\frac{34}{333}$

43. Suggestion: If $b = ar$ and $c = br$, then $b/a = c/b$.

45. Suggestion: If $a_{k+1} = a_k r$, what is $\log a_{k+1} - \log a_k$?

47. 262 cycles per second

Section 58

1. 120   **4.** 126   **5.** 1140

7. $(n + 2)(n + 1)$ **9.** $\dfrac{n + 1}{n}$ **11.** $2n$

13.

1	7	21	35	35	21	7	1	
1	8	28	56	70	56	28	8	1

15. A common denominator for the right side is $k!(n - k + 2)!$. Or use (58.3) three times.

17. $u^6 + 6u^5v + 15u^4v^2 + 20u^3v^3 + 15u^2v^4 + 6uv^5 + v^6$

19. $a^6 - 6a^5b + 15a^4b^2 - 20a^3b^3 + 15a^2b^4 - 6ab^5 + b^6$

21. $16u^4 - 32u^3v^2 + 24u^2v^4 - 8uv^6 + v^8$

23. 300   **25.** $a^{20} + 20a^{18}b^3 + 180a^{16}b^6 + 960a^{14}b^9$

27. $x^{100} + 100x^{99}y + 4950x^{98}y^2 + 161{,}700x^{97}y^3$ **29.** 210

31. With $a = b = 1$, the left side of (58.4) equals 2^n, and the right side is the desired sum.

33. Suggestion: Multiply and divide the left side by the product of the first n positive even integers.

Chapter XIV Review

1. $3, 27, 162, 810, 3^n(n + 1)n/2$ **2.** $\sum\limits_{k=1}^{\infty} k(-10)^{k-1}$

3. $3 + 7 + 11 + \cdots + (4k + 3) = k(2k + 1) + (4k + 3) = 2k^2 + 5k + 3 = (k + 1)(2k + 3)$

4. $1^2 + 3^2 + 5^2 + \cdots + (2k + 1)^2 = \dfrac{k(2k - 1)(2k + 1)}{3} + (2k + 1)^2$

$= \dfrac{4k^3 + 12k^2 + 11k + 3}{3} = \dfrac{(k + 1)(2k + 1)(2k + 3)}{3}$

5. $10 - 45\pi$ **6.** Use $a_1 = 3$ and $a_n = 4n - 1$ in Equation (56.4).

7. $2\sqrt{3}, -6, 6\sqrt{3}, -486$ **8.** $0.1y^2$ **9.** -1705

10. $\dfrac{a - a^{n+1}b^{2n}}{1 - ab^2}$ **11.** $-\frac{1}{5} < t < \frac{1}{5}, \dfrac{1}{1 - 5t}$ **12.** 6

13. \$1103.97   **14.** \$75   **15.** $\dfrac{n + 1}{k}$

17. $a^{10} - 5a^8b + 10a^6b^2 - 10a^4b^3 + 5a^2b^4 - b^5$

18. $1{,}000{,}000x^6 + 60{,}000x^5y + 1500x^4y^2 + 20x^3y^3 + 0.15x^2y^4 + 0.0006xy^5 + 0.000001y^6$

Section 59

1. Directrix $y = \frac{1}{8}$. Focus $(0, -\frac{1}{8})$. Vertex $(0, 0)$. Axis $x = 0$.

3. Directrix $x = 3$. Focus $(-3, 0)$. Vertex $(0, 0)$. Axis $y = 0$.

5. Directrix $x = \frac{1}{4}$. Focus $(-\frac{1}{4}, 0)$. Vertex $(0, 0)$. Axis $y = 0$.

7. Directrix $x = -\frac{7}{4}$. Focus $(-\frac{9}{4}, -2)$. Vertex $(-2, 1)$. Axis $y = 1$.

9. Directrix $y = \frac{11}{2}$. Focus $(3, \frac{1}{2})$. Vertex $(3, 3)$. Axis $x = 3$.

11. Directrix $y = -\frac{23}{8}$. Focus $(0, -\frac{25}{8})$. Vertex $(0, -3)$. Axis $x = 0$.

13. Directrix $y = -\frac{7}{4}$. Focus $(-\frac{3}{2}, -\frac{5}{4})$. Vertex $(-\frac{3}{2}, 0)$. Axis $x = -\frac{3}{2}$.

15. Directrix $y = -\frac{1}{4}$. Focus $(\frac{1}{2}, \frac{1}{4})$. Vertex $(\frac{1}{2}, 0)$. Axis $x = \frac{1}{2}$.

17. $x^2 = -20y$.

19. $(x + 1)^2 = 32(y - 4)$

21. $x^2 = 16(y + 4)$

23. $(y - 1)^2 = -\frac{1}{5}(x - 5)$

25. $\frac{45}{8}$ ft or 5 ft $7\frac{1}{2}$ in.

Section 60

1. Center $(0, 0)$. Foci $(0, -\sqrt{7})$ and $(0, \sqrt{7})$. Endpoints of major axis $(0, -4)$ and $(0, 4)$. Endpoints of minor axis $(-3, 0)$ and $(3, 0)$.

3. Center $(0, 0)$. Foci $(0, -\sqrt{21})$ and $(0, \sqrt{21})$. Endpoints of major axis $(0, -5)$ and $(0, 5)$. Endpoints of minor axis $(-2, 0)$ and $(2, 0)$.

5. Center $(0, -1)$. Foci $(-\sqrt{6}, -1)$ and $(\sqrt{6}, -1)$. Endpoints of major axis $(-3, -1)$ and $(3, -1)$. Endpoints of minor axis $(0, -1 - \sqrt{3})$ and $(0, -1 + \sqrt{3})$.

7. Center $(0, -2)$. Foci $(0, -2 - \sqrt{3})$ and $(0, -2 + \sqrt{3})$. Endpoints of major axis $(0, -4)$ and $(0, 0)$. Endpoints of minor axis $(-1, -2)$ and $(1, -2)$.

9. Center $(-5, 0)$. Foci $(-5 - 3\sqrt{3})$ and $(-5, 3\sqrt{3})$. Endpoints of major axis $(-5, -6)$ and $(-5, 6)$. Endpoints of minor axis $(-8, 0)$ and $(-2, 0)$.

11. Center $(-1, -3)$. Foci $(-1, -6)$ and $(-1, 0)$. Endpoints of major axis $(-1, -8)$ and $(-1, 2)$. Endpoints of minor axis $(-5, -3)$ and $(3, -3)$.

13. $\dfrac{(x - 2)^2}{2^2} + \dfrac{(y - 4)^2}{4^2} = 1$

15. $\dfrac{(x + 3)^2}{3^2} + \dfrac{(y - 2)^2}{4^2} = 1$

17. $\dfrac{x^2}{5^2} + \dfrac{y^2}{4^2} = 1$

19. $35x^2 + y^2 = 36$

21. $25x^2 + 24y^2 = 625$

23. $(2, 1)$ and $(-2, 1)$

25. Use $x = 56.25$ in $\dfrac{x^2}{76.25^2} + \dfrac{y^2}{37.5^2} = 1$. (Why?) The answer is 25 ft 3 in.

27. All of the points that are both inside or on the circle $x^2 + y^2 = 25$ except those inside the ellipse $4x^2 + 9y^2 - 36 = 0$. (Why?)

31. $b = 9.68$

33. $e = 0.0509$

35. 67 million miles

37. 29.41 Earth years

39. 164.62 Earth years

Section 61

1. Center $(0, 0)$. Foci $(-\sqrt{13}, 0)$ and $(\sqrt{13}, 0)$. Endpoints of transverse axis $(-3, 0)$ and $(3, 0)$. Endpoints of conjugate axis $(0, 2)$ and $(0, -2)$.

3. Center $(0, 0)$. Foci $(0, -2\sqrt{5})$ and $(0, 2\sqrt{5})$. Endpoints of transverse axis $(0, -4)$ and $(0, 4)$. Endpoints of conjugate axis $(-2, 0)$ and $(2, 0)$.

5. Center $(2, -1)$. Foci $(2, -5)$ and $(2, 3)$. Endpoints of transverse axis $(2, -4)$ and $(2, 2)$. Endpoints of conjugate axis $(-3, -1)$ and $(7, -1)$.

7. Center $(0, -2)$. Foci $(-\sqrt{6}, -2)$ and $(\sqrt{6}, -2)$. Endpoints of transverse axis $(-3, -2)$ and $(3, -2)$. Endpoints of conjugate axis $(0, -2 - \sqrt{3})$ and $(0, -2 + \sqrt{3})$.

9. Center $(1, -2)$. Foci $(-4, -2)$ and $(6, -2)$. Endpoints of transverse axis $(-3, -2)$ and $(5, -2)$. Endpoints of conjugate axis $(1, -5)$ and $(1, 1)$.

11. Center $(2, -6)$. Foci $(2, -6 - \sqrt{14})$ and $(2, -6 + \sqrt{14})$. Endpoints of transverse axis $(2, -9)$ and $(2, -3)$. Endpoints of conjugate axis $(2 - \sqrt{5}, -6)$ and $(2 + \sqrt{5}, -6)$.

13. $9x^2 - 4y^2 + 36 = 0$

15. $21x^2 - 4y^2 + 84 = 0$

17. $5x^2 - 16y^2 - 80 = 0$

19. $25x^2 - 9y^2 + 225 = 0$

21. $\dfrac{x^2}{3^2} - \dfrac{(y - 3)^2}{4^2} = 1$

23. $(0, -1)$, $(-\sqrt{3}, 2)$, and $(\sqrt{3}, 2)$.

25. $\dfrac{y^2}{b^2} - \dfrac{x^2}{a^2} = 1$

27. $y = \pm x$

Section 62

1. (a) $(-1/\sqrt{2}, -5/\sqrt{2})$ (b) $(5/\sqrt{2}, 5/\sqrt{2})$

3. (a) $(-\sqrt{2}, 3\sqrt{2})$ (b) $(-\sqrt{2}, -\sqrt{2})$

5. Two intersecting lines: $y = \pm 3x$.

7. Two intersecting lines: $y = \pm\tfrac{2}{3}x$.

9. Two parallel lines: $x = \pm 2$.

11. One line: $x = 0$.

13. One point: $(0, 0)$.

15. One point: $(0, 0)$.

17. Two lines: $y = \pm 4$.

19. $\theta = 45°$. $\dfrac{x'^2}{9} - \dfrac{y'^2}{1} = 1$.

21. $\theta = 60°$. $\dfrac{x'^2}{1} + \dfrac{y'^2}{2} = 1.$

23. $\theta = 30°$. $\dfrac{x'^2}{1} + \dfrac{y'^2}{4} = 1.$

25. $\cot 2\theta = -\frac{7}{24}$. $\dfrac{x'^2}{2} + \dfrac{y'^2}{4} = 1.$

27. $\theta = 45°$. $\dfrac{x'^2}{4} + \dfrac{y'^2}{1} = 1.$

29. $\cot 2\theta = \frac{7}{24}$. $y' + 1 = 3(x' - 2)^2.$

31. An ellipse, a circle, a point, or the empty set.

33. A hyperbola or two intersecting lines.

35. An ellipse, a circle, a point, or the empty set.

Section 63

1. $e = 1$. See Figure 63.4*d*.

3. $e = \frac{1}{2}$. See Figure 63.4*b*.

5. $e = \frac{1}{4}$. See Figure 63.4*c*.

7. $e = \frac{3}{4}$. See Figure 63.4*b*.

9. $e = \frac{5}{3}$. See Figure 63.4*c*.

11. $e = \frac{3}{5}$. See Figure 63.4*b*.

13. $r = 9/(4 - 3 \cos \theta)$

15. $r = 20/(1 + \sin \theta)$

17. $r = 2/(1 - \sin \theta)$

19. $[d/2, \pi]$ and $[3d/2, \pi]$.

Section 64

1. $y = -x + 4$. Line.

3. $y = x + 8$. Line.

5. $x - 2y - 1 = 0$. Line.

7. $\dfrac{x^2}{4} + \dfrac{y^2}{25} = 1$. Ellipse.

9. $y = 1/x$. Hyperbola.

11. $\dfrac{x^2}{9} + \dfrac{y^2}{1} = 1$. Ellipse.

13. $x^2 - y^2 = 1$. Hyperbola.

15. $x + y - 1 = 0$.

17. $\dfrac{x^2}{9} + \dfrac{y^2}{4} = 1, 0 \le x \le 3, 0 \le y \le 2$. Part of an ellipse.

19. $t = 0, t = 1, t = \frac{1}{2}$.

21. (a) Symmetric with respect to the x-axis.
    (b) Symmetric with respect to the y-axis.
    (c) Symmetric with respect to the origin.

23. $\dfrac{(y - k)^2}{b^2} - \dfrac{(x - h)^2}{a^2} = 1$. Hyperbola.

25. $\dfrac{(x - h)^2}{a^2} - \dfrac{(y - k)^2}{b^2} = 1$. Hyperbola.

Chapter XV Review

1. Parabola
2. Ellipse
3. Hyperbola
4. Parabola
5. Two intersecting lines
6. Circle
7. Ellipse
8. Ellipse
9. Parabola
10. Empty set
11. Hyperbola
12. Parabola
13. Hyperbola
14. Two parallel lines
15. $x^2 = -20y$
16. $25x^2 + 4y^2 = 100$
17. $\dfrac{(y - 3)^2}{4} - \dfrac{(x + 2)^2}{5} = 1$
18. $y^2 = 12(x - 2)$
19. $4(x + 1)^2 + 12y^2 = 48$
20. $36x^2 - 9y^2 = 324$
21. $\theta = 30°$. $y' = x'^2$.
22. $\theta = 45°$. $x'^2 - 4y'^2 = 4$.
23. $\cot 2\theta = 7/24$. $x'^2 + 25y'^2 = 25$.
24. $\cot 2\theta = -7/24$. $4x'^2 + y'^2 = 4$.
25. Hyperbola or two intersecting lines.
26. Parabola, line, two intersecting lines, or the empty set.
27. $e = 3$. See Figure 63.4a.
28. $e = \frac{1}{2}$. See Figure 63.4b.
29. $e = 3$. See Figure 63.4c.

19. **21.** **23.**

25. (a) $f(-x) = \dfrac{a(-x)}{b(-x)} = \dfrac{a(x)}{b(x)} = f(x)$

(b) Similar to (a).   (c) Similar to (a).

27.   **29.**

Section 20

1. $\dfrac{3}{x+1} - \dfrac{2}{x-2}$

3. $\dfrac{5}{x+2} + \dfrac{1}{x-4}$

5. $\dfrac{1}{3} \cdot \dfrac{1}{x+1} - \dfrac{2}{3} \cdot \dfrac{1}{2x-1}$

7. $\dfrac{3}{x-1} - \dfrac{1}{(x-1)^2}$

9. $\dfrac{-2}{2x-3} + \dfrac{5}{(2x-3)^2}$

11. $\dfrac{3}{x} - \dfrac{1}{x-1} + \dfrac{3}{(x-1)^2}$

13. $\dfrac{4}{x} - \dfrac{3}{x^2+x+1}$

15. $\dfrac{-3}{x} + \dfrac{4}{x^2+2}$

17. $\dfrac{-2}{x^2} + \dfrac{3}{x^2+1}$

19. $\dfrac{x}{x^2+1} - \dfrac{2x-1}{(x^2+1)^2}$

21. $\dfrac{2x-1}{x^2+x+1} + \dfrac{3x}{(x^2+x+1)^2}$

23. $\dfrac{4}{x-1} - \dfrac{3}{(x-1)^2} + \dfrac{1}{(x-1)^3}$

25. $3x - 1 + \dfrac{1}{x} - \dfrac{2}{x+1}$

27. $2x - 1 + \dfrac{x-1}{x^2+1} - \dfrac{2x}{(x^2+1)^2}$

Review Exercises for Chapter V

1. $x(x + 1)(x - 1)(x^2 - x + 1)$
2. $y(y - 2)^2(y^2 + 2y + 4)$
3. $2(m + 1)$ 4. $v/[u(u + 2v)]$
5. $(x + 1)/4$ 6. $4x/(x - 1)$
7. $1/(x^2 - 1)$ 8. $2/[x(x + 1)(x - 2)]$
9. $-ab$ 10. $(d + c)/d$
11. $(-\infty, -2) \cup (2, \infty)$
12. $(-\infty, -2) \cup (0, 1)$

13.

14.

15.

16.

17. $\dfrac{3}{x + 2} - \dfrac{4}{(x + 2)^2}$ 18. $\dfrac{4}{x} - \dfrac{3}{x^2 + 1}$

19. $x + \dfrac{3}{x - 1} + \dfrac{1}{x + 2}$ 20. $x^2 + 1 - \dfrac{1}{x - 1} + \dfrac{5}{x^2 + 2}$

Cumulative Review for Chapters I–V

1. $-\frac{4}{5}, \frac{8}{3}$
2. $(-1 \pm \sqrt{13})/2$
3. $2\sqrt{5}$ cm and $4\sqrt{5}$ cm
4. $5x - 2y + 5 = 0$
5. $2\sqrt{13}$
6. $((-4 + \sqrt{6})/5, (-7 + 3\sqrt{6})/5)$ and $((-4 - \sqrt{6})/5, (-7 - 3\sqrt{6})/5)$
7. $(-\infty, -2) \cup [0, 2) \cup [3, \infty)$
8. $f(x) = 4(x - 2)$

Answers / 30

31. Use De Moivre's Theorem to prove that each number is an nth root. Also explain why the n numbers are all different.
33. Use the suggestion.
35. Use $\sqrt{a^2 + b^2} = \sqrt{a^2 + (-b)^2}$.
37. Use $z\bar{z} = a^2 + b^2$.
39. One method: Use $z = a + bi$, $w = c + di$, $|z/w| = |z\bar{w}/w\bar{w}|$, compute, and simplify.

Section 46

1. $q(z) = z^2 - iz + 2$, $r(z) = 3i$
3. $q(z) = 2z^3 + (-1 + 4i)z^2 + (-8 - i)z + (1 - 16i)$, $r(z) = 33 + 3i$
5. $f(i) = -1 - 2i$, $f(1 + i) = -4 + 6i$
7. $q(z) = z^3 + 2iz^2 - 3z - 6i$
9. $q(z) = z^3 - \sqrt{5}iz^2 - z + \sqrt{5}i$
11. $z^4 + (-1 + 3i)z^3 - 3iz^2 + 4iz - 4i$
13. $x^4 - 4x^3 + 8x^2 - 16x + 16$
15. $(x^2 - 2x + 2)(x^2 + 3)^2$
17. (a) 5, $(-1 + \sqrt{3}i)/2$, and $(-1 - \sqrt{3}i)/2$, each of multiplicity one.
    (b) $(z - 5)\left(z + \dfrac{1}{2} - \dfrac{\sqrt{3}}{2}i\right)\left(z + \dfrac{1}{2} + \dfrac{\sqrt{3}}{2}i\right)$
    (c) $(z - 5)(z^2 + z + 1)$
19. (a) i, $-i$, $2i$, and $-2i$, each of multiplicity one.
    (b) $(z - i)(z + i)(z - 2i)(z + 2i)$
    (c) $(z^2 + 1)(z^2 + 4)$
21. (a) $1 + i$, $1 - i$, and -3, each of multiplicity one.
    (b) $(z - 1 - i)(z - 1 + i)(z + 3)$
    (c) $(z^2 - 2z + 2)(z + 3)$
23. $-1/2$, $\sqrt{3}i$, $-\sqrt{3}i$
25. $1/2$, $2i$, $-2i$
27. 0, 5, $2i$, $-2i$

Chapter XI Review

1. $7 - i$ 2. $-1 - 5i$ 3. 3
4. $24 + 6i$ 5. $-8 + i$ 6. $-10 + 10i$
7. $1 + 2i$ 8. $-\dfrac{15}{26} - \dfrac{3}{26}i$ 9. $4 + 2i$
10. $11 + 2i$
11. $-\dfrac{3}{2} + \dfrac{3\sqrt{3}}{2}i$ 12. $-\dfrac{9\sqrt{2}}{4} + \dfrac{9\sqrt{2}}{4}i$
13. 5, $3\pi/2$, $5(\cos 3\pi/2 + i \sin 3\pi/2)$

14. $10, 7\pi/6, 10(\cos 7\pi/6 + i \sin 7\pi/6)$

15. $6\sqrt{2}, 3\pi/4, 6\sqrt{2}(\cos 3\pi/4 + i \sin 3\pi/4)$

16. $24, \pi, 24(\cos \pi + i \sin \pi)$

17. 0

18. $-512 - 512\sqrt{3}\, i$

19.

$$\cos \frac{2k\pi}{12} + i \sin \frac{2k\pi}{12} \text{ for } k = 0, 1, 2, \ldots, 11.$$

20. $\dfrac{\sqrt{3}}{2} + \dfrac{1}{2}i, \; -\dfrac{\sqrt{3}}{2} + \dfrac{1}{2}i, \; -i$

21. $(1 \pm i)/2$ **22.** $(-3 \pm \sqrt{3}i)/2$

23. $z^4 - iz^3 + 2z^2$ **24.** $z^4 + (-3 + i)z^3 + (1 - 3i)z^2 + (-3 + i)z - 3i$

25. $z^4 - 4z^3 + 8z^2$ **26.** $z^6 + 11z^4 + 19z^2 + 9$

27. (a) $2i, -2i$, and $\frac{3}{2}$, each of multiplicity one.
   (b) $(z - 2i)(z + 2i)(2z - 3)$
   (c) $(z^2 + 4)(2z - 3)$

28. (a) $i/2, -i/2, \sqrt{2}i$, and $-\sqrt{2}i$, each of multiplicity one.
   (b) $(2z - i)(2z + i)(z - \sqrt{2}i)(z + \sqrt{2}i)$
   (c) $(4z^2 + 1)(z^2 + 2)$

Section 47

1. $(5, -1, -2)$ **3.** $(3, \frac{1}{2}, 3)$

5. $\{(5t + 1, -2t, t): \; t \text{ is a real number}\}$ **7.** Inconsistent.

9. $\{(t + 4, -2t - 10, t): \; t \text{ is a real number}\}$ **11.** Inconsistent.

13. $\{(\frac{7}{11}t + \frac{6}{11}, \frac{1}{11}t + \frac{4}{11}, t): \; t \text{ is a real number}\}$

15. Inconsistent.

17. $\{(\frac{3}{4}t + \frac{1}{8}, \frac{1}{4}t + \frac{11}{8}, t): \; t \text{ is a real number}\}$

19. $x = -2, y = 4, z = 3, w = 7$ **21.** Inconsistent.

23. 500 pounds each of B and D.

25. National League teams 20, Yankees 19, other American League teams 11.

27. Cleveland 35 inches, Mobile 67 inches, Phoenix 7 inches.

29. $y = 2x^2 + x$ **31.** $x^3 - 2x^2 + x + 2$ **33.** $v_0 = 24$ ft/sec, $s_0 = 216$ ft

Section 48

1. Inconsistent.
3. $\{(4, -3t - 1, -2t + 7, t): \ t \text{ is a real number}\}$
5. Inconsistent.
7. $(-3, 8, 6, 6)$
9. Inconsistent.
11. $(-4, 6)$
13. $(0, 2, 4)$
15. $\{(5t - \frac{4}{3}, -3t + \frac{2}{3}, t): \ t \text{ is a real number}\}$
17. Inconsistent.
19. $\{(\frac{4}{7}t + \frac{2}{7}, -\frac{1}{7}t + \frac{10}{7}, t): \ t \text{ is a real number}\}$
21. Inconsistent.
23. $(-4, 0, 2, 1)$
25. $(\frac{1}{2}, \frac{3}{2})$
27. $(4, 0)$
29. $\{(t - 3, -2t + 1, t, 2): \ t \text{ is a real number}\}$
31. 7 cm, 17 cm, 21 cm
33. $\frac{1}{3}, 1, \frac{5}{3}$
35. 9 four-game series, 11 five-game series, 8 six-game series, 22 seven-game series.
37. $-x^3 + x + 4$
39. Use the suggestion.

Section 49

1.

3.

5.

7.

9.

11.

13.

15.

17.

19.

21.

23.

25.

27.

29.

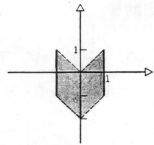

31. $x > 0, y > 0$
33. $x > 0, y < 0$
35. $y > 0, x^2 + y^2 \le 25$

Section 50

In Exercises 1–6, the vertices of the feasible set are at (0, 0), (0, 4), and (2, 0).
  1. Maximum $f(0, 4) = 11$, minimum $f(0, 0) = -1$.
  3. Maximum $f(0, 0) = -2$, minimum $f(2, 0) = -8$.
  5. Minimum $f(0, 0) = 0$, maximum $f(x, y) = 8$ for $\{(x, 4 - 2x): \ 0 \le x \le 2\}$.
In Exercises 7–12, the vertices of the feasible set are at (0, 0), (6, 0), (5, 4), and (0, 3).
  7. Maximum, $f(6, 0) = 13$, minimum $f(0, 3) = -5$.
  9. Maximum $f(6, 0) = 28$, minimum $f(0, 0) = -2$.
  11. Maximum $f(x, y) = 48$ for $\{(x, 24 - 4x): \ 5 \le x \le 6\}$, minimum $f(0, 0) = 0$.
  13. $\frac{5}{6}$ units of chicken and no tuna.
  15. Use 3 bags of brand A and 2 bags of brand B. The total cost will be $100.
  17. No orange juice and 6 cups of tomato juice. 13.2 mg.
  19. Use the suggestions.
  21. Any combination with $a = 3b$ and $b > 0$.

Chapter XII Review

  1. $\{(x, \frac{1}{3}(x - 2)): \ x$ is a real number$\}$
  2. (4, 7)   **3.** $(\frac{1}{3}, -\frac{1}{2})$ **4.** Inconsistent.
  5. Inconsistent.   **6.** $\{(x, \frac{1}{2}, (4x - 3)): \ x$ is a real number$\}$
  7. (0, -2, 4)   **8.** $(\frac{1}{2}, \frac{1}{4}, \frac{3}{4})$
  9. $\{(\frac{4}{3}, t - \frac{5}{3}, t): \ t$ is a real number$\}$
  10. $(\frac{23}{3}, \frac{26}{3}, \frac{5}{3})$ **11.** (8, 2, 0)
  12. Inconsistent.   **13.** (4, -2, 5)
  14. $(\frac{3}{13}, -\frac{5}{13}, \frac{53}{13})$ **15.** $(\frac{5}{3}, -1, -\frac{2}{3})$
  16. $\{(\frac{1}{2}t + \frac{5}{4}, \frac{1}{2}t + \frac{3}{4}, t): \ t$ is a real number$\}$

17. $(5, 6, -2)$ **18.** $(17, 6, 10)$

19. $(-1, 4)$ and $(2, 13)$ **20.** $(-1, 2)$ and $(2, 8)$

21. $\left(\dfrac{3\sqrt{42}}{4}, \dfrac{\sqrt{22}}{4}\right), \left(\dfrac{3\sqrt{42}}{4}, -\dfrac{\sqrt{22}}{4}\right), \left(-\dfrac{3\sqrt{42}}{4}, \dfrac{\sqrt{22}}{4}\right), \left(-\dfrac{3\sqrt{42}}{4}, -\dfrac{\sqrt{22}}{4}\right)$

22. $(3, 2), (3, -2), (-3, 2), (-3, -2)$

23.   **24.**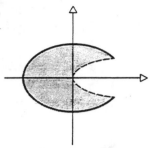

25. Maximum $f(3, 0) = 9$, minimum $f(0, 1) = -9$.

26. Maximum $f(x, y) = 2$ at $\{(x, \tfrac{1}{2}(5 - x)): \ x \text{ is a real number}\}$, minimum $f(0, 0) = -3$.

Section 51

1. $x = -5, y = -4$ **3.** $c = \tfrac{3}{4}, d = 7, x = 1, y = -\tfrac{1}{2}, z = \tfrac{7}{8}$

5. $\begin{bmatrix} -1 & 28 \\ 14 & -8 \end{bmatrix}$ **7.** $\begin{bmatrix} 2 & 6 & -12 \\ -4 & -4 & 16 \end{bmatrix}$ **9.** $\begin{bmatrix} 13 \\ 3 \\ -5 \end{bmatrix}$

11. $\begin{bmatrix} 10 & 1 & 15 \end{bmatrix}$ **13.** 3×1 **15.** $m = 6, p = 7$

17. $\begin{bmatrix} -23 & -52 \\ 9 & -18 \end{bmatrix}$ **19.** $\begin{bmatrix} -16 & -69 & 34 \\ 2 & 27 & -41 \end{bmatrix}$

21. $\begin{bmatrix} -51 & 37 \\ 0 & 0 \\ 46 & 31 \end{bmatrix}$ **23.** $\begin{bmatrix} -41 & 15 & 34 \\ -3 & 5 & 12 \\ -1 & -1 & 10 \end{bmatrix}$ **25.** $\begin{bmatrix} 52 & 18 \\ 26 & 9 \\ 4 & 22 \end{bmatrix}$

27. $\begin{bmatrix} -20 & 24 \\ -59 & -23 \\ 21 & 15 \end{bmatrix}$ **29.** $\begin{bmatrix} -14 & -10 \\ 0 & 0 \\ 10 & -12 \end{bmatrix}$ **31.** $\begin{bmatrix} -25 & 59 \\ 0 & 0 \\ 36 & -23 \end{bmatrix}$

33. $\begin{bmatrix} -49 & 26 & 3 \\ -42 & 9 & -9 \end{bmatrix}$

Section 52

1. $AB = I_2$ **3.** $AB = I_3$

5. $d = -4$, invertible, $\begin{bmatrix} -\tfrac{1}{2} & \tfrac{7}{4} \\ \tfrac{1}{2} & -\tfrac{5}{4} \end{bmatrix}$

7. $d = \frac{1}{12}$, invertible, $\begin{bmatrix} 4 & -3 \\ -4 & 6 \end{bmatrix}$ 9. $d = 0.1$, invertible, $\begin{bmatrix} 30 & 5 \\ 100 & 17 \end{bmatrix}$

11. $d = 140$, invertible, $\begin{bmatrix} \frac{1}{28} & \frac{1}{70} \\ -\frac{1}{4} & \frac{1}{10} \end{bmatrix}$

13. $\begin{bmatrix} -\frac{14}{3} & 1 & \frac{2}{3} \\ -6 & 1 & 1 \\ \frac{17}{3} & -1 & -\frac{2}{3} \end{bmatrix}$ 15. $\begin{bmatrix} -\frac{69}{187} & \frac{13}{187} & \frac{21}{187} \\ -\frac{7}{187} & \frac{23}{187} & -\frac{6}{187} \\ \frac{4}{17} & -\frac{1}{17} & \frac{1}{17} \end{bmatrix}$

17. $\begin{bmatrix} \frac{7}{53} & \frac{15}{106} & -\frac{21}{106} \\ -\frac{8}{53} & \frac{51}{106} & -\frac{29}{106} \\ -\frac{1}{53} & \frac{13}{106} & \frac{3}{106} \end{bmatrix}$ 19. $\begin{bmatrix} \frac{17}{5} & \frac{8}{15} & \frac{16}{15} & -\frac{4}{15} \\ 1 & -\frac{1}{3} & \frac{1}{3} & -\frac{1}{3} \\ -\frac{3}{5} & -\frac{2}{15} & -\frac{4}{15} & \frac{1}{15} \\ -\frac{1}{5} & \frac{1}{15} & \frac{2}{15} & \frac{7}{15} \end{bmatrix}$

21. Not invertible.   23. $x = \frac{13}{2}$, $y = -\frac{19}{2}$

25. $x = \frac{4}{3}$, $y = \frac{1}{12}$, $z = -\frac{5}{12}$ 27. $x = \frac{7}{9}$, $y = \frac{1}{9}$, $z = \frac{21}{9}$

31. 23 million ounces in South Africa, 16 million ounces outside.

33. $C = I = 15.5$ quads. $G = D = 20.5$ quads.

Section 53

1. -4 3. 8   5. -30 7. -4

9. 8   11. 80   13. 215   15. -261 ·

17. 238   19. -70 21. $-\frac{63}{4}$ 23. $x = \frac{2}{7}$, $y = -\frac{6}{7}$

25. $u = \frac{17}{22}$, $v = \frac{1}{11}$ 27. $r = \frac{13}{7}$, $s = \frac{17}{7}$ 29. $x = \frac{24}{7}$, $y = \frac{6}{7}$, $z = \frac{11}{7}$

31. Inconsistent.   33. Inconsistent.   35. Inconsistent.

41. $3 billion in 1970, $42 billion in 1978, $80 billion in 1980.

Section 54

1. -42 3. -30 5. -150 7. 228

9. -150 11. -204 13. -584 15. 4

17. Property IV   19. Property I   21. Property II

23. $(-1, 0, \frac{2}{3}, -\frac{1}{2})$

Chapter XIII Review

1. $\begin{bmatrix} 2 & 23 \\ -2 & 3 \end{bmatrix}$ 2. $\begin{bmatrix} 0 & 3 \\ -3 & -1 \\ 13 & 18 \end{bmatrix}$ 3. $\begin{bmatrix} 1 & -2 \\ 56 & 55 \end{bmatrix}$

4. $\begin{bmatrix} 0 & -5 & 8 \\ 22 & 16 & 2 \\ -1 & -17 & 1 \end{bmatrix}$ 5. $\begin{bmatrix} \frac{2}{13} & -\frac{1}{13} \\ \frac{5}{13} & \frac{4}{13} \end{bmatrix}$ 6. $\begin{bmatrix} 12 & -20 \\ -15 & 30 \end{bmatrix}$

7. $\begin{bmatrix} \frac{1}{9} & \frac{2}{9} & -\frac{2}{9} \\ \frac{25}{18} & -\frac{2}{9} & \frac{13}{18} \\ -\frac{4}{9} & \frac{1}{9} & -\frac{1}{9} \end{bmatrix}$ **8.** Not invertible.   **9.** Not invertible.

10. $\begin{bmatrix} 0 & \frac{1}{13} & -\frac{3}{23} \\ \frac{1}{2} & \frac{1}{2} & \frac{1}{2} \\ 0 & -\frac{6}{23} & -\frac{5}{23} \end{bmatrix}$ **11.** $x = \frac{45}{16}, y = \frac{19}{32}$ **12.** $x = \frac{4}{3}, y = \frac{1}{3}, z = \frac{7}{3}$

13. 170   **14.** 0   **15.** -14

16. $(ac - b^2)(bd - c^2)$ **17.** $x = \frac{2}{3}, y = \frac{7}{5}$ **18.** Inconsistent.

19. Dependent.   **20.** $x = \frac{8}{5}, y = \frac{12}{5}$

Section 55

1. 5, 10, 15, 20, 25, $5n + 5$ **3.** $\frac{1}{2}, \frac{2}{3}, \frac{3}{4}, \frac{4}{5}, \frac{5}{6}, \frac{n+1}{n+2}$

5. $-2, 4, -8, 16, -32, (-2)^{n+1}$

For Exercises 7–23, only the induction step (P_k implies P_{k+1}) is given.

7. $1 + 2 + 2^2 + \cdots + 2^{k+1} = 2^{k+1} - 1 + 2^{k+1} = (2 \cdot 2^{k+1}) - 1 = 2^{k+2} - 1$

9. $5 + 10 + 15 + \cdots + 5(k + 1) = \dfrac{5k(k + 1)}{2} + 5(k + 1)$

$$= \frac{5k(k + 1) + 10(k + 1)}{2} = \frac{5(k + 1)(k + 2)}{2}$$

11. $1^3 + 2^3 + \cdots + (k + 1)^3 = \left[\dfrac{k(k + 1)}{2}\right]^2 + (k + 1)^3$

$$= \frac{k^2(k + 1)^2 + 4(k + 1)^3}{4}$$

$$= \left[\frac{(k + 1)(k + 2)}{2}\right]^2$$

13. $(1 \cdot 2) + (2 \cdot 3) + (3 \cdot 4) + \cdots + (k + 1)(k + 2)$

$$= \frac{k(k + 1)(k + 2)}{3} + (k + 1)(k + 2) = \frac{(k + 1)(k + 2)(k + 3)}{3}$$

15. $\dfrac{1}{1 \cdot 2 \cdot 3} + \dfrac{1}{2 \cdot 3 \cdot 4} + \dfrac{1}{3 \cdot 4 \cdot 5} + \cdots + \dfrac{1}{(k + 1)(k + 2)(k + 3)} = \dfrac{k(k + 3)}{4(k + 1)(k + 2)}$

$$+ \frac{1}{(k + 1)(k + 2)(k + 3)} = \frac{k(k + 3)^2 + 4}{4(k + 1)(k + 2)(k + 3)} = \frac{(k + 1)(k + 4)}{4(k + 2)(k + 3)}$$

17. $\left(1 - \dfrac{1}{4}\right)\left(1 - \dfrac{1}{9}\right)\left(1 - \dfrac{1}{16}\right) \cdots \left(1 - \dfrac{1}{(k + 1)^2}\right) = \left(\dfrac{k + 1}{2k}\right)\left(1 - \dfrac{1}{(k + 1)^2}\right)$

$$= \frac{k + 1}{2k} - \frac{1}{2k(k + 1)} = \frac{(k + 1)^2 - 1}{2k(k + 1)} = \frac{k + 2}{2(k + 1)}$$

19. $2k \leq 2^k$ implies $2(2k) \leq 2^{k+1}$, which implies $2(k + 1) \leq 2^{k+1}$ because $k + 1 \leq 2k$.

21. $\left(1 + \dfrac{1}{2}\right)^k \geq 1 + \dfrac{1}{2^k}$ implies $\left(1 + \dfrac{1}{2}\right)^{k+1} \geq \left(1 + \dfrac{1}{2^k}\right)\left(1 + \dfrac{1}{2}\right) \geq 1 + \dfrac{1}{2^{k+1}}$, which

implies $\left(1 + \dfrac{1}{2}\right)^{k+1} \geq 1 + \dfrac{1}{2^{k+1}}$.

23. $a^k < 1$ and $0 < a < 1$ imply $a^{k+1} < a < 1$, which implies $a^{k+1} < 1$.

25. By connecting appropriately chosen vertices, a $(k + 1)$-sided polygon can be divided into a k-sided polygon and a triangle. From this, the sum of the interior angles will be $(k - 2)180° + 180° = (k - 1)180°$.

27. Induction step: The number of diagonals of a $(k + 1)$-sided polygon is $\dfrac{k(k - 3)}{2} +$

$(k - 1) = \dfrac{(k + 1)(k - 2)}{2}$.

Section 56

1. 5, 8, 11, 14, 17   **3.** 40, 28, 16, 4, −8   **5.** $\frac{3}{2}, \frac{7}{4}, 2, \ldots, \frac{15}{4}$

7. 1, 8, 15, 396   **9.** $\frac{1}{4}, \frac{3}{8}, \frac{1}{2}, \frac{115}{4}$ **11.** 120, 125, 130, 16,050

13. (a) $a_1 = a_n - (n - 1)d$ (b) 28

15. (a) $n = \dfrac{a_n - a_1}{d} 1$ (b) 351   **17.** −455

19. $b_1 + b_2 + b_3 + b_4 + b_5$ **21.** $4 + 5 + 6 + 7 + 8 + 9$

23. $\frac{1}{6} + \frac{1}{7} + \frac{1}{8} + \frac{1}{9} + \frac{1}{10} + \frac{1}{11}$ **25.** $\sum_{k=1}^{10} 3k$

27. $\sum_{k=1}^{20} k \cdot 5^k$ **29.** $\dfrac{5n}{2}(3n + 1)$ **33.** $S_n = \dfrac{n}{2}(a_1 + a_n)$ **35.** 490

37. (a) 482.5 gal   (b) 47th day   **39.** $40

Section 57

1. $\frac{1}{2}$, 2, 8, 32, 128   **3.** $10^{-1}, 10b^{-4}, 10^{-7}, 10^{-10}, 10^{-13}$

5. 100, 10, 1, 10^{-7} **7.** $\dfrac{2^{k-1}}{5^{k-2}}, \dfrac{1031}{125}$

9. $3(-\sqrt{3})^{k-1}, 39 - 12\sqrt{3}$ **11.** $(1 - \sqrt{2})(1 + \sqrt{2})^{k-1}, -1 - 2\sqrt{2}$

13. $\frac{665}{128}$ **15.** $1.5(1 - 0.6^{10}) \approx 1.49$ **17.** $22.\overline{2}$

19. (a) $a_1 = \dfrac{a_n}{r^{n-1}}$ (b) 486

21. (a) $a_1 = \dfrac{S_n(1 - r)}{(1 - r^n)}$ (b) $1 + \sqrt{2}$

23. $15,431.20   **25.** $7958.55   **27.** $19,124.88

29. $3000/32.38 \approx $92.94   **31.** $a_{k+1} = (a_1 r^{k-1})r = a_1 r^k$

35. $\dfrac{a_1 - a_1(-1)^n}{2}$. S_n alternates between 0 and a_1.

37. $\frac{31}{9}$ **39.** $\frac{697}{33}$ **41.** $\frac{34}{333}$

43. Suggestion: If $b = ar$ and $c = br$, then $b/a = c/b$.

45. Suggestion: If $a_{k+1} = a_k r$, what is $\log a_{k+1} - \log a_k$?

47. 262 cycles per second

Section 58

1. 120   **4.** 126   **5.** 1140

7. $(n + 2)(n + 1)$ **9.** $\dfrac{n + 1}{n}$ **11.** $2n$

13.

1	7	21	35	35	21	7	1
1	8	28	56	70	56	28	8	1

15. A common denominator for the right side is $k!(n - k + 2)!$. Or use (58.3) three times.

17. $u^6 + 6u^5v + 15u^4v^2 + 20u^3v^3 + 15u^2v^4 + 6uv^5 + v^6$

19. $a^6 - 6a^5b + 15a^4b^2 - 20a^3b^3 + 15a^2b^4 - 6ab^5 + b^6$

21. $16u^4 - 32u^3v^2 + 24u^2v^4 - 8uv^6 + v^8$

23. 300   **25.** $a^{20} + 20a^{18}b^3 + 180a^{16}b^6 + 960a^{14}b^9$

27. $x^{100} + 100x^{99}y + 4950x^{98}y^2 + 161{,}700x^{97}y^3$ **29.** 210

31. With $a = b = 1$, the left side of (58.4) equals 2^n, and the right side is the desired sum.

33. Suggestion: Multiply and divide the left side by the product of the first n positive even integers.

Chapter XIV Review

1. $3, 27, 162, 810, 3^n(n + 1)n/2$ **2.** $\displaystyle\sum_{k=1}^{\infty} k(-10)^{k-1}$

3. $3 + 7 + 11 + \cdots + (4k + 3) = k(2k + 1) + (4k + 3) = 2k^2 + 5k + 3 = (k + 1)(2k + 3)$

4. $1^2 + 3^2 + 5^2 + \cdots + (2k + 1)^2 = \dfrac{k(2k - 1)(2k + 1)}{3} + (2k + 1)^2$

$= \dfrac{4k^3 + 12k^2 + 11k + 3}{3} = \dfrac{(k + 1)(2k + 1)(2k + 3)}{3}$

5. $10 - 45\pi$ **6.** Use $a_1 = 3$ and $a_n = 4n - 1$ in Equation (56.4).

7. $2\sqrt{3}, -6, 6\sqrt{3}, -486$ **8.** $0.1y^2$ **9.** -1705

10. $\dfrac{a - a^{n+1}b^{2n}}{1 - ab^2}$ **11.** $-\frac{1}{5} < t < \frac{1}{5}, \dfrac{1}{1 - 5t}$ **12.** 6

13. \$1103.97   **14.** \$75   **15.** $\dfrac{n + 1}{k}$

17. $a^{10} - 5a^8b + 10a^6b^2 - 10a^4b^3 + 5a^2b^4 - b^5$

18. $1{,}000{,}000x^6 + 60{,}000x^5y + 1500x^4y^2 + 20x^3y^3 + 0.15x^2y^4 + 0.0006xy^5 + 0.000001y^6$

Section 59

1. Directrix $y = \frac{1}{8}$. Focus $(0, -\frac{1}{8})$. Vertex $(0, 0)$. Axis $x = 0$.

3. Directrix $x = 3$. Focus $(-3, 0)$. Vertex $(0, 0)$. Axis $y = 0$.

ANSWERS TO ODD NUMBERED PROBLEMS

Section 11.1

1 (a) 80-90°F
   (b) 60-72°F
   (c) 60-100°F
11 (a) Decreasing
   (b) Increasing
15 Half wave-length of original
   Speed = 2 seats/sec

Section 11.2

1 B, B, B
3 $(1, -1, -3)$; Front, left, below
9 Cylinder radius 2 along x-axis
11 Q
13 $(1.5, 0.5, -0.5)$
15 $(-4, 2, 7)$
19 $(x-1)^2 + (y-2)^2$
   $+ (z-3)^2 = 25$

Section 11.3

1 (a) Decreases
   (b) Increases
3 (a) Bowl
   (b) Neither
   (c) Plate
   (d) Bowl
   (e) Plate
5 (a) I
   (b) V
   (c) IV
   (d) II
   (e) III
9 (b) Increasing x

Section 11.4

11 (a) A
   (b) B
   (c) A
23 (a) (III)
   (b) (I)
   (c) (V)
   (d) (II)

(e) (IV)
27 (a) (II) (E)
   (b) (I) (D)
   (c) (III) (G)
29 $\alpha + \beta > 1$: increasing
   $\alpha + \beta = 1$: constant
   $\alpha + \beta < 1$: decreasing

Section 11.5

1 $\Delta z = 0.4$; $z = 2.4$
3 $f(x,y) = 2 - \frac{1}{2} \cdot x - \frac{2}{3} \cdot y$
5 $z = 4 + 3x + y$
7 No
9 $f(x,y) = 2x - 0.5y + 1$
11 -1.0
13 $f(x,y) = 3 - 2x + 3y$
19 (a) no
   (b) no
   (c) no
   (e) 0.5 of GPA

Section 11.6

3 (a) I
   (b) II
7 Spheres
9 $9x - \frac{5}{2}y + \frac{1}{3}z + \frac{67}{6}$
11 $-(3/2)x - 3y + 3z - 4$
13 Hyperboloid of two sheets
15 Elliptic paraboloid
17 Ellipsoid
19 Sphere

Section 11.7

3 (b) Yes
5 0
7 0
9 1
13 $\pm\sqrt{(1-c)/c}$.
15 No

Chapter 11 Review

1 Vertical line through $(2, 1, 0)$
3 $(x/5) + (y/3) + (z/2) = 1$
11 Could not be true
13 Might be true
15 True
17 $3x - 5y + 1 = c$
19 $2x^2 + y^2 = k$
23 $g(x,y) = 3x + y$

Section 12.1

1 $\vec{p} = 2\vec{w}$
   $\vec{q} = -\vec{u}$
   $\vec{r} = \vec{u} + \vec{w}$
   $\vec{s} = 2\vec{w} - \vec{u}$
   $\vec{t} = \vec{u} - \vec{w}$
3 $\sqrt{11}$
5 $-15\vec{i} + 25\vec{j} + 20\vec{k}$
7 $\sqrt{65}$
9 $\vec{i} + 3\vec{j}$
11 $-4.5\vec{i} + 8\vec{j} + 0.5\vec{k}$
13 $\sqrt{11}$
15 5.6
17 $\vec{i} + 4\vec{j}$
19 $-\vec{i}$
23 $3\vec{i} + 4\vec{j}$
25 $\vec{a} = \vec{b} = \vec{c} = 3\vec{k}$
   $\vec{d} = 2\vec{i} + 3\vec{k}$
   $\vec{e} = \vec{j}$
   $\vec{f} = -2\vec{i}$
27 $\|\vec{u}\| = \sqrt{6}$
   $\|\vec{v}\| = \sqrt{5}$
29 (a) $(3/5)\vec{i} + (4/5)\vec{j}$
   (b) $6\vec{i} + 8\vec{j}$

Section 12.2

1 Scalar
3 Vector
5 (a) $50\vec{i}$

485

(b) $-50\vec{j}$
(c) $25\sqrt{2}\vec{i} - 25\sqrt{2}\vec{j}$
(d) $-25\sqrt{2}\vec{i} + 25\sqrt{2}\vec{j}$

7 $180\vec{i} + 72\vec{j}$

9 P
   Towards the center

11 $(79.00, 79.33, 89.00, 68.33, 89.33)$

13 $48.3°$ east of north
    744 km/hr

15 548.6 km/hr

Section 12.3

1 -38

3 14

5 238

7 1.91 radians $(109.5°)$

9 $\vec{u} \perp \vec{v}$ for $t = 2$ or -1.
   No values of t make $\vec{u}$ parallel
   to $\vec{v}$.

11 $3\vec{i} + 4\vec{j} - \vec{k}$
    (multiples of)

13 $-x + 2y + z = 1$

15 $2x - 3y + 7z = 19$

17 $3x + y + z = -1$

19 $\vec{a} = -\frac{8}{21}\vec{d} + (\frac{79}{21}\vec{i} + \frac{10}{21}\vec{j} - \frac{118}{21}\vec{k})$

21 $38.7°$

25 Bantus

Section 12.4

1 $-\vec{i}$

3 $-\vec{i} + \vec{j} + \vec{k}$

5 $-2\vec{i} + 2\vec{j}$

7 $\vec{a} \times \vec{b} = -2\vec{i} - 7\vec{j} - 13\vec{k}$
   $\vec{a} \cdot (\vec{a} \times \vec{b}) = 0$
   $\vec{b} \cdot (\vec{a} \times \vec{b}) = 0$

9 Max: 6
   Min: 0

11 $x + y + z = 1$

13 (a) 1.5
    (b) $y = 1$

15 $4x + 26y + 14z = 0$

19 (b) $\vec{c} \perp \vec{a}$ and $\|\vec{c}\| = \|\vec{a}\|$
    (c) $-a_2 b_1 + a_1 b_2$

Chapter 12 Review

3 $\vec{p} = -\frac{4\sqrt{5}}{5}\vec{i} - \frac{2\sqrt{5}}{5}\vec{j}$

5 $-\vec{u}, \vec{v}, \vec{v} - \vec{u}, \vec{u} - \vec{v}$

7 (a) $t = 1$
   (b) no t values
   (c) any t values

9 $-2\vec{k}$

11 $\vec{i} - \vec{j}$

13 $\sqrt{6}/2$

15 $\vec{n} = 4\vec{i} + 6\vec{k}$

17 (a) $(21/5, 0, 0)$
    (b) $(0, -21, 0)$ and $(0, 0, 3)$
         (for example)
    (c) $\vec{n} = 5\vec{i} - \vec{j} + 7\vec{k}$
         (for example)
    (d) $21\vec{j} + 3\vec{k}$
         (for example)

19 $-\vec{i}/2 + \sqrt{3}\vec{j}/2$
    $-\vec{i}/2 - \sqrt{3}\vec{j}/2$

21 Vector

25 (a) $30\vec{i} - 2\vec{k}$
         $20\vec{i} + 15\vec{j} - 5\vec{k}$
         $12\vec{i} + 30\vec{j} + 3\vec{k}$
    (b) $30\vec{i} + \vec{j}$
         $20\vec{i} + 16\vec{j} - 3\vec{k}$
         $12\vec{i} + 31\vec{j} + 5\vec{k}$

27 $38.7°$ south of east.

33 $9x - 16y + 12z = 5$
    0.23

Section 13.1

1 $f_x(3, 2) \approx 2$
   $f_y(3, 2) \approx -1$

3 (c) Positive
   (d) Negative

5 (a) Both negative
   (b) Both negative

7 (a) $\partial P/\partial t$:
        dollars/month
        Rate of change in pay-
        ments with time.

negative
   (b) $\partial P/\partial r$:
        dollars/percentage point
        Rate of change in pay-
        ments with interest rate.
        positive

9 (a) Negative
   (b) Positive

11 $f_T(5, 20) \approx 1$

13 (a) 2.5, 0.02
    (b) 3.33, 0.02
    (c) 3.33, 0.02

15 -1

Section 13.2

1 -1

3 $2xy + 10x^4 y$

5 y

7 $a/(2\sqrt{x})$

9 $21x^5 y^6 - 96x^4 y^2 + 5x$

11 $(a + b)/2$

13 $2B/u_0$

15 $2mv/r$

17 Gm_1/r^2

19 $-2\pi r/T^2$

21 $\epsilon_0 E$

23 $c\cos(ct - 5x)$

25 $(15a^2 bcx^7 - 1)/(ax^3 y)$

27 $[x^2 y(-3\lambda + 10) - 3\lambda^4(8\lambda^2 - 27\lambda + 50)]/2(\lambda^2 - 3\lambda + 5)^{3/2}$

29 $\pi xy/\sqrt{2\pi xyw - 13x^7 y^3 v}$

31 $z_x = 7x^6 + yx^{y-1}$
    $z_y = 2^y \ln 2 + x^y \ln x$

33 13.6

35 (a) 3.3, 2.5
    (b) 4.1, 2.1
    (c) 4, 2

37 (a) Pre^{rt}
    (b) e^{rt}

39 $h_x(2, 5) = -0.38$ ft/seat
    $h_t(2, 5) = 0.76$ ft/second

ADDITION FORMULAS

$$\sin(u + v) = \sin u \cos v + \cos u \sin v$$
$$\cos(u + v) = \cos u \cos v - \sin u \sin v$$
$$\tan(u + v) = \frac{\tan u + \tan v}{1 - \tan u \tan v}$$

SUBTRACTION FORMULAS

$$\sin(u - v) = \sin u \cos v - \cos u \sin v$$
$$\cos(u - v) = \cos u \cos v + \sin u \sin v$$
$$\tan(u - v) = \frac{\tan u - \tan v}{1 + \tan u \tan v}$$

DOUBLE-ANGLE FORMULAS

$$\sin 2u = 2 \sin u \cos u$$
$$\cos 2u = \cos^2 u - \sin^2 u$$
$$\cos 2u = 1 - 2 \sin^2 u$$

$$\cos 2u = 2 \cos^2 u - 1$$
$$\tan 2u = \frac{2 \tan u}{1 - \tan^2 u}$$

HALF-ANGLE FORMULAS

$$\sin \frac{u}{2} = \pm \sqrt{\frac{1 - \cos u}{2}}$$

$$\cos \frac{u}{2} = \pm \sqrt{\frac{1 + \cos u}{2}}$$

$$\tan \frac{u}{2} = \pm \sqrt{\frac{1 - \cos u}{1 + \cos u}}$$
$$\tan \frac{u}{2} = \frac{\sin u}{1 + \cos u}$$
$$\tan \frac{u}{2} = \frac{1 - \cos u}{\sin u}$$

PRODUCT FORMULAS

$$\sin u \cos v = \tfrac{1}{2}[\sin(u + v) + \sin(u - v)]$$
$$\cos u \sin v = \tfrac{1}{2}[\sin(u + v) - \sin(u - v)]$$

$$\cos u \cos v = \tfrac{1}{2}[\cos(u + v) + \cos(u - v)]$$
$$\sin u \sin v = \tfrac{1}{2}[\cos(u - v) - \cos(u + v)]$$

SUM AND DIFFERENCE FORMULAS

$$\sin u + \sin v = 2 \sin\left(\frac{u + v}{2}\right) \cos\left(\frac{u - v}{2}\right)$$

$$\sin u - \sin v = 2 \cos\left(\frac{u + v}{2}\right) \sin\left(\frac{u - v}{2}\right)$$

$$\cos u + \cos v = 2 \cos\left(\frac{u + v}{2}\right) \cos\left(\frac{u - v}{2}\right)$$

$$\cos u - \cos v = -2 \sin\left(\frac{u + v}{2}\right) \sin\left(\frac{u - v}{2}\right)$$

LAW OF COSINES

$$a^2 = b^2 + c^2 - 2bc \cos \alpha$$

LAW OF SINES

$$\frac{\sin \alpha}{a} = \frac{\sin \beta}{b} = \frac{\sin \gamma}{c}$$

THE GREEK ALPHABET

A	α	alpha	I	ι	iota	P	ρ	rho
B	β	beta	K	κ	kappa	Σ	σ	sigma
Γ	γ	gamma	Λ	λ	lambda	T	τ	tau
Δ	δ	delta	M	μ	mu	Y	υ	upsilon
E	ϵ	epsilon	N	ν	nu	Φ	ϕ	phi
Z	ζ	zeta	Ξ	ξ	xi	X	χ	chi
H	η	eta	O	o	omicron	Ψ	ψ	psi
Θ	θ	theta	Π	π	pi	Ω	ω	omega

LINES

The slope of the line through $P_1(x_1, y_1)$ and $P_2(x_2, y_2)$ is

$$m = \frac{\Delta y}{\Delta x} = \frac{y_2 - y_1}{x_2 - x_1}.$$

Point-slope form: $y - y_1 = m(x - x_1)$

Slope-intercept form: $y = mx + b$

DISTANCE FORMULA

The distance between points $P_1(x_1, y_1)$ and $P_2(x_2, y_2)$ is

$$\sqrt{(x_1 - x_2)^2 + (y_1 - y_2)^2}.$$

BINOMIAL THEOREM

$$(a + b)^n = \binom{n}{0} a^n + \binom{n}{1} a^{n-1}b + \binom{n}{2} a^{n-2}b^2 + \cdots + \binom{n}{k} a^{n-k}b^k + \cdots + \binom{n}{n} b^n,$$

where $\binom{n}{k} = \dfrac{n!}{k!(n - k)!}$.

ABSOLUTE VALUE INEQUALITIES

For real numbers y and c such that $c > 0$:

$\quad |y| < c$ iff $-c < y < c$

$\quad |y| > c$ iff $y < -c$ or $y > c$.

GEOMETRIC FORMULAS

Area

Triangle	$A = \frac{1}{2}bh$
Square	$A = s^2$
Rectangle	$A = ab$
Circle	$A = \pi r^2$
Sphere	$A = 4\pi r^2$

Volume

Cube	$V = s^3$
Sphere	$V = \frac{4}{3}\pi r^3$

SPECIAL PRODUCTS AND FACTORS

$$(u + v)^2 = u^2 + 2uv + v^2$$

$$(u - v)^2 = u^2 - 2uv + v^2$$

$$(u + v)^3 = u^3 + 3u^2v + 3uv^2 + v^3$$

$$(u - v)^3 = u^3 - 3u^2v + 3uv^2 - v^3$$

$$u^2 - v^2 = (u + v)(u - v)$$

$$u^3 + v^3 = (u + v)(u^2 - uv + v^2)$$

$$u^3 - v^3 = (u - v)(u^2 + uv + v^2)$$

LAWS OF EXPONENTS

$$a^r a^s = a^{r+s}$$

$$\frac{a^r}{a^s} = a^{r-s}$$

$$(a^r)^s = a^{rs}$$

$$(ab)^r = a^r b^r$$

$$\left(\frac{a}{b}\right)^r = \frac{a^r}{b^r}$$

RADICALS

$$(\sqrt[n]{a})^n = a$$

$$\sqrt[n]{a^n} = |a| \quad (n \text{ even})$$

$$\sqrt[n]{a^n} = a \quad (n \text{ odd})$$

$$\sqrt[n]{ab} = \sqrt[n]{a}\,\sqrt[n]{b}$$

$$\sqrt[n]{\frac{a}{b}} = \frac{\sqrt[n]{a}}{\sqrt[n]{b}}$$

$$\sqrt[m]{\sqrt[n]{a}} = \sqrt[mn]{a}$$

$$\sqrt[n]{a^m} = (\sqrt[n]{a})^m = a^{m/n}$$

QUADRATIC FORMULA

The solutions of $ax^2 + bx + c = 0$ $(a \neq 0)$ are

$$x = \frac{-b \pm \sqrt{b^2 - 4ac}}{2a}.$$

LAWS OF LOGARITHMS

$$\log_b b = 1 \qquad \log_b 1 = 0$$

$$\log_b xy = \log_b x + \log_b y$$

$$\log_b \left(\frac{x}{y}\right) = \log_b x - \log_b y$$

$$\log_b x^r = r \log_b x$$

TRIGONOMETRIC FUNCTIONS

ACUTE ANGLES

$$\sin \alpha = \frac{\text{opposite}}{\text{hypotenuse}} \qquad \csc \alpha = \frac{\text{hypotenuse}}{\text{opposite}}$$

$$\cos \alpha = \frac{\text{adjacent}}{\text{hypotenuse}} \qquad \sec \alpha = \frac{\text{hypotenuse}}{\text{adjacent}}$$

$$\tan \alpha = \frac{\text{opposite}}{\text{adjacent}} \qquad \cot \alpha = \frac{\text{adjacent}}{\text{opposite}}$$

GENERAL ANGLES

$$r = \sqrt{x^2 + y^2}$$

$\sin \theta = y/r \qquad \csc \theta = r/y$

$\cos \theta = x/r \qquad \sec \theta = r/x$

$\tan \theta = y/x \qquad \cot \theta = x/y$

REAL NUMBERS

$\sin t = y \qquad \csc t = 1/y$

$\cos t = x \qquad \sec t = 1/x$

$\tan t = y/x \qquad \cot t = x/y$

RECIPROCAL IDENTITIES

$$\csc t = \frac{1}{\sin t}$$

$$\sec t = \frac{1}{\cos t}$$

$$\cot t = \frac{1}{\tan t}$$

COFUNCTION IDENTITIES

$$\cos t = \sin\left(\frac{\pi}{2} - t\right)$$

$$\cot t = \tan\left(\frac{\pi}{2} - t\right)$$

$$\csc t = \sec\left(\frac{\pi}{2} - t\right)$$

QUOTIENT IDENTITIES

$$\tan t = \frac{\sin t}{\cos t} \qquad \cot t = \frac{\cos t}{\sin t}$$

EVEN-ODD IDENTITIES

$\sin(-t) = -\sin t \qquad \csc(-t) = -\csc t$

$\cos(-t) = \cos t \qquad \sec(-t) = \sec t$

$\tan(-t) = -\tan t \qquad \cot(-t) = -\cot t$

PYTHAGOREAN IDENTITIES

$$\sin^2 t + \cos^2 t = 1$$

$$\tan^2 t + 1 = \sec^2 t$$

$$1 + \cot^2 t = \csc^2 t$$